INORGANIC CHEMISTRY

INORGANIC CHEMISTRY

JACOB KLEINBERG

WILLIAM J. ARGERSINGER, Jr.

ERNEST GRISWOLD

DEPARTMENT OF CHEMISTRY, UNIVERSITY OF KANSAS

D. C. HEATH AND COMPANY · BOSTON

Library of Congress Catalog Card Number
60-5284

TABLE OF CONTENTS

PART I. **Atomic Structure and Properties**

Chapter 1. The Development of Atomic Theory   3

2. Quantum Mechanics and Atomic Structure   17

3. The Periodic Classification of the Elements   58

4. Atomic Structure and Properties of the Elements   69

5. Chemical Binding and Structure   147

PART II. **Some Aspects of Chemical Behavior**

Chapter 6. Coordination Compounds   211

7. Acid-Base Relationships and Inorganic Reactions
in Nonaqueous Systems   268

PART III. **The Chemistry of the Elements**

Section A. The Representative Elements

Chapter 8. Perspective   291

9. Hydrogen   295

10. Group I — The Alkali Metals   301

11. Group II   314

12. Group III   325

13. Group IV   345

14. Group V   378

15. Group VI   422

16. Group VII — The Halogens   456

v

Section B. The Short Transition Series

Chapter 17. Perspective — 487

18. The Titanium Family — 491

19. The Vanadium Family — 499

20. The Chromium Family — 513

21. The Manganese Family — 530

22. The Transition Triads. I — Iron, Cobalt, and Nickel — 545

23. The Transition Triads. II — The Platinum Metals — 565

24. The Copper Family — 589

25. The Zinc Family — 607

Section C. The Long Transition Series

Chapter 26. The Rare-Earth, or Lanthanide, Elements — 623

27. The Actinide Elements — 641

Index — 665

PREFACE

The rapidly increasing emphasis placed on teaching and research in inorganic chemistry within recent years has brought with it an urgent need for textbooks in this area suitable for use by students at a moderately advanced level of training in chemistry. With this need in mind the present book has been written. It is designed primarily as a textbook to be used by students most of whom will have completed the basic courses in the four divisions, general, analytical, organic, and physical chemistry. We believe that a background of this kind is essential to a study of modern inorganic chemistry. To illustrate, the common use of organic molecules as coordinating agents in complex compounds and the occurrence of isomerism in this important class of substances indicate the need of a basic knowledge of organic chemistry. Furthermore, many of the major advances in inorganic chemistry, both theoretical and experimental, have resulted from the application of concepts and techniques from physical chemistry.

The book is divided into three major parts. The first part is concerned at the outset with the structure and general properties of individual atoms, proceeding from the simplest to the more complex. Here the student is provided with the background which will enable him to understand the sources, usefulness, and limitations of the general concepts of atomic structure which underlie the interpretation of atomic properties and the periodic classification of the elements. Against this background the basic theories of chemical binding and structure in relatively simple molecules are developed, preparing the way for later discussions of specific compounds and reactions.

Part II deals with some special aspects of chemical behavior which are of importance in connection with much of the descriptive chemistry which follows. Here the molecular concepts developed in Part I are extended and applied to some actual chemical systems and reactions: to the structure and behavior of typical coordination complexes, to general acid-base behavior, and to some useful types of reactions in nonaqueous systems.

In Part III the chemistry of the elements is discussed in relation to their positions in the periodic classification. Although a substantial amount of chemical information is included in this section of the book, the object has not been to offer an encyclopedic treatment of the compounds of the elements. Instead, compound types have been carefully selected to present the more significant aspects of the chemistry of the various elements and to illustrate characteristic relationships. In so far as possible, the descriptive chemistry has been interpreted in the light of the concepts previously discussed.

In our opinion the chemistry of the transition elements has not in the past received the attention which its importance deserves. The tremendous growth of interest in these elements has encouraged us to put greater emphasis on the discussion of their chemistry, and thus to provide what we believe to be an equitable balance between these elements and the representative elements.

Readers will note the omission of special sections on nuclear chemistry, the inert gases, and organometallic compounds. We feel that nuclear chemistry is properly a special field, the study of which should be based upon a solid foundation in general and inorganic chemistry. As for the inert gases, it seems to us that their very limited chemistry contributes little to a general discussion of properties and reactions of chemical systems. In our treatment of the chemistry of the metallic elements we have for the most part omitted discussion of organometallic compounds. It is our opinion that in order to do justice to this important class of compounds it would be necessary to increase the scope and size of the text beyond the limits which we considered desirable.

Our policy with respect to documentation has been to list a set of general references at the heading of each chapter and, in addition, to include in the body of the text references to material not covered in these general readings or upon which we wish to place special emphasis.

We are indebted to Professor John C. Bailar, Jr., for his critical reading of the entire manuscript and his excellent suggestions for its improvement.

JACOB KLEINBERG
WILLIAM J. ARGERSINGER, JR.
ERNEST GRISWOLD

PART

I

ATOMIC STRUCTURE

AND PROPERTIES

Chapter 1. The Development of Atomic Theory 3

2. Quantum Mechanics and Atomic Structure 17

3. The Periodic Classification of the Elements 58

4. Atomic Structure and Properties of the Elements 69

5. Chemical Binding and Structure 147

THE DEVELOPMENT OF ATOMIC THEORY

The Chemical Development of
Early Atomic Theory

1.1 It is probable that not long after man started to think, he began to ask himself how far he could subdivide a sample of matter. So far as he could observe, there was no limit, and matter to him was continuous and also infinitely variable in nature. The very diversity of types of matter he could observe, however, led him also to ask if perhaps these all might not be derived from just a few simple elementary substances; in such case, subdivision of a given type of matter should ultimately lead to one of these elementary substances, and this should be the limit — in other words, matter would be discrete.

1.2 Both of these opposing views on the structure of matter had schools of adherents among the Greek philosophers. Xenophanes (6th cen. B.C.) and his Eleatic school propounded the theory of the continuous structure of matter; Leukippos (5th cen. B.C.) and Demokritos (late 5th, early 4th cen. B.C.), on the other hand, developed and supported a theory of discrete matter; that is, an

GENERAL REFERENCES

BRISCOE, *The Structure and Properties of Matter*, McGraw-Hill Book Company, Inc., New York, 1935, Ch. I, II.

MELDRUM and GUCKER, *Introduction to Theoretical Chemistry*, American Book Company, New York, 1936, Ch. 1, 2, 5.

PARTINGTON, *A Short History of Chemistry*, The Macmillan Company, New York, 1937.

PARTINGTON, *A Text-Book of Inorganic Chemistry*, Macmillan and Company, Ltd., London, 1939, Ch. II, III, VII, VIII, IX, XIV, XXIV.

TAYLOR, "The Atomic Concept of Matter," Ch. I in Vol. I, *Treatise on Physical Chemistry*, edited by Taylor and Glasstone, D. Van Nostrand Company, Inc., New York, 1942.

WEEKS, *The Discovery of the Elements*, Journal of Chemical Education, Easton, Pa., 1956, Ch. 24, 25.

atomic hypothesis. We have these ideas preserved today not only in the writings of the philosophers themselves, but also in the works of such poets as Epicurus (342?–270 B.C.) and Lucretius (96?–55 B.C.), particularly, who wrote of the atomic hypothesis advanced by the Greeks.

1.3 During the Dark Ages the question lay dormant, except for very slight and incidental consideration by some of the Arabic alchemists. They taught that all metals were derived from mercury and sulfur, and therefore in a sense attributed a discrete nature to such metals. Toward the end of the Middle Ages, European alchemists extended some of these ideas of the constitution of various substances. Van Helmont (1577?–1644), discoverer of carbon dioxide and originator of our word "gas," in one classic experiment, at least, reverted to the old notion of Thales (640?–546 B.C.) that all substances arose from water. Still later, Newton (1642–1727) made use of a form of the atomic hypothesis in attempting to explain some of Boyle's (1627–1691) observations; it might be said that in defining elements Boyle himself implicitly supposed matter to be discrete. In this same period Lemery (1675) and Boerhaave (1724) used the atomic hypothesis in their work.

1.4 The chemical atomic hypothesis as known and used today, however, rests almost entirely on the work of John Dalton (1766–1844), although he was profoundly influenced by Newton's ideas and apparently foreshadowed by the suggestions of William Higgins (1789) on chemical combination. Dalton, who probably was led to the hypothesis along almost purely physical lines, postulated that the elements consist of small discrete ultimate particles, called atoms, which retain their individual physical properties throughout all chemical reactions. According to Dalton, all the atoms of a given element are identical and no two different elements have identical atoms. Moreover, it was he who suggested the determination and use of *relative* weights of atoms, because of the extremely small values of their absolute weights. We also owe to Dalton the conception of the molecule (which unfortunately he termed "compound atom"), as the fundamental entity of a compound and as a simple aggregate of atoms of the constituent elements. Thus attention was fixed on just two properties of the atom, its unchanging mass and its remarkable ability to unite with other atoms to form simple stable combinations. In terms of these two properties the quantitative relations between substances involved in chemical changes could be predicted and described. The Law of Conservation of Mass must follow from the hypothesis that the indestructible atoms have definite constant masses; the Law of Definite Proportions results from this concept and the elementary assumption that atoms of one element unite always in a given simple numerical ratio with atoms of a second element (Dalton supposed this ratio to be 1 : 1 insofar as possible); the Law of Multiple Proportions is derived from the further assumption that in the combination of atoms of two given elements there may be under different circumstances two or more different possible numerical combining ratios; and finally, the so-called Law of Equivalent Proportions is a necessary consequence of this whole set of postulates.

1.5 The central importance of the combining ability of atoms is quite evident, but there were for a number of years practically no suggestions as to the nature of this ability, while great interest developed in the problem of determining the relative weights of atoms. Dalton's clear description of molecules as atomic aggregates, however, did lead almost immediately to one important contribution to the concept of atomic structure. The obvious next step — that of supposing that atoms of all the elements are actually different simple combinations of one or more primary particles — was taken by Prout (1815), who suggested that all atoms are combinations of hydrogen atoms.

1.6 The atomic hypothesis of Dalton was accepted in principle by the chemists of the nineteenth century, who differed greatly, however, in their interpretation and application. This century was marked not only by the discovery of a number of new elements but also by many ingenious attempts to determine atomic weights. Chemists developed new principles and new analytical methods, and their labors resulted in increasingly accurate atomic weight determinations. From his studies of relative volumes of reacting gases, Gay-Lussac (1805, 1808) deduced that these combining volumes are proportional to small whole numbers. Avogadro (1811) postulated that equal volumes of all gases under the same conditions of temperature and pressure contain the same numbers of atoms, or in modern terms, molecules. These two ideas, which are so intimately related to the determination of atomic and molecular weights, were largely ignored during the first half of the nineteenth century. In fact, during this period there was confusion between atoms and molecules, atomic and molecular weights. The observation of Dulong and Petit (1819) that the atomic heat (atomic weight $\times$ specific heat) is approximately the same for different solid elements was of limited usefulness in resolving the uncertainty between atomic and equivalent weights of such elements. During these years Berzelius (1814, 1818, 1826) made use of Dalton's theory by determining atomic weights from measurements of gas volumes, and he also worked with Dulong on specific heats and atomic weights. However, it was not until the time of Cannizzaro (1858), who developed Avogadro's concept of molecules of elements and combined it with tolerably accurate analyses of volatile compounds of the elements, that we began to obtain rather exact determinations of atomic weights. With this advance the atomic hypothesis and the methods for the necessary determination of atomic weights attained a degree of completeness and accuracy sufficient to explain completely the long-known laws of chemical combination, to furnish a basis for numerous and varied analytical techniques, and even to begin to suggest questions about the fundamental nature and behavior of atoms themselves. An international chemical congress in 1860, at which Cannizzaro brilliantly described his arguments, methods, and conclusions, marked the end of the development period and the beginning of a new era of systemization.

1.7 The determination of definite atomic weights was thus a stimulus to Mendeléeff and Lothar Meyer (1869–71) who independently arrived at periodic classifications of the elements based on arrangements in order of increasing atomic weights. The work of Mendeléeff and Meyer had its precursors in the earlier observations of others, among them, Döbereiner, De Chancourtois, and Newlands, each of whom pointed out relationships among the chemical and physical properties of the elements when they were arranged in some manner depending on atomic weights. Döbereiner (1829) pointed out that for certain groups of three elements selected because of their similar chemical properties (*e.g.*, sulfur, selenium, and tellurium) the atomic weights are in an approximate arithmetic progression. De Chancourtois (1860–2) presented some incomplete and only partially correct ideas on the variation of the properties of elements when arranged in order of increasing atomic weight, and Newlands (1863–6) suggested a similar but more clearly conceived arrangement. In Newlands' arrangement, for the lightest elements, at least, elements of similar properties occupy periodic positions apparently eight steps apart. This so-called "Law of Octaves," however, and the other observations as well, were neither widely nor seriously studied or accepted, and it remained for Mendeléeff and Meyer to put the problem of the periodic classification of the elements on a firm scientific foundation.

1.8 Careful and detailed study of the sixty-three elements then known led Mendeléeff and Meyer to the conclusion that the chemical and physical properties of the elements are periodic functions of their atomic weights. The periodic variation of one physical property is illustrated in Figure 1.1, which shows the classic example of the atomic volume, that is, the volume of one gram atomic weight. Other physical properties such as thermal and electrical conductivity or melting and boiling points show qualitatively similar periodic variation with atomic weight. The simplest quantitative indication of periodic variation in chemical properties is the change in valence, which Mendeléeff showed exhibits a periodic variation with increasing atomic weight if one selects for each element its maximum valence (except for copper, silver, and gold, for which their minimum valence of one must be used). Other chemical properties vary similarly: for example, as the atomic weight increases among the lighter elements, the oxides of the first elements (the alkali metals) are strongly basic, while those which follow are successively moderately basic, weakly basic and weakly acidic, moderately acidic, and then strongly acidic. After an intervening element (an inert gas) the cycle is repeated. These and many other periodic relationships are embodied in the periodic table of Mendeléeff shown in Figure 1.2. In this table the elements are arranged in order of increasing atomic weight in successive horizontal rows; properties generally proceed through a cycle in each horizontal row, so that elements with similar properties are found below one another in vertical columns of the table, emphasizing the periodicity of properties such as valence. The regular and repetitive variation in both physical and chemical properties is so pronounced that one can hardly credit it to chance. Furthermore, one may consider the properties as characteristic of the location within the table, even if perhaps the appropriate element itself has not yet been studied.

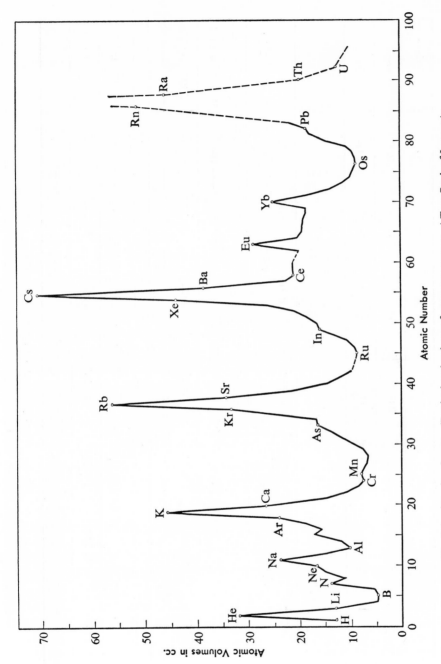

Fig. 1.1 Atomic volumes. (Revised and redrawn from PARTINGTON, *A Text-Book of Inorganic Chemistry*, Macmillan and Company, Ltd., London, 1939, Fig. 209)

SERIES	I	II	III	IV	V	VI	VII	VIII
	—	—	—	RH₄	RH₃	RH₂	RH	—
	R₂O	RO	R₂O₃	RO₂	R₂O₅	RO₃	R₂O₇	RO₄
1	H = 1							
2	Li 7	Be 9.4	B 11	C 12	N 14	O 16	F 19	
3	Na 23	Mg 24	Al 27.3	Si 28	P 31	S 32	Cl 35.5	
4	K 39	Ca 40	——44	Ti 48	V 51	Cr 52	Mn 55	Fe 56 Co 59 Ni 59 Cu 63
5	(Cu 63)	Zn 65	——68	——72	As 75	Se 78	Br 80	
6	Rb 85	Sr 87	(?)Yt 88	Zr 90	Nb 94	Mo 96	——100	Ru 104 Rh 104 Pd 106 Ag 108
7	(Ag 108)	Cd 112	In 113	Sn 118	Sb 122	Te 125	I 127	
8	Cs 133	Ba 137	(?)Di 138	(?)Ce 140	—	—	—	
9	(——)							
10	—	—	(?)Er 178	(?)La 180	Ta 182	W 184	—	Os 195 Ir 197 Pt 198 Au 199
11	(Au 199)	Hg 200	Tl 204	Pb 207	Bi 208	—	—	
12	—	—	—	Th 231	—	U 240	—	

Fig. 1.2 Mendeléeff's revised periodic table (1871).

Thus the table furnishes a convenient means of correlating the vast amount of information already available on the elements and a remarkable tool for the guidance of further investigation.

1.9 The periodic table of Mendeléeff is probably the greatest generalization of chemistry; this classification systematized the entire study of chemistry and led it into new channels. Research for new elements was stimulated, study of known elements as family members was intensified, and a search for the key to regular behavior was encouraged. The classic illustration of the impetus given to research by Mendeléeff's work is the response to his prediction of the properties of the then unknown elements of atomic numbers 21, 31, and 32. These elements were postulated in 1871 in order to maintain the regularity observed among the known elements, and they were assigned chemical and physical properties to suit their presumed locations in the periodic table. The predictions were brilliantly and almost completely verified by the discovery of gallium by Lecoq de Boisbaudran in 1875, scandium by Nilson in 1879, and germanium by Winkler in 1886. In later years the search for elements 43, 61, 85, and 87, and the transuranic elements was similarly stimulated and aided by the concepts embodied in the periodic table. The table, however, was far from perfect. The positions assigned to members of several pairs of elements, for example tellurium and iodine, on the basis of their chemical properties, were in reverse order of atomic weights; the position of hydrogen was ambiguous; and what we now call the long periods were little understood, entirely because of the undue emphasis on an eight-element period.

1.10 It is remarkable that, with the exception of Prout's hypothesis, the enormous advances in our knowledge of the structure of matter made through the time of Mendeléeff involved no considerations of the internal structure of atoms. It is also extremely remarkable that the end of this era in chemistry coincides with the beginnings of the physical experiments from which our knowledge of internal atomic structure was derived.

The Physical Development of Concepts
of Atomic Structure

1.11 The earliest conceptions of an atom as a sort of microscopic billiard ball treated its properties as intrinsic and unchanging attributes of the particle itself, and not as consequences of an internal structure. In fact, atoms as ultimate particles can logically have no internal structure. That a billiard ball atom should possess mass was entirely reasonable; that it should also have the property of joining with other atoms only in simple numerical ratios to produce molecules of demonstrated stability was not evident from the primitive picture but was accepted from necessity. As time went on, however, it became clear that the binding of atoms into molecules implies some sort of fundamental physical characteristics of the atoms which can explain the phenomena of valence. In at least some of the early hypotheses advanced to explain chemical reactivity, the notion seems implicit that chemical combination has its basis in electrical properties, and elements were classed as electropositive or electronegative, the assignments being based on evidence obtained from electrolysis. The valences of the elements were considered positive or negative for metals and nonmetals respectively, and it seemed inescapable that the atoms themselves should have some electrical properties to account for this. Unfortunately, perhaps, the element carbon constituted a great difficulty for such theories, especially in view of the very large number of known stable compounds which carbon forms with both positive and negative elements. Chemical evidence, which was quite sufficient to organize the elements, could not immediately determine the structure of the atoms. This problem could be solved only by new concepts and experiments in physics, although we shall see subsequently that chemical generalizations were extremely valuable in extending to complex atomic systems the physical concepts developed quantitatively for simple atoms.

1.12 As early as 1750 Benjamin Franklin speculated that "electrical matter consists of particles extremely subtle," and although the direct evidence is weak, Faraday in 1833 may have conceived of fundamental electrical particles as well. On the basis of Faraday's Laws, Stoney suggested in 1874 the existence of an ultimate particle of electricity; this particle was first called the electryne but eventually was named the electron. Stoney's suggestion, amplified by Helmholtz in 1881, led to an intensification of the investigation of electrical discharges in gases at low pressures, which had been studied since Plücker's early work in 1859, with the result that such discharges were soon recognized as streams of electrical particles. Thus began the direct conscious observation of particles of atomic and electronic magnitudes. Perrin (1895) showed that the cathode rays discovered by Crookes (1876–9) are negatively charged particles, and in 1897 J. J. Thomson determined the ratio of charge to mass, e/m, for cathode rays, using electrical and magnetic deflection methods. He showed that this ratio is the same for cathode rays in all gases; in other words, it is a universal constant for all matter. On the other hand, Thomson also demonstrated that in the positive rays discovered by Goldstein in 1886 the ratio e/m is different for

GENERAL REFERENCES

DANIELS and ALBERTY, *Physical Chemistry*, John Wiley and Sons, Inc., New York, 1955, Ch. 20.

GLASSTONE, *Textbook of Physical Chemistry*, D. Van Nostrand Company, Inc., New York, 1954, Ch. I, II.

MELDRUM and GUCKER, *Introduction to Theoretical Chemistry*, American Book Company, New York, 1936, Ch. 17, 18, 19.

PARTINGTON, *A Text-Book of Inorganic Chemistry*, Macmillan and Company, Ltd., London, 1939, Ch. XXV.

STRANATHAN, The *"Particles" of Modern Physics*, The Blakiston Company, Philadelphia, 1952.

TAYLOR, "The Atomic Concept of Matter," Ch. I in Vol. I, *Treatise on Physical Chemistry*, edited by Taylor and Glasstone, D. Van Nostrand Company, Inc., New York, 1942.

different gases. One must conclude, therefore, that in some way in strong electrical fields identical ultimate negatively charged particles (electrons) are stripped from different gas particles (molecules) leaving different charged residues (positive ions). Subsequently it was discovered that metals emit charged particles when heated (thermionic emission) or irradiated by ultraviolet light (photoelectric effect). These particles were demonstrated to be identical for all metals under various conditions, and identical to the electrons observed in the gas discharge processes. The conclusion that electrons are fundamental constituents of all matter was anticipated in part by Ampère in 1825 and by Weber in 1871; Lorentz developed his electron theory between 1880 and 1895 with this concept as a basic postulate.

1.13 Not long after the discovery of radioactive elements by Becquerel in 1896 and the Curies in the years following, careful study showed that the radiations from these substances also consist, at least in part, of streams of very energetic, electrically charged particles. Deflection experiments by Rutherford proved these charged particles to be of two kinds: electrons, or beta particles, and positive ions with the same ratio of charge to mass as the positive ions derived from helium; these latter were named alpha particles. Obviously these particles originated in the atoms of the radioactive elements, and so the evidence, direct and indirect, was further strengthened for a detailed atomic architecture.

1.14 The first suggestion that the atom has a definite internal structure resulted in 1903 from experiments by Lenard on the scattering of electrons by atoms. Lenard concluded from his observations that the atom has an open structure and proposed as a model for the atom a small positive nucleus surrounded by a cloud of electrons. His hypothesis was followed in the very next year by an alternative suggestion from Thomson that an atom consists of a definite number of electrons "enclosed in a sphere of uniform positive electrification." It is interesting that Thomson was able to show that with increasing numbers of electrons, atoms of this sort should exhibit variations in properties like those observed among the chemical elements in the periodic table. Nevertheless, Lenard's hypothesis of atomic structure was confirmed and greatly extended by Rutherford and his co-workers (1911–22), who from their classic experiments of the scattering of alpha particles by atoms, not only could support Lenard's model of the atom, but were actually able to calculate the magnitude of the positive charge and approximate size of the nucleus.

1.15 The next step in the elucidation of atomic structure grew from another fundamental advance made at the very end of the nineteenth century — the discovery of X-rays by Roentgen in 1895. These rays, which arise when a target is bombarded with sufficiently energetic electrons, were found to consist of electromagnetic radiation of very short wavelength, qualitatively similar to but much more penetrating than ordinary light. Moseley (1913–14) studied the frequencies of the X-rays emitted by thirty-eight different elements, using diffraction from a crystal of known dimensions to determine the wavelength, and hence the frequency, of the X-rays from the various targets. He showed (see

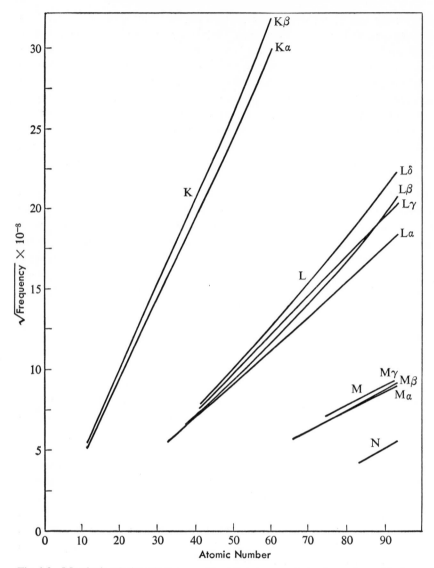

Fig. 1.3   Moseley's relationship between X-ray frequency and atomic number.   (Redrawn from PARTINGTON, *A Text-Book of Inorganic Chemistry*, Macmillan and Company, Ltd., London, 1939, Fig. 224)

Fig. 1.3) that these frequencies are related in a simple way to the atomic numbers, which are the ordinal numbers assigned to the elements arranged, with only three exceptions, in order of increasing atomic weight.   The overwhelming evidence presented by Moseley established the fundamental character of the atomic number and its identity with the number of electronic units of positive charge on the nucleus of the atom, and thus verified the hypothesis advanced in

1913 by Broek and used that same year by Bohr. The apparent dependence of certain physical and chemical properties of the atom on atomic weight was seen to be accidental, because the atomic weight, barring a few inconsistencies, increases fairly uniformly with the atomic number or nuclear charge. Rutherford had shown from his alpha particle scattering experiments that the positive nuclear charge in electronic units is equal to approximately one half the atomic weight, and from studies of the scattering of X-rays by matter, Barkla (1907–9) had arrived at the equivalent result that the number of electrons in the atom is approximately one half the atomic weight. The Periodic Law, therefore, is best stated in the form: "The chemical and physical properties of the elements are periodic functions of the atomic number."

1.16 Moseley's work was truly significant in the development of the theory of atomic structure and its correlation with chemical properties. His work was also of immediate practical importance to chemists because it showed which elements were yet missing from the periodic table (*i.e.*, he found gaps in his simple numerical order of atomic numbers) and how many rare earth elements there could be. It confirmed the fact that the positions of argon and potassium, cobalt and nickel, and tellurium and iodine in the periodic table are in reverse order in each instance to that indicated by their atomic weights, but it did not explain why this is so.

1.17 After the alpha and beta particles released in radioactive disintegration had been identified, the emphasis in research with radioactive materials shifted toward two areas: the study of the elements concerned, and the use of the particles as projectiles in the investigation of atomic structure by the scattering technique of Rutherford. The suggestion of Rutherford and Soddy (1903) was shown to be correct, that the phenomenon of radioactivity is one of spontaneous disintegration of an atom of one element to produce the observed particle and a residual atom of a different element; the particular elements concerned were identified in many cases. Sequences of successive disintegrations were discovered, notably that series leading from uranium through radium, and ultimately to lead (Radium G). The relationship between the disintegrating atom and the atom produced from its disintegration was clearly stated in 1913 by Russell, Fajans, and Soddy: in a disintegration process yielding an alpha particle the product belongs to a group in the periodic system two places to the left of that to which the original atom belongs, and its atomic weight is four units less; in a disintegration process yielding a beta particle the product belongs to a group one place to the right of that of the original atom, and its atomic weight is the same. In this simple statement is the description of a multitude of examples of transmutation, a phenomenon which the early alchemists had sought without success. The transmutation, however, is a spontaneous one which apparently cannot be induced, prevented, or controlled in any manner by variation of experimental conditions.

1.18 Rutherford and Chadwick (1919–22), extending their work on the scattering of alpha particles to gaseous targets such as nitrogen, found that new nuclei were formed with the simultaneous emission of long-range particles. These long-range particles were shown to be identical with the positive ions derived from hydrogen and which were named protons by Rutherford. This first artificial transmutation, like the natural transmutations already observed and described in the investigation of radioactive elements, indicated that atoms of different elements probably differ only slightly in constitution; the particular result was reminiscent of Prout's hypothesis, which seemed to have been thoroughly discredited by the increasingly accurate atomic weight determinations of the nineteenth century.

1.19 In continuing his work on the study of the ratio of charge to mass of positive rays, Thomson (1912) developed his "parabola method," in which a stream of positive ions is caused to pass through parallel electric and magnetic fields. Regardless of their initial velocities, all ions of the same charge/mass ratio are focused along a parabolic arc on a photographic plate; ions with different charge/mass ratios strike the photographic plate on different parabolic arcs. Using this method, Thomson found that the positive rays from neon give two different values of the charge/mass ratio corresponding to atomic masses of 20 and 22. Thus neon consists of two physically different but chemically identical kinds of atoms. The investigations of Soddy and his students (1913) demonstrated conclusively that certain radioactive elements consist of several species of atoms which differ individually in mass and radioactive properties but have identical chemical properties. Soddy proposed the name *isotopes* for the different species of an element. In the next year he showed the existence of nonradioactive isotopes of lead. The existence of isotopes explains why atomic weights which are determined chemically are usually fractional, for these are average weights. It also explains the apparent reversals in the Mendeléeff periodic classification. The techniques of Thomson have been developed and advanced by Aston, Bainbridge, Dempster, and Nier and now furnish the most precise determination of atomic masses.

1.20 The Rutherford model of the atom assigned nearly the entire mass of the atom to the nucleus, the external electrons possessing almost negligible mass (the mass of the electron is approximately 1/1836 that of the proton). The constitution of the nucleus, then, is of considerable interest. Since both the charge and mass (in round numbers) of the proton are unity, and, as was mentioned earlier, the atomic weight is very roughly twice the atomic number for the lighter elements, it was evident that nuclei can not be made up only of protons. At first it was suggested that a nucleus of atomic number Z and atomic weight A contains A protons and $A - Z$ electrons, but it was soon realized that such combinations can not possibly be stable in the close proximity dictated by nuclear dimensions.

1.21 In 1920 Harkins and Rutherford independently suggested the existence of an uncharged particle with the mass of the proton. Such a particle was discovered by Chadwick in 1932 as a product of the bombardment of beryllium by alpha particles. The particle was named the neutron and was soon recognized both as a fundamental particle of matter and as the necessary uncharged constituent of nuclei. Because of its lack of electrical charge, the neutron is a particularly efficient projectile for bombarding the positively charged nuclei of atoms and producing new isotopes.

1.22 The work of Rutherford and others in establishing the occurrence of nuclear reactions has been enormously extended. In general, such reactions may be described as arising from the bombardment of a target nucleus by a particle projectile, resulting in the emission of one or more particles and the production of a residual nucleus. The reaction discovered by Chadwick is referred to as an α,n reaction, specifically $Be(\alpha,n)C$, because the product nucleus in this case is carbon. Among the many other types of nuclear reactions which have been studied are n,α; n,p and p,n where p represents a proton; $n,2n$; n,γ where γ represents a photon, *i.e.*, a quantum of radiation; reactions involving the deuteron (charge 1, mass 2) or triton (charge 1, mass 3) as projectile or product; energetic reactions in which larger composite particles or large numbers of light particles are "chipped off" the target nucleus (spallation); and nuclear fission, in which nuclei disintegrate into two roughly comparable fragments, usually releasing several neutrons in the process. These nuclear reactions illustrate not only the transmutation of elements but also the equivalence and interconversion of matter and energy predicted by Einstein; among them are processes in which the mass decreases and energy appears as radiation or as kinetic energy of the reaction products, and others in which energy is absorbed and matter appears in its place.

1.23 A fairly well-defined concept of the structure of the atom has been developed on the basis of the experiments we have discussed. The neutral atom appears to consist of a positively charged nucleus surrounded at distances of the order of 10^{-8} cm by electrons equal in number to the nuclear charge. The nucleus is believed to be a tightly bound collection of neutrons and protons; its dimensions are of the order of 10^{-13} cm, and its density is therefore enormous. The nucleus of atomic number Z and atomic weight (mass number) A contains Z protons and $A - Z$ neutrons. The binding forces between these nuclear particles (nucleons) are of very short range but of great magnitude, and are not similar to any forces experienced in ordinary macroscopic systems. They are believed to involve "exchange" phenomena between neutrons and protons, and also to involve those particles known as mesons which have masses intermediate between those of electrons and protons.

1.24 Radioactive disintegration is a nuclear phenomenon in which unstable nuclei eject energetic particles which are produced from the protons and neutrons present. Thus a radioactive atom may emit alpha particles (helium nuclei), which are tightly bound groups of two protons and two neutrons having, therefore, a charge of two units and a mass of four units, or it may emit beta particles (energetic electrons) through the conversion of a neutron to a proton, $n \rightarrow p + \beta^-$. Certain unstable nuclei are observed to produce positrons, which are particles of a single positive charge and mass equal to that of the electron, by the converse of this reaction: $p \rightarrow n + \beta^+$. In nuclear reactions nucleons may thus be converted, but their total number is conserved; similarly the total electrical charge is constant.   Equations for nuclear reactions may therefore be balanced just like those for ordinary chemical reactions; the electrical charge is usually written as a subscript and the total number of nucleons, or mass number, as a superscript.

$$\begin{aligned}
{}^{9}_{4}\text{Be} + {}^{4}_{2}\alpha &\rightarrow {}^{1}_{0}n + {}^{12}_{6}\text{C} &\quad\text{or}\quad& {}^{9}_{4}\text{Be}(\alpha,n){}^{12}_{6}\text{C} \\
{}^{27}_{13}\text{Al} + {}^{1}_{0}n &\rightarrow {}^{4}_{2}\alpha + {}^{24}_{11}\text{Na} &\quad\text{or}\quad& {}^{27}_{13}\text{Al}(n,\alpha){}^{24}_{11}\text{Na} \\
{}^{102}_{46}\text{Pd} + {}^{1}_{0}n &\rightarrow {}^{1}_{1}p + {}^{102}_{45}\text{Rh} &\quad\text{or}\quad& {}^{102}_{46}\text{Pd}(n,p){}^{102}_{45}\text{Rh} \\
{}^{113}_{48}\text{Cd} + {}^{1}_{0}n &\rightarrow {}^{0}_{0}\gamma + {}^{114}_{48}\text{Cd} &\quad\text{or}\quad& {}^{113}_{48}\text{Cd}(n,\gamma){}^{114}_{48}\text{Cd} \\
{}^{7}_{3}\text{Li} + {}^{2}_{1}d &\rightarrow {}^{1}_{0}n + {}^{8}_{4}\text{Be} &\quad\text{or}\quad& {}^{7}_{3}\text{Li}(d,n){}^{8}_{4}\text{Be} \\
{}^{9}_{4}\text{Be} + {}^{2}_{1}d &\rightarrow 2{}^{4}_{2}\alpha + {}^{3}_{1}\text{H} &\quad\text{or}\quad& {}^{9}_{4}\text{Be}(d,2\alpha){}^{3}_{1}\text{H}
\end{aligned}$$

When an unstable heavy nucleus undergoes fission upon collision with a neutron, the process yields a variety of products of intermediate charge and mass; a typical example may be represented by the equation

$$ {}^{239}_{94}\text{Pu} + {}^{1}_{0}n \rightarrow {}^{99}_{40}\text{Zr} + {}^{139}_{54}\text{Xe} + 2{}^{1}_{0}n. $$

The energy changes in radioactive disintegrations and in nuclear reactions, reflecting modifications in the binding of nucleons by the exceedingly strong nuclear forces, are generally 10^5 to 10^6 times as great as the energies associated with ordinary chemical changes.

1.25 The chemical properties of the atoms depend primarily on the number and distribution of external electrons and consequently on the atomic number or nuclear charge Z.   The atomic weight or mass number A is almost an incidental property so far as chemical behavior is concerned.   Different isotopes of an element consist of atoms whose nuclei contain the same numbers of protons but different numbers of neutrons, and, except for the very lightest elements, they have essentially identical chemical properties.   In the following chapters we shall investigate further the relationships between the electronic structure of the atoms and the chemical properties of the elements.

CHAPTER 2

QUANTUM MECHANICS AND ATOMIC STRUCTURE

The Bohr Model for Atomic Structure

Introduction

2.1 In the long history of science a number of truly crucial researches have determined for years to come the direction of advance in a particular field. One of these certainly is that of Ernest Rutherford on the scattering of alpha particles by matter. Fairly simple experiments combined with shrewd insight in interpretation led to the concept of the nuclear atom. It is true that such a structure had been suggested earlier by Lenard, but the work of Rutherford was much more convincing, and the nuclear atom was soon almost universally accepted.

2.2 The concept of a nuclear atom describes a physical model — that of a small, dense, positively charged nucleus surrounded by electrons. The similarity to the solar system is inescapable, and so it is not surprising that attempts were made to describe the atom in the same way as the solar system is described, with classical mechanical concepts. Immediately, difficulties arose — two principal difficulties suffice to describe the situation, although others also exist. According to the laws of classical physics (mechanics and electrodynamics) an accelerating charged body must radiate energy; an electron moving in any closed path about a nucleus must accelerate and therefore should radiate energy in the form of

GENERAL REFERENCES

CARTMELL and FOWLES, *Valency and Molecular Structure*, Academic Press, Inc., New York, 1956, Ch. 1, 2.

EYRING, WALTER and KIMBALL, *Quantum Chemistry*, John Wiley and Sons, Inc., New York, 1947, Ch. I.

GLASSTONE, *Textbook of Physical Chemistry*, D. Van Nostrand Company, Inc., New York, 1954, Ch. I.

PAULING and WILSON, *Introduction to Quantum Mechanics*, McGraw-Hill Book Company, Inc., New York, 1935, Ch. II.

RICE, *Electronic Structure and Chemical Binding*, McGraw-Hill Book Company, Inc., New York, 1940, Ch. V.

TAYLOR, "The Atomic Concept of Matter," Ch. I in Vol. I, *Treatise on Physical Chemistry*, edited by Taylor and Glasstone, D. Van Nostrand Company, Inc., New York, 1942.

electromagnetic waves. As the energy is lost, the electron should spiral down into the nucleus and be captured; the life of an orbital electron would be very short, and terminated by catastrophe. Obviously such atoms cannot exist as atoms are known to do. A second difficulty lies in the application of the classical law of equipartition of energy, according to which all the particles in an atom, electrons included, should contribute to the heat capacity of the atom. This is not observed experimentally, even for the simplest cases, the monatomic inert gases.

2.3 One must conclude that either the concept of the structure of the atom is incorrect, or classical physics is incapable of treating such a system. It is fortunate that Bohr actually made the second choice when he evolved his quantum mechanical model of the atom. Bohr set aside the conflicting parts of classical mechanics and saved the useful parts, just as Planck had done when faced with a similar Gordian knot in the problem of black body radiation.

2.4 Bohr accepted the planetary model of the atom, but assumed that the atom can exist in nonclassical stationary energy states. The stationary states were first defined as those states for which the total angular momentum is a multiple of $\dfrac{h}{2\pi}$, a universal constant, and then later by certain arbitrary general quantum restrictions on the action integrals for the system. When an atom undergoes transition from one stationary state to another, energy is absorbed or emitted in definite amounts corresponding to the absorption or emission of light of definite frequency. Bohr first considered only circular electron orbits, but the work was soon extended to include elliptical orbits as well.

2.5 Formally the postulates of the Bohr-Wilson-Sommerfeld theory may be set down as follows:

1. Atoms are dynamical systems of electrons and positive nuclei exerting classical Coulombic forces. This is the Rutherford model.

2. The behavior of the atomic systems is determined entirely by the laws of classical dynamics subject to certain quantum conditions: namely, only those states are realized for which the action integral for a complete cycle of the motion for each degree of freedom is an integral multiple of Planck's constant, the quantum of action.

$$I_i = \oint p_i \, dq_i = n_i h \qquad \begin{array}{l} i = 1, 2 \cdots 3N \\ n_i = 1, 2, 3, \cdots \end{array}$$

(In this expression q_i is one of the $3N$ independent coordinates in a system of N particles, p_i is the momentum corresponding to motion along this coordinate, and the integral is taken over a complete cycle of motion; noncyclic motions cannot be treated in this framework. The integer n_i is a "quantum number," and h is Planck's constant, which has the value 6.625×10^{-27} erg seconds.)

3. When an atomic system undergoes transition from a stationary state of energy E_1 to a different stationary state of energy E_2, energy is radiated (or absorbed) in quanta $h\nu$ such that $h\nu = E_1 - E_2$, where ν = frequency.

The Hydrogen Atom

2.6 Since the Bohr concept of the atom is still widely used with modifications and reservations in the discussion of problems of chemical reactivity, it seems worthwhile to discuss the treatment in detail. The hydrogen atom alone is capable of exact treatment, but the results are basic in the study of all atomic properties and they illustrate the method. The physical problem is that of determining the orbits of an electron about a proton, subject to the action (quantum) restrictions. Each such orbit corresponds to a particular possible stationary energy state, and in each case the energy is determinable. With the aid of postulate 3, then, differences of these calculated values may be compared with results from experiments in spectroscopy.

2.7 The first step is the solution of the simple classical two-body problem in a Coulombic central force field; the orbits are the conic sections described by

$$r = \frac{l}{1 - \epsilon \cos \theta}$$

$$l = \frac{\alpha_1^2}{\mu e^2}$$

$$\epsilon = \sqrt{1 + \frac{2\alpha_1^2 E}{\mu e^4}}.$$

In these relations above, r and θ are the polar coordinates describing the planar orbit of the electron of reduced mass μ and charge e about the nucleus; ϵ is the eccentricity of the orbit and α_1 and E are the constant angular momentum and total energy respectively of the system. For closed, *i.e.*, elliptic, orbits, the total energy E is negative and is in fact equal to the negative of the average kinetic energy of the electron in its orbit. Since classically both α_1 and E may vary continuously, these relations describe a continuously varying infinite set of closed electronic orbits.

2.8 The quantum conditions for the hydrogen atom are three — one associated with each of the three polar coordinates. (Since the problem is a simple central force problem, the motion is planar and the expressions for the orbits do not include the third polar coordinate, the co-latitude angle ϕ.) The three quantum conditions are

$$\oint p_\phi \, d\phi = mh$$

$$\oint p_\theta \, d\theta = n_\theta h$$

$$\oint p_r \, dr = n_r h.$$

2.9 The first is immediately integrated because p_ϕ is constant; the result is

$$2\pi p_\phi = mh \quad \text{or} \quad p_\phi = m\frac{h}{2\pi}, \quad \text{where } m = \pm1, \pm2, \pm3 \cdots.$$

The quantity p_ϕ is the component of angular momentum of the system along the Z-axis, and can assume only those values which are integral multiples of $\frac{h}{2\pi}$. The number m is called the magnetic quantum number and describes the orientation in space of the plane of the electronic orbit.

2.10 The second is similarly integrated, because p_θ is also constant, and equal to the quantity α_1 in the relations given above. Thus one obtains

$$2\pi\alpha_1 = n_\theta h \quad \text{or} \quad \alpha_1 = n_\theta \frac{h}{2\pi}, \quad \text{where } n_\theta = 1, 2, 3 \cdots.$$

The total angular momentum is thus also quantized and may assume only values which are integral multiples of $\frac{h}{2\pi}$, which may be considered as the quantum of angular momentum. The number n_θ is called the azimuthal quantum number; it is often represented by the letter k. Since angular momentum is a vector, one may write

$$p^2 = p_x{}^2 + p_y{}^2 + p_z{}^2 \quad \text{or} \quad \alpha_1{}^2 = (p_x{}^2 + p_y{}^2) + p_\phi{}^2,$$

and then it is evident that $(p_x{}^2 + p_y{}^2)$ is always positive and that

$$\alpha_1{}^2 \geq p_\phi{}^2 \quad \text{or} \quad n_\theta{}^2 \geq m^2.$$

The two quantum numbers are not entirely independent, but rather the values of m may be given as $\pm 1, \pm 2, \cdots \pm n_\theta$. The value zero for n_θ is excluded because the corresponding orbit is a degenerate ellipse which would require the electron to pass through the nucleus.

2.11 The third quantum condition is evaluated with rather more difficulty using the relations

$$p_r = m \frac{dr}{dt} = m \frac{dr}{d\theta} \frac{d\theta}{dt}; \quad \frac{d\theta}{dt} = \frac{\alpha_1}{mr^2}; \quad r = \frac{l}{1 - \epsilon \cos \theta}.$$

The result of integration, in terms of the radial quantum number n_r, is

$$E = \frac{-2\pi^2 \mu e^4}{(n_r + n_\theta)^2 h^2}; \quad n_r = 0, 1, 2 \cdots.$$

It is convenient to define a new quantum number n,

$$n = n_r + n_\theta; \quad n = 1, 2, 3 \cdots,$$

which is called the principal or total quantum number. Evidently the total and azimuthal quantum numbers are not entirely independent, but

$$n_\theta = 1, 2, 3 \cdots, n.$$

Then the allowed energy values are given by the expression

$$E_n = \frac{-2\pi^2 \mu e^4}{n^2 h^2}; \quad n = 1, 2, 3 \cdots$$

and depend on only the total quantum number. It is of some interest that if the problem is treated by the methods of relativistic mechanics the energy is found to depend slightly on the azimuthal quantum number also.

2.12 Thus, out of all the classically possible orbits only those which satisfy these three quantum restrictions are actually possible. Each choice of n, n_θ, and m specifies a distinct stationary dynamical state of the system. The principal quantum number n determines the total energy, the azimuthal quantum number n_θ determines the angular momentum, and the magnetic quantum number m determines the component of angular momentum along the Z-axis. In general, several distinct values of n_θ and m are possible for a given value of n, that is, several distinct states of different angular momentum or different spatial orientation may have the same total energy; such an energy state is said to be degenerate or multiple.

2.13 As was mentioned earlier, the energies of the closed orbits are always negative; the zero of energy corresponds to $n = \infty$ and to complete ionization of the atom. The lowest, or ground, state of hydrogen is characterized by the value unity for the total quantum number ($n = 1$, $n_\theta = 1$, $m = \pm 1$) and has the energy E_1.

$$E_1 = \frac{-2\pi^2 \mu e^4}{1^2 h^2} = \frac{-Rhc}{1^2},$$

where the Rydberg constant $R = \dfrac{2\pi^2 \mu e^4}{ch^3}$ has been introduced; c is the velocity of light. This energy value represents the energy required to ionize the normal hydrogen atom and is a very large quantity. Its value may be variously expressed as $E_H = 109677.58$ cm^{-1} = 2.1779×10^{-11} ergs = 13.596 ev = 313.56 kcal./mole, in which the two commonly used energy units, wave numbers (cm^{-1}) and electron-volts (ev) are introduced. In the former, the factor hc is suppressed, so that an energy of one wave number (1 cm^{-1}) corresponds to hc ergs, or 1.986×10^{-16} ergs. In the latter case, one electron-volt (1 ev) is the energy acquired by an electron falling through a potential difference of one volt, and is thus $1 \times 1.60186 \times 10^{-19}$ volt-coulombs or 1.60186×10^{-12} ergs.

2.14 The higher, or excited, states of the hydrogen atom possess energies given by the expression

$$E_n = \frac{-Rhc}{n^2}, \quad \text{where } Rhc = E_H, \text{ the energy of the ground state.}$$

The first excited state, for $n = 2$, is quite high relative to the ground state; its energy is $\dfrac{-Rhc}{4}$ and thus the difference in energy between the two lowest states is $\dfrac{3Rhc}{4} = \dfrac{3}{4} E_H$ which corresponds to 10.197 ev or 235.17 kcal./mole. This energy is referred to as the first excitation energy.

2.15 These energy states may be represented on a wide one-dimensional graph

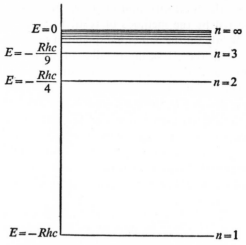

Fig. 2.1   Energy levels of the hydrogen atom.

called an energy level diagram which is illustrated in Figure 2.1. The energies above $E = 0$ correspond to states of the ionized atom; these states form a continuum and the energy therefore may vary continuously.

2.16 An atom may undergo transition from one state to another, emitting or absorbing energy in the process. When the atom undergoes transition from an energy state defined by the total quantum number n_1 to another state defined by the total quantum number n_2, the energy emitted is given by

$$\Delta E = E_{n_1} - E_{n_2} = h\nu_{n_1 \to n_2},$$

in which h is Planck's constant and $\nu_{n_1 \to n_2}$ is the frequency of radiation emitted in the transition. The frequency is thus given by

$$\nu_{n_1 \to n_2} = Rc\left(\frac{1}{n_2^2} - \frac{1}{n_1^2}\right),$$

or in terms of wave numbers (reciprocal wavelengths)

$$\tilde{\nu}_{n_1 \to n_2} = R\left(\frac{1}{n_2^2} - \frac{1}{n_1^2}\right).$$

2.17 This result is one of the major triumphs of Bohr's treatment of the hydrogen atom; the frequencies of the line spectrum of hydrogen had been previously found experimentally to obey just this law, in which n_1 and n_2 are integers. Furthermore, the value of Rydberg's constant R calculated from Bohr's theoretical expression in terms of other universal constants is in very close agreement with that determined experimentally, well within the limits of experimental error. Rarely is such seemingly exact verification of a theoretical prediction encountered.

2.18 It is clear that transitions may occur in groups or series the members of which involve the same final state but different initial states. Thus all transitions from higher states to the ground state, $n = 1$, give rise to spectral lines in the Lyman series. Since the energy differences are all necessarily large, the frequencies are quite high, the wavelengths are quite short and the spectral lines are found in the ultraviolet region.

2.19 The Balmer series of lines in the visible and near ultraviolet regions arises from transitions from higher states to the lowest excited state, $n = 2$. These lines, for obvious reasons, were the first to be studied and the relation shown above for the frequencies, with $n_2 = 2$, was found empirically. The agreement between observed wavelengths and wavelengths calculated from the theoretical Bohr formula is shown in the table for the first three lines in the Balmer series for hydrogen.

n_1	λ calculated	λ observed (corrected to vacuo)
3	6564.70 Å	6564.6 Å
4	4862.74	4862.8
5	4341.73	4341.7

2.20 As n_1 (the total quantum number of the initial state) becomes very large, the states crowd together and hence the spectral lines do also. In the limit as n_1 approaches infinity, the continuum of states of the ionized atom is reached and the spectral lines are replaced by a region of continuous emission. The wavelength in the Balmer series at which this occurs is accurately predicted by the Bohr formula and is given by the relations

$$\tilde{\nu}_\infty = \frac{R}{4} = 27,419.4 \text{ cm}^{-1} \quad \text{or} \quad \lambda_\infty = 3647.05 \text{ Å}.$$

2.21 Transitions from higher states to those states for which $n_2 = 3, 4,$ and 5 give rise to the Paschen, Brackett, and Pfund spectral series, respectively. All three series are in the infrared region of the spectrum.

2.22 The stationary states have been shown to correspond to particular orbits or sets of orbits for the electron about the nucleus, or more properly, about the center of mass of the system. These orbits are ellipses, the number, shape, and size of which are determined by the values of the quantum numbers n and n_θ. (It will be seen that the value of m determines only the orientation of the orbit). Each distinct dynamical state of the system corresponds to a particular orbit and is characterized by a set of specific values of the quantum numbers; the energy, however, (except for small relativistic corrections) is determined only by the total quantum number n, which also determines the major axis of the elliptical orbit. Since there are n different values of n_θ possible for a given value of n ($n_\theta = 1, 2, \cdots n$) there are n elliptical orbits of different eccentricities corresponding to that single energy state characterized by the total quantum number n. One of these, that for $n_\theta = n$, is circular and corresponds to the maximum possible angular momentum; the smaller values of n_θ describe elliptical orbits of smaller total angular momentum. The most eccentric orbit is found for $n_\theta = 1$, and in this orbit the electron may come very close to the nucleus; a hypothetical orbit for $n_\theta = 0$ would be a degenerate line ellipse through the nucleus.

2.23 It is convenient to measure distances within the atom in terms of a unit equal in length to the radius of the circular orbit for the ground state of hydrogen. This distance, the Bohr radius, is given by the expression

$$a_0 = \frac{h^2}{4\pi^2 \mu e^2} = 0.5292 \text{ Å.}$$

From the equations given above which describe the elliptical orbits one finds for the semi-major and semi-minor axes respectively

$$a = n^2 a_0, \quad b = n n_\theta a_0 = \frac{n_\theta}{n} a.$$

The allowed orbits for the three lowest states of the hydrogen atom are shown in Figure 2.2. These figures illustrate the increasing size of the atom as the

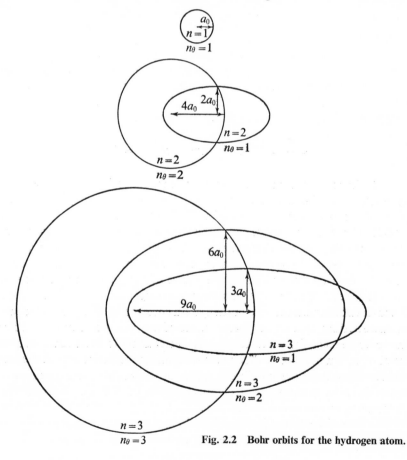

Fig. 2.2   Bohr orbits for the hydrogen atom.

quantum number increases, the increasing eccentricity of the orbit, and hence the decreasing distance of closest approach but increasing average distance, as n_θ decreases for a given value of n_1; and finally, the increasing degeneracy (number of different orbits) as the energy increases.

2.24 In the absence of an electric or magnetic field, there is no particular Z-direction specified, and the quantization associated with the quantum number m is essentially trivial. In the presence of a field, however, a direction is specified, and the orientation of the electronic orbits in space is restricted by the quantum rules; so long as the applied field is weak, the energies of the various states are unchanged, as is indicated by the fact that the expression for the energy does not contain the quantum number m.

2.25 Angular momentum is a vector quantity. The total angular momentum of the atomic system is represented by a vector normal to the plane of the orbit and of length $n_\theta \dfrac{h}{2\pi}$. The Z-component of the angular momentum must also

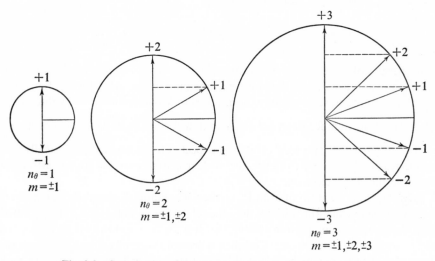

Fig. 2.3 Quantization of angular momentum in the hydrogen atom.

be an integral multiple of $\dfrac{h}{2\pi}$, and thus only certain orientations of the orbit are allowed. These are shown in Figure 2.3 for $n_\theta = 1$, 2, and 3. For $n_\theta = 1$ (the lowest possible state), there are two possibilities only: in each case the plane of the orbit is perpendicular to the Z-direction, and the two states correspond to motion in either the clockwise or counterclockwise sense. For $n_\theta = 2$, four orientations are possible, and for $n_\theta = 3$, six. In every case the value $m = 0$ is excluded, and the value $m = \pm n_\theta$ corresponds to an orbit whose plane is perpendicular to the Z-direction.

2.26 Where the applied fields are not weak, then there is an interaction energy of the atom with the field. The observed fact that the spectral lines of an atom are split by a magnetic field (the Zeeman effect) was at first considered to be due entirely to this interaction energy which must slightly displace the energies for different m-values and hence lead to sets of closely spaced spectral lines instead of the single lines expected in the absence of such interaction. It was found, however, that this explanation is only partially satisfactory; the electron has an intrinsic angular momentum, or spin, and hence an intrinsic magnetic moment which also interacts with applied fields, and incidentally, with the magnetic fields associated with the orbital motion of the electrons to produce closely spaced energy levels in more complex atoms.

Complex Atoms

2.27 If one considers an atomic system consisting of a nucleus of charge $+Ze$ and a single electron (the He^+ or Li^{2+} ions, for example), it is easily seen that the description given for the hydrogen atom need be only slightly modified for the new system. Thus one finds the energies

$$E_n = -\frac{2\pi^2\mu Z^2 e^4}{n^2 h^2} = -Z^2\frac{Rhc}{n^2}; \quad n = 1, 2, 3 \cdots.$$

The energies of the possible states for a single electron increase as the square of the atomic number Z, and thus may become quite large. One further finds that the semi-major and semi-minor axes of the elliptic orbits for a given value of the total quantum number decrease as $\frac{1}{Z}$, so that for hydrogenlike atoms of higher atomic numbers the specified orbits are expected to be smaller. Physically this seems reasonable because the greater nuclear charge exerts a greater attractive force on the single electron.

2.28 The neutral atom of atomic number Z contains Z electrons; each inter-acts with the nucleus and with all the other electrons as well. It is to be expected that the electronic interactions should deform and expand the orbits calculated for a single isolated electron. Complex representations of many-electron atoms have been devised in which hydrogenlike one-electron orbits are assigned to each electron, different orbits and orbital orientations being selected to minimize the interactions among the electrons occupying them. The idea of labeling each of the electrons of a complex atom with quantum numbers like those of the electron in a hydrogenlike atom was thus introduced, and spectroscopic observa-tions of the various levels of complex atoms were used in attempts to determine the required labeling. The Zeeman effect particularly, which showed the mul-tiplicity of the energy levels in the atom, indicated that electrons with a given value of the quantum number $k \, (= n_\theta)$ possess at most $2(2k - 1)$ levels, and it was a short step to assume that therefore an atom could contain at most $2(2k - 1)$ such electrons of quantum number k. On this basis, Stoner and Main-Smith in 1924 suggested a system of electron configurations which ac-counted qualitatively for the periodic arrangement of the elements. It was shown, however, that the electronic interactions in a complex atom are not sufficient alone to account in any quantitative sense for the experimentally observed atom size in the terms of the simple Bohr description. The explanation will be found in the application of the Pauli Exclusion Principle to the stationary states determined from wave mechanics.

2.29 The concepts of stationary states and transitions between them were applied by many investigators to describe the spectra of complex atoms. An extensive system of nomenclature for spectroscopy was developed, in which the stationary states of atoms were rather well described in terms of energy and momentum. However, in order to produce pictorial models for complex atoms analogous to that for the hydrogen atom, Sommerfeld and others had to introduce more and more complicated effects such as precession of elliptical orbits, relativistic mass changes, and quantum defects or effective quantum numbers. The result, although piecewise successful, became more and more cumbersome and top-heavy, and was eventually replaced in many of its elements by wave mechanical concepts. The basic concepts of stationary states and transitions between them nevertheless still remain as fundamental building blocks in the theory of atomic structure and atomic spectra. The Bohr theory, with reservations, is a useful introduction and approximation to the more complete and more complex wave mechanical theory of atomic structure. Because of these necessary reservations, however, we shall not attempt to apply the Bohr theory in detail to the structure of complex atoms; it is more profitable to proceed to the newer formulation given by the methods of wave mechanics.

The Wave Mechanical Model of the Hydrogen Atom

Introduction

2.30 In 1900 Planck suggested that radiant energy is not emitted or absorbed continuously but in discrete units, or quanta, of magnitude proportional to the

GENERAL REFERENCES

BOHM, *Quantum Theory*, Prentice-Hall, Inc., New York, 1951, Part I.

CARTMELL and FOWLES, *Valency and Molecular Structure*, Academic Press, Inc., New York, 1956, Ch. 1, 3, 4.

COULSON, *Valence*, The Clarendon Press, Oxford, 1952, Ch. II, III.

DUSHMAN, "Quantum Theory of Atomic Spectra and Atomic Structure," Ch. II in Vol. I, *Treatise on Physical Chemistry*, edited by Taylor and Glasstone, D. Van Nostrand Company, Inc., New York, 1942.

EYRING, WALTER and KIMBALL, *Quantum Chemistry*, John Wiley and Sons, Inc., New York, 1947, Ch. III, IV, V, VI.

GLASSTONE, *Theoretical Chemistry*, D. Van Nostrand Company, Inc., New York, 1944, Ch. I, II.

PAULING and WILSON, *Introduction to Quantum Mechanics*, McGraw-Hill Book Company, Inc., New York, 1935, Ch. III, IV, V.

PITZER, *Quantum Chemistry*, Prentice-Hall, Inc., New York, 1953, Ch. 1, 2, 3, 4.

RICE and TELLER, *The Structure of Matter*, John Wiley and Sons, Inc., New York, 1949, Ch. 1, 2.

frequency. His revolutionary proposal was designed to explain the nature of the frequency distribution of radiation from a body in thermal equilibrium, but it actually became the cornerstone for the development of modern quantum mechanics. The concept was successfully applied by Einstein and then by Debye to the theory of the heat capacity of solid crystals, by Einstein to the study of the photoelectric effect, and by others in the treatment of various physical problems. In 1913, as we have seen, Bohr extended the quantum concept to the problem of atomic structure when he postulated stationary states for atomic systems and transitions between the states which give rise to the emission or absorption of energy quanta. Where Planck had supposed the energy quantized, Bohr and his successors, Wilson and Sommerfeld, assumed the angular momentum or action quantized, and were thus able to determine for simple atoms certain distinct stationary states in which electrons travel in specified geometrical orbits. The spectacular success of the theory in predicting the line spectrum of hydrogen was unfortunately not matched in its applications to more complex systems, and Bohr's quantum mechanical methods were utterly incapable of predicting spectral intensities, that is, the probabilities of transitions between stationary states.

2.31 In 1925 Heisenberg introduced a new scheme of mechanics centered about the experimentally observable spectral frequencies and intensities rather than the unobservable electron orbits of the Bohr theory. His general symbolic methods, based on the use of the mathematics of matrices (arrays of elements defined in certain ways), were extended to several areas of physical theory. In particular, Pauli studied the hydrogen atom with the new mechanics and obtained the same results for the energies of the stationary states as were derived from the Bohr theory; no specific orbits were predicted, but it was possible to predict probabilities of transition between the stationary states. This success and others served to establish the importance of a symbolic description of physical systems and phenomena as contrasted to the highly detailed structural description of classical mechanics and of the older Bohr quantum mechanics.

2.32 A fundamental part of Heisenberg's new mechanics was embodied in the so called "Uncertainty Principle." He postulated that there is an inherent limitation to the precision with which dynamical variables may be measured, the limitation being most easily given in the form

$$\Delta p \Delta q \sim h,$$

in which Δp and Δq are respectively the uncertainties in a momentum p and its conjugate coordinate q, and h is Planck's constant. It is clear that the Bohr theory contravenes this principle because it predicts precisely defined orbits (*i.e.*, zero uncertainty in position) of precisely defined energy or momentum. The Uncertainty Principle generally relates any two "canonically conjugate variables" (dynamical variables whose product has the dimensions of action) and is important also in the form

$$\Delta E \Delta t \sim h,$$

E being energy and t time: the energy of a state may be precisely defined ($\Delta E = 0$) only if its lifetime is infinite, in other words, if it is a stationary state.

2.33 In 1924 and 1925 de Broglie introduced and discussed the brilliant hypothesis that electrons possess a wave-particle duality just as does radiant energy; specifically, that to an electron of momentum p there corresponds a plane wave of wavelength $\lambda = \dfrac{h}{p}$, a relation analogous to that proposed by Einstein when he attributed to light quanta of wavelength λ and energy $h\nu$ the momentum $p = \dfrac{h\nu}{c} = \dfrac{h}{\lambda}$. Schrödinger extended de Broglie's suggestions for free electrons to systems generally and developed a new formulation of quantum mechanics. He applied his wave mechanics to several systems with success, and, in particular, found for the hydrogen atom those stationary energy states already shown by Bohr to be in agreement with experiment. Schrödinger demonstrated that his wave mechanics and Heisenberg's matrix mechanics are entirely equivalent formulations of the new quantum mechanics, embodying the same basic principles and concepts in two complementary mathematical descriptions.

2.34 In the following we shall very briefly describe some of the principles and methods of wave mechanics and their application to the hydrogen atom and then to more complex structures. The reader may thus observe the evolution, from fundamental physical bases, of those principles of atomic structure and chemical binding which may already be familiar as independent chemical concepts.

Elementary Principles of Wave Mechanics

2.35 The state of a physical system is described as completely as natural restrictions permit by a certain mathematical function Ψ of the time and coordinates. This function, called the wave function, is the solution of a differential equation formulated by Schrödinger and subject to appropriate boundary conditions for the system considered. Each dynamical variable (*e.g.*, energy, angular momentum) is associated with a mathematical operator, a symbol which represents a set of directions for mathematical operations $\left(e.g., \sqrt{}, \dfrac{\partial}{\partial x} \right)$. In general, the operator P and wave function Ψ are such that

$$P\Psi = \alpha\Psi,$$

in which α is one of a specified set of values and is the expected result of the measurement of that dynamical variable represented by P in the system in the state represented by Ψ. The α values are called eigenvalues of P, and the appropriate wave functions, eigenfunctions of P.

2.36 The operator corresponding to the energy is the so-called "Hamiltonian." For the systems of interest here the Hamiltonian is written in the form

$$H = \frac{-h^2}{8\pi^2} \sum_{k=1}^{N} \frac{1}{m_k} \nabla_k^2 + V(q_1 \cdots q_{3N}),$$

in which m_k is the mass and ∇_k^2 the Laplacian operator

$$\nabla_k^2 \equiv \frac{\partial^2}{\partial x_k^2} + \frac{\partial^2}{\partial y_k^2} + \frac{\partial^2}{\partial z_k^2}$$

for the k-th particle of the N particles present, and V is the potential energy which depends only on the coordinates $q_1 \ldots q_{3N}$. The eigenfunctions of the Hamiltonian are independent of the time and thus describe the stationary states of the system. Since in general only certain such states may exist, the defining equation may be written

$$H\psi_n\ldots - E_n\ldots\psi_n\ldots = 0,$$

in which $\psi_n\ldots$ describes a particular stationary state characterized by the set of quantum numbers represented by $n \ldots$ and possessing energy given by the eigenvalue E_n. This is Schrödinger's amplitude equation, commonly called the wave equation.

2.37 The square of ψ, written as $\psi^*\psi$ because in general ψ may be complex, is interpreted as a probability distribution function for the configuration. Thus the probability that the coordinate q_1 lies between q_1 and $q_1 + dq_1$, q_2 between q_2 and $q_2 + dq_2 \cdots$ is given by

$$\psi^*(q_1 \cdots q_{3N})\psi(q_1 \cdots q_{3N})dq_1 \cdots dq_{3N}.$$

This interpretation of ψ and the natural boundary conditions of physical systems require ψ to be "well-behaved," that is, to be finite, continuous and single-valued. Furthermore, ψ must satisfy the obvious requirement ("normalization")

$$\int \cdots \int \psi^*\psi \, dq_1 \cdots dq_{3N} = 1,$$

which merely states that the system possesses a configuration of some sort. The probability interpretation of ψ makes possible in principle the prediction of atomic and molecular structures from basic physical relationships described in the potential function V and the amplitude equation. In general, only probabilities of certain structures rather than precisely described configurations may be determined because of the limitations of the Uncertainty Principle. For the hydrogen atom, for example, instead of discrete precisely located electronic orbits we shall find only a smoothed out average electron density in all directions about the nucleus.

2.38 The eigenfunctions ψ_n of the Hamiltonian operator may be used to describe an arbitrary state ψ of the system as a superposition of the stationary states in arbitrary proportions:

$$\psi = \sum_n A_n\psi_n.$$

The coefficient A_n represents the contribution of the stationary state ψ_n to the arbitrary state ψ; the quantity $A_n{}^*A_n$ represents the probability that a measurement of the energy E of the system in the arbitrary state will yield the value E_n. Clearly the restriction $\sum\limits_{n} A_n{}^*A_n = 1$ obtains. The average energy $\bar{E}$ may thus be represented as

$$\bar{E} = \sum_{n} A_n{}^*A_n E_n$$

but is often more conveniently represented in the form

$$\bar{E} = \int \cdots \int \psi^* H\psi \; d\tau,$$

where H is the Hamiltonian operator, $d\tau \equiv dq_1 \cdots dq_{3N}$, and ψ represents the arbitrary state.

2.39 If ψ_m and ψ_n are two eigenfunctions of H, then for any operator P there exists the set of *matrix elements*

$$\alpha_{mn} \equiv \int \cdots \int \psi_m{}^* P\psi_n \; d\tau$$

which constitute the matrix (table of quantities) of the operator P. The nondiagonal (i.e., $m \neq n$) elements of the matrix of the Hamiltonian operator itself are all zero, as is true also for any operator P' which commutes with H, that is, an operator such that the order of application of P' and H is immaterial:

$$P'(H\phi) \equiv H(P'\phi).$$

2.40 The diagonal elements (α_{nn}) give the precise values of the appropriate dynamical variables in the indicated stationary states which are eigenstates of both operators H and P'. Thus it is possible to specify simultaneous precise values of those dynamical variables whose operators commute, but not otherwise. Position and momentum operators do not commute and hence there cannot be states in which both position and momentum are precisely defined; this is the essential content of the Heisenberg principle.

2.41 The most important operators in the study of atomic structure are the Hamiltonian (total energy) and the angular momentum operators. Since the angular momentum is a vector, operators are associated with its three components; these may be written in Cartesian coordinates

$$M_x = \frac{h}{2\pi i}\left(y\frac{\partial}{\partial z} - z\frac{\partial}{\partial y}\right)$$
$$M_y = \frac{h}{2\pi i}\left(z\frac{\partial}{\partial x} - x\frac{\partial}{\partial z}\right)$$
$$M_z = \frac{h}{2\pi i}\left(x\frac{\partial}{\partial y} - y\frac{\partial}{\partial x}\right).$$

The square of the total angular momentum is represented by the operator

$$M^2 \equiv M_x{}^2 + M_y{}^2 + M_z{}^2,$$

in which $M_x{}^2$ implies two successive applications of the operator M_x. The operator M^2 commutes with the Hamiltonian in atomic systems and thus there are states in which both total energy and total angular momentum are precisely defined.

2.42 The angular momentum operators in spherical coordinates involve only the angular coordinates. In particular, the operator M_z, corresponding to the component of angular momentum along a specified Z-axis, has the very simple form

$$M_z = \frac{h}{2\pi i}\frac{\partial}{\partial \phi},$$

where ϕ is the azimuthal angle measured around the specified axis. It may be shown that the operators M_z and M^2 commute in atomic systems; precise values, therefore, of both the total angular momentum and its Z-component may be simultaneously specified. For atomic systems we shall therefore expect to find stationary states in which the total energy, the total angular momentum, and the Z-component of total angular momentum are all simultaneously precisely specified. Conversely, all three of these quantities must be specified in order to characterize a particular stationary state. The wave mechanical treatment of the hydrogen atom will illustrate this circumstance quite clearly.

The Hydrogen Atom

2.43 The hydrogen atom is the simplest of all ordinary chemical atoms; the study of its structure by means of any system of mechanics is important in developing for that system the basis of the treatment of more complex atoms and molecules. Because of the simplicity of the structure of the hydrogen atom, the problem may be said to be solved exactly in either the old or the new quantum mechanics. The application of the Bohr theory led to the assignment of distinct electronic orbits about the nucleus, corresponding to distinct energy states of the atom. The theory predicted the sizes and shapes of the orbits and the energies of the states. As has been seen, the agreement between calculated and observed spectral frequencies was extremely good. The application of wave mechanics to the same problem is similarly fundamental and successful. Since the methods and results constitute the starting point for all discussions of atomic and molecular structure, they will be very briefly sketched.

2.44 The physical behavior of a hydrogenlike atom consists of its translational motion as a single unit, coupled with its internal motion; for the latter, which is the important part, the nucleus may be imagined fixed while the electron of mass μ moves about it under the influence of the Coulombic potential energy function $V = \dfrac{-Ze^2}{r}$, $+Ze$ being the nuclear charge, $-e$ the electronic charge, and r the distance between the two particles. The wave equation then has the form

$$-\frac{h^2}{8\pi^2\mu}\nabla^2\psi - \frac{Ze^2}{r}\psi - E\psi = 0,$$

which is a second order differential equation in the three coordinates which specify the position of the electron relative to the nucleus. The solutions will describe states of the hydrogenlike atom.

2.45 Because of the particularly simple nature of the potential function, the wave equation may be separated into three distinct equations, one for each of the three polar coordinates r, θ, ϕ which are properly used to describe the configuration. If $\psi(r, \theta, \phi) \equiv R(r)\Theta(\theta)\Phi(\phi)$, the first equation, that in the azimuthal angle ϕ, is

$$\frac{d^2\Phi}{d\phi^2} = -m^2\Phi,$$

in which m^2 is the first of two unknown constants which arise in the separation process. The solution of this equation is well known; it contains two arbitrary constants A and B:

$$\Phi = A \sin m\phi + B \cos m\phi.$$

Now the wave function must be single-valued; it must have the same value at ϕ as at $\phi + 2\pi$, $\phi + 4\pi$, $\cdots$, because these angles all correspond to the same configuration. This can be true only if m is an integer, positive or negative. Thus a quantum number has appeared quite automatically in requiring a well-behaved solution of the wave equation. The number $m = 0, \pm 1, \pm 2 \cdots$ is equivalent to the magnetic quantum number of the Bohr theory.

2.46 The equation in the co-latitude angle θ is rather more complex:

$$\frac{1}{\sin\theta}\frac{d}{d\theta}\left(\sin\theta\frac{d\Theta}{d\theta}\right) + \left(\beta - \frac{m^2}{\sin^2\theta}\right)\Theta = 0.$$

The number β is the second unknown separation constant. The equation is found by standard mathematical methods to possess well-behaved solutions only if the constant β is of the form $l(l + 1)$, l being a positive integer not less than $|m|$ (the value of m regardless of sign). Thus a second quantum number, the azimuthal quantum number, has appeared naturally in seeking a proper wave function. The combined Φ and Θ solutions, which are appropriate for any system in which the potential depends only on r, have long been known as *spherical harmonics* and may be represented in the form

$$\Phi(\phi)\Theta(\theta) = \Phi_m(\phi)\Theta_{lm}(\theta) = e^{im\phi}P_l^{|m|}(\cos\theta),$$

in which $l = 0, 1, 2 \cdots$ and $m = 0, \pm 1, \pm 2 \cdots \pm l$.

2.47 The third equation in the radial distance r introduces for the first time the energy E:

$$\frac{1}{r^2}\frac{d}{dr}\left(r^2\frac{dR}{dr}\right) + \left[\frac{8\pi^2\mu}{h^2}\left(E + \frac{Ze^2}{r}\right) - \frac{l(l+1)}{r^2}\right]R = 0.$$

Proper solutions of the equation may be found for all positive values of the energy E. These solutions represent ionized states of the atom, and the continuously distributed eigenvalues of the energy permit in transitions the experimentally observed continuous absorption or emission of radiation of all frequencies. The Bohr theory is incapable of treating these states.

2.48 For negative total energies, well-behaved solutions of the equation are found only for specified values of E, namely,

$$E_n = -\frac{2\pi^2\mu Z^2 e^4}{n^2 h^2},$$

in which n is a positive integer not less than $l + 1$. Thus a third quantum number, the principal quantum number n, appears naturally and not as a consequence of an arbitrary quantization process as in the Bohr theory. The solutions of the radial equation are also well-known functions, the associated Laguerre polynomials $L_{n+l}^{2l+1}(\rho)$, where ρ is proportional to r. If n takes on the values 1, 2, 3, . . ., then $l = 0, 1, 2, \cdots (n-1)$.

2.49 The result for E_n, with $Z = 1$ for the hydrogen atom itself, is identical with that obtained in the Bohr treatment of the hydrogen atom. The essentially complete agreement with experiment has already been discussed and must of course apply equally well, so far as energies are concerned, to the wave mechanical results. Thus the observed simple line spectra of hydrogenlike atoms conform to the predictions of the theory. In addition, the wave theory allows the calculation of transition probabilities between states and hence the intensities of spectral lines, and the results are in essential agreement with experiment. The Bohr theory could not predict intensities.

2.50 The complete wave function may now be written

$$\psi(r, \theta, \phi) = N_{nl}\rho^l e^{-\rho/2}L_{n+l}^{2l+1}(\rho)e^{im\phi}P_l^{|m|}(\cos\theta)$$
$$n = 1, 2, 3\cdots; \quad l = 0, 1, 2\cdots(n-1); \quad m = -l, -l+1\cdots0\cdots+l.$$

In this, N_{nl} is an unimportant normalization factor; $\rho = \dfrac{r}{a} = \dfrac{2Z}{n}\dfrac{r}{a_0}$; $a_0 = \dfrac{h^2}{4\pi^2\mu e^2}$, the radius of the first Bohr orbit; and L and P are respectively the associated Laguerre and Legendre polynomials. The quantity $a = \dfrac{na_0}{2Z}$ is a characteristic length for each energy state of a given hydrogenlike atom. Clearly, it is smaller the greater the positive charge on the nucleus, because this holds the electron the more tightly. Furthermore, for a given atom, it increases as n increases and hence as the energy rises — the more energetic the electron the greater its average distance from the nucleus. The normalized wave functions for hydrogenlike atoms for $n = 1, 2$, and 3 are listed in Table 2.1; in the functions given,

$$\sigma = \frac{Zr}{a_0} = \frac{n}{2}\rho.$$

2.51 The solutions $\psi_{n,l,m}$ which have been obtained are the correct eigenfunctions for the system. Each such solution, specified by a particular set of

TABLE 2.1

Normalized Wave Functions of Hydrogenlike Atoms

n	l	m	State	ψ
1	0	0	$1s$	$\psi_{1s} = \dfrac{1}{\sqrt{\pi}}\left(\dfrac{Z}{a_0}\right)^{3/2} e^{-\sigma}$
2	0	0	$2s$	$\psi_{2s} = \dfrac{1}{4\sqrt{2\pi}}\left(\dfrac{Z}{a_0}\right)^{3/2}(2-\sigma)e^{-\sigma/2}$
2	1	0	$2p_z$	$\psi_{2p_z} = \dfrac{1}{4\sqrt{2\pi}}\left(\dfrac{Z}{a_0}\right)^{3/2}\sigma e^{-\sigma/2}\cos\theta$
2	1	± 1	$2p_x$	$\psi_{2p_x} = \dfrac{1}{4\sqrt{2\pi}}\left(\dfrac{Z}{a_0}\right)^{3/2}\sigma e^{-\sigma/2}\sin\theta\cos\phi$
			$2p_y$	$\psi_{2p_y} = \dfrac{1}{4\sqrt{2\pi}}\left(\dfrac{Z}{a_0}\right)^{3/2}\sigma e^{-\sigma/2}\sin\theta\sin\phi$
3	0	0	$3s$	$\psi_{3s} = \dfrac{2}{81\sqrt{3\pi}}\left(\dfrac{Z}{a_0}\right)^{3/2}(27-18\sigma+2\sigma^2)e^{-\sigma/3}$
3	1	0	$3p_z$	$\psi_{3p_z} = \dfrac{2}{81\sqrt{\pi}}\left(\dfrac{Z}{a_0}\right)^{3/2}\sigma(6-\sigma)e^{-\sigma/3}\cos\theta$
3	1	± 1	$3p_x$	$\psi_{3p_x} = \dfrac{2}{81\sqrt{\pi}}\left(\dfrac{Z}{a_0}\right)^{3/2}\sigma(6-\sigma)e^{-\sigma/3}\sin\theta\cos\phi$
			$3p_y$	$\psi_{3p_y} = \dfrac{2}{81\sqrt{\pi}}\left(\dfrac{Z}{a_0}\right)^{3/2}\sigma(6-\sigma)e^{-\sigma/3}\sin\theta\sin\phi$
3	2	0	$3d_{z^2}$	$\psi_{3d_{z^2}} = \dfrac{1}{81\sqrt{6\pi}}\left(\dfrac{Z}{a_0}\right)^{3/2}\sigma^2 e^{-\sigma/3}(3\cos^2\theta-1)$
3	2	± 1	$3d_{xz}$	$\psi_{3d_{xz}} = \dfrac{2}{81\sqrt{\pi}}\left(\dfrac{Z}{a_0}\right)^{3/2}\sigma^2 e^{-\sigma/3}\sin\theta\cos\theta\cos\phi$
			$3d_{yz}$	$\psi_{3d_{yz}} = \dfrac{2}{81\sqrt{\pi}}\left(\dfrac{Z}{a_0}\right)^{3/2}\sigma^2 e^{-\sigma/3}\sin\theta\cos\theta\sin\phi$
3	2	± 2	$3d_{x^2-y^2}$	$\psi_{3d_{x^2-y^2}} = \dfrac{1}{81\sqrt{2\pi}}\left(\dfrac{Z}{a_0}\right)^{3/2}\sigma^2 e^{-\sigma/3}\sin^2\theta\cos 2\phi$
			$3d_{xy}$	$\psi_{3d_{xy}} = \dfrac{1}{81\sqrt{2\pi}}\left(\dfrac{Z}{a_0}\right)^{3/2}\sigma^2 e^{-\sigma/3}\sin^2\theta\sin 2\phi$

values of the three quantum numbers n, l, and m, describes in the quantum mechanical sense a distinct dynamical state of the system, giving the total energy, the total angular momentum, and the component of angular momentum along a specified axis (the Z-axis). The wave functions which have been found as eigenfunctions of the Hamiltonian or energy operator H are also eigenfunctions of the operator for the square of the total angular momentum, M^2, and that for the Z-component of angular momentum M_z, because for atomic systems all these operators commute. Thus the values of these three properties in the stationary states are all simultaneously eigenvalues and are given by the scheme shown.

Operator	Dynamical Variable	Eigenvalues
H	Total Energy	$\dfrac{-2\pi^2 \mu^2 e^4}{n^2 h^2}$
M^2	Square of total angular momentum	$l(l+1)\left(\dfrac{h}{2\pi}\right)^2$
M_z	Z-component of angular momentum	$m\,\dfrac{h}{2\pi}$

2.52 We have already seen that the eigenvalues of the energy are precisely those obtained in the Bohr theory. It is evident also that the eigenvalues of the Z-component of total angular momentum are the same for the two methods of calculation. It is equally evident that the results for the square of the total angular momentum are different; the Bohr theory predicts the values $n_\theta^2 \left(\dfrac{h}{2\pi}\right)^2$, where n_θ is an integer. This difference is not trivial and is related to the circumstance previously mentioned (see 2.29) that the old Bohr quantum mechanical treatment had eventually to be arbitrarily modified, among other ways, by the incorporation of half-integral quantum numbers.

2.53 It is customary to arrange the various dynamical states of the hydrogen-like atoms in order of the energies, each energy state being specified by a particular value of n. In general, however, there are for each value of n several possible values of l $(0, 1 \cdots (n-1))$; furthermore, for each l value there are $2l+1$ different values of m possible $(-l, -l+1 \cdots 0 \cdots +l)$. Since each particular set of values of n, l, and m specifies a distinct dynamical state, then a single energy state may correspond to several different dynamical states, or it is said to be degenerate or to have a certain multiplicity. The multiplicity of the energy state E_n is easily shown to be n^2, which is just $\sum_{l=0}^{n-1} (2l+1)$. The degeneracy associated with the quantum number m arises from symmetry in rotations and is therefore termed "necessary"; that associated with the quantum number l arises from the particular form of the Coulombic potential function and is termed "accidental." Finally, we shall see subsequently that the necessary incorporation of electron spin in these considerations will just double the degeneracy already calculated, and this result will be intimately connected with modern concepts of the structure of complex atoms and the periodic relationships of the elements.

2.54 The several states are usually designated by giving first the value of n and then a letter $s, p, d, f \ldots$ according as $l = 0, 1, 2, 3 \cdots$. Thus the state for $n = 1$ and $l = 0$ is called a $1s$ state, and that for $n = 3$ and $l = 2$ a $3d$ state. For a given assignment of n and l, the several different states corresponding to the various allowed values of the magnetic quantum number m are usually not described directly by the angular factors derived earlier but by equivalent linear combinations of these factors which become common trigonometric expressions describing functions with maxima in certain directions in space. These directions are implied by subscripts on the state designations; the notation is illustrated in the wave functions listed in Table 2.1.

2.55 The configuration of the atom in its several states may be determined from the fundamental interpretation of $\psi^*\psi$ as a probability density function. Because $\psi_{n,l,m}$ for the hydrogenlike atom depends on r, θ, and ϕ, which locate the electron relative to the nucleus, $\psi_{n,l,m}^*\psi_{n,l,m}$ describes the probability of position of the electron around the nucleus. Whereas the Bohr theory placed the electron in a precisely defined orbit for a specified energy, the newer theory gives only the probability distribution. We shall examine separately the radial and angular aspects of this distribution.

2.56 The radial parts, R_{nl}, of the first several wave functions of hydrogen are shown in Figure 2.4. The radial function vanishes at $r = 0$ for all states except s states which have zero angular momentum. Each radial function vanishes at $r = \infty$ and also at $n - l - 1$ smaller values of r.

2.57 The probability that the electron lies in any direction whatsoever in a shell of thickness dr at the distance r from the nucleus is obtained by integrating $\psi^*\psi$ over all directions in space; the result is

$$P(r)\ dr = [R_{nl}(r)]^2 r^2\ dr.$$

The radial probability function $P(r)$ is shown in Figure 2.5 for the lower energy states of the hydrogen atom. Each curve possesses $n - l$ maxima, the major maximum in each case being that at the largest distance. The radial distance of the major maximum electron density increases with increasing n; in other words, the most probable radius of the atom is larger in the higher energy states. For a given value of n (fixed energy) the most probable radius decreases as l increases (as the angular momentum increases), which corresponds in the Bohr description to decreasing eccentricity of the orbit and decreasing average distance between electron and nucleus.

2.58 The average distance between electron and nucleus may be calculated from $P(r)$ and is found to be $\frac{3}{2}a_0$ for the $1s$ ground state of hydrogen. As may be seen from the figure, the most probable value of r in this state is just a_0, the radius of the circular orbit corresponding to the state of lowest energy in the Bohr theory. Quite generally, the most probable radius for any state in which $l = n - 1$ is equal to the radius of the circular Bohr orbit for that energy state.

2.59 It is customary in speaking of a hydrogenlike atom in a specified state indicated as $1s$, $2s$, $3d$ ... to refer to the electron as a $1s$, $2s$, $3d$ ... electron. In these terms, one may conclude from the radial distribution curves that for a given nucleus, electrons of a given type specified by one of the letters s, p, d ... are progressively further removed from the nucleus as the principal quantum number n increases. For a given value of the principal quantum number n, the s electron is farthest from the nucleus, and p, d, f ... electrons are progressively

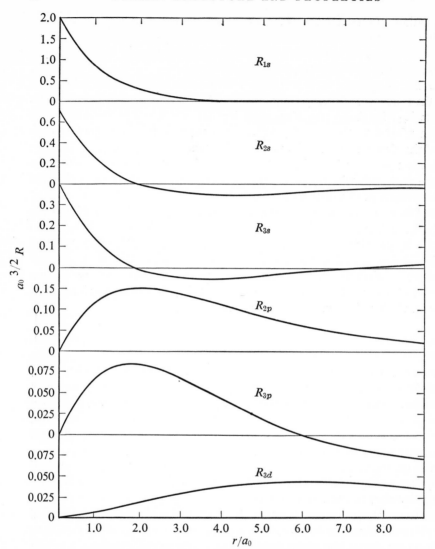

Fig. 2.4   Radial part of wave functions of the hydrogen atom.

closer. Thus an electron in a given state may be located on the average nearer the nucleus than an electron of lower energy (n smaller), provided the first electron is in a state of sufficiently large angular momentum (l larger). This will be of some interest in the study of complex atoms with several electrons.

2.60 The s states of the hydrogenlike atoms ($l = 0$) have zero angular momentum and spherically symmetrical electronic distribution functions. These states should not be identified, however, with the circular Bohr orbits; in fact, the circular orbits correspond to states of maximum angular momentum, $l = n - 1$, and one must seek the analog of the s state in the limiting ellipses of maximum

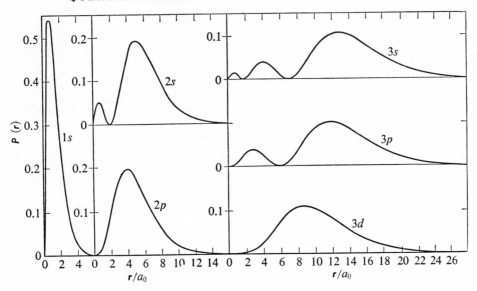

Fig. 2.5   Radial probability function P(r) for lower states of hydrogen.

eccentricity of the Bohr theory. In the latter, the nearly linear motion of the electron corresponds to minimum angular momentum, and the motion of the electron very near the nucleus corresponds in wave mechanical terms to a finite probability of finding the electron at short distances from the nucleus, as is true for *s* states. Thus, although the Bohr theory is still useful in picturing atomic structure and behavior, it must be used carefully. The difficulty in making direct analogies between the wave mechanical and Bohr results for low values of the principal quantum number emphasizes the only approximate nature of the Bohr theory.

2.61 States of nonzero angular momentum, for $l > 0$, have electron distribution functions with varying densities along different directions in space. In certain directions the angular part of $\psi^*\psi$ exhibits maximum values, and in these directions the electron density is maximum. For *p* states the directions may be taken as the Cartesian axes *x*, *y*, and *z*; the relative electron density is shown for 2*p* states in Figure 2.6 in which only the angular part is indicated. The three distributions for 2*p* states are identical except for their orientation in space. In the case of *d* states, five patterns of distribution are found with maxima in different but equivalent directions. Although these directional factors for the electron density are not immediately important for single isolated hydrogenlike atoms, we shall see later that for complex atoms and especially for chemical bonds between atoms these factors become extremely important. The directional character of these functions is of primary importance in determining the directional character of chemical bonds.

2.62 To summarize, for hydrogenlike atoms the methods of wave mechanics

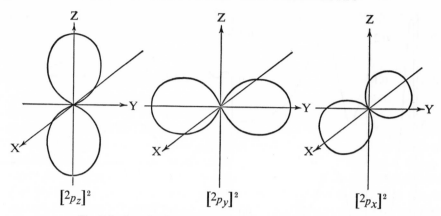

Fig. 2.6   Angular dependence of electron density in $2p$ states.

predict energy levels which agree with the observations of spectra; in general these energy levels are degenerate, possessing several different sub-states of the same energy but of different total angular momenta or different Z-components of total angular momentum; and to each dynamical state there corresponds a probability distribution function which describes the probable configuration of the nucleus-electron system, rather than a distinct elliptical orbit as predicted by the Bohr theory.   The quantizing conditions which Bohr introduced in an *ad hoc* manner have appeared naturally in the search for well-behaved wave functions, and are embodied in the quantum numbers *n*, *l*, and *m*, which specify the simultaneous precise values of the total energy, total angular momentum, and Z-component of angular momentum, respectively, in the distinct dynamical state represented by the function $\psi_{n,l,m}$.

Many-Electron Atoms: the Electronic Configurations of the Elements

Electron Spin

2.63 Many energy levels of atoms as deduced from spectroscopic data are found to consist of several closely spaced yet nevertheless distinct levels.   Even such relatively simple atoms as those of the alkali metals, with one valence electron, present doublet levels, and the energy levels of the alkaline earth metals may be divided into singlets and triplets.   This multiplicity cannot be accounted for if the electron possesses no other properties than mass and charge, because these alone cannot provide any additional small variable interaction to explain the small energy differences in the multiplets.   To solve the problem, Uhlenbeck and Goudsmit suggested that the electron possesses an intrinsic angular momentum, the component of which in any specified direction is $\pm \frac{1}{2}\frac{h}{2\pi}$ with a concomitant magnetic moment of $\pm \frac{1}{2}\cdot\frac{e}{\mu c}\frac{h}{2\pi}$.   The multiplet energy levels arise from the interaction between this intrinsic magnetic moment of the electron and the magnetic field associated with the orbital motion of the electron or electrons about the nucleus of the atom. The intrinsic angular momentum is referred to as "spin" and clearly is quantized, its value being determined by the spin quantum number m_s which may have either of the two allowed values $+\frac{1}{2}$ and $-\frac{1}{2}$.

2.64 The spin property is not unique for electrons, but is exhibited by all particles. It is sometimes useful to imagine it as arising from the actual rotation or spinning of an electronic charge, but this is neither a necessary nor an entirely correct conception. It is generally preferable to treat spin as an additional intrinsic property of the particle not directly derivable from classical considerations. It should be remarked that a complete relativistic theory of the electron introduces the spin automatically, but the complexities of the treatment prevent its ready extension to larger systems.

2.65 Since the interaction between the spin and orbital motion is small, the Hamiltonian operator for one electron in a hydrogenlike atom may be written approximately as the sum of two independent parts

$$H = H_{\text{space}} + H_{\text{spin}},$$

where H_{space} is the Hamiltonian previously considered (see 2.44) and H_{spin} arises from the inclusion of spin. The eigenfunctions of H may then be written as simple products of eigenfunctions of H_{space} and eigenfunctions of H_{spin}. The former are the wave functions $\psi_{n,l,m}$ previously obtained, and the latter, of which only two are possible because the spin is restricted to but two values, are commonly designated α and β to correspond to the eigenvalues $+\frac{1}{2}$ and $-\frac{1}{2}$

GENERAL REFERENCES

CARTMELL and FOWLES, *Valency and Molecular Structure*, Academic Press, Inc., New York, 1956, Ch. 5.

COULSON, *Valence*, The Clarendon Press, Oxford, 1952, Ch. II.

DIEKE, "Atomic and Molecular Physics," Section 7 of *American Institute of Physics Handbook*, edited by Gray, McGraw-Hill Book Company, Inc., New York, 1957.

DUSHMAN, "Quantum Theory of Atomic Spectra and Atomic Structure," Ch. II in Vol. I, *Treatise on Physical Chemistry*, edited by Taylor and Glasstone, D. Van Nostrand Company, Inc., New York, 1942.

EYRING, WALTER and KIMBALL, *Quantum Chemistry*, John Wiley and Sons, Inc., New York, 1947, Ch. IX.

GLASSTONE, *Textbook of Physical Chemistry*, D. Van Nostrand Company, Inc., New York, 1954, Ch. I.

GLASSTONE, *Theoretical Chemistry*, D. Van Nostrand Company, Inc., New York, 1944, Ch. I.

HERZBERG, *Atomic Spectra and Atomic Structure*, Dover Publications, New York, 1944, Ch. III.

PAULING and WILSON, *Introduction to Quantum Mechanics*, McGraw-Hill Book Company, Inc., New York, 1935, Ch. VIII, IX.

PITZER, *Quantum Chemistry*, Prentice-Hall, Inc., New York, 1953, Ch. 5.

RICE and TELLER, *The Structure of Matter*, John Wiley and Sons, Inc., New York, 1949, Ch. 3.

RICE, *Electronic Structure and Chemical Binding*, McGraw-Hill Book Company, Inc., New York, 1940, Ch. VI, VII.

of the spin quantum number m_s. The complete eigenfunctions for the hydrogenlike atoms may then be written

$$\psi = \psi_{n,l,m,m_s} = \psi_{n,l,m}\alpha_{+\frac{1}{2}} \quad \text{or} \quad \psi_{n,l,m}\beta_{-\frac{1}{2}}.$$

2.66 Thus for a hydrogenlike atom there are four quantum numbers, n, l, m, and m_s, which may be considered to be assigned to the electron and which describe completely, in quantum mechanical terms, the behavior of the electron. Because the actual magnitude of the spin-orbit interaction is generally small, it is convenient to retain the description of energy levels previously obtained without spin, each of which was specified by the value of the principal quantum number n and possessed the multiplicity or degeneracy n^2. Now, however, since the electron may have spin $+\frac{1}{2}$ or $-\frac{1}{2}$, each such energy level consists of $2n^2$ distinct dynamical states, each specified by a particular set of values of the four quantum numbers n, l, m, and m_s.

2.67 It is convenient to define spin operators S^2 and S_z analogous to the orbital angular momentum operators M^2 and M_z. The new operators may be shown to commute with the Hamiltonian operator and hence the eigenfunctions ψ of the latter are also eigenfunctions of the spin operators. The appropriate eigenvalues are indicated in the relations:

$$S^2\psi = S(S+1)\left(\frac{h}{2\pi}\right)^2\psi \qquad S = \tfrac{1}{2}$$

$$S_z\psi = m_s\frac{h}{2\pi}\psi \qquad m_s = \pm\tfrac{1}{2}.$$

The Pauli Exclusion Principle

2.68 Consider a system containing, perhaps among other particles, two identical particles. Two configurations of the system which differ only in the interchange of these two particles are not distinguishable in any way, and the calculated probability distribution function must be exactly the same for the two configurations. If ψ is the wave function for the first configuration and ψ' that for the second, with the identical particles interchanged, then

$$\psi^*\psi \equiv \psi'^*\psi', \quad \text{or} \quad \psi^2 \equiv \psi'^2$$

if ψ may be supposed real. This relation implies that

$$\psi' = +\psi \quad \text{or} \quad \psi' = -\psi,$$

that is, that the interchange of identical particles must leave the wave function unchanged (ψ is symmetric) or else merely change its sign (ψ is antisymmetric).

2.69 The Pauli Exclusion Principle summarizes experience in the statement that the complete wave function must be antisymmetric in the coordinates of identical elementary particles (*e.g.*, electrons or protons). For the interchange of composite particles it is evident that the complete wave function must be symmetric if the composite particle consists of an even number of elementary particles (*e.g.*, deuterons), and antisymmetric if the composite particle consists of an odd number of elementary particles (*e.g.*, tritons).

2.70 If each of the electrons in a complex atom is assigned a set of quantum numbers as was suggested earlier in the study of the Bohr model and as will be developed in somewhat greater detail later in this section, then Pauli's original form of the Exclusion Principle (the form usually cited by chemists) states that no two electrons in the same atom may have identical sets of all four quantum numbers. It may be shown that this statement is derivable from the more general form of the Exclusion Principle.

Many-Electron Atoms

2.71 In the neutral atom of atomic number Z the nucleus of charge $+Ze$ is surrounded by Z electrons each of charge $-e$ and, if the nucleus is presumed fixed, of the effective mass μ. If r_i is the radial distance from nucleus to the ith electron and r_{ij} the distance between the ith and jth electrons, then the Hamiltonian operator is approximately

$$H = \frac{-h^2}{8\pi^2\mu} \sum_i \nabla_i^2 - \sum_i \frac{Ze^2}{r_i} + \sum_{i<j} \frac{e^2}{r_{ij}},$$

in which spin-orbit interactions have been ignored. Let us now for the moment suppose that each electron can be instructed to interact normally with the nucleus but to ignore completely all the other electrons in the atom. This truly drastic simplification leads to

$$H \sim H_0 = \frac{-h^2}{8\pi^2\mu} \sum_i \nabla_i^2 - \sum_i \frac{Ze^2}{r_i} = \sum_i H_i^0,$$

where H_i^0 is the Hamiltonian operator for a hydrogenlike atom consisting of the nucleus and the ith electron alone; thus the operator H_0 is a sum of independent terms, one for each electron. The solution of the wave equation $H_0\psi_0 - E_0\psi_0 = 0$ may therefore be written as a corresponding product of independent factors

$$\psi_0 = \psi_1^0\psi_2^0 \cdots = \prod_i \psi_i^0.$$

It is then easily shown that each factor is an eigenfunction of the one-electron Hamiltonian H_i^0 and contributes its eigenvalue E_i^0 to the total energy $E_0 = \sum_i E_i^0$. Thus the wave function of the entire atom is a product of hydrogenlike wave functions, one for each electron. Each function has its own set of quantum numbers n, l, m, and m_s which may be associated with the corresponding electron.

2.72 The product functions which formally satisfy the wave equation (and are well-behaved) do not in general satisfy the Exclusion Principle, which here requires the complete wave function ψ_0 to be antisymmetric in the coordinates of pairs of electrons. If the factor ψ_i^0 in ψ_0 is assigned to electron j and ψ_j^0 to electron i, the new product function ψ'_0 is an equally good wave function. In fact, every new product function derived from ψ_0 by permuting coordinates of electrons in the manner indicated is an equally good wave function for the complex atom, and so also is any linear combination (*i.e.*, sum with arbitrary coefficients) of all of these products. There is one linear combination which is antisymmetric in the coordinates of pairs of electrons and is an entirely acceptable wave function. It may be written in the interesting and useful determinantal form shown. In this expression, $\psi_i^0(k)$ is the ith one-electron eigenfunction

$$\psi_0 = \frac{1}{\sqrt{Z!}} \begin{vmatrix} \psi_1^0(1) & \psi_1^0(2) & \psi_1^0(3) \cdots \psi_1^0(Z) \\ \psi_2^0(1) & \psi_2^0(2) & \psi_2^0(3) \cdots \psi_2^0(Z) \\ \psi_3^0(1) & \psi_3^0(2) & \psi_3^0(3) \cdots \psi_3^0(Z) \\ \cdot & \cdot & \cdot & \cdot \\ \cdot & \cdot & \cdot & \cdots & \cdot \\ \cdot & \cdot & \cdot & \cdot \\ \psi_z^0(1) & \psi_z^0(2) & \psi_z^0(3) \cdots \psi_z^0(Z) \end{vmatrix}$$

(hydrogenlike atom wave function) the arguments of which are the coordinates of the kth electron. The subscript i represents a whole set of quantum numbers $(n, l, m, m_s)_i$. The factor $\dfrac{1}{\sqrt{Z!}}$ is merely a normalization factor.

2.73 The well-known rule for evaluating determinants — form all the products which have an element from each row and each column and add these with positive or negative signs according to a certain scheme — shows us that the determinant is in fact a linear combination of all the possible product functions. Furthermore, the physical operation of interchanging electrons k and l is precisely equivalent to interchanging the kth and the lth columns of the determinant; this merely changes its sign and therefore the function is antisymmetric and satisfies the Pauli Principle. Finally, suppose the ith and jth one-electron functions are identical, so that they have identical sets of the four quantum numbers. The ith and the jth rows of the determinant then are identical and the determinant vanishes. In other words, there can be no wave function for the entire complex atom in which two hydrogenlike wave functions, or more loosely, two electrons have identical sets of values of the four quantum numbers. This is the older, narrower and, to chemists, more common statement of the Pauli Exclusion Principle.

2.74 Let us now construct the hypothetical complex atom in its most stable, or ground, state. We choose for the one-electron wave functions those of lowest energy, subject to the restriction discussed above. The functions will be chosen in order of increasing principal quantum number n; in the simplified case under consideration there is no preference among the several functions corresponding to different l values for a single n value. Thus for an atom of atomic number 7, for example, we should choose the functions specified by the following sets of quantum numbers.

n	l	m	m_s	Function	Number	
1	0	0	$\pm\frac{1}{2}$	$1s$	2	
2	0	0	$\pm\frac{1}{2}$	$2s$	2	Eight equivalent
2	1	0	$\pm\frac{1}{2}$			functions; choose
				$2p$	6	any five.
2	1	±1	$\pm\frac{1}{2}$			

For atomic number 26, we should choose all of these ten functions and sixteen more from the eighteen equivalent functions for $n = 3$: $3s$ (two), $3p$ (six) and $3d$ (ten). In this way we build up the "electronic configuration" of the hypothetical complex atom. For the first example, had we chosen both $2s$ functions and three $2p$ functions we should write $(1s)^2 (2s)^2 (2p)^3$ for the electronic configuration, and for the second example we might have $(1s)^2 (2s)^2 (2p)^6 (3s)^2 (3p)^6$ $(3d)^8$ or perhaps $(1s)^2 (2s)^2 (2p)^6 (3s)^1 (3p)^5 (3d)^{10}$, since in the simplified model all functions for $n = 3$ give the same energy. Evidently the ground states of most of these hypothetical atoms are degenerate; in fact this degeneracy is exhibited by all such atoms except those for which we have no choice in assigning functions of the lowest energy. Those are said to have "closed shells" of electrons; they are the atoms of atomic number 2, 10, 28, 60, 110 . . .. Other atoms, except hydrogen, necessarily have closed shells of lower energy and one unfilled group or shell of electrons. These configurations are relatively less stable than those with only closed shells.

2.75 The treatment of the hypothetical complex atoms in which the electrons interact only with the nucleus and not with one another is thus fairly simple and complete, and quite suggestive to the reader who has already had some experience with electronic configurations and the periodic system of the elements. It is evident, however, that the implications of the model are not entirely correct, and so we must avoid the temptation to pursue the simple theory too far. The physical approximation of neglecting completely the electronic interactions in the atom is really a very drastic one, sufficiently so that the quantitative results are quite in error, and the qualitative results somewhat in error so far as the order of filling the higher electronic shells is concerned. The general notions here developed, however, are correct, and the example serves to introduce the concepts of electronic configurations, closed shells, and the filling of the various electronic levels in order of increasing energy. We shall now return to the original description of the complex atom and attempt a more rigorous treatment.

2.76 The electronic interactions in a complex atom cannot easily be explicitly taken into account in solving the wave equation. Their average effect may however be observed as a modification of the potential function. Thus if the ith electron is far from the nucleus and the other electrons, the latter screen the nucleus and decrease its effective charge nearly to just $+e$ so that the potential function for the ith electron tends toward $\dfrac{-e^2}{r_i}$ when r_i is much larger than all the r_j's. On the other hand, if r_i is much less than the r_j's, the other electrons behave like a charged outer shell which produces a constant contribution to the potential inside, so that the potential for the ith electron tends toward $-Z\dfrac{e^2}{r_i}$ + constant. Effective potential functions $V(r_i)$ may be defined which behave in the manner described for r_i when it is either very large or very small and which otherwise represent the average effect of all the other electrons on electron i. Then to a good approximation

$$H = \frac{-h^2}{8\pi^2\mu} \sum_i \nabla_i{}^2 + \sum_i V(r_i) + H' = H^0 + H' \sim H^0,$$

in which H' is a small term ("perturbing" Hamiltonian) which may be neglected if $V(r_i)$ is carefully chosen. Rewriting H^0 as

$$H^0 = \sum_i \left[\frac{-h^2}{8\pi^2\mu} \nabla_i{}^2 + V(r_i) \right] = \sum_i H_i,$$

we see that it is a sum of independent terms — one for each electron. Thus again the wave function of the whole atom with Z electrons may be written as a product of Z factors which are eigenfunctions of the modified one-electron Hamiltonian H_i, and the energy of the atom is the sum of the corresponding energy eigenvalues for all the Z electrons.

2.77 The eigenfunctions of H_i are known as "atomic orbitals." They consist of an angular part which is identical with that for hydrogenlike atom wave functions and thus introduces the same quantum numbers l and m; a radial part which is not greatly different from that of the hydrogenlike functions and which introduces the principal quantum number n; a spin part which is either α or β as before and which thus adds the spin quantum number m_s. Each atomic orbital is thus identified by the set of four quantum numbers and is often referred to as a $1s$, $2p$, $3d$ . . . orbital to indicate the values of n and l.

2.78 The energies of the general atomic orbitals depend on both n and l but not on m or m_s in the present degree of approximation. Thus the energies of the $3s$, $3p$, and $3d$ atomic orbitals are not identical but increase in the indicated order. For a given value of n the energy increases with increasing values of l, and this spread of energy for each given principal quantum number may become so great for higher values of n that the sub-levels overlap for different n values. The actual displacements vary from atom to atom, but generally the energies of the several orbitals increase in the order $1s$, $2s$, $2p$, $3s$, $3p$, $4s$, $3d$, $4p$, $5s$, $4d$, $5p$, $6s$, $4f$, $5d$, $6p$, $7s$, $5f$, $6d$.

2.79 The reason for the variation of energy with l lies in what is called "screening" of the outer electrons from the nucleus by the inner electrons. The outer electrons are acted upon by an effective field arising from the nucleus and the inner electrons, the latter acting, in effect, to diminish the nuclear field.

Those electrons which do not penetrate near the nucleus are well screened by inner electrons and hence are more loosely held than are electrons which approach the nucleus closely and are thereby less well screened. The probability distribution functions for various sets of quantum numbers show that an electron whose behavior is described by a d orbital does not in general penetrate as near the nucleus as one described by a p orbital for the same value of n; in like manner, the electron described by a p orbital lies on the average outside one described by an s orbital. For a given value of n, the s electrons penetrate most deeply of all; these electrons then are least completely screened and most tightly held. The result is that the energies of the atomic orbitals increase in the order $s, p, d, f \ldots$ for a given value of the principal quantum number.

2.80 The process of constructing ground states of complex atoms as outlined for the hypothetical atom with noninteracting electrons may now be applied with the more satisfactory atomic orbitals. The wave function for the ground state is made up of atomic orbitals including spin, one for each electron, chosen in order of increasing energy (decreasing binding energy) starting with the $1s$ orbital so that the total energy is the lowest possible. Two s orbitals may be used, six p orbitals, ten d orbitals and fourteen f orbitals. The selection made defines the normal electronic configuration of the atom, and although we cannot assign particular electrons to specified orbitals, it is customary to speak of the $1s, 2p, 3d \ldots$ electrons in a complex atom. An electron may be said to "occupy" a given orbital if that orbital is one of those selected as factors for an approximate product wave function.

2.81 Hydrogen has its one electron in a $1s$ orbital; helium, both of its electrons in $1s$ orbitals with opposite spins. In a complex atom no more $1s$ orbitals may be used, however, and lithium requires for its third electron one of the $2s$ orbitals. Beryllium uses the second $2s$ orbital and boron must place its fifth electron in one of the six equivalent $2p$ orbitals. As the atomic number is increased the remaining $2p$ orbitals are occupied until with the element neon of atomic number 10, all six of the $2p$ orbitals are required. Neon has only closed shells of electrons and its configuration is described as $(1s)^2 (2s)^2 (2p)^6$. Sodium, of atomic number 11, uses the same orbitals as neon and must add another, a $3s$ orbital. The neon configuration is repeated in all elements between sodium and argon and describes an electronic kernel of the atom which remains qualitatively unchanged while electrons are added successively to a new sequence starting with the single $3s$ electron of sodium and ending with the sixth $3p$ electron of argon. The electrons in this growing set are termed "valence electrons." Argon, like neon, has only closed shells of electrons which are described in the electronic configuration $(1s)^2 (2s)^2 (2p)^6 (3s)^2 (3p)^6$.

2.82 Atoms of larger atomic number than argon will all have the same basic configuration for the first eighteen electrons, with added orbitals for the remaining electrons. Thus the expected configurations for the normal states of all complex atoms may be built up from the atomic orbitals; their relative energies and the Pauli Exclusion Principle determine which orbitals are to be selected.

It must be remembered that the order of energies is not exactly the same for all atoms and there will be a few discrepancies or deviations from the expected order in the case of atoms of moderate to large atomic number.

2.83 It is evident that by continuing the process just described electronic configurations may be postulated for atoms even of very large atomic number. That such atoms do not exist — an atom of atomic number 122, for example, which might have the electronic configuration $(1s)^2$ $(2s)^2$ $(2p)^6$ $(3s)^2$ $(3p)^6$ $(3d)^{10}$ $(4s)^2$ $(4p)^6$ $(4d)^{10}$ $(4f)^{14}$ $(5s)^2$ $(5p)^6$ $(5d)^{10}$ $(5f)^{14}$ $(6s)^2$ $(6p)^6$ $(6d)^{10}$ $(6f)^1$ $(7s)^2$ $(7p)^6$ $(7d)^1$ $(8s)^2$ — seems not to result from chemical factors concerned with the extranuclear electrons and stability of the nucleus-electron system, but rather from physical considerations of stability within the atomic nucleus itself.

2.84 Let us now return briefly to the wave equation and its approximate solution which depends on the choice of the effective potentials $V(r_i)$. The square of the wave function represents the electron density in the atom and thus may be used to compute a new and more nearly correct effective potential $V(r_i)$. This, in turn, leads to a better approximation to the wave function, and the whole process may be repeated until eventually the computed wave function is essentially identical with that assumed in the determination of $V(r_i)$. This method of successive approximation, introduced by Hartree and extended by Fock, is usually referred to as the method of "self-consistent fields." The method has been used for a number of different atoms and the results constitute probably the best atomic orbitals available.

2.85 The electron density distributions for the ground states of several complex atoms as determined by the method of self-consistent fields are shown in Figure 2.7. The curves show peaks corresponding to the several groups of electrons: that for Na^+, for example, has a first peak for the two $1s$ electrons and a second for the eight $2s$ and $2p$ electrons. The curve for Rb^+ possesses two analogous peaks and in addition two others corresponding to the two groups of electrons with $n = 3$ and $n = 4$. The groups, labeled $K, L, M, N \ldots$, are more commonly referred to as "shells" of electrons. It may be seen that as n increases for a given atom the maximum in the distribution curve becomes less sharp indicating a more diffuse distribution of the less tightly held electrons. It is also seen that as the nuclear charge Z increases, the inner electrons are held more and more tightly to the nucleus, the peaks becoming considerably sharper and located at progressively smaller distances. Thus the simplified picture of shells of electrons about the nucleus, arising from qualitative considerations of the construction of acceptable wave functions for the atom, is found to have some physical basis in the actual electronic distribution, at least within the limits of approximation of the Hartree method of calculation. Since the calculation is at best an approximation, however, in that it replaces actual fields dependent on all instantaneous coordinates of all electrons by average central fields dependent only on the radial coordinate of the particular electron, the distribution curves thereby deduced are not to be taken as precise descriptions of the electronic distribution within the atom. A measure of the extent of approximation is

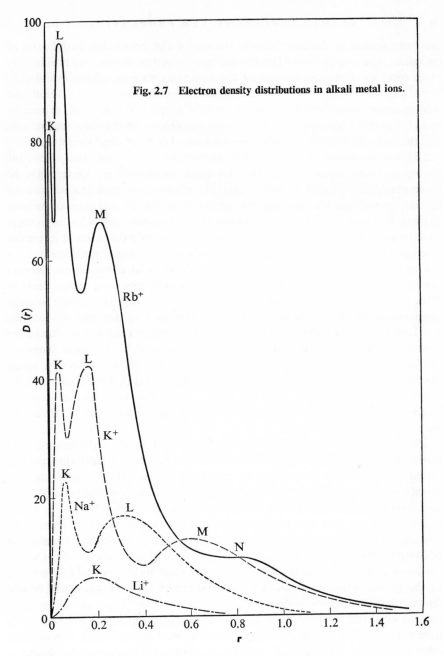

Fig. 2.7 Electron density distributions in alkali metal ions.

afforded by the computation of the energies of the atoms, which on the average are found to be incorrect by about 0.5 volt per electron.

Atomic Spectra and Atomic Structure

2.86 We have previously discussed the energy level diagram for the hydrogen atom (see 2.15). The diagrams for other hydrogenlike atoms (*e.g.*, He⁺, Be³⁺)

are quite similar in structure, almost the only differences being in the scale of energies. The energy level diagrams for many-electron atoms are considerably more complex, however, because of the numerous ways in which several electrons may exhibit both electrostatic and spin-orbit interactions. While the field of spectroscopy and the detailed study of energy level diagrams cannot be included in this book, it is of some interest to examine briefly these interactions and their effects, thereby introducing some useful concepts and definitions.

2.87 Let us consider an atomic system containing, for example, two p electrons having the same value of the principal quantum number n; these might be those outside the closed $1s$ and $2s$ shells in the spectroscopic ground state of carbon, or perhaps the two electrons in a very highly excited state of helium. If there is no interaction at all between these electrons (and with any others which are in the atom), then the energy state is explicitly defined and its energy given by the relations previously discussed. When the electrostatic interactions are considered, however, as is done approximately in constructing effective potential functions, we find that this hypothetical energy state corresponds to three distinct energy states, differing in the way in which the orbital angular momenta of the electrons are combined. For each of the two p electrons $l = 1$, and these combine vectorially to give a quantized resultant L, a quantum number for the atom, which can have the values 0, 1, or 2. The three states are labeled respectively S, P, and D states, in analogy with the states of a single electron; of these, the P state is of lowest energy and is degenerate, and the S state is of highest energy. In the general case where the resultant L of the l values for all electrons might have larger values, the letters F, G, $H \ldots$ are used for $L = 3, 4, 5 \ldots$.

2.88 When the spin-orbit interaction is included in the calculations, then further splitting is observed for the P but not for the S or D states; this splitting of course indicates a multiplicity in the simple levels. The value of the spin quantum number is $\frac{1}{2}$ for each electron and these also combine vectorially to give a quantized resultant S, a second quantum number for the atom, which can have for two electrons the values 0 and 1. In the former case there is no splitting, in the latter a splitting into three components. In general, the number of components is $2S + 1$, corresponding to the actual spin values $-S$, $-S + 1$ $\cdots 0 \cdots + S$, and is indicated by a left superscript in the symbol of the state. In the present example singlet ($S = 0$) and triplet ($S = 1$) states will be observed; in other systems doublets ($S = \frac{1}{2}$), quartets ($S = \frac{3}{2}$), quintets ($S = 2$) $\cdots$ may be observed. A system containing N electrons outside closed shells will have values of S which are integral or half-integral according as N is even or odd; for N even, states of odd multiplicity will be observed, and *vice versa*.

2.89 For each of the two p electrons $m = -1, 0$, or $+1$, and there are six independent combinations of the m values. For each of three of these the two m values are equal and since n and l are also the same for the two electrons, the Pauli Principle requires their m_s values to be different. Thus for these states $S = 0$. That one of the three for which both m values are zero necessarily belongs to the S level for which $L = 0$; the other two belong to the D level for which $L = 2$.

2.90 Each of the other three combinations possesses different m values for the two electrons; consequently they may have paired spins so that $S = 0$, or parallel spins so that $S = 1$. The former three states belong to the D level which thus has a total of five, all with $S = 0$; and the latter three, for which $L = 1$, to the P level. Thus we have found the multiplicities of the ^1S, ^3P, and ^1D levels.

2.91 To determine the splitting for $S = 1$ we consider the ways in which the angular momenta may combine. Measuring angular momenta in units of $\dfrac{h}{2\pi}$, we find that the total orbital angular momentum is $\sqrt{L(L + 1)}$ and the total spin angular momentum is $\sqrt{S(S + 1)}$. These combine to give the total angular momentum $\sqrt{J(J + 1)}$, where J is the quantized vectorial resultant of L and S and hence assumes the values $|L - S|$, $|L - S| + 1 \cdots L + S$, a total of either $2S + 1$ or $2L + 1$ different values according as L is greater than or less than S. The value of the quantum number J is written as a right subscript on the symbol for the state. The state ^1S has $L = 0$, $S = 0$ and hence $J = 0$; when spin-orbit interaction is included we have the $^1S_0$ state; the complete symbol $^1S_0$ is called the *term symbol*. Similarly the ^1D state has $L = 2$, $S = 0$ and so $J = 2$, which gives the $^1D_2$ state. Finally for the ^3P state, $L = 1$ and $S = 1$, so $J = 0$, 1, or 2. Actual computation of the spin-orbit interaction shows that the states are $^3P_0$, $^3P_1$, and $^3P_2$ in order of increasing energy, and the amount of the interaction is proportional to the upper J value so that the $^3P_1 - {}^3P_2$ spacing is twice the $^3P_0 - {}^3P_1$ spacing.

2.92 The three states for which $J \neq 0$ are degenerate, but only the application of an external magnetic field can induce further splitting. In the external field the interaction is determined by the Z-component of total angular momentum, hence by the quantum number M which may have the values $-J$, $-J + 1$ $\cdots 0 \cdots +J$. Thus a state of a given J value is $(2J + 1)$-fold degenerate and in an external field is split into as many components which may be shown to be evenly spaced. The $^3P_2$ and $^1D_2$ states each have five components, for $M = -2, -1, 0, +1, +2$; the $^3P_1$ state has three, for $M = -1, 0, +1$; the $^3P_0$ and $^1S_0$ states have but one component each, for $M = 0$.

2.93 All the relationships developed here are illustrated qualitatively in Figure 2.8. Similar diagrams may be constructed for other electronic configurations; if there are more than two electrons, if the electrons are of different types (*i.e.*, different l values), or if the L values are high, then the diagram may become exceedingly complex. The total number of different states in an external magnetic field is found to be just the number of equivalent independent product functions, including spin, permitted by the Pauli Principle for the specified electronic configuration. Thus we found fifteen for the configuration p^2, and for $1s2p$ there are twelve or for $2s3d$, twenty.

2.94 As the atomic number increases, and especially for atoms with nearly complete shells, the relative magnitude of the spin-orbit interaction increases

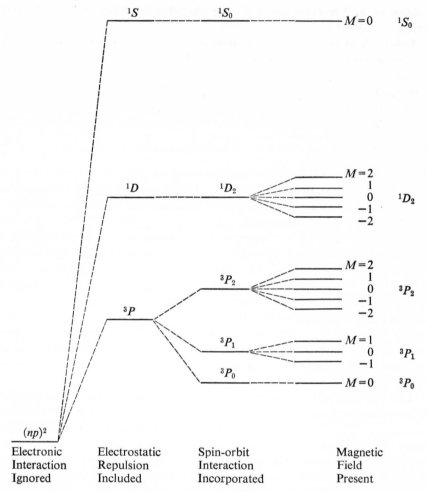

Fig. 2.8   Energy levels for the electronic configuration $(np)^2$**.** (Adapted from Eyring, Walter and Kimball, *Quantum Chemistry*, John Wiley and Sons, Inc., New York, 1947, Fig. 9.1.)

and ultimately becomes considerably larger than the electrostatic effect. In such cases, which we shall not further discuss, the spin-orbit interaction is considered first in deriving the system of energy states, and a different method of combining momenta must be used.

2.95 The only state possible for a completely closed configuration, such as $1s^2$, $1s^2 2s^2$, $2p^6$ or $3p^6 3d^{10}$, is the $^1S_0$ state. For other configurations only the electrons in incomplete shells need be considered in determining the possible states. Thus we find the same kinds of states in the same order of energy for the two configurations $2s2p$ and $1s^2 2s^2 2p^6 3s3p$, or for the pair $1s^2 2s^2 2p^2$ and $1s^2 2s^2 2p^6 3s^2 3p^2$. Finally, we find the same kinds of states, although not usually in the same order of energy, for two configurations, one of which possesses a specified number of electrons in a given sub-shell and the other an equal number of vacancies in that sub-shell; the pairs $2p^2$ and $2p^4$ or $3d^3$ and $3d^7$ are examples. The order of energy of the allowed states and the choice of the lowest or ground state may generally be determined with the aid of certain empirical rules.

2.96 The permitted transitions between the energy states of an atomic system may be described by so-called "selection rules." These rules, usually introduced

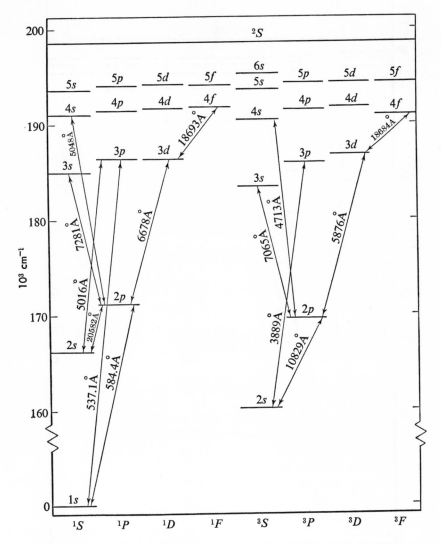

Fig. 2.9 Energy level diagram of He. Ground state configuration is $1s^2$ and in higher states one electron is excited to state indicated. Upper line is at ionization potential and ^2S is the ground state of the ion.

as empirical generalizations, may also in general be derived from considerations of quantum mechanical transition probabilities. The effect of the rules is to eliminate or forbid many conceivable transitions in an atomic system, but, nevertheless, the complexity of energy levels is sufficiently great in most instances to furnish a wealth of spectral lines, especially in the transition and rare earth types of elements.

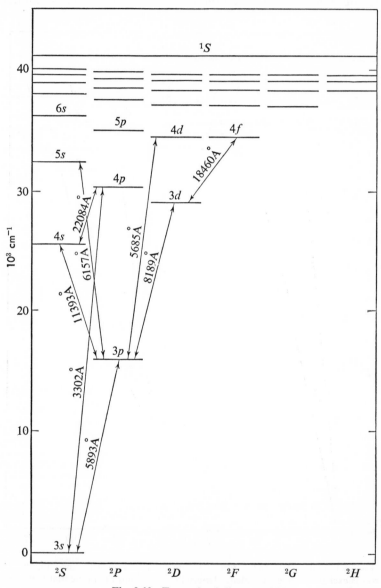

Fig. 2.10   Energy level diagram of Na.

2.97 The generalizations as to states observed, the order of the states, and the allowed transitions are illustrated for several atoms in the energy level diagrams of Figures 2.9 through 2.11; these are of course incomplete in the higher levels, and only a few more or less typical transitions are indicated, with corresponding wavelengths in Ångstrom units appended.

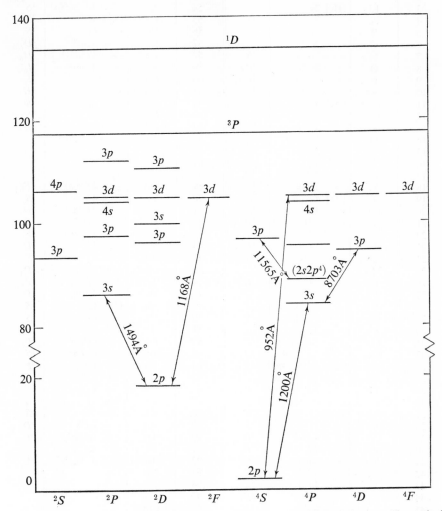

Fig. 2.11 Energy level diagram of N. Two ionization potentials are shown. The excited state is $2s^2 2p^2 nx$, nx indicated on each level. In the ^4P state $(2s2p^4)$ one s electron is excited.

Electronic Configurations of the Elements

2.98 The electronic configurations of all the common elements are shown in Table 2.2. With a very few exceptions, for which reasonable assignments are

TABLE 2.2
Electronic Configurations of the Elements

Atomic Number	Element	Electronic Configuration	Ground State	Atomic Number	Element	Electronic Configuration	Ground State
1	H	$1s$	^2S	52	Te	—— $4d^{10}5s^25p^4$	$^3P_2$
2	He	$1s^2$	^1S	53	I	—— $4d^{10}5s^25p^5$	$^2P_{3/2}$
3	Li	[He] $2s$	^2S	54	Xe	—— $4d^{10}5s^25p^6$	^1S
4	Be	—— $2s^2$	^1S	55	Cs	[Xe] $6s$	^2S
5	B	—— $2s^22p$	$^2P_{1/2}$	56	Ba	—— $6s^2$	^1S
6	C	—— $2s^22p^2$	$^3P_0$	57	La	—— $5d6s^2$	$^2D_{3/2}$
7	N	—— $2s^22p^3$	^4S	58	Ce	—— $4f5d6s^2$	$^3H_5$
8	O	—— $2s^22p^4$	$^3P_2$	59	Pr	—— $4f^36s^2$	$^4I_{9/2}$
9	F	—— $2s^22p^5$	$^2P_{3/2}$	60	Nd	—— $4f^46s^2$	$^5I_4$
10	Ne	—— $2s^22p^6$	^1S	61	Pm	—— $4f^56s^2$	$^6H_{5/2}$
11	Na	[Ne] $3s$	^2S	62	Sm	—— $4f^66s^2$	$^7S_0$
12	Mg	—— $3s^2$	^1S	63	Eu	—— $4f^76s^2$	^8S
13	Al	—— $3s^23p$	$^2P_{1/2}$	64	Gd	—— $4f^75d6s^2$	$^9D_2$
14	Si	—— $3s^23p^2$	$^3P_0$	65	Tb	—— $4f^85d6s^2$	
15	P	—— $3s^23p^3$	^4S	66	Dy		
16	S	—— $3s^23p^4$	$^3P_2$	67	Ho		
17	Cl	—— $3s^23p^5$	$^2P_{3/2}$	68	Er		
18	Ar	—— $3s^23p^6$	^1S	69	Tm	—— $4f^{13}6s^2$	$^2F_{7/2}$
19	K	[Ar] $4s$	^2S	70	Yb	—— $4f^{14}6s^2$	^1S
20	Ca	—— $4s^2$	^1S	71	Lu	—— $4f^{14}5d6s^2$	$^2D_{3/2}$
21	Sc	—— $3d4s^2$	$^2D_{3/2}$	72	Hf	—— $4f^{14}5d^26s^2$	$^3F_2$
22	Ti	—— $3d^24s^2$	$^3F_2$	73	Ta	—— $4f^{14}5d^36s^2$	$^4F_{3/2}$
23	V	—— $3d^34s^2$	$^4F_{3/2}$	74	W	—— $4f^{14}5d^46s^2$	$^5D_0$
24	Cr	—— $3d^54s$	^7S	75	Re	—— $4f^{14}5d^56s^2$	^6S
25	Mn	—— $3d^54s^2$	^6S	76	Os	—— $4f^{14}5d^66s^2$	$^5D_4$
26	Fe	—— $3d^64s^2$	$^5D_4$	77	Ir	—— $4f^{14}5d^76s^2$	$^4F_{9/2}$
27	Co	—— $3d^74s^2$	$^4F_{9/2}$	78	Pt	—— $4f^{14}5d^96s$	$^3D_3$
28	Ni	—— $3d^84s^2$	$^3F_4$	79	Au	[*] $6s$	^2S
29	Cu	—— $3d^{10}4s$	^2S	80	Hg	—— $6s^2$	^1S
30	Zn	—— $3d^{10}4s^2$	^1S	81	Tl	—— $6s^26p$	$^2P_{1/2}$
31	Ga	—— $3d^{10}4s^24p$	$^2P_{1/2}$	82	Pb	—— $6s^26p^2$	$^3P_0$
32	Ge	—— $3d^{10}4s^24p^2$	$^3P_0$	83	Bi	—— $6s^26p^3$	^4S
33	As	—— $3d^{10}4s^24p^3$	^4S	84	Po	—— $6s^26p^4$	$^3P_2$
34	Se	—— $3d^{10}4s^24p^4$	$^3P_2$	85	At	—— $6s^26p^5$	
35	Br	—— $3d^{10}4s^24p^5$	$^2P_{3/2}$	86	Rn	—— $6s^26p^6$	^1S
36	Kr	—— $3d^{10}4s^24p^6$	^1S	87	Fr	[Rn] $7s$	^2S
37	Rb	[Kr] $5s$	^2S	88	Ra	—— $7s^2$	^1S
38	Sr	—— $5s^2$	^1S	89	Ac	—— $6d7s^2$	$^2D_{3/2}$
39	Y	—— $4d5s^2$	$^2D_{3/2}$	90	Th	—— $6d^27s^2$	$^3F_2$
40	Zr	—— $4d^25s^2$	$^3F_2$	91	Pa	—— $6d^37s^2$	
41	Nb	—— $4d^45s$	$^6D_{1/2}$	92	U	—— $5f^36d7s^2$	$^5L_6$
42	Mo	—— $4d^55s$	^7S	93	Np		
43	Tc	—— $4d^55s^2$	^6S	94	Pu		
44	Ru	—— $4d^75s$	$^5F_5$	95	Am		
45	Rh	—— $4d^85s$	$^4F_{9/2}$	96	Cm		
46	Pd	—— $4d^{10}$	^1S	97	Bk		
47	Ag	—— $4d^{10}5s$	^2S	98	Cf		
48	Cd	—— $4d^{10}5s^2$	^1S	99	Es		
49	In	—— $4d^{10}5s^25p$	$^2P_{1/2}$	100	Fm		
50	Sn	—— $4d^{10}5s^25p^2$	$^3P_0$	101	Md		
51	Sb	—— $4d^{10}5s^25p^3$	^4S	102	No		

* Structure of closed shells [Xe] $4f^{14}5d^{10}$.

made on the basis of chemical or other indirect evidence, these configurations are derived from spectroscopic data. The table lists in order the atomic number Z, the symbol, the electronic configuration of the ground state, and the spectroscopic term symbol for the ground state. In the table, systems of closed levels corresponding to the configurations for the inert gases are represented in the electronic configurations of the succeeding elements by the bracketed symbol of the inert gas.

2.99 The building up of complex atoms is seen to follow a simple and regular pattern for the first twenty elements, and then to exhibit somewhat more erratic behavior. Hydrogen has a single 1s electron, helium has two 1s electrons and completes the shell. Lithium adds a 2s electron and beryllium a second, thus completing that level. Boron starts the 2p sub-shell which is complete with neon. The 3s and 3p levels are complete at magnesium and argon, respectively. Because of the variation of energy with the quantum number l, the energy of the 3d level is generally somewhat higher than that of the 4s sub-shell, and therefore the latter is filled first, being completed at calcium. In the succeeding elements the 3d level is filled but not perfectly regularly because the 3d and 4s shells do not differ greatly in energy. Toward the end of the series the 3d level seems to fill preferentially, and with copper the 3d level is completed by transferring an electron out of the 4s sub-shell. The elements zinc through krypton then use up the 4s and 4p levels. The behavior is repeated for the 5s, 4d, and 5p levels in the elements rubidium through xenon. At element 55, cesium, a similar pattern begins with the 6s sub-shell, but this sequence is further complicated by the existence of the 4f level, the energy of which generally is quite near that of the 5d level. The 6s level is complete at barium and the 5d sub-shell is started with lanthanum, but thereafter the 4f sub-shell seems to be of somewhat lower energy and in the elements cerium through lutetium the 4f orbitals are added, often at the expense of the 5d orbital originally used at lanthanum. When all the 4f orbitals have been occupied, then the previous pattern is resumed; the 5d sub-shell is complete at gold and the 6p level at radon. With francium the same general procedure starts again with two important modifications; first, the 6d shell seems relatively lower than the 5f level for the earlier members of the series, so that 5f occupancy seems not to start until the element uranium; second, limitations of nuclear stability terminate the series of elements before the entire 7s, 6d, 5f, 7p series can be constructed, the final, perhaps hypothetical, element in such a series being the element of atomic number 118.

2.100 The process just described is based on energy considerations in choosing appropriate factors of an approximate wave function for the complex atom. The result, however, is a remarkable structure which arranges the elements in a manner which naturally correlates and illustrates not only physical but also chemical properties. The configurations which have been derived follow a periodic pattern and in fact fit almost precisely the requirements of a periodic system of the elements. In the next section this periodic arrangement will be examined in considerably greater detail.

CHAPTER 3

THE PERIODIC CLASSIFICATION OF THE ELEMENTS

3.1 In the preceding chapter we developed a periodic assignment of electronic configurations of the elements. These configurations, in abbreviated form with the closed shells of electrons omitted, are shown in Figure 3.1 in the so-called "long period" form of the periodic chart of the elements. The arrangement is such that all the elements in a column, or group as it is to be called, have similar electronic configurations with respect to the number and kind of outer electrons. Except in the central part of the table where d orbitals are being filled and in the two series of elements where f orbitals are being filled, the correspondence of electronic configurations outside closed shells of electrons is exact in each group. This correspondence is indicated in the spectroscopic term values, which depend only on the electrons outside closed shells. Thus hydrogen and the alkali metals of group I, each of which has a single s electron outside a closed shell of electrons, all have the same spectral designation ^2S, which describes this type of configuration. Similarly in group VIII all the inert gases with completely filled orbitals have the ground state ^1S, and the group VI elements oxygen through polonium the ground state $^3P_2$, the lowest of several states corresponding to two unfilled p orbitals in the atom.

GENERAL REFERENCES

BRISCOE, *The Structure and Properties of Matter*, McGraw-Hill Book Company, Inc., New York, 1935, Ch. III.

DUSHMAN, "Quantum Theory of Atomic Spectra and Atomic Structure," Ch. II in Vol. I, *Treatise on Physical Chemistry*, edited by Taylor and Glasstone, D. Van Nostrand Company, Inc., New York, 1942.

EYRING, WALTER and KIMBALL, *Quantum Chemistry*, John Wiley and Sons, Inc., New York, 1947, Ch. IX.

GLASSTONE, *Textbook of Physical Chemistry*, D. Van Nostrand Company, Inc., New York, 1954, Ch. I.

GLASSTONE, *Theoretical Chemistry*, D. Van Nostrand Company, Inc., New York, 1944, Ch. I.

PARTINGTON, *A Text-Book of Inorganic Chemistry*, Macmillan and Company, Ltd., London, 1939, Ch. XXV.

WEEKS, *The Discovery of the Elements*, Journal of Chemical Education, Easton, Pa., 1956, Ch. 24.

Periodic table — REPRESENTATIVE / SHORT TRANSITION SERIES (TRANSITION TRIADS)

I	II									I	II	III	IV	V	VI	VII	VIII
1. H $1s$																	2. He $1s^2$
3. Li $2s$	4. Be $2s^2$											5. B $2s^2 2p$	6. C $2s^2 2p^2$	7. N $2s^2 2p^3$	8. O $2s^2 2p^4$	9. F $2s^2 2p^5$	10. Ne $2s^2 2p^6$
11. Na $3s$	12. Mg $3s^2$											13. Al $3s^2 3p$	14. Si $3s^2 3p^2$	15. P $3s^2 3p^3$	16. S $3s^2 3p^4$	17. Cl $3s^2 3p^5$	18. Ar $3s^2 3p^6$
19. K $4s$	20. Ca $4s^2$	21. Sc $3d 4s^2$	22. Ti $3d^2 4s^2$	23. V $3d^3 4s^2$	24. Cr $3d^5 4s$	25. Mn $3d^5 4s^2$	26. Fe $3d^6 4s^2$	27. Co $3d^7 4s^2$	28. Ni $3d^8 4s^2$	29. Cu $3d^{10} 4s$	30. Zn $3d^{10} 4s^2$	31. Ga $-4p$	32. Ge $-4p^2$	33. As $-4p^3$	34. Se $-4p^4$	35. Br $-4p^5$	36. Kr $-4p^6$
37. Rb $5s$	38. Sr $5s^2$	39. Y $4d 5s^2$	40. Zr $4d^2 5s^2$	41. Nb $4d^4 5s$	42. Mo $4d^5 5s$	43. Tc $4d^5 5s^2$	44. Ru $4d^7 5s$	45. Rh $4d^8 5s$	46. Pd $4d^{10}$	47. Ag $4d^{10} 5s$	48. Cd $4d^{10} 5s^2$	49. In $-5p$	50. Sn $-5p^2$	51. Sb $-5p^3$	52. Te $-5p^4$	53. I $-5p^5$	54. Xe $-5p^6$
55. Cs $6s$	56. Ba $6s^2$	57. La* $5d 6s^2$	72. Hf $-5d^2 6s^2$	73. Ta $-5d^3 6s^2$	74. W $-5d^4 6s^2$	75. Re $-5d^5 6s^2$	76. Os $-5d^6 6s^2$	77. Ir $-5d^7 6s^2$	78. Pt $-5d^9 6s$	79. Au $-5d^{10} 6s$	80. Hg $-5d^{10} 6s^2$	81. Tl $-6p$	82. Pb $-6p^2$	83. Bi $-6p^3$	84. Po $-6p^4$	85. At $-6p^5$	86. Rn $-6p^6$
87. Fr $7s$	88. Ra $7s^2$	89. Ac† $6d 7s^2$															

* Lanthanides

58. Ce $4f 5d 6s^2$	59. Pr $4f^3 6s^2$	60. Nd $4f^4 6s^2$	61. Pm $4f^5 6s^2$	62. Sm $4f^6 6s^2$	63. Eu $4f^7 6s^2$	64. Gd $4f^7 5d 6s^2$	65. Tb $4f^8 5d 6s^2$	66. Dy	67. Ho	68. Er	69. Tm $4f^{13} 6s^2$	70. Yb $4f^{14} 6s^2$	71. Lu $4f^{14} 5d 6s^2$

† Actinides

90. Th $6d^2 7s^2$	91. Pa $6d^3 7s^2$	92. U $5f^3 6d 7s^2$	93. Np	94. Pu	95. Am	96. Cm	97. Bk	98. Cf	99. Es	100. Fm	101. Md	102. No

Fig. 3.1 The periodic system of the elements.

3.2 In a horizontal row of the table, or period, as it is specifically designated, the configurations change fairly regularly as the atomic number and the number of extranuclear electrons increase uniformly. In each period the configurations go through a cycle from the beginning of occupancy of a new set of orbitals to its completion. The periods are of increasing length, 2, 8, 8, 18, 18, 32, . . . elements, a natural result of the operation of the Pauli Exclusion Principle and the existence of degeneracy in the principal energy levels of the original hydrogenlike wave functions. The numbers 2, 8, 18, 32 are just the numbers of available orbitals, including spin, for $n = 1, 2, 3, 4$; or in the more common usage of chemists, twice the number of orbitals, each of which can accommodate two electrons. The delay in filling $3d$ levels makes the third period only eight elements long and places the elements which fill $3d$ orbitals in the fourth period with those which fill $4s$ and $4p$ orbitals. In the same way there are two periods of eighteen elements because the filling of the $4f$ level is still further delayed, and the corresponding elements are to be found in the sixth period with those which fill the $6s$, $5d$, and $6p$ orbitals.

3.3 The chemical properties of an element are determined primarily by the electronic configuration of its atoms. The elements within a group therefore may be expected to have similar properties. However, since the configurations do differ in the nature and number of closed shells of electrons, and in the average radial distance and binding energy of the valence or outer electrons, we may also expect gradations in chemical properties within a group. These gradations, which will be discussed later in detail, should be fairly uniform, and in some degree the relative gradations in chemical properties should be similar for different groups.

3.4 Within each period we may expect a much wider variation in properties than that exhibited within a group; furthermore, a similar variation will be repeated in each subsequent period. In the long periods of eighteen elements, and especially in the very long periods of nominally thirty-two elements, the variation in properties is rapid at the beginning and near the end, and very much less pronounced in the central regions, where the electronic configurations vary only in fairly deep portions of the atom and the outer electron configurations remain nearly fixed.

3.5 It is clear that the configuration of the outermost electrons, that is, those with the highest value of the principal quantum number, does not alone determine the properties of an element, for otherwise all the elements from calcium through nickel, for example, would have the same properties, and so also would potassium and copper, or more interestingly, perhaps, cesium and gold. In the latter instances the difference in reactivity is related to the difference in ionization potential. The outermost s electron of the alkali metal is less tightly held than that of the second element because the screening due to the completely closed configuration of electrons in the inert gas preceding the alkali metal is quite effective, but in the case of the second element, copper or gold, the less penetrating d or f electrons which are added as the nuclear charge increases in the period are less effective in screening the outermost s electron from the nucleus.

3.6 The metals in group II, the elements zinc, cadmium, and mercury, the inert gases of group VIII, and certain transition elements, palladium and ytterbium for example, are seen to have completely closed levels of electrons in the ground state. Since obviously these elements have far from identical chemical properties, one must take into consideration relative energies as well as ground state configurations. Among the elements listed, the inert gases have high ionization potentials and the others relatively low ionization potentials; the gradual filling up of a p level to produce an inert gas adds electrons to the outermost shell, where they are relatively inefficient in screening each other from the nucleus, with the result that as the nuclear charge is increased all the outermost electrons become quite firmly bound.

3.7 The chemical properties of an element in many cases correspond not to the spectroscopically determined ground state but to one derived from it by relatively minor shifts in configuration. When we discuss chemical binding between atoms we shall find that a determining factor is the number of unpaired electrons in the atoms concerned, and that atoms with no unpaired electrons do not form stable bonds. All of the atoms mentioned in the paragraph above contain only paired electrons in the ground states described (this is always indicated by the spectroscopic term symbol ^1S). The formation of chemical bonds is made possible by the "promotion" of an electron in a closed shell to a shell of only slightly higher energy, which produces two unpaired electrons. The promotion of a $2s$ electron to the $2p$ state in the elements beryllium through carbon, which requires relatively little energy because the levels are quite near together, is responsible for the normal chemical behavior of those elements. On the other hand, the $1s$ and $2s$ levels in helium are far apart, as are the np and $(n+1)s$ levels for the heavier inert gases, and promotion is not observed. Thus helium is an inert gas instead of an alkaline earth metal. Promotion is responsible for the chemical reactivity of the other nongaseous elements cited in the previous paragraph.

3.8 When filling s orbitals there is no uncertainty in the order of occupancy: of the two (two, because we include spin explicitly) equivalent orbitals one is chosen first, and then the other. In the case of p, d, or f orbitals, however, we must look a little further to determine the order of filling. The p, d, and f orbitals possess maxima in different directions in space. If for example the orbital $p_z\alpha$ were chosen first, to choose next $p_z\beta$ would be to localize the electrons in each other's vicinity and lead to mutual repulsion. On the other hand, if the second electron were to be described by any of the other four available orbitals, $p_x\alpha$, $p_x\beta$, $p_y\alpha$, or $p_y\beta$, the repulsion would be considerably less and the configuration more stable. Thus we expect p, d, or f orbitals generally to be filled up in such a manner that the electrons remain unpaired as long as possible, and, experiments indicate, with parallel spins in the different equivalent orbitals. This is sometimes referred to by chemists as the *Principle of Maximum Mul-*

tiplicity. For example, in a notation which is self-evident, we describe the detailed configuration of the *p* electrons of nitrogen as [↑] [↑] [↑] rather than [↑↓] [↑] [ ], and of the *d* electrons of niobium as [↑] [↑] [↑] [↑] [ ] rather than [↑↓] [↑↓] [ ] [ ] [ ].* The conclusion we have reached is intimately related to the observations on chemical binding as determined by the number of unpaired electrons; in fact, there is a close similarity between the dispersion phenomenon involved here and that of promotion discussed in the preceding paragraph.

3.9 A further consequence of the argument on space localization of the *p* electrons is that the addition of the fourth *p* electron must bring about a somewhat larger increase in energy than accompanied the addition of each of the earlier electrons in the group. The increase in energy, or decrease in binding energy, arising from the interaction of the two electrons in the same space orbital, is reflected in the sudden decrease in the first ionization potential between groups V and VI in the otherwise regularly increasing values across a period. The situation with respect to the sixth *d* electron or the eighth *f* electron is analogous but complicated by the fact that these are deep in the atom and the effect on ionization potential much less direct and simple. In any case, the effect is to make a half-filled orbital, other than an *s* orbital, rather more stable than its neighbors on either side.

3.10 In the construction of electronic configurations we saw that each element was derived from its predecessor by the addition of one extranuclear electron. The positive charge on the nucleus was of course increased by one, and although this is only of secondary importance chemically, the mass usually increased as well. The approximate wave function was modified, generally but not always without other change, by the incorporation of an additional one-electron atomic orbital, which may be supposed for the sake of discussion to be occupied by the additional electron. Thus the changes which distinguish one element from its predecessor (in order of increasing atomic number) may be attributed to the last electron added; this electron is referred to as the "differentiating electron."

3.11 The nature of the differentiating electron, as described approximately by its own atomic orbital, and the nature of its interactions with the electrons already present determine the configuration and behavior of the resulting atom. The eleventh electron in sodium, for example, which differentiates sodium from neon, must occupy a 3*s* orbital. This electron is on the average farther removed from the nucleus than any of neon's electrons, and is detached from the atom with relative ease. Those properties of atoms which result from the presence of loosely held electrons — metallic conduction or ionic bond formation as we shall see subsequently — are much more pronounced in sodium than in neon; in fact the very tightness with which the electrons are held in neon makes these differences from sodium almost differences in kind rather than in degree. On the other hand, the electron which differentiates europium from samarium is a

---

* The directions of the arrows in this notation are unimportant; dots may convey the same information about the pairing of electrons in the orbitals.

$4f$ electron, enters a shell already well started but one yet of sufficient capacity that after the addition it is still quite incomplete, and in general produces only a slight modification in properties of the element, as illustrated by the ionization potentials which are 5.67 and 5.6 volts, respectively.

3.12 The structure of the periodic system of elements and the energetic and spatial relationships previously discussed suggest that in considering the different types of differentiating electrons, s and p orbitals be considered together. The d and f orbitals, however, filling up as they do in delayed steps corresponding to the addition of electrons to inner shells of the atom, are of a different nature and their differentiating electrons are conveniently considered in separate categories. Thus we are led to a classification of the elements according to the type of orbital which the differentiating electron enters. We shall discuss three classes of elements.

1. The representative (or regular) elements: the differentiating electron enters an s or p level
2. The short transition series elements: the differentiating electron enters a d level
3. The two long transition series of elements: the differentiating electron enters an f level

3.13 The classification given here is similar to one due to Bohr, who suggested that the elements be grouped into four classes according to the number of incomplete shells of electrons in the atoms.

1. No incomplete shells of electrons
2. One incomplete shell of electrons
3. Two incomplete shells of electrons
4. Three incomplete shells of electrons

In this classification a "shell" implies the set of orbitals for a given n, except that the outermost shell (highest value of n) is complete at eight electrons, and the next outermost shell complete at eighteen electrons. The actual grouping of elements is the same in the two systems except that the Bohr classification divides the first group of regular or representative elements into two, one containing the inert gases and the other the remaining regular elements. In the Bohr classification, emphasis is placed on the role of the entire configuration in determining the properties of the element; in the differentiating electron classification, this emphasis is maintained but the effect of successive additions of an electron in modifying the properties of the elements is also stressed. This point of view will be found particularly valuable in the discussion of horizontal variations of properties within the periods of the usual long period chart.

3.14 The strict application of the differentiating electron criterion places the elements of the zinc, cadmium, and mercury family among the representative elements. This leads, of course, to the unfortunate result that the elements of this family and those of group II are classed together, a circumstance not realized

for any other group. Some of the chemical properties of these elements, however, may suggest, with increasing emphasis for the heavier elements, that they
be classed among the transition elements and be considered the terminal elements of each of the three short transition series. The chemistry of these
elements will be discussed from this viewpoint. If the d level did not fill up
preferentially at the expense of the succeeding s shell in the immediately preceding elements, there would of course be no question about this assignment.
Furthermore, as a point of interest only, if one applies the concept of the differentiating electron to the doubly charged ions of the elements of the copper and
zinc groups, group III, and the following groups, then zinc, cadmium, and
mercury are unequivocally classed with the transition elements and these are
distinct from the representative elements which follow. With this arrangement,
then, the classification of the elements may be made as follows:

3.15 The representative elements comprise those in the first two and last six
columns of the long period chart; the short transition series elements are those
in the intermediate ten columns; the two long transition series are those shown
separately, one, the lanthanides consisting of the elements cerium through
lutetium and the other, the actinides which start with thorium and run on as far
as the presently known elements extend.

3.16 We shall expect certain fundamental similarities or relationships among
the elements of each class, and definite differences between the elements of
different classes. We shall consider briefly the horizontal and vertical relationships among the three classes of elements.

3.17 The class of representative elements contains all of the nonmetallic elements and all of the most reactive metallic elements. The representative
elements in each period except the first illustrate an almost complete cycle of
behavior starting with a reactive metal and proceeding through less reactive
metals, relatively unreactive and then more reactive nonmetals to an inert gas
at the end. The behavior is repeated in the next period with a shift toward more
metallic characteristics all along the period. The metallic representative elements of groups I and II characteristically exhibit but one oxidation state,
numerically equal to the group number; the nonmetallic representative elements, however, exhibit several oxidation states, prominent among which, especially for the elements of groups V, VI, and VII, are negative oxidation states.
The vertical group relationships are quite pronounced among the representative
elements. The similarity of the alkali metals of group I, for example, is evident
in both their physical properties (they are soft, easily fusible, malleable and
ductile metals, and very good conductors of heat and electricity) and their
chemical properties (they are reactive metals forming compounds in which they
exhibit the oxidation state of $+1$, and the compounds of the alkalis with a given
anion resemble one another quite closely in color, solubility and other common
properties). In the same way, the elements of the halogen group exhibit a
similarity of properties which can result only from a fundamental similarity in
structure. This group illustrates, as well, the gradation of properties within a

group: physically, as the atomic weight increases one observes a difficultly con-densible and then an easily condensible gas, a volatile liquid, and a somewhat volatile solid; chemically, there is a change from a highly reactive nonmetal with a predominant −1 oxidation state through decreasingly reactive nonmetals to a considerably less reactive nonmetal which exhibits a relatively much greater tendency toward positive oxidation states. The other groups of representative elements show the same sort of fundamental similarity with superimposed grada-tions of properties. In general, the gradation of chemical properties with increasing atomic weight will be toward greater reactivity for the most metallic elements (*i.e.*, groups I and II) and toward lesser reactivity in the case of the nonmetallic elements. The rate of such variation, insofar as one can describe such a rate, is approximately the same in all groups of representative elements. The trends in the physical properties of the representative elements within a given group are generally somewhat more rapid for the nonmetals than for the metallic elements.

3.18 The set of representative elements in a period is derived from the filling-up of both *s* and *p* orbitals. Although the completion of the *s* orbital, at the group II alkaline earth and the zinc group element, in the long periods, does not give a highly stable configuration such as is obtained in completing the *p* orbital at the inert gas, there is generally observed a break in the otherwise fairly smooth horizontal variation of properties at this point. Thus the first ionization potential increases for the *s* electrons in groups I and II, then de-creases upon the addition of the first *p* electron in group III, and then increases regularly again across the period, except for the break between groups V and VI. In the long periods the interposition of the transition series complicates the situation to some extent; the ionization potential of the group III element (gallium, indium, thallium) is lower than that of its immediate predecessor in the zinc-cadmium-mercury family, but except for the lightest element is higher than that of the corresponding alkaline earth metal. The explanation for this latter fact in terms of structure is analogous to that offered for the difference between potassium and copper, for example: the *d* or *d* and *f* electrons added in the transition series do not penetrate deeply and thus do not shield completely the *s* and *p* electrons from the increased nuclear charge.

3.19 In general, the electropositive nature of the representative elements decreases as one moves across a period from the left, and increases as one moves down a group from the top. One obvious consequence is that the most electro-positive, and hence most reactive metal is the heaviest alkali metal, while the most electronegative, and therefore most reactive nonmetal is the lightest halogen. A second consequence is the "diagonal relationship" between an element and its neighbor one group to the right and one period down. The two steps at least partially compensate in their effects on electronic behavior with the result that in type and strength of chemical bond and general properties of resulting compounds, although not of course in the numerical valence or com-pound formula, such pairs as lithium and magnesium, beryllium and aluminum, boron and silicon, and even oxygen and chlorine, are found to be rather similar. As may be evident in the choice of examples, these diagonal relationships are of greater interest for the lighter than for the heavier elements.

3.20 The elements in each of the second and third classes are all metals, and most of them are characterized by several different positive oxidation states. In either a short transition or long transition series there is not the sweeping variation which is exhibited in the series of representative elements within a period; all the elements of a short transition series are fundamentally similar in chemical and in most physical properties, and in the long transition series the similarity is even greater, so much so that the separation of lanthanide or actinide mixtures is a difficult task. In addition, it is considered no great inconvenience to place each long transition series of elements in a single location in the periodic table, although in other cases each location is presumed to specify a single set of properties for the element it contains. In the usual periodic chart, the horizontal relationships among the long transition series of elements are rather more interesting and important than the vertical or group relationships. This fact was partly responsible in the early days of periodic classification for a great deal of difficulty in arranging the elements. The "short period" form of table folded the longer periods to produce sub-groups of elements, the numbering of which persists in some of the long period charts; these sub-groups in many ways seemed unaccountably different from each other within a single group. The elements copper, silver, and gold accompanied the alkali metals; chromium, molybdenum, and tungsten fell in group VI with oxygen and sulfur; and the "transition triads" (iron, cobalt, and nickel; ruthenium, rhodium, and palladium; or osmium, iridium, and platinum) were found with the inert gases of group VIII unless these were transferred to a new group 0, as was often done. Attempts to justify such assignments in terms of vertical group relationships were necessarily not very successful, and we now see the reason in the configurations of the elements concerned.

3.21 In general, the metallic elements of the short transition series exhibit several different oxidation states, the higher oxidation states being relatively more stable for the intermediate elements in each series. Their ions are often colored and often paramagnetic, these properties being associated with incomplete inner shells of electrons. Both the elements and their compounds frequently show considerable catalytic activity in a variety of specific types of reactions. Complex formation is quite common, and complexes often stabilize unusual oxidation states which are not observed in simple compounds. With increasing atomic number the reactivity of the elements in a short transition series generally decreases but not in a regular fashion.

3.22 The corresponding elements of a given group in the three short transition series show resemblances in physical and chemical properties, the similarities being greatest at either end of the series and least in the region occupied by the transition triads near the middle of the series. The elements scandium, yttrium, and lanthanum, which introduce the three transition series, are sufficiently similar in chemical properties that their separation is a fairly difficult chemical problem, as is the separation of hafnium and zirconium in the next group. Within the groups at the beginning of the series there is a regular increase in electropositive character and reactivity with increasing atomic weight, but in the later groups the variation is less regular, principally because of the insertion of the series of rare-earth metals in the sixth period. Thus we find gold less reactive than silver, and mercury less reactive than cadmium.

3.23 The transition elements of the iron, cobalt, and nickel families constitute in each period a transition triad. In the older short period form of the periodic table these sets of elements serve somewhat the same purpose as the inert gases in linking the end of a sequence of elements to the beginning of the next more or less similar sequence. The element following each triad resembles, as we have seen, the alkali metal preceding, and similarly for succeeding groups, at least to the extent that a moderately reasonable and useful short period table could be constructed. The members of a transition triad resemble one another fairly closely, especially in the two heavier triads, and generally resemble chemically the elements immediately preceding rather more than those immediately following; this behavior, however, is considerably more pronounced in the fourth period than in the sixth. In a given triad, reactivity decreases with increasing atomic number. The elements of the triad in the fourth period are markedly more reactive than those of the subsequent triads; these latter, often referred to as the "platinum metals" or "noble metals," are relatively inert. The three respective pairs of elements in the ruthenium and osmium triads exhibit close analogies in physical and chemical behavior, but the iron triad elements differ from these in many respects. In addition to their greater reactivity, one observes relatively greater stability of their lower oxidation states, ferromagnetic behavior of the metals, and rather important differences in fusibility, hardness, tensile strength, and similar physical properties.

3.24 It is of incidental interest that the chemical atomic weights of the three elements in any triad do not differ greatly one from another. The differences within a triad are generally rather less than the average atomic weight increments for the other elements of the same long period.

3.25 The two long transition series consist of elements whose electronic configurations are built up step-wise by the addition of successive f electrons to an inner shell, the configuration of the outer shell remaining fixed or nearly so. The addition of electrons to the $4f$ level produces the fourteen elements following lanthanum, the lanthanides, and the $5f$ electrons produce the actinides, of which there is not a complete series. There is some question as to whether thorium should be considered the second element in the fourth short transition series or the first element of the rare-earth metal type in the second long transition series. Physical and chemical evidence seem to favor somewhat the former assignment, but in any event the situation is not nearly so clear as with cerium in the first rare-earth series. (See Ch. 27.)

3.26 The members of a long transition series are characterized by a common oxidation state of $+3$, and in addition, many of the elements exhibit other positive oxidation states as well. The ions are often colored and paramagnetic. The elements resemble one another very closely in physical properties and chemical reactivity, and their corresponding compounds are quite similar in color, solubility, and other usual properties. There is a slight diminution in reactivity as the atomic number increases within one of the series. The somewhat irregular pattern of filling $4f$ and $5d$ shells in the lanthanide series is not reflected in gross variations in chemical behavior because the electrons are deep in the atom; thus no difficulty is experienced at the terminal element lutetium analogous to that considered at the ends of the short transition series.

3.27 Since the actinide series is incomplete, no entirely inclusive statement may be made about vertical relationships between the two series. In general, analogies are observed between corresponding elements in the two series or between compounds of corresponding elements with a given nonmetal or nonmetallic radical. The actinide elements generally are relatively more stable in higher oxidation states, and only for uranium and the heavier elements is a fairly stable common $+3$ oxidation state observed. For the later elements in the actinide series the expected similarities with the lanthanide elements in solubilities and electrode potentials, for example, were used in designing experimental methods for separation of the synthetically prepared elements.

3.28 The detailed properties and behavior of elements in the three classes will be taken up in subsequent chapters after the discussion of the general relations between electronic configurations and the chemical and physical properties of atoms.

CHAPTER 4

ATOMIC STRUCTURE AND PROPERTIES OF THE ELEMENTS

Atomic Sizes and Size Relationships

Atomic Volumes

4.1 In the development of the atomic hypothesis it was evident from the first that atoms are necessarily small — much smaller than the limit of ordinary vision. The determination of just how small the atoms actually are, however, was not possible with the experimental techniques available until recent years, and only the most indirect means could be used to afford an estimate. The order of magnitude and relative sizes, and their variation with atomic weight could be inferred for elements in the solid state from measurements of the atomic volume, *i.e.*, the volume of one gram-atomic weight of an element. If the atomic weight is W and the density D, then the atomic volume $V = W/D$. The density may be determined by any of numerous methods, and the atomic weight by Cannizzaro's method or by the combination of equivalent weight determination with a specific heat measurement for the application of the approximate Dulong-

GENERAL REFERENCES

BREWER, BROMLEY, GILLES and LOFGREN, "The Thermodynamic Properties of the Halides," Paper 6 in *The Chemistry and Metallurgy of Miscellaneous Materials: Thermodynamics*, edited by Quill, McGraw-Hill Book Company, Inc., New York, 1950.

CLARK, *The Electronic Structure and Properties of Matter*, Chapman and Hall, Ltd., London, 1934, Ch. VII, VIII, X.

GLASSTONE, *Textbook of Physical Chemistry*, D. Van Nostrand Company, Inc., New York, 1954, Ch. V.

PAULING, *The Nature of the Chemical Bond*, Cornell University Press, Ithaca, N.Y., 1940, Ch. V, X.

RICE and TELLER, *The Structure of Matter*, John Wiley and Sons, Inc., New York, 1949, Ch. 8.

RICE, *Electronic Structure and Chemical Binding*, McGraw-Hill Book Company, Inc., New York, 1940, Ch. XVI.

STILLWELL, *Crystal Chemistry*, McGraw-Hill Book Company, Inc., New York, 1938, Ch. II.

WHITE, "X-ray Analysis of the Solid State," Ch. IV in Vol. II, *Treatise on Physical Chemistry*, edited by Taylor and Glasstone, D. Van Nostrand Company, Inc., New York, 1951.

Petit rule. The atomic volume is not the volume of the atom itself, but rather the entire volume occupied by Avogadro's number of atoms and the intervening spaces. The cube root of the volume/atom measures the mean distance between atomic centers in the solid element; if all solid elements contained spherical atoms arranged in contact in the same sort of crystal lattice, then these distances would be accurately proportional to the atomic diameters of the several elements. It will be seen that the volume/atom reflects not only actual atomic size and the strength of interatomic forces, but also the formation of molecules, their size, and their intermolecular forces. Thus the atomic volume, valuable as it was in Lothar Meyer's reasoning about the elements, is not a clear guide to the properties of the atoms themselves.

4.2 Table 4.1 lists the atomic volumes of several of the more common elements; the data refer to 20° except for hydrogen ($-250°$, liquid), chlorine ($-102°$, solid), and argon ($-223°$, solid). The successive sections give values for the alkali metals, the third period of elements, the common alkaline earth metals, the common halogens, and four other randomly selected elements.

4.3 We see immediately that atomic dimensions are in Ångstrom units, that

TABLE 4.1

Selected Atomic Volumes

Atomic Number	Element	Atomic Volume	Volume/atom	$\sqrt[3]{Volume/atom}$
1	Hydrogen	12.5 cc.	20.8 Å³	2.75 Å
3	Lithium	13.1	21.7	2.79
11	Sodium	23.9	39.7	3.41
19	Potassium	45.6	75.8	4.23
37	Rubidium	56.0	93.0	4.53
55	Cesium	70.6	117	4.89
11	Sodium	23.9	39.7	3.41
12	Magnesium	14.4	23.9	2.88
13	Aluminum	10.0	16.6	2.55
14	Silicon	11.8	19.6	2.70
15	Phosphorus	17.2	28.6	3.06
16	Sulfur	15.7	26.1	2.97
17	Chlorine	18.8	31.2	3.15
18	Argon	24.2	40.1	3.42
20	Calcium	26.3	43.7	3.52
38	Strontium	34.2	56.7	3.84
56	Barium	38.4	63.7	3.99
17	Chlorine	18.8	31.2	3.15
35	Bromine	23.6	39.2	3.40
53	Iodine	26.0	43.1	3.51
26	Iron	7.2	11.9	2.28
47	Silver	10.4	17.2	2.58
57	Lanthanum	22.5	37.4	3.34
82	Lead	18.3	30.4	3.12

is, of the order of 10^{-8} cm. The numbers in the last column are larger than atomic diameters, but at least are roughly proportional to them and indicate the range of variation to be expected. Mendeléeff pointed out that in general the elements of large atomic volume are chemically reactive and those of small atomic volume relatively unreactive; the inert gases which do not fit into this generalization were not then known.

4.4 The table exhibits two characteristic features: the atomic volume increases more or less regularly with increasing atomic number within a group, and it varies cyclically from a large to a small and back to a large value as the atomic number increases within a period. Both of these were evident in the graph of atomic volume vs. atomic weight first produced by Meyer and mentioned in an earlier chapter (see 1.8). The subsequent discussion of atomic structure furnishes the key to these variations; we shall ignore at first the existence of molecular entities in the solid elements, particularly the nonmetals. The outer electrons of successive elements in a group are in nearly identical electronic configurations with the number of shells in the kernels (*i.e.*, nucleus + completed shells of electrons) increasing regularly from one period to the next by the addition of successive completed electron shells. Particular specified shells are closer to the nucleus for the larger atoms, but the extra shells increase the total volume occupied by the atom. Furthermore, the elements within a group having similar chemical and physical properties may be expected generally to form similar crystalline arrays in the solid state; thus we shall expect the atomic volume to increase as one goes down a group.

4.5 It is observed that within a group the rate of increase of atomic volume with atomic number is generally much greater for the metals than for the nonmetals. In the groups of metallic elements, increasing atomic number is often accompanied by decreasing melting point, indicating a weakening of effective interatomic forces, so that the interatomic distances may be expected to increase more rapidly than is required just by the increase in size of the atom itself. On the other hand, in the case of the nonmetals, the effective forces become stronger with increasing atomic number, as is evidenced in the sequence gaseous fluorine and chlorine, liquid bromine, and solid iodine. Thus going down the group one observes increasingly tight binding in the crystal as the actual atoms themselves increase in size; the effect, opposite to that described for the metals, results in a much smaller rate of increase of atomic volume with atomic number. The elements bromine and iodine, for example, have nearly equal atomic volumes although, as we shall see subsequently, the iodine atom itself is considerably larger than the bromine atom.

4.6 The variation of atomic volume with increasing atomic number within a period also requires for its explanation both the decrease in the actual size of the atoms and the rather more pronounced effect of the change of the nature and strength of interatomic forces as the properties of the atoms vary. As we move across a period we find the atoms at first exerting increasing attraction on one another leading eventually to the formation of actual chemical bonds among all the atoms in the crystal in the case of the elements near the middle of the period. Still further along the period, however, the attractive forces lead to the formation of distinct molecules such as N_2, P_4, S_8; and the solid crystal is made up of these. Within the molecules the atoms are very near one another, but the molecules themselves being saturated structures exert relatively weak attractive forces on one another and the distances between them are large. These intermolecular forces may be ascribed to interactions depending in magnitude on the polarizability (see 5.45) of the molecules. The element at the end of the period, the inert gas, then exhibits the weakest intermolecular forces because its molecule, which is a single atom, is least polarizable. The inert gas has a very large atomic volume, comparable with that for the initial metal of the period, although its atom may actually be smaller. It may be remarked on this latter point that the regular decrease of actual atomic size as the atomic number increases within a period terminates with the halogen in group VII, and the inert gas is rather larger. The effects we have considered are consistent with the observed decrease through a minimum and subsequent increase of atomic volume as the atomic number increases across a period of the periodic table.

Ionic Radii

4.7 The atomic volume is an explicitly defined physical quantity susceptible to almost direct measurement. The radius of an ion or atom, however, is not a definite physical or geometrical quantity but rather depends on an arbitrary definition which may be modified for different purposes. In the modern view of an atom or ion, there is no single characteristic radius of the sort defined for the hard sphere visualized in the early conceptions of the atom. It is necessary to speak of a mean radius with respect to some specified property. Thus, for example, one may define a radius of an atom or ion such that the total electronic charge at all smaller distances from the nucleus is just equal to the total electronic charge at all greater distances; or the radius might be taken as that corresponding to the greatest density of electronic charge. In general, these defined radii will not be equal. Most commonly, however, just as in the case of molecular diameters, atomic or ionic radii are defined in terms of equilibrium distances between pairs of particles, like or unlike, in appropriate systems.

4.8 Ionic radii are characteristic distances assigned to the several ions such that the sum of the radii for two oppositely charged ions is equal to the equilibrium distance between the ions in contact in their stable crystal; more specifically, these are the crystal ionic radii. Evidently there may be corrections necessary in certain cases to bring about agreement between theoretical values and experimental values as measured by X-ray diffraction, and not all predictions of equilibrium distances can be tested directly because the required stable crystals are not known. Since the interionic distance in a crystal depends not only on the electronic distributions in the ions themselves and on their extension in space but also on the nature of their interaction (in terms of valence), the structure of the crystal, and the ratio of the radii of the ions, then the ionic radii defined in this manner must be to some extent mean values averaged for each ion over a number of combinations with other ions. The first reasonably successful attempt to determine crystal ionic radii was made by Landé in 1920. His approximate results were refined first by Wasastjerna in 1923 and further refined and greatly extended by Goldschmidt in 1926 and Pauling in succeeding years.

4.9 Any atomic system which is not electrically neutral is an ion; the number of extranuclear electrons is greater than the nuclear charge (anions) or less than the nuclear charge (cations). For the majority of the elements the ions of principal chemical interest are those which result from the loss of all valence electrons or the complete filling of the several vacancies in the outermost or valence shell of the atom. For the regular or representative elements these ions have the electronic configuration of either an inert gas in which the outer shell contains eight electrons, or a pseudo-inert gas structure in which it contains eighteen; the ions derived from the nonmetals immediately preceding and the metals immediately following an inert gas will all have the same configuration as, or be isoelectronic with, that inert gas. One may also consider within a single period an isoelectronic sequence of ions derived from the atoms by the complete removal of all the valence electrons from each atom. Such a sequence is illustrated by the series Ne, Na^+, Mg^{2+}, Al^{3+}, Si^{4+}, P^{5+}, S^{6+}, Cl^{7+}, while a sequence of the first type is illustrated by O^{2-}, F^-, Ne, Na^+, Mg^{2+}. Among the transition elements and to some extent among the heavier metallic representative elements of the groups toward the right of the periodic table, chemically important ions also result from the loss of only a part of what might be classed as the group of valence electrons. In this case a variety of valences, or oxidation states, is observed for the element.

4.10 In an isoelectronic sequence, the size of the ion itself depends only on the effective nuclear charge and in fact is inversely proportional to that effective charge. The screening effects of the electrons in the ions have been independently determined; and it is therefore possible, as Pauling has shown, to calculate relative radii from these known screening constants and the actual nuclear charges for all members of the sequence. Actual values of the radii are based on measured distances in an ionic crystal made up of the singly charged cation and anion in the sequence, i.e., Na^+ and F^- in the sequence given. These radii are called univalent ionic radii, and represent the relative sizes of the outer electron shells of the ions in the sequence. They do not, however, take into account variations in valence which modify the interaction between ions and the type of crystal structure produced, so that in general these radii do not possess the additivity characteristic of the crystal ionic radii. If the ions under consideration were to interact with one another as if they were singly charged while retaining their actual electron distributions, then the interionic distances in the crystal would be the univalent ionic radii. The two types of radius are identical for singly charged ions, and within limits, the crystal radius may be computed from the univalent radius and the ionic charge. For ions of multiple charge

TABLE 4.2

Ionic Radii in Isoelectronic Sequences of Elements* (in Ångstrom units)

F^{7+} 0.07 (0.19)	Cl^{7+} 0.26 (0.49)	Mn^{7+} 0.46 (0.75)	Br^{7+} 0.39 (0.62)	Tc^{7+}	I^{7+} 0.50 (0.77)		At^{7+}
O^{6+} 0.09 (0.22)	S^{6+} 0.29 (0.53)	Cr^{6+} 0.52 (0.81)	Se^{6+} 0.42 (0.66)	Mo^{6+} 0.62 (0.93)	Te^{6+} 0.56 (0.82)		Po^{6+}
N^{5+} 0.11 (0.25)	P^{5+} 0.36 (0.62)	V^{5+} 0.59 (0.88)	As^{5+} 0.46 (0.70)	Nb^{5+} 0.70 (1.00)	Sb^{5+} 0.63 (0.90)		Bi^{5+} 0.75 (0.99)
C^{4+} 0.15 (0.29)	Si^{4+} 0.41 (0.65)	Ti^{4+} 0.68 (0.96)	Ge^{4+} 0.53 (0.76)	Zr^{4+} 0.80 (1.09)	Sn^{4+} 0.71 (0.96)	Ce^{4+} 1.01 (1.27)	Pb^{4+} 0.84 (1.06)
B^{3+} 0.25 (0.44)	Al^{3+} 0.52 (0.74)	Sc^{3+} 0.81 (1.06)	Ga^{3+} 0.60 (0.79)	Y^{3+} 0.96 (1.23)	In^{3+} 0.81 (1.04)	La^{3+} 1.16 (1.40)	Tl^{3+} 0.95 (1.15)
Be^{2+} 0.38 (0.54)	Mg^{2+} 0.66 (0.83)	Ca^{2+} 0.99 (1.18)	Zn^{2+} 0.72 (0.86)	Sr^{2+} 1.15 (1.34)	Cd^{2+} 0.96 (1.13)	Ba^{2+} 1.37 (1.55)	Hg^{2+} 1.10 (1.25)
Li^{+} 0.71 (0.71)	Na^{+} 0.95 (0.95)	K^{+} 1.33 (1.33)	Cu^{+} 0.93 (0.93)	Rb^{+} 1.47 (1.47)	Ag^{+} 1.21 (1.21)	Cs^{+} 1.74 (1.74)	Au^{+} 1.37 (1.37)
He (0.93)	Ne (1.12)	Ar (1.54)		Kr (1.69)		Xe (1.90)	
H^{-} 2.12 (2.12)	F^{-} 1.34 (1.34)	Cl^{-} 1.80 (1.80)		Br^{-} 1.90 (1.90)		I^{-} 2.23 (2.23)	
	O^{2-} 1.35 (1.70)	S^{2-} 1.84 (2.19)		Se^{2-} 1.98 (2.32)		Te^{2-} 2.21 (2.50)	
	N^{3-} 1.71 (2.47)	P^{3-} 2.12 (2.79)		As^{3-} 2.22 (2.85)		Sb^{3-} 2.45 (2.95)	
	C^{4-} 2.60 (4.14)	Si^{4-} 2.71 (3.84)		Ge^{4-} 2.72 (3.71)		Sn^{4-} 2.94 (3.70)	

* The upper figure is the crystal radius; the lower figure, in parentheses, is the univalent radius.

the crystal radius is smaller than the univalent radius, and the ratio decreases as the ionic charge (valence) increases. For considerations of the size of individual ions, independent of their interaction with other ions, the univalent radius is the more useful; for chemical considerations, however, the crystal ionic radius is the more useful and more commonly discussed. Unfortunately, the term "ionic radii" is sometimes used for either set of values without further specifications; this results in some confusion, particularly for ions of large charge.

4.11 The values of the ionic radii of most of the common elements are shown in Tables 4.2 and 4.3. The crystal radii are also shown graphically in Figure 4.1.

TABLE 4.3

Ionic Crystal Radii * (in Ångstrom units)

Ion	Radius	Ion	Radius	Ion	Radius	Ion	Radius	Ion	Radius
H^+	0.29 Å	Co^{2+}	0.74 Å	Ag^+	1.21 Å	Dy^{3+}	1.00 Å	Bi^{5+}	0.75 Å
H^-	2.12	Ni^{2+}	0.73	Cd^{2+}	0.96	Ho^{3+}	0.99	Bi^{4+}	(0.88)
Li^+	0.71	Cu^{2+}	(0.72)	Cd^+	(1.30)	Er^{3+}	0.98	Bi^{3+}	1.08
Be^{2+}	0.38	Cu^+	0.93	In^{3+}	0.81	Tm^{3+}	0.96	Bi^{2+}	(1.32)
B^{3+}	0.25	Zn^{2+}	0.72	In^{2+}	(1.02)	Yb^{3+}	0.95	Bi^+	1.70
O^{2-}	1.35	Ga^{3+}	0.60	In^+	(1.40)	Yb^{2+}	(1.06)	Ra^{2+}	1.50
F^-	1.34	Ga^{2+}	(0.76)	Sn^{4+}	0.71	Lu^{3+}	0.93	Ac^{3+}	1.11
Na^+	0.95	Ga^+	(1.08)	Sn^{2+}	1.10	Ta^{4+}	(0.88)	Th^{4+}	0.99
Mg^{2+}	0.66	Ge^{2+}	(0.84)	Sb^{5+}	0.63	W^{2+}	(0.87)	Th^{3+}	1.08
Al^{3+}	0.52	As^{5+}	0.46	Sb^{3+}	0.92	Re^{3+}	(0.78)	Pa^{5+}	0.90
P^{5+}	0.36	As^{3+}	0.69	I^-	2.23	Re^{2+}	(0.86)	Pa^{4+}	0.96
P^{3+}	(0.55)	Br^-	1.90	Cs^+	1.74	Os^{3+}	(0.78)	Pa^{3+}	1.05
S^{2-}	1.84	Rb^+	1.47	Ba^{2+}	1.37	Os^{2+}	(0.88)	U^{6+}	0.83
Cl^-	1.80	Sr^{2+}	1.15	La^{3+}	1.16	Ir^{3+}	(0.80)	U^{5+}	0.87
K^+	1.33	Y^{3+}	0.96	Ce^{4+}	1.01	Ir^{2+}	(0.92)	U^{4+}	0.93
Ca^{2+}	0.99	Zr^{3+}	(0.82)	Ce^{3+}	1.14	Ir^+	(1.16)	U^{3+}	1.03
Sc^{3+}	0.81	Zr^{2+}	(0.9)	Ce^{2+}	(1.2)	Pt^{3+}	(0.83)	Np^{6+}	0.82
Ti^{3+}	0.64	Nb^{3+}	(0.78)	Pr^{4+}	0.99	Pt^{2+}	(0.96)	Np^{5+}	0.88
Ti^{2+}	(0.85)	Nb^{2+}	(0.85)	Pr^{3+}	1.12	Pt^+	(1.24)	Np^{4+}	0.92
V^{3+}	0.69	Mo^{2+}	(0.83)	Nd^{3+}	1.10	Au^{3+}	(0.87)	Np^{3+}	1.01
V^{2+}	(0.80)	Ru^{3+}	(0.72)	Pm^{3+}	1.08	Au^{2+}	(1.02)	Pu^{6+}	0.81
Cr^{3+}	0.62	Ru^{2+}	(0.81)	Sm^{3+}	1.07	Au^+	1.37	Pu^{5+}	0.87
Cr^{2+}	(0.80)	Rh^{3+}	0.72	Sm^{2+}	(1.16)	Hg^{2+}	1.10	Pu^{4+}	0.90
Mn^{3+}	0.66	Rh^{2+}	(0.80)	Eu^{3+}	1.05	Hg^+	1.50	Pu^{3+}	1.00
Mn^{2+}	0.78	Rh^+	(1.07)	Eu^{2+}	(1.14)	Tl^{3+}	0.95	Am^{6+}	0.80
Fe^{3+}	0.64	Pd^{3+}	(0.74)	Gd^{3+}	1.03	Tl^{2+}	(1.19)	Am^{5+}	0.86
Fe^{2+}	0.76	Pd^{2+}	(0.85)	Tb^{4+}	0.91	Tl^+	1.59	Am^{4+}	0.89
Co^{3+}	0.63	Ag^{2+}	(0.91)	Tb^{3+}	1.02	Pb^{2+}	1.27	Am^{3+}	0.99

* Figures in parentheses are estimated values.

4.12 The univalent ionic radii are determined by two factors, the atomic number or nuclear charge, and the electronic configuration. So long as we deal with members of an isoelectronic sequence of the sort defined above, the electronic configurations always consist of precisely the same collection of closed shells, and thus their effect, as measured by the screening of the nucleus from

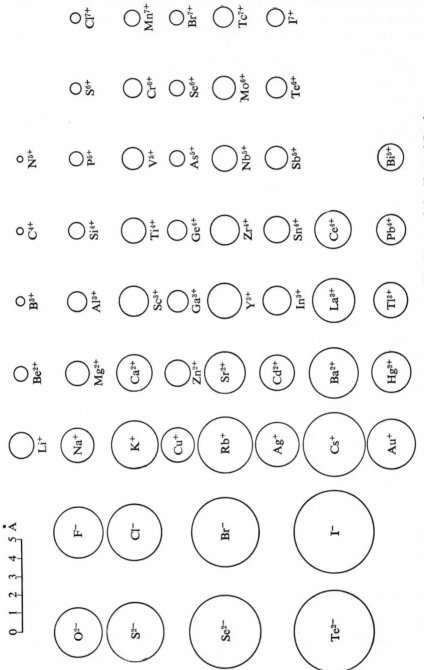

Fig. 4.1 Ionic crystal radii. (Redrawn from PAULING, *The Nature of the Chemical Bond,* Cornell University Press, Ithaca, N.Y., 1940, Fig. 44–2)

the outer electrons, is the same for all members of the sequence. In other words, the effective nuclear charge is less than the actual nuclear charge by the same amount for each of the ions and increases uniformly in unit steps as one progresses along the isoelectronic sequence. This increase brings about the regular decrease in ion size illustrated by the horizontal rows in the table and graph, because as the effective nuclear charge increases, the attractive force on the extranuclear electrons must increase and there is no compensating change in the repulsive forces arising from electronic interactions and the operation of the Exclusion Principle. Consequently new equilibrium mean separations result at decreasing distances from the nucleus.

4.13 When we compare the members of one isoelectronic sequence with the corresponding members from another period, we expect a difference arising from the different complete electronic configurations for the two. In the period containing the heavier elements, the larger number of extranuclear electrons is responsible for a larger absolute constant amount of screening; the increase, however, is not generally quite as great as the increase in actual nuclear charge (eight units between the C^{4-} and Si^{4-} sequences, for example), with the result that the effective nuclear charges are somewhat larger for the sequence of heavier ions. On the other hand, these ions have one entire shell of electrons more than their lighter counterparts, and this shell necessarily lies outside those present in the lighter series, even though the latter are somewhat drawn in. The first factor alone tends to produce smaller ionic radii for the heavier elements, the second to produce larger ionic radii. It is seen that the second effect is considerably more important and that the ionic radii are larger for the heavier sequence, except for the corresponding lightest, most negatively charged ions, for which the order is reversed. It has been pointed out that in a given isoelectronic sequence the radius varies inversely with the effective nuclear charge; among these ions, then, the ones with small nuclear charge are those whose radius is most affected by variation in nuclear charge. For two sequences, the result of variation in effective screening will be greatest for the ions of smallest nuclear charge, and as a consequence, for these ions this factor outweighs the effect of incorporating an added electron shell. Hence the univalent ionic radius is smaller for the ion of larger nuclear charge, the heavier ion. With increasing complexity of electronic structure the increase in screening more nearly balances the increment in actual nuclear charge, and the relative importance of the effect here discussed declines. Thus, although the univalent radius of Si^{4-} is considerably less than that of C^{4-}, those of Sn^{4-} and Ge^{4-} are nearly equal. An almost exaggerated illustration of this effect is furnished by the singly negatively charged ions H^-, F^-, Cl^-, Br^-, and I^-. Here the univalent ionic radius of H^- is almost as large as that of I^- and approximately 50 per cent larger than that of F^-, although the progression from F^- to I^- shows a regular increase in radius. The absolute screening in the first isoelectronic sequence is much less than that in the second, but for H^- with its actual nuclear charge of only one, the relative screening is considerably greater than that for F^-, with the result that the effective nuclear charges are in the approximate ratio of one to six. The incorporation of the entire filled L shell of electrons in F^- cannot compensate for this large increase in effective nuclear charge and so we find F^- much smaller in size than H^-.

4.14 We have seen in an earlier chapter that for a given value of the principal quantum number n, the energies of the states increase in the order of increasing l, that is, in the order $s, p, d, f \ldots$. In other words, an ns electron is bound more tightly than an np electron, which is bound more tightly than an nd electron, and so on. This may be interpreted as implying that p electrons screen the nucleus less effectively than s electrons. We say that s electrons are most deeply penetrating and most effective in screening. Thus the L shell in F^-, containing s and p electrons, is not nearly so efficient in screening the large nuclear charge as the K shell in H^- is for its own small nuclear charge.

4.15 The concept of penetration must be rather carefully applied for it may also be shown from simple classical consideration that electrons of high angular momentum (l large) should not be found in the outer reaches of stable atoms. Thus we have $3d$ electrons, for example, not in the outermost shell but inside the $4s$ shell. The answer is evident in the distribution patterns obtained in either the Bohr theory or the wave mechanical treatment: s electrons have fairly high probabilities of being found near the nucleus but their maximum density is at a distance somewhat greater than for electrons of higher l values for the same n value. The Bohr orbits for s electrons (for large n) are eccentric ellipses, the electron traveling very near the nucleus at perihelion, and at aphelion being far outside the electrons of higher angular momentum which travel less eccentric paths.

4.16 Returning to the consideration of ionic radii, we see that in the long periods it is not feasible to consider a single isoelectronic series but rather, as is suggested in Figure 4.1, two are involved, the first built around the appropriate inert gas and the second starting with the singly positively charged ion of the element of the copper family. Such a sequence as this illustrates the effect of increasing atomic number at constant screening, which brings about a regular decrease in ionic radius, as is evidenced in the series Cu^+ to Br^{7+}. On the other hand, the radii are all considerably smaller than those of the elements in the earlier sequence in the same period. If we compare K^+ with Cu^+, for example, we find in each case three complete levels of electrons, but the outer shell of Cu^+ contains eighteen ($3s^2 3p^6 3d^{10}$) electrons and that of K^+ contains only eight ($3s^2 3p^6$) electrons, and the actual nuclear charge is ten units greater for Cu^+ than for K^+. The extra $3d$ electrons in Cu^+ are not deeply penetrating and thus afford relatively little added screening, certainly less than that required to neutralize completely the ten units of increased nuclear charge. Thus the effective nuclear charge is several units greater for Cu^+ than for K^+, and the shells of electrons are correspondingly more compact. The same situation obtains, of course, for succeeding pairs such as Ca^{2+} and Zn^{2+} or Sc^{3+} and Ga^{3+}.

4.17 The ionic radii of the elements in a sequence of the sort under discussion increase as one goes from the first long period to the next heavier period, just as was observed among the sequences built around the inert gas configurations. The reason is quite the same, the effect of increased effective nuclear charge being more than compensated for by the incorporation of an extra completed shell of electrons. In the present instance, furthermore, the nuclear charges are relatively greater than for the ions of the first type of sequence, and therefore the first ions in the sequences do not exhibit the exceptional behavior noted earlier. The ionic radii of the short transition series elements of the second and third long periods, however, are very nearly the same. The interposition of the lanthanides increases the effective nuclear charge and one observes a corresponding decrease in ionic radius. The effect among the long period transition elements is known as the *lanthanide contraction*.

4.18 The crystal ionic radii depend not only on nuclear charge and electronic configuration but also on the ionic charge and the type of crystal structure. The effect of ionic charge is to make the crystal radii of multicharged ions less than the univalent radii, for multicharged ions exert greater attractive forces on one another than would be the case if they were singly charged, without other changes in the forces in the crystal; thus the equilibrium distances must be less than would be predicted from the univalent radii. The interionic distances in ionic crystals made up of ions from a given isoelectronic sequence decrease fairly regularly with increasing valence: thus we observe 3.29 Å for $K^+ - Br^-$ and 2.96 Å for $Ca^{2+} - Se^{2-}$, or 2.81 Å for $Na^+ - Cl^-$ and 2.54 Å for $Mg^{2+} - S^{2-}$. In either comparison, the electronic distributions are essentially the same but the ions of higher charge are closer together at equilibrium. The stronger attractive forces in the ion pairs of higher valence are also responsible for enhanced hardness and diminished volatility; within an isoelectronic sequence the melting points of ionic compounds increase with increased valence.

4.19 The ions in the solid crystals NaF, KCl, RbBr, and CsI (all in the standard sodium chloride arrangement) exhibit a radius ratio (cation radius/anion radius) of about 0.75. These are often used for reference in determining crystal radii. Now if the radius ratio is much less than this, the relatively large anions in the lattice come in contact and the repulsions in the crystal are different from, and greater than, those expected in the reference arrangement, with the result that the actual interionic distance is larger than the sum of the crystal radii. Pauling and others have shown, however, that this effect may be treated theoretically and that quantitative corrections may be computed which bring about very close agreement between predicted and observed equilibrium interionic distances for crystals such as LiI, in which the radius ratio is quite small. The same crystals, in the group of alkali halides, for which the actual distances markedly exceed the predicted values, are those which exhibit anomalies in associated properties; for example, their melting and boiling points are lower than would be expected on the basis of simple regular variation with interionic distance. Calculations of crystal energies with the radius ratio effect taken into account provide a means of "correcting" the observed results, however, to correspond to a series of hypothetical alkali halides with the observed distances but the standard radius ratio of 0.75. For these crystals, in which interactions should all be similar and vary only with the interionic distance, such properties as melting point, boiling point, heats of fusion and sublimation, and solubility all vary monotonically for a series of halides of a given alkali or of alkali salts of a given halogen. The parametric curves of the value of the corrected property against the atomic number of the ion being varied, in contradistinction to the actual experimental curves, are separate, roughly parallel, always in order of increasing atomic number of the ion taken as parameter, and do not intersect.

4.20 In other symmetric crystals such as MgSe, for example, the radius ratio effect is also operative, and the observed interionic distance is greater than the sum of the crystal radii. In unsymmetrical crystals such as CaF_2 or Li_2S the effect seems rather less important. For these, the additivity relation is quite well satisfied with the usual crystal radii, which more or less automatically compensate for the effect of dissimilar valences.

4.21 The final factor to be considered here in its effect on equilibrium interionic distances is the coordination number of the metal, *i.e.*, the number of anion neighbors about a cation in the stable crystal. Pauling has shown that the coordination numbers are related to the repulsive forces in the crystal; the change for a given pair of ions from one structure to another of higher coordination number is generally accompanied by an increase in interionic distance. The reference structures normally chosen are the sodium chloride and rutile (TiO_2) structures in each of which the cation has six neighboring anions. A correction must be applied if we wish to compute interionic distances from tabulated crystal radii for the ions in a crystal structure of different coordination number. Such corrections were suggested on empirical grounds by Goldschmidt and have been computed from theoretical considerations by Pauling; it is found that the sum of the crystal radii is to be multiplied by approximately 1.035 for a structure with coordination number eight (cesium chloride or fluorite structures), or by approximately 0.955 for a structure with coordination number four (β-quartz, sphalerite, or wurtzite structures). The corrected values are usually in quite good agreement with experimentally determined distances. Similar correction factors may be applied with moderate success for other coordination numbers, even in complex crystals such as the metallic fluorosilicates, where the metal to fluorine distances are predictable although the fluorine atoms are bonded covalently to the silicon atom.

4.22 There are two other cases of interest in the consideration of ionic radii; the first is that of more than one ion derived from a given atom, and the second and much more important one is that of similarly charged ions in a short transition series or more particularly a long transition series. The ionic radius of successively more positively charged ions from a given atom (*e.g.*, Fe^{2+}, Fe^{3+}) decreases rapidly because the effective nuclear charge increases. In many such instances, of course, the ions also have quite different electronic configurations; the addition of one or more electrons to the more highly charged ionic structure increases the total repulsive effect, perhaps partly because of the necessity for pairing spins with electrons already present in the orbital entered, and may even involve the addition of a new outer shell (*e.g.*, Ce^{4+} to Ce^{3+}). All these factors contribute to an increased ionic radius for the less positively charged cation. The same considerations lead to the result that in the much rarer case of more than one simple anion derived from a given atom, the larger the ionic charge the larger the ionic radius.

4.23 The members of a series of ions of equal charge derived from the successive elements in a transition series (*e.g.*, Mn^{2+}, Fe^{2+}, Co^{2+}, and Ni^{2+}) generally exhibit a slow decrease in ionic radius with increasing atomic number, because the increment in screening effect at each step does not quite suffice to counteract the increment in actual nuclear charge; thus the effective nuclear charge increases and the ions decrease in size. For the lanthanides with ionic charge $+3$ the effect is relatively small because the structural variation in the series is in the $4f$ shell, but the atoms all possess the $5s^2 5p^6$ shell outside this. Thus the crystal ionic radii of all trivalent rare-earth ions may be given as 0.90 ± 0.05 Å, but there is a nearly regular decrease from La^{3+} to Lu^{3+}; this is the lanthanide contraction.

4.24 In terms of the crystal radii of the simple ions (of inert gas or pseudo-inert gas structure) of the elements arranged in the long form of the periodic table, the various relationships we have discussed may be briefly summarized as follows: the ionic radius increases as one goes down a group, with the exceptions already noted, namely, H^- and F^-, C^{4-} and Si^{4-}, and the short transition series elements of the second and third long periods; the ionic radius decreases rapidly for the cations, changes discontinuously to a much larger value for the anions, and then decreases again, as one goes across a period from left to right. In the long periods an earlier abrupt increase is observed immediately following the transition triads (*i.e.*, at the element in the copper group, where the nature of the ion changes), and the subsequent decrease is less rapid than in the short periods. In the long transition elements the decrease is still less rapid but nonetheless real and important.

Covalent (Atomic) Radii

4.25 The third common measure of atomic size is the so-called "covalent radius," a quantity intended to represent the effective size of an atom in ordinary covalent combination with other atoms. The nature of chemical linking will be discussed in a subsequent chapter; for the time being we remark only that covalent bonding involves the sharing of electron pairs between nuclei. The equilibrium distance between the bound nuclei may be considered the sum of the radii of two spheres representing the two atoms. These radii are the "normal covalent radii" of the elements concerned; they refer to compounds in which the atoms form their usual complement of single covalent bonds (*i.e.*, shared pairs of electrons), the number being equal to the negative oxidation number (*i.e.*, four for carbon, three for nitrogen, two for oxygen, one for fluorine).

4.26 Experience has shown that in a series of related molecules in which the environment of a particular covalent bond is not greatly changed, the bond distance is quite constant and may be supposed to be determined almost solely by the atoms themselves and the type of bond. Further investigation has demonstrated that the characteristic bond distance for a given bond between two specified atoms, like or unlike, is in fact only an insensitive function of the environment within the molecule. In other words, only fairly drastic changes in the surrounding atoms and their bonds bring about appreciable variation in the bond distance under consideration. Thus the distance between two carbon atoms joined by a single covalent bond is 1.54 ± 0.03 Å for a remarkable diversity of molecules including diamond itself, straight chain, branched, and cyclic paraffins, most unsaturated hydrocarbons, many substituted aromatic systems, and the multitude of nominal derivatives of these containing functional groups such as for example the carbonyl, hydroxyl, carboxyl, nitrile, and amino groups. Deviations are observed for single bonds between atoms of which both are parts of aromatic systems or are multiply bonded to other atoms in aliphatic systems, and between atoms of which one is triply bound to the remainder of the molecule. Similarly, for heteronuclear bond distances nearly constant results are obtained: the single bond carbon-oxygen and carbon-nitrogen distances are 1.43 ± 0.03 Å and 1.47 ± 0.03 Å, respectively, in a great variety of compounds.

4.27 The single bond distance between carbon and chlorine is found to be 1.76 ± 0.02 Å in a number of compounds, and the equilibrium interatomic distance in the chlorine molecule is 1.98 Å. The carbon-chlorine distance is seen to be the arithmetic mean of the carbon-carbon distance (1.54 A) and the chlorine-chlorine distance. The same sort of additive relationship is observed for most of the bond distances for simple bonds and this circumstance permits us to assign individual covalent radii to the several atoms. The figures given for the carbon-carbon and chlorine-chlorine distances immediately fix the single bond covalent radii for carbon and chlorine as one half of these respective figures, or 0.77 Å for carbon and 0.99 Å for chlorine. Proceeding then to the carbon-nitrogen and carbon-oxygen distances given earlier, we conclude that the covalent radii of nitrogen and oxygen are respectively 0.70 and 0.66 Å. In this way we may build up, as Pauling and Huggins did in 1934, a whole set of radii assigned to the several elements and appropriate for single covalent bonds. We shall see later that the predicted bond distances may have to be corrected for effects arising from charges on the atoms, differences in electronegativity of the bonded atoms, or multiple bonding in adjacent positions.

4.28 In the examples already given we have combined results for solids (*e.g.*, diamond) with those for gases (*e.g.*, Cl_2). It is important that in doing so comparable molecular situations are involved. It has been pointed out by Schomaker and Stevenson that the radii here derived for nitrogen and oxygen correspond to bonds with a significant average amount of ionic character, and that the covalent radii for these atoms in compounds without such ionic character (hydrazine and hydrogen peroxide) should be given as 0.74 Å in each case. These values, with similarly increased values of 0.72 Å for fluorine and 0.37 Å for hydrogen (from the hydrogen molecule itself), are consistent with metallic radii derived for the other elements of the first period. In his extensive analysis of the whole system of atomic radii and interatomic distances Pauling has argued that these metallic radii are essentially covalent radii.

4.29 In all that has gone before, we have referred to single bond radii, but of course many atoms form multiple bonds and the corresponding bond distances are also of importance. It is found that multiple bond distances are also nearly independent of molecular environment and are additive as well, so that double and triple bond covalent radii may be assigned to individual atoms in a manner quite analogous to that used to obtain single bond radii. These multiple bond radii are smaller than the single bond radii; the most common example, perhaps, is furnished by carbon for which the single, double, and triple bond covalent radii are respectively 0.771 Å, 0.665 Å, and 0.602 Å. For other atoms the corresponding decreases in radius are approximately the same.

4.30 In solid crystals the actual interatomic distances are somewhat dependent on the atomic arrangement, even though the different arrangements may both exhibit only single bonds. Thus there are defined for various elements, particularly transition metals, tetrahedral, octahedral, and square covalent radii to be used in predicting bond distances when the atom is surrounded tetrahedrally by four other atoms, octahedrally by six other atoms, or in a coplanar arrangement by four other atoms. The tetrahedral radii are the same as the normal single bond covalent radii for the lighter elements — in fact for many they must be identical — but are somewhat smaller for the heaviest, most electronegative elements. Where comparison is possible, the octahedral and square radii are approximately equal and generally larger than the tetrahedral radius for a given atom. We shall return to these considerations in the next chapter, where the nature of the bonding is discussed.

4.31 Bond distances may be determined from X-ray diffraction measurements of crystals or from electron diffraction or spectroscopic studies of gas molecules. The detailed investigation of X-ray interference patterns from crystalline solids began with the suggestion by Laue in 1912 that crystals should provide appropriate interference gratings for the very short wavelengths of the X-rays. Investigation progressed through the contributions of the Braggs starting in 1913, Debye and Scherrer in 1916, Hull in 1917, Weissenberg in 1924, Patterson in 1935, and very many others, so that today use of X-ray interference patterns has become a well-developed, accurate, and widely applicable method for the determination of crystal structure and bond distances. In the earlier years X-ray studies served to corroborate the basic structural features of molecules derived indirectly from the study of reactions, and then to resolve the finer details, but more recently X-ray investigations have often preceded the classical chemical structural analysis of complex organic molecules, as was true in the case of penicillin.

4.32 There are several different experimental techniques used in X-ray diffraction work and several ways of analyzing the observed diffraction data, most of them somewhat indirect in that an approximate structure is assumed and then refined by use of the diffraction data. More direct indication of structure is given through the use of electron density patterns computed from the experimental data, which give a type of image of the actual molecule, emphasizing the heavy scattering centers. In no method can the positions of hydrogen atoms be fixed because they are too inefficient as scattering centers for X-rays. In recent years the scattering of beams of neutrons has become of increasing interest and importance because such diffraction may be used to determine hydrogen positions in molecules.

4.33 In 1915 Debye suggested that X-ray diffraction could be applied to the study of individual and nearly independent molecules in the gaseous state. He developed the basic methods for the determination of structure from diffraction data, but the method itself was quite inconvenient with X-rays and little was accomplished. After the earliest diffraction experiments with electron beams on crystalline metals in 1928, the application of electron beams to the study of structure of gaseous molecules was inevitable. Mark and Wierl in 1930 used the diffraction of electron beams and Debye's theoretical treatment to determine configurations and bond distances in a number of simple molecules, and the technique of electron diffraction was rapidly developed and applied to many molecules by Pauling, Brockway, and numerous others during the succeeding years. Just as in the case of X-ray diffraction from crystals, there are both direct and indirect methods of determining structures from the experimental observations; the direct method, which is rather approximate, may be used for rough determinations and then the bond angles and distances may be more accurately determined by extended and at times laborious computations from the observed scattered intensities and the positions and shapes of their maxima.

4.34 The rotational energy levels of molecules are determined in part by the moments of inertia, and these, of course, by the masses and relative distances between the atoms in the molecule. For molecules of moderately simple configuration it is possible to compute bond distances from measured moments of inertia. Studies of pure rotation spectra or of rotational fine structure in vibrational spectra furnish the requisite moments of inertia. For diatomic molecules this method probably provides the best value for the interatomic distances because of the high accuracy which spectroscopic measurements have attained. For symmetrical, small polyatomic molecules of various configurations the method is also applicable, but it cannot be used for more complex molecules because the observations furnish too few independent quantities to fix the several generally different bond distances in the molecule.

4.35 In 1920 Bragg suggested a set of values of atomic radii without distinguishing between different kinds of chemical bonds in the crystals. This distinction was made very shortly and resulted in the development of systems of ionic radii on the one hand and covalent radii on the other. In 1926 Huggins and Goldschmidt independently proposed sets of values of covalent radii and in 1932 and subsequent years Pauling refined and enlarged the tables of values.

TABLE 4.4

Tetrahedral Covalent Radii (in Ångstrom units)

	Be	B	C	N	O	F
	0.89	0.80	0.77	0.74	0.74	0.72
	Mg	Al	Si	P	S	Cl
	1.40	1.26	1.17	1.10	1.04	0.99
Cu	Zn	Ga	Ge	As	Se	Br
1.35	1.31	1.26	1.22	1.18	1.14	1.11
Ag	Cd	In	Sn	Sb	Te	I
1.53	1.48	1.44	1.40	1.36	1.32	1.28
Au	Hg	Tl	Pb	Bi		
1.50	1.48	1.47	1.46	1.46		

TABLE 4.5

Octahedral Covalent Radii (in Ångstrom units)

Ti IV	Fe IV	Fe II				
1.36	1.20	1.23				
		Co III	Co II			
		1.22	1.32			
		Ni IV	Ni III	Ni II		Se IV
		1.21	1.30	1.39		1.40
Zr IV		Ru II			Sn IV	Te IV
1.48		1.33			1.45	1.52
		Rh III	Rh II			
		1.32	1.43			
		Pd IV		Pd II		
		1.31		1.50		
				Ag III		
				1.49		
		Os II			Pb IV	
		1.33			1.50	
		Ir III	Ir II			
		1.32	1.43			
		Pt IV		Pt II		
		1.31		1.50		
			Au IV	Au III		
			1.40	1.49		

Values of the covalent radii of many of the important elements are listed in Tables 4.4–4.6 and shown in Figure 4.2.

TABLE 4.6

Multiple Bond Covalent Radii (in Ångstrom units)

Atom	Single Bond	Double Bond	Triple Bond	Atom	Single Bond	Double Bond
C	0.771 Å	0.665 Å	0.602 Å	Ge	1.223	1.12
N	0.74	0.60	0.55	As	1.21	1.11
O	0.74	0.55	0.50	Se	1.17	1.07
Si	1.173	1.07	1.00	Sn	1.412	1.30
P	1.10	1.00	0.93	Sb	1.41	1.31
S	1.04	0.94	0.87	Te	1.37	1.27

4.36 Like ionic radii, covalent radii are determined primarily by the nuclear charge (atomic number) and electronic configuration. In the case of solid compounds the effect of crystalline arrangement is evident in the distinction between tetrahedral and octahedral radii, for example. Similarly the effect of multiple bonding between the atoms is shown in the values of single, double, and triple bond covalent radii. The actual interatomic distance in a given molecule will depend not only on the intrinsic atomic radii but, in addition, on other factors involved in the binding of the atoms and their immediate neighbors; this will be discussed later.

4.37 The single bond covalent radii decrease as one progresses along a period. As the atomic number increases the actual nuclear charge increases uniformly; at each step an additional electron is added to the valence shell, but its screening effect is small, and therefore the effective nuclear charge increases. The atoms are all similarly bonded by a single shared electron pair, but as the nuclear charge increases uniformly it tends to draw the electron pair closer so that the radius decreases. In the short periods the effect becomes less pronounced toward the end of the period, but in the long periods the covalent radius decreases more slowly (or even increases slightly) between the group IV and group V representative elements than at the ends of the period. The explanation of this latter behavior is probably to be found in a modification of the bonding mechanism. It is to be noted that in only these periods, the tetrahedral and normal covalent radii are different for the heavier atoms, and the sequence of tetrahedral radii, which reflect a more nearly constant mode of binding, exhibits a uniform decrease with increasing atomic number.

4.38 Within a group the single bond covalent radii increase more or less regularly as the atomic number increases. The atoms in a group have the same outer electron configuration and tend therefore to form the same kind and number of chemical bonds. The atoms, like the corresponding ions previously discussed, must increase in size with increasing atomic number because of the

Fig. 4.2 Single bond covalent radii of the elements. (Values in Ångstrom units)

I	II	Sc	Ti	V	Cr	Mn	Fe	Co	Ni	Cu	Zn	III	IV	V	VI	VII	VIII
1. H 0.37																	2. He
3. Li 1.225	4. Be 0.889											5. B 0.80	6. C 0.771	7. N 0.74	8. O 0.74	9. F 0.72	10. Ne
11. Na 1.572	12. Mg 1.364											13. Al 1.248	14. Si 1.173	15. P 1.10	16. S 1.04	17. Cl 0.994	18. Ar
19. K 2.025	20. Ca 1.736	21. Sc 1.439	22. Ti 1.324	23. V 1.224	24. Cr 1.172	25. Mn 1.168	26. Fe 1.165	27. Co 1.157	28. Ni 1.149	29. Cu 1.173	30. Zn 1.249	31. Ga 1.245	32. Ge 1.223	33. As 1.21	34. Se 1.17	35. Br 1.142	36. Kr
37. Rb 2.16	38. Sr 1.914	39. Y 1.616	40. Zr 1.454	41. Nb 1.342	42. Mo 1.291	43. Tc	44. Ru 1.241	45. Rh 1.247	46. Pd 1.278	47. Ag 1.339	48. Cd 1.413	49. In 1.497	50. Sn 1.412	51. Sb 1.41	52. Te 1.37	53. I 1.334	54. Xe
55. Cs 2.35	56. Ba 1.981	57. La * 1.690	72. Hf 1.442	73. Ta 1.343	74. W 1.299	75. Re 1.278	76. Os 1.255	77. Ir 1.260	78. Pt 1.290	79. Au 1.336	80. Hg 1.440	81. Tl 1.549	82. Pb 1.538	83. Bi 1.52	84. Po 1.53	85. At	86. Rn
87. Fr	88. Ra 1.981	89. Ac †															

SHORT TRANSITION SERIES — (TRANSITION TRIADS)

* Lanthanides

58. Ce 1.646	59. Pr 1.648	60. Nd 1.642	61. Pm	62. Sm 1.66	63. Eu 1.850	64. Gd 1.614	65. Tb 1.592	66. Dy 1.589	67. Ho 1.580	68. Er 1.567	69. Tm 1.562	70. Yb 1.699	71. Lu 1.557

† Actinides

90. Th 1.652	91. Pa	92. U 1.421	93. Np	94. Pu	95. Am	96. Cm	97. Bk	98. Cf	99. Es	100. Fm	101. Md	102. No

incorporation of successive new electron shells. The increase in nuclear charge is nearly compensated by the screening due to the added electrons in the neutral atoms. The rate of increase is greater for the groups at either end of a period than for the groups of transition metals or of the elements immediately following the transition series, because in the latter the effect of enhanced screening is relatively greater. As a matter of fact, just as in the case of ionic radii, the corresponding short transition series elements of the second and third long periods have very nearly the same covalent radii, a consequence of the lanthanide contraction. Atoms with next outermost shells of eighteen electrons are always smaller than corresponding atoms with next outermost shells of eight electrons, and their radii also change more slowly with atomic number in either a horizontal fashion within a period or in vertical fashion within a group.

4.39 The equilibrium interatomic distance in elementary hydrogen is 0.74 Å, corresponding to a value of 0.37 Å for the single bond covalent radius. In very many molecules containing bonds between hydrogen and nonmetallic atoms such as carbon, nitrogen, oxygen, fluorine, sulfur, chlorine, bromine, or iodine, the covalent radius of hydrogen computed from the observed interatomic distance and the accepted value of the covalent radius of the second atom is considerably less than this, varying in general from 0.28 to 0.32 Å. Pauling chose the average value 0.30 Å; Schomaker and Stevenson gave the value 0.37 Å derived from the hydrogen molecule as the correct value for bonds without ionic character, analogous to the value 0.74 Å they chose for oxygen and nitrogen.

4.40 The variation in apparent radius from one bond to another is due to variation in ionic character of the bond, and thus to variation in the electrical nature of the second bonded atom. Because of the small intrinsic size and simple structure of the hydrogen atom, relatively slight changes in the ionic character of the bond are reflected in quite appreciable variations in the interatomic distance or in the apparent covalent radius of hydrogen. The relation between interatomic distance and ionic character of the bond may be given approximately in the form

$$r_{AB} = r_A + r_B - \beta \Delta x$$

in which r_{AB} is the interatomic distance between the bonded A and B atoms, r_A and r_B their covalent radii, β a small constant, and Δx the difference in electronegativity between A and B, regardless of sign. Electronegativity measures the innate attraction of an atom of an element for electrons, and as we shall see subsequently, electronegativity difference measures the ionic character of bonds between atoms. For most atom pairs, the term $\beta \Delta x$ is of the order of a few hundredths of an Ångstrom unit; it is quite appreciable relative to the small value of r_A for a hydrogen atom and thus accounts generally for the difference between the apparent radius of hydrogen in elementary hydrogen and that in its compounds with other elements.

4.41 Huggins has suggested an alternative relationship describing the variation of interatomic distance with the nature of the bond. He found that for very many covalent bonds a quantity r^*_{AB}, called the "constant-energy distance" and defined as

$$r^*_{AB} = r_{AB} + \tfrac{1}{2} \log_{10} D_{AB},$$

where r_{AB} and D_{AB} are the bond length and bond energy respectively, is quite accurately represented as the sum of constant-energy radii for the two bonded atoms. These radii, which are generally about 0.4 Å larger than the usual covalent radii, may be used for the computation of bond lengths.

$$r_{AB} = r^*_A + r^*_B - \tfrac{1}{2} \log_{10} D_{AB}$$

The values thus obtained are in very good agreement with results from experiment except for bonds with hydrogen. The constant-energy radius which must be assigned to hydrogen decreases from 0.88 Å for the H_2 molecule and 0.86 Å for bonds with first row elements down to 0.82 Å for bonds with fourth row elements. The variation may be due to neglect of electronegativity differences but more probably is due to failure of the additivity relation for the very small hydrogen atom.

4.42 In some molecules, the atoms which are covalently joined may themselves be electrically charged, as is true in substituted ammonium ions, for example. A positive charge on an atom tends to decrease slightly its covalent radius, a negative charge to increase slightly the radius. The differences are usually of the order of 0.02–0.03 Å, and in a sense illustrate the effect of variation of screening of the nucleus by extranuclear electrons. If but one atom of a bonded pair is electrically charged, the interatomic distance will be slightly less (for a positive charge) or slightly more (for a negative charge) than the sum of the usual radii; if the two bonded atoms are equally but oppositely charged, then the effects will nearly cancel and the interatomic distance will be rather close to the sum of the ordinary covalent radii.

4.43 Elements which can exhibit the same crystalline atomic arrangement in different oxidation states, like some of the transition triad metals in their octahedral configurations, for example, illustrate an analogous effect which may be interpreted in terms of a formal charge corresponding to the oxidation state of the metal. Thus the octahedral covalent radii of Ni(II), Ni(III), and Ni(IV) decrease more or less regularly in that order, and similarly for the several oxidation states of cobalt and iron.

4.44 The carbon-carbon distance in benzene and related aromatic structures is found experimentally to be 1.39 Å, intermediate between the single bond (1.54 Å) and double bond (1.33 Å) distances. The distance between bonded carbon atoms in a single atomic plane in graphite is 1.42 Å. In either case it may be inferred that the bond itself is intermediate between a single and a double bond, the double bond contribution being larger for benzene than for graphite. The conception of bonds of intermediate multiplicity derives from the perhaps more fundamental conception of resonance between bonding structures. Although this concept will be treated in greater detail in a subsequent chapter, its barest outline may be introduced here in connection with the bond distances mentioned above.

4.45 The benzene molecule is known to be planar, the six equivalent carbon atoms arranged in the form of a regular hexagon with one hydrogen atom adjacent to each carbon atom, symmetrically placed outside the hexagonal ring but coplanar with it. The principal features of this structure were first deduced from the number and distribution of isomeric substitution products and the stoichiometry of hydrogen addition, and were substantiated by X-ray analysis after 1920. The distribution of the four normal covalences of each carbon atom was for many years one of the outstanding problems in chemistry, inasmuch as the properties and reactions of benzene argued against any type of ordinary unsaturated structure (linear, branched, or cyclic) with fixed double bonds. In an example of rare insight, and perhaps unconscious anticipation of the concepts and results of quantum mechanics, Kekulé suggested in 1866 that the actual structure is a composite of two, each of which would now be described as having alternate single and double bonds between adjacent carbon atoms in a six-membered ring. The failure to observe two ortho-substituted isomers, for example, was explained by a very rapid oscillation between the two forms, and this same oscillation was held responsible, in an unexplained fashion, along with the only partially unsaturated nature of the bonds in the ring, for the relatively unreactive character of benzene.

4.46 In more modern terms we suppose the actual structure of benzene to be a synthesis of several energetically equivalent limiting structures or resonance forms; the two principal resonance structures are those of Kekulé, although other structures such as those of Dewar involving stretched bonds across the ring may make minor contributions to the actual structure. Each of the resonance structures is an approximate representation of the actual structure. Now a general theorem of quantum mechanics states that the corresponding energy of such an approximate representation is necessarily greater than that of the actual structure. In other words, the molecule in its equilibrium state is different from those structures hypothesized because the actual molecule possesses a lower energy. Thus we see that the actual molecule is more stable than any of the resonance structures written to describe it. The difference in energy is sometimes referred to as the resonance energy, or it is said that the molecule is stabilized by resonance.

4.47 If we attempt to represent the actual state of a system as a synthesis or superposition of several limiting or resonance states, it is evident that the larger the number of such equivalent approximate descriptions available, the better will be the representation of the actual state. The general theorem mentioned above then predicts a greater relative stability for that molecule represented by a large number of resonance structures than for a different configuration for which only a small number of resonance structures are available. This qualitative argument is often of use in predicting the product of a chemical reaction or the relative rates or equilibria for two similar processes.

4.48 Resonance is not to be considered as a rapid change from one limiting form to another; the resonance structures are not tautomers, which differ in nuclear configuration, and they cannot be resolved. The properties of the resonating molecules are the average properties of the resonance structures, modified by the resonance phenomenon itself: the energy has been shown to be less than that of any resonance structure by at least the amount of the resonance energy.

4.49 Let us now return to the question of the bond distances in benzene. On the average each bond is one half single and one half double, or is said to have one half double bond character. The actual benzene molecule is more stable, however, than either hypothetical cyclohexatriene resonance structure, and this extra stability is associated with a diminution in bond length, so that the carbon-carbon distance is less than a simple average of the single and double bond distances. Thus we observe 1.39 Å rather than $\frac{1}{2}(1.54 + 1.33) = 1.44$ Å for a nonresonating bond of multiplicity one and one half. The energy of the molecule is always less than that calculated from the several possible resonance structures, and the actual bond distances are always somewhat less than those averaged from the possible resonance structures.

4.50 Graphite consists of parallel planes of carbon atoms, about 3.40 Å apart, the forces between which are relatively weak and not properly considered chemical valence forces at all but rather van der Waals forces. In the atomic planes the carbon atoms are arranged hexagonally at interatomic distances of 1.42 Å; the carbon atoms are tightly bound throughout the entire array which may properly be termed a single molecule. Each carbon atom possesses four valences for binding to its three neighboring carbon atoms. For the sheet-like molecule, then, many equivalent resonance structures exist, in each of which every carbon atom forms one double and two single bonds with its neighbors, and every carbon-carbon bond has one third double bond character. One might expect for any resonance form an average bond distance of $\frac{2}{3}(1.54) + \frac{1}{3}(1.33)$ $= 1.47$ Å. The greater strength of the actual bonds in the resonating molecule corresponds to the smaller bond distance observed.

4.51 The relations discussed here for carbon-carbon resonating single-double bonds in benzene and graphite have been extended semi-quantitatively by Pauling to bonds between other atoms and to triple bonds between carbon atoms. Measurements of actual bond distances in resonating molecules may therefore be used to indicate the degree of multiple bond character.

Ionization Potential and Electron Affinity

Ionization Potential

4.52 The electronic configuration of an atomic or ionic system largely determines the chemical behavior of that system, and chemical processes which the system undergoes are associated with changes in the electronic configuration.

The ease with which such processes may be accomplished is evidently determined by the magnitude of the energy increments corresponding to the changes in electronic configuration. Thus if a metal atom participates in chemical reaction by losing its outermost *s* valence electron, then the work required to remove that electron from the atom governs the tendency toward such reaction: if the electron is very easily removed, the atom is highly reactive, and if the electron is removed only with difficulty, the atom exhibits a much less reactive character. Similarly, if in a chemical reaction an atom of a nonmetal must gain a single electron to saturate its configuration, then its reactivity is the larger the more easily the electron is picked up. Evidently a quantitative measure of the energies involved in gain or loss of electrons by atomic systems will be one factor — but not the only one — in predicting the nature of and tendency toward chemical binding between the atoms.

4.53 We have found for an isolated, *i.e.*, gaseous atom, a system of energy levels. Each level corresponds to a certain possible state of the system, and in the simple systems, at least, the several states differ one from another only in respect to one valence electron. For example, in the hydrogen atom, the states are just the possible states for the single valence electron, and a change from one atomic energy state to another involves the transition of the electron from one level to another. A similar situation obtains for the more complex alkali atoms, the lower energy levels of which correspond in general to different states for the valence electron and essentially unchanged states for the inner inert gas electronic configuration. Atoms of elements in the periodic groups of higher order exhibit states which correspond to excitation of one or more electrons from the ground state. For all atoms there are energy levels which correspond to complete removal of one or more electrons, that is, to ionization of the atom. The energy difference between the ground state and the state of ionization is called the ionization potential, and is the amount of energy required to remove completely the most loosely bound electron from the gaseous atom. Ionization

GENERAL REFERENCES

DIEKE, "Atomic and Molecular Physics," Section 7 of *American Institute of Physics Handbook*, edited by Gray, McGraw-Hill Book Company, Inc., New York, 1957.

DUSHMAN, "Quantum Theory of Atomic Spectra and Atomic Structure," Ch. II in Vol. I, *Treatise on Physical Chemistry*, edited by Taylor and Glasstone, D. Van Nostrand Company, Inc., New York, 1942.

GLASSTONE, *Textbook of Physical Chemistry*, D. Van Nostrand Company, Inc., New York, 1954, Ch. I, V, VIII.

HERZBERG, *Atomic Spectra and Atomic Structure*, Dover Publications, New York, 1944, Ch. VI.

LATIMER, *The Oxidation States of the Elements and Their Potentials in Aqueous Solutions*, 2nd Edition, Prentice-Hall, Inc., New York, 1952, Ch. 2.

PAULING, *The Nature of the Chemical Bond*, 2nd Edition, Cornell University Press, Ithaca, N.Y., 1940, Ch. II, X.

PRITCHARD and SKINNER, "The Concept of Electronegativity," *Chem. Rev.* **55**, 745 (1955).

RICE and TELLER, *The Structure of Matter*, John Wiley and Sons, Inc., New York, 1949, Ch. 3, 8.

potentials are given in volts, and measure in electron-volts the work required to remove the electron from the atom; one electron-volt is equivalent to 23,060 cal./mole. Evidently for all atoms except hydrogen there are several ionization potentials, the first, second, third ... ionization potentials being defined respectively as the work required to remove completely the first, second, third ... electron from the original neutral atom. The second ionization potential of magnesium, for example, is the energy difference between the ground states of Mg^+ and Mg^{2+}. An atom of the element of atomic number Z has in principle Z ionization potentials, for Z electrons may be removed from the atom, but generally only the first few potentials are known or are sufficiently small that the corresponding processes are physically realizable or of significance in chemical phenomena.

4.54 Ionization potentials depend principally upon four main factors: atomic size, nuclear charge, the shielding effect of inner electrons, and the type of electron removed. The effect of variation of any one factor is easily predicted, but in general the factors are not independent and the actual magnitude of the ionization potential varies in a not entirely regular fashion with uniform change of atomic structure.

4.55 The effect of changing atomic radius alone on the ease of removal of outer electrons is easily predicted from simple electrostatic considerations: an increase of atomic radius without other change must bring about a decrease in ionization potential because the more distant electron is held less tightly by the nucleus. Since, however, there cannot be two different kinds of atoms for which the other three factors are all the same (notably the nuclear charge), the size effect cannot be tested alone. Two different atoms for which the effective nuclear charge (actual nuclear charge − shielding effect) is about the same and for which the electrons to be removed occupy the same type of orbital — atoms of two consecutive representative elements in a group, for example — illustrate the effect of size: the larger atom possesses the smaller ionization potential.

4.56 Similarly, the increase of nuclear charge without other change is responsible for an increase in ionization potential, because the electron is more tightly held. This situation is nearly realized in the elements samarium through dysprosium, the atoms of which are nearly constant in size and exhibit an approximately constant amount of electronic shielding of the nucleus. The first ionization potential, for the removal of either a $4f$ or a $5d$ electron in all cases, increases monotonically as the nuclear charge increases.

4.57 The ease of removal of an electron from an atom is obviously determined not by the actual nuclear charge but rather by the effective nuclear charge which describes the field operative on the electron. The effective nuclear charge is less than the actual charge for all atoms except hydrogen because the other electrons to some degree screen the nucleus from the valence electron. An increase in the shielding effect, without other change, must cause a decrease in ionization potential, and conversely a decrease in the shielding effect must cause an increase in ionization potential. The successive ionization potentials of a given atom with several valence electrons of the same type illustrate this effect: the removal of the first electron does not change the actual nuclear charge nor does the atomic radius decrease markedly, but the amount of electrostatic screening available decreases and the effective nuclear charge increases. The second ionization potential is greater than the first, and each succeeding ionization potential, in general, is greater than the one before. The variation to be predicted is not simple, however, because the efficiency of screening is different for electrons in different types of orbitals. In any one shell the electrons which penetrate most deeply, the *s* electrons, in general are more effective screening electrons than *p* or *d* electrons, and *f* electrons are the least effective. On that account, the loss of an *f* electron does not change the total screening effect greatly, and we should expect successive high order ionization potentials of the heavier rare-earth elements not to increase rapidly. Since more work is always required to remove an electron from a more highly positively charged residue, however, these ionization potentials will increase to some extent with increasing order for a given element.

4.58 The electron which is removed in the process here considered is of course the most loosely bound electron in the atomic system. Depending on the configuration of the element, this electron may be an *s*, *p*, *d*, or *f* electron. We have seen that the *s* electrons have the most eccentric orbits, corresponding to the minimum value of angular momentum described by the zero value of the quantum number *l*. These electrons in any one shell thus penetrate nearest to the nucleus; consequently, the actual shielding the *s* electrons experience in any one level from the other electrons in the atom is least of all the four possible types, *s*, *p*, *d*, or *f*. The *s* electrons are therefore held most tightly; and if other factors are constant or nearly so, we expect the ionization potential for the removal of an *s* electron to be highest, next highest for a *p* electron, lower for the removal of a *d* electron, and lowest of all for the removal of an *f* electron. The effect is partially responsible, along with decrease of size and amount of shielding, for the rather abrupt increase in successive ionization potentials observed for atoms whose valence shells contain electrons of more than one type. Thus the first, second, and third ionization potentials of boron are 8.296, 25.149 and 37.920 volts, corresponding to the removal in turn of a *p* and then two *s* electrons. Similarly the first four ionization potentials of oxygen, for the removal of *p* electrons, increase by steps of roughly 20 volts each, but the fifth ionization potential is about 35 volts greater than the fourth, for in this case an *s* electron must be removed.

4.59 For a metallic atom possessing *N* valence electrons, all of the first *N* ionization potentials are of chemical interest and importance; for a nonmetallic atom the higher potentials among the first *N* are not of direct interest except in indicating the extreme improbability that the ionization process as such may be involved in chemical combination. In either case ionization potentials may be defined and measured for the removal of electrons beyond those of the valence shell. These electrons are all much more closely and tightly held than the valence electrons, and the screening is less effective, so the higher order ionization potentials are much larger than those related to the removal of valence electrons. There is thus a large increase in ionization potential after the last valence electron is removed: for beryllium, for example, the four successive ionization potentials are 9.320, 18.206, 153.850, and 217.657 volts; and for aluminum the second, third, and fourth potentials are 18.823, 28.44, and 119.96 volts.

4.60 In general, for an element possessing several valence electrons there is no change of configuration of the residue when the first valence electron is removed. For example, the outer electron configurations of calcium and its singly and doubly charged ions, Ca, Ca$^+$, and Ca^{2+}, are respectively ... $3s^23p^64s^2$, ... $3s^23p^64s^1$, and ... $3s^23p^6$. In the case of transition elements the same behavior is usually observed but there are significant exceptions. When the most stable configuration of the ion differs from that of the atom with its most loosely bound electron removed, then the configuration must change upon ionization. Thus the outer configurations of vanadium and its singly charged ion are respectively ... $3d^34s^2$ and ... $3d^4$; similarly we observe ... $3d^74s^2$ and ... $3d^8$ for cobalt, ... $3d^84s^2$ and ... $3d^9$ for nickel, ... $5d^16s^2$ and ... $5d^2$ for lanthanum, and ... $4f^15d^16s^2$ and ... $4f^26s^1$ for cerium. The changed configuration of the first ion often is responsible then for an otherwise unexpectedly large increase from the first to the second ionization potential, just as it explains the low value of the first ionization potential. Schematically the situation is illustrated in Figure 4.3, where simplified energy level diagrams give the ground states of the atoms and ions. Evidently the effect here considered is exactly analogous to that observed at the copper group elements and elsewhere in the building up of electronic configurations; the order of stability of the several orbitals may vary slightly with nuclear charge and with the state of ionization of the atomic system.

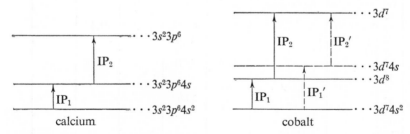

Fig. 4.3 Simplified energy level diagrams for ground states of atoms and ions of calcium and cobalt.

4.61 In Table 4.7 are listed the known values of the ionization potentials of the elements. The list is incomplete because of experimental difficulties of measurement, particularly for potentials of higher order of the elements with many valence electrons and for the newer and scarcer elements.

TABLE 4.7
Ionization Potentials of the Elements

Atomic Number	Symbol	Valence Configuration	IONIZATION POTENTIAL IN ELECTRON-VOLTS							
			I	II	III	IV	V	VI	VII	VIII
1	H	$1s^1$	13.595							
2	He	$1s^2$	24.580	54.403						
3	Li	$2s^1$	5.390	75.619	122.420					
4	Be	$2s^2$	9.320	18.206	153.850	217.657				
5	B	$2s^22p^1$	8.296	25.149	37.920	259.298	340.127			
6	C	$2s^22p^2$	11.264	24.376	47.864	64.476	391.986	489.84		
7	N	$2s^22p^3$	14.54	29.605	47.426	77.450	97.863	551.925	666.83	
8	O	$2s^22p^4$	13.614	35.146	54.934	77.394	113.873	138.080	739.114	871.12
9	F	$2s^22p^5$	17.418	34.98	62.646	87.23	114.214	157.117	185.139	953.60
10	Ne	$2s^22p^6$	21.559	41.07	64	97.16	126.4	157.91		
11	Na	$3s^1$	5.138	47.29	71.65	98.88	138.60	172.36	208.44	264.155
12	Mg	$3s^2$	7.644	15.03	80.12	109.29	141.23	186.86	225.31	265.97
13	Al	$3s^23p^1$	5.984	18.823	28.44	119.96	153.77	190.42	241.93	285.13
14	Si	$3s^23p^2$	8.149	16.34	33.46	45.13	166.73	205.11	246.41	303.87
15	P	$3s^23p^3$	10.55	19.65	30.156	51.354	65.007	220.414	263.31	309.26
16	S	$3s^23p^4$	10.357	23.4	35.0	47.29	72.5	88.029	280.99	328.80
17	Cl	$3s^23p^5$	13.01	23.80	39.90	53.5	67.80	96.7	114.27	348.3
18	Ar	$3s^23p^6$	15.755	27.62	40.90	59.79	75.0	91.3	124.0	143.46
19	K	$4s^1$	4.339	31.81	46	60.90		99.7	118	155
20	Ca	$4s^2$	6.111	11.87	51.21	67	84.39		128	147
21	Sc	$3d^14s^2$	6.56	12.80	24.75	73.9	92	111.1		159
22	Ti	$3d^24s^2$	6.83	13.57	28.14	43.24	99.8	120	140.8	
23	V	$3d^34s^2$	6.74	14.65	29.7	48	65.2	128.9	151	173.7
24	Cr	$3d^54s^1$	6.764	16.49	(31)	(50.4)	(72.8)			
25	Mn	$3d^54s^2$	7.432	15.64	(32)	(52)	(75.7)			
26	Fe	$3d^64s^2$	7.90	16.18						
27	Co	$3d^74s^2$	7.86	17.05						
28	Ni	$3d^84s^2$	7.633	18.15						
29	Cu	$3d^{10}4s^1$	7.724	20.29	29.5					
30	Zn	$3d^{10}4s^2$	9.391	17.96	40.0					
31	Ga	$3d^{10}4s^24p^1$	6.00	20.51	30.6	63.8				
32	Ge	$3d^{10}4s^24p^2$	7.88	15.93	34.07	45.5	93.0			
33	As	$3d^{10}4s^24p^3$	9.81	20.2	28.0	49.9	62.5			
34	Se	$3d^{10}4s^24p^4$	9.75	21.5	33.9	42.72	72.8	81.4		
35	Br	$3d^{10}4s^24p^5$	11.84	21.6	25.7	(50)				
36	Kr	$3d^{10}4s^24p^6$	13.996	24.56	36.8	(68)				
37	Rb	$5s^1$	4.176	27.5	(47)	(80)				
38	Sr	$5s^2$	5.692	11.027						
39	Y	$4d^15s^2$	6.377	12.233	20.4					
40	Zr	$4d^25s^2$	6.835	12.916	24.00	33.8				
41	Nb	$4d^45s^1$	6.881	13.895	24.2					
42	Mo	$4d^55s^1$	7.131	15.72						
43	Tc	$4d^55s^2$	7.23	14.87						
44	Ru	$4d^75s^1$	7.365	16.597						
45	Rh	$4d^85s^1$	7.461	15.92						
46	Pd	$4d^{10}$	8.33	19.42						
47	Ag	$4d^{10}5s^1$	7.574	21.48	35.9					
48	Cd	$4d^{10}5s^2$	8.991	16.904	38.0					
49	In	$4d^{10}5s^25p^1$	5.785	18.828	27.9	57.8				
50	Sn	$4d^{10}5s^25p^2$	7.332	14.63	30.5	39.4	80.7			
51	Sb	$4d^{10}5s^25p^3$	8.639	19	24.7	44.0	55.5			

TABLE 4.7 (*continued*)
Ionization Potentials of the Elements

Atomic Number	Symbol	Valence Configuration	I	II	III	IV	V	VI	VII	VIII
52	Te	$4d^{10}5s^25p^4$	9.01	21.5	30.5	37.7	60.0	(72)		
53	I	$4d^{10}5s^25p^5$	10.44	19.0						
54	Xe	$4d^{10}5s^25p^6$	12.127	21.21	32.0	(46)	(76)			
55	Cs	$6s^1$	3.893	25.1	(35)	(51)	(58)			
56	Ba	$6s^2$	5.210	10.001						
57	La	$5d^16s^2$	5.61	11.43	20.4					
58	Ce	$4f^15d^16s^2$	(6.91)	14.8						
59	Pr	$4f^36s^2$	(5.76)							
60	Nd	$4f^46s^2$	6.3							
61	Pm	$4f^56s^2$								
62	Sm	$4f^66s^2$	5.6	11.2						
63	Eu	$4f^76s^2$	5.67	11.24						
64	Gd	$4f^75d^16s^2$	6.16	12						
65	Tb	$4f^85d^16s^2$	(6.74)							
66	Dy	$4f^{10}6s^2$	(6.82)							
67	Ho	$4f^{11}6s^2$								
68	Er	$4f^{12}6s^2$								
69	Tm	$4f^{13}6s^2$								
70	Yb	$4f^{14}6s^2$	6.22	12.10						
71	Lu	$4f^{14}5d^16s^2$	6.15	14.7						
72	Hf	$4f^{14}5d^26s^2$	5.5	14.9						
73	Ta	$5d^36s^2$	7.7							
74	W	$5d^46s^2$	7.98							
75	Re	$5d^56s^2$	7.87							
76	Os	$5d^66s^2$	8.7							
77	Ir	$5d^76s^2$	9.2							
78	Pt	$5d^96s^1$	9.0	18.56						
79	Au	$5d^{10}6s^1$	9.22	20.5						
80	Hg	$5d^{10}6s^2$	10.434	18.751	34.3	(72)	(82)			
81	Tl	$5d^{10}6s^26p^1$	6.106	20.42	29.7	50.5				
82	Pb	$5d^{10}6s^26p^2$	7.415	15.028	(31.9)	42.11	69.4			
83	Bi	$5d^{10}6s^26p^3$	7.287	19.3	25.42	45.1	55.7			
84	Po	$5d^{10}6s^26p^4$	8.43							
85	At	$5d^{10}6s^26p^5$								
86	Rn	$5d^{10}6s^26p^6$	10.745							
87	Fr	$7s^1$								
88	Ra	$7s^2$	5.277	10.14						
89	Ac	$6d^17s^2$								
90	Th	$6d^27s^2$			29.4					
91	Pa	$6d^37s^2$								
92	U	$5f^36d^17s^2$	4							
93	Np									
94	Pu									
95	Am									
96	Cm									
97	Bk									
98	Cf									
99	Es									
100	Fm									
101	Md									
102	No									

4.62 The four factors (atomic size, nuclear charge, shielding effect, electron type) combine to determine the actual ionization potentials of the elements and their variation with position in the periodic table. In a given period of representative elements the first ionization potentials generally increase from left to right as the effective nuclear charge increases and the atomic radius decreases slightly. For the lighter elements (Be—B, Mg—Al and Ca—Ga) there is a decrease in ionization potential at the group III elements of the boron-aluminum family because with these the first p electron is removed from the valence shell. The p electron penetrates less closely to the nucleus than the s electrons removed for the preceding two metallic elements, and hence is less tightly held and more easily removed. The group IV elements show the same variation in their second ionization potentials. For the heavier elements (Sr—In, Ba—Tl) this effect is more than compensated for by the decrease in radius following the transition series. With the succeeding elements of the period, the first ionization potential increases fairly regularly for the reasons given until the group VI elements exhibit a second relative decrease in potential. This latter effect is probably due to the somewhat enhanced stability of the just half-filled p level of the resultant ion. The same phenomenon is exhibited, as one might expect, in the second ionization potentials of the group VII elements. In both instances the magnitude of the effect decreases markedly with increasing atomic number, because as the electronic structures become more complex the difference in binding of an s and a p electron in a given shell and the excess stability of a half-filled level both become relatively less important.

4.63 The increase of first ionization potential across a period leads to the maximum value for the terminal inert gas. The next element in order of increasing atomic number adds its differentiating s electron to a new outer and more distant level. The valence electron is well shielded by the inner complete electronic shells and therefore is quite easily removed. Thus the alkali metal has a very low ionization potential, and with it starts another period exhibiting the variations described above. The first ionization potentials, and indeed the ionization potentials of any given order, show a periodic dependence on atomic number quite similar to that observed for other physical properties.

4.64 The short transition series show considerably less variation of first ionization potential as the atomic number increases. The effective nuclear charge increases quite slowly because each increment in actual nuclear charge is nearly compensated for by the addition of a new electron to an inner level where its screening efficiency is high. The slow decrease in size with increasing atomic number is then mainly responsible for the general increase in first ionization potential through the series. The same factors operate in the long transition series to a greater extent to bring about nearly constant ionization potential; it is not possible to detect a regular trend in either direction, the small variations generally arising as much from the more or less irregular variations in electronic configurations of the atom or the singly charged ion as from regular variations in nuclear charge, screening effect, or atomic radius.

4.65 The variation of ionization potential with atomic number within a group, that is, the vertical variation in the periodic table, is generally toward lower values for the heavier elements. The elements within a group have similar electronic configurations so that usually an electron of the same type is to be removed in all cases, and their effective nuclear charges are roughly the same. The atomic radius increases uniformly with increasing atomic number and so the ionization potential decreases in the same order. The principal exception is noted for the elements tantalum through lead immediately following the lanthanides, which have larger ionization potentials than the corresponding elements of the same groups but of the preceding period. The reasons for this behavior are found in the lanthanide contraction, that is, the decrease in size through the rare-earth series, and in the increase in nuclear charge in the same region: the effective nuclear charge increases more from lanthanum to hafnium than from yttrium to zirconium, and this is responsible for a greater increase in ionization potential.

4.66 We shall see later that ionization potentials are often important in determining the chemical properties of the elements. Since the potentials describe the tendency toward electron loss, they are directly involved in considerations of chemical binding involving such loss, that is, in ionic bond formation by metallic elements. Indirectly, the potentials are involved in nonionic types of bonding as well, but other factors must also be considered. The magnitudes of the potentials are of interest in another way: the very large values for highly positively charged simple cations, corresponding to energies much larger than those normally available in chemical reactions, make the existence of such ions in ordinary chemical compounds extremely improbable. Finally, it must be remembered that the ionization potentials refer to the gaseous atom and ion, and in actual chemical processes other changes such as volatilization or solvation also introduce energy effects which may be of comparable importance.

Electron Affinity

4.67 In the preceding section we have discussed the energy involved in the process $M \rightarrow M^+ + e^-$, where M is an atom, M^+ the resulting positive ion, and e^- an electron; the energy absorbed in the process is the ionization energy or the ionization potential. Now we may equally well conceive of the process $X + e^- \rightarrow X^-$, where X is an atom and X^- the uninegative ion resulting from the capture of an electron by atom X. The energy released in this process when atom and ion are in their respective lowest energy states is termed the electron affinity of the element. Just as in the case of the ionization potential of M, the process strictly involves the isolated gaseous atom and ion, and the corresponding energy quantity may be only one factor in actual processes involving vaporization and solvation effects as well. The energy may be expressed in either calories or volts (*i.e.*, electron-volts).

4.68 The electron affinity is not nearly so easily measured as the ionization potential and consequently is known for only a few elements. Although, in principle, affinities of higher order may be defined, *e.g.*, the energy release for the process $O^- + e^- \rightarrow O^{2-}$, these are not usually known or even discussed. More commonly, as will be seen below for the group VI elements, the electron affinity for two (or more) electrons may be determined as the energy released, for example, in the process $O + 2e^- \dashrightarrow O^{2-}$. The values of the electron affinity are positive for only a few of the lighter nonmetallic elements, and in all cases presumably only for the first step of ionization, because work must be done to attach an extra electron to a large atom with an inherent tendency to lose electrons (as dictated by the electron configuration) or to an atom bearing a negative charge.

4.69 The electron affinity depends primarily on the size of the atom and the effective nuclear charge; the basic electronic configuration of the element suggests immediately the sign and approximate magnitude of the electron affinity because only atoms with but one or two vacancies in the valence shell, and this fairly close to the nucleus, exhibit large positive affinities. In general, the affinity decreases rapidly with increasing atomic radius because the attractive force on electrons due to the nucleus must decrease with increasing distance. For the same sort of reason the affinity increases with increasing effective nuclear charge, thus with increasing nuclear charge (atomic number) or decreasing effectiveness of screening by inner electrons.

4.70 Since the electron affinity of an element is essentially the same as the ionization potential of its singly negatively charged ion, one may treat the variations in magnitude in the same terms as those used for ionization potential. It is evident that the affinity is determined to some extent by the type of orbital in which the added electron is located; if other factors are constant, then the affinity is greater if the added electron enters an *s* orbital, and in principle decreases in order for *p*, *d*, and *f* orbitals. Such processes, however, are of little more than theoretical interest except for *s* and *p* electrons.

4.71 We shall see later that certain processes of chemical combination involve the gain of electrons by nonmetallic atoms. In these cases the electron affinity of the atom will be one of the energy factors important in determining the tendency toward the particular combination process and the stability of the product. Broadly, the process in which the atom gains electrons may be referred to as reduction; the atom itself, in removing electrons from another portion of the system, oxidizes that portion, and thus the electron affinity measures roughly the oxidizing power of the nonmetallic element. Similarly, those metallic elements which have small ionization potentials lose electrons readily and are thus good reducing agents.

4.72 Electron affinities may be determined indirectly from thermodynamic data for binary compounds and the elements and the directly measured ionization potential of the metallic atom concerned. The determination makes use of a simple form of thermodynamic cycle known as the Born-Haber cycle and illustrated in the diagram. Here one imagines a complete cycle in which the metallic atom M and nonmetallic atom X, both in the gaseous state, are con-

$$M(g) + X(g) \xrightarrow{I-A} M^+(g) + X^-(g)$$

$$S \Big\uparrow +\tfrac{1}{2}D \qquad\qquad\qquad \Big\downarrow -U$$

$$M(g) + \tfrac{1}{2}X_2(g) \xleftarrow{\ Q\ } MX(s)$$

Born-Haber Cycle

verted to their respective ions M^+ and X^-, absorbing the energy $I - A$, I being the ionization potential of M and A the electron affinity of X. The gaseous ions then condense to the crystalline solid MX and the latter is decomposed to the two elements in their standard states; the corresponding energy absorptions are respectively $-U$, where U is the lattice or crystal energy, and Q, the energy of formation of MX. Finally, the elements in their standard states are converted to the gaseous atoms, the initial state of the entire system, by the absorption of the sublimation energy S for the metal and one half the molar energy of dissociation D of the nonmetal. Since in the cycle the system returns precisely to its initial state, the total energy absorbed must vanish and

$$(I - A) + (-U) + Q + (S + \tfrac{1}{2}D) = 0$$

or

$$A = I - U + Q + S + \tfrac{1}{2}D.$$

Of these energy quantities U may be calculated with moderate accuracy from the known structure of the crystalline compound; in principle the remaining four quantities — I, Q, S, and D — may be determined experimentally. Computations are usually made for a number of different binary compounds of a given nonmetallic atom and the apparent values of A averaged; under optimum conditions agreement within a few per cent may be obtained.

4.73 Electron affinities may be determined rather more directly by methods involving the experimental study of the equilibrium system $X(g) + e^- \rightleftharpoons X^-(g)$. The results generally agree within a few kcal./mole with those based on the Born-Haber cycle and the computed crystal energies.

4.74 A few electron affinities are listed in Table 4.8. The value for hydrogen

TABLE 4.8

Electron Affinities of Several Elements

Element	Electron Affinity		Element	Electron Affinity	
	Electron-Volts	Kcal./Mole		Electron-Volts	Kcal./Mole
F	3.63	83.8	O	−7.3	−170 Total affinity
Cl	3.78	87.2	S	−3.4	−79 for *two*
Br	3.54	81.7	Se	−4.2	−97 electrons
I	3.24	74.7			
O	2.2	51	Li	0.54	12.5
S	2.4	55	Na	0.74	17.1
H	0.75	17.2	He, Ne, Ar, Kr, Xe, Rn	0	0

is based on quantum mechanical calculations for the atom and ion, H and H^-, the others generally on Born-Haber calculations or extrapolation through ionization potentials. The second values for oxygen and sulfur and the value for selenium refer to the total process for two electrons, $X + 2e^- \rightarrow X^{2-}$.

4.75 As is to be expected, the affinity decreases with increasing atomic number within a group, and increases with increasing atomic number within a period. An inert gas cannot accept an extra electron in its outer shell because of the restrictions described by the Pauli Principle, and the energy of binding of an electron in a new shell farther out is essentially zero because of the almost complete shielding of the nucleus by the intervening closed shells of electrons; thus the inert gases exhibit zero electron affinity.

Electronegativity

4.76 Chemical combination is discussed, as we shall see later, almost entirely in terms of behavior of electrons in the fields of atomic kernels. Accordingly, the attraction which atoms exert on electrons is a fundamental property basic to the consideration of chemical behavior. Unfortunately, perhaps, the chemist is interested in this property not only of single neutral atoms in the gas phase but also of atoms bonded to others in molecules, and what he terms "electronegativity" is intended to describe the general property of the atom regardless of its environment. Obviously, the two precisely defined properties we have discussed, ionization potential and electron affinity, are different but related illustrations of the general tendency of atoms to attract electrons. From our discussion of these two properties it is possible to describe, at least semi-quantitatively, the variation of electronegativity with position in the periodic table: quite generally, electronegativity increases as one moves to the right in a period, and decreases as one goes down a group. Fluorine is the most electronegative atom, and the heaviest alkali metals the least electronegative, or the most electropositive. Small atoms with nearly filled valence shells have high electronegativities, and the electronegativity decreases as the atom becomes larger or as the occupancy of the valence shell decreases.

4.77 Mulliken first, and then Pauling, have remarked that the ionization potential measures the average attraction of atom and singly charged cation for an electron, the electron affinity measures the average attraction of the atom and singly charged anion for an electron, and the average of the ionization potential and electron affinity, in the same units, of course, should measure the electronegativity of the atom. Since, however, the simple relationship is valid only for monovalent elements and electron affinities are known for but a few elements, this definition of electronegativity is not normally used. An alternative approach is based on considerations of bond energies and their dependence on the electrical character of the bound atoms.

4.78 The strength of a chemical bond between atoms is measured by the energy required to break the bond, that is, to separate the atoms from their molecular grouping and leave them distinct isolated gaseous atoms. For homonuclear or heteronuclear univalent elements bound in diatomic molecules only one bond is concerned, and the energy is merely the dissociation energy of the molecule, which may be determined by a variety of spectroscopic or thermochemical methods. For diatomic molecules containing atoms of valence greater than one, e.g., nitrogen or oxygen, the dissociation energy may equally well be determined, but it corresponds to rupture of a multiple bond between the atoms. It is not possible to deduce from such a measurement the energy for a single bond; this must be determined indirectly as described below. Multiple bonds between atoms of the second row in the periodic table are found to be extremely strong, which accounts in part, for example, for the low reactivity of nitrogen and the relative instability of numerous compounds capable of decomposition with nitrogen as a product.

4.79 For polyatomic molecules, several bonds are involved, and the energy required to disrupt any given bond depends on which, if any, of the other bonds have already been ruptured. Thus different amounts of energy are required to break the first, second, and third N—H bonds in ammonia. Still, the symmetry and the indistinguishability of the three hydrogen atoms require the actual bond strengths in the molecule to be identical, and so the average of the three values may be taken as the energy of the N—H bond. If the polyatomic molecule possesses more than one kind of bond, as is true, for example, for hydrogen peroxide with two H—O bonds and one O—O bond, then the thermochemical data give only the total energy required to break all the bonds, and other data or added assumptions are needed to evaluate each of the several bond energies. In this particular case, the bond energy for the H—O bond is assumed to be the same as in the water molecule, evaluated as one half the total energy required to disrupt the water molecule into atoms, and therefore the O—O bond energy may be calculated by difference. By analogous methods the energies of the single bonds between pairs of atoms in many simple molecules may be calculated from the measured heats of formation of the molecules and energies of dissociation of the elements in their standard states into gaseous atoms. In Table 4.9 are listed values of such single bond energies for a number of atom pairs.

4.80 For molecules consisting of atoms exhibiting their normal covalences (e.g., two for oxygen, four for carbon) and for which a single valence bond structure may be assigned in the classical fashion, the total energy is given quite well, generally within one or two kcal./mole, as the sum of the bond energies (see Table 4.9). The bond energies may therefore be used in certain cases to decide between alternative bonding arrangements.

4.81 If one assumes that a given single bond energy consists of two contributions, one from each atom, then bond energies should be additive; that is to say, the bond energy of the C—H bond, for example, should be equal to one half the sum of the C—C and H—H bond energies. Now it is true that the C—H bond energy is intermediate between those for C—C and H—H bonds, but the quantitative relation is not verified. In general, bond energies are not additive; the energy of a single bond between unlike atoms is usually

TABLE 4.9

Selected Single Bond Energies (in kcal./mole)

H—H	104	C—C	82	F—Br	61	Cl—Br	52
H—Li	58	C—N	64	F—Sb	108	Cl—Rb	101
H—C	100 *	C—O	83	Na—Na	18	Cl—Sn	77
H—N	84	C—F	102	Na—Cl	98	Cl—Sb	74
H—O	111	C—Si	75	Si—Si	50	Cl—I	50
H—F	135	C—S	61	Si—S	60	K—K	12
H—Na	47	C—Cl	79	Si—Cl	90	Ge—Ge	42
H—Si	81	C—Br	66	Si—Br	73	Ge—I	55
H—P	76	C—I	52	Si—I	53	As—As	38
H—S	81	N—N	32	P—P	51	As—Br	58
H—Cl	103	N—F	56	P—Cl	78	As—I	42
H—K	43	N—Cl	37	P—Br	64	Se—Se	50
H—Cu	62	O—O	33	P—I	49	Br—Br	46
H—As	59	O—F	45	S—S	49	Br—Sn	65
H—Se	66	O—Si	106	S—Cl	61	Br—Sb	62
H—Br	88	O—Cl	50	S—As	50	Br—I	42
H—Rb	39	O—As	74	S—Br	51	Rb—Rb	11
H—Ag	53	O—Sb	74	Cl—Cl	58	Sn—Sn	36
H—Te	57	F—F	37	Cl—K	101	Sb—Sb	35
H—I	71	F—Si	136	Cl—Cu	83	Sb—I	44
H—Cs	41	F—S	71	Cl—Ge	80	Te—Te	49
Li—Li	26	F—Cl	61	Cl—As	73	I—I	36
Li—Cl	118	F—As	111	Cl—Se	58	Cs—Cs	10

* The energies for all bonds involving carbon are based on the value 172 kcal./mole for the heat of sublimation of graphite; if the lower value 137 kcal./mole is adopted, the energy for the C—C bond must be decreased to 64 kcal./mole, and the energies for all other bonds containing carbon must be decreased by about 9 kcal./mole.

rather greater than the average of the bond energies for the separate pairs of like atoms. The excess energy increases as the difference in electronegative character between the bonded atoms increases: the excess in bonds involving hydrogen atoms increases monotonically across the second period from 7 kcal./mole for the C—H bond through 16 and 43 kcal./mole respectively for N—H and O—H bonds to the very high value of 65 kcal./mole for the H—F bond. In the bonds between hydrogen and halogen atoms the excess energy decreases with increasing atomic number, and therefore with decreasing difference in electronegative character between hydrogen and halogen, through the values 65, 22, 13, and 1 kcal./mole, respectively, for the H—F, H—Cl, H—Br, and H—I bonds. Thus the rather qualitative concept of electronegative character of the elements is related to the quantitative concept of bond energies, and the latter may therefore be used to measure electronegativity quantitatively.

4.82 The excess bond energies themselves cannot be expressed as differences of terms for the two bound atoms, but Pauling has shown that the square roots of the excess bond energies can be so expressed to a good approximation. Values may be assigned to the several elements such that the square of their difference for a given pair of atoms is proportional to the excess bond energy for the single bond between the atoms. These quantities, in appropriate units, are the electronegativity values for the elements. The scale is chosen so that the energy is given in electron-volts, and because only differences are involved, the arbitrary zero point is selected to make the electronegativities of the first row elements carbon to fluorine have values from 2.5 to 4.0. In these terms, then, the energy, $D(A—B)$, of the single bond between atoms A and B may be expressed in kcal./mole in the form

$$D(A—B) = \tfrac{1}{2}\{D(A—A) + D(B—B)\} + 23.06(x_A - x_B)^2,$$

where x represents the electronegativity value and 23.06 is the conversion factor from electron-volts to kilocalories. This relation is quite well satisfied, generally to within a few kcal./mole except when the electronegativity difference is very large, or when experiment shows, as it sometimes does, a negative excess bond energy. In this latter case, Pauling has introduced a "postulate of the geometric mean," which suggests as the expected value of the A—B single bond energy the geometric rather than arithmetic mean of the values for the A—A and B—B bonds; the excess bond energy on this basis is almost always positive and rather well represented in terms of the assigned electronegativity values.

4.83 The first two sets of electronegativity values given in Table 4.10 were determined by Pauling and by Huggins with the method described above. The Pauling values have been shown to be in essential agreement, in the cases where comparison is possible, with those calculated from the ionization potential and electron affinity according to Mulliken's postulate. The Pauling values are listed because they form a consistent and fairly complete set useful in certain

TABLE 4.10

Electronegativities of the Elements

	Pauling	Huggins *	Sanderson †		Pauling	Huggins	Sanderson
F	4.0	3.90	3.92	Sn	1.7	1.90	2.02
O	3.5	3.50	3.46	Ti	1.6		1.56
N	3.0	3.05	2.93	Zr	1.6		1.56
Cl	3.0	3.15	3.28	Be	1.5		1.37
Br	2.8	2.95	2.96	Al	1.5		1.39
C	2.5	2.60	2.47	Sc	1.3		1.35
S	2.5	2.60	2.66	Y	1.3		1.30
I	2.5	2.65	2.50	Mg	1.2		1.21
Se	2.4	2.55	2.76	Li	1.0		0.86
H	2.1	2.20	2.31	Ca	1.0		1.06
P	2.1	2.15	2.16	Sr	1.0		1.00
Te	2.1	2.30	2.34	Na	0.9		0.85
B	2.0		1.88	Ba	0.9		0.96
As	2.0	2.10	2.53	K	0.8		0.80
Si	1.8	1.90	1.74	Rb	0.8		0.77
Sb	1.8	2.05	2.19	Cs	0.7		0.76
Ge	1.7	1.90	2.31				

* HUGGINS, *J. Am. Chem. Soc.*, **75**, 4123 (1953).
† SANDERSON, *J. Chem. Phys.*, **23**, 2467 (1955).

discussions in Part III of this text. The Huggins values are newer and rest on a more detailed survey of bond energies, but most metallic atoms are not included.

4.84 The third set of electronegativity values in Table 4.10 is that of Sanderson and is based on an entirely different approach. Sanderson has defined the "stability ratio" of an atom as the ratio of its mean electron density to that of an equivalent inert gas atom; this comparison value is obtained by linear interpolation between the values for the neighboring actual inert gas atoms. The stability ratios are less than unity for metals, which tend to increase in electron density in bonding because of the decrease in radius; similarly, the ratios are greater than unity for nonmetals, which tend to decrease in electron density in bonding. Sanderson then obtained an empirical relationship between these ratios and electronegativities on the Pauling scale, and thus was able to compute essentially from atomic numbers and atomic radii alone the values given in Table 4.10. Sanderson has extended these concepts with considerable success to the calculation of interatomic distances in simple molecules. It is assumed that in chemical bonding the stability ratios of the two atoms change to a common final value which is the geometric mean of the initial values. The final value determines an "adjusted radius" for each atom, and the bond length is the sum of these.

4.85 It is evident with either set of values that the electronegativity decreases with increasing atomic size, best measured, perhaps, by the normal covalent radius; the electronegativity also decreases with decreasing number of valence electrons. These two principal factors bring about a periodic variation of electronegativity with atomic number.

4.86 In our later discussion of chemical bonds we shall learn that in general the excess bond energy measures the contribution of ionic structures to the strength of a chemical bond. Bonds between atoms of most unlike electronegativities are most ionic in character and may be nearly entirely so. Thus electronegativities may be used to predict bond character, bond strength, and stabilities of compounds, and may be useful indirectly in estimating other properties such as electron affinity or even electrode potential.

Electrode Potentials

Introduction

4.87 When pieces of copper and zinc are supported in aqueous solutions of their respective sulfates, and the two solutions brought into mutual contact through a porous barrier, a difference of electrical potential is observed between the two dissimilar metals. The system, which is an example of a galvanic cell and is known, in at least some of its forms, as a Daniell cell, is a source of electrical energy and is capable of doing electrical work; it will cause an electrical current to flow through an external resistance connected between the two metals, or electrodes. In the normal spontaneous operation of the usual Daniell cell, electric current is observed to flow in the external circuit from the copper electrode to the zinc electrode. The observed difference of potential between the two poles depends on the concentrations of the aqueous solutions and on the temperature, and under ordinary conditions is of the order of one or two volts.

4.88 If the system is carefully examined after it has been allowed to operate for a time as a galvanic cell giving up electrical energy, it is found to have changed chemically: zinc has left the metallic electrode and appeared in solution as zinc sulfate, while the copper sulfate concentration has been diminished and additional copper has been deposited on the copper electrode. These changes may be represented by the equation

$$Zn(s) + CuSO_4(aq) = ZnSO_4(aq) + Cu(s)$$

in which the notations (s) and (aq) indicate the pure solid phase and the aqueous solution phase respectively. In the isothermal operation of the simplest form of the Daniell cell no other changes may be detected and the process given must therefore be the source of the electrical energy; rather, the cell which has been devised furnishes a means of converting chemical to electrical energy.

4.89 One may connect the system we have described to some convenient external source of a potential difference opposite to and greater than that of the cell. Under these conditions it is observed that the chemical process is reversed; *i.e.*, that copper dissolves and zinc plates out. By very careful adjustment of the external potential difference, as with the use of a potentiometer circuit, it is possible to obtain a state of balance such that a very small change in either direction, properly a differential change, in the applied potential difference causes a corresponding change in the direction of the chemical process. Under these conditions the chemical change proceeds reversibly, and the galvanic cell is said to operate reversibly. The value of the external balancing potential difference is the reversible electromotive force, or EMF, of the cell; it is this quantity which has precise thermodynamic significance for the cell and process considered.

4.90 Corresponding to the process as it has been written above, the cell may be described in the self-explanatory notation

$$Zn(s) \mid ZnSO_4(aq) \mid CuSO_4(aq) \mid Cu(s).$$

For this cell, in which the cell process normally is spontaneous in the direction written (from left to right), the EMF has a positive value. We note that the

GENERAL REFERENCES

DANIELS and ALBERTY, *Physical Chemistry*, John Wiley and Sons, Inc., New York, 1955, Ch. 15.

GLASSTONE, *Textbook of Physical Chemistry*, D. Van Nostrand Company, Inc., New York, 1954, Ch. XII.

HARNED and OWEN, *The Physical Chemistry of Electrolytic Solutions*, Reinhold Publishing Corp., New York, 1950, Ch. 10.

LATIMER, *The Oxidation States of the Elements and Their Potentials in Aqueous Solutions*, 2nd Edition, Prentice-Hall, Inc., New York, 1952.

LATIMER and HILDEBRAND, *Reference Book of Inorganic Chemistry*, 3rd Edition, The Macmillan Company, New York, 1951, Appendices I, II, III.

PAUL, *Principles of Chemical Thermodynamics*, McGraw-Hill Book Company, Inc., New York, 1951, Ch. 9.

cell process describes an *oxidation* occurring at the *left* electrode of the cell as written; this illustrates the commonly accepted American sign convention for EMF values. Had the cell been described in the reverse order, the corresponding cell process would be given also in the reverse order, involving oxidation of the copper, and the EMF would be negative, which is taken to mean that the spontaneous operation of the cell is in the direction opposite to that indicated by the equation for the corresponding cell process.

4.91 The electromotive force of the cell may be considered as the difference of two potentials, one at each electrode. Since only the difference is susceptible of experimental measurement, there is no natural zero for such potentials and an arbitrary base must be chosen. One defines a cell such as

$$Zn(s) \mid ZnSO_4(aq) \mid H_2SO_4(aq, std.) \mid H_2(g, 1 \text{ atm})$$

in which H_2SO_4(aq, std.) represents a certain aqueous sulfuric acid solution to be specified subsequently, and H_2(g, 1 atm) represents hydrogen gas at a standard pressure of one atmosphere. The EMF of this cell is the difference of the two potentials,

$$E_{cell} = E_{Zn} - E_H^\circ,$$

and by definition E_H° is taken as zero. Thus $E_{cell} = E_{Zn}$ and the potential of the zinc electrode may be determined experimentally as the EMF of the particular galvanic cell described. The potentials defined according to the conventions here described are known as oxidation potentials.

4.92 Just as the EMF of the cell may be considered as the difference of two oxidation potentials, so also may the cell process be considered as the difference of two oxidation processes, or in more conventional terms, the sum of an oxidation process at the left electrode and a reduction process at the right electrode. In this division, however, we see immediately a fundamental feature of oxidation and reduction processes taken separately — the presence of electrons as a product in the oxidation or as a reactant in the reduction. Let us first simplify the cell description and cell process to

$$Zn(s) \mid Zn^{2+}(aq) \mid Cu^{2+}(aq) \mid Cu(s)$$
$$Zn(s) + Cu^{2+}(aq) = Zn^{2+}(aq) + Cu(s),$$

wherein at present we merely indicate the presence in solution of the indicated ions and ignore questions of the degree of ionization of the solute or the degree of hydration of the ions. The separate processes at the electrodes may be written as follows.

$$Zn(s) = Zn^{2+}(aq) + 2e^- \text{ at the left electrode}$$
$$Cu^{2+}(aq) + 2e^- = Cu(s) \text{ at the right electrode.}$$

Each electrode process involves a reduced state and an oxidized state of a system; the two states are often referred to as a "couple." The general process occurring at an electrode may be written as an oxidation.

$$\text{Reduced state} \rightarrow \text{Oxidized state} + ne^-.$$

4.93 The separate processes here described suggest the source of the electrode potential: at the zinc, for example, atoms lose electrons and leave the solid phase to enter the solution phase as ions; the electrons discarded on the electrode charge the electrode, and in the convention adopted, raise its potential from the presumed initial zero value. At the copper electrode, conversely, ions from solution pick up electrons and are discharged as atoms. The deficiency of electrons thus brought about charges the electrode positively, and, again in terms of the accepted convention, is responsible for a lowered potential.* For any electrode, an analogous process may be visualized, leading to some charged condition which determines the potential of the electrode. Although the potential of the standard hydrogen electrode is taken as zero, it is not to be supposed that the process

$$\tfrac{1}{2}H_2(g, 1 \text{ atm}) = H^+(aq, std.) + e^-$$

does not occur; the potential of an arbitrary electrode describes the tendency of its charging process to occur relative to the tendency for the analogous process to occur at the standard hydrogen electrode.

4.94 When a galvanic cell operates to drive a current through an external resistance, the useful electrical work done is equal to the product of the charge and the EMF. If the cell operates reversibly, then the cell process is reversible and we know from thermodynamics that the available useful work is equal to $-\Delta F$, that is, to the decrement in free energy for the process. If the cell process as written involves in the oxidation (or reduction, because these two must balance) a transfer of n faradays of electricity, we find

$$-\Delta F = n\mathfrak{F}E$$

in which $\mathfrak{F}$ is the value of the faraday; if $\mathfrak{F}$ is given in coulombs and E in volts, then ΔF is in joules and must be multiplied by 0.2390 to be converted to calories. Now the EMF, E, is taken as the difference of two potentials, one for each electrode, and the cell process is similarly taken as the difference of two oxidation processes; we associate the potential of each electrode with the free energy decrement for its own oxidation process, and conclude that, except for an unimportant additive constant arising from the arbitrary choice of a zero of potential, the electrode oxidation potential, in appropriate units, is the free energy change for the corresponding electrode oxidation process. Approximately, the electrode oxidation potential is the negative of the energy required to bring about the electrode oxidation process.

4.95 The electrode oxidation processes we have thus far considered, the conversion of metallic atoms to ions in aqueous solution, are similar to the processes for which the ionization potential measures the energy change. The significant difference is the difference in state of both reactants and products. Consider the processes and corresponding energy absorptions ΔE:

---

* The situation here described, in which the zinc electrode becomes *negatively* charged but by the convention adopted is said to possess a *positive* potential, is responsible for the alternative convention widely used by polarographers and others, in which the potentials and electromotive forces have the opposite signs to those dictated by the convention used in the present discussion.

$$M(g) = M^+(g) + e^- \qquad \Delta E \sim I$$
$$M(s) = M^+(aq) + e^- \qquad \Delta E \sim -E$$

The product of the electrode reaction is a hydrated ion, the extent of hydration and free energy of formation of which depend on the composition of the solution and temperature. It is conventional to define for the ion in solution a standard state which is described as a state of unit activity. The activity is in effect a thermodynamic concentration and approaches in dilute solution the actual concentration; the ratio of activity to concentration is known as the "activity coefficient," and this approaches unity for infinitely dilute solutions, is less than unity at moderate concentrations, and may for some electrolytes greatly exceed unity at high concentrations. The activity coefficient measures departure of the ionic solutions from ideal behavior, principally because of interactions among the solute ions or between the ions and the solvent molecules, and its deviation from unity is greatest for the smallest, most highly charged ions. We see, therefore, that a state of unit activity is not generally one of unit concentration, but the latter may serve as a rough approximation to the standard state for the ion or ions considered in the electrode processes. All other substances involved in the electrode processes will also be considered in their usual thermodynamic standard states, pure crystalline solids, pure liquids, or pure gases under a pressure of one atmosphere. Under these conditions, and at a specified temperature which is usually 25°, the electrode oxidation potentials are referred to as standard oxidation potentials. They are a measure of the tendency of the electrode process to occur, and the most positive values are those for the processes with the greatest tendency to occur. Since the processes are conventionally written as oxidations, *i.e.*, with the reducing agent on the left and the oxidizing agent, with electrons, on the right, the most positive values of the oxidation potential are associated with the strongest reductants, and the most negative values with the strongest oxidants. A positive value of the oxidation potential specifically implies that the reduced form of the couple is a stronger reducing agent than elementary hydrogen; a negative value of the oxidation potential implies that the oxidized form of the couple is a stronger oxidizing agent than the hydrogen ion in solution. Under standard conditions of unit activity, the reduced form of a couple will reduce the oxidized form of any couple which has a more negative standard oxidation potential, and the oxidized form of a couple will oxidize the reduced form of any couple which has a more positive standard oxidation potential. Tables of standard oxidation potentials are usually arranged with the most positive values at the top so that the best reducing agents are at the top and the best oxidizing agents at the bottom.

4.96 In principle, oxidation potentials are simply determined from measurements of EMF of galvanic cells as described above. In practice, difficulty is often experienced in designing suitable cells and alternative methods based on other types of thermodynamic data must be used. By one means or another a very large number of standard potentials have been determined and the values most recently given by Latimer are listed in Table 4.11; the data all refer to

TABLE 4.11

Standard Oxidation Potentials *

ACID SOLUTION

Couple	$E°$ (volts)	Couple	$E°$ (volts)
$HN_3 = \frac{3}{2}N_2 + H^+ + e^-$	3.09	$AsH_3 = As + 3H^+ + 3e^-$	0.60
$Li = Li^+ + e^-$	3.045	$Tl + Cl^- = TlCl + e^-$	0.557
$K = K^+ + e^-$	2.925	$Ga = Ga^{3+} + 3e^-$	0.53
$Rb = Rb^+ + e^-$	2.925	$SbH_3(g) = Sb + 3H^+ + 3e^-$	0.51
$Cs = Cs^+ + e^-$	2.923	$P + 2H_2O = H_3PO_2 + H^+ + e^-$	0.51
$Ra = Ra^{2+} + 2e^-$	2.92	$H_3PO_2 + H_2O = H_3PO_3 + 2H^+$	
$Ba = Ba^{2+} + 2e^-$	2.90	$\qquad + 2e^-$	0.50
$Sr = Sr^{2+} + 2e^-$	2.89	$Fe = Fe^{2+} + 2e^-$	0.440
$Ca = Ca^{2+} + 2e^-$	2.87	$Eu^{2+} = Eu^{3+} + e^-$	0.43
$Na = Na^+ + e^-$	2.714	$Cr^{2+} = Cr^{3+} + e^-$	0.41
$La = La^{3+} + 3e^-$	2.52	$Cd = Cd^{2+} + 2e^-$	0.403
$Ce = Ce^{3+} + 3e^-$	2.48	$H_2Se = Se + 2H^+ + 2e^-$	0.40
$Nd = Nd^{3+} + 3e^-$	2.44	$Ti^{2+} = Ti^{3+} + e^-$	ca. 0.37
$Sm = Sm^{3+} + 3e^-$	2.41	$Pb + 2I^- = PbI_2 + 2e^-$	0.365
$Gd = Gd^{3+} + 3e^-$	2.40	$Pb + SO_4^{2-} = PbSO_4 + 2e^-$	0.356
$Mg = Mg^{2+} + 2e^-$	2.37	$In = In^{3+} + 3e^-$	0.342
$Y = Y^{3+} + 3e^-$	2.37	$Tl = Tl^+ + e^-$	0.3363
$Am = Am^{3+} + 3e^-$	2.32	$\frac{1}{2}C_2N_2 + H_2O = HCNO + H^+ + e^-$	0.33
$Lu = Lu^{3+} + 3e^-$	2.25	$Pt + H_2S = PtS + 2H^+ + 2e^-$	0.30
$H^- = \frac{1}{2}H_2 + e^-$	2.25	$Pb + 2Br^- = PbBr_2 + 2e^-$	0.280
$H(g) = H^+ + e^-$	2.10	$Co = Co^{2+} + 2e^-$	0.277
$Sc = Sc^{3+} + 3e^-$	2.08	$H_3PO_3 + H_2O = H_3PO_4 + 2H^+$	
$Pu = Pu^{3+} + 3e^-$	2.07	$\qquad + 2e^-$	0.276
$Al + 6F^- = AlF_6^{3-} + 3e^-$	2.07	$Pb + 2Cl^- = PbCl_2 + 2e^-$	0.268
$Th = Th^{4+} + 4e^-$	1.90	$V^{2+} = V^{3+} + e^-$	0.255
$Np = Np^{3+} + 3e^-$	1.86	$V + 4H_2O = V(OH)_4^+ + 4H^+$	
$Be = Be^{2+} + 2e^-$	1.85	$\qquad + 5e^-$	0.253
$U = U^{3+} + 3e^-$	1.80	$Sn + 6F^- = SnF_6^{2-} + 4e^-$	0.25
$Hf = Hf^{4+} + 4e^-$	1.70	$Ni = Ni^{2+} + 2e^-$	0.250
$Al = Al^{3+} + 3e^-$	1.66	$N_2H_5^+ = N_2 + 5H^+ + 4e^-$	0.23
$Ti = Ti^{2+} + 2e^-$	1.63	$S_2O_6^{2-} + 2H_2O = 2SO_4^{2-} + 4H^+$	
$Zr = Zr^{4+} + 4e^-$	1.53	$\qquad + 2e^-$	0.22
$Si + 6F^- = SiF_6^{2-} + 4e^-$	1.2	$Mo = Mo^{3+} + 3e^-$	ca. 0.2
$Ti + 6F^- = TiF_6^{2-} + 4e^-$	1.19	$HCOOH(aq) = CO_2 + 2H^+ + 2e^-$	0.196
$Mn = Mn^{2+} + 2e^-$	1.18	$Cu + I^- = CuI + e^-$	0.185
$V = V^{2+} + 2e^-$	ca. 1.18	$Ag + I^- = AgI + e^-$	0.151
$Nb = Nb^{3+} + 3e^-$	ca. 1.1	$Sn = Sn^{2+} + 2e^-$	0.136
$Ti + H_2O = TiO^{2+} + 2H^+ + 4e^-$	0.89	$HO_2 = O_2 + H^+ + e^-$	0.13
$B + 3H_2O = H_3BO_3 + 3H^+ + 3e^-$	0.87	$Pb = Pb^{2+} + 2e^-$	0.126
$Si + 2H_2O = SiO_2 + 4H^+ + 4e^-$	0.86	$Ge + 2H_2O = GeO_2 + 4H^+ + 4e^-$	0.15
$2Ta + 5H_2O = Ta_2O_5 + 10H^+$		$W + 3H_2O = WO_3 + 6H^+ + 6e^-$	0.09
$\qquad + 10e^-$	0.81	$HS_2O_4^- + 2H_2O = 2H_2SO_3 + H^+$	
$Zn = Zn^{2+} + 2e^-$	0.763	$\qquad + 2e^-$	0.08
$Tl + I^- = TlI + e^-$	0.753	$Hg + 4I^- = HgI_4^{2-} + 2e^-$	0.04
$Cr = Cr^{3+} + 3e^-$	0.74	$H_2 = 2H^+ + 2e^-$	0.00
$H_2Te = Te + 2H^+ + 2e^-$	0.72	$Ag + 2S_2O_3^{2-} = Ag(S_2O_3)_2^{3-} + e^-$	−0.01
$Tl + Br^- = TlBr + e^-$	0.658	$Cu + Br^- = CuBr + e^-$	−0.033
$2Nb + 5H_2O = Nb_2O_5 + 10H^+$		$UO_2^+ = UO_2^{2+} + e^-$	−0.05
$\qquad + 10e^-$	0.65	$HCHO(aq) + H_2O = HCOOH(aq)$	
$U^{3+} = U^{4+} + e^-$	0.61	$\qquad + 2H^+ + 2e^-$	−0.056

* All data are taken directly from Latimer, *The Oxidation States of the Elements and Their Potentials in Aqueous Solutions*, 2nd Edition, Prentice-Hall, Inc., New York, 1952, pp. 340–8.

TABLE 4.11 (*continued*)
Standard Oxidation Potentials

ACID SOLUTION

Couple	$E°$ (*volts*)	Couple	$E°$ (*volts*)
$PH_3(g) = P + 3H^+ + 3e^-$	−0.06	$Te + 2H_2O = TeO_2 + 4H^+ + 4e^-$	−0.529
$Ag + Br^- = AgBr + e^-$	−0.095	$2I^- = I_2 + 2e^-$	−0.5355
$Ti^{3+} + H_2O = TiO^{2+} + 2H^+ + e^-$	−0.1	$3I^- = I_3^- + 2e^-$	−0.536
$SiH_4 = Si + 4H^+ + 4e^-$	−0.102	$CuCl = Cu^{2+} + Cl^- + e^-$	−0.538
$CH_4 = C + 4H^+ + 4e^-$	−0.13	$Ag + BrO_3^- = AgBrO_3 + e^-$	−0.55
$Cu + Cl^- = CuCl + e^-$	−0.137	$Te + 2H_2O = TeOOH^+ + 3H^+ + 4e^-$	−0.559
$H_2S = S + 2H^+ + 2e^-$	−0.141	$HAsO_2 + 2H_2O = H_3AsO_4 + 2H^+ + 2e^-$	−0.559
$Np^{3+} = Np^{4+} + e^-$	−0.147	$Ag + NO_2^- = AgNO_2 + e^-$	−0.564
$Sn^{2+} = Sn^{4+} + 2e^-$	−0.15	$MnO_4^{2-} = MnO_4^- + e^-$	−0.564
$2Sb + 3H_2O = Sb_2O_3 + 6H^+ + 6e^-$	−0.152	$2H_2SO_3 = S_2O_6^{2-} + 4H^+ + 2e^-$	−0.57
$Cu^+ = Cu^{2+} + e^-$	−0.153	$Pt + 4Br^- = PtBr_4^{2-} + 2e^-$	−0.58
$Bi + H_2O + Cl^- = BiOCl + 2H^+ + 3e^-$	−0.16	$2SbO^+ + 3H_2O = Sb_2O_5 + 6H^+ + 4e^-$	−0.581
$H_2SO_3 + H_2O = SO_4^{2-} + 4H^+ + 2e^-$	−0.17	$CH_4 + H_2O = CH_3OH(aq) + 2H^+ + 2e^-$	−0.586
$CH_3OH(aq) = HCHO(aq) + 2H^+ + 2e^-$	−0.19	$Pd + 4Br^- = PdBr_4^{2-} + 2e^-$	−0.6
$Hg + 4Br^- = HgBr_4^{2-} + 2e^-$	−0.21	$Ru + 5Cl^- = RuCl_5^{2-} + 3e^-$	−0.60
$Ag + Cl^- = AgCl + e^-$	−0.222	$U^{4+} + 2H_2O = UO_2^+ + 4H^+ + e^-$	−0.62
$(CH_3)_2SO + H_2O = (CH_3)_2SO_2 + 2H^+ + 2e^-$	−0.23	$Pd + 4Cl^- = PdCl_4^{2-} + 2e^-$	−0.62
$As + 2H_2O = HAsO_2(aq) + 3H^+ + 3e^-$	−0.247	$CuBr = Cu^{2+} + Br^- + e^-$	−0.640
$Re + 2H_2O = ReO_2 + 4H^+ + 4e^-$	−0.252	$Ag + C_2H_3O_2^- = AgC_2H_3O_2 + e^-$	−0.643
$Bi + H_2O = BiO^+ + 2H^+ + 3e^-$	−0.32	$2Ag + SO_4^{2-} = Ag_2SO_4 + 2e^-$	−0.653
$U^{4+} + 2H_2O = UO_2^{2+} + 4H^+ + 2e^-$	−0.334	$Au + 4CNS^- = Au(CNS)_4^- + 3e^-$	−0.66
$Cu = Cu^{2+} + 2e^-$	−0.337	$PtCl_4^{2-} + 2Cl^- = PtCl_6^{2-} + 2e^-$	−0.68
$Ag + IO_3^- = AgIO_3 + e^-$	−0.35	$H_2O_2 = O_2 + 2H^+ + 2e^-$	−0.682
$Fe(CN)_6^{4-} = Fe(CN)_6^{3-} + e^-$	−0.36	$3NH_4^+ = HN_3 + 11H^+ + 8e^-$	−0.69
$V^{3+} + H_2O = VO^{2+} + 2H^+ + e^-$	−0.361	$H_2Te = Te + 2H^+ + 2e^-$	−0.70
$Re + 4H_2O = ReO_4^- + 8H^+ + 7e^-$	−0.363	$H_2N_2O_2 = 2NO + 2H^+ + 2e^-$	−0.71
$HCN(aq) = \frac{1}{2}C_2N_2 + H^+ + e^-$	−0.37	$OH + H_2O = H_2O_2 + H^+ + e^-$	−0.72
$S_2O_3^{2-} + 3H_2O = 2H_2SO_3 + 2H^+ + 4e^-$	−0.40	$Pt + 4Cl^- = PtCl_4^{2-} + 2e^-$	−0.73
$Rh + 6Cl^- = RhCl_6^{3-} + 3e^-$	−0.44	$C_2H_4 = C_2H_2 + 2H^+ + 2e^-$	−0.73
$2Ag + CrO_4^{2-} = Ag_2CrO_4 + 2e^-$	−0.446	$Se + 3H_2O = H_2SeO_3 + 4H^+ + 4e^-$	−0.74
$S + 3H_2O = H_2SO_3 + 4H^+ + 4e^-$	−0.45	$Np^{4+} + 2H_2O = NpO_2^+ + 4H^+ + e^-$	−0.75
$Sb_2O_4 + H_2O = Sb_2O_5 + 2H^+ + 2e^-$	−0.48	$2CNS^- = (CNS)_2 + 2e^-$	−0.77
$2Ag + MoO_4^{2-} = Ag_2MoO_4 + 2e^-$	−0.49	$Ir + 6Cl^- = IrCl_6^{3-} + 3e^-$	−0.77
$2NH_3OH^+ = H_2N_2O_2 + 6H^+ + 4e^-$	−0.496	$Fe^{2+} = Fe^{3+} + e^-$	−0.771
$ReO_2 + 2H_2O = ReO_4^- + 4H^+ + 3e^-$	−0.51	$2Hg = Hg_2^{2+} + 2e^-$	−0.789
$S_4O_6^{2-} + 6H_2O = 4H_2SO_3 + 4H^+ + 6e^-$	−0.51	$Ag = Ag^+ + e^-$	−0.7991
$C_2H_6 = C_2H_4 + 2H^+ + 2e^-$	−0.52	$N_2O_4 + 2H_2O = 2NO_3^- + 4H^+ + 2e^-$	−0.80
$Cu = Cu^+ + e^-$	−0.521	$Rh = Rh^{3+} + 3e^-$	ca. −0.8
		$Os + 4H_2O = OsO_4 + 8H^+ + 8e^-$	−0.85
		$H_2N_2O_2 + 2H_2O = 2HNO_2 + 4H^+ + 4e^-$	−0.86
		$CuI = Cu^{2+} + I^- + e^-$	−0.86
		$Au + 4Br^- = AuBr_4^- + 3e^-$	−0.87
		$Hg_2^{2+} = 2Hg^{2+} + 2e^-$	−0.920

TABLE 4.11 (*continued*)
Standard Oxidation Potentials

ACID SOLUTION

Couple	$E°$ (volts)	Couple	$E°$ (volts)
$HNO_2 + H_2O = NO_3^- + 3H^+$ $+ 2e^-$	-0.94	$N_2H_5^+ + 2H_2O = 2NH_3OH^+$ $+ H^+ + 2e^-$	-1.42
$PuO_2^+ = PuO_2^{2+} + e^-$	-0.93	$Au + 3H_2O = Au(OH)_3 + 3H^+$ $+ 3e^-$	-1.45
$NO + 2H_2O = NO_3^- + 4H^+ + 4e^-$	-0.96	$\frac{1}{2}I_2 + H_2O = HIO + H^+ + e^-$	-1.45
$Au + 2Br^- = AuBr_2^- + e^-$	-0.96	$Pb^{2+} + 2H_2O = PbO_2 + 4H^+$	
$Pu^{3+} = Pu^{4+} + e^-$	-0.97	$+ 2e^-$	-1.455
$Pt + 2H_2O = Pt(OH)_2 + 2H^+$ $+ 2e^-$	-0.98	$Au = Au^{3+} + 3e^-$	-1.50
$Pd = Pd^{2+} + 2e^-$	-0.987	$H_2O_2 = HO_2 + H^+ + e^-$	-1.5
$IrBr_6^{4-} = IrBr_6^{3-} + e^-$	-0.99	$Mn^{2+} = Mn^{3+} + e^-$	-1.51
$NO + H_2O = HNO_2 + H^+ + e^-$	-1.00	$Mn^{2+} + 4H_2O = MnO_4^- + 8H^+$ $+ 5e^-$	-1.51
$Au + 4Cl^- = AuCl_4^- + 3e^-$	-1.00	$\frac{1}{2}Br_2 + 3H_2O = BrO_3^- + 6H^+$	
$VO^{2+} + 3H_2O = V(OH)_4^+ + 2H^+$ $+ e^-$	-1.00	$+ 5e^-$	-1.52
$IrCl_6^{3-} = IrCl_6^{2-} + e^-$	-1.017	$\frac{1}{2}Br_2 + H_2O = HBrO + H^+ + e^-$	-1.59
$TeO_2 + 4H_2O = H_6TeO_6$ $+ 2H^+ + 2e^-$	-1.02	$2BiO^+ + 2H_2O = Bi_2O_4 + 4H^+$ $+ 2e^-$	-1.59
$2NO + 2H_2O = N_2O_4 + 4H^+ + 4e^-$	-1.03	$IO_3^- + 3H_2O = H_5IO_6 + H^+ + 2e^-$	-1.6
$Pu^{4+} + 2H_2O = PuO_2^{2+} + 4H^+$ $+ 2e^-$	-1.04	$Bk^{3+} = Bk^{4+} + e^-$	-1.6
		$Ce^{3+} = Ce^{4+} + e^-$	-1.61
$2Cl^- + \frac{1}{2}I_2 = ICl_2^- + e^-$	-1.06	$\frac{1}{2}Cl_2 + H_2O = HClO + H^+ + e^-$	-1.63
$2Br^- = Br_2(l) + 2e^-$	-1.0652	$AmO_2^+ = AmO_2^{2+} + e^-$	-1.64
$2HNO_2 = N_2O_4 + 2H^+ + 2e^-$	-1.07	$HClO + H_2O = HClO_2 + 2H^+$ $+ 2e^-$	-1.64
$Cu(CN)_2^- = Cu^{2+} + 2CN^- + e^-$	-1.12	$Au = Au^+ + e^-$	ca. -1.68
$Pu^{4+} + 2H_2O = PuO_2^+ + 4H^+ + e^-$	-1.15	$Ni^{2+} + 2H_2O = NiO_2 + 4H^+$ $+ 2e^-$	-1.68
$H_2SeO_3 + H_2O = SeO_4^{2-} + 4H^+$ $+ 2e^-$	-1.15	$PbSO_4 + 2H_2O = PbO_2 + SO_4^{2-}$ $+ 4H^+ + 2e^-$	-1.685
$NpO_2^+ = NpO_2^{2+} + e^-$	-1.15	$Am^{3+} + 2H_2O = AmO_2^{2+} + 4H^+$ $+ 3e^-$	-1.69
$4Cl^- + C + 4H^+ = CCl_4 + 4H^+$ $+ 4e^-$	-1.18	$MnO_2 + 2H_2O = MnO_4^- + 4H^+$ $+ 3e^-$	-1.695
$ClO_3^- + H_2O = ClO_4^- + 2H^+ + 2e^-$	-1.19	$Am^{3+} + 2H_2O = AmO_2^+ + 4H^+$ $+ 2e^-$	-1.725
$\frac{1}{2}I_2 + 3H_2O = IO_3^- + 6H^+ + 5e^-$	-1.195		
$HClO_2 + H_2O = ClO_3^- + 3H^+$ $+ 2e^-$	-1.21	$2H_2O = H_2O_2 + 2H^+ + 2e^-$	-1.77
$2H_2O = O_2 + 4H^+ + 4e^-$	-1.229	$Co^{2+} = Co^{3+} + e^-$	-1.82
$2S + 2Cl^- = S_2Cl_2 + 2e^-$	-1.23	$Fe^{3+} + 4H_2O = FeO_4^{2-} + 8H^+$ $+ 3e^-$	-1.9
$Mn^{2+} + 2H_2O = MnO_2 + 4H^+$ $+ 2e^-$	-1.23	$NH_4^+ + N_2 = HN_3 + 3H^+ + 2e^-$	-1.96
$Tl^+ = Tl^{3+} + 2e^-$	-1.25	$Ag^+ = Ag^{2+} + e^-$	-1.98
$Am^{4+} + 2H_2O = AmO_2^+ + 4H^+$ $+ e^-$	-1.26	$2SO_4^{2-} = S_2O_8^{2-} + 2e^-$	-2.01
$2NH_4^+ = N_2H_5^+ + 3H^+ + 2e^-$	-1.275	$O_2 + H_2O = O_3 + 2H^+ + 2e^-$	-2.07
$HClO_2 = ClO_2 + H^+ + e^-$	-1.275	$H_2O + 2F^- = F_2O + 2H^+ + 4e^-$	-2.1
$PdCl_4^{2-} + 2Cl^- = PdCl_6^{2-} + 2e^-$	-1.288	$Am^{3+} = Am^{4+} + e^-$	-2.18
$N_2O + 3H_2O = 2HNO_2 + 4H^+$ $+ 4e^-$	-1.29	$H_2O = O(g) + 2H^+ + 2e^-$	-2.42
$2Cr^{3+} + 7H_2O = Cr_2O_7^{2-} + 14H^+$ $+ 6e^-$	-1.33	$H_2O = OH + H^+ + e^-$	-2.8
$NH_4^+ + H_2O = NH_3OH^+ + 2H^+$ $+ 2e^-$	-1.35	$N_2 + 2H_2O = H_2N_2O_2 + 2H^+$ $+ 2e^-$	-2.85
$2Cl^- = Cl_2 + 2e^-$	-1.3595	$2F^- = F_2 + 2e^-$	-2.87
		$2HF(aq) = F_2 + 2H^+ + 2e^-$	-3.06

TABLE 4.11 (continued)

Standard Oxidation Potentials

BASIC SOLUTION

Couple	$E°$ (volts)	Couple	$E°$ (volts)
$Ca + 2OH^- = Ca(OH)_2 + 2e^-$	3.03	$W + 8OH^- = WO_4^{2-} + 4H_2O + 6e^-$	1.05
$Sr + 2OH^- + 8H_2O = Sr(OH)_2 \cdot 8H_2O + 2e^-$	2.99	$Mo + 8OH^- = MoO_4^{2-} + 4H_2O + 6e^-$	1.05
$Ba + 2OH^- + 8H_2O = Ba(OH)_2 \cdot 8H_2O + 2e^-$	2.97	$Cd + 4CN^- = Cd(CN)_4^{2-} + 2e^-$	1.03
$H(g) + OH^- = H_2O + e^-$	2.93	$Zn + 4NH_3 = Zn(NH_3)_4^{2+} + 2e^-$	1.03
$La + 3OH^- = La(OH)_3 + 3e^-$	2.90	$Fe + S^{2-} = FeS_{(\alpha)} + 2e^-$	1.01
$Lu + 3OH^- = Lu(OH)_3 + 3e^-$	2.72	$In + 3OH^- = In(OH)_3 + 3e^-$	1.0
$Mg + 2OH^- = Mg(OH)_2 + 2e^-$	2.69	$Pb + S^{2-} = PbS + 2e^-$	0.95
$2Be + 6OH^- = Be_2O_3^{2-} + 3H_2O + 4e^-$	2.62	$CN^- + 2OH^- = CNO^- + H_2O + 2e^-$	0.97
$Sc + 3OH^- = Sc(OH)_3 + 3e^-$	ca.2.6	$2Tl + S^{2-} = Tl_2S + 2e^-$	0.96
$Hf + 4OH^- = HfO(OH)_2 + H_2O + 4e^-$	2.50	$Pu(OH)_3 + OH^- = Pu(OH)_4 + e^-$	0.95
$Th + 4OH^- = Th(OH)_4 + 4e^-$	2.48	$Sn + S^{2-} = SnS + 2e^-$	0.94
$Pu + 3OH^- = Pu(OH)_3 + 3e^-$	2.42	$SO_3^{2-} + 2OH^- = SO_4^{2-} + H_2O + 2e^-$	0.93
$U + 4OH^- = UO_2 + 2H_2O + 4e^-$	2.39	$Se^{2-} = Se + 2e^-$	0.92
$Al + 4OH^- = H_2AlO_3^- + H_2O + 3e^-$	2.35	$Sn + 3OH^- = HSnO_2^- + H_2O + 2e^-$	0.91
$Zr + 4OH^- = H_2ZrO_3 + H_2O + 4e^-$	2.36	$Ge + 5OH^- = HGeO_3^- + 2H_2O + 4e^-$	0.9
$U(OH)_3 + OH^- = U(OH)_4 + e^-$	2.2	$HSnO_2^- + H_2O + 3OH^- = Sn(OH)_6^{2-} + 2e^-$	0.90
$U + 3OH^- = U(OH)_3 + 3e^-$	2.17	$PH_3 + 3OH^- = P + 3H_2O + 3e^-$	0.89
$P + 2OH^- = H_2PO_2^- + e^-$	2.05	$Fe + 2OH^- = Fe(OH)_2 + 2e^-$	0.877
$B + 4OH^- = H_2BO_3^- + 3e^-$	1.79	$Ni + S^{2-} = NiS_{(\alpha)} + 2e^-$	0.83
$Si + 6OH^- = SiO_3^{2-} + 3H_2O + 4e^-$	1.70	$H_2 + 2OH^- = 2H_2O + 2e^-$	0.828
$U(OH)_4 + 2Na^+ + 4OH^- = Na_2UO_4 + 4H_2O + 2e^-$	1.61	$Cd + 2OH^- = Cd(OH)_2 + 2e^-$	0.809
$H_2PO_2^- + 3OH^- = HPO_3^{2-} + 2H_2O + 2e^-$	1.57	$Fe + CO_3^{2-} = FeCO_3 + 2e^-$	0.756
$Mn + 2OH^- = Mn(OH)_2 + 2e^-$	1.55	$Cd + CO_3^{2-} = CdCO_3 + 2e^-$	0.74
$Mn + CO_3^{2-} = MnCO_3 + 2e^-$	1.48	$Co + 2OH^- = Co(OH)_2 + 2e^-$	0.73
$Zn + S^{2-} = ZnS + 2e^-$	1.44	$Hg + S^{2-} = HgS + 2e^-$	0.72
$Cr + 3OH^- = Cr(OH)_3 + 3e^-$	1.3	$Ni + 2OH^- = Ni(OH)_2 + 2e^-$	0.72
$Zn + 4CN^- = Zn(CN)_4^{2-} + 2e^-$	1.26	$2Ag + S^{2-} = Ag_2S + 2e^-$	0.69
$Zn + 2OH^- = Zn(OH)_2 + 2e^-$	1.245	$As + 4OH^- = AsO_2^- + 2H_2O + 3e^-$	0.68
$Ga + 4OH^- = H_2GaO_3^- + H_2O + 3e^-$	1.22	$AsO_2^- + 4OH^- = AsO_4^{3-} + 2H_2O + 2e^-$	0.67
$Zn + 4OH^- = ZnO_2^{2-} + 2H_2O + 2e^-$	1.216	$2FeS + S^{2-} = Fe_2S_3 + 2e^-$	0.67
$Cr + 4OH^- = CrO_2^- + 2H_2O + 3e^-$	1.2	$Sb + 4OH^- = SbO_2^- + 2H_2O + 3e^-$	0.66
$Cd + S^{2-} = CdS + 2e^-$	1.21	$Co + CO_3^{2-} = CoCO_3 + 2e^-$	0.64
$6V + 33OH^- = 16H_2O + HV_6O_{17}^{3-} + 30e^-$	1.15	$Cd + 4NH_3 = Cd(NH_3)_4^{2+} + 2e^-$	0.597
$Te^{2-} = Te + 2e^-$	1.14	$ReO_2 + 4OH^- = ReO_4^- + 2H_2O + 3e^-$	0.594
$HPO_3^{2-} + 3OH^- = PO_4^{3-} + 2H_2O + 2e^-$	1.12	$Re + 8OH^- = ReO_4^- + 4H_2O + 7e^-$	0.584
$S_2O_4^{2-} + 4OH^- = 2SO_3^{2-} + 2H_2O + 2e^-$	1.12	$S_2O_3^{2-} + 6OH^- = 2SO_3^{2-} + 3H_2O + 4e^-$	0.58
$Zn + CO_3^{2-} = ZnCO_3 + 2e^-$	1.06	$Re + 4OH^- = ReO_2 + 2H_2O + 4e^-$	0.576
		$Te + 6OH^- = TeO_3^{2-} + 3H_2O + 4e^-$	0.57

TABLE 4.11 (*continued*)
Standard Oxidation Potentials

BASIC SOLUTION

Couple	$E°$ (volts)	Couple	$E°$ (volts)
$Fe(OH)_2 + OH^- = Fe(OH)_3 + e^-$	0.56	$Mn(OH)_2 + OH^- = Mn(OH)_3 + e^-$	−0.1
$O_2^- = O_2 + e^-$	0.56	$Pt + 2OH^- = Pt(OH)_2 + 2e^-$	−0.15
$2Cu + S^{2-} = Cu_2S + 2e^-$	0.54	$Co(OH)_2 + OH^- = Co(OH)_3 + e^-$	−0.17
$Pb + 3OH^- = HPbO_2^- + H_2O$ $+ 2e^-$	0.54	$PbO(r) + 2OH^- = PbO_2 + H_2O$ $+ 2e^-$	−0.248
$Pb + CO_3^{2-} = PbCO_3 + 2e^-$	0.506	$I^- + 6OH^- = IO_3^- + 3H_2O + 6e^-$	−0.26
$S^{2-} = S + 2e^-$	0.48	$PuO_2OH + OH^- = PuO_2(OH)_2$ $+ e^-$	−0.26
$Ni + 6NH_3(aq) = Ni(NH_3)_6^{2+}$ $+ 2e^-$	0.47	$Ag + 2SO_3^{2-} = Ag(SO_3)_2^{3-} + e^-$	−0.30
$Ni + CO_3^- = NiCO_3 + 2e^-$	0.45	$ClO_2^- + 2OH^- = ClO_3^- + H_2O$ $+ 2e^-$	−0.33
$2Bi + 6OH^- = Bi_2O_3 + 3H_2O$ $+ 6e^-$	0.44	$2Ag + 2OH^- = Ag_2O + H_2O$ $+ 2e^-$	−0.344
$Cu + 2CN^- = Cu(CN)_2^- + e^-$	0.43	$ClO_3^- + 2OH^- = ClO_4^- + H_2O$ $+ 2e^-$	−0.36
$Hg + 4CN^- = Hg(CN)_4^{2-} + 2e^-$	0.37	$Ag + 2NH_3 = Ag(NH_3)_2^+ + e^-$	−0.373
$Se + 6OH^- = SeO_3^{2-} + 3H_2O$ $+ 4e^-$	0.366	$TeO_3^{2-} + 2OH^- = TeO_4^{2-} + H_2O$ $+ 2e^-$	−0.4
$2Cu + 2OH^- = Cu_2O + H_2O$ $+ 2e^-$	0.358	$OH^- + HO_2^- = O_2^- + H_2O + e^-$	−0.4
$Tl + OH^- = Tl(OH) + e^-$	0.3445	$4OH^- = O_2 + 2H_2O + 4e^-$	−0.401
$Ag + 2CN^- = Ag(CN)_2^- + e^-$	0.31	$2Ag + CO_3^{2-} = Ag_2CO_3 + 2e^-$	−0.47
$Cu + CNS^- = Cu(CNS) + e^-$	0.27	$Ni(OH)_2 + 2OH^- = NiO_2$ $+ 2H_2O + 2e^-$	−0.49
$OH + 2OH^- = HO_2^- + H_2O + e^-$	0.24	$I^- + 2OH^- = IO^- + H_2O + 2e^-$	−0.49
$Cr(OH)_3 + 5OH^- = CrO_4^{2-}$ $+ 4H_2O + 3e^-$	0.13	$Ag_2O + 2OH^- = 2AgO + H_2O$ $+ 2e^-$	−0.57
$Cu + 2NH_3 = Cu(NH_3)_2^+ + e^-$	0.12	$MnO_2 + 4OH^- = MnO_4^{2-} + 2H_2O$ $+ 2e^-$	−0.60
$Cu_2O + 2OH^- + H_2O$ $= 2Cu(OH)_2 + 2e^-$	0.080	$RuO_4^{2-} = RuO_4^- + e^-$	−0.60
$HO_2^- + OH^- = O_2 + H_2O + 2e^-$	0.076	$Br^- + 6OH^- = BrO_3^- + 3H_2O$ $+ 6e^-$	−0.61
$TlOH + 2OH^- = Tl(OH)_3 + 2e^-$	0.05	$ClO^- + 2OH^- = ClO_2^- + H_2O$ $+ 2e^-$	−0.66
$Ag + CN^- = AgCN + e^-$	0.017	$IO_3^- + 3OH^- = H_3IO_6^{2-} + 2e^-$	−0.7
$Mn(OH)_2 + 2OH^- = MnO_2$ $+ 2H_2O + 2e^-$	0.05	$N_2H_4 + 2OH^- = 2NH_2OH + 2e^-$	−0.73
$NO_2^- + 2OH^- = NO_3^- + H_2O$ $+ 2e^-$	−0.01	$2AgO + 2OH^- = Ag_2O_3 + H_2O$ $+ 2e^-$	−0.74
$Os + 9OH^- = HOsO_5^- + 4H_2O$ $+ 8e^-$	−0.02	$Br^- + 2OH^- = BrO^- + H_2O$ $+ 2e^-$	−0.76
$2Rh + 6OH^- = Rh_2O_3 + 3H_2O$ $+ 6e^-$	−0.04	$3OH^- = HO_2^- + H_2O + 2e^-$	−0.88
$SeO_3^{2-} + 2OH^- = SeO_4^{2-} + H_2O$ $+ 2e^-$	−0.05	$Cl^- + 2OH^- = ClO^- + H_2O$ $+ 2e^-$	−0.89
$Pd + 2OH^- = Pd(OH)_2 + 2e^-$	−0.07	$FeO_2^- + 4OH^- = FeO_4^{2-} + 2H_2O$ $+ 3e^-$	−0.9
$2S_2O_3^{2-} = S_4O_6^{2-} + 2e^-$	−0.08	$ClO_2^- = ClO_2 + e^-$	−1.16
$Hg + 2OH^- = HgO(r) + H_2O$ $+ 2e^-$	−0.098	$O_2 + 2OH^- = O_3 + H_2O + 2e^-$	−1.24
$2NH_4OH + 2OH^- = N_2H_4$ $+ 4H_2O + 2e^-$	−0.1	$OH^- = OH + e^-$	−2.0
$2Ir + 6OH^- = Ir_2O_3 + 3H_2O + 6e^-$	−0.1		
$Co(NH_3)_6^{2+} = Co(NH_3)_6^{3+} + e^-$	−0.1		

25° C, or 298° K.   These values constitute a consistent set; although new thermodynamic data are available for several couples, no revision of Latimer's 1952 values has been attempted.

Variation of Standard Potentials

4.97 In the discussion of other properties of the elements we have become accustomed to finding more or less regular variation with position in either group or period in the periodic table.   The standard oxidation potentials, however, do not at first glance seem to exhibit such regular variation; we note, for example, that the lightest alkali metal, lithium, appears with the most positive potential and is then followed by the other alkali metals approximately in order of decreasing atomic weight from cesium to sodium.   Interspersed among these are the alkaline earth metals, and many transition metals are found with not much less positive standard oxidation potentials.   The nonmetallic elements are considerably more regular in their variation of potential with atomic number within a group.   Although there are numerous exceptions, the standard oxidation potential becomes more negative as one moves to the right in a period, and becomes more negative as one goes up in a group of nonmetals; among the metals the situation is too complex for generalization.   Evidently other factors than ionization potential or electron affinity must be considered to account for the complex trends and the exceptions.   Furthermore, the table of standard oxidation potentials includes many couples involving an element in two oxidation states different from zero; the variation of these standard oxidation potentials is determined by the relative stabilities of the different oxidation states in aqueous systems.   It should be remarked that the standard potentials in the table all refer to aqueous systems in which the ions are hydrated, and in nonaqueous systems the potentials may be considerably different and often in quite different order.

4.98 The several factors which determine the standard oxidation potential of an element may be best illustrated by means of a Born-Haber thermodynamic cycle similar to that discussed earlier in connection with electron affinities.   The electrode oxidation process in the case of a metallic element is equivalent to a series of three steps: the sublimation of the solid metal, the ionization of the gaseous metallic atom, and the hydration of the gaseous cation. The four processes may therefore be combined in a cycle of the form shown,

$$M(s) \xrightarrow{-nE} M^{n+}(aq) + ne^-$$
$$-S \uparrow \qquad \qquad \downarrow H$$
$$M(g) \xleftarrow{-I} M^{n+}(g) + ne^-$$

in which E is the standard oxidation potential of the metal M, S is the energy absorbed in its sublimation, I is its ionization potential, and H is the energy released in the hydration of the cation M^+; each such term is written as an energy absorption in the process indicated by the corresponding arrow. The actual energy of hydration of a single ion is not susceptible to direct determination, but relative hydration energies may be determined and the quantity H may be taken as the hydration energy relative to the value 256 kcal./mole for the proton. Thus the basis for the arbitrary zero of energy for H is the same as for E, the standard oxidation potential; the two unknown energy quantities however do not cancel each other because E still contains an additive term involving the dissociation and ionization of hydrogen and the transfer of electrons between phases. Accordingly, we shall obtain relative rather than actual standard oxidation potentials; the latter are more positive than those calculated directly from the relation given by approximately 4.8 volts or 110 kcal./mole. The total absorption of energy for the entire cycle must vanish, and hence for a univalent metal

$$-E + H - I - S = 0$$

or

$$E = H - I - S.$$

4.99 Strictly, the energy quantities are free energy changes. The standard oxidation potential E measures a free energy change (in volts divided by n, as shown above), but the other energy quantities are most commonly determined from heat effects. It is necessary to know independently the entropy changes for the processes, since $\Delta F = \Delta H - T\Delta S$ for each of the isothermal changes. In many cases the entropy changes are not precisely known but are small, so that the known enthalpy changes (ΔH, or heat effect) are fair approximations to the desired free energy changes (ΔF). Furthermore, for a sequence of similar elements, qualitative considerations based partly on variations of enthalpy changes instead of free energy changes will be valid because the entropy effects very approximately cancel one another. It is evident, of course, that all energy quantities must be expressed in the same units.

4.100 The standard oxidation potential of a metal is seen to be greater the larger its hydration energy and the smaller its ionization potential and energy of sublimation. The latter two quantities usually vary in the same manner as atomic structure is changed; the hydration energy often varies in the same manner but at a different rate. Thus, in the sequence of alkali metals, all three energy terms decrease more or less uniformly, but the hydration energy decreases relatively more than either the ionization or sublimation energy with the result that E varies but slightly. The hydration energy of lithium is anomalously high because of the very small size of the bare ion, and the standard oxidation potential of lithium is more positive than that of cesium. In certain nonaqueous systems where the difference in solvation energy may not be so large, the potential of lithium is less than that of cesium, and lithium is a poorer reducing agent than cesium.

4.101 In comparisons of alkali or alkaline earth metals with the much less reactive metals of groups of higher order, the hydration energy differences are relatively less important, and the considerably larger ionization and sublimation energies of the less reactive metals lead to much less positive standard oxidation potentials. For these metals (*e.g.*, copper, silver, platinum), the hydration energy is usually small compared to the ionization and sublimation energies, the standard oxidation potentials are of negative sign, and their variation is determined primarily by the variation in the ionization and sublimation energies. It may be noted that the nobility of metals is as much due to large sublimation energies as to large ionization energies.

4.102 For gaseous nonmetallic elements, the analogous cycle involves three steps equivalent to the electrode process: dissociation into gaseous atoms, the addition of one or more electrons to the atom, and the hydration of the gaseous anions. For liquid or solid elements an additional vaporization step is required before the dissociation into atoms. Considering for the sake of simplicity only the former case, we write down four processes in the form of a cycle. Here

$$
\begin{array}{ccc}
X^{n-}(aq) & \xrightarrow{-nE} & \tfrac{1}{2}X_2(g) + ne^- \\[2pt]
{\Big\uparrow}{\scriptstyle -H} & & {\Big\downarrow}{\scriptstyle D} \\[2pt]
X^{n-}(g) & \xleftarrow{-A} & X(g) + ne^-
\end{array}
$$

again, each energy term is written as an energy absorption in the direction indicated by the arrow. E is the standard oxidation potential of the gaseous nonmetal X_2, D is its dissociation energy per atom, A its electron affinity, and H the energy released in the hydration of the gaseous anion X^{n-}. The total absorption of energy for the complete cycle must be zero and therefore for a univalent nonmetal

$$-E + D - A - H = 0$$

or
$$E = D - A - H.$$

4.103 The standard oxidation potential of a nonmetal is thus dependent on three energy quantities just as is that of a metal: the potential is the more negative the larger the electron affinity and hydration energy and the smaller the dissociation energy. As the atomic structure is varied in a sequence of nonmetals in such a way that the electron affinity increases, the hydration energy usually also increases, a principal factor in both cases being a decrease in atomic size; at the same time the generally much smaller dissociation energy also increases, but at a slower rate. Thus in a sequence of nonmetals such as the halogens the variation of standard oxidation potential is determined primarily by the variation in electron affinity and hydration energy. In the case of the heavier, larger, and considerably less volatile nonmetals the hydration energy may be relatively less important and the dissociation energy (which will include a vaporization energy as well) may become relatively more important.

4.104 Reducing power is associated with large positive values of the standard oxidation potential, and oxidizing power with large negative values. Thus, reducing power increases with decreasing ionization potential and the parallel decrease in sublimation energy, the concomitant decrease in hydration energy being generally too small to affect markedly the direction of change. For the representative elements such increase of reducing power may be expected, in general, to be observed with increase in atomic number within a group of metals or with decrease in atomic number within a period. Similarly, for nonmetals oxidizing power increases generally with decreasing atomic number within a group and with increasing atomic number within a period, these being the directions in which electron affinity and hydration energy increase.

Applications of Electrode Potentials; the Direction of Chemical Change

4.105 The tendency for an oxidation-reduction reaction to occur is determined by both the reducing power of the reductant and the oxidizing power of the oxidant. Thus, for practical applications the oxidation potentials for both reductant and oxidant (properly, both couples) must be considered. We have seen that a spontaneous process is indicated by a positive value of the EMF, which corresponds to a negative value of ΔF, the free energy increase for the reaction. Since the EMF is the difference of the two electrode oxidation potentials, the tables of standard oxidation potentials may be used to determine the direction of spontaneous change in reactions in which each reactant or product is in its standard state. Consider the reaction previously discussed

$$\text{Zn(s)} + \text{Cu}^{2+}(\text{aq, std.}) = \text{Zn}^{2+}(\text{aq, std.}) + \text{Cu(s)}$$

in which solid zinc reduces copper ion in solution at constant unit activity to produce solid copper and zinc ion in solution at constant unit activity. By our conventions the EMF of the corresponding cell, which may be written as $E°$ where the superscript indicates that all reactants and products are in their standard states, is simply given by the relation

$$E° = E°_{\text{Zn}} - E°_{\text{Cu}}$$

$E°_{\text{Zn}}$ and $E°_{\text{Cu}}$ being the standard oxidation potentials of zinc and copper, respectively. From the tables we find at 25°

$$E° = 0.763 - (-0.337) = +1.100 \text{ v.}$$

and conclude that under standard conditions at 25° the reaction proceeds spontaneously to the right, or in other words, zinc spontaneously reduces copper ion.

4.106 Consider next the slightly more complex reaction

$$\tfrac{1}{2}\text{I}_2(\text{s}) + \text{Fe}^{2+}(\text{aq, std.}) = \text{I}^-(\text{aq, std.}) + \text{Fe}^{3+}(\text{aq, std.})$$

in which each substance is in its standard state. The EMF of the appropriate cell at 25° is given by

$$E° = E°_{\text{Fe}^{2+}} - E°_{\text{I}} = -0.771 - (-0.5355) = -0.236 \text{ v.}$$

In this case the negative sign of $E°$ indicates that the reaction spontaneously proceeds under the given experimental conditions in the direction opposite to that written; in other words iodide ion reduces iron(III) ion to produce iron(II) ion and solid iodine, all ions being at unit activity or approximately at unit molality.

4.107 The relative stabilities of different oxidation states may be inferred from considerations of standard oxidation potentials. Let us consider two cases representing disproportionations,

$$3Au^+ = 2Au + Au^{3+} \quad \text{and} \quad 3Fe^{2+} = 2Fe^{3+} + Fe,$$

where the notation describing the standard states for all species is omitted. At 25° the potentials for the two systems are respectively

$$E_1^\circ = E_{Au^+,Au^{3+}}^\circ - E_{Au,Au^+}^\circ = -1.41 - (-1.68) = +0.27 \text{ v.}$$
and $$E_2^\circ = E_{Fe^{2+},Fe^{3+}}^\circ - E_{Fe,Fe^{2+}}^\circ = -0.771 - (0.440) = -1.211 \text{ v.}$$

The positive sign of E_1° indicates that under the specified conditions of unit activity, gold(I) ion is unstable with respect to disproportionation to gold(III) ion and gold; in exactly the same way one concludes from the negative sign of E_2° that under these same conditions of unit activity iron(III) ion spontaneously reacts with iron to produce iron(II) ion. The standard oxidation potentials of the several tin couples lead directly to a similar conclusion: metallic tin is oxidized by hydrogen ion at unit activity to produce tin(II) ion, but not tin(IV) ion; rather, under standard conditions tin(IV) ion is reduced by hydrogen to tin(II) ion.

4.108 Let us consider finally whether, again under standard conditions, manganese dioxide should be expected to oxidize tellurium dioxide to telluric acid in aqueous acid solution. The reaction may be written

$$MnO_2 + 2H^+ + TeO_2 + 2H_2O = Mn^{2+} + H_6TeO_6,$$

which is the difference of the two separate electrode processes

$$TeO_2 + 4H_2O = H_6TeO_6 + 2H^+ + 2e^- \qquad E_1^\circ = -1.02 \text{ v.}$$
$$Mn^{2+} + 2H_2O = MnO_2 + 4H^+ + 2e^- \qquad E_2^\circ = -1.23 \text{ v.}$$

The potential for the overall process is $E^\circ = E_1^\circ - E_2^\circ = -1.02 - (-1.23) = +0.21$ v., and since its sign is positive one concludes that the reaction will proceed spontaneously in the indicated direction.

4.109 It should be remarked that in these considerations the term "spontaneous change" is used in the thermodynamic sense. If a change actually occurs, then it will be in the direction dictated by the sign of the EMF or of ΔF, but no prediction can be made as to the velocity of such change, and, in fact, it may often happen that the predicted spontaneous change proceeds at essentially zero velocity. Furthermore, it may also happen that the postulated change, although thermodynamically spontaneous overall, actually proceeds by a mechanism consisting of two or more steps one of which is not spontaneous in this same sense; thus the free energy increment ΔF may be negative for the entire process, denoting spontaneity, but consist of two terms, one for each of two sub-processes, and of these one is positive. Then the corresponding change cannot occur and so the overall net process will not be observed. An alternative explanation is that the original postulated spontaneous change is followed by a second spontaneous change, the reverse of the previously mentioned subprocess with positive ΔF, so that the observed net change is not that predicted. For example, under standard conditions, hydrogen ion should spontaneously oxidize iron to iron(III) ion, but hydrogen gas will also spontaneously reduce iron(III) ion to iron(II) ion. The observed change is then the oxidation of iron to iron(II) and not iron(III) ion. Similarly, at unit activities in aqueous acid solutions, silver ion should spontaneously oxidize thallium to thallium(III) ion ($E = +0.079$ v.), but actually thallium(I) ion is produced because the reduction of thallium(III) ion by silver is so highly spontaneous ($E = +0.450$ v.). The standard oxidation potentials predict the direction of spontaneous change for a specified reaction but do not of themselves predict the actual reactions to be observed.

4.110 The examples given above illustrate the combination of electrode reactions to give complete chemical reactions. For these, the standard EMF is the difference of the standard oxidation potentials of the two couples concerned, irrespective of the numbers of electrons involved in the two electrode processes. When electrode processes are combined to give other electrode processes, however, the free energy changes rather than the potentials must be combined. For example, the standard potential of the chromium-chromium(II) ion couple may be calculated as follows:

$$\begin{array}{llll}
\text{Cr} & = \text{Cr}^{3+} + 3e^- & E^\circ = +0.74 & \Delta F^\circ = -3\mathfrak{F}(+0.74) \\
\text{Cr}^{2+} & = \text{Cr}^{3+} + \ e^- & E^\circ = +0.41 & \Delta F^\circ = - \ \mathfrak{F}(+0.41) \\
\hline
\text{Cr} & = \text{Cr}^{2+} + 2e^- & & \Delta F^\circ = - \ \mathfrak{F}(+1.81)
\end{array}$$

But for the indicated electrode process $\Delta F^\circ = -n\mathfrak{F}E^\circ = -2\mathfrak{F}E^\circ$ and so $E^\circ = +0.90$ v., the standard oxidation potential of the chromium-chromium(II) couple at 25°. The thoughtful student will recognize that there is no real distinction between the two methods of combining standard potentials. The second method described is the general method, consistent with thermodynamics, and the first is but a special case which arises when the total amount of electricity expressed in Faraday units, n, is the same for both couples, a requisite for writing a complete chemical reaction.

4.111 While valuable information may be derived from the standard oxidation potentials which refer to systems under conditions of unit activity and hence approximately at unit molalities for ionic species, most chemical reactions are carried out at arbitrary and variable concentrations. In order to predict the direction of spontaneous change in reactions under arbitrary conditions of concentration, it is necessary to know how the EMF's of the corresponding cells change with the concentrations. The relationship, sometimes referred to as the Nernst equation, may be obtained in the following way. We have already seen that the reversible electrical work to be obtained from a cell is $n\mathfrak{F}E$, and this must be equal to $-\Delta F$, the decrement in free energy for the change which occurs during the operation of the cell. Now for any species, the free energy F and activity a are related by the expression

$$F = F^\circ + RT \ln a,$$

where $F°$ is the free energy of the species in its standard state, the state of unit activity; R is the gas constant and T the absolute temperature. If the chemical change which occurs during the operation of the cell is

$$uU + vV + \cdots = xX + yY + \cdots$$

then ΔF for this change is given by

$$
\begin{aligned}
\Delta F &= xF_X + yF_Y + \cdots - uF_U - vF_V - \cdots \\
&= x(F_X° + RT \ln a_X) + y(F_Y° + RT \ln a_Y) + \cdots \\
&\quad - u(F_U° + RT \ln a_U) - v(F_V° + RT \ln a_V) - \cdots \\
&= xF_X° + yF_Y° + \cdots - uF_U° - vF_V° - \cdots \\
&\quad + RT[x \ln a_X + y \ln a_Y + \cdots - u \ln a_U - v \ln a_V - \cdots] \\
&= \Delta F° + RT \ln \frac{a_X^x a_Y^y \cdots}{a_U^u a_V^v \cdots} = \Delta F° + RT \ln Q.
\end{aligned}
$$

4.112 The quantity $\Delta F°$ is called the standard free energy change for the reaction at the specified temperature and is evidently the increase in free energy when the reaction occurs with each substance in its own standard state. The quantity Q is termed the reaction quotient and its definition in terms of the activities of the various products and reactants is indicated in the equation above. Now if the chemical change involves n faradays, then because $\Delta F = -n\mathfrak{F}E$ and $\Delta F° = -n\mathfrak{F}E°$, we obtain

$$E = E° - \frac{RT}{n\mathfrak{F}} \ln \frac{a_X^x a_Y^y \cdots}{a_U^u a_V^v \cdots} = E° - \frac{RT}{n\mathfrak{F}} \ln Q.$$

Inasmuch as the activities are related to the concentrations of the several products and reactants, the EMF of the cell or the oxidation potential of a reaction system varies with these concentrations according to this Nernst equation. Since the majority of applications refer to 25° and common logarithms are often used, it is convenient to write the relation in the specific form

$$E = E° - \frac{0.05914}{n} \log Q.$$

Here E is the EMF of the cell or the oxidation potential of the reaction system under arbitrary concentration conditions, $E°$ is the corresponding potential under standard activity conditions (both at 25°), and n is the number of faradays involved in the cell reaction for which the reaction quotient Q is defined.

4.113 It is evident that

$$E° = E_L° - E_R°,$$

where $E_L°$ is the standard oxidation potential for the left-hand electrode in the cell, that is, for the couple the reduced form of which appears on the left-hand side of the equation for the reaction; analogously $E_R°$ is the standard oxidation potential for the right-hand electrode, or the couple the reduced form of which appears on the right-hand side of the equation. In addition, the perceptive student will note that expressions similar to that for the cell EMF may be written for each of the separate electrodes, giving the potential of the electrode as a function of the activities, or approximately, the concentrations of the substances concerned in the electrode process. Thus one may write for the electrode Zn(s) | Zn²⁺(aq) the electrode reaction

$$Zn(s) = Zn^{2+}(aq) + 2e^-$$

and the expression for the electrode potential

$$E_{Zn} = E^\circ_{Zn} - \frac{RT}{2\mathfrak{F}} \ln a_{Zn^{2+}}.$$

Metallic zinc is in its own standard state and hence its activity is unity and is not generally explicitly included; the electrons by convention are excluded. Similarly for the electrode Ag(s), AgCl(s) | Cl⁻(aq) one writes

$$Ag(s) + Cl^-(aq) = AgCl(s) + e^-$$

$$E_{Ag, AgCl} = E^\circ_{Ag, AgCl} - \frac{RT}{\mathfrak{F}} \ln \frac{1}{a_{Cl^-}} = E^\circ_{Ag, AgCl} + \frac{RT}{\mathfrak{F}} \ln a_{Cl^-}.$$

As a final example consider the electrode consisting of metallic platinum in contact with solid manganese dioxide and an aqueous solution of hydrogen and manganese(II) ions. The electrode may be formulated as Pt(s), $MnO_2(s)$ | Mn^{2+}(aq), H⁺(aq), and the oxidation process which occurs is

$$Mn^{2+}(aq) + 2H_2O \rightarrow MnO_2(s) + 4H^+(aq) + 2e^-.$$

The oxidation potential of this electrode (or of the $Mn^{++} - MnO_2$ couple) is

$$E = E^\circ - \frac{RT}{2\mathfrak{F}} \ln \frac{a^4_{H^+}}{a_{Mn^{2+}}a^2_{H_2O}}.$$

In most applications the solutions are sufficiently dilute that water may be considered to be in its standard state and the term a_{H_2O} is dropped from the reaction quotient; in general a_{H_2O} will be only a few per cent less than unity and this corresponds for the given couple at 25° to only about 0.25 mv. difference in E per unit per cent difference in a_{H_2O}.

4.114 The effect of acidity on reducing strength of a given couple is quite evident in the example just considered. If the activities of manganese(II) ion and water are kept constant at unity, then the potential of the electrode is given by

$$E = E^\circ - \frac{2RT}{\mathfrak{F}} \ln a_{H^+} = -1.23 + 0.118 \text{ pH at } 25°,$$

where the definition pH $\equiv -\log a_{H^+}$ has been substituted. It is obvious that an increase of one unit of pH brings about an increase of 0.118 v. in the oxidation potential of the couple. In other words, manganese(II) ion becomes a progressively stronger reducing agent as the solution is made less and less acid; at the same time manganese dioxide becomes a progressively weaker oxidizing agent as the solution is made less acid. Since many couples in aqueous solution involve hydrogen ion as a product, this increase of reducing power with increasing pH is rather general; conversely, for these same couples the oxidizing power increases with increasing acidity, a fact generally known from direct chemical evidence. If the reaction associated with a given couple or electrode does not involve hydrogen ion as reactant or product, then of course variation in pH will have no effect on the potential. In other cases increase in pH may cause a change in the electrode reaction itself because of the insolubility of many metallic hydroxides. Thus consider the two possible reactions involving nickel in the oxidation states zero and $+2$:

$$Ni(s) = Ni^{2+}(aq) + 2e^- \qquad \text{acid solution}$$
$$Ni(s) + 2OH^-(aq) = Ni(OH)_2(s) + 2e^- \qquad \text{basic solution}$$

The potential in the first reaction is independent of pH; that in the second increases with increasing pH.

$$E_2 = E° - \frac{RT}{2\mathfrak{F}} \ln \frac{1}{a^2_{OH^-}} = E° - \frac{RT}{\mathfrak{F}} \ln \frac{a_{H^+}}{K_W} = E°' + 0.059 \text{ pH at } 25°.$$

We note that the standard oxidation potentials for the two systems are not equal, even though the same two oxidation states of nickel are involved. This same observation may be made for most of the systems listed in the tables of standard oxidation potentials; the several systems involving different pairs of oxidation states of manganese are particularly interesting and important for practical applications.

4.115 Let us now consider the chloride-chlorate couple, for which we write the equation

$$Cl^-(aq) + 3H_2O = ClO_3^-(aq) + 6H^+(aq) + 6e^-.$$

The potential for arbitrary activity conditions is (with a_{H_2O} approximately unity)

$$E = E° - \frac{RT}{6\mathfrak{F}} \ln \frac{a_{ClO_3^-}a^6_{H^+}}{a_{Cl^-}} = -1.45 - \frac{0.059}{6} \log \frac{a_{ClO_3^-}a^6_{H^+}}{a_{Cl^-}} \text{ at } 25°.$$

If all ionic activities are unity, then $E = E° = -1.45$ v. Suppose that

$$a_{Cl^-} = 5, \ a_{ClO_3} = 0.05, \ a_{H^+} = 0.1; \text{ then the potential becomes}$$

$$E = -1.45 - \frac{0.059}{6} \log \frac{0.05(0.1)^6}{5} = -1.45 + 0.08 = -1.37 \text{ v.}$$

Under these conditions, as compared with standard conditions of unit activities, chloride ion is a slightly improved reducing agent and chlorate ion a slightly less efficient oxidizing agent. In either case, however, the potential of the electrode is negative, indicating that the reducing agent (chloride ion) is weaker than hydrogen under standard conditions.

4.116 To return now to the consideration of complete chemical reactions let us first take up the reduction of lead(II) ion by metallic tin.

$$Sn(s) + Pb^{2+}(aq) = Sn^{2+}(aq) + Pb(s)$$

$$E = E^\circ - \frac{RT}{2\mathfrak{F}} \ln \frac{a_{Sn^{2+}}}{a_{Pb^{2+}}} = 0.136 - 0.126 - \frac{0.059}{2} \log \frac{a_{Sn^{2+}}}{a_{Pb^{2+}}} \text{ at } 25^\circ$$

$$= 0.010 - \frac{0.059}{2} \log \frac{a_{Sn^{2+}}}{a_{Pb^{2+}}}.$$

Obviously under standard conditions metallic tin reduces lead ion. Now, however, suppose we make $a_{Sn^{2+}} = 2$ and $a_{Pb^{2+}} = 0.5$; under these conditions we find

$$E = 0.010 - \frac{0.059}{2} \log \frac{2}{0.5} = 0.010 - 0.018 = -0.008 \text{ v. at } 25^\circ.$$

The calculated EMF now has a negative sign which indicates that the reaction proceeds spontaneously in the opposite direction to that written; in other words, metallic lead reduces tin(II) ion when the activity of the latter is somewhat larger than unity and that of lead ion somewhat smaller than unity. If concentrations are substituted for activities the qualitative observation is still valid but the computed result for the EMF is only approximate.

4.117 The oxidation state of thallium in aqueous solutions is easily influenced by pH as well as temperature. For the reaction

$$H_2O + Tl^{3+}(aq) = \tfrac{1}{2}O_2(g) + Tl^+(aq) + 2H^+(aq)$$

we may write for the EMF at 25°

$$E = E^\circ - \frac{RT}{2\mathfrak{F}} \ln Q = -1.229 - (-1.25) - \frac{0.059}{2} \log \frac{a_{O_2}^{1/2} a_{Tl^+} a_{H^+}^2}{a_{Tl^{3+}}}.$$

The activity of oxygen is approximately equal to its partial pressure, 0.21 atm in the normal atmosphere. Upon substitution we obtain

$$E = +0.03 - 0.030 \log \frac{a_{Tl^+}}{a_{Tl^{3+}}} + 0.059 \text{ pH}.$$

At zero pH ($a_{H^+} = 1$), water reduces thallium(III) ion so long as $\dfrac{a_{Tl^+}}{a_{Tl^{3+}}}$ is less than 10; if the latter ratio exceeds 10, however, E becomes negative and the direction of spontaneous change is to the left, toward the oxidation to thallium(III) ion. For more acid solutions the critical (equilibrium) value of the ratio is smaller: when pH $= -0.7$ ($a_{H^+} = 5$), water reduces thallium(III) ion so long as the $\dfrac{a_{Tl^+}}{a_{Tl^{3+}}}$ ratio is less than approximately 0.5, so that thallium(III) ion is somewhat more stable than thallium(I) ion in these aqueous acid solutions in contact with the atmosphere. With increasing pH the thallium(I) ion becomes relatively more stable in aqueous solutions.

Electrode Potentials and Chemical Equilibrium

4.118 The consideration of relative stability in the previous illustration is in effect a discussion of equilibrium in the system involved. When temperature and pressure are maintained constant, as is true for the types of systems we have been discussing, the thermodynamic criterion for equilibrium in a reaction is that $\Delta F = 0$. Since $\Delta F = -n\mathfrak{F}E$, this is equivalent to the statement that $E = 0$ at equilibrium, a condition previously mentioned. Therefore, if equilibrium obtains in an oxidation-reduction system,

$$E = 0 = E° - \frac{RT}{n\mathfrak{F}} \ln Q_e,$$

in which Q_e is the reaction quotient evaluated for the equilibrium activities of the several reactants and products. The equilibrium reaction quotient Q_e is easily recognized as identical with the usual equilibrium constant K defined for the general reaction introduced previously:

$$Q_e = \left[\frac{a_X^x \, a_Y^y \cdots}{a_U^u \, a_V^v \cdots}\right]_{\text{at equilibrium}} = K.$$

Thus we obtain

$$E° = \frac{RT}{n\mathfrak{F}} \ln K = \frac{0.05914}{n} \log K \text{ at } 25°.$$

The same result might of course be obtained directly from the general thermodynamic relations $\Delta F° = -RT \ln K$ and $\Delta F° = -n\mathfrak{F}E°$. Since the value of $E°$ for a complete chemical reaction may be determined from the standard oxidation potentials of the couples involved, equilibrium constants may be calculated from these tables. It should be recognized that in actual practice the process has often been reversed, so that values of standard oxidation potentials are sometimes determined in part from independent measurements of equilibrium constants.

4.119 Let us calculate the equilibrium constant for the oxidation of copper by bromate ion in aqueous acid solution at $25°$. The equation is

$$3Cu(s) + BrO_3^-(aq) + 6H^+(aq) \rightarrow 3Cu^{2+}(aq) + Br^-(aq) + 3H_2O,$$

and six faradays of electricity are involved in the change. For the reaction

$$E° = E°_{Cu, \, Cu^{2+}} - E°_{Br^-, \, BrO_3^-} = -0.337 - (-1.44) = +1.10 \text{ v. at } 25°.$$

When all reactants and products are in their standard states, the reaction proceeds spontaneously to the right. The equilibrium constant is given by

$$\log K = \frac{nE°}{0.059} = \frac{6(1.10)}{0.059} = +112 \qquad K = 10^{112}.$$

The very large value of the constant implies that bromate ion is extremely unstable in these circumstances.

4.120 Suppose finely divided metallic silver is shaken with a solution of mercury(I) nitrate. Let us calculate the equilibrium constant for the displacement reaction:

$$Ag(s) + \tfrac{1}{2}Hg_2^{2+}(aq) = Ag^+(aq) + Hg(l); \quad n = 1$$

$$E° = E°_{Ag, Ag^+} - E°_{Hg, 1/2Hg_2^{2+}} = -0.7991 - (-0.789) = -0.010 \text{ v. at } 25°.$$

$$\log K = \frac{-0.010 \times 1}{0.059} = -0.17 \qquad K = 0.68.$$

In this example the equilibrium constant is nearly unity and we conclude that equilibrium will obtain when silver has displaced an appreciable fraction (about one fourth in a solution originally $1M$ in Hg_2^{2+}) of the mercury in solution, so that the equilibrium activities of the two cations, and approximately their concentrations, are of the same order of magnitude and very roughly equal.

4.121 As a final example of equilibrium let us consider the problem of the solubility of iron(II) hydroxide:

$$Fe(OH)_2(s) = Fe^{2+}(aq) + 2OH^-(aq).$$

The equilibrium constant for this reaction, which is the solubility product constant for iron(II) hydroxide, may be calculated from the table of standard oxidation potentials if we imagine the reaction to consist of two half-reactions in opposition:

I $Fe(s) = Fe^{2+}(aq) + 2e^-$ $E° = +0.440$ v. at $25°$
II $Fe(s) + 2OH^-(aq) = Fe(OH)_2(s) + 2e^-$ $E° = +0.877$ v. at $25°$.

The difference I − II is the desired reaction for which

$$E° = E°_I - E°_{II} = +0.440 - 0.877 = -0.437 \text{ v.}$$

$$\log K = -\frac{0.437 \times 2}{0.05914} = -14.8 \qquad K = 1.7 \times 10^{-14}.$$

The small value of K implies that iron(II) hydroxide is extremely insoluble in water at $25°$. If no other electrolytes are present, the ionic activities are very well approximated by the ionic molalities and one easily calculates that the solubility is about 1.6×10^{-5} molal. If other electrolytes are present in appreciably larger concentrations, then the ionic activity coefficients may deviate markedly from unity so that ionic concentrations are but poor approximations to the ionic activities.

4.122 Ionic activity coefficients in aqueous systems depend on the temperature and very strongly on the concentration of electrolytes in the solution. Thus, in systems of variable, large electrolyte concentration, it becomes necessary to consider the difference between activity and concentration. As was mentioned earlier, each ionic activity may be represented as a product of its stoichiometric molality and its ionic activity coefficient. For the electrode $Pt(s) \mid Fe^{2+}(aq)$, $Fe^{3+}(aq)$, for which we write the electrode reaction

$$Fe^{2+}(aq) = Fe^{3+}(aq) + e^-,$$

we may write the potential expression

$$E = E^\circ - \frac{RT}{\mathfrak{F}} \ln Q = E^\circ - \frac{RT}{\mathfrak{F}} \ln \frac{a_{Fe^{3+}}}{a_{Fe^{2+}}} = E^\circ - \frac{RT}{\mathfrak{F}} \ln \frac{m_{Fe^{3+}} \gamma_{Fe^{3+}}}{m_{Fe^{2+}} \gamma_{Fe^{2+}}}.$$

Here γ is the ionic activity coefficient and m the molality. Let us write

$$E = \left(E^\circ - \frac{RT}{\mathfrak{F}} \ln \frac{\gamma_{Fe^{3+}}}{\gamma_{Fe^{2+}}} \right) - \frac{RT}{\mathfrak{F}} \ln \frac{m_{Fe^{3+}}}{m_{Fe^{2+}}}.$$

Suppose now we deal with a solution of practical interest in which the ratio $\frac{m_{Fe^{3+}}}{m_{Fe^{2+}}}$ may vary over a rather wide range although the molalities themselves are usually rather small, and the concentrations of other solute species remain sensibly constant, generally at rather large values such as would be encountered in a solution made $1M$ in sulfuric acid. Under these circumstances the ratio $\frac{\gamma_{Fe^{3+}}}{\gamma_{Fe^{2+}}}$ remains nearly constant and we obtain

$$E = E_f^\circ - \frac{RT}{\mathfrak{F}} \ln \frac{m_{Fe^{3+}}}{m_{Fe^{2+}}}.$$

The formal potential E_f° of an electrode is a constant at a given temperature for a specified concentration of a particular electrolyte, often an acid such as sulfuric or hydrochloric acid. Such potentials are of particular convenience in analytical chemistry where it is often necessary to relate measured EMF values and ionic molalities in solutions which may be made constant in concentration of an electrolyte present in gross amounts. For example we might consider the reaction

$$Fe^{2+}(aq) + Ce^{4+}(aq) = Fe^{3+}(aq) + Ce^{3+}(aq)$$

carried out in $1M$ sulfuric acid solution. We may write for the reaction

$$E = E_{Fe^{2+}}^\circ - E_{Ce^{3+}}^\circ - \frac{RT}{\mathfrak{F}} \ln \frac{a_{Fe^{3+}}}{a_{Fe^{2+}}} \cdot \frac{a_{Ce^{3+}}}{a_{Ce^{4+}}}$$

or

$$E = (E_{f_{Fe^{2+}}}^\circ - E_{f_{Ce^{3+}}}^\circ) - \frac{RT}{\mathfrak{F}} \ln \frac{m_{Fe^{3+}}}{m_{Fe^{2+}}} \cdot \frac{m_{Ce^{3+}}}{m_{Ce^{4+}}}.$$

The quantity $E_{f_{Fe^{2+}}}^\circ - E_{f_{Ce^{3+}}}^\circ \equiv E_f^\circ$ is very nearly constant, independent of variation in the ratios of molalities, so long as the concentration of sulfuric acid is held constant and the total molalities of active ionic species are fairly small. Although E_f° is not generally calculable from the standard oxidation potentials, appropriate values are rather easily determined from experiment. The usefulness of the expression given is quite evident for potentiometric titrations in the iron(II)-cerium(IV) system.

Electrode Potentials and the Stabilization of Oxidation States of Metals

4.123 The standard oxidation potential for the electrode $M(s) \mid M^{n+}(aq)$ measures the ease of occurrence of the reaction

$$M(s) = M^{n+}(aq) + ne^-.$$

The cation M^{n+} is hydrated in aqueous solution, to an indefinite extent in the case of the highly reactive alkali metals and alkaline earth metals, or often to a definite extent represented by such a formula as $M(H_2O)_r^{n+}$, r integral, in the case of many of the transition elements. Let us rewrite the reaction as

$$M + wH_2O = M(H_2O)_w^{n+} + ne^- \qquad E_1^\circ$$

for which the same value of the standard oxidation potential applies. Suppose now we consider the analogous process occurring in a system containing a different ligand X; then

$$M + xX = MX_x^{n+} + ne^- \qquad E_2^\circ.$$

In general the two ionic species $M(H_2O)_w^{n+}$ and MX_x^{n+} are not equally stable, and this is indicated by different values of the standard potentials in the two cases. Specifically, if the standard potential for the first electrode reaction, E_1°, is more positive than that for the second, E_2°, then one must conclude that the hydrated ion is more stable than the ion containing the ligand X. For the displacement reaction

$$MX_x^{n+} + wH_2O = M(H_2O)_w^{n+} + xX$$

we find $E^\circ = E_1^\circ - E_2^\circ > 0$ and $\ln K = \dfrac{n\mathscr{F}E^\circ}{RT} > 0.$

Since $\ln K > 0$, then $K > 1$ and equilibrium favors the hydrated ion. Under unit activity conditions, water displaces the ligand X to produce the more stable hydrated ion. If several possible complexed structures for the $n+$ oxidation state of the metal are possible, then these decrease in relative stability in order of decreasingly positive standard oxidation potential.

4.124 An analogous situation exists when the complexed structure happens to be an electrically neutral soluble weak electrolyte or insoluble compound. Consider the reactions

$$M(s) + nY^-(aq) = MY_n(aq) + ne^- \qquad E_3^\circ$$
$$M(s) + nZ^-(aq) = MZ_n(s) + ne^- \qquad E_4^\circ$$

of which specific examples are respectively

$$B(s) + 3OH^-(aq) = H_3BO_3(aq) + 3e^-$$
$$Pb(s) + 2I^-(aq) = PbI_2(s) + 2e^-.$$

The standard oxidation potentials for these processes indicate, for conditions of unit activity, the relative tendency toward the formation of the several species. For example, if E_3° is more positive than E_1°, then under standard conditions the weak electrolyte MY_n is formed in preference to the hydrated ion. Thus, in considerations of the relative stability of the $n+$ oxidation state of the metal M in various systems, reactions and potentials of this latter type may be incorporated in a list of reactions and potentials for the formation of ionic species. In such a list arranged in order of decreasing standard oxidation potential the most stable species is found at the top and the stability decreases monotonically as the potential becomes more negative. For the +2 oxidation state of the metals zinc and nickel in aqueous solutions of the appropriate ion or ligand we find the following potentials at 25°.

$$
\begin{aligned}
&Zn + S^{2-} &&= ZnS(s) + 2e^- &&& E° = 1.44 \text{ v.} \\
&Zn + 4CN^- &&= Zn(CN)_4^{2-} + 2e^- &&& E° = 1.26 \\
&Zn + 2OH^- &&= Zn(OH)_2(s) + 2e^- &&& E° = 1.245 \\
&Zn + 4OH^- &&= ZnO_2^{2-} + 2H_2O + 2e^- &&& E° = 1.216 \\
&Zn + CO_3^{2-} &&= ZnCO_3(s) + 2e^- &&& E° = 1.06 \\
&Zn + 4NH_3 &&= Zn(NH_3)_4^{2+} + 2e^- &&& E° = 1.03 \\
&Zn + 3C_2O_4^{2-} &&= Zn(C_2O_4)_3^{4-} + 2e^- &&& E° = 1.02 \\
&Zn + wH_2O &&= Zn(H_2O)_w^{2+} + 2e^- &&& E° = 0.763 \\
&Ni + S^{2-} &&= NiS(s) + 2e^- &&& E° = 0.83 \\
&Ni + 2OH^- &&= Ni(OH)_2(s) + 2e^- &&& E° = 0.72 \\
&Ni + 6NH_3 &&= Ni(NH_3)_6^{2+} + 2e^- &&& E° = 0.47 \\
&Ni + CO_3^{2-} &&= NiCO_3(s) + 2e^- &&& E° = 0.45 \\
&Ni + wH_2O &&= Ni(H_2O)_w^{2+} + 2e^- &&& E° = 0.250
\end{aligned}
$$

4.125 The addition of an ion or ligand which forms a stable complex, weak electrolyte, or insoluble compound of the metal in the specified oxidation state increases the reducing power of the metal, or which is equivalent, decreases the oxidizing power of the oxidized state of the metallic element. Thus, in principle at least, we should predict from the two couples

$$
\begin{aligned}
&Hg &&= Hg^{2+} + 2e^- &&& E° = -0.854 \text{ v.} \\
&Hg + 4I^- &&= HgI_4^{2-} + 2e^- &&& E° = +0.04
\end{aligned}
$$

that under conditions of unit activity hydrogen gas will reduce simple mercury(II) ion but not the tetraiodomercurate(II) complex ion. Similarly from the couples

$$
\begin{aligned}
&Cd + 4CN^- = Cd(CN)_4^{2-} + 2e^- &&& E° = +1.03 \text{ v.} \\
&H_2 + 2OH^- = 2H_2O + 2e^- &&& E° = 0.828 \\
&Cd + 4NH_3 = Cd(NH_3)_4^{2+} + 2e^- &&& E° = 0.597
\end{aligned}
$$

we predict that in these basic solutions under standard conditions cadmium metal may reduce water in the presence of the strong complexing agent cyanide ion but not in the presence of the weaker complexing agent ammonia. It should be emphasized, of course, that these predictions refer to equilibrium situations and indicate nothing about the rates of the reactions.

4.126 Let us now consider the problem of the relative stability of different oxidation states of a given metal in various aqueous systems. Two problems may be considered: the stabilization of a low oxidation state which otherwise may reduce the solvent liberating hydrogen or disproportionate to metal and higher oxidation state, or the stabilization of a high oxidation state which otherwise may oxidize the solvent liberating oxygen. Obviously, in actual systems other processes must be considered involving the anions present and often atmospheric oxygen as well.

4.127 The potential of the $Cu^+ - Cu^{2+}$ couple, -0.153 v., indicates that fairly mild oxidizing anions such as nitrate ion will oxidize copper(I) ion and therefore copper(I) salts of such anions may not exist in aqueous systems. Combining this potential with that for the $Cu - Cu^+$ couple we find that simple copper(I) ion is unstable with respect to disproportionation:

$$2Cu^+ = Cu + Cu^{2+} \qquad E° = -0.153 - (-0.521) = +0.368 \text{ v. at } 25°.$$

However, the copper(I) state may be stabilized in the presence of various ions or molecules such as iodide, cyanide or thiocyanate ion or the organic ligand acetonitrile. Thus

$$2CuI = Cu + Cu^{2+} + 2I^- \qquad E° = -0.86 - 0.19 = -1.04 \text{ v. at } 25°$$
$$CuI + H^+ = Cu^{2+} + I^- + \tfrac{1}{2}H_2 \qquad E° = -0.86 - 0 = -0.86 \text{ v. at } 25°,$$

the negative sign of $E°$ indicating stability of the copper(I) state relative to either disproportionation or oxidation by hydrogen ion. The effect of adding excess cyanide to a solution of copper(II) ion is known to all students of qualitative analysis and is represented by the equation

$$Cu^{2+} + 3CN^- = Cu(CN)_2^- + \tfrac{1}{2}(CN)_2 \qquad \begin{aligned} E° &= +0.19 - (-1.12) \\ &= +1.31 \text{ v. at } 25° \end{aligned}$$

where the positive sign of $E°$ indicates spontaneous formation of the cyanocuprate(I) complex ion at the expense of copper(II) ions. In general, reducing anions stabilize the copper(I) state, and simple copper(II) salts of such reducing anions are difficult or impossible to prepare. The copper(II) state may be stabilized by certain organic ligands with the result that bis (ethylenediamine) copper(II) salts of reducing anions are quite stable.

4.128 Tripositive manganese is a strong oxidizing agent, as is indicated by the potential of the couple

$$Mn^{2+} = Mn^{3+} + e^- \qquad E° = -1.51 \text{ v. at } 25°.$$

Soluble simple compounds of manganese in this oxidation state are not stable in water:

$$Mn^{3+} + \tfrac{1}{2}H_2O = Mn^{2+} + \tfrac{1}{4}O_2 + H^+ \qquad \begin{aligned} E° &= -1.229 - (-1.51) \\ &= +0.28 \text{ v. at } 25°. \end{aligned}$$

The $+3$ oxidation state may be stabilized, however, by the formation of an insoluble compound such as the orthophosphate or a soluble complex such as that with the cyanide ion. For the latter

$$Mn(CN)_6^{4-} = Mn(CN)_6^{3-} + e^- \qquad E° = +0.22 \text{ v. at } 25°,$$
$$\text{and} \quad Mn(CN)_6^{4-} + \tfrac{1}{2}(CN)_2 = Mn(CN)_6^{3-} + CN^- \qquad \begin{aligned} E° &= +0.22 - 0.19 \\ &= +0.03 \text{ v. at } 25°. \end{aligned}$$

An analogous and almost exaggerated situation is observed for the $+2$ and $+3$ oxidation states of cobalt, where we find

$$Co^{2+} = Co^{3+} + e^- \qquad\qquad E^\circ = -1.82 \text{ v. at } 25^\circ$$
$$CN^- + [Co(CN)_5(H_2O)]^{3-} = Co(CN)_6^{3-} + H_2O + e^- \quad E^\circ = +0.83 \text{ v. at } 25^\circ.$$

The cyanide complex of the cobalt(III) ion is so stable that it may be produced by the oxidation of the cobalt(II) complex by water:

$$CN^- + [Co(CN)_5(H_2O)]^{3-} = Co(CN)_6^{3-} + \tfrac{1}{2}H_2 + OH^-$$
$$E^\circ = +0.83 - (0.828) \sim 0.$$

Since the pressure of hydrogen is generally considerably less than one atmosphere, and the concentration of hydroxyl ion generally not large, equilibrium obtains well to the right in the system described. Even in the presence of the much less tightly bound ligands ammonia and hydroxyl ion, the cobalt(III) complex is easily produced by the oxidation of the cobalt(II) complex by air:

$$Co(OH)_2 + \tfrac{1}{4}O_2 + \tfrac{1}{2}H_2O = Co(OH)_3 \qquad\qquad E^\circ = -0.17 - (-0.401)$$
$$= +0.23 \text{ v. at } 25^\circ$$
$$Co(NH_3)_6^{2+} + \tfrac{1}{4}O_2 + \tfrac{1}{2}H_2O = Co(NH_3)_6^{3+} + OH^- \qquad E^\circ = -0.1 - (-0.401)$$
$$= +0.3 \text{ v. at } 25^\circ.$$

4.129 Examples of stabilization of particular oxidation states are known for a large number of metals. The ligands found to be effective are in many cases organic molecules such as ethylenediamine, phenanthroline, pyridine, and their derivatives. While qualitative arguments may be made along the lines developed above, quantitative predictions are difficult and rarely possible because of the paucity of appropriate standard potential data.

Magnetic and Electrical Properties

Magnetic Properties of Matter

Introduction **4.130** When a sample of matter is placed in an inhomogeneous magnetic field it tends generally to move in the field. If the specimen tends to move toward the weaker regions in the field the material is said to be *diamagnetic* and to be more repellent than a vacuum to magnetic lines of force. If the specimen tends to move toward the stronger parts of the field the material is termed *paramagnetic* and is said to be more permeable than a vacuum to magnetic lines of force. Certain substances exhibit this latter property in an enormously magnified degree, so that the magnetic lines of force may be concentrated in them by a factor of the order of a million; these are called *ferromagnetic*. Diamagnetism is a universal property characteristic of all matter but experimentally can be easily observed only in the absence of the much more pronounced para- or ferromagnetism, which easily mask it. Paramagnetic substances are fairly common in all three states of aggregation, and paramagnetic ions, both simple and complex, are widely studied. Ferromagnetism is a much rarer property restricted to a few elements (*e.g.*, Fe, Co, and Ni) and particular alloys (*e.g.*, Fe–Co, Fe–Ni, or Ni–Mn alloys, Co amalgams) or compounds (*e.g.*, Fe_3O_4, γ-Fe_2O_3, Fe_3Si_2, $SnMn_2$, $SnMn_4$). Unlike dia- and paramagnetism, which are fundamentally atomic or molecular in nature, ferromagnetism is a structural or group property deriving from a certain kind of interaction between atoms or groups of atoms and is nonexistent except in sufficiently large collections of atoms, in other words, in crystals of dimensions greater than a minimum estimated to be of the order of a few tens of Ångstrom units. In systems of this size other modes of interaction give rise to two additional types of magnetic behavior termed *antiferromagnetism* and *ferrimagnetism;* these will be discussed briefly together with ferromagnetism.

4.131 The magnetic properties of a substance may be characterized by its magnetic moment. For a simple magnetic dipole (*i.e.*, an elementary bar magnet) the orienting effect of an applied magnetic field is proportional to the strength of the poles of the magnet and to the distance between them, and thus the magnetic moment may be defined as the product of these two quantities. Similarly, for an elementary loop or circuit carrying an electric current — or an orbit traversed by an electron — the orienting effect of an external magnetic field is proportional to the electric current and to the area of the loop, and so the magnetic moment of this system is defined in a consistent fashion as the product of these two quantities. For more complex systems the observed magnetic moment is the resultant of such elementary moments, ultimately of the electrons themselves. These magnetic moments either are intrinsic properties of the electron, corresponding to its spin, or result from the orbital motion of the electron within the atom; in either case, the motion of an electric charge — a current — gives rise to a magnetic field just as is observed in macroscopic systems, but the analogy is incomplete and somewhat misleading. The manner

GENERAL REFERENCES

ANGELLO, "Properties of Metallic Conductors," Section 5g of *American Institute of Physics Handbook*, edited by Gray, McGraw-Hill Book Company, Inc., New York, 1957.

DUSHMAN, "Quantum Theory of Atomic Spectra and Atomic Structure," Ch. II in Vol. I, *Treatise on Physical Chemistry*, edited by Taylor and Glasstone, D. Van Nostrand Company, Inc., New York, 1942.

GARNER, *Chemistry of the Solid State*, Butterworth's Scientific Publications, London, 1955, Ch. 5.

GLASSTONE, *Textbook of Physical Chemistry*, D. Van Nostrand Company, Inc., New York, 1954, Ch. VIII.

MOORE, *Physical Chemistry*, 2nd Edition, Prentice-Hall, Inc., New York, 1955, Ch. 11, 13.

PITZER, *Quantum Chemistry*, Prentice-Hall, Inc., New York, 1953, Ch. 10, 12.

RICE and TELLER, *The Structure of Matter*, John Wiley and Sons, Inc., New York, 1949, Ch. 8, 9.

SELWOOD, *Magnetochemistry*, Interscience Publishers, New York, 1956.

SHOENBERG, *Superconductivity*, 2nd Edition, Cambridge University Press, London, 1952.

VAN VLECK, *Theory of Electric and Magnetic Susceptibilities*, Oxford University Press, London, 1932.

in which these elementary electronic magnetic moments combine determines the overall magnetic properties of the material.

4.132 A sample in an inhomogeneous magnetic field is acted upon by a force F which is proportional to the strength H of the field, to the gradient of the field $\frac{\partial H}{\partial S}$ (its rate of change of strength with change of position in the direction of S), and to the volume V of the sample; the proportionality constant, κ, is called the [volume] susceptibility of the sample material. Thus

$$F = \kappa V H \frac{\partial H}{\partial S},$$

and the susceptibility may be determined from an experimental measurement of the force on a given specimen in a known magnetic field. Most commonly, chemists discuss susceptibility on a weight basis, using the gram susceptibility, χ, or the molar susceptibility, χ_M, which are defined by the relations

$$\chi = \frac{\kappa}{d}, \quad \chi_M = \frac{\kappa M}{d},$$

in which d is the density and M the molecular weight of the material. Since κ is also the ratio of the intensity of the induced magnetic field to that of the applied field, it is dimensionless; for that reason χ has the dimensions of reciprocal density, but these are often suppressed or loosely given as "units per gram" in older literature. For diamagnetic materials χ is negative and of the order of 10^{-6} cc./g. or merely 10^{-6}; for paramagnetic substances χ is positive and generally larger by about one order of magnitude. The susceptibility of a ferromagnetic substance is very much greater and therefore in making magnetic measurements it is extremely important to remove all traces of ferromagnetic impurities.

Diamagnetism **4.133** All atoms contain electrons which move freely in orbits, or in specified states, without gain or loss of energy. When a magnetic field is applied, a superimposed current — electron motion — is induced which persists so long as the field remains because there is no energy loss. The magnetic effect of the induced current is necessarily opposed to that of the applied field, and approximately proportional to the field; the ratio is essentially the diamagnetic susceptibility which we have seen is negative. Because the phenomenon involves the internal electronic orbits, or energy levels, the temperature is unimportant and the diamagnetic susceptibility is generally observed to be independent of temperature. It is also independent of the field strength, a circumstance which allows its determination even in the presence of small amounts of ferromagnetic impurity: ferromagnetism varies with field strength and may be allowed for by judicious extrapolation of data obtained at several different field strengths. The induction effect must occur with all atomic systems of electrons and therefore diamagnetism must be a universal property of matter, analogous to electric polarizability which it strongly resembles.

4.134 Diamagnetic behavior is observed for molecular systems which contain only paired electrons, and for atomic or ionic systems which contain only completely filled orbitals and hence only paired electrons. In all such structures both the spin and orbital electronic moments cancel out, there is no permanent magnetic moment, and only the induction phenomenon remains to produce diamagnetism. The molecular systems are of relatively little interest, although, of course, they include the great majority of all compounds. The atomic systems include the species possessing inert gas configurations ($\ldots ns^2np^6$, *e.g.*, O^{2-}, F^-, Ne, K^+, Sr^{2+}, La^{3+}), pseudo-inert gas configurations ($\ldots (n-1)d^{10}$, *e.g.*, Pd, Ag^+, Cd^{2+}, Tl^{3+}), and those configurations characterized by the "inert pair" ($\ldots (n-1)d^{10}ns^2$, *e.g.*, Ga^+, Sn^{2+}, Bi^{3+}). It is necessary (but not sufficient) that the system, whether molecular, atomic or ionic, contain an even number of electrons in order to exhibit diamagnetic behavior, except in certain special cases where opposing paramagnetic effects happen to be very small. All substances which do not have the particular atomic or structural features required for para-, ferro-, antiferro-, or ferrimagnetism must demonstrate diamagnetic behavior.

Paramagnetism **4.135** If an atomic system contains unpaired electrons their spin and orbital magnetic moments are not completely canceled and there remains a permanent magnetic moment. In an external magnetic field the permanent moment tends to orient itself parallel to the field, just as a compass needle aligns itself with the earth's magnetic field. The orienting tendency is opposed by the usual thermal motion; the extent of alignment therefore must decrease with rising temperature. The net effect is measured by the magnetic susceptibility which is found to be positive and to vary with temperature according to the Curie or Curie-Weiss laws:

$$\chi = \frac{K_c}{T} \quad \text{or} \quad \chi = \frac{K_{cw}}{T+\Delta}.$$

(The Curie-Weiss law is not to be applied at temperatures below the Curie point $T_c = -\Delta$; for such temperatures the material possesses ferromagnetic properties.)

4.136 The quantum mechanical treatment of the interaction between the elementary moment and the applied field yields for the molar susceptibility χ_M the result

$$\chi_M = \frac{N\mu^2}{3kT} + N\alpha,$$

in which μ is the permanent magnetic moment, α is the diamagnetic part plus a small temperature independent paramagnetic contribution, and N, k, and T have their usual significance. This expression, due to Van Vleck, is identical, except for the addition of the term $N\alpha$, to one obtained long ago by Langevin by classical methods. The evaluation of μ and α, however, is possible only in quantum mechanical terms because they involve intrinsic structural and energetic features of atoms. For μ different expressions are obtained according as the spacing of the degenerate spin levels is small compared to kT,

$$\mu = \beta\sqrt{4S(S + 1) + L(L + 1)} \qquad (A)$$

or large compared to kT,

$$\mu = \beta \cdot g\sqrt{J(J + 1)}. \qquad (B)$$

Here β is the magnitude of the Bohr magneton, which is the electronic unit of magnetic moment and has the value $\beta = \dfrac{eh}{4\pi mc} = 0.917 \times 10^{-20}$ erg oersted^{-1}; S, L, and J are the quantum numbers associated respectively with the resultant spin, the resultant orbital angular momentum, and the total angular momentum (vector sum of S and L); and g the Landé splitting factor, a known explicit function of the quantum numbers S, L, and J. A more involved result is obtained for the intermediate case. Clearly both spin and orbital contributions are included in either expression and must generally be considered.

4.137 Neighboring ions in the crystalline or liquid state or in solution interact strongly with one another. If the interactions are so strong that the orbital angular momentum cannot be oriented by an applied magnetic field, the orbital contribution to the magnetic moment does not appear and is said to be "quenched." In the case of simple ions of representative and short transition series elements, in which the unpaired electrons are near the surface and are almost entirely unscreened from the fields of the neighboring ions, the orbital contributions to the magnetic moment are found to be almost completely quenched. Under these circumstances, expression (A) for μ may be simplified by dropping the orbital term to yield

$$\mu = \beta\sqrt{4S(S + 1)} \quad \text{or} \quad \mu_B = 2\sqrt{S(S + 1)} \quad \text{in Bohr magnetons.}$$

TABLE 4.12

Calculated and Observed Magnetic Moments of Transition Element Ions

Ion	3d Electrons	Unpaired Electrons	μ Calc. $= \sqrt{n(n + 2)}$	μ Obs.
Sc^{3+}, Ti^{4+}, V^{5+}	0	0	0.00	0.0
Ti^{3+}, V^{4+}	1	1	1.73	1.77–1.79
V^{3+}	2	2	2.83	2.76–2.85
V^{2+}, Cr^{3+}, Mn^{4+}	3	3	3.87	3.68–4.00
Cr^{2+}, Mn^{3+}	4	4	4.90	4.80–5.06
Mn^{2+}, Fe^{3+}	5	5	5.92	5.2–6.0
Fe^{2+}	6	4	4.90	5.0–5.5
Co^{2+}	7	3	3.87	4.4–5.2
Ni^{2+}	8	2	2.83	2.9–3.4
Cu^{2+}	9	1	1.73	1.8–2.2
Cu^{1+}, Zn^{2+}	10	0	0.00	0.0

Now the total spin S is just half the number n of unpaired electrons, each with spin $\frac{1}{2}$, so we may also write

$$\mu_B = \sqrt{n(n+2)},$$

which immediately shows that unpaired electrons are required for paramagnetism, and also that the number of unpaired electrons may be determined from experimental measurement of the paramagnetic susceptibility. In Table 4.12 are listed the calculated and observed moments for a number of common ions of the 3d transition elements.

4.138 The agreement is generally good except for cobalt which exhibits abnormally high values under nearly all experimental circumstances. The deviation is presumably due in part to incomplete quenching of orbital moments, which is more pronounced for the second than the first half of the series, and in part to extensive complex formation. Cobalt exhibits a high degree of magnetic anisotropy, *i.e.*, dependence of susceptibility on direction in the crystal, and this is related to the anomalous high values of the observed moments.

4.139 The ions of the long transition series, either lanthanide or actinide, behave differently. The shells containing their unpaired electrons are deep in

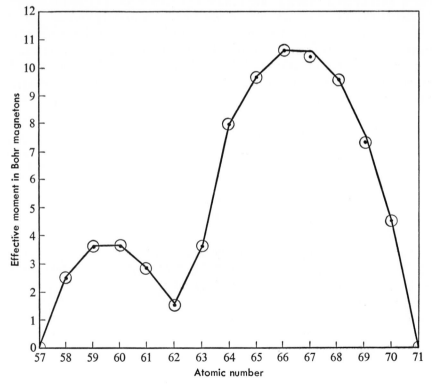

Fig. 4.4 **Magnetic moments of the trivalent lanthanide ions at 25° C.** Circles are experimental points and solid line shows theoretical calculated values.

the atom and are shielded by outer electrons from the effects of the fields of neighboring ions. Their orbital moments are unaffected and contribute to the overall magnetic moment. For these ions expression (B) or the corresponding relation for the intermediate case must be used. The computations are straight-forward if the S, L, and J values are correctly identified; this was first done by Hund in a classical investigation with the older quantum mechanics and has been modernized and extended by Van Vleck. The results for the trivalent lanthanide ions are shown in Figure 4.4.

4.140 The detailed agreement between theory and experiment is quite clearly demonstrated by the figure. The binodal form of the curve results from the coupling of spin and orbital contributions to the total moment. If the orbital contributions were quenched as for the $3d$ transition element ions, then the curve should show a single peak with a maximum at atomic number 63, Gd^{3+}, which has seven unpaired electrons just half filling all the available $4f$ orbitals.

4.141 All molecules containing an odd number of electrons (*e.g.*, NO, NO_2, ClO_2, $(C_6H_5)_2NO$, NaO_2, organic free radicals) are necessarily paramagnetic. Other molecules may also be paramagnetic if they contain unpaired electrons, albeit the total number of electrons is even. Thus, molecular oxygen is found to be strongly paramagnetic, with a moment corresponding to two unpaired electrons in the diatomic molecule. Certain complex organic molecules containing an even number of electrons have been shown to be paramagnetic, at least at higher temperatures; they may be in equilibrium with diamagnetic forms at lower temperatures. These so-called *biradicals*, of which the high temperature form of porphyrindine shown is an example, possess two unpaired electrons in the paramagnetic state.

4.142 Measurements of magnetic properties are widely used in determining the nature of binding in specific structures, particularly coordination compounds. Both bond type and stereochemistry may be inferred from the number of unpaired electrons. Magnetic measurements have also been applied to the elucidation of the electronic configuration and valence of various ions and atoms, notably of the actinide elements. These and other applications will be described in subsequent chapters.

Ferromagnetism **4.143** In discussing paramagnetic behavior it was implicitly assumed that the elementary magnetic moments are quite independently oriented in the absence of an applied field. It is only reasonable to suppose, however, that in dense systems they interact in some manner and that there will be possible various configurations of neighboring magnetic moments. In many crystalline materials the orbital contributions to the magnetic moment are quenched by the crystal field but the spins persist, and the problem of orientation may be discussed at least approximately in terms of spin only.

4.144 We shall see in Chapter 5 that electron spins tend to align themselves in an antiparallel fashion in forming a covalent chemical bond. The reason for this behavior is found in the Pauli Exclusion Principle which requires anti-symmetric character for the entire wave function; in chemical binding the part of the wave function depending only on space coordinates is symmetric for the stable low energy state and thus the spin part must be antisymmetric, requiring the electrons to have antiparallel spins. In such a material as crystalline iron, where an excess of available electron orbits is available, it seems that the state of lowest energy may correspond to an antisymmetric space function. Consequently the spin part must be symmetric and electron spins are aligned in parallel fashion.

4.145 The parallel alignment of electron spins necessarily aligns the magnetic moments of certain of the electrons in a whole region or domain of the crystal lattice. The result is to enhance the susceptibility very greatly, for in a given crystal instead of N elementary magnetic dipoles of moment μ each, corresponding to the individual electron spins, there are $\dfrac{N}{n}$ of moment $n\mu$ each, where n is the average number of elementary moments aligned per domain. The expression for the susceptibility becomes

$$\chi_M \sim \frac{1}{3kT}\frac{N}{n}(n\mu)^2 = \frac{N\mu^2}{3kT} \cdot n$$

and the susceptibility may become many orders of magnitude greater than the paramagnetic value, because large numbers of magnetic moments may be aligned in a single domain.

4.146 At low temperatures the spins in a domain may be considered perfectly ordered. As the temperature is raised the spin orientation becomes more random and the net moment of each domain decreases. Furthermore, the phenomenon is cooperative in that as each magnetic dipole assumes a random orientation it diminishes the ordering effect on its neighbors and favors their disordering as well. Thus the disorder increases more and more rapidly with rising temperature and becomes complete at the sharp temperature known as the Curie point. Here the net moment of the domain becomes zero but residual interactions between the elementary moments account for very high values of the paramagnetism. Curie temperatures generally lie in the range 500–1500° K, from which we may infer that the energy of coupling between spins is considerably smaller than the energy of ordinary chemical binding. In a ferromagnetic material the interacting electrons are rather far removed from each other, whereas in a chemical bond they are quite near together and the interaction energy is much larger.*

4.147 Ferromagnetic materials are not easily characterized according to structure, although elements with but a few vacancies in the $3d$ level (Fe, Co, Ni) predominate greatly. Metallic copper, with the $3d$ level filled, and manganese with too large a number of vacancies, are not ferromagnetic; copper-manganese alloys are ferromagnetic. Gadolinium and dysprosium are ferromagnetic and presumably other rare-earth metals also are at low temperatures. Very many alloys containing iron, cobalt, or nickel are ferromagnetic, as well as a variety of others including gadolinium amalgams and alloys of manganese, aluminum, and copper. Among the large number of known ferromagnetic compounds are many oxides, sulfides, silicides, carbides, and nitrides of iron; cobalt, nickel or other short transition series metals; and more unusual examples such as CrO_2, AgF_2, and mixtures of $LaMnO_3$ with $CaMnO_3$.

4.148 The parallel alignment of elementary magnetic moments in ferromagnetic materials results from one of several possible kinds of interaction. In some substances the interaction gives rise to antiparallel arrangements, in two sublattices, or of two kinds of elementary moments. If these are equivalent, the substance is antiferromagnetic; if they are not equivalent, the substance is ferrimagnetic. Just as in ferromagnets, the phenomenon vanishes at temperatures above a characteristic Curie point for each substance. Below the Curie point, the susceptibility of an antiferromagnetic substance decreases with decreasing temperature, which distinguishes it from ferromagnetic materials. Among the diverse substances which exhibit antiferromagnetism are MnO, MnS, FeF_2, VO_2, $CuCl_2 \cdot 2H_2O$, and Cr_2S_3. Ferrimagnetism is shown by a variety of substances such as $FeCr_2O_4$ and certain other chromites and thiochromites, and $NiFe_2O_4$ and similar ferrites; these substances characteristically possess two kinds of magnetic ion.

Magnetic Resonance Techniques **4.149** When an elementary magnetic dipole is placed in a magnetic field H, its energy levels are split to give several perturbed levels corresponding to the several possible quantized orientations of the dipole. In the simplest case, that of particles of spin $\frac{1}{2}$, each unperturbed energy level E_k gives rise to two perturbed levels, $E_k \pm \mu H$, where μ is the magnetic

---

* Heisenberg has developed an approximate quantum mechanical theory which may be used to predict the value of the Curie temperature in the form

$$T_c = -\Delta = \frac{2Z}{3k} S(S+1)J'$$

where Z is a geometrical factor determined by the nature of the lattice, S the spin and J' the exchange integral, which is a quantum mechanical quantity describing the interaction between the electrons (see 5.64). Clearly, if the exchange integral is negative, as it is for chemical binding, there is no real Curie point and the material is paramagnetic at all temperatures. If the exchange integral is positive, however, then a real positive Curie temperature exists below which the material is ferromagnetic and above which it is paramagnetic. Thus one may associate positive exchange integrals with ferromagnetism.

moment. At thermal equilibrium in a system of such elementary magnets in a magnetic field, there is a very slight excess of dipoles in the lower energy state (for protons the fraction excess in the ground state is about 10^{-5} at 300° K in a field of 7000 gauss). If transitions occur from the lower of these states to the upper, energy in amount $2\mu H$ must be absorbed; this energy quantity may be characterized by the frequency which is given by the usual relation

$$h\nu = \Delta E = 2\mu H.$$

Resonance methods provide a means by which this frequency or energy can be measured with precision and hence a method of determining the magnetic moment μ. Three ranges of energy transfer, as measured by the appropriate frequencies, are of importance: a few megacycles per second, corresponding to moments observed in nuclei, of the order of one thousandth of typical atomic moments; several thousand megacycles per second, corresponding to atomic moments or unpaired spins in paramagnetic substances; several tens of thousands of megacycles per second, corresponding to the large magnetic moments of the domains in ferromagnetic materials. These three areas are termed respectively *nuclear magnetic resonance* (NMR), *paramagnetic* (or *electron spin*) *resonance* (PMR), and *ferromagnetic resonance*, currently the least developed and least important in the study of chemical problems.

4.150 Although details necessarily vary for techniques in the three areas, the basic scheme is the same for all. The sample to be studied is placed between the poles of a large magnet. Energy is fed into the sample from an appropriate oscillator source through a coil or similar device, and transitions are detected by means of either the small electromotive force induced in a receiver coil by the motion of the magnetic dipoles in the field, or the change in impedance in the energy input system. The characteristic feature is that when the energy fed into the sample is of just the correct frequency for the transition between states, then the output signal is greatly magnified by resonance effects. In usual practice the oscillator frequency is fixed at a convenient value and the field strength is varied or modulated by a low frequency current in an auxiliary parallel winding; the varying field recurrently scans the resonance state and the output shows peaks at those values of field strength for which the applied frequency matches the level spacing.

4.151 The almost unbelievably detailed structural information which can be obtained and the enormous sensitivity of the NMR method are illustrated in Figure 4.5, which shows the output plotted against the field strength in a study of the proton resonance in ethyl alcohol; the energy input is a 30 megacycle radio frequency, the field strength is 7050 gauss, and the entire sweep width (horizontal axis) is only 38 milligauss. The peak at the left is identified as being due to the protons of the methyl group, that in the center to those of the methylene group, and that on the right to the hydroxyl proton. The areas under the three peaks are as 3 : 2 : 1, the numbers of protons in the three different groups. The three kinds of proton have slightly different resonant frequencies,

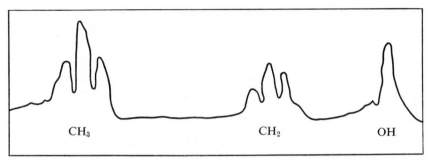

Fig. 4.5 **Proton resonance in ethyl alcohol at 30 mc and 7050 gauss, with sweep width of 38 milligauss.** (From MOORE, *Physical Chemistry*, 2nd. Edition, Prentice-Hall, Inc., Englewood Cliffs, N.J., 1955, Fig. 11.14)

or energy level spacing, because their magnetic environments in the molecule are slightly different; these slight differences are referred to as "chemical shifts." Furthermore, each peak has a fine structure, the interpretation of which is beyond the scope of this discussion.

4.152 If atomic or molecular motion in a system is sufficiently rapid and vigorous that all nuclei of a given kind (*e.g.*, protons) have essentially the same environment, then the NMR peak will be quite narrow; in the absence of such motion the peak will be wide because of variations in environment. Thus NMR measurements may reveal the nature and extent of molecular motions in liquids and solids, as has been done for water. Such motions may also be studied by observing the relaxation time, which is the time required for the elementary moments to exchange energy with the lattice. A sharp decrease in the relaxation time, as is observed for ammonium bromide at 88° K (from 32 to 0.01 sec.), indicates the onset of internal molecular motion such as rotation on the crystal lattice.

4.153 Because paramagnetic atomic moments are so very much larger than nuclear moments, they decrease relaxation times very markedly, and consequently NMR measurements may be applied to the determination of small amounts of paramagnetic substances. The theory is as yet incompletely worked out and the method must be considered empirical. NMR has also been extensively applied in the study of catalysis and adsorption.

4.154 Paramagnetic resonance investigations are not subject to diamagnetic corrections which in other methods of study may be quite appreciable. The detection, determination, and detailed study of paramagnetic ions and of free radicals have been greatly facilitated by resonance techniques. PMR has been applied in reaction rate studies, structure determination, elucidation of electronic configurations and bond types, especially in coordination compounds, and in the investigation of luminescent solids, solutions of metals in liquid ammonia, and semiconductors.

Electrical Properties of Metals   **4.155** Metals in the macroscopic solid or liquid state are characterized by certain properties which may be attributed to the individual atoms (*e.g.*, ionization potential, chemical reactivity) and other properties which may result either wholly or in part from the nature of the forces which hold the metallic atoms together. Pure metals which are soft and pliable generally exhibit relatively low melting points as well, because these properties alike result from the existence of weak forces between the atoms. In general, the physical properties of metals derive from and reveal much about the binding forces.

4.156 Metals conduct electricity and heat very well. The conductivity is invariably large for the most chemically reactive metals, although other much less reactive metals may show large conductivities as well. Because no gross material transport accompanies electrical conduction it must be concluded that a flow of electrons is responsible. Thus, a structure is suggested in which relatively free electrons circulate among fixed cations on a crystal lattice; the electrons are the valence electrons stripped from the original metallic atoms, and the fixed cations are the residues. This conception of an "electron gas," (due to Drude, Lorentz, and others) explains moderately well a number of characteristic properties of metals, foremost of which is their electrical conductivity. The high thermal conductivity of metals is believed due also to the free electrons which can easily and efficiently transport kinetic energy through a crystalline metal. In either case, the metal with the most loosely held electrons would be expected to be the best conductor, as is observed experimentally.

4.157 The electrons in a metal in equilibrium may not escape because of the Coulombic forces exerted by the lattice ions. If energy is supplied, however, we should expect that electrons might escape from the metal. This is precisely what is observed: if the energy is supplied as heat, then the phenomenon is termed *thermionic emission;* if the energy is supplied in the form of short wavelength radiation, then we observe the *photoelectric effect.* In either case there is a minimum energy (temperature or frequency) below which the effect is not observed, because the electron is not given sufficient energy to overcome the attractive forces at the surface and thus surmount the barrier to its escape.

4.158 The system of nearly free electrons is capable of absorbing and almost immediately re-emitting radiation over a wide range of frequencies. Again, this is just what is observed for metals, for they are opaque, lustrous, and generally somewhat gray in color. No characteristic absorption or reflection is observed except for gold and copper.

4.159 Other physical properties of metals can tell us something about the essentially fixed portion of the structure, the ions on the crystalline lattice. Metals are quite dense as compared to simple molecular crystals and we conclude that the structure must be close packed. The malleability and ductility of metals imply that the forces in the lattice are nondirectional or nearly so; yet these forces must be strong, because the system is solid, resists deformation to some extent, and is only very slightly compressible. Finally, the heat capacity of the metal and its variation with temperature suggest that the lattice sites are occupied generally by single ions rather than by clusters analogous to molecules in the case of covalent chemical compounds.

4.160 The electronic heat capacity of metals is considerably less than that normally expected for a monatomic gas ($\frac{3}{2}R$ per mole), which implies that the classical electron gas description is oversimplified. Quantum mechanical treatments of the problem are much too complex for our discussion, but the qualitative result may be given. In essence, a wave function is found which is analogous to a molecular orbital for one electron in the field of the entire lattice. Part of the function resembles closely that for a free electron and accounts, through the standard descriptions of quantum mechanics, for those properties, notably electrical conductance, which seem to require free electrons for their explanation. The remainder of the wave function is a complex periodic factor related to the crystal lattice geometry, which describes in a certain way the possible energy states for electrons in the metal. These states fall in groups of N each for a crystal of N atoms, and are almost continuously distributed within a band or zone (Brillouin zone), which itself is separated in energy very greatly from the other bands or zones. An elementary lattice is then imagined to be produced by adding electrons to the appropriate levels, filling them up from the lowest level in the lowest band or zone; each band may accommodate $2N$ electrons because of spin. Just as completely filled inner shells may be ignored in considering chemical binding, so also may they be ignored in the present treatment, because the electrons which just fill the inner atomic shells exactly suffice to fill the corresponding bands for the crystal. Consequently we need add only valence electrons to valence electron bands. If the last band is only partially filled, then the substance is a metal and exhibits the characteristic properties of metals. If all of the electronic energy levels of the last band are filled, however, then the substance is an insulator, because there are no levels within the band to which an electron may be transferred, and the next band is located at a much higher energy.

4.161 Certain substances are neither conductors nor insulators, but have small electrical conductances generally increasing with rising temperature. The current may be carried by migration of ions, which simultaneously accomplishes matter transport, or by migration of electrons in the special case of semiconductors. In these latter substances the last band is presumed filled but there exist either low lying conduction bands or special local defect levels associated with physical defects in the lattice, which may be missing, misplaced, or substituted ions. Substances like germanium, for which a conduction band lies not far above the last filled band, are termed intrinsic semiconductors. At somewhat elevated temperatures electrons are excited to the conduction band and the material becomes conducting. In the defect semiconductors, the defect level may contain a few electrons and lie not far below a vacant band to which the electrons are easily excited and where they may yield conduction; or the defect level may be vacant but lie not far above the filled band from which electrons may be easily excited, leaving vacancies or "holes" in the band which can account for electrical conduction. Crystalline zinc oxide containing a few zinc atoms in excess is an example of the first type of semiconductor, and copper(I) oxide (Cu_2O) an example of the second type. The special levels themselves are localized and cannot be directly responsible for conduction. The electronic semiconductors most often involve the metallic elements of representative groups III, IV, and V, although examples involving other elements are also known. They have become important commercially because of their application in transistor devices. Their study has also helped elucidate the crystal structure and behavior of metals and their compounds.

4.162 The electrical conductance of a normal metallic conductor decreases with rising temperature, very roughly as $\frac{1}{T}$. The explanation for the decrease lies in the collisions between electrons and lattice ions, the frequency of which increases with rising temperature. On the other hand, the electrical conductance of a semiconductor increases with rising temperature, approximately as $e^{-E/RT}$. In this instance, we are dealing in effect with a distribution between a lower nonconducting and an upper conducting state, E is approximately the energy difference between them, and the law cited describes the distribution as determined by the temperature.

4.163 As the temperature is lowered toward the absolute zero the electrical resistance of an ordinary metallic conductor decreases and approaches a very low value (probably not zero because of the zero point lattice energy). In a certain class of metallic conductors, however, the electrical resistance decreases with decreasing temperature and becomes zero at a finite determinable transition temperature T_c. At lower temperatures than T_c, a current once induced in a ring of such a conductor continues to flow indefinitely. These are termed *superconductors*. The transition temperatures of a number of metals are given in Table 4.13.

4.164 It has been shown that the transition temperature for a given metal varies with its isotopic composition. It is inferred, therefore, that the superconduction phenomenon is associated in some way with lattice vibrations, because these must vary as the nuclear masses are changed. The transition tem-

TABLE 4.13

Transition Temperatures of Superconductors

Metal	T_c °K	Metal	T_c °K	Metal	T_c °K
Hf	0.374	Ga	1.103	Hg	4.17
Ru	0.47	Al	1.175	Ta	4.38
Zr	0.546	U	1.25	La	4.71
Ti	0.558	Th	1.32	V	4.89
Cd	0.602	Tl	2.38	Pb	7.26
Os	0.71	In	3.37	Nb	9.22
Zn	0.93	Sn	3.69	Tc	11.2

perature also varies with the strength of an applied magnetic field, decreasing with increasing field strength. There exists thus for each superconductor a critical field strength H_c for which $T_c = 0$; for $H \geq H_c$, only normal conduction may be observed. Superconductors must also be nearly perfectly diamagnetic, that is, have almost infinite value of the diamagnetic susceptibility so that there is no magnetic field within the conductor regardless of the external field.

4.165 Various theories have been proposed to account for superconductivity, but none has yet been completely successful or completely accepted. The most likely are based in part on models with at least two states, normal and superconducting, with an appreciable energy gap between them; they usually involve detailed consideration of lattice interactions with electrons in the two states. It is interesting that the very interactions which account for increasing resistance at higher temperatures seem also responsible for the phenomenon of superconductivity at very low temperatures. Thus, metals which are ordinarily poor conductors might be expected to behave as superconductors at low temperatures, and the good conductors, with weak electron-lattice interactions, are not superconductors; this is verified experimentally for the metals lead, mercury, and titanium, which are superconductors, and for copper, silver, gold, and the alkali metals, which are not superconductors.

CHAPTER 5

CHEMICAL BINDING AND STRUCTURE

Ionic or Electrovalent Binding

Introduction

5.1 In the first half of the nineteenth century the concept of valence as a numerical measure of combining capacity was introduced and accepted, and the valences of many elements were determined as more and more accurate analyses were developed and precise atomic weights found. Even though the electrical structure of the atom was not yet realized, an electrical basis for valence was suggested by Berzelius and related to the commonly accepted positive valences for metals and negative valences for nonmetals, determined primarily on the basis of evidence from electrolysis. The existence of such pairs of compounds as methane and carbon tetrachloride, however, posed a real problem for those who would assign an invariable positive or negative valence for each atom, and of course a simple picture of this sort was incapable of ex-

GENERAL REFERENCES

BREWER, "The Fusion and Vaporization Data of the Halides," Paper 7 in *The Chemistry and Metallurgy of Miscellaneous Materials: Thermodynamics*, edited by Quill, McGraw-Hill Book Company, Inc., New York, 1950.

BREWER, BROMLEY, GILLES and LOFGREN, "The Thermodynamic Properties of the Halides," Paper 6 in *The Chemistry and Metallurgy of Miscellaneous Materials: Thermodynamics*, edited by Quill, McGraw-Hill Book Company, Inc., New York, 1950.

COULSON, *Valence*, The Clarendon Press, Oxford, 1952, Ch. I.

DUSHMAN, "Quantum Theory of Atomic Spectra and Atomic Structure," Ch. II in Vol. I, *Treatise on Physical Chemistry*, edited by Taylor and Glasstone, D. Van Nostrand Company, Inc., New York, 1942.

GLASSTONE, *Textbook of Physical Chemistry*, D. Van Nostrand Company, Inc., New York, 1954, Ch. V.

LATIMER, *The Oxidation States of the Elements and Their Potentials in Aqueous Solutions*, Prentice-Hall, Inc., New York, 1952, Ch. 2.

PALMER, *Valency, Classical and Modern*, Cambridge University Press, London, 1944, Ch. I, II.

PAULING, *The Nature of the Chemical Bond*, 2nd Edition, Cornell University Press, Ithaca, N.Y., 1940, Ch. X.

RICE, *Electronic Structure and Chemical Binding*, McGraw-Hill Book Company, Inc., New York, 1940, Ch. XI, XIV.

SIDGWICK, *The Electronic Theory of Valency*, The Clarendon Press, Oxford, 1927, Ch. IV.

147

plaining the stability of the diatomic gaseous elements such as hydrogen, nitrogen, and oxygen. We know today that the difficulty lies in the fact that there are chemical bonds of different types: the bond in sodium chloride, for example, for which the simple concept of a $+1$ valence for sodium and a -1 valence for chlorine seems quite satisfactory, is fundamentally different in nature from the bond in the gaseous chlorine molecule.

5.2 A stable molecule is a group of atoms whose distances of separation are of the order of atomic diameters, a few Ångstroms at most, and which are held together by forces which we call valence forces. These latter forces are different from those acting between, say, inert molecules in a real gas or electrically charged pith balls hung on strings, in that they may be saturated; that is to say, the valence forces due to a particular atom suffice to attach to that atom a specified integral number of other atoms and no more. It is this characteristic of the forces which results in the property of simple numerical valence of the elements.

5.3 The forces which give rise to chemical binding must have their source in the structure of the atoms. It is not surprising that progress in the understanding of chemical binding has gone hand in hand with progress in the elucidation of atomic structure. The accepted picture of an atom as a system of electrons surrounding a positively charged nucleus implies that these entities alone are concerned in chemical binding. The retention of nuclear properties of the atom in its molecules and the existence of certain universal characteristics of all chemical bonds imply further that chemical binding involves the electrons in the atoms. Finally, we have seen in our previous discussion of atomic structure that the electrons in inner completed shells are almost inert and we must conclude that chemical binding involves the electrons in outer (not necessarily the outermost) incomplete shells. Anticipating and oversimplifying the discussion to follow, we remark that the bonding process involves either the transfer of such electrons from one atom to another, or the sharing of such electrons between atoms. Electron transfer gives rise to ionic or electrovalent bonds, and sharing to covalent bonds. In most chemical bonds one mechanism or the other predominates greatly, but in many, the two mechanisms make roughly comparable contributions.

5.4 Although Thomson suggested tentatively that chemical binding is a consequence of electrostatic attraction between oppositely charged atomic structures resulting from the transfer of electrons from one atom to another, the first definite hypotheses on the role of electrons in binding were those of Kossel and Lewis in 1916. Their views were more or less complementary. Kossel emphasized the transfer of electrons and Lewis their sharing, but they proceeded necessarily from the same generalizations: the observation that inert gas electronic configurations are extremely stable and the atoms chemically unreactive, and the assumption that atoms possessing electronic configurations different from that of a neighboring inert gas tend to attain that stable configuration in chemical combination. At first, attention was centered on the elements of the first three periods (hydrogen through argon), particularly on carbon with its multitude of compounds and on the heavier elements but one or two groups removed from the inert gases. For this reason, emphasis was placed on a stable arrangement of eight electrons, i.e., an octet. The so-called "Rule of Eight," which requires the gain, loss, or sharing of electrons to bring about such an eight electron group, applies strictly to many but not all by far of the known stable compounds of the elements.

5.5 Kossel suggested that atoms of the strongly electropositive elements immediately following inert gases in order of increasing atomic number lose one or more electrons in chemical combination to produce positively charged ions with inert gas configurations. Similarly atoms of the strongly electronegative elements immediately preceding inert gases gain one or more electrons to produce negatively charged ions with inert gas structures. The electrostatic attraction between such oppositely charged ions accounts for the high stability of the chemical bond between a strongly electropositive atom and a strongly electronegative atom. The ions possess rather less stability than that of a neutral inert gas structure in which the resultant zero spin and orbital momenta preclude interaction with electrons in other atoms. This difference is due to their electrical charges which lead to electrostatic interactions with other systems. The isolated ions, however, are essentially the same as inert gas atoms, as is indicated by comparative ionization potentials.

5.6 The fundamental feature of the Kossel concept is the attainment of a configuration in which the electronic shells are filled; the inert gases illustrate special cases of such configurations. In these terms, however, other configurations are also quite stable. We may expect to find cases where atoms enter into chemical binding by gaining or losing electrons to attain, for example, the configuration of palladium ($1s^2 2s^2 2p^6 3s^2 3p^6 3d^{10} 4s^2 4p^6 4d^{10}$) or of zinc ($1s^2 2s^2 2p^6 3s^2 3p^6 3d^{10} 4s^2$), and there are still other stable configurations containing incompletely filled levels, for example, that of Mn^{2+}. In general, these electronic configurations are not as stable as the inert gas structures, as is evidenced by the relative chemical reactivity, but there are many examples of ions of these types among the metals. Stable negative ions of nonmetals almost invariably have inert gas structures.

5.7 Elements rather far removed from the inert gases nevertheless form stable chemical bonds, and the resulting compounds in general do not have properties indicating the presence of ionic constituents. For example, the extremely large amount of energy required to produce C^{4+} and the very strong electric field about the ion both militate against its stable existence under any conditions except possibly in the very dilute gas. However, carbon forms thousands upon thousands of stable compounds; evidently Kossel's concept of electron transfer is inapplicable in such cases and an alternative is required.

5.8 Lewis proposed that inert gas structures may be attained by the sharing of electrons between atoms, the shared electrons being counted for both atoms in reckoning the occupancy of the outermost level. For example, a hydrogen atom attains the helium configuration by possessing a share in two electrons, and carbon may attain the neon configuration for its L shell by possessing a share in each of eight electrons. The attractive force between the bonded atoms is not quite so simply visualized as for the ionic bonds postulated by Kossel, but very crudely, at least, one may picture the necessarily somewhat positive atomic kernels or residues being attracted to opposite sides of a negatively charged region occupied by the shared electrons. The stability of the negative electron cloud itself is not evident from classical considerations and the problem must be postponed for treatment according to quantum mechanical concepts and methods.

5.9 It was soon realized that in the vast majority of shared electron, or covalent, bonds the electrons are shared in pairs. A bonded hydrogen atom is stable because it shares a pair of electrons with a second atom (which may be another hydrogen atom, so that the product is the very stable hydrogen molecule), and a bonded carbon atom shares four pairs of electrons with other atoms in most of its compounds. There seems to be some evidence that one- or three-electron bonds exist in a few special cases. The near universality of electron pair sharing, however, is recognized in the "Rule of Two" which describes a more fundamental and more general characteristic of nature than the "Rule of Eight." We shall see later (sec. 5.68 *ff.*) that the pairing of electrons leads to states of minimum energy for a given molecular configuration because the electronic spins are thereby neutralized; the electron pair with its resultant zero spin momentum then interacts much less strongly with the rest of the system than do two electrons with parallel spins. The pairing phenomenon, if such it may be called, is closely related to the operation of the Pauli Exclusion Principle: the total capacity of an orbital in an atom, bonded or not, is realized within the restrictions of the Exclusion Principle only when the electrons occur in pairs with opposite spins.

5.10 The forces briefly described in the foregoing are not the only forces recognized in chemical binding. It is necessary to discuss as well ion-dipole forces or dipole-dipole forces, interactions arising from the polarization of atomic systems, and the forces operative in solid metals either pure or in combination. In the sections to follow we shall elaborate the simple concepts of electron transfer and electron sharing, and treat these additional topics in somewhat less detail.

Ionic or Electrovalent Binding

5.11 Let us consider the potassium and chlorine atoms: the potassium atom possesses the electronic configuration $1s^22s^22p^63s^23p^64s^1$, and the chlorine atom the configuration $1s^22s^22p^63s^23p^5$. Neither has an inert gas structure but rather possesses an incomplete shell of electrons. It is quite evident from the configurations, however, that each differs very little from that for the intervening inert gas argon, $1s^22s^22p^63s^23p^6$; the loss of a single electron in the one case and the gain of a single electron in the second leads directly to the stable argon configuration for each, and the electrostatic attraction between the oppositely charged ions should be responsible for a stable ionic bond.

5.12 In general we have seen that the $4s$ level is at a higher energy than the $3p$ level. The relative levels vary somewhat with atomic number, it is true, but one might expect no great difference for these three consecutive elements chlorine through potassium. One might also expect that the transfer of the electron from the $4s$ level in potassium to the $3p$ level in chlorine should lead to the evolution of energy and to a more stable configuration. This crude picture is not generally correct, however, as may be seen by considering the transfer process in detail.

$$K(g) = K^+(g) + e^-$$
$$Cl(g) + e^- = Cl^-(g)$$

The energy absorbed in the first step is the ionization energy of potassium, and that evolved in the second step is the electron affinity of chlorine. The experimental values of these two quantities are 4.3 and 4.0 volts respectively, and thus the energy to be evolved in the attachment of the electron to the chlorine atom is insufficient to bring about the removal of the electron from the potassium atom. It is important to note, however, that the difference is not large. If a potassium ion and a chlorine ion are brought together, their large energy of interaction greatly exceeds this small difference and the net result is that the pair of ions $K^+ - Cl^-$ is much more stable than the pair of atoms $K - Cl$.

5.13 The argument above implies that the pair cesium-fluorine should furnish a much more favorable case, for then the process involves the transfer of an electron from the $6s$ level in cesium to the $2p$ level in fluorine. Similarly, the pair lithium-iodine should provide a considerably less favorable case involving the transfer from a $2s$ level to $5p$ level. As Table 5.1 shows, these predictions are borne out, but the interesting fact is again that the differences are not very large. The variation of energy of a given level with atomic number (nuclear charge) is such that the $6s$ electron in cesium behaves much like the $2s$ electron in lithium, and the $5p$ electron in iodine like the $2p$ electron in fluorine.

5.14 In Table 5.1 are given the values of the excess $A - I$ of the electron affinity A of the nonmetal over the ionization energy I of the metal, for the pairs involving the common alkali metals and hydrogen as electron donors, and the common halogens and hydrogen as electron acceptors; all values are given in electron-volts.

5.15 Ionization energies have been quite accurately determined, but electron affinities are much less accurately known, and precise quantitative significance must not be attached to the values listed in the table, particularly the very small values or the very small differences between values. Even so, one may conclude that the cesium-fluorine pair exhibits an exothermic electron transfer reaction, as do perhaps the rubidium-fluorine and cesium-chlorine pairs, and possibly even the potassium-fluorine pair, and in all other pairs the electron transfer process is endothermic. Excluding the pairs involving hydrogen, however, we

TABLE 5.1

Ionization Energies and Electron Affinities (*in Electron-volts*)

Metal Nonmetal	Li $I = 5.4$	Na $I = 5.1$	K $I = 4.3$	Rb $I = 4.2$	Cs $I = 3.9$	H $I = 13.6$
F $A = 4.3$	−1.1	−0.8	0	+0.1	+0.4	−9.3
Cl $A = 4.0$	−1.4	−1.1	−0.3	−0.2	+0.1	−9.6
Br $A = 3.8$	−1.6	−1.3	−0.5	−0.4	−0.1	−9.8
I $A = 3.4$	−2.0	−1.7	−0.9	−0.8	−0.5	−10.2
H $A = 0.7$	−4.7	−4.4	−3.6	−3.5	−3.2	−12.9

note that these energy differences do not exceed 2.0 volts, or approximately 46 kcal./mole, for even the least favorable case. The energy released upon the mutual approach of the oppositely charged ions to the distances commonly observed in electrovalent compounds, a very few Ångstroms at most, is of the order of 100 to 300 kcal./mole and hence greatly exceeds this amount; thus, quite strong chemical bonds are produced.

5.16 The element hydrogen is included in the comparison above, although the great majority of its compounds are not of the ionic type, as one would predict from the values of $A − I$ given in Table 5.1. The large ionization energy, as compared to that for the alkali metals, and the small electron affinity relative to the halogens, lead to energy deficiencies in the neighborhood of 10 volts for the hydrogen-halogen pairs. The electrostatic interaction energy is not sufficient to outweigh such a large deficiency and consequently combination in these pairs does not come about primarily through electron transfer. We shall see (sec. 5.115) that the bonds in the hydrogen halides are covalent in nature but contain an appreciable ionic contribution, the magnitude of which is greatest with fluorine and least with iodine, as would be predicted from the tabulated values of the energy deficiency $A − I$.

5.17 The energy differences are considerably smaller for the alkali metal-hydrogen pairs, although still greater than for the alkali metal-halogen pairs, by an amount of the order of three to ten. The energy of electrostatic interaction is large enough that these metallic hydrides exist, although they are quite generally considerably less stable than the corresponding halides. In these ionic compounds the hydrogen is present as the hydride ion, H^-, and it is not surprising that the compounds are powerful reducing agents.

5.18 The case of the pair hydrogen-hydrogen is of particular interest: at large distances of separation the system $H \ldots H$ is more stable than the system $H^+ \ldots H^-$ (or its equivalent $H^- \ldots H^+$) by 12.9 volts, or approximately 300 kcal./mole. As the ions approach each other, their interaction energy cancels a part of this difference but far from all of it. If the ions approach so closely as to make the interaction energy 300 kcal./mole, then the energy deficiency in the electron transfer process is no longer simply given as $A - I$, where A and I are evaluated individually for isolated atoms. Thus the ionic structures do not make the major contribution to the strong chemical bond in the hydrogen molecule; nevertheless, there is an appreciable ionic contribution to the fundamentally covalent bond between the two hydrogen atoms.

5.19 The specific pairs discussed above suggest that ionic bonds are formed only between pairs of atoms of which one is strongly electropositive and the other strongly electronegative. Low ionization potentials and high electron affinities therefore favor ionic bond formation, and we find such bonds restricted roughly to the elements of groups I and II among the representative metals and groups VI and VII among the nonmetals, although certain reactive transition metals may form predominantly ionic bonds with highly electronegative elements. Those factors which lead to low ionization potentials, namely large radius, efficient shielding by inner electrons and resultant low effective nuclear charge, and a stable configuration of completely filled electronic shells in the resulting ion, all favor ionic bond formation by a metal (see 4.54–59). In an analogous manner, small radius, high effective nuclear charge, and a stable configuration of the product ion favor ionic bond formation by a nonmetal. It is evident that the tendency toward formation of an ionic bond is determined not just by the properties of one of the atoms, but by those of both atoms. Finally, the strength of the bond depends greatly on the interaction between the two oppositely charged ions, or in the crystalline state, the interaction among all of the ions of both signs.

General Properties of Ionic Compounds

5.20 Under ordinary conditions, the stable state of practically all ionic compounds is the crystalline solid. At elevated temperatures the solid melts or sublimes but even in the liquid and vapor states, ions or ion pairs are observed. In solution in appropriate polar solvents the constituents are the ions, generally solvated, which interact with one another. The interaction of the ions in the crystalline solid, however, is the fundamentally important factor in any consideration of the stability and properties of ionic compounds. A considerable quantity of energy is released when equivalent large numbers of cations and anions are transferred from the dilute gas phase, where the distances between ions are very large and the interactions very small, to the actual crystalline solid, in which the distances between ions are quite small and the interactions quite large. This energy, per mole of the crystalline compound, is termed the lattice energy or crystal energy of the compound. The lattice energy, by this definition, is also the amount of energy which must be supplied to disrupt completely one mole of a crystalline compound and transfer the constituent ions to very large mutual separations in the gas phase. It represents the total potential energy of interaction of the ions at their specific distances in the particular crystalline lattice structure characteristic of the solid compound and is thus susceptible of calculation from basic principles, as well as of experimental measurement.

5.21 The calculation of the lattice energy rests primarily on the work of Born, Landé, and Mayer. The lattice energy consists of four principal contributions:

- a. The purely electrostatic interaction between simple presumably fixed ions
- b. The interactions between the polarizabilities (*i.e.*, the capacities for distortion in instantaneous fields) of neighboring ions
- c. The van der Waals repulsion energy which arises from the close range interaction of the electronic structures of the two ions and which operates to fix equilibrium distances of separation in the stable crystal
- d. The zero point vibrational energy of the ions in the crystal lattice.

Of these the first two are positive, the second two, negative contributions to the lattice energy. The first is calculable from simple classical electrostatic theory, the last is known accurately from measured lattice frequencies, but the remaining two are much more difficult to treat. Their detailed calculation from quantum mechanical principles is exorbitantly difficult or even impossible, and resort is made to approximate representation of the effects by simple relations involving two or three parameters. The particular relations chosen, shown below, are based on semiquantitative arguments on approximate wave functions and electron density functions for the system, and the values of the parameters are determined from experimental measurements of other properties of the crystal such as the compressibility and density, the theoretical treatment of which necessarily involves these same concepts, relations, and parameters. In these terms, the energy of interaction of a pair of nearest neighbors, an anion and a cation of charges z_1e and z_2e distant r apart, is given by

$$u = \frac{Az_1z_2e^2}{r} + Be^{-r/p} - \frac{C}{r^6} + \varepsilon_0.$$

A is the geometrical Madelung constant, a number of the order of unity which results from the summation of contributions from all ions in the lattice and therefore describes the effect of the electrostatic fields of neighboring ions on the pair considered and is determined by the type of crystal lattice. B, C, and p are parameters to be determined from the requirement of equilibrium in the crystal and the independent measurements of density and compressibility; ε_0 is the zero point energy of the two ions on the lattice. When the ions have their equilibrium separation r_0 the energy u is a minimum; therefore

$$\left(\frac{\partial u}{\partial r}\right)_{r=r_0} = -\frac{Az_1 z_2 e^2}{r_0^2} - \frac{B}{p}e^{-r_0/p} + \frac{6C}{r_0^7} = 0$$

$$u_0 = \frac{Az_1 z_2 e^2}{r_0}\left(1 - \frac{p}{r_0}\right) - \frac{C}{r_0^6}\left(1 - \frac{6p}{r_0}\right) + \varepsilon_0.$$

The lattice energy U defined for a mole of the crystal is Nu_0, N being Avogadro's number:

$$U = \frac{NAz_1 z_2 e^2}{r_0}\left(1 - \frac{p}{r_0}\right) - \frac{NC}{r_0^6}\left(1 - \frac{6p}{r_0}\right) + N\varepsilon_0.$$

5.22 An alternative and somewhat simpler expression may be analogously derived by ignoring the zero point energy and representing the combined second and third terms by an inverse power of the distance. The result may be written

$$U = \frac{NAz^2 e^2}{r_0}\left(1 - \frac{1}{n}\right),$$

in which z is the largest common factor of z_1 and z_2 and n is a parameter of the order of ten, characteristic of the electronic configurations of the ions; its value may be calculated theoretically or determined from the experimental compressibility, and the two results are generally in fair agreement. It is evident that an uncertainty of ten per cent in n introduces an uncertainty of only one or two per cent in U.

5.23 The second expression for the lattice energy U illustrates the effect of the two principal factors z and r_0. The lattice energy increases rapidly with the valence of the ions in the crystalline compound, and also increases rapidly with decreasing interionic separation in the lattice, which may come about because of decreasing radius of either cation or anion or both. It is important to note that for a given range of change of radius of one ion, the effect on U is the greater the smaller the radius of the second ion. Thus the range of values of the lattice energy of the alkali metal fluorides is greater than that for the iodides, and that for the lithium halides greater than that for the cesium halides. A third factor in determining the crystal energy U is the polarization or deformation of the ions, particularly of the anion in the intense field of the cation. In general the polarization effect increases and hence the lattice energy increases as the ionic charges increase, the cation radius decreases, the anion radius increases, or as the cation changes from an eight- to an eighteen-electron configuration. Although, as we shall see subsequently (sec. 5.25–32), other factors are also involved in the stability of ionic compounds, in general the larger the lattice energy the more stable the crystalline ionic compound.

5.24 The magnitudes of the lattice energy and of the individual contributions described above are shown for the alkali metal halides in Table 5.2. The fluorides are omitted for lack of complete data, and the zero point energies, averaging about 0.07 ev, are omitted. The table also includes some experimental results for lattice energies obtained from measurements of ionic concentrations

TABLE 5.2

Lattice Energies of Alkali Halides (*in Electron-volts*)

Compound	Electrostatic Energy	Polarizability Interaction	Van der Waals Repulsion	Calculated Lattice Energy	Experimental Lattice Energy
LiCl	9.75	0.16	1.17	8.63	8.74
LiBr	9.07	0.14	0.98	8.16	8.23
LiI	8.23	0.16	0.79	7.56	7.60
NaCl	8.92	0.13	1.03	7.94	7.86
NaBr	8.41	0.12	0.90	7.58	7.65
NaI	7.77	0.14	0.74	7.10	7.23
KCl	7.99	0.17	0.94	7.17	7.22
KBr	7.62	0.16	0.82	6.71	6.90
KI	7.10	0.16	0.69	6.54	6.59
RbCl	7.68	0.20	0.87	6.95	
RbBr	7.30	0.17	0.76	6.67	6.56
RbI	6.82	0.17	0.67	6.30	
CsCl	7.08	0.33	0.77	6.51	
CsBr	6.80	0.30	0.71	6.34	
CsI	6.40	0.29	0.63	6.04	6.13

in the vapor phase in equilibrium at high temperatures with the crystalline solid. All values in the table are given in electron-volts; 1 ev = 23.06 kcal./mole.

5.25 It has been shown (see 4.72) that the lattice or crystal energy may be related through a Born-Haber cycle to the other thermochemical quantities for the elements concerned. We found there the result

$$U = I - A + Q + S + \tfrac{1}{2}D$$

for the crystal energy U of a compound such as an alkali metal halide. I is the ionization energy of the metal, A the electron affinity of the nonmetal, Q the energy of formation of the solid compound from the elements in their standard states, S the sublimation energy of the metal, and D the energy of dissociation of the diatomic nonmetallic element into atoms. If independent values of the electron affinities are known, crystal energies may be computed from this relation and the other known energy quantities; most commonly, however, theoretical values of lattice energy have been used to determine electron affinities, as was described earlier.

5.26 In Table 5.3 are listed the values, in kcal./mole, of the appropriate energy quantities and the calculated lattice energies for the alkali metal halides. The calculated lattice energies have been adjusted to give constant values for the electron affinity of each halogen; the corrections do not exceed ±2.5 kcal./mole.

5.27 The effect of ionic radius on the crystal energy U is clearly evident in the table: the values of U decrease uniformly as the anionic radii increase from fluorine to iodine or as the cationic radii increase from lithium to cesium. The dependence of U on the individual energy quantities, although explicitly indicated in the relation derived above, is nonetheless complex, because it involves the heat of formation Q, which like the crystal energy, is a function of the properties of both combining elements. In fact, if we may assume the crystal energy known from theoretical calculations, the Born-Haber result is conveniently written

$$Q = U - I + A - S - \tfrac{1}{2}D$$

and used as a means of predicting theoretical values of the standard heat of formation of the compound. Such heats of formation give an indication of the thermal stability of the compound.

5.28 For the sequence lithium through cesium the quantity $I + S$ decreases from 161.3 to 108.5 kcal./mole as the atomic and ionic radii increase; for the fluorides of these metals the quantity $A - \tfrac{1}{2}D$ is, of course, constant but the lattice energy U decreases with increasing cation radius even more rapidly than $I + S$ because of the small size of the fluoride ion. Thus the heats of formation of the fluorides decrease from lithium to cesium. For the chlorides, bromides, and iodides, with their considerably larger ions, the lattice energies decrease more slowly than $I + S$ for the sequence with the result that the heats of formation of the chlorides, bromides, and iodides increase from lithium to cesium. Effects such as these, arising primarily from the very small size of the fluoride ion, are responsible for the often anomalous properties of simple fluorine compounds; striking instances in aqueous systems are the very low solubility of calcium fluoride and the very high solubility of silver fluoride.

5.29 For the halides of a given alkali metal, the heat of formation Q decreases in the order fluoride to iodide in every case, but the decrease is much more pronounced for the lithium compounds than for those of the other metals. The reason is again the small size of the ion; the lattice energy is therefore large but

		Li $S = \ 37.1$ $I = 124.2$	Na 26.0 118.4	K 21.5 100.0	Rb 20.5 96.3	Cs 18.8 89.7
F	$A = 81.0$ * $\tfrac{1}{2}D = 18.3$ *	$Q = 146.3$ $U = 244.9$	136.0 217.7	134.5 193.3	131.3 185.4	126.9 172.7
Cl	$A = 87.1$ $\tfrac{1}{2}D = 29.0$	$Q = \ \ 97.7$ $U = 200.9$	98.2 184.5	104.2 167.6	102.9 161.6	103.5 153.9
Br	$A = 80.7$ $\tfrac{1}{2}D = 26.7$	$Q = \ \ 83.7$ $U = 191.0$	86.0 176.4	93.7 161.2	93.0 155.8	94.3 148.8
I	$A = 73.5$ $\tfrac{1}{2}D = 25.5$	$Q = \ \ 64.8$ $U = 178.1$	68.8 165.2	78.3 151.8	78.5 147.3	80.5 141.0

TABLE 5.3

Thermochemical Data for Alkali Halides (in kcal./mole)

* The older value of about 32 kcal./mole for $\tfrac{1}{2}D$ corresponds to a value of about 95 kcal./mole for A for fluorine. This value, although high, was formerly considered to be in line with those for the other halogens.

decreases rapidly with increasing radius of the anion. We have noted (see 4.100) that the standard oxidation potential of lithium is anomalous; this is also due primarily to the very small size of the bare lithium ion and to the unusually large value of its hydration energy, a quantity in some respects similar to the crystal energy.

5.30 The large lattice energies of ionic compounds result from strong forces between the ions in the crystal lattice. These forces must be overcome in order to vaporize the crystal to gaseous ions, to fuse the solid, or to vaporize the liquid or solid to gaseous molecules or ion pairs. In either the fusion or the vaporization process, however, the total energy requirement is less than the total lattice energy because of the interaction, respectively, of either the mobile but neighboring ions in the liquid phase or the two ions of the ion pair in the gas phase. Nevertheless, it is to be expected that the strong interionic forces in ionic compounds will be responsible for relatively large heats of fusion, sublimation, and vaporization and high values of the melting and boiling points as compared with analogous quantities for most covalent compounds. In Table 5.4 are listed incomplete data for the melting and boiling points of a number of halides of metals of representative groups I and II.

TABLE 5.4

Melting and Boiling Points of Halides of Groups I and II Metals

Non-Metal	F		Cl		Br		I	
Metal	Melting Point, °C	Boiling Point, °C	Melting Point, °C	Boiling Point, °C	Melting Point, °C	Boiling Point, °C	Melting Point, °C	Boiling Point, °C
Li	870	1676	613	1353	547	1265	446	1190
Na	992	1705	801	1430	755	1390	651	1300
K	880	1500	776	1500	730	1376	723	1330
Rb	760	1410	715	1390	682	1340	642	1300
Cs	684	1250	646	1290	636	1300	521	1280
Be	800 (subl.)		405	488	490	520	510	590
Mg	1396	2239	708	1412	700		ca. 700	
Ca	1360		772	>1600	765	810	575	718
Sr	1450	2489	873		643		402	
Ba	1285	2137	962	1560	847		740 (dec.)	
Ra			1000		728			

5.31 With the obvious exceptions of the values for beryllium chloride, bromide, and iodide, which are predominantly covalent, these high melting and boiling points may be compared with the much lower values for such compounds as methane, ethyl alcohol, ammonia, and other covalent compounds. The heats of fusion of most of the halides of the alkali metals and alkaline earth metals lie between 4.0 and 8.0 kcal./mole, and all of them fall between 2.5 and 13.9 kcal./mole except that for lithium fluoride, which is only 1.4 kcal./mole.

These values may be compared with the values 1.4, 2.4 and 2.0 kcal./mole respectively for water, benzene, and carbon dioxide. Similarly, the heats of vaporization of these same metallic halides generally lie in the range 30 to 60 kcal./mole, and the heats of vaporization of water, benzene, and carbon dioxide are in order 9.7, 8.4, and 3.8 kcal./mole. It is evident that the strong forces between the oppositely charged ions in either the crystalline solid or the liquid phase lead to high melting and boiling points and large heats of fusion and vaporization. It should be pointed out, however, that while ionic compounds are characterized by such behavior, certain covalent structures, notable among which are diamond and silicon carbide, also exhibit these refractory properties. In such cases the extremely strong forces in the crystal are essentially chemical bonds rather than the much weaker forces operative between saturated molecules.

5.32 The same strong forces which bring about high melting and boiling points of ionic compounds also are responsible for other physical properties characteristic of these compounds: the solid crystals are generally hard, dense, rigid, and relatively incompressible and nonvolatile as compared to crystalline covalent compounds, and the liquid state is also generally denser and less compressible and volatile than the liquid state of most covalent compounds.

5.33 The strength of ionic bonds and the stability of the ionic crystals might lead us to expect that these compounds are generally not very soluble, because the solution process implies the separation of the crystal units to give mobile and, in dilute solution, nearly independent particles. It is found experimentally that ionic compounds in general are nearly insoluble in nonpolar solvents such as carbon tetrachloride, but are soluble to varying extents in polar solvents like methanol and may be extremely soluble in highly polar solvents like water. The process of dissolution must involve rupture of the ionic crystal lattice to produce the solute species; these latter may be ion pairs or even larger clusters in solvents of low polarity, but in most polar solvents they are individual, solvated ions. The energy needed for the lattice rupture is provided in the main by that released by the solvation process. Thus solvents whose molecules do not exert the attractive forces of solvation on the ions cannot dissolve appreciable quantities of ionic compounds. Polar solvents consist of polar molecules which do exert such attraction for ions (ion-dipole forces, sec. 5.41–6) and hence may dissolve ionic compounds. The solubility measures the relative strength of the solvation and crystal forces.

5.34 Polar solvents diminish the attractive forces between the ions because of their high dielectric constants. The force between two charges q_1 and q_2, a distance l apart, in a vacuum is $\frac{q_1 q_2}{l^2}$, but in a medium of dielectric constant D the force is $\frac{q_1 q_2}{D l^2}$. The total energy of a given configuration of charges (solvated ions, for example) relative to the isolated charges in the gas phase is correspondingly less for a material medium for which $D > 1$ than for a vacuum, and thus the configuration is less stable or the charges more mobile in the medium of high dielectric constant. Solvents such as water, for which $D = 78.5$ at $25°$, are therefore good solvents for ionic compounds.

5.35 The energy quantities concerned in the solution process may be related by a cycle of the Born-Haber type. The process of solution of the ionic halide MX, for example, is equivalent to the rupture of the lattice to give isolated gaseous ions, following by the solvation of the isolated gaseous ions to produce the actual solvated ions at standard concentration (properly, activity) in solution. For aqueous systems we may write the cycle shown, in which L is the

$$MX(s) \xrightarrow{\quad L \quad} M^+(aq) + X^-(aq)$$
$$-U \searrow \qquad \nearrow H$$
$$M^+(g) + X^-(g)$$

energy absorbed in the solution process, H the hydration energy and U the crystal or lattice energy. Each energy term is written as an absorption for the indicated process and the total energy absorption must vanish for the cyclic process. Therefore

$$L + H - U = 0 \quad \text{or} \quad L = U - H.$$

5.36 This particularly simple result may be stated generally: the energy absorbed in dissolving is equal to the energy absorbed in disrupting the lattice plus the energy absorbed in solvating the ions. Since the two energies U and H are of comparable magnitude, it is not too surprising to find that some ionic compounds in water, for example, exhibit positive and some negative heats of solution; although to be sure, those with positive heats of solution (heat is absorbed in the solution process) predominate, and hence the solubility of most ionic compounds in water increases with rising temperature. It is often observed that an anhydrous ionic compound dissolves exothermically in water but the corresponding hydrated compound dissolves endothermically: for the two crystalline solids the lattice energy U may be expected to be roughly comparable, but the solvation energy generally is much greater for the anhydrous compound than for the hydrated compound in which the ions are already extensively solvated. Thus in the range of ordinary temperatures the solubility of sodium sulfate decahydrate increases sharply with rising temperature but that of the anhydrous sodium sulfate decreases with rising temperature. The solubility of calcium chloride hexahydrate increases with rising temperature more rapidly than does that of the tetrahydrate, and this in turn more rapidly than the solubility of the dihydrate.

5.37 As was mentioned previously in the discussion of the Born-Haber cycle for oxidation potentials, the energy terms must be all of the same type, that is, all must be changes in internal energy, or changes in enthalpy, or changes in free energy. Thus far we have implicitly supposed them to be internal energy changes or enthalpy changes. Let us now suppose them to be free energy changes; this is equivalent to ignoring entropy changes, assuming that they cancel, or restricting the results to the absolute zero of temperature, which is obviously inconvenient for discussions of liquid solution behavior. In any event, we suppose that a variation in the quantity $U - H$ measures approximately the corresponding variation in the standard free energy change $\Delta F°$ for the solution process. Since $\Delta F° = -RT \ln K$, and the equilibrium constant K for the solution process is a direct measure of the solubility, a variation in $U - H$ measures approximately the variation in solubility, the solubility decreasing as $U - H$ becomes more positive.

5.38 The solvation energy H increases with increasing dielectric constant of the solvent, but the lattice energy U does not vary. Therefore the solubility of an ionic compound generally increases with increasing polarity and dielectric constant of the solvent. Both H and U increase with increasing ionic charge (valence or oxidation number), but U generally increases more rapidly. Thus alkaline earth metal salts are generally less soluble than the corresponding salts of the neighboring alkali metals. In the same way both H and U decrease with increasing ionic radii, but the lattice energy varies the more rapidly, especially for small values of the radii. As the ionic radii increase, $U - H$ generally becomes more negative and the solubility increases. Finally, as we have seen above, the lattice energy is strongly dependent on polarization of the anions by the cations. Since generally the polarizing effect of the cation on the polar solvent molecules is rather less important, the solvation energy is less affected and consequently an increase in polarization because of variation of ionic charge, ionic radius, or electronic configuration usually leads to decreased solubility of the ionic compound in polar solvents.

5.39 Ionic compounds are made up of ionic species whether in the crystalline solid state, the liquid state, or in solution in polar solvents. The application of an electric field causes the ions to migrate in any of these states, although in the solid the effect is appreciable only at high temperatures just below the fusion point. The ionic migration is responsible for the transport of electric charge, hence an electric current, but in addition appreciable quantities of matter are also transported; this distinguishes ionic conductance in these systems from electronic conductance in metals. The conductance of an ionic compound in the crystal, liquid, or solution phase is also dependent on the factors which have been discussed, although the dependence is quite complex. In a very general way factors which tend to increase lattice energy or other ionic interactions tend to give low conductance, and conversely.

5.40 In summary, ionic compounds are characterized generally by high melting and boiling points; fairly high heats of fusion, sublimation, and vaporization; hard, dense, nearly incompressible crystals; very low solubility in nonpolar solvents and much greater solubility in polar solvents; and high electrical conductance in solution in polar solvents, in the pure liquid state, or in the crystalline state near the melting point.

Electrostatic Dipole Interactions

5.41 Neutral atoms or molecules attract one another weakly at relatively large distances; the force of attraction increases with decreasing separation until at quite small distances either the two particles combine chemically or else the attractive force is replaced by a repulsive force. Attractive forces are also observed between ions and neutral atoms or molecules. All of these forces depend for their existence on the extended structure of the neutral atom or molecule, because simple uncharged point masses could not interact in the way described. Because these forces seem to be responsible for certain chemical combinations, often nearly stoichiometric, it is necessary to examine them in somewhat greater detail, and it is convenient to do so in this discussion of chemical binding. The attractions are sometimes termed chemical bonds, but they are generally longer and considerably weaker than typical ionic or covalent bonds, and do not involve either electron transfer or electron sharing.

5.42 A system consisting of two electrical charges q, of equal magnitude but opposite sign, separated by the distance d, is called a dipole of moment $\mu = qd$. The total charge is zero. In the field of a single charge Q the dipole tends to orient itself to bring its oppositely charged end nearer Q, and thus a net attractive force results regardless of the sign of Q. This is an ion-dipole force. If now a second single charge $-Q$ is placed near Q, producing a second dipole, the orientation of the first dipole is determined by the nearer of the two charges, which it attracts; the more distant charge is repelled, but the force of repulsion is smaller than that of attraction. Thus, there is an attractive force between the two dipoles even though each possesses zero net electrical charge; this is the dipole-dipole force.

5.43 Dipoles may be of two kinds, permanent and induced. A stable structure with centers of positive and negative electricity displaced from each other possesses a permanent dipole moment. In diatomic molecules, a difference in electronegativity guarantees the existence of such permanent moments; homonuclear diatomic molecules necessarily have zero moments, and if the two different atoms of a heteronuclear molecule have nearly equal electronegativities (in other words, if the bond is essentially nonpolar) then such molecules also have essentially zero moments. A few dipole moments of diatomic molecules in the gaseous state are listed in Table 5.5; the values are given in Debye units, $1D = 10^{-18}$ c.g.s. units.

TABLE 5.5

Dipole Moments of a Few Diatomic Molecules

Molecule	H_2	HF	HCl	HBr	HI	NaI	KCl	KI	CO	NO
Moment	0	1.9	1.03	0.78	0.38	4.9	6.3	6.8	$\sim$0	$\sim$0

5.44 Polyatomic molecules in general possess nonzero dipole moments unless their several bonds happen to be more or less symmetrically oriented and cancel each other's contributions. Carbon tetrachloride and carbon dioxide thus have zero moments, but chloroform, ethyl bromide, ammonia, and water all have quite appreciable permanent dipole moments. The zero moment for carbon dioxide strongly suggests that the molecule possesses the symmetrical linear O—C—O structure, just as the value $\mu \sim 1.8\ D$ for water suggests an angular

configuration $\begin{array}{c} \text{O} \\ \diagup\ \diagdown \\ \text{H}\qquad\text{H} \end{array}$.

5.45 When a body containing electrical charges which are more or less free to move is placed in an electric field, the charges are displaced, the positive in one direction and the negative in the opposite, to an extent determined by the properties of the body and the strength of the field. The displaced charges constitute an induced dipole whose moment $\mu = \alpha F$, F being the field strength, and α the polarizability of the material. Atoms and molecules behave in this manner, giving rise to induced dipoles in electric fields; the most common electric fields in this regard are those due to ions, to permanent dipoles, or to instantaneous dipoles produced by random fluctuations in charge distribution in molecules whose average moment is zero. Because the induced dipole results directly from the polarizability, its interactions with ions or permanent dipoles are sometimes referred to as ion- or dipole-polarizability interactions.

5.46 There are five different interactions which may now be considered, approximately in order of decreasing strength; two are of the ion-dipole type and three of the dipole-dipole type. The ion-permanent dipole interaction is particularly important in many coordination compounds and in systems involving polar solvents such as water or liquid ammonia. The ion-induced dipole or ion-polarizability interaction is also concerned in certain complex ions involving easily polarizable species; the triiodide ion, I_3^-, is an example. The strongest of the three dipole-dipole interactions is that involving only permanent dipoles; it is responsible for much of the order in molecular crystals and for extensive association in polar liquids. Permanent dipole-induced dipole, or dipole-polarizability, interactions are rather weaker but may be responsible for such species as the reported inert gas hydrates. Finally, the polarizability-polarizability interaction is the weakest of all; it operates in the liquefaction and crystallization of the inert gas elements.

5.47 The polarizability of an atom or ion measures the ease with which its electronic distribution may be distorted; it depends on the size, mean electrical density, and environment (see 5.122–124). For structures with inert gas configurations, the polarizability increases with increasing size. Thus for the inert gases helium through xenon the values of the polarizability are in order 0.20, 0.39, 1.63, 2.46, and 4.00 Å^3. This increase in polarizability is the principal reason for the increase of melting and boiling points with increasing atomic number in the group of inert gases. The trend is also illustrated by the series of values 1.05, 3.68, 4.80, and 7.15 Å^3 for the polarizabilities of F^-, Cl^-, Br^-, and I^-. The polarizability of a given elementary anion is decreased when it becomes bonded to a cationic center; the smaller and more highly charged the cationic center, the greater is the diminution in polarizability. For example, the molar refraction, which is approximately proportional to the polarizability, of O^{2-} as a free ion is 7.0 cm.[3], but in CaO, MgO, and BeO the values are 6.1, 4.2, and 3.2 cm.[3], respectively; similarly, the values in PO_4^{3-}, SO_4^{2-} and ClO_4^- are 4.0, 3.6, and 3.3 cm.[3], respectively.

5.48 When a cation and an anion approach one another, the field surrounding each ion polarizes the other ion to an extent determined by its polarizability. The major effect is usually the polarization of the anion by the cation. If the polarization is quite small, an ionic bond results; if the polarization is extensive, the electrons are drawn toward the cation and the bond has an appreciable covalent character. On the basis of these concepts, first pointed out by Fajans in 1923–4, covalent bonding is favored by large charges on either ion, a small cationic radius, a large anionic radius, and a pseudo inert gas configuration rather than an inert gas configuration for the cation, because these factors all enhance the polarization. In a crystalline solid such as sodium chloride, polarization is slight because the symmetrical distribution of oppositely charged neighbors is responsible for a small net polarizing force on any given ion. In the vapor phase, however, this canceling of forces is not possible and ions are involved as single anion-cation pairs, in which polarization is considerably more extensive and the bond considerably more covalent than in the crystalline state.

5.49 The tendency of an anion or anionic group to form a covalent bond with a cation — *i.e.*, to coordinate covalently with the cation — is markedly dependent on the polarizability. Thus F^- has a smaller tendency than does I^- to coordinate with less electropositive ions such as In^{3+}; presumably the cation polarizes I^- much more extensively and forms a stronger covalent link with it than is possible with F^-. In general SO_4^{2-} coordinates somewhat more readily than ClO_4^- because the oxygen atoms in ClO_4^- are less polarizable than those in SO_4^{2-}; NO_3^- usually occupies an intermediate position because, although the nominal charge on the central nitrogen atom is less than that on the sulfur atom in SO_4^{2-}, the central atom is also smaller, and consequently the oxygen atoms have low polarizabilities.

5.50 A very important example of electrostatic interaction involving dipole strength and polarizability is furnished by the so-called hydrogen bond in which a hydrogen atom links two strongly electronegative atoms. Because the bond may also involve some covalent nature and resonance behavior it will be considered later (see 5.125 *ff.*).

Covalent Bonding: Fundamental Basis and Development

Introduction

5.51 The idea of covalent bonding was introduced on an empirical basis before any real developments in the quantum mechanical theory of chemical binding were possible. The subsequent treatment of molecular systems, although generally only approximate in nature, verified the fundamental concepts introduced by Lewis and Langmuir and constituted not only a tribute to their insight and ingenuity but also a further indication of the essential validity of quantum mechanical methods.

5.52 In 1927 Heitler and London, in what was in effect the first quantum mechanical treatment of the chemical bond, discussed the structure of the hydrogen molecule. Their methods, based on the notion of approximating a wave function as a sum of wave functions for related simple atomic systems, led directly to the concepts of electron pairing of spins, and the sharing of more or less localized electron pairs between the bonded atoms. The basic ideas were rapidly extended by Pauling and Slater, among others, to the treatment of more complex molecules. The characteristic features of the bonds were found to be the pairing of spins of electrons (one initially on each of the bonded atoms), the concentration of the shared electron pairs between the bonded atoms, the directional properties of the bonds formed by polyvalent atoms, and in general, a molecular structure which stressed the original atomic nature of the system and the localized bonds between the atoms in the molecule. An alternative approach was developed by Hund and Mulliken, based on the behavior of electrons in the field of two nuclei in diatomic molecules; their extensions to larger molecules introduced the concept of molecular orbitals and the construction of molecules by the addition of electrons to successive orbitals just as was done for atomic systems. The result, which gives a less detailed picture of bonding, is particularly useful in the consideration of unsaturated systems. The different approaches are often complementary and, at least in some simple systems, may be shown to be essentially equivalent.

5.53 In the following sections we shall briefly discuss the simplest molecular systems in approximate terms, introducing on theoretical grounds the concepts of electron sharing and exchange, resonance between equivalent structures, hybridization and directed valence, and the dominant role of the electron pair

GENERAL REFERENCES

CARTMELL and FOWLES, *Valency and Molecular Structure*, Academic Press, Inc., New York, 1956, Part II.

COULSON, *Valence*, The Clarendon Press, Oxford, 1952, Ch. V, VI, VIII.

DUSHMAN, "Quantum Theory of Atomic Spectra and Atomic Structure," Ch. II in Vol. I, *Treatise on Physical Chemistry*, edited by Taylor and Glasstone, D. Van Nostrand Company, Inc., New York, 1942.

EYRING, WALTER and KIMBALL, *Quantum Chemistry*, John Wiley and Sons, Inc., New York, 1947, Ch. XII, XIII.

GLASSTONE, *Theoretical Chemistry*, D. Van Nostrand Company, Inc., New York, 1944, Ch. III.

PAULING, *The Nature of the Chemical Bond*, 2nd Edition, Cornell University Press, Ithaca, N.Y., 1940, Ch. I, III, IV, VI.

PAULING and WILSON, *Introduction to Quantum Mechanics*, McGraw-Hill Book Company, Inc., New York, 1935, Ch. XII, XIII.

PITZER, *Quantum Chemistry*, Prentice-Hall, Inc., New York, 1953, Ch. 8.

RICE and TELLER, *The Structure of Matter*, John Wiley and Sons, Inc., New York, 1949, Ch. 7.

RICE, *Electronic Structure and Chemical Binding*, McGraw-Hill Book Company, Inc., New York, 1940, Ch. X, XI, XII, XV.

in covalent binding. We shall examine the factors which influence the tendency toward covalent bond formation and the strength of such bonds, and discuss the general properties of the compounds containing these bonds. Finally, we shall discuss briefly the nature and properties of bonds in metals and of hydrogen bonds.

The Hydrogen Molecule Ion — A One-Electron Bond

5.54 The simplest molecular structure which can be built from the ordinary chemical atoms is the hydrogen molecule ion, H_2^+, the properties of which are known from spectroscopic investigation. The dissociation energy D is 2.79 ev or 64.3 kcal./mole, and the equilibrium internuclear separation is 1.06 Å. We have seen (see 5.18) that the hydrogen molecule, H_2, cannot be a simple ionic compound bound by electrostatic attraction between the two ions H^+ and H^-, and it seems obvious that the electrostatic attraction between an ion and an atom H^+ and H must be still weaker. Nevertheless, the molecular structure exists in a stable state (stable relative to dissociation into ion and atom) and we must seek an explanation as illustrative of covalent binding in its most elementary form.

5.55 The hydrogen molecule ion consists of two protons and an electron; it thus constitutes a three body problem for which the Schrödinger wave equation is to be solved. It is possible to separate the variables in the equation if elliptical coordinates are used. Just as we found in the study of the hydrogen atom, the separation of variables and the requirement that the solutions be well-behaved lead naturally to the introduction of three quantum numbers, which may be written λ, τ, and ϵ in the present instance. The quantum numbers determine the energy of the various states of the system as a function of the internuclear separation R. The quantum number λ is particularly important because it behaves for the molecular system just as m does for an atomic system; in fact, if the internuclear separation R in the molecular system is made to approach zero, so that the "united atom" results, in this case He^+ (the isotope of mass two if the hydrogen atoms are ordinary atoms of mass one), then λ passes over into the quantum number m of the united atom. The solutions of the wave equation which have been obtained in numerical form by Burrau, Hylleraas, Jaffe, and Teller are known as molecular orbitals. They describe the behavior of a single electron in the field of two nuclei in the same way that atomic orbitals (hydrogenlike one-electron wave functions) describe the behavior of a single electron in the field of a single nucleus. The allowed values of λ are the positive or negative integers, including zero, and the several molecular orbitals are designated σ, π, δ ... according as $|\lambda| = 0$, 1, 2 .... A δ molecular orbital must reduce for the united atom to an atomic orbital with $|m| = 2$, thus to a d, f... atomic orbital but not to an s or p orbital. The complete designation of these molecular orbitals specifies the state of the united atom as well, so that we may have $1s\sigma$, $2s\sigma$, $2p\sigma$, $2p\pi$, $3s\sigma$, $3p\sigma$, $3p\pi$, $3d\sigma$, $3d\pi$, $3d\delta$, $4s\sigma$ ... molecular orbitals. For a σ orbital, $\lambda = 0$ and there is but one state;

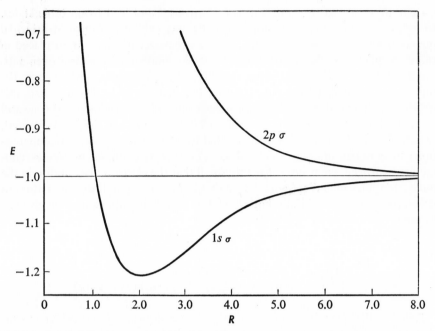

Fig. 5.1 **Calculated total energy of H_2^+.** E in units of E_H, the energy of an isolated hydrogen atom, and R in units of a_0, the first Bohr radius.

for a π, δ ... orbital $\lambda = \pm |\lambda|$ and such a state is doubly degenerate. The numbers of states are of course doubled if we include spin. The total energy of the H_2^+ system as a function of the internuclear distance R is shown for the two lowest states, $1s\sigma$ and $2p\sigma$, in Figure 5.1.

5.56 The minimum in the curve of energy versus internuclear separation for the $1s\sigma$ state implies a state of the H_2^+ system stable with respect to dissociation. Since chemists emphasize the two nuclei in the molecule, it must be concluded that the nuclei are chemically bound, and the bond can consist only of the electron; in the approach here adopted the electron is not localized but is shared equally by the two nuclei. Thus we have a type of covalent bond; since but one electron is involved, spin considerations are of no interest.

5.57 Molecular orbitals like those found for the H_2^+ system may be used, in suitably modified form, for complex diatomic molecules: the electrons in the molecular system are fed into molecular orbitals consistent with their capacities and the Pauli Principle. It is found that certain molecular orbitals preserve their principal quantum numbers as the internuclear separation R decreases to give the united atom; these are termed "bonding orbitals" and the electrons they contain are called "bonding electrons." On the other hand, for "anti-bonding orbitals," the principal quantum number increases as the transition is made from separate atoms to united atom; these orbitals in the molecular system are occupied by "anti-bonding electrons," and lead to unstable states. In a few exceptional cases bonding orbitals may exhibit a change in principal quantum number as R decreases. When all the electrons have been placed in the molecular orbitals in order, the excess in number of bonding over anti-bonding electrons determines the stability of the molecule, and in fact, the number of electron pair bonds between the two nuclei is just one half this difference. The order of filling molecular orbitals is not rigidly fixed (one will recall that the order of filling atomic orbitals is also not rigidly fixed) and, therefore, experimental evidence is needed to determine the electron configurations of complex diatomic molecules. For several diatomic molecules containing hydrogen, an atom sufficiently small that the electron distribution in the molecule approximates to some degree that in the corresponding united atom to which the molecular orbital notation relates, the configurations may be given as follows.

$$H_2 \quad (1s\sigma)^2$$
$$CH \quad (1s\sigma)^2(2s\sigma)^2(2p\sigma)^2\ 2p\pi$$
$$HF \quad (1s\sigma)^2(2s\sigma)^2(2p\sigma)^2(2p\pi)^4$$
$$HCl \quad (1s\sigma)^2(2s\sigma)^2(2p\sigma)^2(2p\pi)^4(3s\sigma)^2(3p\sigma)^2(3p\pi)^4$$

5.58 For diatomic molecules containing larger atoms the internuclear separation cannot be made quite small and the united atom concept becomes less useful. On the other hand, the separated atoms furnish but a poor approximation to the molecule itself. Under these circumstances the molecular orbitals are less precisely defined by the terms $z\sigma$, $y\sigma$, $x\sigma$, $w\pi$, $v\pi$, $u\sigma$ ..., in which z, y, x ... are equivalent to sets of (n,l) values for the atom (as in the notation $1s\sigma$ or $3p\pi$), and the molecular orbitals are listed approximately in order of decreasing stability after the orbitals occupied by the four most tightly held electrons from the K shells of the two bonded atoms; these four are represented by the symbol KK. At equilibrium internuclear separations the orbitals $z\sigma$, $x\sigma$, $w\pi$ ... are bonding orbitals, and $y\sigma$, $v\pi$, $u\sigma$ ... are anti-bonding orbitals. In these terms, the configurations are given below for several compounds of first period elements; for each, the number of shared pairs is listed.

Li_2	$KK(z\sigma)^2$	1	bond
B_2	$KK(z\sigma)^2(y\sigma)^2(x\sigma)^2$	1	bond
C_2	$KK(z\sigma)^2(y\sigma)^2(w\pi)^2(x\sigma)^2$	2	bonds
BO or CN	$KK(z\sigma)^2(y\sigma)^2(w\pi)^3(x\sigma)^2$	$2\frac{1}{2}$	bonds
CO or N_2	$KK(z\sigma)^2(y\sigma)^2(w\pi)^4(x\sigma)^2$	3	bonds
NO	$KK(z\sigma)^2(y\sigma)^2(x\sigma)^2(w\pi)^4(v\pi)^1$	$2\frac{1}{2}$	bonds
O_2	$KK(z\sigma)^2(y\sigma)^2(x\sigma)^2(w\pi)^4(v\pi)^2$	2	bonds
F_2	$KK(z\sigma)^2(y\sigma)^2(x\sigma)^2(w\pi)^4(v\pi)^4$	1	bond

5.59 Molecular orbitals are of considerable use and importance in the study of diatomic molecules and in extended form in the study of polyatomic molecules. Their further detailed treatment is beyond the scope of the present discussion.

5.60 An approximate treatment of the H_2^+ system is perhaps more instructive and productive of qualitative concepts which can be extended to more complex molecules. If we imagine that the two nuclei are separated to a very great distance, then, clearly, there can be two equivalent asymptotic states, I with the single electron near nucleus a, and II with the electron near nucleus b. These states may be represented graphically.

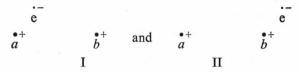

$$\text{I} \qquad\qquad \text{II}$$

5.61 At large internuclear separation the interactions are all vanishingly small except that between the electron and the nearby nucleus, which together constitute a simple hydrogen atom; the separated nucleus behaves as a free particle. The wave function for either asymptotic state may therefore be written as a product of a wave function for the appropriate hydrogen atom — an atomic orbital — and the function ψ_0 for an independent particle, which may simply be suppressed in the present discussion. (The nuclear motions are very much slower than those of the electrons and to a good approximation the nuclei may be considered fixed while electronic behavior is investigated.) Thus we may write

$$\psi_I = \psi_a(1)\psi_0 \rightarrow \psi_a(1); \quad \psi_{II} = \psi_0\psi_b(1) \rightarrow \psi_b(1),$$

in which ψ_0 refers to the separate bare nucleus and $\psi_a(1)$ is an atomic orbital the arguments of which are the coordinates of electron 1 relative to nucleus a.

5.62 Now the actual state of the H_2^+ system is neither I nor II, except in the limit of very great internuclear separations. At smaller distances R between a and b, the state presumably is intermediate between I and II, or may be imagined a composite of both. We attempt to describe the actual state by an approximate wave function ψ which is a linear combination of ψ_I and ψ_{II}:

$$\psi = C_I\psi_I + C_{II}\psi_{II}.$$

The standard methods of quantum mechanics then lead to the evaluation of the constants C_I and C_{II}. In particular, for H_2^+ we obtain two possible wave functions,

$$\psi_S = \frac{\psi_I + \psi_{II}}{N_S} = \frac{\psi_a(1) + \psi_b(1)}{N_S} \quad \text{and} \quad \psi_A = \frac{\psi_I - \psi_{II}}{N_A} = \frac{\psi_a(1) - \psi_b(1)}{N_A},$$

in which N_S and N_A are normalization constants. The subscript S or A refers to the symmetric or antisymmetric character of ψ with respect to interchange of the two identical nuclei a and b. The corresponding energies of the system, E_S and E_A, are functions of the internuclear distance R and are in fact approximately those shown in Figure 5.1 for the two lowest states $1s\sigma$ and $2p\sigma$, respectively. Clearly, the symmetric state described by ψ_S is one in which binding occurs between the two nuclei as evidenced by the minimum in the curve, which represents a state stable with respect to dissociation. The values of the energy and internuclear separation at the minimum in the curve (1.76 ev and 1.32 Å, respectively) agree approximately with the experimentally observed values for these quantities. It is equally clear that the state represented by ψ_A is not stable toward dissociation but is characterized by repulsion between the nuclei at all internuclear distances. The symmetric state is termed a bonding state, the antisymmetric an anti-bonding state.

5.63 It is of interest to compute the approximate average electron density in the neighborhood between the two nuclei in the two states: this density is given by the square of the wave function ψ. At the midpoint between the two nuclei $\psi_a(1) = \psi_b(1)$ so that

$$\rho_S = \psi_S^2 = \frac{4\psi_a^2}{N_S^2} \neq 0, \quad \text{but} \quad \rho_A = \psi_A^2 = 0.$$

Thus in the symmetric state there is a quite appreciable electron density between the two nuclei, and the electrical attraction between this charge accumulation and the nuclei may be considered as the chemical bond in the stable molecule. In the antisymmetric state the electron density at the midpoint between the nuclei is zero; there is no bond of this type, and in fact the relatively unscreened nuclei repel each other at all distances, hence the designation "anti-bonding." The concentration of electric charge between nuclei in states described by symmetric wave functions has been found quite generally to be characteristic of bonded states, and the qualitative interpretation in terms of electrical attraction is at least approximately correct.

5.64 The energies of the two states may be represented in the form (in so-called atomic units of energy)

$$E_S = E_H + \frac{1}{R} + \frac{J + K}{1 + \Delta} \quad \text{and} \quad E_A = E_H + \frac{1}{R} + \frac{J - K}{1 - \Delta},$$

in which E_H is the energy of an isolated hydrogen atom, $\frac{1}{R}$ the energy of interaction between the two nuclei, and J a quantity (the "Coulomb integral") which represents the average energy of interaction between one nucleus and an electron more or less localized on the other nucleus with a distribution presumed unaffected by the presence of the first nucleus. Δ is a quantity dependent upon R but generally small compared to unity, and K (the "exchange integral") is defined by the expression

$$K = \int \psi_I \left(\frac{-1}{R_a}\right) \psi_{II} \, d\tau = \int \psi_a(1) \left(\frac{-1}{R_a}\right) \psi_b(1) \, d\tau.$$

$\psi_a(1)$ and $\psi_b(1)$ were defined above, R_a is the instantaneous distance between the electron 1 and nucleus a, and the integration is carried out over all space. The factor $\psi_a(1)$ in the integrand represents the electron near nucleus a, the factor $\psi_b(1)$ represents the electron near nucleus b; the integral K is said to represent the net result of this exchange. The existence of the exchange integral is a necessary result of the arbitrary choice of the approximate method of describing the system; the exchange integral involves, among other effects, that of the second nucleus in disturbing the electronic distribution about the first nucleus. Thus E_H is not exactly the energy of the electron and its nearby nucleus, and J is not exactly the interaction energy between this electron and the second more distant nucleus; K includes the deviations. Because the formulation here adopted has been found generally convenient, the exchange integral has become an important quantity in the treatment of chemical bonds, and it is important to understand both its nature and its role.

5.65 Since Δ is small relative to unity, comparison of E_S and E_A shows that the exchange energy is primarily responsible for binding in this system. Furthermore, because we know that $E_S < E_A$, it is clear that the exchange energy term is negative, a general result for the exchange of electrons between different nuclei. From these two considerations we conclude — and this will subsequently be generalized (see 5.75–76) — that the larger the exchange integral the stronger or more stable the bond. Finally, if one examines the behavior with time of an arbitrary state of the H_2^+ system, it may be shown that such a state may be represented as oscillating or resonating between two extremes, one with the electron localized about nucleus a and the other with the electron near b, with a high frequency given approximately by $h\nu = -2K$, or $\nu = -2\dfrac{K}{h}$. This often helpful but misleadingly simple picture ought not to be taken literally, however, as a description of an actual physical phenomenon, or a type of high frequency tautomerism. It may be remarked that for the H_2^+ system the exact numerical quantum mechanical treatment previously mentioned does not lead to exchange integrals or resonance phenomena; these arise from the nature of the approximate method here considered and should be discussed and used within the framework of the limitations imposed by that approximate method.

5.66 The quantity Δ may be called the "overlap integral"; it is defined by the expression

$$\Delta = \int \psi_I \psi_{II} \, d\tau = \int \psi_a(1)\psi_b(1) \, d\tau$$

and represents the extent to which the orbitals for the two nuclei overlap. Since the magnitude of these orbitals decreases rapidly with increasing distance from their nuclei, Δ also decreases rapidly as the nuclei are separated. The integrals Δ and K behave similarly, and in more complex systems it may be assumed that configurations which maximize Δ, the overlap of two orbitals on different nuclei, also maximize the corresponding exchange integral K and hence, as well, the stability of the bond between the two nuclei. In the present instance of the H_2^+ molecule, the integrals may be evaluated analytically and if the orbitals chosen for the two nuclei are ordinary $1s$ atomic orbitals, as they should be when the ground state of the molecule is sought, the results are

$$K = e^{-R}(1 + R) \quad \text{and} \quad \Delta = e^{-R}\left(1 + R + \frac{R^2}{3}\right),$$

which illustrate the close similarity of the two quantities.

5.67 We have seen that a stable chemical bond may result between two nuclei of which each possesses an orbital that may be used to describe approximately the behavior of an electron, and that the strength of the bond is the greater the larger is the exchange integral, or approximately, the overlap integral, between these two orbitals. The bond is pictured physically as an electronic concentration between the two nuclei, and may be treated figuratively as resulting from a very high frequency oscillation or resonance between two equivalent states in which the binding electron is associated with first one and then the other of the two nuclei. These concepts, developed in the study of this simplest molecule, H_2^+, will be extended to more complex systems.

The Hydrogen Molecule

5.68 The hydrogen molecule consists of two hydrogen atoms, that is, of two protons and two electrons (the molecules HD, HT, DT, D_2, and T_2 are not fundamentally different with regard to their chemical binding). Proceeding as for the H_2^+ case, we recognize four important asymptotic states for the molecule.

Of these the first two tend toward neutral atomic structures as the internuclear separation is increased, and the second two toward ionic structures. Our previous discussion of ionic bonding suggests that the ionic structures III and IV are much less important than the nonionic structures and that they may be neglected in a first approximation. States I and II are described by different approximate wave functions and must be recognized as distinct possible asymptotic states of the system in this sense. The approximate wave functions for the two states may be taken as products of the appropriate atomic wave functions or atomic orbitals; in an obvious notation we write

$$\psi_I = \psi_a(1)\psi_b(2) \quad \text{and} \quad \psi_{II} = \psi_a(2)\psi_b(1).$$

5.69 Now neither of these can represent in any significant manner the actual state of the bound atoms because it is precisely the binding which is ignored in writing the approximate functions. Just as the physical state of the system may be supposed to be intermediate between these two limiting states, however, so also shall we suppose that the wave function representing approximately the actual state may be considered as being intermediate between ψ_I and ψ_{II}. In other words we shall attempt to describe the system by a wave function which is a linear combination of those for the two limiting nonionic structures:

$$\psi = C_I\psi_I + C_{II}\psi_{II} = C_I\psi_a(1)\psi_b(2) + C_{II}\psi_a(2)\psi_b(1).$$

We may imagine a peculiar hypothetical molecule in which each nucleus interacts only with one electron and each electron interacts only with one nucleus. Such a molecule is represented exactly by either ψ_I or ψ_{II}, so that the state of the molecule is doubly degenerate. We may then suppose that the other actual interactions between nuclei, between electrons, and between a nucleus and an electron are introduced as perturbations of the hypothetical state. The methods of quantum mechanics then lead to a calculation of the approximate effect of the perturbations and permit the evaluation of the coefficients C_I and C_{II} in ψ and of the approximate energy levels of the perturbed system. In the present case, as we did for H_2^+, we find two solutions; we use $1s$ orbitals for ψ_a and ψ_b, these being the functions corresponding to lowest energy for the isolated atoms and hence, presumably, to lowest energy for the actual H_2 molecule:

$$\psi_S = \frac{\psi_I + \psi_{II}}{\sqrt{2(1 + \Delta)}} \quad \text{and} \quad \psi_A = \frac{\psi_I - \psi_{II}}{\sqrt{2(1 - \Delta)}}.$$

The corresponding energies are given in atomic units by the expressions

$$E_S = 2E_H + \frac{J + K}{1 + \Delta} \quad \text{and} \quad E_A = 2E_H + \frac{J - K}{1 - \Delta},$$

in which, as before, E_H is the energy of an isolated hydrogen atom, J the Coulomb integral which here represents approximately the average interaction between two unperturbed atoms, K the exchange integral, and Δ the overlap integral. If we represent by H' those perturbing terms in the Hamiltonian operator which describe interactions between a nucleus or electron in one atom and a nucleus or electron in the other, these integrals are written as follows.

$$J = \int \psi_I H' \psi_I \, d\tau = \int \psi_a(1)\psi_b(2)H'\psi_a(1)\psi_b(2) \, d\tau$$
$$K = \int \psi_I H' \psi_{II} \, d\tau = \int \psi_a(1)\psi_b(2)H'\psi_a(2)\psi_b(1) \, d\tau$$
$$\Delta = \int \psi_I \psi_{II} \, d\tau = \int \psi_a(1)\psi_b(2)\psi_a(2)\psi_b(1) \, d\tau$$

5.70 The energies E_S and E_A are functions of internuclear separation R and their variation qualitatively resembles that shown earlier for the H_2^+ system. The lower energy is E_S, corresponding to ψ_S which describes a symmetric state;

there is a minimum in the energy curve and thus a stable configuration of the H_2 system. The very approximate calculation here described predicts 0.87 Å and 3.14 ev for the equilibrium internuclear distance and the energy of dissociation respectively, to be compared with the experimental values 0.74 Å and 4.72 ev. The higher energy E_A corresponds to the wave function ψ_A, which describes an antisymmetric state with no stable binding but rather repulsion between the nuclei at all distances of separation. Again, the principal part of the binding energy is given by the exchange integral K.

5.71 Up to this point, the calculations have ignored the spin of the electrons; because the effect on the energy is negligible, the spin part of the problem may be factored out. The spin must be taken into account, however, in considering the symmetry properties of the wave function. The Pauli Exclusion Principle requires the complete wave function to be antisymmetric in the coordinates of the two electrons: the symmetric space function ψ_S must be combined with an antisymmetric spin function for the two electrons in order to satisfy the Exclusion Principle. The antisymmetric spin function represents two electrons with paired or opposed spins, and thus we find that in the stable or bonding state for H_2 the two electrons must be paired, that is, have opposed spins. We shall see (sec. 5.75–76) that for molecules generally, bonding states are described by symmetric space functions and hence involve antisymmetric electron spin functions and paired or antiparallel electron spins. Parallel electronic spins, on the other hand, belong to unstable states.

5.72 Let us now briefly consider an alternative approach based on the results for the H_2^+ system in which a single electron moves in the field of two nuclei and, in the symmetric state, forms a bond between them. In H_2 there are two electrons moving in the field of the two nuclei and interacting with each other as well. If this latter electronic interaction is neglected, however, the wave function for H_2 may be written as the product of two molecular orbitals, one for each electron, these being solutions for the H_2^+ system. The reader will recognize the analogy to the treatment of complex atoms in terms of atomic orbitals derived from the study of the hydrogen atom (see 2.74).

5.73 We have found for H_2^+ the lowest orbital $1s\sigma$; this may be used for each of two electrons if their spins are paired. The molecular orbitals known in numerical form may be used to compute the energy, but it is more instructive to consider the approximations to molecular orbitals previously derived. Thus

$$\psi_{1s\sigma}(1) \sim \frac{\psi_a(1) + \psi_b(1)}{N_S} \quad \text{and} \quad \psi_{H_2} \sim \psi_{1s\sigma}(1)\psi_{1s\sigma}(2)$$

and so

$$\psi_{H_2} \sim \frac{1}{N_S{}^2} [\psi_a(1)\psi_b(2) + \psi_a(2)\psi_b(1) + \psi_a(1)\psi_a(2) + \psi_b(1)\psi_b(2)].$$

It is noted that the first two terms correspond to atomic or covalent limiting structures, and the last two to ionic structures. If the latter are suppressed, then the result is identical to that obtained for the symmetric state by the previous method. If the expression for ψ_{H_2} is used unchanged, however, then the ionic structures are much too heavily weighted, that is, equally with the covalent structures, and the predicted values for the equilibrium internuclear separation and dissociation energy, 0.85 Å and 2.65 ev respectively, are more in error than those derived from the previous atomic orbital calculation. Clearly, improved agreement between theory and experiment may be obtained by introducing a variable contribution of the ionic structures.

5.74 Consider now a slightly different way of building up the H_2 system: let the first electron be placed in a $1s\sigma$ molecular orbital and the second in the next higher $2p\sigma$ orbital. We found (see 5.62) for the latter orbital the approximate form

$$\psi_{2p\sigma}(1) \sim \frac{\psi_a(1) - \psi_b(1)}{N_A},$$

so that ψ'_{H_2}, the approximate wave function for this state of the H_2 system, may be given by

$$\psi_{H_2} \sim \psi_{1s\sigma}(1)\psi_{2p\sigma}(2)$$

or $$\psi'_{H_2} \sim \frac{1}{N_A N_S} [\psi_a(1)\psi_b(2) - \psi_a(2)\psi_b(1) - \psi_a(1)\psi_a(2) + \psi_b(1)\psi_b(2)].$$

If the ionic terms in ψ'_{H_2} are suppressed, the result is seen to be the same as the previously found ψ_A which describes the antisymmetric, anti-bonding state of energy E_A. The energy E_A is greater than the energy E_S of the bound state for all internuclear separations; we conclude, therefore, that in order to produce the most stable state of the hydrogen molecule, the molecular orbitals are to be completely filled in order, each accommodating two electrons with paired spins. This principle is generally valid for molecules and, as we have seen above, one may describe approximately the states of many-electron molecules in terms of the assignment of the electrons, two at a time with paired spins, to molecular orbitals in order of increasing energy.

5.75 In either formulation, in terms of atomic orbitals or in terms of approximate molecular orbitals, equivalent results are obtained. Although the use of molecular orbitals is perhaps intuitively more appealing in that the description of the physical system is somewhat less artificial, the atomic orbital approach has been widely used and the concepts it introduces have been extensively applied in the study of chemical bonds. In these terms, the covalent bond in the hydrogen molecule consists of a pair of electrons, with opposed spins, shared between the two nuclei; their behavior is described by bonding orbitals, one for each electron, the orbitals belonging to the two nuclei which are bonded. The actual system is intermediate (*i.e.*, "resonates") between two limiting states differing only in the interchange of electrons between nuclei, and the principal part of the bonding energy is given by the exchange integral related to this electronic interchange and proportional in magnitude very roughly to the extent of the "overlap" in space of the bonding orbitals of the two nuclei.

The Electron Pair Bond

5.76 The concepts introduced above in the study of the H_2^+ and H_2 systems may be extended generally to more complex systems. A covalent bond between two nuclei a and b is qualitatively the same as that between the two hydrogen nuclei in the hydrogen molecule, and the description in the preceding paragraph may be generally applied. Thus the stable molecule LiH may be described by the symmetric function ψ_{LiH} (we ignore for the present the major ionic contribution to the structure of LiH)

$$\psi_{\mathrm{LiH}} \sim \frac{\psi_{\mathrm{Li}}(1)\psi_{\mathrm{H}}(2) + \psi_{\mathrm{Li}}(2)\psi_{\mathrm{H}}(1)}{N_S}$$

representing resonance between two limiting states differing only in the assignment of electrons to nuclei, or in other words, sharing of the two electrons between the bonded nuclei. The complete description of the system is obtained by combining ψ_{LiH} with the antisymmetric spin function for two electrons, which represents pairing of the electron spins. The strength of the bond is determined mainly by the magnitude of the exchange integral for the electronic interchange and hence by the degree of overlap of the bonding orbitals. For lithium, ψ_{Li} must be a $2s$ wave function because the $1s$ orbitals are already occupied by the first two electrons in the completely filled K shell of the atom. The $2s$ wave function of lithium and the $1s$ orbital of hydrogen do not overlap as extensively, at the required internuclear separation, as the $1s$ orbitals on two hydrogen atoms, and thus the bond in LiH is not as strong as that in H_2.

5.77 Hydrogen atoms may be bonded similarly to other atoms with one valence electron and an available orbital. This class includes, of course, not only the alkali metals but also the halogens, as we shall see below. Furthermore, covalent bonding between any two univalent atoms, identical as in the diatomic hydrogen or chlorine molecules or different as in LiH or ICl, may be described in analogous terms. The actual bonds may not be entirely covalent because ionic contributions become large as the difference in inherent electronegativity of the two atoms increases.

5.78 Since the formation of a covalent electron pair bond involves pairing of the spins of the two electrons, electrons with already paired spins in an atom cannot generally participate in such bond formation. Consequently the maximum number of covalent bonds an atom may form (*i.e.*, its covalency) is generally equal to the number of electrons with unpaired spins within the atom. Thus the covalency of hydrogen or lithium is one; similarly fluorine, with the electronic configuration $1s^2 2s^2 2p^5$, has but a single unpaired electron and therefore a covalency of one. Oxygen has the configuration $1s^2 2s^2 2p^4$ and its total spin S is unity, indicating two unpaired electrons or that one $2p$ orbital is completely filled and the other two each half-filled; thus oxygen is divalent. Nitrogen has three unpaired electrons because each of the three $2p$ orbitals is half-filled; its normal covalency is three. In the case of carbon, the lowest electronic configuration is $1s^2 2s^2 2p^2$ indicating two unpaired electrons and a covalency of two, in disagreement with observation for by far the majority of the vast number of carbon compounds. The next lowest configuration, $1s^2 2s 2p^3$ arising from the "promotion" of an electron from the $2s$ to the $2p$ level, describes a state in which the total spin S is two, thus a state with four unpaired electrons occupying the orbitals $2s$, $2p_x$, $2p_y$, and $2p_z$. Carbon in this state should exhibit a covalency of four, and we conclude that in almost all of its compounds carbon does in fact possess this configuration. The energy required for the $2s \rightarrow 2p$ promotion is considerably less than that furnished by the formation of the two additional bonds, which incidentally are stronger than the bonds formed by the $2p$ orbitals without the participation of the $2s$ orbital. Promotion of this sort is to be expected whenever the energy gained (by the formation of more or stronger bonds) exceeds that required for the promotion; the perturbation of atomic energy levels in the process of molecule formation usually makes the energy required for promotion considerably less than the energy difference between the corresponding levels in the isolated gaseous atom. Promotion of an electron to a level of higher principal quantum number is not generally observed.

5.79 If the bonds in a molecule arise from the sharing of electrons with paired spins, and if all electrons originally unpaired in the atoms are involved in the binding, then clearly the molecule contains no unpaired electrons and its total spin must be zero. It has long been known that with but a handful of exceptions, chemical molecules contain an even number of electrons, and the exceptions, so-called "odd molecules," are usually unstable, particularly with respect to dimerization. Similarly most molecules are found to have zero spin but there are certain exceptions which imply that the simple description is not complete. The oxygen molecule, for example, stable as it is, seems to contain two unpaired electrons (see 5.91, 5.113).

5.80 When an atom forms more than one bond, as do oxygen, nitrogen, and carbon, the relative orientation of the several bonds may be determined experimentally from electron or X-ray diffraction studies or in some cases from spectroscopic data. The simple model we have developed for the covalent bond permits at least a qualitative treatment of the directional properties of these bonds. Let us consider oxygen, for which the bonding orbitals may be taken as the $2p_x$ and $2p_y$ orbitals, each of which contains an unpaired electron. A covalent bond formed by one of these orbitals and an appropriate orbital on another atom, say a $1s$ orbital on a hydrogen atom, is most stable when the exchange integral is a maximum and thus when the two orbitals overlap to the greatest extent. The two $2p$ orbitals have their maximum values along two orthogonal axes, the x and y axes in the present instance, and hence the overlap and bond stability should be maximum when the two bonds from the oxygen atom form a bond angle of 90°. The experimentally observed H—O—H bond angle in water is 105°, which implies that the very simple interpretation given here is incomplete.

5.81 In nitrogen we should expect to form three covalent bonds with the three $2p$ orbitals and appropriate orbitals on the other bonded atoms. Because the nitrogen orbitals exhibit their maximum values along the orthogonal x, y, and z axes, overlap and bond stability should be maximum in these directions and bond angles of 90° should also be expected for simple nitrogen compounds. Actually, the H—N—H bond angle in ammonia is about 108°, a discrepancy even greater than that observed for oxygen.

5.82 The carbon atom in which one electron has been promoted may form four simple covalent bonds using the orbitals $2s$, $2p_x$, $2p_y$, and $2p_z$. It might be supposed from the previous arguments that these would consist of three bonds along the rectangular axes and a fourth in a random direction; experience, however, contradicts this suggestion and requires, at least in such symmetrical compounds as methane or carbon tetrachloride, that all four bonds be equivalent in nature and relative orientation. The difficulty is resolved when it is realized that the particular set of orbitals mentioned is not unique, but an almost accidentally chosen set, and that equivalent orbitals taken as linear combinations of those described furnish equally good solutions to the wave mechanical problem. Thus we define four equivalent bonding orbitals, $\psi_1 \dots \psi_4$,

$$\psi_k = a_k\psi_{2s} + b_k\psi_{2p_x} + c_k\psi_{2p_y} + d_k\psi_{2p_z}; \qquad k = 1, 2, 3, 4,$$

which must be normalized and mutually orthogonal, and finally are so chosen that the overlap with a bonding orbital on a second atom, hydrogen for example, is a maximum. These requirements, fourteen in number, serve to determine four equivalent orbitals known as "hybrid" SP^3 orbitals which may be described in the form:

$$\psi_1 = \tfrac{1}{2}[\psi_{2s} + \psi_{2p_x} + \psi_{2p_y} + \psi_{2p_z}]$$
$$\psi_2 = \tfrac{1}{2}[\psi_{2s} + \psi_{2p_x} - \psi_{2p_y} - \psi_{2p_z}]$$
$$\psi_3 = \tfrac{1}{2}[\psi_{2s} - \psi_{2p_x} + \psi_{2p_y} - \psi_{2p_z}]$$
$$\psi_4 = \tfrac{1}{2}[\psi_{2s} - \psi_{2p_x} - \psi_{2p_y} + \psi_{2p_z}]$$

5.83 These orbitals exhibit their maximum values along axes tetrahedrally disposed in space; thus we expect the carbon atom, using these SP^3 orbitals, to form four bonds arranged at the tetrahedral angle of approximately 109° 28' (*i.e.*, $\cos^{-1} - \tfrac{1}{3}$). For symmetrical molecules like methane the experimentally observed values of the bond angles are all equal to this value; for unsymmetrically substituted methanes the bond angles may be slightly different, but rarely deviate by more than a very few degrees from the tetrahedral value.

5.84 We have seen that promotion in the carbon atom serves to explain the observed covalence of four and permits hybridization of the orbitals, which in turn explains the tetrahedral orientation of the four bonds. Still another important factor is seen to be involved if we investigate the actual magnitudes of the several orbitals and the strength of the bonds they form with an appropriate orbital from a second atom at a given interatomic distance. If the value of a $2s$ orbital is taken as unity, the same in all directions because the $2s$ orbital is spherically symmetrical, then the maximum value for a $2p$ orbital is $\sqrt{3}$ along its own axis, and its strength is zero in the plane perpendicular to this axis. Each hybrid SP^3 orbital, however, may be shown to have a strength or maximum value of 2 along its own bond axis, and this is the largest value obtainable from any combination of $2s$ and $2p$ orbitals. Thus an SP^3 orbital overlaps an orbital of another atom more extensively than any other possible orbital for a carbon atom, and those bonds involving the SP^3 orbitals of the carbon atom are therefore the strongest and the resulting molecules the most stable. Tetrahedral bonding should be the normal behavior of the carbon atom, and variations in the nature of the bonded atoms should generally change the bond angles slightly without significantly modifying the relative spatial relationships. This conclusion will need to be modified only in the case of multiple bonding between a carbon atom and a second atom. It is evident that the tetrahedral or near-tetrahedral bonding in carbon compounds will be responsible, in those cases where four different atoms or groups are bound to the carbon atom, for the existence of two mirror image nonsuperimposable configurations, and hence the nature of the binding is related to the phenomenon of optical isomerism in these compounds.

5.85 We have thus far implicitly restricted our considerations to single covalent bonds, although very many stable molecules containing multiple bonds are known, particularly among the compounds of carbon. Such structures may be treated qualitatively by methods analogous to those described above, and the concepts of promotion and hybridization are both useful. Let us consider ethylene: structurally, it possesses two joined carbon atoms each of which carries two hydrogen atoms; the six atoms all lie in one plane; the existence of *cis* and *trans* geometrical isomers of substituted ethylenes implies that the bond between the carbon atoms is very rigid and resistant to rotation. In terms of the approximate quantum mechanical treatment of binding, each carbon atom possesses four unpaired electrons (because promotion presumably is operative) and four bonding orbitals which may be combined with appropriate bonding orbitals on a second atom, hydrogen or carbon, to produce covalent or shared electron pair bonds, the strength of which is approximately proportional to the extent of spatial overlap of the orbitals involved. The orbitals need not be either the original $2s$, $2p_x$, $2p_y$, and $2p_z$ or the hybrid equivalent SP^3 orbitals, however; in fact, an alternative formulation is more convenient. To meet the minimum bonding requirements of the known structure we form three hybrid orbitals from the $2s$ and two $2p$ orbitals, $2p_x$ and $2p_y$, for example. These new combinations, normalized, mutually orthogonal, and chosen to give maximum overlap along their bond directions, are known as hybrid SP^2 orbitals. They may be expressed in the form:

$$\psi_1 = \frac{1}{\sqrt{3}}\, \psi_{2s} + \frac{\sqrt{2}}{\sqrt{3}}\, \psi_{2p_x}$$

$$\psi_2 = \frac{1}{\sqrt{3}}\, \psi_{2s} - \frac{1}{\sqrt{6}}\, \psi_{2p_x} + \frac{1}{\sqrt{2}}\, \psi_{2p_y}$$

$$\psi_3 = \frac{1}{\sqrt{3}}\, \psi_{2s} - \frac{1}{\sqrt{6}}\, \psi_{2p_x} - \frac{1}{\sqrt{2}}\, \psi_{2p_y}.$$

Their directions of maximum strength are equally spaced at 120° angles in a plane, and their maximum strength is $\frac{1}{\sqrt{3}} + \sqrt{2} = 1.992$ as compared with the value 2.000 for the hybrid SP^3 orbital. These SP^2 orbitals suffice to bond two hydrogen atoms, with their $1s$ orbitals, to each carbon atom and the two carbon atoms together to give the basic ethylene skeleton.

5.86 Each carbon atom has one more valence electron and one orbital, the $2p_z$ orbital, which exhibits its maximum strength along the z axis perpendicular to the plane of the three already established bonds. If the $2p_z$ orbitals on the two carbon atoms are used for the formation of a second link between the atoms, these overlap to the maximum extent when their axes are parallel, and the most stable configuration then is one in which all six atoms are coplanar and the structure resists rotation about the C—C bond. These are precisely the structural features already described.

5.87 The bonds formed by the use of the SP^2 orbitals are sometimes referred to as σ bonds and the bond involving the $2p_z$ orbitals is termed a π bond. The σ bond is rather stronger than a π bond (1.992 as compared to 1.732 as the maximum strength of the orbital), and this may be interpreted as involving a greater concentration of electrons between the nuclei in a σ bond than in a π bond. In addition, the electron density exhibits cylindrical symmetry about a σ bond but is concentrated in regions above and below but not in or symmetrically around a π bond. Because the π bond between carbon atoms is weaker than the σ bond, the energy of a double bond is less than twice that of a single bond: the values for C═C and C—C are respectively 145 and 80.5 kcal. In ethylene itself, the H—C—H and H—C═C angles both are found experimentally to be equal to 120°, but in substituted ethylenes the corresponding angles may not be exactly equal to each other, the R—C—R bond generally being the smaller. The difference may be due to variation in repulsive forces between the atoms or groups joined to the carbon atom; furthermore, a more refined treatment of the bonding problem indicates that the three hybrid SP^2 orbitals need not be equivalent, but the $2s$ contribution may be concentrated in the carbon-carbon bond, leaving the carbon-hydrogen bonds very much like SP^3 tetrahedral bonds with their characteristic tetrahedral angle smaller than 120°.

5.88 An analogous treatment may be applied to the triple bond in acetylene or its derivatives. The acetylene molecule is linear or cylindrically symmetrical, and consists of two bonded carbon atoms each of which in turn is bonded to a terminal hydrogen atom. These minimum structural features require for each carbon atom two bonds and therefore two bonding orbitals; we choose these as hybrid orbitals made up from $2s$ and $2p_z$, say, by the application of the same requirements and method as in the previous cases. The SP hybrid orbitals so derived may be described in the form

$$\psi_1 = \frac{1}{\sqrt{2}} (\psi_{2s} + \psi_{2p_z})$$

$$\psi_2 = \frac{1}{\sqrt{2}} (\psi_{2s} - \psi_{2p_z}).$$

These orbitals have their maximum strength $\left(\frac{1 + \sqrt{3}}{\sqrt{2}} = 1.932 \right)$ in opposite directions along the z axis, in other words, at a bond angle of 180°. The bonds formed with the SP orbitals and appropriate orbitals on a second atom may be termed σ bonds like those involving SP^2 orbitals. In the case of acetylene itself, each carbon forms one bond with a hydrogen atom and a second with the other carbon atom, thus providing the basic structure of the molecule with the symmetrical properties mentioned earlier.

5.89 The remaining electrons on the carbon atoms occupy the $2p_x$ and $2p_y$ orbitals which cause them to spread out from the molecular axis to some extent. The orbitals on the two atoms overlap to produce π bonds. There is no preferred plane of electron concentration because the x and y directions, perpendicular to the bond axis, contribute equally so that the electron density is cylindrically symmetrical. The strength of either of these π bonds is less than that of a σ bond, and in addition, because each electron distribution repels somewhat the other and decreases its binding power, the combined strength of the two π bonds is less than that of a $\sigma - \pi$ double bond. The bond energy of C$\equiv$C is 198 kcal., to be compared with the values previously given for the C$=$C and C$-$C bonds.

5.90 We are led to the concept that a double bond consists of a σ bond and a weaker π bond, and a triple bond of a σ bond (weaker than that in the double bond) and two π bonds. This model, developed for carbon compounds, may be extended to other atoms as well; thus the double bonds C$=$N, C$=$O, N$=$N, N$=$O, and O$=$O are similarly treated with obvious modification arising from the different numbers of electrons available on the atoms. Whereas each atom in the C$=$C bond carries two electron pairs each forming a bond to another atom or group, the nitrogen atom in these structures carries one unshared pair of electrons and one shared pair which constitutes a covalent bond to an atom or group; the oxygen atom in general bears two unshared electron pairs and is thus not bonded to any other atom. The unshared electron pair on the nitrogen probably occupies the $2s$ orbital and the bonding or valence orbitals are therefore the three $2p$ orbitals with their maxima directed along the three axes at right angles one to another. If the double bond is imagined to result from distortion of the normal bonding directions, tetrahedral for carbon but at right angles for nitrogen, then the C=C bond is more strained and less stable than either the C=N or N=N bond. The orbitals used by the oxygen atom are also $2p$ orbitals and similar conclusions may be drawn. In either case, the double bond is rigid, but of course the lack of substituents (other than unshared electron pairs) on the oxygen atom prevents isomerism in the oxygen compounds.

5.91 The O=O double bond is unique in that no other atoms are bound to the two concerned in the double bond, cylindrical symmetry necessarily results, and the torsional rigidity of the double bond is a meaningless concept. Furthermore, the orbitals available for both bonding and accommodating the unshared electrons may be so selected that the binding electrons have parallel spins instead of the opposed spins commonly required. It is observed experimentally that the ground state of the oxygen molecule is a triplet state, that is, its total spin is unity, corresponding to a total of two unpaired spins, and oxygen is a paramagnetic substance.

5.92 The oxygen atom may not participate in triple bond formation; with the electrons and orbitals available, only two bonds are possible. Nitrogen, however, may form triple bonds like those of carbon. As we have seen, the strain in C≡N or N≡N bonds is less than in C≡C bonds, and the bond is stronger. In fact, the N≡N bond is so extraordinarily strong that molecular nitrogen is almost inert in a chemical sense, and chemical reactions which produce molecular nitrogen usually do so with the liberation of very large quantities of energy. Because the only additional bonding possible in the C≡N systems attaches another atom to the carbon by means of an SP orbital with its maximum directed out from the carbon but along the triple bond axis, all such structures will exhibit cylindrical symmetry, *i.e.*, a linear configuration.

5.93 Let us now return to the consideration of single covalent bonds of the period lithium to neon. The lowest electron configuration of beryllium is $1s^2 2s^2$, which implies that beryllium should be quite inert chemically; the actual existence of numerous beryllium compounds indicates strongly that promotion occurs to give the configuration $1s^2 2s 2p$, the $2p$ orbital being any one of the three equivalent orbitals. It is to be expected that beryllium will use the two hybrid SP orbitals in bond formation; these orbitals overlap those of the second atom most extensively in directions 180° apart, *i.e.*, in opposite directions along the same line, and so such compounds as BeH_2, the covalent beryllium halides, and beryllium alkyl compounds should be linear with the R—Be—R bond angle equal to 180°. Analogous results are observed for the heavier but similar mercury atom which forms linear halide molecules X—Hg—X and X—Hg—Hg—X. The radical CH_2 probably has a similar linear structure, using hybrid SP orbitals rather than simple p orbitals which would give an angular configuration like that of the water molecule. In the CH_2 radical the remaining two unshared electrons on the carbon atom then must occupy the two $2p$ orbitals not used for bonding between carbon and hydrogen atoms.

5.94 The boron atom possesses the lowest electronic configuration $1s^2 2s^2 2p$;

experience here also suggests promotion, which will permit a covalence of three instead of one. The configuration $1s^22s2p^2$ provides the orbitals $2s$, $2p_x$, and $2p_y$, say, which may be hybridized to the planar SP^2 orbitals previously described. These three orbitals then may be used to form three covalent bonds with other atoms such as fluorine; the three bonds will be coplanar and the bond angles will all be 120° unless the bonded atoms or groups are different and their several interactions not all equivalent. The molecule boron trimethyl, $B(CH_3)_3$, is known experimentally to be flat with three equal bond angles of 120° each.

5.95 Since the boron atom has but three valence electrons, no more than three normal bonds may be formed; and the bonds involving these SP^2 orbitals are necessarily somewhat weaker than tetrahedral SP^3 bonds would be. We shall see later that a fourth bond may be formed with another atom if the latter is able to provide both electrons to be shared. The four bonds then are the stronger tetrahedral bonds and the molecule may be extremely stable; examples are furnished by the ammonia addition compounds of $B(CH_3)_3$ or BF_3, in which the nitrogen atom contributes an unshared pair of electrons to form the fourth bond about the boron atom. Physically, it may be imagined that the approach of the unshared electron pair toward one face of the planar bonded boron structure forces back the shared pair bonds to yield a pyramidal structure in which the F—B—F angles are all equal and not greatly different from the F—B—N angle, so that all four are near the tetrahedral value.

5.96 The radical CH_3 might be supposed to have the flat structure described above, in which each bond consists of overlapping $1s$ (from hydrogen) and hybrid SP^2 (from carbon) orbitals containing a pair of electrons with opposed spins. The carbon atom possesses one additional electron, however, which occupies the remaining $2p_z$ orbital and thus is located outside the CH_3 plane with equal probability on either side. Because this unshared electron interacts repulsively with the electrons in the C—H bonds, the latter may be forced back slightly to produce a flat pyramidal arrangement with the unshared electron at the apex. Such a structure corresponds to the partial inclusion of the $2p_z$ orbital in the hybrid orbitals; if the hybridization includes all the orbitals completely, which is unlikely, then a tetrahedral structure is to be expected with hydrogen atoms at three corners and the single unshared electron at the fourth corner.

5.97 The previous discussion of the bonding of nitrogen and oxygen now needs to be re-examined. The use of $2p$ orbitals alone leads to predicted bond angles of 90° in both water and ammonia, but experiment gives 105° and 108°, respectively. These larger angles, near the tetrahedral value, suggest that bonding in these molecules involves some promotion of a $2s$ electron to a $2p$ state and a partial contribution of the s orbital to the hybrid orbitals actually used in bonding. If the promotion is complete in oxygen, for example, the configuration becomes $1s^22s2p^5$, or in an expanded form, $1s^22s2p_x^22p_y^22p_z$, and there are still but two unpaired electrons. We may exclude the filled $2p_x$ and

$2p_y$ orbitals and obtain as the appropriate hybrid bonding orbitals the two linear SP orbitals which produce a bond angle of 180°. In these terms, partial promotion will increase the bond angle from 90° but certainly not all the way to 180°. One may alternatively include in the hybridization all the orbitals and then use two of the four SP^3 hybrid orbitals to accommodate the unshared electron pairs on the oxygen atom; in this case, the expected bond angle is the tetrahedral angle. In the same way for nitrogen, complete promotion produces the electron configuration $1s^2 2s 2p_x 2p_y 2p_z^2$, and if the completely filled $2p_z$ orbital is excluded, then the strongest available bonding orbitals are the hybrid SP^2 orbitals with coplanar bonds 120° apart. Thus promotion and hybridization tend to flatten the right-angle structure predicted from consideration of the $2p$ orbitals above to produce larger bond angles. Again as for oxygen, all s and p orbitals may be included in hybridization and the resultant hybrid tetrahedral SP^3 orbitals used, three in the bonding of nitrogen to hydrogen and one to accommodate the unshared electron pair. The resultant structure in either view is similar to that described earlier for the CH_3 radical except that the fourth position is occupied by the unshared pair instead of by a single electron.

5.98 Promotion in nitrogen and oxygen is not complete, however, because the energy required is larger than for the carbon atom. Furthermore, for carbon, promotion increases the covalence from two to four, but for nitrogen and oxygen, promotion cannot increase the covalence: the configuration of nitrogen $1s^2 2s^2 2p^3$ with three unpaired electrons becomes after promotion $1s^2 2s 2p^4$, also with three unpaired electrons, and similarly $1s^2 2s^2 2p^4$ for oxygen becomes by promotion $1s^2 2s 2p^5$, and each configuration exhibits two unpaired electrons and therefore a covalence of two. Thus no additional energy may be gained by the formation of a larger number of bonds by the atom after promotion.

5.99 It seems clear that for both nitrogen and oxygen, promotion occurs to some extent, but the tendency to form the strongest bonds from SP^3 hybrid orbitals is countered by the tendency to place the unshared pair or pairs of electrons in the most stable s orbitals, making these unavailable for bonding. The decreased availability of the s orbital as compared to the p orbitals suggests that SP^3 rather than SP (for oxygen) or SP^2 (for nitrogen) orbitals are the proper ones to consider in predicting bond angles. Thus, the angles in water and ammonia are not quite as large as the tetrahedral angle, and considerably less than the maximum (180° for water or 120° for ammonia).

5.100 The approximate conclusions based on exchange integrals and orbital overlap alone may be modified by more detailed calculations. For example, consideration of the interaction between the two hydrogen atoms in the water molecule shows a repulsive force operative which serves to increase the H—O—H bond angle over the value 90° predicted for simple bonding with $2p$ orbitals. Similarly, repulsion among the several atoms bonded to a nitrogen atom may bring about a slight "opening up" of the molecule and cause bond angles to exceed the predicted 90° value. If the bonded atoms are not all alike, then the mutual repulsions may differ and the bond angles in the substituted ammonia molecule will not all be the same. In the heavier analogs of water (hydrogen sulfide and hydrogen selenide) and of ammonia (phosphine and arsine), the hydrogen atoms are farther apart and bear somewhat smaller effective nuclear charges. In these molecules, then, the repulsive force is less and the bond angle not increased so much over the expected right angle. The experimental values are respectively 92° and 91° for the water analogs and 93° and 92° for those of ammonia. In the near tetrahedral configuration with the oxygen or nitrogen atom at the center, two positions in the former case and one in the latter are occupied by unshared pairs of electrons. Optical isomerism is not observed for the asymmetrically substituted ammonia compounds, however, because the electron pair is not sufficiently rigidly located.

5.101 The atoms of the third period of the periodic table possess five $3d$ orbitals in addition to their $3s$ and $3p$ orbitals. They may therefore exhibit covalences greater than four. In the earlier empirical picture of covalent binding based on the concept of the stability of the octet arrangement, this behavior was viewed as a distinct phenomenon and referred to as "expansion of the valence shell." In terms of the picture here developed, however, covalences larger than four are entirely natural for atoms which may possess more than four unpaired electrons. Thus the molecule PBr_5 probably contains five covalent bonds involving s, p, and d orbitals of the M electron shell. Very many similar compounds, however, involve bonds to highly electronegative atoms, which implies considerable ionic character in the bonds and perhaps only four covalent bonds are actually present. This type of molecule, of which examples are furnished by PF_5 or SF_6, possesses a composite structure or resonates among several limiting structures, each with perhaps four shared pair links and one or two ionic bonds.

5.102 An atom of the fourth or of a heavier period may also form bonds involving s, p, and d orbitals of its valence shell; such seems to be the case for $MoCl_5$, for example, and for charged complexes such as $SnBr_6^{2-}$. The use of d orbitals from the shell next below the valence shell, however, is much more important and widespread. These d orbitals generally have energies not greatly different from those of the s and p orbitals of next higher principal quantum number, and therefore hybridization is quite probable and may lead to very strong bonding orbitals. The inclusion of d orbitals is quite common in structures in which coordination numbers larger than four are observed. Although detailed discussion of such systems will be given in subsequent sections (see Ch. 6), some of the hybrid orbitals are included in Table 5.6, which lists a number of coordination numbers and bond arrangements.

5.103 Not all of the theoretically possible bond arrangements and hybrid orbitals are actually observed in nature. Those forming the strongest bonds are preferred, and the most common hybrid bonding orbitals seem to be SP^3, DSP^2, and D^2SP^3 with relative strengths of 2.000, 2.694, and 2.923, respectively. Strength in chemical bonds and shortness go together, and we should

TABLE 5.6

Hybrid Bonding Orbitals and Bond Directions *

Coordination Number	Hybrid Orbitals	Bond Arrangement
2	SP	Linear
	P^2	Angular (90°)
3	SP^2	Trigonal plane
	P^3	Trigonal pyramid
4	SP^3	Tetrahedral
	DSP^2	Tetragonal plane
	D^4	Tetragonal pyramid
5	DSP^3	Bipyramid
	D^2SP^2	Tetragonal pyramid
	D^3P^2	Pentagonal plane
	D^5	Pentagonal pyramid
6	D^2SP^3	Octahedral
	D^4SP	Trigonal prism
	D^3P^3	Trigonal antiprism
7	D^3SP^3	Distorted octahedron
	D^4SP^2	Distorted trigonal prism
8	D^4SP^3	Dodecahedron
	D^5SP^2	Face-centered prism

* Taken from Eyring, Walter and Kimball, *Quantum Chemistry*, John Wiley and Sons, Inc., N.Y., p. 231.

expect to observe some relation between covalent bond radii and the types of bonds used. In a previous section (see 4.30) it was pointed out that normal single bond radii and tetrahedral radii are identical for the lighter electronegative elements, but for the heavier elements of the same groups (*i.e.*, As—Br and Sb—I) the tetrahedral radii are somewhat smaller than the normal single bond radii. We conclude that the normal bonding with these atoms is not completely tetrahedral and the full strength of SP^3 bonds is not used. Secondly, it was observed that octahedral and square radii are generally nearly equal and different from tetrahedral radii: the difference between strengths of the DSP^2 and D^2SP^3 hybrid orbitals is fairly small, but each of these is quite appreciably stronger than the SP^3 tetrahedral orbital. We should, then, expect square and octahedral radii to be smaller than tetrahedral radii; this is true for Ag and Au, but the evidence is not conclusive because the comparison involves different oxidation states. A rather larger number of examples is known in which the octahedral radius exceeds the tetrahedral radius. In these, of which structures involving the +4 oxidation states of Ti, Zr, Sn, Pb, Se, and Te are examples, the bonding involves not D^2SP^3 but SP^3D^2 hybrid orbitals, that is, the use of higher d orbitals of the valence shell itself, which are relatively more energetic, so that the bonds are somewhat less stable and longer than would otherwise be expected.

5.104 The hybrid orbitals may be used to form covalent bonds or to accommodate unshared pairs, which in some respects behave like and may be directed like covalent bonds. It is generally observed that triatomic molecules are linear if the central atom bears no unshared pairs

$$O = C = O, \quad S = C = S, \quad N^- = N^+ = O, \quad N^- = N^+ = N^-$$

and angular if an unshared pair is present

$$\overset{H}{\underset{H-O:}{|}}, \quad \overset{H}{\underset{H-S:}{|}}, \quad \overset{O}{\underset{O-N}{|^-}} .$$

It is observed also that molecules of the type MX_3 are planar if M possesses no unshared electron pairs

and pyramidal if an electron pair is present on M

The importance of unshared pairs in determining the choice of hybrid orbitals and resulting molecular geometry is thus quite evident.

Resonance

5.105 In the previous study of the H_2^+ and H_2 systems we found that the actual structure may be pictured as a superposition of two distinct but more or less equivalent structures differing in the details of electron assignment. The energy of the system is less than that of either of the so-called resonance structures by an amount which may be called the resonance energy. The resonance energy is associated with the processes or motions which convert one resonance structure to the other. In the case of simple systems like the hydrogen molecule or the methane molecule, the phenomenon involves only the interchange of indistinguishable electrons between essentially identical structures, and the resonance is more often referred to merely as exchange, and the resonance energy as the exchange energy. In more complex systems, however, an analogous phenomenon exists in which the equivalent resonating structures differ in the actual placement of electron pair bonds, unshared electron pairs, or sometimes unpaired electrons, relative to the nuclear skeleton. Thus the structure of ozone may be assumed to involve resonance among four structures described by the usual diagrams as shown. Each line joining two oxygen atoms represents an

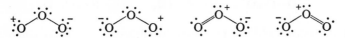

electron pair bond of the type discussed previously. It is clear that the first two of these four structures have identical energies, differing effectively only in the labeling of identical oxygen nuclei; the structures of the second pair also have identical energies for the same reason. The energies of the two pairs are very nearly the same as well, but this is not evident from the structures shown. The O—O bond distances are slightly different in the four hypothetical resonance structures, ranging approximately from 1.10 Å for a double bond to 1.48 Å for a single bond; the experimentally observed value of the distance between the center and either terminal atom in the actual molecule is 1.26 ± 0.02 Å.

5.106 The four diagrams shown for ozone represent limiting structures which may be expected to make contributions to the actual structure of the molecule. In quantum mechanical terms, the wave function for the actual molecule may be approximated as a sum of terms, each being a fraction of the wave function of one of the resonance forms. If the approximation is to be at all valid, clearly all of the resonance forms must be not greatly different from the actual structure nor from each other: thus they must have equal or nearly equal energies and nearly identical nuclear configurations. Close approximations cannot be expected if the structures differ markedly in charge distributions or in the numbers of unpaired electrons. The larger the number of equivalent resonance forms which may contribute, the better the description of the actual state furnished by the superposition of the resonance forms; this latter generalization is sometimes loosely held to predict greater stability for the system made up of the larger number of resonating structures, and may be of use in predicting which of several possible reaction paths may be favored in a chemical change.

5.107 It should be emphasized that the resonance concept is an arbitrary one, chosen for the sake of convenience in representing the actual states of molecules in terms of conventional bonding diagrams. Just as the molecular orbital approach for the H_2^+ and H_2 systems led to quantitative results without mention of exchange integrals or resonance between limiting states, so also may detailed yet approximate treatments of more complex systems be undertaken without assuming the resonance concept. As a practical matter, however, such treatments are quite difficult, the quantitative results are generally of very slight interest, and useful qualitative conclusions as to structure and stability may be developed with the use of the resonance concept. Thus, for ozone, although no one of the structures shown would be expected to represent a very stable molecule, the combination or superposition gives a moderately stable result; the indicated polar structures combine to give an essentially nonpolar resulting molecule, and the actual bond distances are intermediate between the limits corresponding to the structures of the resonance forms. Similarly for carbon dioxide, for which we may write the resonance structures

$$:\!\ddot{O}\!=\!C\!=\!\ddot{O}:, \quad :\!\overset{-}{\underset{\cdot\cdot}{O}}\!-\!C\!\equiv\!O\overset{+}{:}, \quad \text{and} \quad :\!\overset{+}{O}\!\equiv\!C\!-\!\overset{-}{\underset{\cdot\cdot}{O}}:,$$

of which the second and third are exactly equivalent and make equal contributions presumably somewhat less important than that of the first structure, we expect a stable nonpolar molecule with the two C—O bond distances equal and probably slightly shorter than the usual C=O value of 1.22 A (the experimental value for carbon dioxide is 1.15 Å). As a third example consider cyanogen, $(CN)_2$, for which four resonance structures have been suggested:

$$:\overset{-}{\underset{\cdot\cdot}{N}}{=}C{=}C{=}\overset{+}{N}:$$

$$:N{\equiv}C{-}C{\equiv}N: \quad :N{=}C{=}C{=}N:$$

$$:\overset{+}{N}{=}C{=}C{=}\overset{-}{\underset{\cdot\cdot}{N}}:$$

The second structure contains unpaired electrons not present in the other forms; its contribution must be quite small and it may be ignored. The last two are equivalent, differing only in the labeling of the atomic kernels (here we ignore the possibility of having different isotopes of a given element in the several locations the element may occupy in the molecule); these two differ from the first two quite markedly in their charge distribution. Only the first structure shows each atom with a stable octet, that is, with all the orbitals in its valence shell suitably occupied. From these observations we conclude that the first structure is the most important and predict that the linear molecule is symmetrical and nonpolar, the C—C distance is less than the usual single bond distance (1.54 Å) but greater than the double bond value (1.33 Å), and the C—N distance greater than that in HCN, for example (1.05 Å), or in other structures containing the —C≡N system. Experiment gives 1.37 Å for the C—C distance and 1.16 Å for the C—N distance.

5.108 Let us now consider the resonance energy. For this we choose benzene, a particularly important molecule which is characteristic of all organic aromatic molecules in resonance energy. The five important resonance structures for benzene are the two equivalent Kekulé structures (a) and the three equivalent Dewar structures (b).

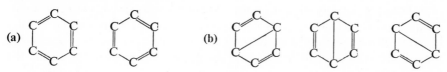

Each carbon atom in these structures is bonded to a hydrogen atom not shown. The Dewar structures are of slightly higher energy than the Kekulé structures (because of the longer covalent bonds involved) and to a first approximation may be neglected. Other covalent structures involving crossed bonds may be ignored, and structures with larger numbers of long covalent bonds or with ionic features arising from charge transfers possess considerably higher energies and therefore make negligible contribution to the ground state of the benzene molecule. If, therefore, we take the Kekulé structures as the only contributing resonance structures, the resonance energy is the difference between the energy of one of these and the actual energy of the benzene molecule. From thermochemical data it may be shown that 1308 kcal. must be supplied to rupture all the chemical bonds in benzene, but the energy of the hypothetical cyclohexatriene Kekulé structure is estimated from established bond energies to be about

1266 kcal. (98.2 kcal. for each of six C—H bonds, 145 kcal. for each of three C=C bonds, and 80.5 kcal. for each of three C—C bonds). The resonance energy of the benzene molecule is thus 42 kcal. and is seen to be a significant fraction of the total; in fact, the relative stability and hence the saturated character of benzene and other aromatic systems as compared to aliphatic unsaturated systems is accounted for just by the resonance here described between the two Kekulé structures.

5.109 Although the detailed quantum mechanical treatment of the benzene molecule is not within our scope, it is of interest to mention very sketchily several points involved. Very approximately, each carbon atom, using SP^2 hybrid orbitals, forms bonds with its own hydrogen atom and its two neighboring carbon atoms in the six-membered ring. This minimal structure determines a symmetrical, hexagonal, planar configuration. Each carbon atom then has one more electron to accommodate and one more $2p$ orbital for use. In a valence bond approach to the problem, the $2p$ orbitals are taken in adjacent pairs, overlapping to produce π bonds containing the two electrons with paired spins. The two independent ways of selecting three pairs of adjacent atoms, that is, of placing the three π bonds, correspond to the two Kekulé structures. An approximate quantitative treatment of the problem then gives the energy of the system as a sum of a Coulomb term and an exchange term; the energy of one of the resonance forms is found to be equal to the sum of the same Coulomb term and a slightly different exchange term. If α represents the exchange integral for exchange of electrons between the $2p$ orbitals on the two adjacent atoms, then the difference of the exchange terms or the resonance energy is found to be equal to 0.9α if only two Kekulé structures are considered, or 1.1α if the Dewar structures are taken into account as well. Thus the exchange integral α must be approximately 40 kcal./mole. As would be expected, analogous treatments of other aromatic systems lead to expressions for their resonance energies in terms of the same exchange integral α. Such calculations have been made for a large number of molecules, and the approximate agreement among the various calculated values of the exchange integral α lends support to the basic resonance concept involved.

5.110 An alternative molecular orbital approach may also be used in which we do not seek to localize the last six electrons in π bonds as above, but rather accommodate them in the molecule as a whole in molecular orbitals made up of all six of the available atomic orbitals. The molecular orbitals are found to correspond to the energies, in increasing order, $Q + 2\beta$, $Q + \beta$, $Q + \beta$, $Q - \beta$, $Q - \beta$, $Q - 2\beta$, where Q is a Coulomb term and β an exchange integral similar to α. Since each molecular orbital may accommodate two electrons with paired spins, feeding six electrons into these orbitals gives a structure of energy $6Q + 8\beta$. A similar treatment of a cyclohexatriene Kekulé structure gives the molecular orbitals of energies $Q + \beta$, $Q + \beta$, $Q + \beta$, $Q - \beta$, $Q - \beta$, $Q - \beta$, and the structure then must have the energy $6Q + 6\beta$. Clearly the resonance energy is equal to 2β and the actual structure is more stable than the

Kekulé structure, because β, like α and exchange integrals on different atoms generally, is negative. Again, analogous calculations for a variety of aromatic molecules give consistent values for β in the vicinity of 20 kcal.

5.111 Although the valence bond and molecular orbital methods give consistent results in this study of resonance, they are in a sense complementary. The former method, as here applied, ignores ionic contributions entirely and, with the two Kekulé structures alone, cannot explain the characteristic directing influence of substituents. The latter method, just as it does in the hydrogen molecule, exaggerates the contribution of the ionic structures implicit in the independent motion of electrons from atom to atom in the molecule. In general, resonance in molecular systems may involve to arbitrary extents both covalent and ionic structures, provided these have nearly equal energies, quite similar nuclear configurations, and equal numbers of unpaired electrons.

The Three-Electron Bond

5.112 The helium molecule ion, He_2^+, is stable with respect to dissociation; its dissociation energy and equilibrium internuclear separation are, respectively, 58 kcal./mole and 1.09 Å, as determined from spectroscopic data. The system consists of two helium nuclei and three electrons, and these latter may be said to constitute the chemical bond between the helium nuclei. The system resembles the H_2^+ system rather closely, and may be imagined to involve resonance between two principal limiting structures

$$He: \quad \cdot He^+ \quad \text{and} \quad He\cdot^+ \quad :He$$

An approximate treatment on this basis predicts a stable molecular configuration, with a symmetric wave function for the ground state just as was found for the simpler H_2^+ and H_2 systems. Analogous exchange phenomena are evident, and the bond, arising principally from this exchange or resonance, is approximately as strong as the one-electron bond in H_2^+ or about one half as strong as the electron pair bond in the hydrogen molecule.

5.113 One- and three-electron bonds are possible only between identical nuclei or nuclei of nearly identical electronegativities, because only in these circumstances do the postulated limiting structures arising from electron transfer possess essentially equal energies. Resonance in an electron pair bond, however, is possible whether the bound nuclei are alike or different because the electron interchange leaves equivalent resonance structures. It is not surprising, then, that only a very few one- and three-electron bonds are known, but literally thousands upon thousands of compounds contain two-electron bonds. In addition to H_2^+, the boranes may furnish examples of one-electron bonds, although even this seems unlikely. Three-electron bonds are probably present in such structures as :O⋮⋮O:, :N⩵O: and :Ö—Cl⋮⋮Ö: (two equivalent covalent resonance forms possible); such molecules, which possess unpaired electrons, are paramagnetic and most of them are colored. All three kinds of bonds owe most of their stability to the exchange of electrons which may be said to be shared between the two bonded atoms, and all three bonds are properly termed covalent.

Covalent Binding: Types of Bonds and General Properties

Normal, Coordinate, and Polar Covalent Bonds

5.114 We have seen (sec. 5.52) that the usual covalent bond may be supposed to consist of an electron pair, with matching spins, occupying two overlapping orbitals, one on each of the bonded atoms. The strength of the bond is roughly proportional to the degree of overlap of the two orbitals, and is believed to be due principally to the exchange of the two electrons between the orbitals. In a crude picture, the two somewhat positively charged nuclei are attracted to the negatively charged electronic concentration between them; the two electrons, although similarly charged, are permitted to stay close together because their spins are paired.

5.115 In the covalent bonds of such simple structures as those of hydrogen, water, or saturated hydrocarbons, each atom of the bonded pair contributes one electron to the pair which constitutes the bond. Such bonds are termed *normal* covalent bonds and are perhaps the most common chemical bonds. The concept of shared electron pair bonds does not demand, however, that each atom contribute one electron, but only that an electron pair be available to occupy the overlapping orbitals contributed by the bonded atoms. Thus, there exists a class of covalent bonds in which both electrons may be presumed to have been contributed by one atom, the donor, and the second atom merely accepts a share in the electron pair, making available, of course, a suitable orbital for the bonding. Such a bond is called a *coordinate* covalent link; it has also been

GENERAL REFERENCES

CARTMELL and FOWLES, *Valency and Molecular Structure*, Academic Press, Inc., New York, 1956, Part II.

COULSON, *Valence*, The Clarendon Press, Oxford, 1952, Ch. I, VIII, XII.

DUSHMAN, "Quantum Theory of Atomic Spectra and Atomic Structure," Ch. II in Vol. I, *Treatise on Physical Chemistry*, edited by Taylor and Glasstone, D. Van Nostrand Company, Inc., New York, 1942.

EYRING, WALTER and KIMBALL, *Quantum Chemistry*, John Wiley and Sons, Inc., New York, 1947, Ch. XII, XIII.

GLASSTONE, *Theoretical Chemistry*, D. Van Nostrand Company, Inc., New York, 1944, Ch. III.

PALMER, *Valency, Classical and Modern*, Cambridge University Press, London, 1944, Ch. I, II, IV, V, VI.

PAULING, *The Nature of the Chemical Bond*, 2nd Edition, Cornell University Press, Ithaca, N.Y., 1940, Ch. II, III, VII, VIII, IX, XI.

PAULING and WILSON, *Introduction to Quantum Mechanics*, McGraw-Hill Book Company, Inc., New York, 1935, Ch. XII.

PITZER, *Quantum Chemistry*, Prentice-Hall, Inc., New York, 1953, Ch. 8.

RICE and TELLER, *The Structure of Matter*, John Wiley and Sons, Inc., New York, 1949, Ch. 7.

RICE, *Electronic Structure and Chemical Binding*, McGraw-Hill Book Company, Inc., New York, 1940, Ch. XII, XVI, XVIII.

SIDGWICK, *Some Physical Properties of the Covalent Link in Chemistry*, Cornell University Press, Ithaca, N.Y., 1933.

WELLS, *Structural Inorganic Chemistry*, 2nd Edition, Oxford University Press, London, 1950, Ch. I–V incl.

called a *dative* link, or a *semi-polar* bond, the latter name referring to the usual asymmetry of charge distribution resulting from the unequal contribution of electrons by the bonded atoms.

5.116 The stable compound formed by the union of ammonia and boron trifluoride is presumed to result from the formation of a coordinate covalent link between the nitrogen and boron atoms, the nitrogen atom serving as donor and the boron atom as acceptor.

$$
\begin{array}{ccccc}
\text{H} & & \text{F} & & \text{H} \quad \text{F} \\
| & & | & & | \quad\quad | \\
\text{H—N:} & + & \text{B—F} & \rightarrow & \text{H—N}^+\text{:}^-\text{B—F} \\
| & & | & & | \quad\quad | \\
\text{H} & & \text{F} & & \text{H} \quad \text{F}
\end{array}
$$

In the product molecule the nitrogen atom necessarily bears a positive charge and the boron atom a negative charge; thus, in addition to the covalent bond between the two, there is a strong ionic attraction, and the total bond may be considered almost as a charged double bond. Now the product molecule may be equally well considered as having resulted from the formation of a normal covalent bond between the two energetic ionic species.

$$
\begin{array}{ccccc}
\text{H} & & \text{F} & & \text{H} \quad \text{F} \\
| & & | & & | \quad\quad | \\
\text{H—N}^+\cdot & + & \cdot^-\text{B—F} & \rightarrow & \text{H—N}^+\text{:}^-\text{B—F} \\
| & & | & & | \quad\quad | \\
\text{H} & & \text{F} & & \text{H} \quad \text{F}
\end{array}
$$

Or suppose by some means we bring together a donor atom (one with an unshared electron pair) bearing a negative charge and an acceptor atom bearing a positive charge; the molecule produced by coordinate bond formation will be indistinguishable from that resulting from the formation of a normal covalent bond between the appropriate neutral atoms or radicals.

$$
\begin{array}{ccccccc}
\text{H}\text{:}^- & + & \text{H}^+ & \rightarrow & \text{H}\text{:}\text{H} & \leftarrow & \text{H}\cdot & + & \cdot\text{H} \\
\end{array}
$$

$$
\begin{array}{ccccccccc}
\text{H} & & \text{H} & & \text{H} \quad \text{H} & & \text{H} & & \text{H} \\
| & & | & & | \quad\quad | & & | & & | \\
\text{H—C}\text{:}^- & + & {}^+\text{C—H} & \rightarrow & \text{H—C}\text{:}\text{C—H} & \leftarrow & \text{H—C}\cdot & + & \cdot\text{C—H} \\
| & & | & & | \quad\quad | & & | & & | \\
\text{H} & & \text{H} & & \text{H} \quad \text{H} & & \text{H} & & \text{H}
\end{array}
$$

The distinction between normal and coordinate bonds, then, is arbitrary and depends on what are understood to be the original reactants in producing the bond. The reactants, however, will usually be taken to be neutral atoms or normally bound atoms in molecules, and under these circumstances it is often convenient to make the distinction.

5.117 A rather more fundamental distinction among covalent bonds may be made on the basis of the charge distribution in the bond and the atoms it joins. Clearly, in any covalent bond joining identical groups, such as that in hydrogen or chlorine, the central bonds in hydrogen peroxide or ethane, or even the carbon-carbon links in cyclohexane, the equilibrium distribution of electrical charge must be perfectly symmetrical and the bond nonpolar. On the other hand, bonds between dissimilar atoms or radicals, or even between identical atoms in different environments, that is, with different substituents, are polar in principle and generally are polar in fact as well, in terms of the actual distribution of electrical charge. Coordinate bonds formed between originally neutral atoms, either free or already bound in molecules, are necessarily polar, the donor atom bearing a positive charge and the acceptor a negative charge. Normal covalent bonds between unlike atoms are also polar unless the bonded atoms happen to have equal electronegativities; in the latter case the shared electron pair is equally attracted to the two atoms and its equilibrium position is midway between them, giving a symmetrical charge distribution. Thus the C—H bonds in hydrocarbons are almost nonpolar because of the nearly equal electronegativities of carbon and hydrogen, but the C—Cl bonds in the corresponding substituted chlorine compounds are quite polar. As the difference in electronegativity between the two bonded atoms increases, we approach the extreme opposite to the covalent bond in the homonuclear diatomic molecule; that is, the pure ionic bond between a strongly electropositive metallic atom and a strongly electronegative nonmetallic atom. Thus, although there is considerable convenience in treating chemical bonds as either ionic or covalent, in actual fact relatively few bonds are completely ionic or completely covalent. There is undoubtedly some degree of covalent character in such ionic bonds as those in the alkali metal halides, the extent of covalent character decreasing with increasing atomic number of the metal or with decreasing atomic number of the halogen. Even in the case of the homonuclear diatomic molecules, ionic structures have some small importance, contributing a few per cent in the overall resonance description of the molecule.

5.118 The polarity or ionic character of a covalent bond in a diatomic molecule is indicated simply by the dipole moment of the molecule, a quantity which measures the product of electrical charge and displacement. Thus the dipole moment of the hydrogen chloride molecule is 1.03×10^{-18} c.g.s. units, which corresponds, for example, to a structure with positive and negative charges equal in magnitude to that of the electron (4.80×10^{-10} e.s. units), separated by a distance of 0.215 Å. From the study of band spectra or other data, we determine that the actual internuclear distance is 1.28 Å in this molecule; the average value of the displaced electrical charge is therefore $\dfrac{1.03}{1.28 \times 4.80} = 0.168$ electronic charges. The bond in hydrogen chloride might on this basis be classed as being 17% ionic in character; similar analyses give 11% for the bromide, 5% for the iodide, and 43% for the fluoride, which is rather less than the estimate of 60% which had been previously made.

5.119 The dipole moment of a polyatomic molecule measures the resultant of the charge displacements in several bonds. If the bonds are symmetrically placed and directed relative to the center of the molecule, as in benzene or carbon tetrachloride, for example, the dipole moment is zero regardless of the polarity of the individual bonds. In other cases, the observed moment may be resolved into individual moments for the bonds in the molecule if these are few in number and their geometry is known. Thus the observed moment of 1.85×10^{-18} c.g.s. units for the water molecule may be interpreted as the resultant of two bond moments at the observed bond angle of $104° 40'$, each of length 0.96 Å (the observed H—O bond distance) and displaced charge equal to

$$\frac{1.85 \times 10^{-18}}{2 \cos \dfrac{104° 40'}{2}} \cdot \frac{1}{4.80 \times 10^{-10} \times 0.96 \times 10^{-8}} = 0.33 \text{ electronic charges. The}$$

H—O bond may then be said to possess 33% ionic character. For reasons relating to the resonance in the water molecule among the covalent and two preponderant ionic structures, this estimate is considered somewhat high and the value 28% is preferred. Similar calculations may be made for ammonia, and the simple hydrides and oxides of heavier elements, but for more complex molecules the analysis is quite difficult.

5.120 Clearly the degree of polarity or ionic character in a bond is related to the difference in electronegativity between the two bonded atoms. Although no satisfactory relationship has been derived on theoretical grounds, empirical equations have been developed to fit the data for the hydrogen halides, the ionic character being determined from dipole moment measurements and the electronegativities from bond energy additivity defects. The equation of Hannay and Smyth,

$$\text{Ionic character (in percent)} = 16 \Delta x + 3.5 (\Delta x)^2,$$

in which Δx is the difference in electronegativity, is simple to use and is certainly valid for $0 \leq \Delta x \leq 2.0$. It lacks the reasonable property of predicting an asymptotic approach to pure ionic character as Δx becomes quite large, a property inherent in the older expression due to Pauling,

$$\text{Ionic character (in percent)} = 100[1 - e^{-0.25(\Delta x)^2}].$$

The Hannay and Smyth relation predicts pure ionic bonds for $\Delta x = 3.5$, but so extended an extrapolation is unjustified. Bonds of 50% or greater ionic character, which we may arbitrarily term ionic, are produced if the electronegativity difference Δx exceeds 2.1.

5.121 The very high electronegativity of fluorine is responsible for greater than 50% ionic character in its bonds with all elements of electronegativity less than 1.9; the only predominantly covalent bonds of fluorine are those with moderately or strongly electronegative elements such as the other halogens, the lighter elements of representative groups V and VI, and carbon. With oxygen the situation is similar but, because of its lower electronegativity, the number of covalent bonds is greater and the range of predominantly ionic bond formation more restricted. Similarly, for other nonmetallic elements, as the electronegativity is decreased the ionic character of bonds with metallic atoms decreases while the covalent character of bonds with other nonmetals increases. Similar generalizations are easily made for the behavior of the metallic elements.

Broadly speaking, the bonds between atoms greatly differing in electronegativity are essentially ionic, and those between atoms of similar electronegativity are predominantly covalent. Furthermore, predominantly ionic bonds are the stronger the greater is the electronegativity difference, and predominantly covalent bonds are the stronger the smaller the difference. The latter generalization must be tempered, of course, if resonance among mixed bonding types is important in a particular instance. If we recall the relation between bond energy of the A—B bond and the electronegativity difference for the two atoms (see 4.82),

$$D_{AB} \sim \tfrac{1}{2}[D_{AA} + D_{BB}] + 23 \, (\Delta x)^2$$

we easily see that as the electronegativity difference Δx increases, the bond energy and ionic character increase. The first term in the expression for D_{AB} is essentially the covalent term, that in Δx represents the additional energy ascribed to resonance with ionic structures. As the participation of these ionic structures increases, so also does the stability of the actual bond.

5.122 An alternative approach to the consideration of the mixed ionic and covalent character of chemical bonds may be made from the point of view of an ionic bond modified by the interaction of the ions to embody a greater or lesser degree of electron sharing. When oppositely charged ions draw close together their structures are deformed by their mutual attractive and repulsive forces, the effect generally being considerably more pronounced on the relatively large and diffuse anion than on the smaller and electrically more dense cation. The anion thus polarized effectively loses some share of its negative electron complement to the cation; this decreases the charges of both ions from their original values when isolated, and accounts for a diminished tendency toward ionic bond formation and at the same time brings about some degree of electron sharing, or covalence, between the two atoms. Covalent binding will therefore be favored by those factors which tend to increase the polarization we have described. The most common of these are a large charge on either ion, small size of the cation or large size of the anion, and high polarizability of the anion.

5.123 Highly charged ions exert strong attractive forces on one another and are responsible for extensive deformation, particularly of the anion. Furthermore, highly charged cations are generally quite small, they can approach the anion very closely, and their fields and polarizing effect on the anion are proportionately greater than for cations of small charge. Anions of high charge are large, the binding effect of the nucleus having been decreased by the addition of the extra electrons which, moreover, repel one another; these outer electrons are easily attracted by a cation and thus the anion is easily deformed. Other factors which may increase the effective field strength about a cation of given charge and size (an eighteen electron configuration as compared to an eight electron configuration, for example) or which may increase the polarizability of an anion of given charge and size (such as efficient screening of the nucleus by outer electrons) must also operate to increase the tendency toward covalent bond formation. The importance of the type of electron configuration is well illustrated in the comparison of the chlorides of Na^+ and Cu^+, of cationic radii 0.95 Å and 0.96 Å, respectively; by all standards the former is predominantly ionic, the latter involves an extensive degree of covalent nature.

5.124 Ionic polarizabilities are roughly proportional to the ionic volumes and hence to the cubes of the ionic radii. Among the anions, at least, polarizabilities decrease in the order of increasing electronegativity and may be used in the estimation of crude values of this property. The related properties, polarizability, size, and electronegativity, all operate to bring about an increasing tendency toward covalence with increasing atomic number among the nonmetallic elements and with decreasing atomic number among the metals.

The Hydrogen Bond

5.125 Since almost the beginning of quantitative discussion of valence, hydrogen has been assigned a valence of one, the historical reason being that no stable simple compounds were known in which hydrogen unequivocally was linked to more than one other atom. The concepts subsequently introduced fit these observations and in fact seem to insure that no exceptions can occur: the electronic configuration of hydrogen permits it to accept one electron to form the hydride ion, H^-, in ionic bonds, or to form one covalent bond in which the electron pair completely fills the K shell of the atom. The energy of the L shell is so much higher, and its capacity so great, that no stable systems can result from its involvement in chemical binding. Therefore, hydrogen can form but one bond of any type and its valence should be one.

5.126 It seems quite well established, nonetheless, that in many systems a hydrogen atom is attracted to two different electronegative atoms and, in fact, constitutes a bond between them which has a strength of the order of 5 kcal. Such hydrogen bonds were suggested many years ago as being involved in the structure of trimethylammonium hydroxide, represented by the formula

$$
\begin{array}{c}
\text{Me} \\
| \\
\text{Me---N---H--OH,} \\
| \\
\text{Me}
\end{array}
$$

in the anomalous association of the hydrides of nitrogen, oxygen, and fluorine according to the schemes

$$
\begin{array}{cccc}
\text{H} & & \text{H} & \text{H} \\
| & & | & | \\
\text{H---N---H---N---H,} & \text{H---O---H---O,} & \text{and} & \text{H---F---H---F,} \\
| & & | & \\
\text{H} & & \text{H} &
\end{array}
$$

and in the dimerization of the smaller organic acids like formic and acetic to give structures represented as

$$O\text{-}\text{-}\text{-}H\text{---}O$$
$$H\text{---}C \diagup \diagdown \diagdown \diagup C\text{---}H \quad \text{and} \quad Me\text{---}C \diagup \diagdown \diagdown \diagup C\text{---}Me.$$
$$O\text{---}H\text{-}\text{-}\text{-}O$$

In all of these the short dashed line represents an attractive force between the bonded hydrogen atom and the indicated second electronegative atom. If the hydrogen atom is normally bonded in the usual way to its neighbor then the interaction with the second atom is an electrostatic interaction. The hydrogen atom is strongly positive, the more so as the electronegativity of the atom to which it is bonded increases, and attracts the second electronegative atom, polarizing its electron atmosphere and giving rise to a strong attractive force of the van der Waals type. The result seems to be peculiar to the hydrogen atom because it is the only small atom which can carry a positive charge while it is bonded near the surface of a molecule, and can thus exert large polarizing forces on nearby anion structures. The relatively great strength of the polarizing forces is probably due to the fact that the hydrogen atom possesses no screening electrons. The very small size of the hydrogen atom allows the second electronegative atom to approach quite closely so that the electrostatic interaction is maximized, but prevents more than one such atom from coming near; this accounts for the fact that only two atoms may be linked by the so-called hydrogen bond. It is interesting that in this respect the electrostatic forces resemble chemical forces in the usual covalent bond where saturation is observed.

5.127 It is clear that hydrogen bonds should be formed only between quite highly electronegative atoms, for these will enhance the effective positive charge on the hydrogen atom and account for increased attraction for the nonmetallic atoms. Any factors which increase the electronegative character of the atom originally bearing the hydrogen will increase the tendency toward hydrogen bond formation and the strength of the bonds formed; thus phenols form stronger hydrogen bonds than do aliphatic alcohols because resonance with ionic structures enhances the electronegativity of the oxygen in the phenols. Because the interaction seems to be essentially electrostatic, the tendency to form hydrogen bonds increases with decreasing size of the nonmetallic atom, provided the electronegativity remains sensibly constant. Nitrogen and chlorine have nearly equal electronegativities but nitrogen forms hydrogen bonds more extensively than does chlorine; fluorine tends to form hydrogen bonds much more readily than oxygen which, although it is nearly the same size as fluorine, possesses a much smaller electronegativity. Practically speaking, reasonably stable hydrogen bonds are formed only with nitrogen, oxygen, fluorine, and chlorine, although weaker bonds have been reported with carbon atoms whose electronegativity has been increased through extensive substitution with negative groups such as halogen atoms.

5.128 An alternative formulation of hydrogen bonding has been given in terms of resonance between structures differing only in the location of a shared electron pair joined to the hydrogen atom. Consider first the ion HF_2^-, for which we may write the resonance forms

$$F^- \; H \; :\!\overset{\cdot\cdot}{\underset{\cdot\cdot}{F}}\!:, \quad F^- \; H^+ \; F^-, \quad \text{and} \quad :\!\overset{\cdot\cdot}{\underset{\cdot\cdot}{F}}\!: \; H \; F^-,$$

all of which possess nearly identical configurations and nearly equal energies. Experiment shows that the hydrogen atom is midway between the two fluorine atoms, which implies equal contributions of the two covalent structures and resonance as responsible at least in part for the stability of the hydrogen bonded system.

5.129 The formic acid dimer constitutes a more complex illustration. The simplest conception of a resonance hybrid formed from two essentially equivalent resonance forms of the dimer requires the hydrogen atom to be midway between the two hydrogen-bonded oxygen atoms, and all four C—O bond distances to be equal. Actual experiment leads to the following structure

It is evident that there are two different C—O distances and two different H—O distances. Let us compare these, however, with the corresponding distances for the monomeric formic acid molecules: the C—O distance has decreased from 1.43 Å in the monomer to 1.36 Å, and the C=O distance has increased from 1.22 Å to 1.25 Å; the H—O distance is 0.96 Å in the monomer and 1.07 Å in the dimer, while the H- - -O distance in the dimer is considerably less than the sum of the van der Waals (nonbonding) radii, 2.6 Å, which measures the distance of closest approach of the hydrogen and oxygen atoms in separate nonbonded monomer molecules. Furthermore, the average bond length is diminished, and the bonds are therefore presumably stronger. These are the expected effects of stabilization by resonance. The double bonds lengthen slightly as they gain some single bond character, the single bonds contract rather more as they gain some double bond character, and there results a bond of some covalent nature between the previously separate hydrogen and oxygen atoms.

5.130 The expectation of symmetrical configurations in the resonance hybrid is over-simplified and not justified. The actual structure of a resonating system is intermediate between those of the resonance forms but need not be exactly their average unless the resonance forms are exactly equivalent and are the only structures which make any appreciable contribution. In the present instance, the electrostatic interaction previously described contributes an effect which can account for the asymmetry in the resulting structure. Perhaps the most satisfactory interpretation of hydrogen bonding is to be found in a combination of the resonance and electrostatic interaction effects.

5.131 The effects of hydrogen bonding on the properties of molecules are rather varied. The simple hydrides of the strongly electronegative elements of the second row are extensively associated by hydrogen bond formation and consequently exhibit anomalously high melting points, boiling points, and heats of vaporization and fusion as compared with the values to be predicted from the fairly regular decrease of such quantities with decreasing molecular weight of the hydrides of the appropriate group. These properties and their variations are shown in Table 5.7, which also includes data for the group IV hydrides to

TABLE 5.7

Physical Properties of Nonmetallic Hydrides

Representative Group	Hydride	Melting Point	Boiling Point	Heat of Fusion	Heat of Vaporization
IV	CH_4	91° K	112° K	0.22 kcal./mole	1.96 kcal./mole
	SiH_4	88	162	0.16	2.9
	GeH_4	107	185	0.20	3.36
	SnH_4	123	221	——	4.4
V	NH_3	195	240	1.35	5.58
	PH_3	139	185	0.27	3.49
	AsH_3	157	211	0.56	4.18
	SbH_3	185	256	——	——
VI	H_2O	273	373	1.44	9.72
	H_2S	188	213	0.57	4.46
	H_2Se	207	232	0.60	4.62
	H_2Te	222	271	1.0	5.55
VII	HF	190	293	1.09	7.24
	HCl	159	188	0.48	3.86
	HBr	186	206	0.58	4.21
	HI	222	238	0.69	4.72

serve as a model for the trend to be expected in the absence of hydrogen bonding. The effect of hydrogen bonding in the lightest hydride of each of representative groups V, VI, and VII is evident in all four of the properties listed. The effect may also be noted in the high viscosity and dielectric constant of the liquids and the hardness and rigidity of the crystalline solids.

5.132 Ice is not only harder than might have been expected for a molecular crystal but is also less dense, because extensive hydrogen bonding links the simple H_2O groups into great ordered tetrahedral arrays in which relatively large open spaces may be found. Upon melting, some (but certainly not all — Pauling estimates 15%) of the hydrogen bonds are ruptured, the H_2O groups may rotate slightly and move into the open spaces and thereby decrease the molar volume. Naturally, the bond rupturing process is favored by increasing temperature, and the concomitant molecular relocation and volume decrease are thus responsible for the unusual increase of density with increasing temperature for water over a range of about four degrees immediately above the melting point.

5.133 Hydrogen bonding is held responsible for unexpectedly high solubilities of substances containing functional groups with oxygen or nitrogen in solvents containing one or more hydrogen atoms on a fairly electronegative atom or radical. Thus, for example, organic acid halides are generally more soluble in chloroform than in carbon tetrachloride, liberating heat in the solution process in the former but not in the latter solvent. Hydrogen bonding is strongly suggested between the halogen atom or possibly the oxygen atom, of the solute molecule and the carbon atom of the solvent molecule, the electronegativity of which has been greatly enhanced by the substitution of the three chlorine atoms. The very high solubility of ammonia in water is doubtless due in part to the formation of fairly strong hydrogen bonds between the solvent and solute molecules. The same process occurs in the solution of many other covalent molecules such as alcohols, amines, or organic acids, in water or in similar polar hydrogen-containing solvents. Each of these solutes contains a strongly electronegative atom with which hydrogen bonds may be formed. Many ionic compounds of oxygenated anions owe some part of their solubility in water to hydration of the anion through the formation of hydrogen bonds with the solvent. This hydration of the anion persists even in the crystalline state, and accounts, for example, for the circumstance that many sulfates carry one more molecule of water of hydration than do the corresponding chlorides: $CuSO_4 \cdot 5H_2O$ and $CuCl_2 \cdot 4H_2O$, or $ZnSO_4 \cdot 7H_2O$ and $ZnCl_2 \cdot 6H_2O$ are common illustrations of systems in which the sulfate ion is solvated with a single water molecule, the chloride ion not. Hydrogen bonds are quite prevalent in many crystalline structures both organic and inorganic, and often are responsible for important structural features of the crystal. Thus, hydrogen bonds in crystalline oxalic acid may produce either two-dimensional layer lattices (the α form) or one-dimensional chain configurations (the β form); in substituted amines similar long chains may be produced to give crystals which are preferentially cleaved into strips rather than sheets. The polypeptide chains in proteins form hydrogen bonds, the strength and location of which are extremely important in determining the helical structure of the crystalline proteins.

5.134 In certain molecules the configuration may permit intramolecular as well as intermolecular hydrogen bond formation. For example, salicylaldehyde (o-hydroxybenzaldehyde) is presumed to form a hydrogen bond between the two oxygen atoms as described by the formula given, in which a fairly stable six-membered ring is produced. In the meta and para isomers of this compound the geometry does not permit intramolecular hydrogen bonding; the molecules therefore form intermolecular linkages and the resulting larger molecular assemblies account for the considerably lower volatility of these compounds. The related compound salicylic acid furnishes an interesting combination of intra- and intermolecular hydrogen bonding: two molecules, each bonded intramolecularly like the aldehyde, are linked by hydrogen bonds between the oxygen atoms of their carboxyl groups to produce a dimer analogous to the formic acid dimer previously described.

The product is considerably more acidic than the corresponding dimers of the *meta* and *para* compounds because the interaction of the carboxyl group with the hydrogen atom of the hydroxy group necessarily weakens its interaction with the proton involved in acid-base behavior.

5.135 When a hydrogen bond is formed between two hydroxyl groups, as occurs in the crystals of many metallic hydroxides, in solid hydrates of carboxylic or dicarboxylic acids, or in ice, the bond is often rather longer than most other hydrogen bonds. In most cases it seems quite likely that the hydrogen atom is not symmetrically located in the bond but is nearer one of the oxygen atoms and is definitely linked to it by a covalent bond. In ice, for example, each oxygen atom is surrounded tetrahedrally by four other oxygen atoms at a distance of 2.76 Å; in two of the links a hydrogen atom is located approximately 1.1 Å from the central oxygen atom, and in the other two the hydrogen atom is located approximately 1.6 Å from the central oxygen atom, or 1.1 Å from the second oxygen atom. It seems conclusive that two hydrogen atoms are covalently bonded to each oxygen atom (the normal water molecule), and that the hydrogen bonds in this case involve very little resonance but considerable electrostatic interaction. Bonds of this sort involving two hydroxyl groups are sometimes termed *hydroxyl bonds*. (Unfortunately the rather strong interaction between bonded hydroxyl groups and positive ions, tending to attract the positive ion at approximately a tetrahedral angle to the O—H bond direction, has also been called a hydroxyl bond, but this usage is fairly rare. The term *residual valence* is better used to describe this interaction of an ion with a dipole along the direction of greatest polarizability.)

Electron Deficient Bonds

5.136 The one-electron bond in the hydrogen molecule ion is moderately strong and definitely covalent, but it clearly differs from the usual kind of covalent bond in having too few electrons to form shared pairs between the bonded atoms. Numerous other fairly stable structures are known in which there is an insufficient number of valence electrons to form shared pair bonds; these usually involve such elements as boron, aluminum, and platinum, which possess fewer valence electrons than stable valence shell orbitals, in circumstances in which the element may not form ionic bonds. The boron hydrides generally (diborane, B_2H_6, particularly), the dimer of aluminum trimethyl, $[Al(CH_3)_3]_2$, and the tetramer of platinum tetramethyl, $[Pt(CH_3)_4]_4$, are all examples of substances which do not have enough valence electrons to form ordinary electron pair bonds.

5.137 The structure of diborane has been the subject of very much study and discussion. Ionic structures such as

$$\begin{bmatrix} & \text{H} \quad \text{H} & \\ & | \quad\ | & \\ \text{H}-&\text{B}-\text{B}-\text{H} & \\ & | & \\ & \text{H} & \end{bmatrix}^{-} \text{H}^{+} \quad \text{or} \quad \text{H}^{+}\begin{bmatrix} \text{H} \quad \text{H} \\ | \quad\ | \\ \text{H}-\text{B}-\text{B}-\text{H} \end{bmatrix}^{2-} \text{H}^{+},$$

in which the indicated protons are reasonably labile, are ruled out because the compound has essentially no acid properties. Structures involving one-electron bonds, like

$$
\begin{array}{ccc}
\text{H} \ \ \text{H} & & \text{H} \ \ \text{H} \\
| \ \ \ | & & | \ \ \ \ \ | \\
\text{H} \cdot \text{B} \!-\! \text{B} \cdot \text{H} & \text{or} & \text{H} \!-\! \text{B} \!-\! \text{B} \!-\! \text{H,} \\
| \ \ \ | & & | \ \ \ \ \ | \\
\text{H} \ \ \text{H} & & \text{H} \ \ \text{H}
\end{array}
$$

probably in resonance with the electron pair bonds, now seem rather unlikely. Additional resonance forms contributing to the same ethanelike configuration are those containing "no-electron bonds," the particular nature of the binding force being unspecified.

$$
\begin{array}{ccc}
\text{H} \ \ \text{H} & & \text{H}^{+} \ \text{H} \\
| \ \ \ | & & | \ \ \ \ \ | \ ^{-} \\
\text{H} \!-\! \text{B} \ \ \text{B} \!-\! \text{H} & \text{or} & \text{H} \!-\! \text{B} \!-\! \text{B} \!-\! \text{H.} \\
| \ \ \ | & & | \ \ \ \ \ | \\
\text{H} \ \ \text{H} & & \text{H} \ \ \text{H}
\end{array}
$$

The bulk of the evidence available (magnetic, Raman and infrared, specific heat, electron and X-ray diffraction, nuclear magnetic resonance) seems to favor an ethylenelike structure containing two hydrogen atoms acting as bridges between the boron atoms. In view of the low electronegativity of boron and the known symmetry of the molecule, it is unlikely that these bridges are normal hydrogen bonds. Resonance among various ionic and no-electron bond structures with only paired electrons present in the ethylenelike configuration has been suggested as leading to a so-called resonance link between the boron atoms. Because an electron pair shared between boron and hydrogen atoms is rather loosely held, it has been proposed that such a pair of bonding electrons might serve to form in addition a coordinate link to a second boron atom according to the scheme shown.

5.138 A related concept is that of the "protonated double bond" suggested by Pitzer, in which the electrons are presumed to account for normal bonding of two hydrogen atoms to each boron atom and for a double bond between the two boron atoms. The remaining two protons are located in the electron cloud which constitutes the double bond as indicated. It must be supposed that the protons are very tightly held in order to explain the lack of acidic properties. The actual B—B distance is rather long for such a double bond structure, but the presence of the protons doubtless decreases the tightness of binding ordinarily to be expected in the double bond and accounts for its greater length. It may be remarked that boron trimethyl, $B(CH_3)_3$, does not dimerize, but if one methyl group is replaced by a hydrogen atom, the product exists only as a dimer which possesses a symmetrical coplanar structure analogous to that of tetramethyltehylene.

5.139 The concept of the protonated double bond has been extended to the consideration of the structures of the higher boron hydrides. Such bonds are presumed to be formed between atoms of which each possesses a vacant orbital and an attached hydrogen atom; immediately adjacent bonds of this special type are not possible, and a B—H group between two boron atoms each of which is thus bridged may not form a similar bond. The postulated structures based on these ideas are not completely accepted because the electron diffraction data do not give incontrovertible proof, but they are useful and do reflect many of the properties of the compounds.

5.140 An alternative description of the bonding in the bridged configuration of diborane is furnished by the so-called "three atom" orbitals, which are molecular orbitals made up from orbitals on the two boron atoms and one hydrogen atom. Each orbital is filled with two electrons and links the three atoms together; the four electrons available thus fill two such orbitals and account for the bonding of the two boron atoms and the two bridging hydrogen atoms. In the higher boron hydrides similar molecular orbitals involving three boron atoms are presumed to be involved, and the concept has been extended to the bonding in other electron deficient molecules.

5.141 The dimerization of aluminum trimethyl is believed to be due to electrostatic interaction between the positive aluminum atom of one unit and the negative carbon atom of the second unit; the electric charges are of course effective charges and certainly not integral. Alternative suggestions of hydrogen bonds between carbon and aluminum atoms or a "methylated double bond" between the two aluminum atoms seem most unlikely. The structurally similar dimer of aluminum chloride is almost certainly bound by coordinate links from a donor chlorine atom of one unit to the acceptor aluminum atom of the second, producing two chlorine atom bridges between the two aluminum atoms.

5.142 The problem of the structure of the tetramer of platinum tetramethyl introduces still another suggestion on the bonding in electron deficient systems. Rundle has proposed that under special circumstances an atom may form more than one bond, using a single bond orbital and a single electron pair in the orbital. Thus the carbon atom may give rise to octahedral bonding with two normal bonds involving SP hybrid orbitals and four "half bonds" built from the two remaining p orbitals and appropriate orbitals on the second bonded atom. In the particular case of the platinum compound, a structure has been suggested in which platinum and carbon atoms occupy alternating corners of a near-cube; each platinum atom is bonded octahedrally to three simple methyl groups and to the three adjacent carbon atoms of the near-cube, and each carbon atom is bonded octahedrally to three hydrogen atoms at a short distance and to three platinum atoms at a longer distance. Thus the platinum atoms in the tetramer are linked by three-way methyl bridges; the particular assignment of full and half bonds is immaterial because of resonance.

5.143 An analogous structure for the aluminum trimethyl dimer may be proposed in which the carbon atom links two aluminum and its own three hydrogen atoms in a trigonal configuration in which SP^2 hybrid orbitals are used for bonds to the two aluminum atoms and one hydrogen atom, and two half bonds from the remaining p orbital link the two other hydrogen atoms above and below the plane containing the aluminum and carbon atoms. The remaining methyl groups are tetrahedrally bonded to the aluminum atoms.

The Metallic Bond

5.144 The molecules termed electron deficient in the previous section involve atoms with valence shells less than half filled. Metals, either pure or in one or another form of alloy, consist entirely of such atoms. It is conceivable, then, that there is some similarity between the two types of systems. We have described in an earlier chapter (see 4.155) the characteristic physical properties of metals and both the classical electron gas theory and the quantum mechanical band, or zone, theory. The latter theory has been found quite satisfactory in describing most physical properties of metals in at least a qualitative fashion. Semi-quantitative calculations have been carried out for the magnetic susceptibility, electronic heat capacity and thermal conductivity, electrical conductivity, thermal electromotive force, thermionic emission, and binding energy of the atoms in the metallic crystal lattice. These calculations are outside the scope of the present discussion; we merely remark that the treatment of binding energy demonstrates that the reason for binding between the atoms, alike or different, in a metal is the same as in ordinary covalent electron pair bonds: electrons are found with high probability in the region of low potential energy between the two bonded nuclei.

5.145 The description we have developed, either classical or quantum mechanical, may be termed a physical picture of binding in metals. Pauling has suggested an alternative description, which may be termed chemical in that it makes use of simple bond orbital concepts developed for covalent molecules. It is proposed that resonance exists among very many structures involving one-electron and electron pair bonds in various positions, other pairs of adjacent atoms being unbonded in particular resonance forms. The wealth of vacant bonding orbitals among metallic elements makes possible a large number of such structures and thus should account for considerable resonance stabilization. Thus, effectively, each electron or electron pair uses several orbitals in binding, a circumstance quite similar to that in electron deficient molecules. Pauling's concept of resonating bonds leads to results for interatomic distances and magnetic properties that are in at least qualitative agreement with experiment, and the lack of specific direction of the bonds is consistent with the mechanical properties previously described. It does not permit the calculation of bonding energies or detailed properties of metals.

5.146 The interpretation of metallic binding in chemical terms as contrasted with a physical description is perhaps emphasized in connection with the study of alloys of the type known as *intermetallic compounds* or *intermediate phases*. In these, in contradistinction to what is observed in physical mixtures of insoluble metallic components or in solid solutions of either the substitutional or interstitial type, the metallic constituents are present in fairly simple stoichiometric proportions. These composition ratios, however, seem not at all related to ordinary valences, and commonly involve rather larger integers. They are best expressed in terms of the ratio of total number of valence electrons to total number of atoms in the alloy. Hume-Rothery discovered that this ratio very often has the values $\frac{21}{14}$, $\frac{21}{13}$, and $\frac{21}{12}$, respectively, for three consecutive compounds in a given system of two metals. Although many exceptions are known, these ratios are observed often enough to imply very strongly some fundamental significance. Attempts have been made to explain the ratios in terms of both the physical description involving Brillouin zones and the chemical description in terms of valence bonding; in either case, only qualitative results are obtained.

General Properties of Covalently Bonded Substances

5.147 Covalently bonded substances fall roughly into two classes, those consisting of molecular crystals in the solid state, and those exhibiting atomic crystal formation. In the former, of which solid phosphorus, methane, carbon dioxide, and sulfuric acid are examples, the individual molecules, generally but not always saturated in the chemical sense, are quite stable relative to dissociation, indicating strong chemical binding forces among the various bonded atoms within the molecule; the forces between neighboring molecules in the solid or liquid state, however, are relatively weak. These forces are of the van der Waals type, involving interactions between dipoles (permanent for polar molecules, induced for others) and polarizabilities, and are of relatively short range. Because of the weakness of these intermolecular forces, molecular crystals of covalent substances are generally soft and easily deformed or broken, their melting and boiling points are usually considerably lower than those of ionic crystals, and their vapor pressures usually higher at any given temperature. They tend to be somewhat soluble in nonpolar solvents, but hardly soluble at all in polar solvents unless their bonds are appreciably ionic in character. In the latter case, the solubility increases with increasing ionic character of the bonds, because this increases the energy of interaction between solute and polar solvent. Lacking such electrostatic interaction, only very weakly attractive or even repulsive solute-polar solvent forces are available.

5.148 Substances containing covalent bonds with fairly large amounts of ionic character exhibit properties tending more toward those of ionic compounds. The crystals are harder, higher melting, less volatile, and more soluble in polar solvents. The forces between the molecules in the solid state may be considerably stronger, involving electrostatic effects between strong dipoles. The covalently bonded molecules themselves do not contain ions and thus do not conduct electricity in the fused state. Their conductivity is also essentially zero in solution unless reaction with the solvent produces ions, as is the case in solutions of weak electrolytes like the organic acids in polar solvents such as water.

Ionization of this type is more extensive the more polar are the covalent bonds affected in the reaction. A second property of many covalently bonded inorganic molecules is their color, which is often different from the color of their constituents in either the elementary state or in ionic combination with other atoms. This property is believed to be due to the highly polarized anion structures in the molecules and is exemplified in iodides of small metallic elements or metals of the short transition series, in which compounds the relative ionic sizes bring about extensive anion polarization.

5.149 The second class of covalently bonded substances comprises atomic crystals. These are structures in which the atoms are completely linked in all directions by covalent electron pair bonds. No individual molecules are to be found and the entire crystal, regardless of size, may properly be termed a single molecule. The best known example is the natural diamond, in which all carbon atoms are joined tetrahedrally by single normal covalent bonds. In graphite, resonating single and double normal covalent bonds combine to produce huge sheets of planar hexagonal carbon atom linkages which may be termed two-dimensional giant molecules; the sheets are held together only by weak van der Waals forces. Silicon and titanium carbides, aluminum, scandium, and boron nitrides, and beryllium oxide form atomic crystals in which shared electron pair bonds connect all the atoms in every direction. All such substances are very hard, stiff, and dense; they have generally very high melting and boiling points, low volatilities, essentially zero electrical conductivities, and their solubilities are extremely low in any kind of solvent, unless, of course, a chemical reaction occurs. Each of these properties clearly is a result of the multiplicity of strong covalent bonds which must be broken in order to deform, melt, vaporize, or dissolve the crystal.

PART

II

SOME ASPECTS OF

CHEMICAL BEHAVIOR

Chapter 6. Coordination Compounds   211

7. Acid-Base Relationships and Inorganic Reactions in Non-aqueous Systems   268

CHAPTER 6

COORDINATION COMPOUNDS

Introduction

6.1 There exists a large and important class of substances broadly termed *molecular* or *addition* compounds in which two or more compounds, each capable of existing independently, are united together in definite stoichiometric proportions. Carnallite, $KCl \cdot MgCl_2 \cdot 6H_2O$; tetramminecopper(II) sulfate monohydrate, $Cu(NH_3)_4SO_4 \cdot H_2O$; and potassium ferrocyanide, $K_4Fe(CN)_6$, are familiar examples. Some of these substances maintain their identity as compounds only in the crystalline state and lose it when the crystal is dissolved or melted. An aqueous solution of carnallite, for example, behaves like a simple mixture of its three component ions in water. The term *double salt*, commonly applied to such substances, is a reflection of this behavior. On the other hand, although potassium ferrocyanide may be prepared from potassium cyanide and iron(II) cyanide, and can be formally written $Fe(CN)_2 \cdot 4KCN$, its behavior is very different from that of a typical double salt. Thus in aqueous solution it gives little indication of the presence of iron(II) ion or of cyanide ion, but instead gives evidence of the presence of a more complex entity corresponding to the formulation $[Fe(CN)_6]^{4-}$. Substances of this nature are called *complex* compounds or *coordination* compounds.

6.2 The distinction between double salts and complex compounds is not a sharp one, however. Some complexes, like the ferrocyanide ion and some of the ammonia complexes of cobalt(III), show only a very slight dissociation into their components. Others undergo much more extensive dissociation, and an

GENERAL REFERENCES

The Chemistry of the Coordination Compounds, edited by Bailar, Reinhold Publishing Corporation, New York, 1956, Ch. 1–16.

FERNELIUS, "Structure of Coordination Compounds," *Chemical Architecture*, Sec. III, edited by Burk and Grummitt, Interscience Publishers, Inc., New York, 1948, pp. 53–100.

MARTELL and CALVIN, *Chemistry of the Metal Chelate Compounds*, Prentice-Hall, Inc., New York, 1952, Ch. 1–7.

PAULING, *The Nature of the Chemical Bond*, 2nd edition, Cornell University Press, Ithaca, N.Y., 1940, Ch. III.

WELLS, *Structural Inorganic Chemistry*, 2nd Edition, Oxford University Press, London, 1950, pp. 79–93, Ch. IX, XXI, XXII.

almost continuous gradation in this property is found among various complexes, extending from the extremely stable ones down to the double salts. Even the double salts in aqueous solution may give not only hydrated ions, but appreciable concentrations of other complex species as well. The difference between a double salt and a complex compound, therefore, appears to be one of degree rather than of a more fundamental nature.

6.3 The presence of a complex ion or group may be detected in a variety of ways. Its chemical behavior, different in general from that of its components, may indicate its existence. If it is sufficiently stable with respect to dissociation and substitution it may pass intact through a series of operations, and separation and purification of a compound containing it may be possible. Such properties as color, optical activity, absorption spectrum, solubility behavior, magnetic susceptibility, reduction potential, transference behavior, X-ray pattern, and the like may also give evidence for the presence of a complex. Provided the complex can be isolated in the form of a pure compound, its composition can be determined by ordinary analytical methods. Even when the complex exists in solution but cannot be conveniently isolated, often its composition may be ascertained by one or more of a variety of special methods which have been developed.

6.4 The thermodynamic stability of a complex with respect to dissociation or substitution in a given environment is one of its important properties, as has been implied above. An additional consideration of importance, here as well as in many other chemical systems, is the rate at which the complex proceeds toward equilibrium in such reactions. Great variability in this respect is observed among the reactions in different complexes. When, for example, a solution containing the tetramminecopper(II) ion, $[Cu(NH_3)_4]^{2+}$, is treated with excess hydrochloric acid, the complex is destroyed almost instantaneously, forming ammonium ion and (hydrated) copper(II) ion. When the hexamminecobalt(III) ion, $[Co(NH_3)_6]^{3+}$, is similarly treated, however, the complex appears to be unreactive, and persists almost indefinitely, even though removal of one or more ammonia molecules and replacement by water molecules are thermodynamically favored. Complexes reacting in such very sluggish fashion are frequently said to be "inert," while those coming to equilibrium quite rapidly are described as "labile." The inertness or lability of a complex, as well as its thermodynamic stability, are often important in its detection and characterization.

6.5 Used in a broad sense, the term "complex" applies to such ions as sulfate, nitrate, carbonate, perchlorate, and phosphate, as well as to ferrocyanide, tetramminecopper(II), and the like. In the present discussion, however, this term will be used in a more restricted sense to apply to such entities as $[Fe(CN)_6]^{4-}$, $[Cu(NH_3)_4]^{2+}$, and $[Pt(NH_3)_2Cl_2]$. That is, most of the complex species to be considered here contain a metal atom or ion.

6.6 The earliest description of a complex compound in this narrower sense appeared near the beginning of the nineteenth century, and in the hundred years which followed a great many such compounds were prepared and characterized. Of special interest during this period were the complexes of cobalt(III), platinum(II), and platinum(IV), which can be prepared in great variety, many of them being relatively inert. Some observations on a series of cobaltammines, in particular, provided an important part of the experimental foundation upon which Werner's coordination theory (see 6.9–15) was based, and these are described in the following paragraphs.

6.7 If a solution containing cobalt(II) chloride and ammonium chloride is made strongly ammoniacal and treated for a time with a current of air, then made strongly acid with hydrochloric acid, several products are obtained. Among them are a yellow crystalline compound having the formula $CoCl_3 \cdot 6NH_3$, a beautiful purple solid of formula $CoCl_3 \cdot 5NH_3$, and a green compound $CoCl_3 \cdot 4NH_3$. Because of their colors these compounds were named respectively, luteocobalt chloride, purpureocobalt chloride, and praseocobalt chloride, but they are better called the hexammine-, pentammine-, and tetramminecobalt(III) chlorides.* A fourth member in the series is triamminecobalt(III) chloride, $CoCl_3 \cdot 3NH_3$. A remarkable property of these cobaltammines is that the ammonia in them is not readily removed by acid. They are, for example, quite inert toward hydrochloric acid even when heated to boiling. Treatment with sodium or potassium hydroxide in the cold, moreover, does not precipitate the cobalt, although when the compounds are heated with these reagents they decompose with loss of ammonia. The term "penetration complexes" is sometimes applied to such relatively inert complexes to differentiate them from labile "normal complexes" such as tetramminecopper(II). The distinction is not a fundamental one, however.

6.8 All the ammine groups are inert in the compounds described above, but a very significant difference is found in the behavior of the chlorine atoms. When a freshly prepared solution of the hexammine is acidified and treated in the cold with silver nitrate, all the chlorine is immediately precipitated. Under the same conditions only two thirds of the chlorine in the pentammine is precipitated, only one third in the tetrammine, and none in the triammine. Similar differences appear in other metathetical reactions. For example, corresponding proportions of chloride are lost as hydrogen chloride when these compounds are treated with concentrated sulfuric acid. In a similar series of iridium(III) complexes analogous behavior is observed. The reactions of $IrCl_3 \cdot 6NH_3$, $IrCl_3 \cdot 5NH_3$, and $IrCl_3 \cdot 4NH_3$ with concentrated sulfuric acid, for example, result in the loss of all, two thirds, and one third of the chloride, respectively, while $IrCl_3 \cdot 3NH_3$ loses no hydrogen chloride under these conditions. This difference in behavior among the four types of ammines shown above is not limited to the chlorides. A series of hexammines of the type $CoX_3 \cdot 6NH_3$ may be prepared, in which X represents a negative group such as nitrite or bromide.

---

* Actually two compounds of the formula $CoCl_3 \cdot 4NH_3$ can be obtained. The second, made in a different way and originally called violeocobalt chloride, possesses a dark violet color. As will be pointed out later, these two compounds are geometrical isomers.

In these hexammines all three of the X groups show their characteristic ionic reactions. In the corresponding pentammines, $CoX_3 \cdot 5NH_3$, however, only two of the X groups so behave, in $CoX_3 \cdot 4NH_3$ only one, and in $CoX_3 \cdot 3NH_3$, none. For example, $Co(NO_2)_3 \cdot 3NH_3$ does not react with cold mineral acids to produce nitrous acid, in sharp contrast to the behavior of ionic nitrites. With regard to still lower ammines of these elements, containing fewer than three molecules of ammonia, it is significant that simple diammines of the type $MX_3 \cdot 2NH_3$ are not obtained. Instead, such compounds as $KCo(NO_2)_4 \cdot 2NH_3$ result, in which all four of the negative groups as well as the ammonia molecules are unreactive.

The Werner Coordination Theory

6.9 The significance of the facts outlined above in relation to the structures of the cobaltammines and similar substances was first pointed out by Alfred Werner, whose brilliantly conceived researches, published between about 1893 and 1918, provided a rational explanation of the composition and behavior of these compounds. In his monumental contribution to the subject, Werner described the preparation of a considerable number of new compounds, demonstrated and explained the existence of various types of isomerism, and established the fundamental structures of a great many complexes. He broadened the concepts of valence which had been held previously, and in so doing prepared the way for the modern application of electron theory in the field. So important was Werner's contribution that he was awarded the Nobel Prize in chemistry, and coordination compounds of the kind under discussion are often called "Werner complexes."

6.10 It will be noted that in each member of the cobaltammine series there are six relatively unreactive groups in the molecule besides the metal ion. In the hexammines these are the six ammonia molecules; in the pentammines they include the five ammonia molecules and one negative group, and so on. Werner assumed that these six groups were directly and individually bonded to the metal atom, giving rise to such complexes as those represented by the structural formulas shown. Thus in each of these compounds, according to Werner, there

$$\left[\begin{array}{cc} H_3N & NH_3 \\ & \diagdown \diagup \\ H_3N-Co-NH_3 \\ \diagup \diagdown \\ H_3N & NH_3 \end{array} \right]^{3+} \quad \left[\begin{array}{cc} H_3N & NH_3 \\ & \diagdown \diagup \\ H_3N-Co-NH_3 \\ \diagup \diagdown \\ H_3N & Cl \end{array} \right]^{2+} \quad \left[\begin{array}{cc} H_3N & NO_2 \\ & \diagdown \diagup \\ H_3N-Co-NO_2 \\ \diagup \diagdown \\ H_3N & NO_2 \end{array} \right]^{0} \quad \left[\begin{array}{cc} H_3N & NO_2 \\ & \diagdown \diagup \\ H_3N-Co-NO_2 \\ \diagup \diagdown \\ O_2N & NO_2 \end{array} \right]^{-}$$

    hexammine   pentammine   triammine   diammine

exists around the central metal atom an *inner coordination sphere* consisting of the six groups written inside the brackets, which are directly and more or less firmly attached to the metal atom. Coordinated groups are often called *ligands*. They can be either ions (usually negative, although not always) or certain neutral molecules.

6.11 In the hexammine complex shown there are six electrically neutral ligands coordinated to a tripositive ion, and the resulting complex entity is, of course, a tripositive ion. The corresponding compound must then contain an equivalent number of negative groups, which are not, of course, a part of the inner coordination sphere, but are quite outside it, and in general maintain their ionic character in the compound. In hexamminecobalt(III) chloride, $[Co(NH_3)_6]Cl_3$, for example, all three of the chlorides are of this nature. In the corresponding pentammine, $[Co(NH_3)_5Cl]Cl_2$, however, only two of the chlorides are ionic since the third is part of the inner coordination sphere. The triammine, $[Co(NH_3)_3Cl_3]$, contains no ionic chloride since all three are within the inner coordination sphere. Here the complex is electrically neutral and constitutes the complete molecule.

6.12 Both conductivities and freezing-point depressions have been employed to give information concerning the number of ions actually furnished in aqueous

Molar Conductance
0.001 N solution, 25°

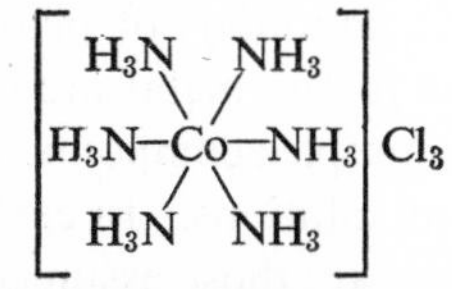

$$\begin{bmatrix} H_3N & NH_3 \\ H_3N-Co-NH_3 \\ H_3N & NH_3 \end{bmatrix} Cl_3 \quad = \quad \begin{bmatrix} H_3N & NH_3 \\ H_3N-Co-NH_3 \\ H_3N & NH_3 \end{bmatrix}^{3+} + 3Cl^- \qquad 431.6$$

hexamminecobalt(III)
chloride

$$\begin{bmatrix} H_3N & NO_2 \\ H_3N-Co-NH_3 \\ H_3N & NH_3 \end{bmatrix} Cl_2 \quad = \quad \begin{bmatrix} H_3N & NO_2 \\ H_3N-Co-NH_3 \\ H_3N & NH_3 \end{bmatrix}^{2+} + 2Cl^- \qquad 246.4$$

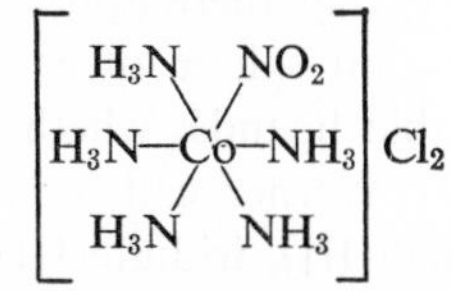

nitropentamminecobalt(III)
chloride

$$\begin{bmatrix} H_3N & NO_2 \\ H_3N-Co-NO_2 \\ H_3N & NH_3 \end{bmatrix} Cl \quad = \quad \begin{bmatrix} H_3N & NO_2 \\ H_3N-Co-NO_2 \\ H_3N & NH_3 \end{bmatrix}^{+} + Cl^- \qquad 98.4$$

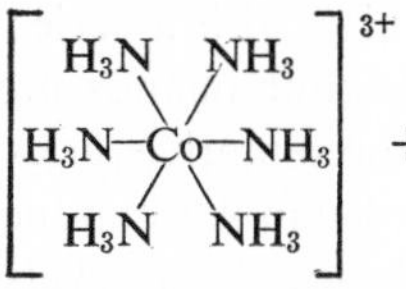

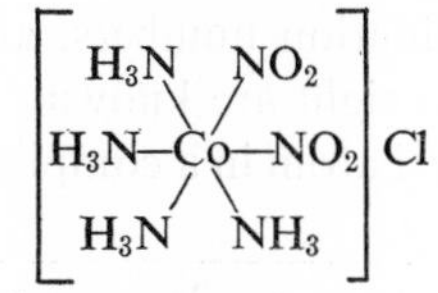

dinitrotetramminecobalt(III)
chloride

$$\begin{bmatrix} H_3N & NO_2 \\ H_3N-Co-NO_2 \\ H_3N & NO_2 \end{bmatrix} \qquad \text{no ionization} \qquad \sim 0$$

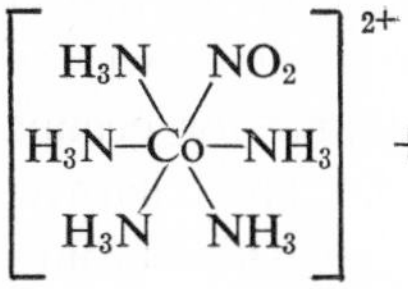

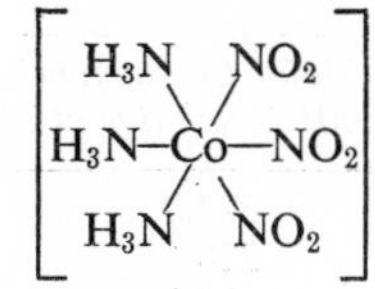

trinitrotriamminecobalt(III)

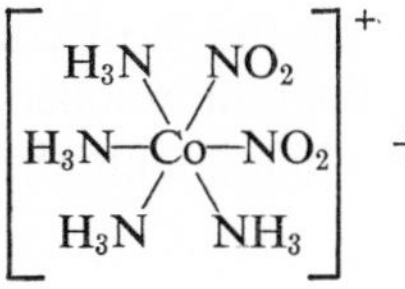

$$K\begin{bmatrix} H_3N & NO_2 \\ H_3N-Co-NO_2 \\ O_2N & NO_2 \end{bmatrix} \quad = \quad K^+ + \begin{bmatrix} H_3N & NO_2 \\ H_3N-Co-NO_2 \\ O_2N & NO_2 \end{bmatrix}^{-} \qquad 99.3$$

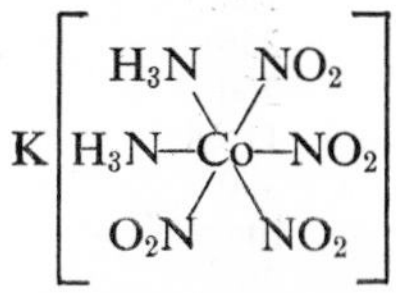

potassium tetranitro-
diamminecobaltate(III)

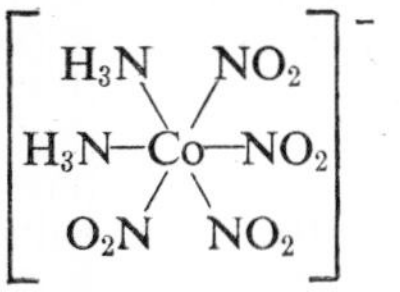

solution by coordination compounds of the type discussed above. Above are given the structures and modes of ionization postulated by the Werner coordination theory for a representative series of cobalt(III) ammines. The molar conductances of approximately 0.001 N solutions at 25° are included. For comparison, the molar conductances of some simple salts under the same conditions may be kept in mind: LiCl, 112.4; $MgCl_2$, 248.2; $LaCl_3$, 411.0.

6.13 It is evident that the observed values of molar conductance are consistent with the mode of ionization proposed by Werner. An analogous series of platinum(IV) ammines shows a similar variation in molar conductance with progressive substitution of negative ligands for ammonia molecules. In these compounds, too, the results indicate the presence of six ligands within the coordination sphere, the residual charge of the complex varying with the number of negative ligands coordinated to the tetrapositive platinum. Differences in valence type are shown also with a series of complex compounds of platinum(II), although here only four ligands are coordinated to the metal atom. In Table 6.1 are listed two representative series of platinum complex compounds, together with the corresponding molar conductances of their solutions. In each formula, the groups shown inside the brackets with the metal are those assumed to be present as ligands within the coordination sphere.

6.14 A striking fact brought out by these observations is that there appears to be a definite number of positions within the coordination sphere of each central atom which are available for occupancy by suitable ligands, whether these be neutral or charged. This characteristic number Werner called the *coordination number* of the particular atom or ion. Cobalt(III), iridium(III), and platinum(IV), for example, possess a coordination number of six in their complexes. In platinum(II) compounds the coordination number is four. Indeed, six and four are by far the most common coordination numbers, although examples of all coordination numbers from two to eight are known.

6.15 The characteristic coordination number of the central atom in a complex

TABLE 6.1

Molar Conductances of Some Platinum(IV) and Platinum(II) Complex Compounds

Name	Formula	Molar Conductance 0.001 N Solution at 25°
Hexammineplatinum(IV) chloride	$[Pt(NH_3)_6]Cl_4$	522.9
Dichlorotetrammineplatinum(IV) chloride	$[Pt(NH_3)_4Cl_2]Cl_2$	228
Trichlorotriammineplatinum(IV) chloride	$[Pt(NH_3)_3Cl_3]Cl$	96.8
Tetrachlorodiammineplatinum(IV)	$[Pt(NH_3)_2Cl_4]$	∼0
Potassium pentachloroammineplatinate(IV)	$K[Pt(NH_3)Cl_5]$	108.5
Potassium hexachloroplatinate(IV)	$K_2[PtCl_6]$	256
Tetrammineplatinum(II) chloride	$[Pt(NH_3)_4]Cl_2$	260
Chlorotriammineplatinum(II) chloride	$[Pt(NH_3)_3Cl]Cl$	115.8
Dichlorodiammineplatinum(II)	$[Pt(NH_3)_2Cl_2]$	∼0
Potassium trichloroammineplatinate(II)	$K[Pt(NH_3)Cl_3]$	106.8
Potassium tetrachloroplatinate(II)	$K_2[PtCl_4]$	267

differs, in general, from the numerical value of its oxidation state, as is seen in the examples given above. To account for the discrepancy between the number of bonds actually established by the central atom and the number which would correspond to its oxidation state alone, Werner postulated the existence of an "auxiliary valence" in addition to the ordinary or principal valence. Thus, in $[Pt(NH_3)_6]Cl_4$ the platinum was considered to use six such auxiliary valences to bind the ammonia molecules, while in $K_2[PtCl_6]$ it uses only two, the remaining four chlorine atoms being held by "principal valences." In terms of the electron theory of valence, the binding between the central metal atom and the attached ligands is to a considerable extent covalent, although the strength and polarity of these bonds may show wide variation. Those bonds which arise from the use of the so-called auxiliary valences are, according to the Lewis theory, co-ordinate covalent bonds (see 5.114–116), in which both electrons in the shared pair are contributed by the ligand. In $[Pt(NH_3)_6]^{4+}$, for example, all six ammonia molecules are regarded as being held by bonds of this type, each ammonia molecule having contributed its unshared pair of electrons for this purpose. On the other hand, $[PtCl_6]^{2-}$ may be considered formally to comprise two chloride ions bonded in this fashion and four neutral chlorine atoms each bound by an ordinary covalent bond in which one electron was contributed by the chlorine atom and one by the platinum atom. These formal distinctions are sometimes represented graphically in structural formulas by the use of arrows to denote coordinate covalent bonds as shown. It must be emphasized, however, that no fundamental difference exists between the two types of bonds, a point which is illustrated by the hexachloroplatinate(IV) ion represented, in which all six chlorines are actually equivalent.

The Effective Atomic Number Concept

6.16 Since, in general, the bonds within a complex possess covalent character, the central atom must have suitable orbitals available for use by the bonding electrons, and its coordination number in the complex would therefore be expected to depend, in part at least, upon its electronic configuration. An indication that such dependence exists is provided by what has been termed the *effective atomic number* [1] (abbreviated E.A.N.), defined as the total number of electrons which the central atom possesses in the complex, including those shared in coordination. In a rather large number of complexes the effective atomic number of the central element is the same as the atomic number of the next inert gas in the periodic system, indicating that in these instances the equivalent of a stable inert gas configuration is being attained by coordination. There are a sufficient number of exceptions, however, to indicate that this condition is not a necessary requirement for complex formation. In the complexes

[1] SIDGWICK, *Trans. Faraday Soc.* **19**, 469 (1923).

of cobalt(III), for example, the effective atomic number of cobalt is 36, corresponding to the atomic number of krypton. On the other hand, iron has an effective atomic number of 35 in iron(III) complexes. The results of these and other similar computations are shown in Table 6.2.

TABLE 6.2

Effective Atomic Numbers of Some Metals in Representative Complexes

Metal	Atomic Number	Example of Complex	Electrons Lost in Ion Formation	Electrons Gained by Coordination	E.A.N.
Fe^0	26	$Fe(CO)_5$	0	10	36 (Kr)
Fe^{II}	26	$Fe(CN)_6^{4-}$	2	12	36
Co^{III}	27	$Co(NH_3)_6^{3+}$	3	12	36
Ni^0	28	$Ni(CO)_4$	0	8	36
Zn^{II}	30	$Zn(CN)_4^{2-}$	2	8	36
Rh^{III}	45	$RhCl_6^{3-}$	3	12	54 (Xe)
Pd^{IV}	46	$Pd(NH_3)_6^{4+}$	4	12	54
Ir^{III}	77	$Ir(NH_3)_6^{3+}$	3	12	86 (Rn)
Pt^{IV}	78	$PtCl_6^{2-}$	4	12	86
Cr^{III}	24	$Cr(NH_3)_6^{3+}$	3	12	33
Fe^{III}	26	$Fe(CN)_6^{3-}$	3	12	35
Co^{II}	27	$Co(NO_2)_6^{4-}$	2	12	37
Pd^{II}	46	$PdCl_4^{2-}$	2	8	52
Pt^{II}	78	$Pt(NH_3)_4^{2+}$	2	8	84

Some Typical Ligands

6.17 Some specific examples of ligands in various complexes have been mentioned above. It is found that a great variety of chemical entities, both ions and neutral molecules, may serve in this capacity. Since, as has been pointed out, the ligands are very commonly attached to the coordination center by coordinate covalent bonds, it is not surprising that the groups which can function as ligands are, with few exceptions, those which possess one or more unshared pairs of electrons in the valence shell, and which can act as electron-pair donors. In a large proportion of such ligands the actual donor atom is a nitrogen, phosphorus, arsenic, oxygen, or sulfur atom, or a halide or sulfide ion, each possessing at least one unshared pair of electrons. Carbon in most of its combinations has no unshared electrons in its valence shell, and does not, in general, act as a donor atom. However, in the complexes of carbon monoxide, cyanide ion, and isonitriles the carbon atom is directly attached to the metal. In these ligands, of course, the carbon atom does have an unshared pair of electrons; moreover, the multiple bond in these groups may make possible an additional stabilizing effect to be discussed later (see 6.128). Complexes of such unsaturated hydrocarbons as ethylene and cyclopentadiene with certain metal ions can be obtained, too, but the bonding is of a somewhat different nature from that just described.

6.18 There are many ligands which possess two or even more donor centers. Provided spatial relations are favorable, a single entity of this kind may occupy two or more coordination positions in a complex. Such a unit is termed a *chelate* group. An important example of a *bidentate* chelating agent, that is, one having two points of attachment, is ethylenediamine, $H_2N—CH_2—CH_2—NH_2$. Each nitrogen atom in this molecule has an unshared pair of electrons, and the molecule forms many complexes with metal ions in which it is essentially equivalent to two molecules of ammonia. With cobalt(III), for example, it forms complexes containing one, two, or three molecules of ethylenediamine (abbreviated en): $[Co(NH_3)_2enCl_2]Cl$, $[Co(NH_3)_2en_2]Cl_3$, $[Co\ en_3]Cl_3$. Some coordinating agents, the carbonate ion and the sulfite ion for example, can occupy either one or two positions. Chelating agents having three or more donor centers within the molecule are also well known. Table 6.3 lists some representative examples of ligands of various types.

TABLE 6.3

Typical Coordinating Ligands

UNIDENTATE		BIDENTATE	
Neutral Molecules	*Negative Ions*	*Neutral Molecules*	*Negative Ions*

6.19 In all of the examples which have been cited thus far, the complex possesses only one coordination center, and is accordingly termed *mononuclear* (or uninuclear). A single complex which contains two or more coordination centers is said to be *polynuclear* (also multinuclear or multinucleate), or more specifically *dinuclear*, *trinuclear*, etc., depending upon the number of centers present. Examples of compounds containing dinuclear complexes are

$$[(H_3N)_5Co\text{---}NH_2\text{---}Co(NH_3)_5](NO_3)_5, \qquad [(H_3N)_4Co \overset{\displaystyle OH}{\underset{\displaystyle OH}{<\quad>}} Co(NH_3)_4](NO_3)_4,$$

and

$$[(H_3N)_4Co \overset{\displaystyle NH_2}{\underset{\displaystyle SO_4}{<\quad>}} Co(NH_3)_4]Cl_3 \cdot 2H_2O.$$

The ligands which link the two metal atoms together are called *bridge groups*.

Nomenclature

6.20 The nomenclature of coordination compounds presents some problems not encountered in simpler inorganic substances, and it has received special consideration. The basic rules adopted by the International Union of Chemistry,[2] together with some additional recommendations which have been proposed,[3] are essentially as follows:

1. In accordance with common practice in naming salts, the cation is named first, the anion last.
2. The names of negative ligands end in *o*. A few examples follow.

Cl^- chloro SCN^- thiocyanato
NO_2^- nitro SO_3^{2-} sulfito
CN^- cyano OH^- hydroxo

   Neutral groups have no distinctive endings. Thus NH_3 ammine, CO carbonyl, and H_2O aquo. No provision was made in the IUC system for naming positive ligands, but it has been proposed that the ending *ium* be used. Two examples are $NH_2\text{---}NH_3^+$ hydrazinium and NO^+ nitrosylium.
3. In listing the ligands, negative ligands are named first, then neutral ones, thus $[Co(NH_3)_3(NO_2)_3]$ trinitrotriamminecobalt. It would seem logical to list positive ligands last as in $[Pd(N_2H_4)(N_2H_5)Cl_2]Cl$ dichlorohydrazinehydraziniumpalladium(II) chloride.

6.21 As the preceding examples indicate, it is customary to follow Werner's system in using the Greek prefixes *di-*, *tri-*, *tetra-*, and so on, to indicate the number of coordinated groups of a particular kind. When the name of the ligand is complex, the terms *bis*, *tris*, *tetrakis*, etc., followed by the name of the ligand enclosed in parentheses seems desirable, in agreement with best usage

[2] JORISSEN, BASSETT, DAMINESS, FICHTER and REMY, *J. Am. Chem. Soc.* **63**, 889 (1941).
[3] FERNELIUS, LARSEN, MARCHI and ROLLINSON, *Chem. and Eng. News*, **26**, 520 (1948).

in the nomenclature of organic compounds. Thus [Co en$_3$]$^{3+}$ would be named tris(ethylenediamine)cobalt(III) ion. Except in cases of this kind the use of parentheses to separate the names of ligands is not considered necessary. Hyphens are not used for this purpose, either, except in the naming of polynuclear complexes.

4. The oxidation state of the central element in the complex is indicated according to the Stock system by a Roman numeral enclosed in parentheses immediately following the name of the metal. In complex anions the name of the central element ends in *ate* (or in *ic* for the acid) and is followed by the Roman numeral in parentheses. An oxidation state of zero is indicated by the symbol (0). This rule is illustrated by the following examples.

[Co(NH$_3$)$_4$SO$_4$](NO$_3$)	sulfatotetramminecobalt(III) nitrate
K[Co(NH$_3$)$_2$(NO$_2$)$_4$]	potassium tetranitrodiamminecobaltate(III)
K$_4$[Fe(CN)$_6$]	potassium hexacyanoferrate(II)
H$_2$[PtCl$_6$]	hexachloroplatinic(IV) acid, or hydrogen hexachloroplatinate(IV)
K$_4$[Ni(CN)$_4$]	potassium tetracyanonickelate(0)

6.22 Neutral complexes are named like cations, although in this case it is often not necessary to indicate the oxidation state if the composition of the complex clearly indicates it. For example, the name of the compound [Ir(NH$_3$)$_3$Cl$_3$] may be written simply *trichlorotriammineiridium*. For that matter, with other complex compounds, especially if the oxidation state of the central element is unknown or is uncertain, indication of the oxidation state may be omitted if the composition of the compound is clearly indicated by the name. Thus for K$_3$[Co(S$_2$O$_3$)$_2$(NO)$_2$] the name *tripotassium dithiosulfatodinitrosylcobaltate* indicates the composition of the compound without making it necessary to specify whether cobalt is unipositive and the NO neutral or the cobalt is tripositive and the NO uninegative.

5. In naming dinuclear complexes it is customary to indicate the bridging group by the Greek letter μ. The following examples will illustrate the recommended usage in this connection.

[(H$_3$N)$_5$Cr—O—Cr(NH$_3$)$_5$]X$_5$ decammine-μ-hydroxodichromium(III) salt
              |
              H

hexammine-μ-trihydroxodicobalt(III) ion

$$\left[\text{en}_2\ \text{Co} \underset{\underset{\displaystyle \overset{|}{\text{H}}}{\text{O}}}{\overset{\overset{\displaystyle \overset{|}{\text{H}}}{\text{N}}}{}} \text{Co en}_2 \right]^{4+}$$

tetrakis(ethylenediamine)-μ-amido-μ-hydroxodicobalt(III) ion

$$\left[(\text{H}_3\text{N})_4\text{Co} \underset{\underset{\displaystyle \overset{|}{\text{H}}}{\text{O}}}{\overset{\overset{\displaystyle \overset{|}{\text{H}}}{\text{O}}}{}} \text{Co(NH}_3)_2\text{Cl}_2 \right] \text{Cl}_2$$

tetramminecobalt(III)-μ-dihydroxodichlorodiamminecobalt(III) chloride

Isomerism

6.23 As might be expected from their rather complex compositions, many coordination compounds have been obtained in two or more isomeric forms. A study of the phenomenon of isomerism has, as a matter of fact, provided a great deal of insight into the structure of these substances, just as similar studies have done in the field of organic chemistry. It is convenient to classify the various cases of isomerism essentially as Werner did into the following types: polymerism, ionization isomerism, hydrate isomerism, ligand isomerism, coordination isomerism, linkage isomerism, and stereoisomerism.

Polymerism **6.24** The phenomenon denoted by this term does not represent true isomerism; it concerns compounds which have the same composition but different formula weights. For example, there are several compounds which have an empirical composition corresponding to $[\text{Pt(NH}_3)_2\text{Cl}_2]_n$. One of these compounds is a yellow, sparingly soluble nonelectrolyte which may be prepared from solid tetrammineplatinum(II) chloride, $[\text{Pt(NH}_3)_4]\text{Cl}_2$, with loss of ammonia, by heating at 250°. Its formula is appropriately written $[\text{Pt(NH}_3)_2\text{Cl}_2]$. A second compound (Magnus's green salt) is precipitated when solutions of tetrammineplatinum(II) chloride and tetrachloroplatinic acid are mixed, and therefore may be formulated $[\text{Pt(NH}_3)_4][\text{PtCl}_4]$. Other compounds of general formula $[\text{Pt(NH}_3)_2\text{Cl}_2]_n$ correspond to the formulas $[\text{Pt(NH}_3)_3\text{Cl}][\text{Pt(NH}_3)\text{Cl}_3]$, $[\text{Pt(NH}_3)_4][\text{Pt(NH}_3)\text{Cl}_3]_2$, and $[\text{Pt(NH}_3)_3\text{Cl}]_2[\text{PtCl}_4]$.

6.25 A number of other examples of polymerism have been encountered, an especially striking one being provided by the series of compounds of general formula $[\text{Co(NH}_3)_3(\text{NO}_2)_3]_n$. The following seven compounds in this series are known.

n		n	
1	$[\text{Co(NH}_3)_3(\text{NO}_2)_3]$	4	$[\text{Co(NH}_3)_6][\text{Co(NH}_3)_2(\text{NO}_2)_4]_3$
2	$[\text{Co(NH}_3)_6][\text{Co(NO}_2)_6]$	4	$[\text{Co(NH}_3)_4(\text{NO}_2)_2]_3[\text{Co(NO}_2)_6]$
2	$[\text{Co(NH}_3)_4(\text{NO}_2)_2][\text{Co(NH}_3)_2(\text{NO}_2)_4]$	5	$[\text{Co(NH}_3)_5(\text{NO}_2)]_3[\text{Co(NO}_2)_6]_2$
3	$[\text{Co(NH}_3)_5(\text{NO}_2)][\text{Co(NH}_3)_2(\text{NO}_2)_4]_2$		

6.26 Polymerism may also involve a polynuclear complex and a simpler complex or two polynuclear complexes, as in the compounds shown.

$$\left[\begin{array}{c} OH \\ (H_3N)_3Co-OH-Co(NH_3)_3 \\ OH \end{array}\right] X_3 \quad and \quad \left[Co\left(\begin{array}{c} OH \\ OH \end{array}Co(NH_3)_4\right)\right]_3 X_6$$

6.27 Before true isomerism can be established between different compounds of the same composition, it is obviously necessary to rule out the possibility that the compounds may, instead, be different polymeric forms. If they are solids it is also necessary to show that they are not simply different crystalline modifications of the same compound. Differences in physical properties, such as colligative properties in suitable solvents, conductivities, absorption spectra, and the like may often be used. Likewise, the chemical behavior and mode of preparation of the compounds may give insight into their nature.

Ionization Isomerism **6.28** An example of ionization isomerism is furnished by the two modifications of $Pt(NH_3)_4SO_4(OH)_2$. One modification is a strong base, giving no test for sulfate ion, and may be formulated $[Pt(NH_3)_4SO_4](OH)_2$. The other form is a neutral compound which gives an immediate precipitate with barium salts, and can be written $[Pt(NH_3)_4(OH)_2]SO_4$. Clearly an interchange of negative groups between the coordination sphere and the "ionization sphere" is here involved. Some other examples follow.

$[Co(NH_3)_5NO_3]SO_4$ and $[Co(NH_3)_5SO_4]NO_3$
$[Co(NH_3)_4(NO_2)Cl]Cl$ and $[Co(NH_3)_4Cl_2]NO_2$
$[Co\ en_2(NO_2)Cl]SCN,\ [Co\ en_2(NO_2)SCN]Cl,\ and\ [Co\ en_2(SCN)Cl]NO_2$

Hydrate Isomerism **6.29** Hydrate isomerism is somewhat analogous to ionization isomerism but involves the interchange of a neutral group with a negative ion. It is illustrated by the three isomeric forms of $CrCl_3 \cdot 6H_2O$. The properties of the three modifications indicate the following respective formulations.

$[Cr(H_2O)_6]Cl_3$ $[Cr(H_2O)_5Cl]Cl_2 \cdot H_2O$ $[Cr(H_2O)_4Cl_2]Cl \cdot 2H_2O$
β-form γ-form α-form
(violet)   (green)   (green)

The violet modification does not lose water when stored over sulfuric acid, its molar conductance is of the same order as that of a terunivalent salt, and all its chloride is immediately precipitated by silver nitrate in cold solution. The γ-form loses one mole of water over sulfuric acid, and only two thirds of its chloride can be immediately precipitated. Its molar conductance corresponds to that of a biunivalent salt. The α-form readily loses two moles of water, and its other properties confirm the formula written above. Another example of hydrate isomerism is that of

$$[Co(NH_3)_4(H_2O)Cl]Cl_2 \quad \text{and} \quad [Co(NH_3)_4Cl_2]Cl \cdot H_2O.$$
(violet)   (green)

An example of both hydrate and ionization isomerism is given by the two compounds

$$[Co(NH_3)_4(H_2O)Cl]Br_2 \quad \text{and} \quad [Co(NH_3)_4Br_2]Cl \cdot H_2O.$$
(violet)   (green)

Ligand Isomerism   **6.30** Isomeric forms of a complex may result from isomerism within a ligand.   For example, three isomers of the formula

$$[Co\ en_2(CH_3C_6H_4NH_2)Cl]Cl_2$$

can be obtained, corresponding to the use of *o-*, *m-*, and *p-*toluidine, respectively. Similarly, the compounds represented by $[Co\ pn_3]Cl_3$ and $[Co\ tmen_3]Cl_3$, in which pn indicates 1,2-diaminopropane (propylenediamine) and tmen stands for 1,3-diaminopropane (trimethylenediamine), are isomeric.

Coordination Isomerism   **6.31** If the complex salt consists of both a complex cation and a complex anion, then an interchange of ligands between the coordination centers may give rise to isomerism, as in the following examples.

$[Co(NH_3)_6][Cr(CN)_6]$	and	$[Cr(NH_3)_6][Co(CN)_6]$
$[Co(NH_3)_4(H_2O)_2][Cr(CN)_6]$	and	$[Cr(NH_3)_4(H_2O)_2][Co(CN)_6]$
$[Co(NH_3)_6][Co(NO_2)_6]$	and	$[Co(NH_3)_4(NO_2)_2][Co(NH_3)_2(NO_2)_4]$
$[Co(NH_3)_6][Co(NH_3)_2(NO_2)_4]_3$	and	$[Co(NH_3)_4(NO_2)_2]_3[Co(NO_2)_6]$
$[Pt(NH_3)_4][PtCl_6]$	and	$[Pt(NH_3)_4Cl_2][PtCl_4]$

An interchange of ligands between the coordination centers in a single polynuclear complex may also result in isomerism as in the compounds

Linkage Isomerism   **6.32** Linkage isomerism, called by Werner "salt isomerism," arises from the possibility that either of two different atoms in a ligand may be attached to the coordination center.   Thus, it is conceivable that cyanide ion might attach itself to the metal by coordination of either the nitrogen atom or the carbon atom.   Similarly, carbon monoxide might use either oxygen or carbon, thiocyanate ion might use either nitrogen or sulfur, and so on. In spite of the apparent possibilities, few authentic cases of linkage isomerism have actually been established.   There is evidence, however, that the nitrite ion when coordinated may be linked either by nitrogen or by oxygen.   For example, two modifications of nitropentamminecobalt(III) chloride have been obtained, in both of which the nitrite ion is in the coordination sphere.   One of them is a brownish-yellow compound from which the nitrite group is not liberated by dilute mineral acids. The other form is red and undergoes spontaneous conversion into the yellow modification upon standing, either in solution or in the solid state. Treatment of the red form with acids yields nitrous acid. The characteristic color of the hexammines of cobalt(III), in which six nitrogens are bonded to cobalt, is yellow, whereas the aquopentammines, $[Co(NH_3)_5OH_2]X_3$, and the nitratopentammines, $[Co(NH_3)_5(ONO_2)]X_2$, which have five nitrogens and one oxygen so attached, are red. By analogy it has been assumed that the two isomeric forms in question may be represented as indicated. The difference

$$\begin{bmatrix} H_3N \quad NO_2 \\ H_3N \rightarrow Co \leftarrow NH_3 \\ H_3N \quad NH_3 \end{bmatrix} Cl_2 \quad \text{and} \quad \begin{bmatrix} H_3N \quad ONO \\ H_3N \rightarrow Co \leftarrow NH_3 \\ H_3N \quad NH_3 \end{bmatrix} Cl_2$$

nitropentamminecobalt(III)   nitritopentamminecobalt(III)
chloride (yellow)   chloride (red)

in stability of the bond between cobalt and the nitrite group in these two compounds with respect to hydrolysis by acids parallels the difference observed between organic nitro-compounds, R—NO_2, and nitrites, R—ONO. Other compounds containing the nitrite ion as ligand have also been obtained in two forms analogous to those described above, and have been formulated in similar fashion, as, for example, $[Co\ en_2(NO_2)_2]X$ and $[Co\ en_2(ONO)_2]X$.

Stereoisomerism **6.33** Among complexes in which the coordination number of the central atom is four or more, the possibilities for geometrical and optical isomerism become important. Discovery of both of these types of isomerism, as a matter of fact, played a very important part in the elucidation of the fundamental structural patterns of four-coordinated and six-coordinated complexes.

6.34 For example, although many four-coordinated complexes have a tetrahedral structure, various lines of evidence (see below) lead to the conclusion that those of platinum(II) are planar. One argument for this view is based on the discovery of two isomeric forms each of such complex compounds as $[Pt(NH_3)_2Cl_2]$, $[Pt(NH_3)_2Br_2]$, and $[Pt(NH_3)_2(CN)_2]$. The two forms appear to be geometrical isomers, of the structure exemplified in Figure 6.1. A tetrahedral structure in the same compound would not, of course, permit isomerism.

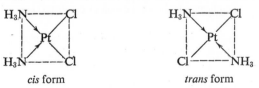

cis form   *trans* form

Fig. 6.1 Geometrical isomerism in the planar complex dichlorodiammineplatinum(II).

6.35 Six-coordinated complexes, in general, appear to possess an octahedral arrangement of the ligand atoms around the coordination center. In support of this structure is the fact that two isomeric forms (but not more than two) of a

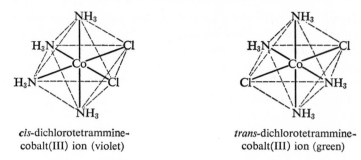

cis-dichlorotetrammine-
cobalt(III) ion (violet)

trans-dichlorotetrammine-
cobalt(III) ion (green)

Fig. 6.2   Geometrical isomerism in an octahedral complex.

number of di-substituted complexes such as $[Co(NH_3)_4Cl_2]^+$ have been obtained. Existence of these two forms is likewise attributed to geometrical isomerism as represented in Figure 6.2.

6.36 Good examples of optical isomerism are furnished by six-coordinated complexes which contain two or three molecules of a bidentate chelating agent as ligands. If the four molecules of ammonia in the violet-colored *cis*-dichloro-tetramminecobalt(III) ion (Fig. 6.2), for instance, are replaced by two molecules of ethylenediamine, the corresponding salts, such as *cis*-[Co en$_2$Cl$_2$]Cl, are found to be racemic mixtures, which by suitable treatment may be resolved into their optically active components.

6.37 The existence of optical isomerism in compounds of this kind can be readily explained in terms of the octahedral structure. In chelate ligands like ethylenediamine, spatial relations are such that the two donor atoms in the molecule cannot occupy coordination positions which are *trans* to each other,

Fig. 6.3   Optical isomerism in the octahedral complex
cis-dichlorobis(ethylenediamine) cobalt(III) ion.

but must occupy adjacent sites in the coordination sphere. There are, accordingly, two nonsuperimposable mirror-image configurations possible for *cis*-[Co en$_2$Cl$_2$]$^+$, as is shown in Figure 6.3. On the other hand, the *trans*-dichloro-bis(ethylenediamine)cobalt(III) ion, as can be seen from Figure 6.4, possesses such symmetry that no optical isomers can be expected. The experimental demonstration that the violet-colored salts of the type [Co en$_2$Cl$_2$]X could be resolved into optical antipodes, whereas the isomeric green compounds could not be, constitutes very good evidence for assigning the *cis* arrangement of

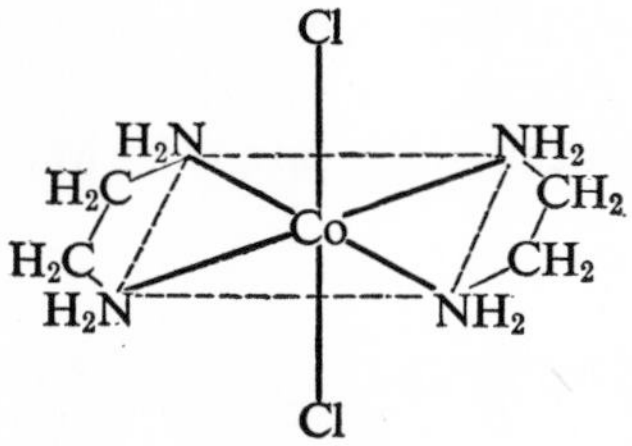

Fig. 6.4 *trans*-Dichlorobis(ethylenediamine)cobalt(III) ion showing lack of asymmetry.

chlorine atoms to the former, the *trans* structure to the latter. Similar results have been obtained with many analogous complexes containing other ligands in place of chlorine, other chelate ligands than ethylenediamine, and other metals than cobalt.

6.38 The actual resolution of a racemic complex compound is effected in essentially the same manner as is used for organic compounds. For example, a racemic *cis*-dichlorobis(ethylenediamine)cobalt(III) salt may be treated with a salt containing an optically active anion such as ammonium d-α-bromocamphor-π-sulfonate, $NH_4(C_{10}H_{14}O_4SBr)$*, yielding a mixture of diastereoisomers as indicated in the following equation.

$$\underbrace{d\text{-}[Co\ en_2Cl_2]Cl + l\text{-}[Co\ en_2Cl_2]Cl}_{\text{original racemic mixture}} + 2NH_4(d\text{-}C_{10}H_{14}O_4SBr) =$$

$$\underbrace{d\text{-}[Co\ en_2Cl_2](d\text{-}C_{10}H_{14}O_4SBr) + l\text{-}[Co\ en_2Cl_2](d\text{-}C_{10}H_{14}O_4SBr)}_{\text{diastereoisomers}} + 2NH_4Cl$$

Diastereoisomers differ in optical activity and in other physical properties, and may in general be separated by taking advantage of differences in solubility. After separation, the individual diastereoisomer may be converted into a salt with an inactive anion. In the present case, treatment of, say,

$$l\text{-}[Co\ en_2Cl_2](d\text{-}C_{10}H_{14}O_4SBr)$$

with hydrochloric acid under suitable conditions yields l-[Co en$_2$Cl$_2$]Cl. Anionic complexes can be similarly resolved by treatment with salts containing an optically active cation. Even neutral complexes have been at least partially resolved by taking advantage of the fact that one enantiomorph in general shows preferential adsorption over the other on optically active quartz.

* As used here d- and l- denote *dextro* and *levo* rotation, respectively, of light of a particular wavelength (the sodium D line). Rotation dispersion curves, *i.e.*, plots of specific rotation *versus* wavelength of light used, in general show considerable variation in rotatory power with wavelength; for some compounds even the direction of rotation may be changed over part of the range. The d- and l-designation conveys no explicit information concerning the absolute configuration of the complex, of course, and the fact that two different complexes may both show the same sign of rotation of sodium D light does not necessarily indicate that they possess the same absolute configuration.

6.39 Octahedral complexes containing three molecules of a bidentate chelate ligand must likewise possess two nonsuperimposable mirror image configurations, as is shown schematically in Figure 6.5. Many complexes of this kind,

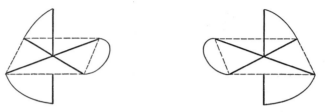

Fig. 6.5 Optical isomers in octahedral complexes containing three bidentate ligands.

such as $[Co\ en_3]^{3+}$, $[Rh\ en_3]^{3+}$, $[Pt\ en_3]^{4+}$, $[Fe\ dipyridyl_3]^{2+}$ and $[Cr(C_2O_4)_3]^{3-}$, to list but a few, have been resolved into their respective enantiomorphs by the use of suitable optically active salts. The existence of optical isomerism in six-coordinated complexes provides very strong evidence for the octahedral structure, of course, and also establishes the chelate character of the bifunctional ligands involved.

6.40 It is true that all of the examples of optically active complexes cited above, and many others which have been studied, contain carbon atoms. To meet the objection that carbon might in some unexplained fashion be responsible for the activity, Werner prepared completely carbon-free polynuclear

$$\left[Co\left(\underset{\underset{H}{O}}{\overset{\overset{H}{O}}{\diagdown\diagup}} Co(NH_3)_4 \right)_3 \right] X_6$$

complex compounds of the type shown and resolved them, obtaining antipodes of exceedingly high specific rotations.

6.41 Once resolution has been accomplished the optically active salt may maintain its original activity for an almost indefinite period, or it may lose it more or less rapidly through spontaneous racemization. For example, d- or l-$[Co\ en_3]Br_3$ is very inert in this respect, and its solutions may even be evaporated to dryness with hydrobromic acid without change in its activity. On the other hand, l-$[Fe\ dipyridyl_3]Br_2$ is reported to lose its activity completely on standing for three hours at room temperature. The possibility of achieving a satisfactory resolution obviously depends in part upon the relative inertness of the complex with respect to racemization.

6.42 Configurational change in an active complex has been shown to occur also in the course of some substitution reactions. For example, when l-$[Co\ en_2Cl_2]^+$ is treated with a carbonate under conditions such that rapid substitution occurs, the product is l-$[Co\ en_2CO_3]^+$. On the other hand, under conditions favoring slow reaction, when one or more of the chlorides is probably replaced by water (a type of reaction often termed *aquation*) previous to treatment with carbonate, the product is d-$[Co\ en_2CO_3]^+$. Obviously a change in configuration analogous to the Walden inversion in organic compounds has occurred in one of these reactions. This point is emphasized by the observation that treatment of *l*-[Co en$_2$CO$_3$]$^+$ with hydrochloric acid yields *d*-[Co en$_2$Cl$_2$]$^+$, whereas the *d*-[Co en$_2$CO$_3$]$^+$ gives *l*-[Co en$_2$Cl$_2$]$^+$ under the same conditions.

Coordination Number and Structure

General

6.43 A variety of chemical and physical methods have been employed in elucidating the structures of coordination complexes. Some applications of stereochemical information to this problem have already been pointed out (see 6.33–39), and other examples of the use of chemical reactions in this connection will be discussed below. Among the physical methods which have been employed X-ray structural analyses have been especially valuable, and measurements of dipole moments, magnetic susceptibilities, and optical properties have also made contributions. Results of such studies show that a group of complexes in which the true coordination number of the central atom is the same, fall into one, or in some cases two, structural patterns characteristic of that particular coordination number. Moreover, the coordination number and the structure can very often be correlated with the electronic configuration and the possibilities for orbital hybridization (see 5.80–102) in the central atom. In the following discussion the structures of various types of complexes are described in relation to the coordination numbers involved, the nature of the evidence for these structures is indicated, and some relationships to electronic configurations are considered.

Coordination Number Two

6.44 Relatively few metals show two-coordination characteristically in their complexes, the most familiar examples being those of monopositive silver and monopositive gold. X-ray examination of crystalline compounds containing the ions Ag(CN)$_2^-$, Ag(NH$_3$)$_2^+$, Au(CN)$_2^-$, and AuCl$_2^-$ has shown them to be linear. Interpreted in terms of the theory of the directed covalent bond (see 5.88), this structure implies the use of *SP* hybrid orbitals by the metal ion. Since silver(I) and gold(I) possess vacant *s* and *p* orbitals in their valence shells, this is possible, although *SP*^{3} hybridization with corresponding tetrahedral bonding might also be expected. Actually, some four-coordinated complexes of this kind are formed by silver(I), and tetrahedral four-coordination is even more characteristic of its homolog, copper(I).

Coordination Number Three

6.45 Although numerous examples of coordination number three for atoms of nonmetallic elements are known, *e.g.*, plane-triangular NO$_3^-$ and CO$_3^{2-}$, and trigonal-pyramidal ClO$_3^-$ and SO$_3^{2-}$, complexes in which a metallic atom actually possesses this coordination number are very uncommon. In solution the stepwise formation of four- or six-coordinated complexes may give rise to three-coordinated complexes in equilibrium with other species, but nothing definite is known about their structure. Three-coordination of copper is observed in solid $KCu(CN)_2$, the structure (see 24.48) suggesting use of modified SP^2 hybrid orbitals (see 5.85).

6.46 It must be pointed out that a number of solid compounds having empirical formulas which suggest three-coordination have been found to have other structures. For example, $CsCuCl_3$ is found by X-ray examination to have anionic chains made up of planar $CuCl_4$ units in which two adjacent chlorines are shared with the two neighboring units in the chain as shown schematically in Figure 6.6. The chain has an empirical composition corresponding to $CuCl^-$,

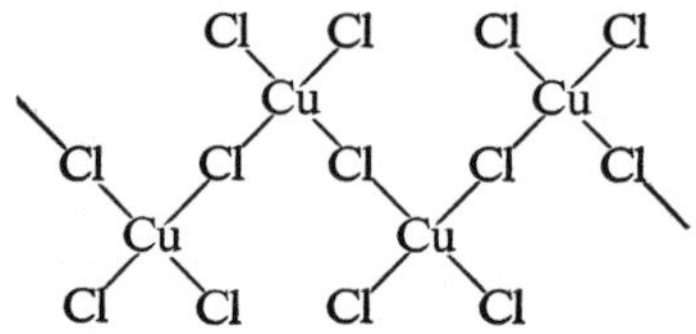

Fig. 6.6   Schematic structure of $(CuCl_3)_n^{n-}$ chains in $CsCuCl_3$.

although the coordination number of copper(II) here is actually four. In solid K_2CuCl_3 and in Cs_2AgCl_3 and Cs_2AgI_3 there are chains of MX_4 tetrahedra in which two corners are shared with two neighbors in the chain. Potassium tricyanonickelate(I), $K_2Ni(CN)_3$, is found to be diamagnetic, which suggests that the anionic complex is probably $[Ni_2(CN)_6]^{4-}$ with the odd electrons on the two nickel(I) ions paired. This hypothesis is supported by X-ray study.

6.47 These examples emphasize the fact that the empirical formula of a compound is by no means a safe guide to the true coordination number of the metal in the complex.

Coordination Number Four

Tetrahedral Structure   **6.48** The tetrahedral structure has been established for many four-coordinated oxy-anions of both metallic and nonmetallic elements. X-ray crystallographic examination of salts of SiO_4^{4-}, PO_4^{3-}, AsO_4^{3-}, VO_4^{3-}, SO_4^{2-}, ClO_4^-, IO_4^-, CrO_4^{2-}, and MnO_4^-, for example, has shown these ions to possess this structure. By the same method, a number of complexes containing other ligands, including $[BeF_4]^{2-}$, $[CoCl_4]^{2-}$, $[Cu(CN)_4]^{3-}$, $[Zn(CN)_4]^{2-}$, $[Cd(CN)_4]^{2-}$, and $[Hg(CN)_4]^{2-}$, have been found to have the tetrahedral structure. A similar pattern for gaseous nickel tetracarbonyl, $Ni(CO)_4$, is indicated by Raman spectra and electron diffraction studies (see 13.60). Some complexes of beryllium(II) and zinc(II) containing two unsymmetrical bidentate groups each have been at least partially resolved into optically active forms, a result which is consistent with tetrahedral coordination, as is illustrated in Figure 6.7 by bis(benzoylacetono)beryllium(II).

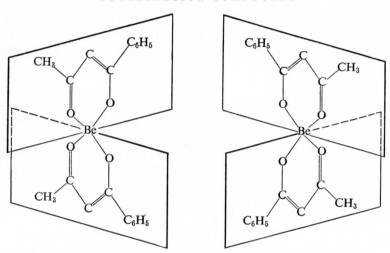

Fig. 6.7 Optical isomerism associated with tetrahedral coordination in bis(benzoylacetono) beryllium(II).

6.49 It would be expected that four-covalent complexes of the representative elements would utilize tetrahedrally directed SP^3 hybrid orbitals (see 5.82) on the central atom for bonding, since in these elements the most stable orbitals in the valence shell are s and p. As indicated by the examples given above, the observed tetrahedral structure of such complexes is in accord with this expectation. An examination of the electron configurations of the short transition series elements nickel, copper, and zinc (Fig. 6.8) shows that also in nickel(0),

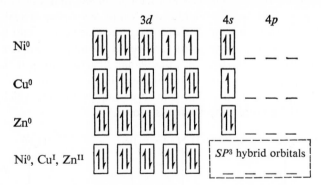

Fig. 6.8 Occupancy of valence orbitals of nickel, copper, zinc, and some tetrahedral complexes.

copper(I), and zinc(II) only s and p orbitals are available, the $3d$ orbitals being completely occupied by unshared pairs. Tetrahedral bonding in the corresponding four-coordinated complexes of these metals, as well as in the analogous complexes of silver(I), cadmium(II), and mercury(II), is thus readily interpreted in terms of the theory of the directed covalent bond.

6.50 Even when the electronegativity difference between central atom and ligand atom is sufficiently great that the bond between them possesses a large degree of ionic character, the tetrahedral arrangement is still to be expected for coordination number four, on the grounds that this configuration corresponds to minimum electrostatic potential energy.

Planar Structure **6.51** Although the tetrahedral structure is widely prevalent among four-coordinated complexes, there is an important group of coordination compounds, involving a comparatively few metals, in which the four donor atoms of the ligands lie on the diagonals of a square in a plane with the central atom.   This structure was first proposed by Werner for the four-coordinated complexes of platinum(II) to explain the existence of isomeric forms among complexes of the type [PtA$_2$B$_2$].   As was mentioned earlier, there are two distinct forms (sometimes designated α- and β-) for each of the compounds [Pt(NH$_3$)$_2$Cl$_2$], [Pt(NH$_3$)$_2$Br$_2$], [Pt(NH$_3$)$_2$(CN)$_2$], and [Pt(NH$_3$)$_2$py$_2$]Cl$_2$,* for example.   In order to be sure that the α- and β-compounds were true isomeric forms, it was necessary to show that the apparent isomerism was not simply a case of polymerism (see 6.24) or of dimorphism, in which the only difference lies in the manner of packing of the molecules in the crystal.   Polymerism has been ruled out by molecular weight determinations in suitable solvents, which have shown both forms to be monomeric.   Dimorphism was excluded, since differences between α- and β-forms persisted even in solution and in various chemical reactions. For example, treatment of, say, α-[Pt(NH$_3$)$_2$Cl$_2$] with appropriate reagents produced only the α-forms of such compounds as [Pt(NH$_3$)$_2$(NO$_3$)$_2$], [Pt(NH$_3$)$_2$Br$_2$], and [Pt(NH$_3$)$_2$(CN)$_2$], whereas similar treatment of β-[Pt(NH$_3$)$_2$Cl$_2$] yielded only the corresponding β-compounds.   Werner concluded that the two forms of these complexes represented examples of *cis* and *trans* geometrical isomerism and that this in turn argued for a planar structure since this would permit such isomerism, whereas a tetrahedral structure would permit no isomerism whatever in these complexes.   Consistent with the planar structure, also, is the fact that several compounds containing four different ligands in the complex, *e.g.*, [Pt(NH$_3$)pyClBr], have been obtained in three isomeric forms which would be expected from the possible arrangements shown.

6.52 The planar structure predicts geometrical isomerism, too, in complexes which contain two unsymmetrical bidentate ligands.   A number of examples of this kind have been observed.   For example, bis(glycino)platinum(II) has been obtained in two forms corresponding, presumably, to the *cis* and *trans* struc-

* py = pyridine

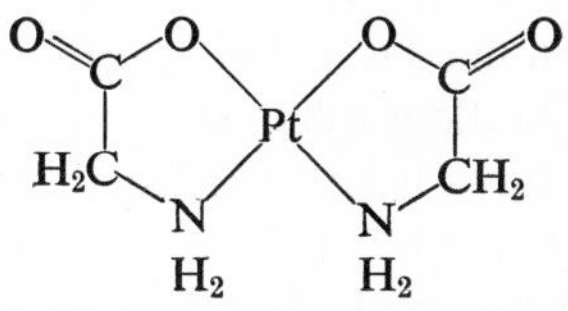

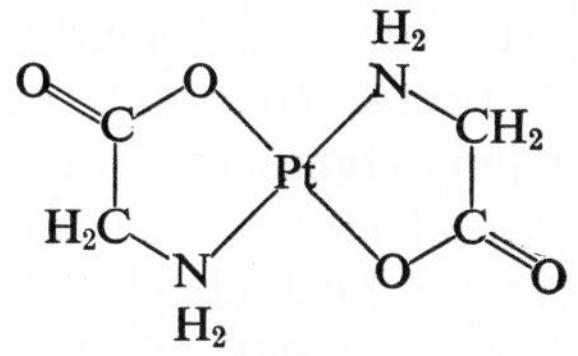

cis

trans

tures shown. Other similar compounds which have been obtained in two modifications include not only additional complexes of platinum(II), but complexes of palladium(II), nickel(II), and copper(II) as well, *e.g.*, bis(glycino)palladium(II), bis(benzylmethylglyoximo)palladium(II), bis(benzylmethylglyoximo)nickel(II), bis(methylglyoximo)nickel(II), and bis(picolinato)copper(II).

6.53 It should be mentioned that *cis-trans* isomerism could occur if the complex had a tetragonal-pyramidal structure with the metal located at the apex of the pyramid. Such an unlikely structure would, however, lead to optical isomerism in a complex containing four unlike ligands, such as

$$[Pt(NH_3)(SO_3)pyCl]^-,$$

and in the *trans* forms of complexes containing two unsymmetrical chelate ligands. Attempts to resolve such materials have been unsuccessful. These results, although admittedly negative, constitute evidence against both the pyramidal and tetrahedral structures, and thus indirectly support the planar structure.

6.54 Evidence of a more positive kind involving optical isomerism has been provided by the preparation of a compound containing the isobutylenediaminestilbenediamineplatinum(II) ion. The two chelate molecules, isobutylenediamine and *meso*-stilbenediamine, are so chosen that if planar coordination of the nitrogen atoms around the platinum occurs (Fig. 6.9) the resulting complex ion

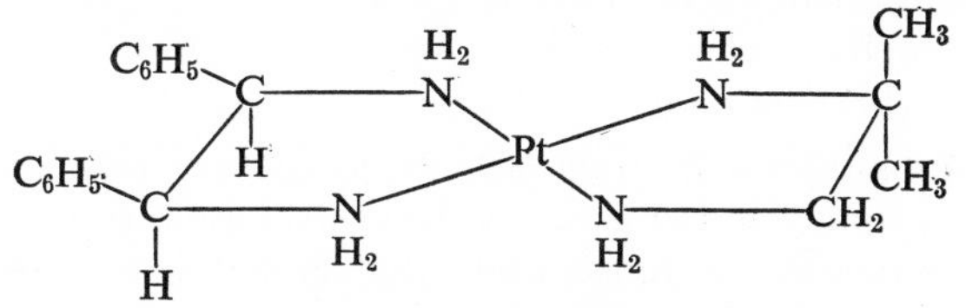

Fig. 6.9 **Isobutylenediaminestilbenediamineplatinum(II) ion showing asymmetric planar structure.**

possesses neither a plane nor center of symmetry, and must exist in optically isomeric forms. On the other hand, if tetrahedral coordination occurs the complex has a plane of symmetry, and optical isomerism will not arise, although geometrical isomerism is possible. This compound and its palladium(II) analog were both found to be resolvable into optical isomers, providing strong additional support for the planar structure of platinum(II) and palladium(II) complexes.

6.55 The most direct and convincing evidence for the planar structure of the four-coordinated complexes of platinum(II), palladium(II), and a few other metal ions comes from X-ray crystallographic studies. Among the compounds for which structural analyses have been made in this manner are $K_2[PtCl_4]$, $[Pt(NH_3)_4]Cl_2 \cdot H_2O$, $K_2[Pt(C_2O_2S_2)_2]$,* $K_2[PdCl_4]$, $[Pd(NH_3)_4]Cl_2$, $K_2[Pd(C_2O_2S_2)_2]$,* $K_2[Ni(C_2O_2S_2)_2]$,* $Na_2[Ni(CN)_4] \cdot 3H_2O$, $K_2[CuCl_4] \cdot 2H_2O$, $[Cu\ py_2Cl_2]$, and $K[AuBr_4] \cdot 2H_2O$. In all of these compounds the central atom in the complex and the four ligand atoms lie in the same plane, with adjacent metal-ligand bonds making essentially 90° angles to each other.

Orbital Theory and Magnetic Properties **6.56** The metal ions for which the square planar structure has been conclusively demonstrated in at least part of the four-coordinated complexes which they form are nickel(II), palladium(II), platinum(II), copper(II), and gold(III). It will be noted that these elements are all members of a short transition series and belong to families near the end of these series. Thus they all have nearly filled but active inner *d* orbitals. In particular, these metals in the oxidation states concerned possess eight or, at most, nine electrons in the *d* level. Nickel(II), for example, has eight 3*d* electrons; copper(II) has nine. Palladium(II), platinum(II), and gold(III) have configurations similar to nickel(II) except that higher principal quantum numbers are involved.

6.57 In the simple dipositive nickel ion, the 4*s* and 4*p* orbitals are vacant and the eight equivalent *d* electrons will normally be distributed in such manner that three of the 3*d* orbitals are fully occupied, while two are singly occupied by unpaired electrons with spins parallel, as represented in Figure 6.10. The two unpaired electrons should make a contribution of 2.83 Bohr magnetons to the magnetic moment of the ion (see 4.137), in essential agreement with observation on various simple nickel salts. If these two electrons were to become paired, occupying a single orbital, the fifth 3*d* orbital would be left completely vacant. With this rearrangement the nickel(II) ion would then have available for bonding one *d* orbital, as well as *s* and *p* orbitals. According to the theory of the directed covalent bond, hybridization of one *d*, one *s*, and two *p* orbitals should give rise to a set of four equivalent bonding orbitals, designated DSP^2, directed toward the corners of a square in the plane of the central atom (see 5.101–102). The square planar structure of four-coordinated complexes of nickel(II), palladium(II), platinum(II), and gold(III) can thus be explained theoretically as resulting from the formation of DSP^2 hybrid orbitals by these ions. The theory suggests (see 5.103) that when formation of either DSP^2 and SP^3 orbitals by a given atom is possible, the former should give somewhat stronger covalent bonds and, other things being equal, will generally be the type formed.

6.58 It is to be noted that use of an $(n - 1)d$, ns, and two np orbitals in this manner leaves no unpaired electrons in square planar complexes of the ions listed above. Such complexes would therefore be expected to have zero spin magnetic

---

* The ligands here are bidentate thio-oxalate ions, in which the sulfur atoms are attached to the metal ion.

moment, and should be diamagnetic. On the other hand, if nickel(II), for example, were to form SP^3 hybrid orbitals, leaving the two unpaired electrons undisturbed, the corresponding tetrahedral complex should be paramagnetic, the spin magnetic moment contribution being 2.83 Bohr magnetons. The electronic configurations corresponding to these various structures are indicated schematically in Figure 6.10.

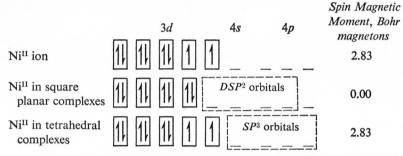

Fig. 6.10 Occupancy of valence orbitals in nickel(II).

6.59 It is a significant fact that of the numerous complexes of platinum(II) and palladium(II) on which magnetic susceptibility measurements have been made, all have been found to be diamagnetic. These results are consistent with a square planar structure for these complexes, since the electronic configurations here would, of course, be analogous to those given above for the corresponding nickel complexes. It should be pointed out, however, that even simple compounds such as $PdCl_2$, PdI_2, $Pd(CN)_2$, and $Pd(SCN)_2$ in the crystalline state are found to be diamagnetic. In at least the first of these, the structure involves coplanar coordination of four anions around each metal ion, each chloride being shared between two metal atoms. It may be that in all their compounds, and even in solution, palladium(II) and platinum(II) are planar quadricovalent. On the other hand, it is possible that these ions do not obey Hund's rule of maximum multiplicity of equivalent electrons (see 3.8), in which case diamagnetic character would not alone suffice to establish the planar structure.

6.60 Magnetic susceptibility measurements on a large number of nickel(II) complexes have shown that, although many of them are diamagnetic, a considerable proportion are paramagnetic. The complexes known to be planar which have been examined, e.g., $[Ni(CN)_4]^{2-}$, $[Ni(C_2O_2S_2)_2]^{2-}$, and glyoximo complexes, are diamagnetic, and it has been generally assumed that all diamagnetic nickel(II) complexes possess the planar structure. On the other hand, it is frequently assumed that the paramagnetic complexes have a tetrahedral structure, although direct evidence on this point is, at present, very meager. It is of interest that complexes in which the donor atoms of the ligands are rather highly electronegative, e.g., those having four oxygen atoms coordinated to the nickel, are predominantly paramagnetic.

6.61 The magnetic criterion cannot be simply used to give an indication of the structure of copper(II) complexes, since one unpaired electron would persist throughout. If SP^3 hybrid orbitals were to be formed, the unpaired electron would remain undisturbed in a $3d$ orbital. The formation of DSP^2 hybrid orbitals from the $3d$, $4s$, and two $4p$ orbitals would require promotion of the odd electron to a $4p$ orbital. It has been suggested that square planar orbitals might also be formed from a $4s$, two $4p$, and one $4d$ orbital, permitting the formation of what may be termed an "outer orbital" complex (see 6.87). In this case the unpaired electron would again remain in a $3d$ orbital. In every case the spin-only contribution to the magnetic moment would be 1.73 Bohr magnetons, although the magnitude of the small orbital contribution might vary somewhat with these various configurations. The diagram represents the different configurations discussed above.

	$3d$	$4s$	$4p$	$4d$
Cu^{II} ion	⇅ ⇅ ⇅ ⇅ ↑	—	— — —	— — — —
Cu^{II} in square planar complexes	⇅ ⇅ ⇅ ⇅	DSP^2 inner orbitals	↑	— — —
Cu^{II} in square planar complexes	⇅ ⇅ ⇅ ⇅ ↑	DSP^2 outer orbitals		— — —
Cu^{II} in tetrahedral complexes	⇅ ⇅ ⇅ ⇅ ↑	SP^3 orbitals		— — —

6.62 Pronounced double refraction is shown by crystals of $CaCO_3$ and $NaNO_3$, where it is attributed to the presence of parallel planar XO_3 ions. Similarly, $K_2[PtCl_4]$ and a series of cyano-complexes of platinum(II), palladium(II), and nickel(II), which also have parallel planar units in the crystal, show strong double refraction. This property of high double refraction (birefringence) is, therefore, used occasionally as evidence for the planar configuration of complex ions or molecules in a crystal.

6.63 Dipole moment determinations have supplied additional support for the planar structure in certain platinum(II) complexes and will be discussed later (see 6.69–71) in connection with the identification of *cis* and *trans* structures.

Identification of Isomers **6.64** The existence of two isomeric forms of complexes of the type $[PtA_2B_2]$ has been pointed out (see 6.51). Accepting the planar structure to be the correct one for these complexes, there remains the important problem of determining which of the isomeric forms of, say, $[Pt(NH_3)_2Cl_2]$ is the *trans* form, which the *cis*. A solution to this problem was first proposed by Werner on the basis of some elimination reactions involving $[Pt(NH_3)_2py_2]Cl_2$. This salt may be obtained in two forms. The α-form can be prepared either by the action of pyridine on α-$[Pt(NH_3)_2Cl_2]$ or by the action of ammonia on α-$[Pt\,py_2Cl_2]$. In an analogous manner β-$[Pt(NH_3)_2py_2]Cl_2$ is obtained from the corresponding β-compounds. When the solid diamminedipyridineplatinum(II) chlorides are heated alone, or when aqueous solutions of them are warmed with concentrated hydrochloric acid, two molecules of neutral ligand are eliminated, and two chloride ions are substituted in their stead. However, the α- and β-forms behave differently with respect to the products formed, this difference being shown in the following equations.

$$[Pt(NH_3)_2py_2]Cl_2 \longrightarrow [Pt(NH_3)pyCl_2] + NH_3 + py$$
$$\quad\alpha \qquad\qquad\qquad\qquad \beta$$

$$[Pt(NH_3)_2py_2]Cl_2 \nearrow [Pt(NH_3)_2Cl_2] + 2py$$
$$\qquad\qquad\qquad\qquad \beta$$
$$\quad\beta \qquad\qquad \searrow [Pt\,py_2Cl_2] + 2NH_3$$
$$\qquad\qquad\qquad\qquad\qquad \beta$$

6.65 These results indicate that the elimination of neutral ligands must not be occurring in random fashion, since in this case all theoretically possible products should be obtained in both reactions. Clearly the elimination is, instead, following some definite pattern. For reasons which will be pointed out below, Werner assumed that after one chloride ion had entered the complex, replacing either a pyridine or an ammonia molecule, the bond to the neutral group which was now *trans* to the chloride was somehow weakened, so that the second chloride would eliminate this *trans* neutral group and replace it. In short, the two neutral ligands which are eliminated and replaced by chlorides must have been *trans* to each other in the original complex. The postulated mechanism of *trans-elimination* leads to the reactions shown for the *cis* and *trans*

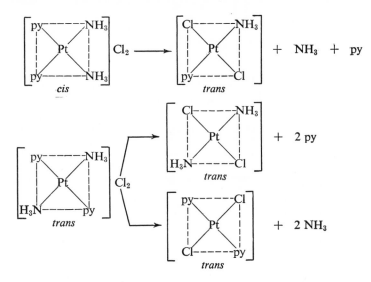

isomers. The sets of products to be expected as a result of *trans*-elimination thus correspond exactly to those which are actually obtained. On the other hand, if *cis*-elimination is postulated, it is easy to show that the products to be expected do not correspond with those experimentally produced. For these reasons Werner concluded that *trans*-elimination must take place in these reactions, and that, therefore, the α-compounds must have the *cis* configuration, the β-compounds the *trans*.

6.66 This assignment of *cis* and *trans* structures is supported by the differences in behavior of the two series of compounds toward bidentate chelating groups. For example, ethylenediamine reacts with α(*cis*)-[Pt(NH₃)₂Cl₂], replacing the two chlorides to give [Pt(NH₃)₂en]Cl₂. It does not react with the β(*trans*)-form, presumably because the two amino groups in the ethylenediamine molecule are not far enough apart to permit chelation across the *trans* positions. Another example is afforded by a series of reactions in which α(*cis*)-[Pt(NH₃)₂Cl₂] is first converted into α-[Pt(NH₃)₂(NO₃)₂], which in turn is found to react with oxalic acid to yield [Pt(NH₃)₂C₂O₄]. By contrast, the β(*trans*)-compound in a similar series of reactions gives [Pt(NH₃)₂(HC₂O₄)₂]. Thus the two chlorides in the α-compound are replaced by a bidentate ligand, whereas in the β-compound, with the chlorides presumably *trans* to each other, two unidentate ligands are required for replacement. Treatment of these last two compounds with hydrochloric acid, incidentally, converts them back into the respective dichloro complexes from which they were obtained.

6.67 The reactions discussed above may be represented schematically as shown.

6.68 Conclusions regarding structure which are based on substitution reactions must necessarily involve the assumption that no change in configuration occurs during substitution, an assumption which can by no means always be justified. The internal consistency of the results just discussed, however, appears to make the assumption a reasonable one in the present case.

6.69 Dipole moment determinations also have been used to distinguish *cis* and *trans* isomers of certain complexes of the type $[PtA_2X_2]$. If A represents a symmetrically substituted phosphine, arsine, or stibine, for example, with X representing a halogen, it is found that one of the two isomeric forms possesses a dipole moment of zero, while the other has a moment of approximately $8 - 12$ Debye units. Results of measurements[4] of this kind are shown in Table 6.4.

TABLE 6.4

Dipole Moments of Some Platinum(II) Complexes of the Type $[PtA_2X_2]$

Compound *	DIPOLE MOMENT (Debye Units)	
	trans-Form	*cis*-Form
$[Pt(PEt_3)_2Br_2]$	~0	11.2
$[Pt(PEt_3)_2I_2]$	~0	8.2
$[Pt(PPr_3)_2Cl_2]$	~0	11.5
$[Pt(PBu_3)_2Cl_2]$	~0	11.5
$[Pt(AsEt_3)_2Cl_2]$	~0	10.5
$[Pt(SbEt_3)_2I_2]$	~0	——
$[Pt(SbEt_3)_2Cl_2]$	——	9.2

* Et = ethyl   Pr = propyl   Bu = butyl

Similar results would be expected for the diammine compounds, $[Pt(NH_3)_2X_2]$, but their lack of solubility in suitable nonpolar solvents has made it difficult to determine dipole moments.

6.70 The permanent dipole moment of a molecule is given by the vector sum of the various effective bond moments. In $[Pt(PEt_3)_2Br_2]$, for example, the moments of the platinum-bromine bond, the platinum-phosphorus bond, and the resultant moment of the phosphine molecule — which is directed along the platinum-phosphorus axis — are involved. In the *trans* planar structure of this complex the two platinum-bromine moments are, of course, of equal magnitude but oppositely directed. Similarly, the two platinum-phosphine ligand moments are equal but opposed. The resultant permanent dipole moment must in consequence be zero. On the other hand, in the *cis* form, the moment will not be zero in general as can be seen in the diagram shown.

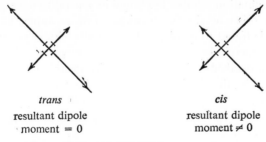

trans
resultant dipole
moment = 0

cis
resultant dipole
moment ≠ 0

4 JENSEN, *Z. anorg. allgem. Chem.*, **229**, 225 (1936).

6.71 These results not only serve to distinguish between the *cis* and *trans* structures, but as a matter of fact offer strong additional evidence for the planar structure as opposed to the tetrahedral or pyramidal models, since neither of the last two would permit zero dipole moment in a series of compounds of this kind.

6.72 Although most metals which form four-coordinated complexes typically form only one kind of structure, either tetrahedral or planar, in some complexes the structure of the ligand forces the other configuration. Beryllium(II) typically forms tetrahedral complexes, as has been mentioned above. However, it forms a complex with the binegative phthalocyanine [5] ion, a quadridentate ligand, in which the structure is planar as represented below. Similar complexes are ob-

tained with zinc(II), cadmium(II), and cobalt(II), which normally show tetra-hedral four-coordination. The phthalocyanine molecule itself, containing two hydrogens in place of the metal, is planar — a structure undoubtedly brought about by the resonating conjugated double-bond system — and presumably forces the metal complex into this arrangement, resulting in a *forced configuration*, different from that formed with other ligands.

Coordination Number Five

6.73 Complexes in which the coordination number of the metal atom or ion is five appear to be very uncommon. Compounds of such composition as to suggest this coordination number are found in general to have structures which actually involve four- or six-coordination. For example, Cs_3CoCl_5 in the crystalline state is found to consist of $CoCl_4$ units with separate ions, Cs^+ and Cl^-. A similar structure is shown by Cs_3ZnCl_5. Crystalline Tl_2AlF_5 consists of Tl^+ and of AlF_6 octahedra linked together in an anionic chain of empirical formula $(AlF_5)_n^{2n-}$ by the sharing of two opposite corners of each octahedron with its neighbors.

[5] LINSTEAD, *J. Chem. Soc.*, 1936, p. 1719; ROBERTSON, *ibid.*, p. 1195; LINSTEAD and ROBERTSON, *ibid.*, p. 1736.

6.74 True five-coordination is exhibited, however, in iron pentacarbonyl, $Fe(CO)_5$, which has been shown by electron diffraction to have the structure of a trigonal bipyramid as shown. The compound of composition corresponding to $Ni(PEt_3)_2Br_3$ is reported [6] to be monomeric in benzene and to have a magnetic moment (1.7–1.9 B.M.) and a dipole moment (2.5 D), which suggest that it may be a five-coordinated complex of nickel(III), probably possessing a tetragonal-pyramidal structure, with the nickel atom at or slightly above the center of the square base.

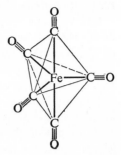

Coordination Number Six

6.75 Complex compounds in which the coordination number of the central atom is six are the most numerous of all and have been extensively studied. Six is the coordination number typically displayed, for example, by most of the elements in the transition series, and by a number of representative elements as well.

6.76 In a complex of the type $[MA_6]$, such as $[Co(NH_3)_6]^{3+}$ or $[Cr(CN)_6]^{3-}$, where A represents a given kind of unidentate ligand, all six of the M-A bonds appear to be equivalent. Among the spatial arrangements of the ligands about the coordination center which would permit six equivalent bonds, three symmetrical configurations suggest themselves, in which the ligands are located,

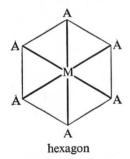 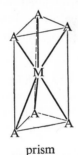 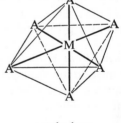

hexagon   prism   octahedron

respectively, (1) at the apices of a regular hexagon coplanar with the metal, (2) at the apices of a trigonal prism with the metal at the center, (3) at the apices of a regular octahedron surrounding the metal. The main lines of evidence which establish the octahedral structure as the correct one are summarized in following sections.

Evidence from Geometrical Isomerism **6.77** All three of the spatial arrangements mentioned above would permit the existence of only one form of what may be called a "monosubstituted" complex of the type $[MA_5B]$, where A and B represent two different kinds of unidentate ligand. However, in a disubsti-

[6] JENSEN, *Z. anorg. allgem. Chem.*, **229**, 265 (1936); JENSEN and NYGAARD, *Acta, Chem. Scand.*, 3, 474 (1949).

tuted complex of the type $[MA_4B_2]$, both the hexagon and the prism models permit three isomeric forms, whereas the octahedron allows only two, a *cis* form and a *trans* form (see 6.35).

6.78 In point of fact, two isomeric forms of a number of such complexes have been obtained, but in no case more than two. For example, two series of salts of type $[Co(NH_3)_4(NO_2)_2]X$ have been prepared, in which X represents any one of a number of anions such as Cl^-, Br^-, NO_3^-, $\frac{1}{2}SO_4^{2-}$, etc. In one series (the *flavo*-salts) the compounds are typically brownish yellow in color. The corresponding isomeric compounds (the *croceo*-series of salts) are generally yellow in color, and show other differences in properties. The existence of compounds containing $[Co(NH_3)_4Cl_2]^+$ in two isomeric forms, one typically green in color (the *praseo*-salts), the other violet (*violeo*-salts), has been mentioned (see 6.35). Two analogous isomeric series of compounds, also displaying green and violet colors, respectively, are obtained in the $[Co\ en_2Cl_2]^+$ compounds. Compounds containing $[Co\ en_2(H_2O)_2]^{3+}$, $[Co\ en_2(H_2O)(OH)]^{2+}$, and $[Co\ en_2(NO_2)Cl]^+$ represent other examples for which two isomeric forms are known. These phenomena are most readily explained in terms of *cis-trans* isomerism in an octahedral structure.

Evidence from Optical Isomerism   **6.79** The resolvability into optical antipodes of complexes such as *violeo*-$[Co\ en_2Cl_2]^+$, $[Co\ en_3]^{3+}$, and $[Co\ en_2(CO_3)]^+$, containing two or three bidentate ligands, can be easily accounted for by use of the octahedral model, as has been pointed out (see 6.37, 6.39). The hexagonal structure would not permit optical isomerism in compounds of this kind, nor would the prismatic structure unless chelation along the diagonals of the square faces of the prism occurred.

Evidence from X-ray Crystallography   **6.80** Structural analyses based on X-ray examination of numerous crystalline compounds containing six-coordinated complexes have shown the octahedral structure to be typical of such complexes. Some representative compounds examined in this way include the following.

$[Co(NH_3)_6]I_3$	$(NH_4)_2[PtCl_6]$	$K_2[SnCl_6]$	$[Co(NH_3)_6][Co(CN)_6]$
$[Cr(NH_3)_6](ClO_4)_3$	$K_2[Pt(SCN)_6]$	$Cs_2[GeF_6]$	$[Co(NH_3)_6][Cr(CN)_6]$
$[Co(NH_3)_5(H_2O)]I_3$	$(NH_4)_3[FeF_6]$	$W(CO)_6$	$[Co(NH_3)_5(H_2O)][Fe(CN)_6]$

Identification of Isomers   **6.81** Accepting the two isomeric forms of complexes of the type $[MA_4B_2]$ to represent *cis* and *trans* arrangements in an octahedral structure, there arises the question of determining which configuration belongs to each compound. Some examples of the manner in which this problem has been attacked are outlined below.

6.82 When carbonatobis(ethylenediamine)cobalt(III) chloride is treated with alcoholic HCl at 0°, or with severely chilled concentrated aqueous HCl, the product obtained is the violet *violeo*-dichlorobis(ethylenediamine)cobalt(III) chloride, rather than the green *praseo*-compound. Since the carbonate ligand must have occupied by chelation two adjacent sites in the coordination sphere of the cobalt, it is assumed that the two chlorides which have replaced the carbonate are also *cis* to each other, and that the *violeo*-compound must therefore have the *cis* configuration. Convincing proof that this assignment is correct comes from the fact that *violeo*-[Co en₂Cl₂]⁺ can be resolved into optical antipodes, whereas the green *praseo*-salt cannot be (see 6.37).

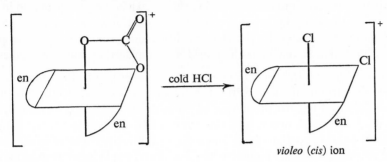

violeo (*cis*) ion

6.83 Because of the similarity in colors, it would seem reasonable to expect the analogous tetrammine complexes, *violeo*- and *praseo*-[Co(NH₃)₄Cl₂]⁺, to possess *cis* and *trans* structures, respectively. Optical activity is not possible here, of course, but a series of chemical reactions outlined below supports this assignment of configurations.

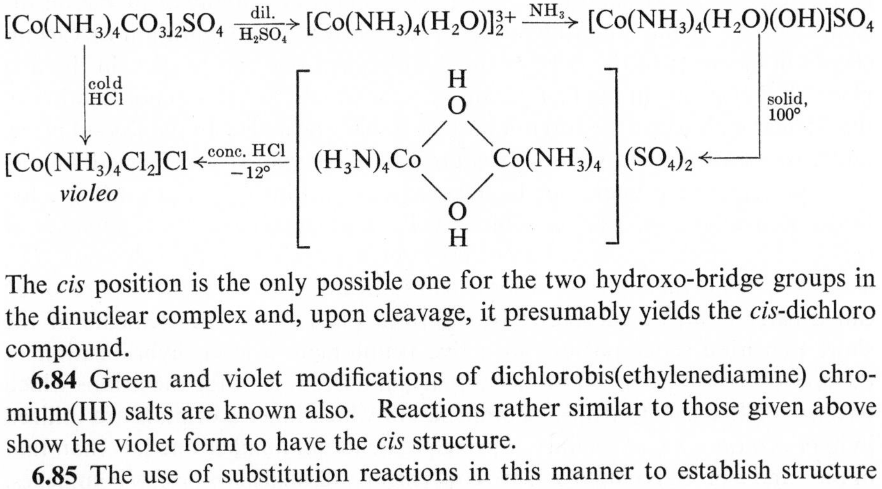

$$[Co(NH_3)_4CO_3]_2SO_4 \xrightarrow[H_2SO_4]{dil.} [Co(NH_3)_4(H_2O)]_2^{3+} \xrightarrow{NH_3} [Co(NH_3)_4(H_2O)(OH)]SO_4$$

$$[Co(NH_3)_4Cl_2]Cl \xleftarrow[-12°]{conc.\ HCl} \left[(H_3N)_4Co \underset{\underset{H}{O}}{\overset{\overset{H}{O}}{\diamond}} Co(NH_3)_4 \right] (SO_4)_2 \longleftarrow$$

violeo

The *cis* position is the only possible one for the two hydroxo-bridge groups in the dinuclear complex and, upon cleavage, it presumably yields the *cis*-dichloro compound.

6.84 Green and violet modifications of dichlorobis(ethylenediamine) chromium(III) salts are known also. Reactions rather similar to those given above show the violet form to have the *cis* structure.

6.85 The use of substitution reactions in this manner to establish structure assumes that no change in configuration occurs during the reaction. This assumption must be used with caution, since many examples of *cis* to *trans* and *trans* to *cis* conversions are known. As a matter of fact the unusual conditions employed in the first reaction given above to convert [Co en₂CO₃]⁺ into *cis*-[Co en₂Cl₂]⁺ were dictated by the fact that in aqueous hydrochloric acid at room temperature the *cis* form undergoes partial conversion into the *trans* form. Evaporation of the acid solution yields predominantly the solid *trans*-[Co en$_2$Cl$_2$]Cl · HCl, which is less soluble than the corresponding *cis* acid salt. On the other hand, evaporation of a neutral solution, prepared from either the *cis* or *trans* salt, yields solid *cis*-[Co en$_2$Cl$_2$]Cl, which is less soluble than the corresponding *trans* neutral salt. Moreover, the carbonato complex may be prepared by treating a solution of either the *cis*- or *trans*-dichloro complex with potassium carbonate. Presumably a mobile equilibrium exists between the *cis* and *trans* forms in solution, which may be displaced in one direction or the other by suitable changes in conditions. The system is made rather more complicated by the fact that in aqueous solution, aquation gradually occurs; that is, one or both chlorides are replaced by water molecules.

Orbital Theory and Magnetic Properties **6.86** According to the theory of the directed covalent bond (see 5.80 *ff.*), a set of six strong equivalent bonding orbitals, directed toward the apices of an octahedron, can be formed by hybridization of two *d*, one *s*, and three *p* orbitals on a given atom; *s* and *p* orbitals belonging to the stable outer shell of principal quantum number *n* would normally be used. However, the *d* orbitals used in hybridization may, in theory, belong either to the penultimate shell with quantum number $(n - 1)$ or to the outer shell with quantum number *n*. Both $(n - 1)D^2nSnP^3$ and $nSnP^3nD^2$ hybridization appear to occur.

6.87 Since in six-coordinated complexes the hybrid orbitals of D^2SP^3 type are occupied by six pairs of electrons supplied by donor atoms of the ligands, it is necessary that a suitable set of vacant orbitals be initially available on the central atom. From a consideration of the electronic configuration of various classes of elements in the light of this requirement one can predict, in the first place, that elements in the first period of eight should not show coordination of this kind at all because they do not possess stable *d* orbitals. In the second place, one also predicts that where six-coordinated complexes are formed among the representative elements of later periods, *e.g.*, [SnCl$_6$]$^{2-}$ and [SbBr$_6$]$^-$, hybridization of *ns*, *np*, and *nd* orbitals will, in general, occur.* Complexes of this kind in which the central atom uses outer *d* orbitals in hybridization, *i.e.*, *d* orbitals from the same principal quantum level as the *s* and *p*, are often called *outer orbital* complexes. In the third place, since the elements of the short transition series possess an active penultimate *d* level, hybridization of the type $(n - 1)D^2nSnP^3$ should be important here, at least for those ions which have six or fewer *d* electrons. Complexes in which inner *d* orbitals are utilized in hybridization, *i.e.*, *d* orbitals of principal quantum number one less than that of the *s* and *p* orbitals employed, are conveniently termed *inner orbital* complexes.

6.88 Octahedral coordination does, in fact, occur very extensively among

---

* It has been suggested that in [SeBr$_6$]$^{2-}$ and in [SbBr$_6$]$^{3-}$ $nP^3nD^2(n + 1)S$ hybridization probably occurs. Both Se^{IV} and Sb^{III} (but not Sb^V) possess a relatively inert pair of *ns* electrons, and it is postulated that these remain undisturbed in the complex, the atom using instead the vacant $(n + 1)s$ orbital. Cited as evidence for this hypothesis is the fact that the octahedral radius deduced for Se^{IV} in [SeBr$_6$]$^{2-}$ is about 23 per cent greater than its tetrahedral radius, whereas the corresponding difference in most complexes where such comparison has been made is less than 5 per cent.

the elements of the short transition series, especially with those ions having six or fewer d electrons. For example, Pt^{IV}, Pd^{IV}, Co^{III}, Ir^{III}, and Fe^{II} all possess six $(n-1)d$ electrons, while Fe^{III}, Mn^{III}, Mn^{II}, and Cr^{III} have less than six. In all these and analogous ions it is theoretically possible to make two vacant $(n-1)d$ orbitals available for use in bonding without promoting any of the electrons out of the d level. In many cases this will require the pairing of some of the d electrons, and will therefore result in a change in magnetic moment. Under such circumstances, magnetic moment values may be used to indicate whether or not inner orbital complexing has occurred. Some examples in which the magnetic criterion may be thus used are discussed below. Electronic configurations of some ions and complexes of this kind, as well as of some for which the magnetic criterion cannot be employed, are shown schematically in Figure 6.11, and magnetic moment values for representative compounds are presented in Table 6.5.

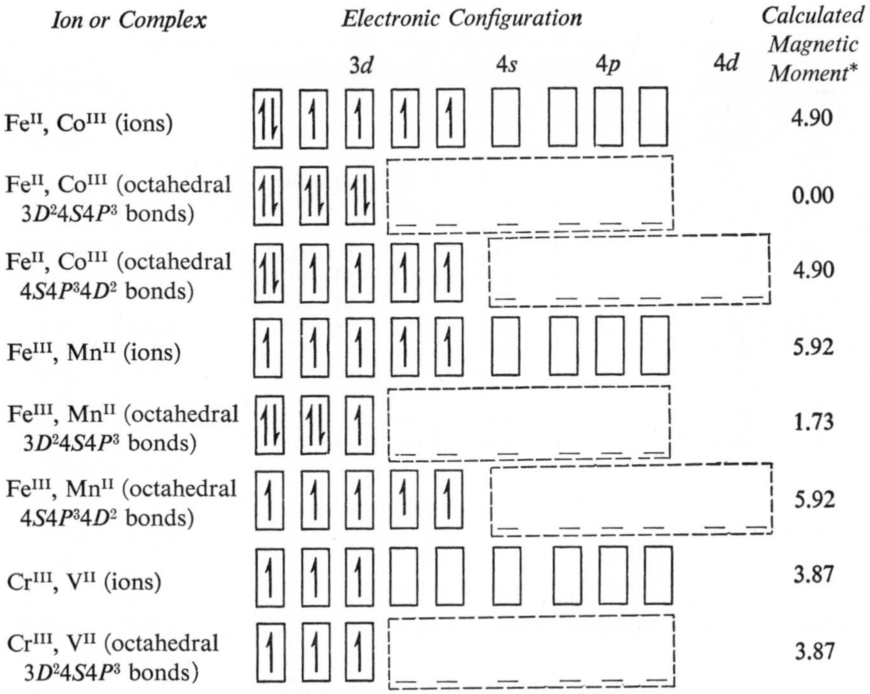

Ion or Complex	Electronic Configuration (3d, 4s, 4p, 4d)	Calculated Magnetic Moment*
Fe^{II}, Co^{III} (ions)		4.90
Fe^{II}, Co^{III} (octahedral $3D^24S4P^3$ bonds)		0.00
Fe^{II}, Co^{III} (octahedral $4S4P^34D^2$ bonds)		4.90
Fe^{III}, Mn^{II} (ions)		5.92
Fe^{III}, Mn^{II} (octahedral $3D^24S4P^3$ bonds)		1.73
Fe^{III}, Mn^{II} (octahedral $4S4P^34D^2$ bonds)		5.92
Cr^{III}, V^{II} (ions)		3.87
Cr^{III}, V^{II} (octahedral $3D^24S4P^3$ bonds)		3.87

*From spin-only formula; in Bohr magnetons.

Fig. 6.11 Electronic configurations and calculated spin magnetic moments of some first-row transition elements.

6.89 The simple iron(III) ion, for example, has five d electrons which, in accordance with Hund's rule of maximum multiplicity, are normally distributed one in each of the $3d$ orbitals. The theoretical spin-only magnetic moment is therefore 5.92 Bohr magnetons. When two of these $3d$ orbitals are used in D^2SP^3 hybridization and by electron pairs from donor atoms, two unpaired electrons enter other singly-occupied $3d$ orbitals, becoming paired with the occupants. The number of unpaired electrons is thus reduced from five to one in this process, and the calculated spin magnetic moment becomes 1.73 Bohr magnetons, as indicated in Figure 6.11.

6.90 The iron(II) ion has six $3d$ electrons, of which four are normally unpaired. In formation of an inner orbital D^2SP^3 complex these four electrons occupy two d orbitals, where they are, of course, paired. The calculated spin moment falls correspondingly from 4.90 Bohr units to zero. Cobalt(III) also has six d electrons, and similar relationships are expected.

Bond Type; Inner and Outer Orbital Complexes   **6.91** Examination of the magnetic moment values in Table 6.5 shows, first, that iron(II) and iron(III) ions

TABLE 6.5

**Magnetic Moments of Simple Salts and Complex Compounds
of Some First-Row Transition Elements**

Compound *	Observed Moment †	Compound *	Observed Moment †
$CrCl_3$	3.81	$[Fe^{II}o\text{-phen}_3]Br_2$ c	0.00
$Cr(NO_3)_3$ (solution)	3.84	$[Fe^{II}(H_2O)_6]SO_4 \cdot H_2O$	5.25
$K_3[Cr^{III}(CN)_6]$	3.8	$[Fe^{II}(NH_3)_6]Cl_2$	5.5
$[Cr^{III}(NH_3)_6]I_3$	3.6	$K_3[Co^{III}(CN)_6]$	0.00
$Fe_2(SO_4)_3$	5.86	$[Co^{III}(NH_3)_6]Cl_3$	0.00
$K_3[Fe^{III}(CN)_6]$	2.4	$[Co^{III}(NH_3)_4Cl_2]Cl$	0.00
$(NH_4)_3[Fe^{III}F_6]$	5.88	$K_3[Co^{III}F_6]$	5.3
$[Fe^{III}acac_3]$ a	5.9	$NiCl_2$	3.24–3.42
$FeCl_2$	5.23	$NiCl_2$ (solution)	3.24
$FeSO_4$	5.27	$[Ni^{II}diarsine_3](ClO_4)_2$ d	0.00
$K_4[Fe^{II}(CN)_6]$	0.00	$[Ni^{II}dipy_3](ClO_4)_2$ b	3.10
$[Fe^{II}dipy_3](ClO_4)_2$ b	0.00	$[Ni^{II}(NH_3)_6]Br_2$	3.23

* Measurements made on solid compounds unless otherwise indicated.
† Bohr magnetons
a acac = acetylacetonate ion
b dipy = α,α'-dipyridyl
c o-phen = *ortho*-phenanthroline
d diarsine = *ortho*-bis(dimethylarsino)benzene

in simple solid compounds do, indeed, possess magnetic moments which approximate those calculated for the number of unpaired electrons expected from Hund's rule. A second important fact brought to light is that, although some of the complexes of these ions have the lower magnetic moment predicted for inner D^2SP^3 orbital complexes, others have essentially the same moment as the simple ion.

6.92 For example, the iron(II) complexes $K_4[Fe(CN)_6]$, $[Fe\ dipy_3](ClO_4)_2$, and $[Fe\ o\text{-phen}_3]Br_2$ are diamagnetic, and thus have no unpaired electrons, in agreement with expectation for inner orbital complexes of iron(II). Similarly, the iron(III) complex $K_3[Fe(CN)_6]$ has a moment corresponding to one unpaired electron as expected. Unquestionably the binding in these complexes is to a large extent covalent, and the term "essentially covalent" is often applied to them. Since penultimate d orbitals are involved, their designation as "inner orbital" complexes is appropriate and is employed in this discussion.

6.93 On the other hand, the compounds

$$[Fe(H_2O)_6] SO_4 \cdot H_2O \quad \text{and} \quad [Fe(NH_3)_6]Cl_2$$

have high magnetic moments indicating the presence of four unpaired electrons. In the iron(III) complexes $(NH_4)_3[FeF_6]$ and $[Fe\ acac_3]$ the moments correspond to five unpaired electrons. The nature of the binding in complexes of this kind has been the subject of much discussion. Since the electronic configuration of the metal in the complex is the same as that of the simple ion, it has been postulated that the binding is predominantly electrostatic, involving either ion-ion interaction, as in Fe^{3+}—F^-, or ion-dipole interaction, as in Fe^{2+}—OH_2. This type of binding entails no difference in the spatial configuration of the complex, since the most favorable arrangement of six negatively-charged entities about a positive ion is an octahedral one. The term "essentially ionic" has been proposed and frequently used to describe these complexes, in contrast to the designation "essentially covalent" applied to complexes like $[Fe(CN)_6]^{3-}$ and $[Fe(CN)_6]^{4-}$.

6.94 Although there is admittedly a discontinuity in bond type of some kind between the two classes of complexes just discussed, it is recognized that the "essentially ionic" complexes do not necessarily represent extreme ionic binding. Tris(acetylacetonato)iron(III), for example, can be readily volatilized, is soluble in nonpolar solvents, and behaves, in general, like a covalent compound, although the magnetic moment (5.9 Bohr magnetons) puts it in the "essentially ionic" category. It has been suggested that the covalent contribution in these complexes may arise from resonance of four bonds formed by use of the $4s$ and $4p$ orbitals among the six positions, or that it may involve the use of $4S4P^34D^2$ hybrid orbitals by the central atom.[7] Because, in general, these bonds possess a significant amount of covalent character, the term "outer orbital" complex has been proposed as an alternative to the designation "essentially ionic."

6.95 On theoretical grounds, hybrid orbitals which use d orbitals from the same principal quantum level as the s and p should show greater extension in space than those employing penultimate d orbitals. Theoretically, also, these more extended orbitals should be most satisfactorily used by electron pairs from highly electronegative donor atoms, which tend naturally to keep the shared pairs rather strongly withdrawn toward the ligands. It is notable that the complexes of iron(II), iron(III), and cobalt(III) with strongly electronegative ligands, e.g., $[Fe^{III}F_6]^{3-}$, $[Fe^{III}acac_3]$, $[Fe^{II}(H_2O)_6]^{2+}$, and $[Co^{III}F_6]^{3-}$, show the

[7] HUGGINS, *J. Chem. Phys.*, **5**, 527 (1937); SUGDEN, *J. Chem. Soc.*, 1943, p. 328; PAULING, *ibid.*, 1948, p. 1461; BURSTALL and NYHOLM, *ibid.*, 1952, p. 3570; CRAIG, MACCOLL, NYHOLM, ORGEL, and SUTTON, *ibid.*, 1954, p. 332.

high magnetic moments consistent with use of $4S4P^34D^2$ orbitals. It seems clear that, regardless of the precise theoretical interpretation of this behavior, the bonds in complexes of this kind are more highly polar than they are in the complexes with less electronegative ligands, e.g., $[Fe^{III}(CN)_6]^{3-}$, $[Fe^{II}(CN)_6]^{4-}$, and $[Co^{III}(NH_3)_6]^{3+}$, in which the magnetic moments correspond to use of $3D^24S4P^3$ bonds.

6.96 The nature of the metal, as well as of the ligand, is important in determining into which category a given complex will fall. For example, all of the complexes of cobalt(III) which have been examined, except $[CoF_6]^{3-}$, are of the inner orbital type. This includes $[Co(H_2O)_6]^{3+}$ and $[Co\ acac_3]$, both of which are diamagnetic, even though there are six strongly electronegative oxygen atoms coordinated to the cobalt atom. On the other hand, $[Fe(H_2O)_6]^{2+}$ and $[Fe\ acac_3]$ belong to the outer orbital type. Again, $[Fe\ dipy_3]^{2+}$ is diamagnetic, indicating an inner orbital complex, whereas $[Ni\ dipy_3]^{2+}$ has essentially the same magnetic moment as the nickel(II) ion, and is therefore to be regarded, presumably, as an outer orbital complex.

6.97 Attempts have been made to bring to light some aspects of chemical behavior which might serve to differentiate sharply between these two types of complexes. Since many of the especially inert complexes (see 6.4) are of the inner orbital kind, it has been suggested that a marked difference in lability or inertness may exist between them, with respect to substitution reactions, racemization of optically active forms, exchange with radioactively-tagged ligands or metal ions, or the like. Broadly speaking, complexes of the outer orbital kind are, in general, more labile than those of the inner orbital class, although other factors than bond type seem also to be concerned here (see below). Outside this rather rough generalization, to which there are numerous exceptions, there appears to be at the present time no single chemical criterion which can be consistently correlated with the classification which has been based on magnetic properties.

6.98 Magnetic moment values fail in some cases to differentiate between inner and outer orbital complexes. Chromium(III), for example, has three d electrons, normally unpaired, and two vacant $3d$ orbitals (Fig. 6.11). Formation of $3D^24S4P^3$ bonds would not be expected to change the number of unpaired electrons, and it is seen from Table 6.5 that $[Cr(CN)_6]^{3-}$ and $[Cr(NH_3)_6]^{3+}$ have magnetic moments indicating the presence of three unpaired electrons (with some orbital contributions also being made to the moment), which is consistent with either $3D^24S4P^3$ or $4S4P^34D^2$ bonds. Since many chromium(III) complexes, including those mentioned above, show slow substitution reactions in solution, it is assumed that they are actually inner orbital complexes.

6.99 It may be mentioned that all of the complexes of platinum(IV) which have been examined are diamagnetic. Inasmuch as platinum(IV), like cobalt(III) and iron(II), has six d electrons, this observation might be interpreted as indicating inner orbital complexing, which is consistent with the general inertness of platinum(IV) complexes. It should be pointed out, however, that it is not certain that Hund's rule of maximum multiplicity (see 3.8) is applicable to platinum; thus the magnetic moment is not necessarily diagnostic here.

Ligand Field Theory **6.100** The preceding discussion has been presented from the point of view of the valence bond theory. An alternative approach, which promises to be a very useful one, employs the ligand field or crystal field theory. Basically, this theory starts with the assumption that most complexes can be treated as relatively simple electrostatic systems consisting of point charges and dipoles. The potential energy of such a system is expressed in terms of classical equations of electrostatics representing contributions which arise from several types of interaction. Among these interactions are (1) attraction between the charged central ion and the ligand charges or dipoles including those induced by the central charge, (2) mutual repulsion between the ligand charges or dipoles, and (3) short range van der Waals' repulsions between the ligands and the central ion. It is clear that on this view, the magnitude of the charge on the central ion, the charge or permanent dipole moment of the ligand, the effective sizes of both ion and ligand, and the polarizability of the ligand should determine in large measure the binding energy of the complex. Calculations based on this model yield values of bond energies which are at least of the right order for a variety of complexes, including some hydrates, ammoniates, and halocomplexes. However, the simple electrostatic theory as outlined above offers no explanation for the magnetic behavior of the inner orbital type of complex. Nor does it account for the marked differences in stability often observed among the complexes of metal ions of essentially the same size and charge.

6.101 The ligand field theory introduces an important modification of the simple electrostatic model by taking account of the effect which the electric field between the central ion and the surrounding ligands has upon the orbitals in the valence shell of the central metal ion. Of particular interest is the effect upon the five d orbitals. According to the theory, in an octahedral complex with six equivalent ligands, the symmetry of the electric field is such that it produces a splitting of the five d orbitals into two groups. One group of two orbitals (d_{z^2} and $d_{x^2-y^2}$, having their maximum concentration along the bond axes) is raised in energy, the other group of three is lowered in energy relative to the level of the original undisturbed set. The magnitude of the splitting between the two groups of orbitals, that is, the energy difference between them, is a function of the radius of the d orbital of the metal and depends also upon the dipole moment (permanent and induced), or charge, of the ligand and the distance between ligand and central ion. The magnitude of the splitting will therefore vary both with the nature of the metal ion and with the ligand.

6.102 The d electrons which the metal ion possesses will occupy the perturbed orbitals of the complex in a manner analogous to that described by Hund's rule. That is, the set of three low-lying orbitals will be at least partially filled first, one electron in each orbital, all three with parallel spins. If the ion possesses only three electrons, *e.g.*, Cr^{3+}, then no electrons enter the two higher orbitals, nor do any electrons lose energy in becoming paired. The system thus acquires a significant amount of stabilization energy, often called "crystal field stabilization energy," and a corresponding gain in bond energy over that to be expected from simple electrostatic considerations.

6.103 If the metal ion has four or five d electrons, the fourth and fifth may be accommodated in either of two ways. In the first of these, the electrons may enter the high-lying orbitals, one electron in each. This would result in a progressive loss in stabilization energy. The spin-only magnetic moment of the metal would, of course, correspond to four or five unpaired electrons, respectively. This distribution of four or five d electrons would be expected only when the energy separation between the two groups of orbitals is relatively small, corresponding to a weak electric field between ion and ligands. In this case it is presumably more economical with respect to energy for the electron to enter the higher orbital than to lose the pairing energy required to enter one of the half-filled lower levels.

6.104 The second possible distribution of the fourth and fifth electrons would be expected to occur if the energy separation between the two groups of d orbitals were relatively large. Here the electron may lose pairing energy and enter a half-filled lower orbital, rather than to go into one of the much higher d orbitals. The spin magnetic moment of the metal ion would now be that associated, respectively, with two unpaired electrons or with one. This situation would correspond to the presence of a strong ligand field.

6.105 Metal atoms with from four to seven d electrons thus have the possibility of forming either of two configurations in octahedral complexes: one of "high spin," the other of "low spin," corresponding, respectively, to the "ionic," or "outer orbital," and the "covalent," or "inner orbital," complexes of valence bond theory. According to the ligand field theory, the choice between these two configurations is determined by the relation between the magnitude of the splitting in the d levels and the electron pairing energy. This relation varies with both metal ion and ligand. In general, high spin complexes are formed when the ligand field is weak, low spin complexes when it is strong. A schematic representation of these effects for a metal ion with six d electrons is given in the accompanying diagram. The weak field case would apply to $[Fe(H_2O)_6]^{2+}$ and $[CoF_6]^{3-}$, for example, whereas the strong field effect would be represented in $[Fe(CN)_6]^{4-}$ and $[Co(NH_3)_6]^{3+}$.

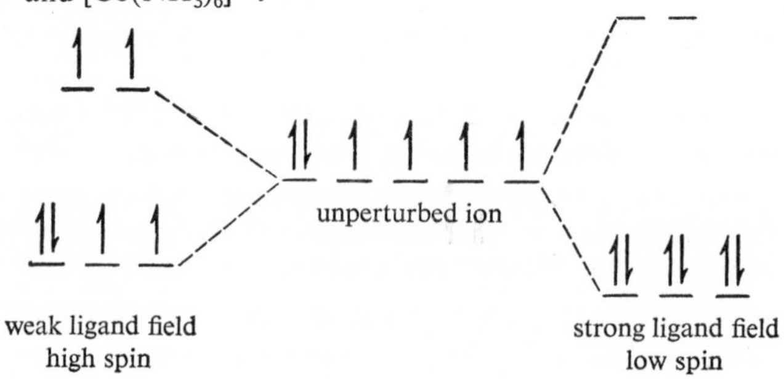

weak ligand field
high spin

unperturbed ion

strong ligand field
low spin

6.106 It should be pointed out that the electric field arising from a tetrahedral arrangement of ligands leads to a different splitting scheme, and the square planar arrangement to still another. These schemes may be employed in a similar manner to account for the magnetic behavior of complexes of these types.

Coordination Number Seven

6.107 Coordination numbers greater than six are of infrequent occurrence in complexes. With few exceptions the metals having such coordination numbers are 4d-, 5d-, or 5f-transition elements in positive oxidation states of four or more in the complex. The ligands include fluoride, oxide, cyanide, and a few chelating agents such as acetylacetonate, 8-hydroxyquinolate, and oxalate ions.

6.108 At least two types of structure involving seven-coordination have been established by X-ray crystallography. One of these is represented by the $[UO_2F_5]^{3-}$ complex in $K_3[UO_2F_5]$ and by $[UF_7]^{3-}$ in $K_3[UF_7]$. Both of these groups have been shown to have the shape of a pentagonal bipyramid (Fig. 6.12(a)).[8] In the former, the five fluorides lie at the apices of an essentially regular pentagon in a plane with the metal atom; the two oxygens lie on the axis perpendicular to this plane, one above and one below, at the apices of the bipyramid. In $[UF_7]^{3-}$ all seven of the U—F distances are equal (2.26 Å).

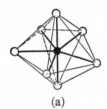 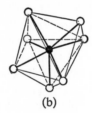

(a) (b) (c)

Fig. 6.12 The structures of some seven-coordinated ions: (a) UF_7^{3-}, (b) ZrF_7^{3-}, (c) NbF_7^{2-}.

The compound $K_3[UF_7]$ occurs in two modifications, one an ordered tetragonal form, the other a disordered cubic form. Both have the same $[UF_7]^{3-}$ structure, but differ in that there is some randomness in orientation of the complex in the latter form. Since the X-ray patterns of $K_3[ZrF_7]$ and $(NH_4)_3[ZrF_7]$ are similar to those of the disordered form of $K_3[UF_7]$, it has been suggested that $[ZrF_7]^{3-}$ probably has the pentagonal bipyramidal structure, also. It should be mentioned, however, that a previously proposed structure for $[ZrF_7]^{3-}$ is also consistent with the X-ray data, though not uniquely required by it. This structure[9] can be approximately described as a distorted octahedron of six fluorides around the metal, outside one triangular face of which the seventh fluoride is located, Figure 6.12(b). The distortion is such that all the Zr—F distances are equal. The $[NbOF_6]^{3-}$ complex in $K_3[NbOF_6]$ is similar to $[ZrF_7]^{3-}$.

[8] ZACHARIASEN, *Acta Cryst.* **7**, 783, 792 (1954).
[9] HAMPSON and PAULING, *J. Am. Chem. Soc.* **60**, 2702 (1938).

6.109 Another type of structure observed is exemplified by $[NbF_7]^{2-}$ in $K_2[NbF_7]$. This is essentially a distorted right trigonal prism with the seventh fluoride situated outside the center of one of the rectangular faces of the prism, Figure 6.12(c).[10] $K_2[TaF_7]$ has a similar structure.

Coordination Number Eight

6.110 Among eight-coordinated complexes two different structural patterns have been established by X-ray crystallography. In one of these, represented by $[TaF_8]^{3-}$ in crystalline sodium octafluorotantalate, the ligand atoms are located at the corners of a square Archimedean antiprism,[11] Figure 6.13(a). A different

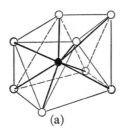
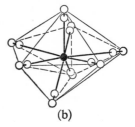

(a)   (b)

Fig. 6.13   The structures of (a) TaF_8^{3-} and (b) $Mo(CN)_8^{4-}$.

structure is displayed by $[Mo(CN)_8]^{4-}$ in $K_4Mo(CN)_8 \cdot 2H_2O$, in which the cyanide groups are located at the eight vertices of a dodecahedron with triangular faces, Figure 6.13(b). The carbon and nitrogen atoms of each cyanide group, incidentally, are collinear with the metal ion. Presumably the analogous tungsten compound, $K_4W(CN)_8 \cdot 2H_2O$, possesses a similar structure.

6.111 Other complexes in which eight-coordination probably occurs include the tetrakis(acetylacetonato) compounds of zirconium, hafnium, thorium, uranium(IV), cerium(IV), and plutonium(IV); the tetrakis(8-hydroxyquinolato) compounds of thorium and plutonium(IV); and the tetrakis(oxalato)uranium(IV) ion.

Polynuclear Complexes

6.112 Although in many coordination compounds the complex entity exists as a discrete ionic or molecular unit with a single coordination center, there are numerous examples of polynuclear complexes possessing two or more coordination centers (see 6.19). From the structural point of view these complexes correspond to groups in which two or more coordination figures (octahedra, tetrahedra, planes, or the like) share a corner, an edge, or even a face. A complex of this kind may be "finite," that is, it may consist of a definite number of coordination polyhedra linked together in a particular way, as in the dinuclear octammine-μ-dihydroxodicobalt(III) ion or the trinuclear trisilicate ion shown. On the other hand the complex may be "infinite" in extent, consisting of a

[10] HOARD, *J. Am. Chem. Soc.* **61**, 1252 (1939).
[11] HOARD, MARTIN, SMITH and WHITNEY, *J. Am. Chem. Soc.*, **76**, 3820 (1954).

structure which is repeated indefinitely. For example, chains of $CuCl_4$ tetrahedra, each sharing two corners with its two neighbors in the chain, occur in K_2CuCl_3 (see 6.46). Similarly linked SiO_4 tetrahedra occur in certain silicates which contain anionic chains of the type $(SiO_3)_n^{2n-}$. Solid palladium(II) chloride is found to be built up of infinite chains of planar $PdCl_4$ groups, each sharing opposite edges with its two neighbors.

6.113 Polynuclear structures in the solid state are found in numerous relatively simple compounds as well as in more complex substances. In such very complex materials as the silicate minerals polynuclear structures are frequent. In aqueous solutions of such salts as those of iron(III), bismuth(III), zirconium(IV), and probably most of the heavy metals, it is believed that under most conditions polynuclear species involving *hydroxo* or *oxo* bridge groups exist. The formation of polynuclear complexes of these kinds is termed *olation* or *oxolation*.

6.114 An important class of polynuclear complexes is represented by the poly-acids and their salts, formed especially by the transition elements in the vanadium and chromium families. The composition of the poly-acids may be formally expressed in terms of water combined with acid anhydride, there being more than one molecule of acid anhydride in each anionic unit. If more than one kind of acid anhydride is contained in the compound it is called a *heteropolyacid*. An example is 6-molybdotelluric acid, $H_6[TeMo_6O_{24}]$, which may be formally written $(H_2O)_3 \cdot TeO_3 \cdot (MoO_3)_6$, although this mode of writing the formula admittedly gives little clue to the structure of the compound. Another example is 12-tungstosilicic acid, $H_4[SiW_{12}O_{40}]$ or $(H_2O)_2 \cdot SiO_2 \cdot (WO_3)_{12}$. If the poly-acid contains only one kind of acid anhydride it is called an *isopoly-acid*. Paramolybdic acid, $H_6Mo_7O_{24}$, and metatungstic acid, $H_8W_{12}O_{40}$, are examples of this class. Formal representation of these compounds in terms of oxides would give $(H_2O)_3 \cdot (MoO_3)_7$ and $(H_2O)_4 \cdot (WO_3)_{12}$, respectively.

6.115 Two of the most common types of heteropoly-acids are represented by the first two examples given above. The 6-heteropoly-acids of the type shown first have the general formula $H_mXR_6O_{24}$, in which R is commonly Mo or W, and X may be one of numerous elements capable of six-coordination, such as I^{VII}, Te^{VI}, Cr^{III}, or Mn^{II}. Various salts of these acids may be prepared; quite frequently the compounds are hydrated. X-ray studies [12] on

$$(NH_4)_6[TeMo_6O_{24}] \cdot 7H_2O$$

have shown that $[TeMo_6O_{24}]^{6-}$ consists basically of a polynuclear ring of six MoO_6 octahedra, each of which shares two edges (not opposite) with its two MoO_6 neighbors. This arrangement provides an inner group of six shared oxygen atoms which are octahedrally arranged around the center. The hetero-atom, tellurium in this case, is located at the center, and is thus surrounded octahedrally by six oxygen atoms, each of which is also shared by two molybdenum atoms. The structure is shown diagrammatically in Figure 6.14.

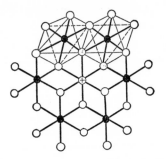

Fig. 6.14 Structure of $[TeMo_6O_{24}]^{6-}$.
$\oplus$, tellurium; ●, molybdenum; ○, oxygen.

6.116 The second type of heteropoly-acid exemplified above consists of the 12-heteropoly-acids of type formula $H_mXR_{12}O_{40}$. Here R is usually Mo or W, while X may be one of a number of elements which characteristically show four-coordination, such as B^{III}, Si^{IV}, P^V and the like. X-ray structural studies [13] of $H_3[PW_{12}O_{40}] \cdot 5H_2O$ and $H_3[PW_{12}O_{40}] \cdot 29H_2O$ have shown the phospho-12-tungstate anion to be a polynuclear "cage" of twelve WO_6 octahedra sharing edges and corners, with the phosphorus atom at the center, surrounded tetra-hedrally by four oxygen atoms. Each of these oxygen atoms is common to a cluster of three WO_6 octahedra each of which, in turn, shares two adjacent edges (ending in the common oxygen atom) with the two other members of the cluster, Figure 6.15(a). There are four such clusters, in all, linked respectively to the four oxygen atoms of the central PO_4 tetrahedron. Every cluster is linked to each of the other three clusters through corner sharing by two adjacent octahedra in the cluster, yielding the arrangement represented in Figure 6.15(b). Crystallographic studies indicate that other 12-polyanions of the same type, such as $[PMo_{12}O_{40}]^{3-}$, $[SiW_{12}O_{40}]^{4-}$, $[SiMo_{12}O_{40}]^{4-}$, and $[BW_{12}O_{40}]^{5-}$, have the same structure.

[12] EVANS, *J. Am. Chem. Soc.*, **70**, 1291 (1948).
[13] KEGGIN, *Proc. Roy. Soc.* (London) **A144**, 75 (1934).

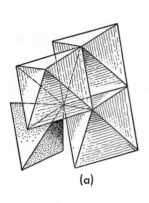

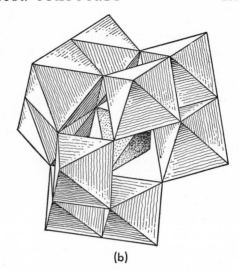

(a)

(b)

Fig. 6.15 Structure of [PW$_{12}$O$_{40}$]$^{3-}$. (a) Cluster of three WO$_6$ octahedra sharing an oxygen atom with a PO$_4$ tetrahedron. (b) Showing nine of the twelve WO$_6$ octahedra surrounding the PO$_4$ tetrahedron.

6.117 A large number of heteropoly-acids and salts of other types have been described, for many of which the structures have not as yet been definitely established.

6.118 The structures of relatively few of the more complex isopoly-acids have been elucidated. It may be mentioned that the paramolybdate ion, [Mo$_7$O$_{24}$]$^{6-}$, resembles the 6-heteropoly-ions described above, having, however, a bent rather than a planar structure, with molybdenum in place of the heteroatom at the center. The analogy is emphasized by comparing the formulation [MoMo$_6$O$_{24}$]$^{6-}$ with [TeMo$_6$O$_{24}$]$^{6-}$. Metatungstic acid, H$_8$W$_{12}$O$_{40}$, appears to have essentially the same arrangement of WO$_6$ octahedra as is found in the 12-heteropoly anions discussed above.

Stability of Complexes

Introduction

6.119 One of the properties of importance in determining the existence and behavior of a complex ion or molecule under given conditions is its thermodynamic stability with respect to dissociation into its components. The dissociation reaction of interest may involve starting with the pure complex compound in its normal physical state and obtaining the products also in their common physical states. However, a large proportion of the data on complex stability refers to the dissociation of the complex in solution. For this reason the term *stability* when applied without further qualification to complexes is most frequently used in this way, although it has been employed, also, not in the thermodynamic sense but in the kinetic sense to denote slowness in attainment of equilibrium. It seems desirable to use a different designation for this latter purpose, however, and the terms "inertness" and "lability" instead of stability and instability seem appropriate.

6.120 A quantitative indication of the stability of a complex in solution is given by the equilibrium constant for the formation of the complex from its components. For example, the numerical value of the equilibrium constant K in the equation

$$\frac{([Cu(NH_3)_4]^{2+})}{(Cu^{2+})(NH_3)^4} = K$$

is an expression of the stability of the tetramminecopper(II) ion in solution. The equilibrium constant given in this way is termed the *stability constant* for the complex. The reciprocal of this constant, corresponding, of course, to a dissociation of the complex, is commonly called the "instability constant."

6.121 It is found experimentally that the formation of a complex in solution usually proceeds in a stepwise manner, and that each step can then be characterized by an equilibrium constant. For example, in the aqueous solution containing copper(II) ion and progressively increased concentrations of ammonia, four steps * are involved.

$$Cu^{2+} + NH_3 = [CuNH_3]^{2+} \qquad \frac{([CuNH_3]^{2+})}{(Cu^{2+})(NH_3)} = k_1$$

$$[CuNH_3]^{2+} + NH_3 = [Cu(NH_3)_2]^{2+} \qquad \frac{([Cu(NH_3)_2]^{2+})}{([CuNH_3]^{2+})(NH_3)} = k_2$$

$$\cdot \qquad\qquad\qquad\qquad\qquad\qquad \cdot$$
$$\cdot \qquad\qquad\qquad\qquad\qquad\qquad \cdot$$
$$\cdot \qquad\qquad\qquad\qquad\qquad\qquad \cdot$$

etc. \qquad\qquad\qquad\qquad\qquad\qquad etc.

The equilibrium constants, k_1, k_2, etc., for the separate steps are often called *formation constants*. The product of the four formation constants in the example above yields the overall stability constant K for the tetrammine complex.

6.122 Although ideally, perhaps, the stability constants should be true thermodynamic constants expressed in terms of the activities of the species in equilibrium, in practice it is often inconvenient to determine such values, and concentration constants may be obtained instead. Frequently these constants are determined at some fixed ionic strength. Moreover, many coordination compounds possess such low solubility in water as to make it expedient to use a modified solvent, such as a dioxane-water mixture, for stability studies. Facts such as these need to be kept in mind when comparisons are made among the stabilities of different complexes.

* There is evidence that a fifth molecule of ammonia can be coordinated with copper(II) ion in solution, but the corresponding formation constant is very much smaller than those for the first four steps.

Factors Which Influence Stability

6.123 To account for the stability of a complex in solution consideration must be given to the metal-ligand bond energy, the heats of solvation of the various species, and the entropy changes involved. These quantities in turn depend upon (1) temperature, (2) the nature of the solvent, (3) the nature of the metal atom or ion, and (4) the nature and number of the ligands. Identification of the precise characteristics of solvent, of metal, and of ligand which are important in this connection, and determination of the interrelationships among these characteristics and the extent to which each affects stability, present a very complex problem which is by no means solved. A number of interesting and useful correlations have been discovered, however, which permit certain limited and rather rough generalizations to be made. Some of these generalizations, especially as they relate to the nature of the metal and of the ligand, are discussed below, although a detailed consideration of this problem is outside the scope of this book.

Nature of the Metal **6.124** If the binding between the central ion and the ligand in a complex is predominantly electrostatic, that is, of the ion-ion or ion-dipole type, the strongest bonds with a given ionic or dipolar ligand should be formed by those central ions possessing the strongest peripheral electric fields. Such fields are favored by small ionic radius and large charge; the combined effect is sometimes expressed in terms of a single parameter called the ionic potential, defined from the relation

$$\text{Ionic Potential} = \frac{\text{Ionic Charge (in Electronic Units)}}{\text{Crystal Radius (in Ångstrom Units)}}.$$

Ions having large ionic potentials, therefore, should be the best complex formers, at least insofar as electrostatic interaction contributes to the strength of the metal-ligand bond. In a general way it is true that the best complex-forming ions are those for which the ionic potential is relatively large. The comparatively small, highly charged ions of the $3d$ transition series, for example, are much better complex formers than the large univalent alkali metal ions. Moreover, within a series of complexes involving closely similar metal ions and a particular ligand, the trend in stability frequently corresponds to the trend in ionic potential. For example, the stability constants of magnesium, calcium, strontium, and barium ions with any one of the ligands oxalate, malonate, succinate, glycinate, acetate, or propionate are found to increase in the order Ba < Sr < Ca < Mg. A similar correlation is seen in the complexes of the tripositive lanthanide ions, where again complex stability is observed to increase with decreasing radius of the rare-earth ion.

6.125 It must be emphasized at once, however, that the ionic potential cannot be used indiscriminantly to predict complex stability. A consideration of the ionic potential would, for example, predict the complexes of magnesium ion (radius 0.66 Å) to be more stable than the corresponding complexes of copper(II) (radius about 0.72 Å), whereas in fact, just the reverse is true. Again, aluminum ion (radius 0.52 Å) should form more stable complexes than cobalt(III) (radius 0.63 Å). This, too, is contrary to fact. In these instances, of course, the ions being compared possess distinctly different outer electron configurations. Thus magnesium and aluminum ions both have an eight-electron inert gas type outer shell, whereas both copper(II) and cobalt(III) possess d-transition series shells. It seems clear that properties other than, or in addition to, the ionic potential must be considered.

6.126 In many complexes the bond between the central atom and the ligand possesses a significant amount of covalent character. Since this involves the sharing of a pair of electrons between the ligand donor and the central atom acceptor, the strength of the bond might be expected to depend, in part at least, upon the magnitude of the attraction for electrons exerted by the central atom. An indication of the strength of this attraction for electrons on the part of a metal ion is given by the ionization potentials of the corresponding atom. Such data indicate that the ratio of ionic charge to ionic radius cannot be correlated closely with ionization potentials, except within groups of very similar elements. This fact is illustrated by comparing ionization potentials of such pairs of atoms as sodium and copper, potassium and gold, calcium and cadmium. Although the radii of monopositive sodium (0.95 Å) and copper (0.93 Å) are almost the same, the corresponding first ionization potentials, 5.12 and 7.74 v., show the marked difference which these ions exhibit in their attraction for an electron. Potassium and gold likewise differ sharply in first ionization potentials, 4.32 and 9.18 v., respectively, although the radii of their monopositive ions, 1.33 Å for K+ and 1.37 Å for Au+, are not very different. Similarly, calcium ion (0.99 Å) and cadmium ion (0.96 Å), although possessing approximately the same radii, show distinctly different strengths of attraction for electrons, as is indicated by comparing the sums of the first and second ionization potentials for the respective atoms: 17.98 v. for calcium and 25.90 v. for cadmium. In comparing two ions of equal size and charge, the one whose formation from the atom requires the larger amount of work presumably exerts a stronger polarizing effect upon a ligand because of its greater attraction for electrons, and therefore should tend to form a stronger covalent bond with the ligand, especially if the latter is easily polarized.

6.127 It is true that metallic ions frequently acquire through coordination more electrons than would be required, if free, to restore electrical neutrality to the ion. In such cases ionization potentials may not give an adequate indication of the strength of electron attraction. Additional effects, such as the availability of inner d orbitals on the acceptor and the possibility of multiple bonding between metal and ligand atom, may also enter. In terms of the ligand field theory, the crystal field stabilization energy is an important consideration for many complexes.

6.128 Multiple bonding as an additional stabilizing effect has been postulated to occur especially in complexes of the d transition elements with ligands which themselves contain multiple bonds, such as cyanide ion or carbon monoxide. This theory assumes that double bonds between metal atom and one or more ligands may be formed, provided the metal atom possesses one or more pairs of unshared d electrons, and provided the ligand can accept such a pair into one of its own orbitals. For example, in ferrocyanide ion the electronic configuration of the iron may be represented as follows. The iron has three unshared

Fe in Fe(CN)$_6^{4-}$ ⇅ ⇅ ⇅ | D^2SP^3 hybrid orbitals |

pairs of d electrons available for establishing a resonating system of three double bonds with the cyanide groups, as indicated by the structure shown. Similarly,

in nickel tetracarbonyl the configuration of nickel is as shown. Here five un-shared pairs of d electrons, four * of which might be contributed by nickel, are

Ni in Ni(CO)$_4$ ⇅ ⇅ ⇅ ⇅ ⇅ | SP^3 hybrid orbitals |

available to establish double bonds as indicated in the model. In both of these

examples the ligand group, because of its own multiple bond system, can accept a pair of d electrons in this manner. Certain other ligand atoms, such as arsenic, phosphorus, and sulfur, may likewise be able to accept a pair of d electrons from the metal atom into one of their otherwise vacant d orbitals. On the other hand it would not be possible to establish a multiple bond between the metal and ammonia or water, for example, since the nitrogen and oxygen valence shells do not expand in this manner.

6.129 Proponents of the metal-ligand multiple bond theory have cited the fact that the metal-carbon bond distance in nickel tetracarbonyl, for example, is distinctly shorter than the value calculated from the single bond radii commonly assumed for these elements. Moreover, it has been emphasized that stable cyanide complexes are formed almost exclusively by d transition elements. Theoretical arguments in support of the theory have also been advanced.

---

* Because of symmetry considerations only two strong bonds of this kind should be formed.

6.130 The dependence of complex stability upon metal-ligand bond strength and this, in turn, upon such properties as have been discussed above, as well as upon properties of the ligand, would be of major importance if the equilibrium involved *gaseous* species only, as for example, in the following reaction.

$$Cd^{2+}(g) + 4NH_3(g) = [Cd(NH_3)_4]^{2+}(g)$$

In solution, however, the situation becomes much more complicated, since in general one or more of the species will have interacted in some manner with the solvent itself, forming a solvate or a complex. For example, in aqueous solution the above reaction is more accurately represented by the following equation.

$$[Cd(H_2O)_n]^{2+} + 4NH_3 = [Cd(NH_3)_4]^{2+} + nH_2O$$

The stability constant of the tetramminecadmium ion in aqueous solution therefore expresses more nearly the stability of this ion relative to that of the aquo ion than it does the intrinsic stability of the complex itself. This relative stability depends not only upon the metal-ammonia bond energy but upon the metal-water bond energy and any other heats of hydration that may be involved, as well as upon the entropy changes which occur in the course of the reaction. The fact that a particular metal ion does not form an ammonia complex in aqueous solution may simply mean that its aquo complex is more stable than its ammine complex.

6.131 Metal ions differ markedly in their readiness to exchange water molecules for various other ligands, and in their apparent preference for one type of ligand atom over another. Sidgwick [14] has pointed out, for example, that a rough division of the metal ions into three groups can be made, based upon the relative tendencies of these ions to form complexes with oxygen as the donor atom, on the one hand, or with nitrogen as the donor atom, on the other. These groups are as follows:

1. Those ions which, in general, complex more readily with oxygen than with nitrogen: Mg^{II}, Ca^{II}, Sr^{II}, Ba^{II}, Ga^{III}, In^{III}, Tl^{III}, Ti^{IV}, Zr^{IV}, Th^{IV}, Ge^{IV}, Sn^{IV}, V^{IV}, V^{V}, Nb^{V}, Ta^{V}, Mo^{V}, U^{IV}, U^{VI}, Fe^{III}, and Co^{II}.
2. Those showing about equally strong tendencies to coordinate with oxygen and nitrogen: Be^{II}, Cr^{III}, Fe^{II}, and the platinum metal ions.
3. Those which complex more readily with nitrogen than with oxygen: Cu^{I}, Cu^{II}, Au^{I}, Cd^{II}, Hg^{II}, V^{III}, Co^{III}, and Ni^{II}.

In a similar fashion, some ions form complexes with the halide ions more readily than do others, and some show relatively strong tendencies to complex with sulfur.

6.132 In the light of this discussion it is not to be expected that the metal ions can be arrayed in a single invariable order which will represent the relative stabilities of their complexes with all ligands. In general, variations in order

[14] SIDGWICK, *J. Chem. Soc.*, 1941, p. 433.

occur as the nature of the ligand is changed, except, perhaps, within certain rather restricted series of similar elements. For example, the dipositive $3d$ transition metals from manganese through copper appear to show the same order in the stability of their four-coordinated complexes no matter what the ligand. Here the order of increasing stability is $Mn^{II} < Fe^{II} < Co^{II} < Ni^{II} < Cu^{II}$. In this series the ionic radii are progressively smaller from left to right, while the sums of the first and second ionization potentials are larger progressively in the same order. Irving and Williams [15] have pointed out that if electrostatic binding is indeed favored by increasing charge-to-size ratio, and covalent bonding by increasing ionization potential, the order of complex stability observed for these ions is just what would be expected, regardless of the nature of the ligand. Moreover, all of the elements in this series possess "active" $3d$ electrons so that possible secondary effects involving d orbitals may be similar here, or may vary in regular fashion, also.

Nature of the Ligand **6.133** Electrostatic interaction between a given metal ion and an ionic or dipolar ligand is expected to depend upon the effective charge carried by the ligand atom and upon the closeness with which the center of this charge can approach the central ion. In other words, small negatively charged ions, such as fluoride and hydroxide ions, or molecules of large dipole moment in which the negative end is small, such as water, should lend themselves best to strong electrostatic binding. Covalent bonding, on the other hand, should be favored by high polarizability (see 5.122–124) of the ligand, and may perhaps be affected, also, by its size and by the availability of an orbital on the ligand which can be used for multiple bond formation with the metal (see 6.128). Experiment has shown, moreover, that complex stability is also affected by chelation, by the number, size, and nature of the chelate rings formed, and by steric effects which may arise from structural features of the ligands.

6.134 The relative influence of such properties of the ligand as charge, dipole moment, size, polarizability, electronic configuration, and structure upon the stability of a complex will be expected to vary according to the nature of the central atom itself, and it is not to be expected, therefore, that within a large group of ligands of different types a single order can be found which will represent the relative stabilities of their complexes with all metals. This is evident from Sidgwick's grouping of the metal ions with respect to their tendencies to complex with nitrogen or with oxygen as the donor atom in the ligand (see 6.131). Nevertheless, within a restricted series of ligands of similar structure it is frequently possible to discern a correlation between the trend in one or more of the properties mentioned above and the relative stability of their complexes with a given metal atom. Some examples of such correlation are discussed below.

6.135 Ammonia and its derivatives the alkyl amines afford an interesting example of apparent correlation between complex-forming ability and permanent dipole moment. The stability of the complexes formed by these com-

[15] IRVING and WILLIAMS, *J. Chem. Soc.*, 1953, p. 3192.

pounds with a given metal ion appears to decrease generally in the order ammonia $\simeq$ primary amine > secondary amine > tertiary amine. There is a corresponding decrease in permanent dipole moment in the series, as is illustrated by the following values [16] (in Debye units): ammonia, 1.47; ethylamine, 1.22; diethylamine, 0.92; triethylamine, 0.66. Moreover, molar refraction studies [17] indicate a decrease in polarizability, also, in the same order. Analogous behavior is shown by water and its alkyl derivatives. Here again the complex-forming ability, permanent dipole moment, and polarizability all decrease with progressive substitution of alkyl groups for hydrogen, that is, in the order water > alcohol > ether.

6.136 In contrast to the behavior of these nitrogen and oxygen compounds, progressive substitution of alkyl groups for hydrogen in the phosphine molecule is accompanied by an increase in stability of the corresponding complexes. Thus phosphine complexes themselves, in general, have a low stability, whereas tertiary phosphines form numerous very stable complexes. It is to be noted that, also unlike the trend with ammonia and the amines, the permanent dipole moment of phosphine is low (0.55 D), and the moments of its alkyl substitution products are reported to increase in the order $PH_3 < RPH_2 < R_2PH < R_3P$. Parallel behavior is shown by hydrogen sulfide and its derivatives where complex-forming tendency and dipole moment both increase in the order $H_2S < RSH < R_2S$. In both of these series there is an opposing decrease in polarizability of the electrons on the ligand atom, but this change is relatively quite small.

6.137 Since electron-pair donors, according to the Lewis concept, are to be regarded as bases, some correlation might be expected between the basic strength of a ligand, which essentially reflects its tendency to coordinate with hydrogen ion, and the stability of its complexes with metal ions. Several instances of this kind of correlation have been pointed out in series of ligands possessing very similar structural features.

6.138 One such example is provided by a series of β-diketones of the type $RCOCH_2COR'$, in which R and R' represent various ring groups such as phenyl, thenyl, or furyl. As the basic character of the corresponding enolate ion becomes more pronounced, through suitable variation in R and R', the stability of the respective chelate complexes with copper(II) or nickel(II) is found to increase in the same order. A similar relationship has been observed between the basicity of pyridine and some of its methyl derivatives and the stability of their respective complexes with silver ion. Attempts to apply this relation more broadly, however, to include ligands of different structural types have been generally unsuccessful. A case in point is provided by triethylamine and ethylamine. Although these compounds are of about the same basic strength, the latter forms the more stable complex with silver ion, for example.

[16] MARYOTT and BUCKLEY, *Table of Dielectric Constants and Electric Dipole Moments of Substances in the Gaseous State*, Nat'l. Bur. Stands. Circular No. 537 (1953).

[17] SMYTH, *Dielectric Constant and Molecular Structure*, Chemical Catalog Co., New York (1931), p. 152.

6.139 Ligands having a structure permitting formation of a chelate ring with the central atom generally form complexes of high stability. Complexes containing the bidentate chelating ligand ethylenediamine, for example, are more stable than those containing an equivalent number of molecules of ammonia or alkylamine. This is illustrated by comparing the stability constant of bis-(ethylenediamine)zinc ion ($K = 1.2 \times 10^{11}$) with that of tetramminezinc ion ($K = 3.2 \times 10^9$).

6.140 Increasing the number of chelate rings has a similar effect. A comparison of the two copper complexes I and II shows that, although they have nearly identical structures except for the number of chelate rings present, compound I has a distinctly higher stability than compound II. Another example

is provided by the calcium(II) complexes with ethylenediaminetetraacetic acid and methylamine-N,N-diacetic acid. The first of these, in the form of its tetra-

ethylenediaminetetraacetic acid

methylamine-N,N-diacetic acid

negative ion, gives a complex of type CaY^{2-} in which the ligand is apparently sexadentate, utilizing the two nitrogen atoms and the four carboxylate groups in coordination. The second compound, as the corresponding dinegative ion, is terdentate, and two such ions coordinate to give a complex of type CaX_2^{2-}, in which there are again two nitrogens and four carboxylate groups in all attached to the calcium ion. Nevertheless the stability constant of the first compound ($K = 4 \times 10^{10}$) is approximately a thousand times as large as that of the second ($K = 3 \times 10^7$).

6.141 The size of the chelate ring formed also appears to have a bearing upon the stability of a complex. By far the most common, and therefore presumably the most stable, are five-membered and six-membered rings (counting the metal atom). Five-membered rings frequently appear to be favored when the atoms of the ring are linked by single bonds only. Complexes formed by ethylenediamine are more stable, in general, than the corresponding complexes of tri-methylenediamine, $H_2NCH_2CH_2CH_2NH_2$, which must form a six-membered ring. Similarly, polyhydroxy compounds form chelates with boric acid, the most stable of which are those in which hydroxyl groups on adjacent carbon atoms are utilized, establishing a five-membered ring with the boron atom. When two or more double bonds are included in the ligand, the rings formed are six-membered more often than not. The spatial requirements of the central atom in relation to the dimensions of the chelating ligand may also be of influence in determining the most stable ring size.

6.142 In chelate rings containing two or more double bonds, resonance among essentially equivalent structures has been postulated as an additional stabilizing influence. The enolate ion of acetylacetone, for example, affords the possibility for such resonance, as is indicated in I and II. This ligand forms very stable complexes with many metal ions. It is of interest to compare it with the phenolate ion of salicylaldehyde, which will also form a similar six-membered chelate ring III. In spite of the similarity in the rings and the fact that as bases

both ligand ions have nearly the same strength, the stability constant of the bis(acetylacetonato)copper(II) complex is approximately ten thousand times as large as that of the corresponding complex with the phenolate of salicylaldehyde. In the latter compound one of the carbon-carbon double bonds is part of the conjugated double bond system of the benzene ring. Presumably its involvement in the benzene resonance reduces its contribution to resonance in the chelate ring, with a corresponding reduction in stability. A number of similar cases have been cited, also, as evidence for a resonance effect upon complex stability.

Stabilization of Oxidation States

6.143 When a metal is capable of exhibiting two or more oxidation states in its compounds, the stability of the complexes which the corresponding ions form with a given ligand may differ sharply. As a result of such difference the stability of one particular oxidation state to another with respect to oxidation or reduction may be distinctly enhanced (see 4.123–129). Excellent examples of such stabilization are afforded by some of the complexes of iron(II) and iron(III). In aqueous medium the standard oxidation potential of the iron(II)-iron(III) couple is

$$Fe^{2+} = Fe^{3+} + e^- \qquad E° = -0.771 \text{ v.}$$

Comparison of this value with that for the ferrocyanide-ferricyanide couple

$$[Fe(CN)_6]^{4-} = [Fe(CN)_6]^{3-} + e^- \qquad E° = -0.36 \text{ v.}$$

shows that in the form of the hexacyano-complexes, iron(II) is more easily oxidized to iron(III) than is hydrated iron(II) to hydrated iron(III). In this case, therefore, some stabilization of the tripositive state in aqueous solution can be said to have occurred as a result of complex formation with cyanide. On the other hand, complex formation with o-phenanthroline results in increased stabilization of the iron(II) state, as is indicated by the oxidation potential value

$$[\text{Fe } o\text{-phen}_3]^{2+} = [\text{Fe } o\text{-phen}_3]^{3+} + e^- \qquad E^\circ = -1.06 \text{ v.}$$

6.144 The stabilization of cobalt(III) with respect to reduction to cobalt(II) through complex formation represents another striking example of this phenomenon. The large negative potential for the couple

$$\text{Co}^{2+} = \text{Co}^{3+} + e \qquad E^\circ = -1.82 \text{ v.}$$

indicates that the (hydrated) cobalt(III) ion would be unstable in aqueous solution, reacting with water and yielding oxygen and cobalt(II). In the presence of ammonia and many other complexing agents, however, oxidation of dipositive cobalt may readily be accomplished, and the resulting cobalt(III) complex becomes markedly more stable with respect to reduction.

Lability and Inertness

6.145 The existence and behavior of a complex in a given environment depend not alone upon its thermodynamic stability with respect to dissociation, substitution, and the like, but also upon its kinetic behavior, that is, upon the rate at which equilibrium in a thermodynamically possible reaction is approached. Brief mention has already been made (see 6.4) of the marked difference in the rates of the two following reactions.

$$[\text{Cu(NH}_3)_4]^{2+} + 4\text{H}^+ + n\text{H}_2\text{O} = [\text{Cu(H}_2\text{O})_n]^{2+} + 4\text{NH}_4^+$$
$$[\text{Co(NH}_3)_6]^{3+} + \text{H}^+ + \text{H}_2\text{O} = [\text{Co(NH}_3)_5(\text{H}_2\text{O})]^{2+} + \text{NH}_4^+$$

The first reaction reaches equilibrium in essentially the time required to mix the reactants, whereas the second is extremely slow, even though thermodynamically favored. Again, the reactions for the formation of $[\text{Fe(H}_2\text{O})_n\text{Cl}]^{2+}$ complex in aqueous solution from (hydrated) iron(III) ion and chloride ion, and its dissociation upon subsequent dilution, attain equilibrium without noticeable delay. On the other hand, the formation of the analogous green $[\text{Cr(H}_2\text{O})_n\text{Cl}]^{2+}$ complex from the violet (hydrated) chromium(III) ion and the reverse reaction both proceed very slowly. Numerous other examples of both very rapid and very slow reactions are encountered among complexes. The marked differences shown in kinetic behavior appear to bear no necessary relation to the differences in stability of the respective complexes, and cannot be safely taken as an indication of the relative strengths of the metal-ligand bonds.

6.146 Attempts to correlate lability or inertness with outer orbital or inner orbital bond type, as indicated by magnetic moment values (see 6.97), have suggested that, although bond type may have an important bearing upon lability, other features of the complex must also be considered.

6.147 A promising approach to this problem has been made by Taube,[18] who points out that certain types of electronic configuration of the central ion almost invariably yield complexes of the inert class, while others produce complexes of the labile class. Six-coordinated complexes of the inner orbital type may, in general, be divided into a labile group and an inert group, according to Taube, depending upon whether or not there are one or more unoccupied inner d orbitals on the central ion as it exists in the complex. If there is such a vacant orbital the complex is labile, but if all the d orbitals are occupied by one or two electrons each, the complex is inert. An example of discontinuity in rates of reaction between the two classes is provided by vanadium(III), the complexes of which are labile, and chromium(III), which forms inert complexes. Occupancy of valence orbitals on the metal in the complexes of vanadium(III) is represented by the configuration $d^1d^1d^0 \; D^2SP^3$, whereas in chromium(III) complexes the configuration is $d^1d^1d^1 \; D^2SP^3$. Other examples are listed in the classification outlined below. It has been suggested that the vacant inner d orbital may provide a point of attack by the electron pair of the entering substituent, and that a transient seven-coordinated activated complex may be formed, providing a path of relatively low activation energy for the substitution. As a result the rate of the reaction might be much greater than for similar complexes in which this mechanism is impossible because of occupied d orbitals. More information on the mechanisms of reactions among complexes is required, however, before the general validity of this hypothesis can be determined.

6.148 Among the complexes of the outer orbital type differentiation between labile and inert members is not as sharp as within the inner orbital class. Many such complexes are labile, but in general the lability decreases as the charge on the central atom increases. In the series AlF_6^{3-}, SiF_6^{2-}, PF_6^-, SF_6, for example, the lability, as indicated by the rate of hydrolysis, decreases progressively from AlF_6^{3-} through SF_6.

6.149 The following outline presents some electronic configurations and examples of the various types of complexes corresponding to Taube's classification. For some of the ions listed below, evidence justifying their inclusion in a particular category is admittedly inconclusive. Generally, however, such evidence as there is does not seem to be in definite disagreement with the ideas on which the classification is based.

I. Inner orbital complexes

   A. Labile group

      (1) $d^0d^0d^0 \; D^2SP^3$: Sc(III), Y(III), tripositive rare-earth ions, Ti(IV), Zr(IV), Hf(IV), Nb(V), Ta(V), Mo(VI), W(VI), Np(III), Np(IV), Pu(III), Pu(IV)

      (2) $d^1d^0d^0 \; D^2SP^3$: Ti(III), V(IV), Mo(V), W(V), Re(VI)

      (3) $d^1d^1d^0 \; D^2SP^3$: Ti(II), V(III), Nb(III), Ta(III), W(IV), Re(V), Ru(VI)

[18] TAUBE, *Chem. Revs.*, **50**, 69 (1952).

B. Inert group

   (1) $d^1 d^1 d^1$ $D^2 SP^3$: V(II), Cr(III), Mo(III), W(III), Mn(IV), Re(IV)

   (2) $d^2 d^1 d^1$ $D^2 SP^3$: $Cr(CN)_6^{4-}$, $Mn(CN)_6^{3-}$, Re(III), Ru(IV), Os(IV).

   (3) $d^2 d^2 d^1$ $D^2 SP^3$: $Mn(CN)_6^{4-}$, Re(II), $Fe(CN)_6^{3-}$, Fe o-phen$_3^{3+}$, Fe dipy$_3^{3+}$, Ru(III), Os(III), Ir(IV)

   (4) $d^2 d^2 d^2$ $D^2 SP^3$: $Fe(CN)_6^{4-}$, Fe o-phen$_3^{2+}$, Fe dipy$_3^{2+}$, Ru(II), Os(II), Co(III) in all but F^- complexes, Rh(III), Ir(III), Pd(IV), Pt(IV)

II. Outer orbital complexes

A. Examples of ions forming labile complexes: Al(III), Mn(II), Fe(II), Fe(III), Co(II), Ni(II), Zn(II), Cd(II), Hg(II), Ga(III), In(III), Tl(III)

B. Examples of inert complexes: SiF_6^{2-}, PF_6^-, AsF_6^-, $SbCl_6^-$, SF_6, SeF_6, TeF_6

CHAPTER 7

ACID–BASE RELATIONSHIPS AND INORGANIC REACTIONS IN NONAQUEOUS SYSTEMS

7.1 The successive appearance of the various concepts of acids and bases has been closely related to the development of our ideas of chemical binding. Each of the major concepts of acid-base relationships to be presented in this chapter has its circle of adherents; each has its critics. Each has been of considerable value in stimulating research in all phases of chemistry. We are particularly concerned with the value of these concepts in relation to the development of the inorganic chemistry of nonaqueous systems.

Early History of the Acid-Base Concept [1,2,3,4]

7.2 It is natural that early acid-base concepts emphasized behavior in water. Although the story of the development of these concepts is an interesting chapter in the history of chemistry, only a few of the more important ideas will be discussed here.

7.3 Experimental criteria for characterizing acids and bases were employed at an early date. Thus, Boyle (1627–1691) defined acids as substances whose aqueous solutions possess the following properties: they are capable of dissolving many substances; they precipitate sulfur from alkaline solutions; they turn blue plant dyes red; they lose all the above characteristics when brought in contact with alkalies.

7.4 The strictly experimental outlook was in large measure forsaken with the advent of Lavoisier's *oxygen* concept. Lavoisier in 1787 proposed that all acids were composed of two parts, one of which is oxygen, the so-called *acidifying principle*, and the other an *acidifiable base*, i.e., an element such as phosphorus or sulfur. The *oxygen* concept, widely accepted for many years, finally was

[1] WALDEN, *Salts, Acids and Bases*, McGraw-Hill Book Co., Inc., New York, 1929.

[2] *Acids and Bases*, Journal of Chemical Education, Easton, Pa., 1941.

[3] LUDER and ZUFFANTI, *The Electronic Theory of Acids and Bases*, John Wiley and Sons, Inc., New York, 1946.

[4] AUDRIETH, *Acids, Bases and Non-Aqueous Systems*, Department of Chemistry, The Pennsylvania State College, State College, Pa., 1949.

abandoned after its opponents, Humphry Davy in particular (1811), showed repeatedly that it was not necessary that an acid contain oxygen (*e.g.*, HCl, H$_2$S) and also that many binary oxygen compounds (*e.g.*, CaO, K$_2$O, etc.) did not possess acid properties.

7.5 With the abandonment of the belief that oxygen was a necessary constituent of all acids, there arose another one-element concept of acids, namely the *hydrogen* concept. Liebig, its chief proponent, stated (1838) that an acid must contain hydrogen, but that not all hydrogen compounds are acids; only those substances possessing hydrogen replaceable by metals are acids.

7.6 The advent of the Arrhenius theory of electrolytic dissociation (1884) was accompanied by a redefinition of the *hydrogen* concept of acids, with the emphasis placed on the role of water as an ionizing solvent. According to this theory, an acid is a hydrogen-containing compound which dissociates in water solution yielding hydrogen ions, and a base is a compound which is ionized in solution yielding hydroxyl ions. Reaction between an acid and a base (a neutralization reaction) produces a salt and water. The Arrhenius definitions were generally adopted and in modified form are still useful with regard to reactions in aqueous solutions.

7.7 The restriction of the Arrhenius concept to aqueous solutions, and the fact that it fails to bring together many related phenomena observed in these solutions, soon made it apparent that the concept was of limited utility. The increasing number of researches dealing with the chemistry of nonaqueous solutions and the realization that reactions which could be interpreted as acid-base phenomena could take place in these solutions called for a broadening of the acid-base concept.

7.8 At present three concepts of acids and bases — the *Brönsted-Lowry*, the *Solvent System*, and the *Lewis Electronic* concepts — have wide acceptance. These are discussed in the sections which follow, particular emphasis being placed on their utility with regard to inorganic reactions in nonaqueous systems.

The Brönsted-Lowry Concept [5,6]

7.9 The Arrhenius concept of acids and bases has been greatly broadened by the definitions proposed independently in 1923 by Brönsted and Lowry. These definitions attribute characteristic acid-base properties to the molecules of the acids and bases themselves. An acid is characterized by its tendency to release a proton and a base by its tendency to accept a proton. These definitions can be formulated by the following equation.

$$\text{Acid} \rightleftharpoons \text{Conjugate base} + \text{Proton}$$
$$(\text{A} \rightleftharpoons \text{B} + \text{H}^+)$$

The release of the proton cannot occur to a large degree unless the acid is brought into contact with some base which has a higher proton affinity than the

[5] BRÖNSTED, *Rec. trav. chim.*, **42**, 718 (1923); *Chem. Revs.*, **5**, 231 (1928); *Ber.*, **61B**, 2049 (1929).

[6] LOWRY, *Trans. Faraday Soc.*, **20**, 13 (1924).

conjugate base with which the proton is associated in the original molecule or ion. This is illustrated by the following general equation.

$$Acid_1 + Base_2 \rightleftharpoons Acid_2 + Base_1$$

The reversible protolytic reaction (*i.e.*, reaction involving transfer of the proton) therefore occurs in the direction which favors the formation of the weaker of the two possible acids and the weaker of the two possible bases. It is apparent that, although the acid-base definitions make no mention of solvent, the presence of the latter, if it is potentially an acid or base, has a profound effect on the manifestation of acidic or basic character by a solute.

7.10 Some typical acid-base equilibria in water are shown in Table 7.1. It is

TABLE 7.1

Acid-Base Equilibria in Water

Acid$_1$		Base$_1$
HClO$_4$		ClO$_4^-$
HNO$_3$		NO$_3^-$
HCl		Cl$^-$
H$_2$SO$_4$		HSO$_4^-$
HSO$_4^-$		SO$_4^{2-}$
H$_3$PO$_4$	Base$_2$ Acid$_2$	H$_2$PO$_4^-$
HC$_2$H$_3$O$_2$	+ H$_2$O $\rightleftharpoons$ H$_3$O$^+$ +	C$_2$H$_3$O$_2^-$
Fe(H$_2$O)$_6^{3+}$		Fe(OH)(H$_2$O)$_5^{2+}$
H$_2$CO$_3$		HCO$_3^-$
H$_2$S		HS$^-$
NH$_4^+$		NH$_3$
HCO$_3^-$		CO$_3^{2-}$
H$_2$O		OH$^-$

(Left margin: Decreasing Acid Strength ↓; Right margin: Decreasing Basic Strength ↑)

evident that on the basis of the Brönsted-Lowry definitions the "neutralization" reaction, *i.e.*, reaction between an acid and base yielding a salt and water, loses its special significance and becomes merely a protolytic reaction in which water is a product.

$$H_3O^+ + OH^- = 2H_2O$$

The reactions listed also demonstrate that "molecules exert their acid or basic functions independently of their electric charges." This permits the classification of hydrolysis as a specialized case of protolysis. (See reaction of Fe(H$_2$O)$_6^{3+}$ with water.) Relative strengths in terms of extent of reaction with water (for Acid$_1$) or with hydronium ion (for Base$_1$) are designated in Table 7.1; these illustrate the inverse relationship which exists between the strength of an acid and that of its conjugate base.

7.11 The terms *acid* and *base* as used in the Brönsted-Lowry sense are merely relative. Many substances are amphiprotic, *i.e.*, they are capable of acting as either acids or bases. Thus, water is capable of acting as a proton donor toward ammonia and a proton acceptor toward such substances as acetic acid.

$Acid_1$		$Base_2$		$Acid_2$		$Base_1$
H_2O	$+$	NH_3	$\rightleftharpoons$	NH_4^+	$+$	OH^-
$HC_2H_3O_2$	$+$	H_2O	$\rightleftharpoons$	H_3O^+	$+$	$C_2H_3O_2^-$

The amphiprotic nature of water is further illustrated by its mode of self-ionization.

H_2O	$+$	H_2O	$\rightleftharpoons$	H_3O^+	$+$	OH^-
$Acid_1$		$Base_2$		$Acid_1$		$Base_2$

7.12 It should be pointed out that the very "strong" acids, such as nitric acid, perchloric acid, sulfuric acid, hydrogen bromide, and hydrogen chloride, are of approximately equal strength in aqueous solution. Water is therefore described as a leveling solvent for "strong" acids. This leveling effect can be attributed to the relatively high basicity of water, which is responsible for the *complete* reaction of "strong" acids in dilute solution to form hydronium ion. The latter is therefore the strongest acid that can exist to any extent in water medium. The so-called "strong" acids are not, however, of equal strengths in solvents which are less basic, *i.e.*, possessing a lesser proton affinity, than water. For example, in acetic acid, which may be characterized as a differentiating solvent toward "strong" acids, the relative strengths of the acids listed above, as determined by conductance measurements, are in the order [7]

$$HClO_4 > HBr > H_2SO_4 > HCl > HNO_3.$$

7.13 It has already been stated that although the Brönsted-Lowry definitions say nothing of solvent, the latter may have a marked effect on the manifestation of acidic or basic character. The role of acetic acid as a differentiating solvent toward "strong" acids has just been noted. The general effects of solvents with regard to the exhibition of acidic or basic character by solutes may be brought out by a classification of solvents in terms of their basicity.[4,8] Solvents may be classified as (a) basic, (b) acidic, (c) amphiprotic, and (d) aprotic.

7.14 Basic solvents, such as ammonia and the organic amines, have a relatively high affinity for protons. Many acids which are relatively weak in water appear to undergo marked reaction (proton transfer to a high degree) with ammonia and amines. Thus the acidic character of the "weak acids" is enhanced in basic solvents.

7.15 On the other hand, acidic solvents, such as acetic acid, sulfuric acid, and hydrogen fluoride, are poor proton acceptors. In these solvents the basic character of "weak bases" is enhanced. For example, urea, a substance which in aqueous medium is a very weak base, can be titrated as a rather strong base by solutions of perchloric acid in glacial acetic acid. The fact that urea is an

[7] KOLTHOFF and WILLMAN, *J. Am. Chem. Soc.*, **56**, 1007 (1934).
[8] HALL, *Chem. Revs.*, **8**, 191 (1931).

acid in the strongly basic solvent liquid ammonia, serves to emphasize the importance of the role of solvent.

7.16 Mention has been made of the amphiprotic nature of water as a solvent. The alcohols may also be included among those solvents which are intermediate between those of pronounced basicity and those of marked acidity.

7.17 The aprotic solvents are those in which there is no apparent reaction between solute and solvent — *e.g.*, benzene, carbon tetrachloride, chloroform, etc. Here the manifestation of acid character is determined by the tendency of the solute to release the proton to other solutes which are capable of acting as bases. The leveling effect which water exerts on "strong" acids and bases is absent in these solvents. Studies in aprotic media have permitted the approximate determination of the so-called "intrinsic acidity" of various acids.

7.18 Insofar as inorganic reactions are concerned the utility of the Brönsted-Lowry concept is in large measure limited to protonic solvents and to certain high-temperature ansolvous systems (to be discussed in sections 7.55–60). Many reactions take place in such nonprotonic solvents as sulfur dioxide, carbonyl chloride (phosgene), and selenium(IV) oxychloride which are interpretable in terms of acid and base behavior. The classic investigations of Franklin on reactions in liquid ammonia led to the development of a *Solvent System* concept of acids and bases which is applicable to both protonic and nonprotonic solvents provided they are capable of undergoing limited self ionization. The Solvent System concept has been of extreme importance in the development of the inorganic chemistry of nonaqueous solvents.

The Solvent System Concept [2,3,4]

7.19 The beginning of liquid ammonia research in this country, and hence the origin of the Solvent System concept of acid-base relationships, was a result of the suggestion of H. P. Cady that liquid ammonia would probably be found to resemble water in both its physical and chemical properties.[9] The extensive investigations which followed, particularly those of Franklin and Kraus, brilliantly demonstrated the validity of Cady's suggestion.

7.20 A comparison of the properties of water with those of liquid ammonia brings out striking similarities. As a solvent for salts, liquid ammonia is second only to water. It closely approaches water in its ability to act as an ionizing medium for electrolytes; some salts are even better conductors in ammonia solution than they are in water. It readily forms solvates with many salts; in this respect it even surpasses water. The high heat of vaporization and abnormally high boiling point ($-33.35°$) as compared to the values of the hydrides of other members of its group indicate, as they do in water, a high degree of association through hydrogen bonding.

7.21 Equally striking are the close similarities in properties and reactions between derivatives of ammonia and those of the analogous compounds of

[9] FRANKLIN, *The Nitrogen System of Compounds*, Reinhold Publishing Corp., New York, 1935, p. 10. This monograph is the source of most of the material dealing with liquid ammonia (sections 7.19–25).

water. On the basis of these similarities Franklin developed the "nitrogen system of compounds." We are concerned with those aspects of this development which are related particularly to the system of acids, bases, and salts in liquid ammonia and in general to the Solvent System concept of acid-base relationships.

7.22 Ammonia may be considered to undergo an autoionization similar to that of water.

$$2NH_3 \rightleftharpoons NH_4^+ + NH_2^-$$
$$2H_2O \rightleftharpoons H_3O^+ + OH^-$$

The amide ion and the hydroxyl ion may therefore be considered as analogous groups when related to the corresponding parent substances, and amides should be expected to be bases in liquid ammonia. Similarly, compounds yielding the ammonium ion should be expected to behave like acids in liquid ammonia. An extension of these analogies between oxygen and nitrogen compounds (some of which are noted in Table 7.2) permitted the formulation of the ammonia system of acids, bases, and salts.

TABLE 7.2

Ammono and Corresponding Aquo Compounds

Ammono Compounds	Corresponding Aquo Compounds
KNH_2, potassium amide	KOH
$PbNH$, lead imide	PbO
Hg_3N_2, mercury(II) nitride	HgO
$K_2Zn(NH)_2 \cdot 2NH_3$, potassium ammonozincate $[K_2Zn(NH_2)_4]$	$K_2Zn(OH)_4$
$C(NH)(NH_2)_2$, guanidine	$CO(OH)_2$
H_2NCN, cyanamide	
$HN{=}PN$, phospham	$HO \cdot PO_2$
K_2CN_2, dipotassium cyanamide	K_2CO_3
KN_3, potassium azide	KNO_3

7.23 That the formal analogies cited above are valid is demonstrated by their experimental verification. Solutions of ammonium salts in liquid ammonia do have the properties of acids, being capable of dissolving many metals with the liberation of hydrogen, affecting indicators, and neutralizing ammono bases. Thus, liquid ammonia solutions of the active metals sodium, potassium, and calcium react with ammonium chloride with the evolution of hydrogen and the formation of the corresponding metal chloride.

$$2Na + 2NH_4Cl = H_2 + 2NaCl + 2NH_3$$

Solutions of ammonium salts also react with metallic amides, imides, and nitrides (ammono bases) in what may be considered typical "neutralization" reactions.

$$NH_4Cl + KNH_2 = KCl + 2NH_3$$
$$2NH_4I + PbNH = PbI_2 + 3NH_3$$
$$3NH_4I + BiN \quad = BiI_3 + 4NH_3$$

That these are indeed true acid-base reactions can be demonstrated by the use of indicators. Thus, the red color of a liquid ammonia solution of potassium amide containing phenolphthalein is discharged upon the addition of the appropriate quantity of ammonium chloride.

7.24 Metathetical reactions resulting in the precipitation of ammono bases from liquid ammonia solutions can be effected; the analogy between these reactions and corresponding ones in aqueous medium is brought out by the equations which follow.

$$AgNO_3 + KNH_2 = AgNH_2\downarrow + KNO_3$$
$$PbI_2 + 2KNH_2 = PbNH\downarrow + NH_3 + 2KI$$
$$3HgI_2 + 6KNH_2 = Hg_3N_2\downarrow + 4NH_3 + 6KI$$

$$2AgNO_3 + 2KOH = Ag_2O\downarrow + 2KNO_3 + H_2O$$
$$Pb(NO_3)_2 + 2KOH = Pb(OH)_2\downarrow + 2KNO_3$$
$$HgCl_2 + 2KOH = HgO\downarrow + 2KCl + H_2O$$

7.25 A striking additional confirmation of the validity of the analogies between the nitrogen and oxygen systems of compounds comes from the demonstration that certain amides and imides are amphoteric in liquid ammonia. Many metallic amides and imides, *e.g.*, $Zn(NH_2)_2$, $PbNH$, $Al(NH_2)_3$, react with potassium amide in liquid ammonia to yield compounds which are strictly analogous to those formed by reaction between the corresponding hydroxides and potassium hydroxide in aqueous medium.

$$Zn(NH_2)_2 + 2KNH_2 = K_2Zn(NH)_2 \cdot 2NH_3 \quad \text{or} \quad K_2Zn(NH_2)_4$$
$$Zn(OH)_2 + 2KOH = K_2Zn(OH)_4$$

7.26 The classic investigations on the ammonia system of compounds stimulated research into the chemistry of many other nonaqueous solvents. The concept of solvents as parent substances in systems of acids, bases, and salts was extended to both protonic * and nonprotonic media. Acid-base definitions were thus proposed for such solvents as hydrazine, hydrogen sulfide, hydroxylamine, acetic acid, carbonyl chloride, sulfur dioxide, and selenium(IV) oxychloride. These media were investigated, with varying degrees of success, as parent solvents. The result has been a tremendous increase in our knowledge of the inorganic reactions which may take place in these solvents.

7.27 Various definitions of acids and bases with regard to behavior in solvents which undergo a slight degree of self ionization have been proposed. The simplest proposal for the general treatment of acid-base relationships in such solvents is that of Cady and Elsey.[10] An acid is defined as a solute which gives rise to a cation characteristic of the solvent, and a base as a solute which gives rise to a characteristic solvent anion. The ions characteristic of a solvent are determined by its manner of autoionization. Proposed modes of autoionization for a number of solvents are shown in Table 7.3.

7.28 Thus, on the basis of the proposed mechanism of the self ionization of liquid sulfur dioxide, compounds such as thionyl chloride can be regarded as

---

* It should be pointed out that both the Brönsted-Lowry concept and the general Solvent System concept which will soon be described are equally applicable to protonic solvents.

[10] CADY and ELSEY, *J. Chem. Educ.*, **5**, 1425 (1928).

TABLE 7.3

Autoionization of Typical Solvents

$H_2O + H_2O \rightleftharpoons H_3O^+ + OH^-$

$NH_3 + NH_3 \rightleftharpoons NH_4^+ + NH_2^-$

$HC_2H_3O_2 + HC_2H_3O_2 \rightleftharpoons (HC_2H_3O_2 \cdot H)^+ + C_2H_3O_2^-$

$H_2SO_4 + H_2SO_4 \rightleftharpoons (H_2SO_4 \cdot H)^+ + HSO_4^-$

$SO_2 + SO_2 \rightleftharpoons SO^{2+} + SO_3^{2-}$

$COCl_2 + COCl_2 \rightleftharpoons (COCl \cdot COCl_2)^+ + Cl^-$

$SeOCl_2 + SeOCl_2 \rightleftharpoons (SeOCl \cdot SeOCl_2)^+ + Cl^-$

acids, whereas substances possessing or giving rise to the sulfite ion can be considered to be bases. The Cady and Elsey concept and the proposed autoionizations are extremely useful in interpreting the behavior of a large number of substances in nonaqueous solvents in terms of acid-base relationships. The situation with respect to acid-base behavior in liquid ammonia has already been described. Application of the concept to reactions in several other solvents, namely acetic acid, liquid sulfur dioxide, and selenium(IV) oxychloride, will be briefly considered below.[11]

7.29 Anhydrous acetic acid (m.p., 16.7°; b.p., 118.1°) is a solvent whose solutions can be studied over a very convenient temperature range. As would be expected from its low dielectric constant (ca. 6 at 25°), acetic acid is a better solvent for covalent than for ionic compounds, and effects of interionic attraction are rather large for solutions of the latter. The value for the ion-product of acetic acid (2.5×10^{-13}) indicates a degree of self ionization comparable with that of water.

$$2HC_2H_3O_2 \rightleftharpoons (HC_2H_3O_2 \cdot H)^+ + C_2H_3O_2^-$$

7.30 On the basis of the definitions which have been proposed, substances giving the solvated proton $(HC_2H_3O_2 \cdot H)^+$ in solution may be regarded as acids, and those yielding the acetate ion may be considered to be bases.

7.31 It has been demonstrated that acetic acid solutions of the "stronger" inorganic acids ($HClO_4$, H_2SO_4, HCl) and the sulfonic acids can be used as titrants for solutions of metal acetates and organic amines, the reactions being followed potentiometrically and also with indicators.[12] The amines function as bases by virtue of the reaction indicated.

$$RNH_2 + HC_2H_3O_2 = RNH_3^+ + C_2H_3O_2^-$$

It is possible to titrate such "weakly basic" substances as acetamide and acetanilide, which cannot be titrated in aqueous medium. Perchloric acid, the most

---

[11] The discussion which follows is adapted from the monograph by AUDRIETH and KLEINBERG, *Non-Aqueous Solvents: Applications as Media for Chemical Reactions*, John Wiley and Sons, Inc., New York, 1953.

[12] HALL and CONANT, *J. Am. Chem. Soc.*, **49**, 3047 (1927); CONANT and HALL, *ibid.*, **49**, 3062 (1927); HALL and WERNER, *ibid.*, **50**, 2367 (1928); HALL, *ibid.*, **52**, 5115 (1930); CONANT and WERNER, *ibid.*, **52**, 4436 (1930); HALL, *Chem. Revs.*, **8**, 191 (1931).

highly dissociated of the "strong" acids in acetic acid, is commonly used as the titrant for bases; it has already been pointed out (see 7.12) that acetic acid acts as a differentiating medium toward "strong" acids. However, even perchloric acid, and also the strongest bases, are relatively weak electrolytes in acetic acid, as a result of the large interionic effects which arise in a solvent of low dielectric constant.

7.32 The solubility of metal acetates in acetic acid emphasizes the similarity between these compounds and their analogous hydroxides in water.[13] The alkali metal and barium acetates are readily soluble, whereas the solubility of most of the other acetates is small. A similar situation exists for the metal hydroxides in water. The solubility of metal acetates in acetic acid appears to be related to their ability to form solvates; in general the tendency for solvate formation and solubility go hand in hand.

7.33 Solubility effects which may be attributed to the amphoteric nature of certain metal acetates in acetic acid have been observed. For example, zinc acetate may be precipitated by the addition of a small quantity of an acetic acid solution of sodium acetate to a similar solution of zinc chloride. The addition of an excess of sodium acetate solution results in the dissolution of the precipitated zinc acetate. The behavior of zinc acetate in acetic acid may be considered to be analogous to that of zinc hydroxide in water which dissolves upon treatment with an excess of sodium hydroxide solution. The following equations may therefore be formulated.

$$ZnCl_2 + 2NaC_2H_3O_2 = Zn(C_2H_3O_2)_2\downarrow + 2NaCl$$
$$Zn(C_2H_3O_2)_2 + 2NaC_2H_3O_2 = Na_2Zn(C_2H_3O_2)_4$$
$$ZnCl_2 + 2NaOH = Zn(OH)_2\downarrow + 2NaCl$$
$$Zn(OH)_2 + 2NaOH = Na_2Zn(OH)_4$$

That the analogy is valid is shown by a solubility study of the ternary system $Zn(C_2H_3O_2)_2$-$NaC_2H_3O_2$-$HC_2H_3O_2$. Figure 7.1 shows that the solubility behavior, at constant temperature, of zinc acetate in acetic acid solutions which contain varying concentrations of sodium acetate is remarkably like that of zinc hydroxide in aqueous sodium hydroxide solutions. In each case, the compositions of the solid compounds which appear at high concentrations of the sodium compound are also quite similar: in acetic acid, $Na_2Zn(C_2H_3O_2)_4 \cdot 4HC_2H_3O_2$; in water, $Na_2Zn(OH)_4 \cdot 2H_2O$.

7.34 The solubility behavior of acetic acid solutions of zinc acetate toward added ammonium acetate is exactly like that toward added sodium acetate.[14] In view of the fact that ammonium acetate has been shown to be a "strong" base in acetic acid, this similarity in behavior is not unexpected. Solubility studies on copper(II) acetate have shown that this substance is also amphoteric in acetic acid.

7.35 A nonprotonic solvent which has been investigated from the Solvent System viewpoint with considerable success is liquid sulfur dioxide. This

[13] DAVIDSON, *Chem. Revs.*, **8**, 175 (1931).
[14] DAVIDSON and GRISWOLD, *J. Am. Chem. Soc.*, **57**, 423 (1935).

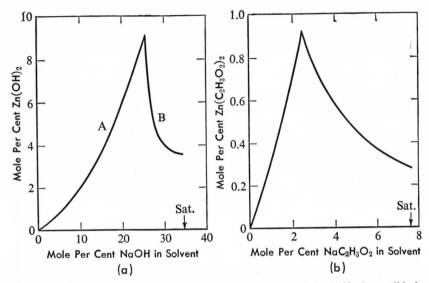

Fig. 7.1 (a) Effect of NaOH upon the solubility of $Zn(OH)_2$ in H_2O at 30°. A — solid phase $Zn(OH)_2$; B — solid phase $Zn(OH)_2 \cdot 2NaOH \cdot 2H_2O$. (b) effect of $NaC_2H_3O_2$ upon the solubility of $Zn(C_2H_3O_2)_2$ in $HC_2H_3O_2$ at 28.5°. (From DAVIDSON, *Chem. Revs.*, 8, 175, 1931)

medium, although it possesses a low boiling point ($-10.2°$), is readily handled in Dewar flasks without appreciable losses due to evaporation, or in sealed containers at room temperature at a few atmospheres pressure. It undergoes autoionization to about the same extent as does water, as is indicated by the value for its specific conductance, 4×10^{-8} ohm^{-1}. Possessing a relatively low dielectric constant (12.35 at 22°), it is a considerably more effective solvent for covalent inorganic compounds than for ionic ones. Moreover, interionic effects are large in solutions of the latter.

7.36 It has already been stated that, on the basis of the proposed self ionization (see 7.28), of liquid sulfur dioxide, thionyl compounds, potential sources of SO^{2+} ions, and sulfites, sources of SO_3^{2-} ion, may be considered to be acids and bases, respectively. Jander and co-workers [15] have utilized these definitions for the development of a "sulfito" chemical system.*

[15] JANDER, *Die Chemie in Wasserähnlichen Lösungmitteln*, Springer-Verlag, Berlin, 1949, Ch. VIII; an excellent summary of liquid sulfur dioxide chemistry.

* Recent work strongly indicates that the proposed mode of self ionization of liquid sulfur dioxide is of minor importance in this solvent. Thus, it has been found that no isotopic sulfur exchange takes place at room temperature when sulfur trioxide is dissolved in liquid sulfur dioxide or when sulfur dioxide is dissolved in liquid sulfur trioxide [HUSTON, *J. Am. Chem. Soc.*, 73, 3049 (1951)]. Moreover, exchange between liquid sulfur dioxide and $SOCl_2$ or $SOBr_2$ is extremely slow [JOHNSON, NORRIS, and HUSTON, *J. Am. Chem. Soc.*, 73, 3052 (1951)]. This suggests that thionyl compounds yield a negligible amount of SO^{2+}, and would thus appear to necessitate modification of Jander's conception of simple ionic mechanisms for reactions involving thionyl compounds (for example, neutralization reactions). In spite of these observations, the Jander approach to inorganic reactions in liquid sulfur dioxide is described because it has proved to be of considerable utility.

7.37 In accordance with the definitions, reaction between thionyl compounds and sulfites to give solvent molecules may be regarded as a typical "neutralization" reaction.

$$SO^{2+} + SO_3^{2-} = 2SO_2$$

Experimental verification for such reactions has been obtained with a number of thionyl compounds and sulfites. The course of the reactions has been followed both conductometrically and by the isolation and identification of reaction products. Figure 7.2 depicts a conductometric titration of thionyl chloride with

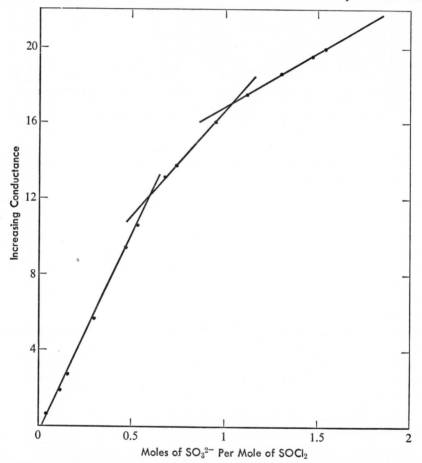

Fig. 7.2 Conductometric titration of thionyl chloride with tetramethylammonium sulfite. (JANDER & WICKERT, Z. physik. Chem., A178, **57**, 1936)

tetramethylammonium sulfite. The first break in the curve presumably corresponds to the formation of an acid salt; however, this salt could not be isolated.

7.38 The reaction of sulfur dioxide solutions of thionyl chloride with metallic iron lends additional support to the hypothesis that thionyl halides are acids in liquid sulfur dioxide. At room temperature the products isolated are iron(II) chloride and free sulfur. Presumably the mechanism of interaction is the following.

$$2Fe + 2SOCl_2 = 2FeCl_2 + 2SO$$
$$2SO = S + SO_2$$

This reaction may be regarded as being analogous to that between iron and hydrochloric acid in aqueous medium.

7.39 A number of metallic sulfites exhibit amphoterism in liquid sulfur dioxide. An interesting example involves the behavior of aluminum sulfite, the sulfur dioxide analog of aluminum hydroxide. Aluminum sulfite is precipitated when an aluminum chloride solution in sulfur dioxide is treated with a solution of tetramethylammonium sulfite. The precipitate dissolves in an excess of tetramethylammonium sulfite solution. When thionyl chloride (an acid) is added to the solution so formed, aluminum sulfite is reprecipitated. The reactions just noted were followed conductometrically and may be described stoichiometrically by the following equations.

$$2AlCl_3 + 3[(CH_3)_4N]_2SO_3 = Al_2(SO_3)_3\downarrow + 6[(CH_3)_4N]Cl$$
$$Al_2(SO_3)_3\downarrow + 3[(CH_3)_4N]_2SO_3 = 2[(CH_3)_4N]_3Al(SO_3)_3$$
$$2[(CH_3)_4N]_3Al(SO_3)_3 + 3SOCl_2 = 6[(CH_3)_4N]Cl + 6SO_2 + Al_2(SO_3)_3\downarrow$$

Other substances that are amphoteric in liquid sulfur dioxide, as demonstrated by the fact that they undergo reactions similar to those described for aluminum sulfite, are the following: $SnO_2 \cdot xSO_2$, $Bi_2O_3 \cdot xSO_2$, $Ga_2O_3 \cdot xSO_2$, $Sb_2O_3 \cdot xSO_2$, and $Sb_2O_5 \cdot xSO_2$.

7.40 Tin exhibits a reaction in liquid sulfur dioxide which is comparable to that of the metal in aqueous sodium hydroxide. Thus, the metal foil reacts with an excess of the base tetramethylammonium sulfite in accordance with the following equations.

$$Sn + [(CH_3)_4N]_2SO_3 + 4SO_2 = [(CH_3)_4N]_2Sn(SO_3)_3 + 2SO$$
$$2SO = SO_2 + S$$
$$[(CH_3)_4N]_2SO_3 + S = [(CH_3)_4N]_2S_2O_3$$

With equimolecular proportions of tin and the base, tin(IV) oxide solvate is precipitated.

7.41 A solvent which, at first glance, would appear to be useful for the study of inorganic reactions is selenium(IV) oxychloride. The freezing (10.9°) and boiling (176°) points imply its utility over a wide and convenient liquid range. Its high dielectric constant (ca. 46 at 20°) indicates a high solvent power for ionic substances. Unfortunately, its usefulness as a medium for chemical reactions is limited by the fact that at elevated temperatures, and in some cases at lower temperatures, it is a powerful oxidizing agent. Nevertheless, it has been demonstrated that selenium(IV) oxychloride may function as a parent solvent for a system of acids, bases, and salts.[16]

[16] SMITH, *Chem. Revs.*, **23**, 165 (1938).

7.42 In accordance with the proposed autoionization of selenium(IV) oxychloride,

$$2SeOCl_2 \rightleftharpoons (SeOCl \cdot SeOCl_2)^+ + Cl^-,$$

substances yielding the $SeOCl^+$(solvated) cation in solution may be regarded as acids and those yielding chloride ion, as bases. Thus, tin(IV) chloride is an acid and pyridine a base in selenium(IV) oxychloride.

$$SnCl_4 + 2SeOCl_2 = 2SeOCl^+ + SnCl_6^{2-}$$
$$C_5H_5N + SeOCl_2 = C_5H_5NSeOCl^+ + Cl^-$$

7.43 There is evidence that the above formulations are valid. Solutions of pyridine in selenium(IV) oxychloride are excellent conductors of electric current. Moreover, well-defined mono- and disolvates have been obtained from such solutions.[17] Such metals as magnesium, calcium, lead, copper, and zinc are in general more reactive and more soluble in a 20 per cent solution of tin(IV) chloride than in selenium(IV) oxychloride alone. The solvate $SnCl_4 \cdot 2SeOCl_2$ can be isolated from selenium(IV) oxychloride solutions of tin(IV) chloride. A formulation analogous to that proposed for tin(IV) chloride also explains the powerful solvent action of selenium(IV) oxychloride solutions of sulfur trioxide, which are capable of dissolving a variety of metallic oxides.[18]

7.44 Typical "neutralization" reactions giving rise to salts have been shown to take place in selenium oxychloride. Conductometric titrations [17] involving a number of acids and bases demonstrate definite compound formation between these substances. For example, titration of tin(IV) chloride (acid) with calcium chloride (base) shows the formation of three compounds, one being of the composition $CaCl_2 \cdot SnCl_4$. The mechanism of the formation is probably as shown.

$$SnCl_4 + SeOCl_2 = 2SeOCl^+ + SnCl_6^{2-}$$
$$2SeOCl^+ + SnCl_6^{2-} + Ca^{2+} + 2Cl^- = Ca^{2+}, SnCl_6^{2-} + 2SeOCl_2$$

Table 7.4 summarizes the acid-base reactions which have been studied.

TABLE 7.4

Conductometric Acid-Base Titrations in $SeOCl_2$

System	Titrant	Compounds Formed	System	Titrant	Compounds Formed
$SnCl_4$-C_5H_5N	$SnCl_4$ C_5H_5N	$SnCl_4 \cdot 2C_5H_5N$ $2SnCl_4 \cdot 1C_5H_5N$ $SnCl_4 \cdot C_5H_5N$ $SnCl_4 \cdot 2C_5H_5N$ $SnCl_4 \cdot 3C_5H_5N$	$FeCl_3$-C_5H_5N	C_5H_5N	$FeCl_3 \cdot C_5H_5N$ $FeCl_3 \cdot 2C_5H_5N$ $FeCl_3 \cdot 3C_5H_5N$
$SnCl_4$-KCl	$SnCl_4$	$2SnCl_4 \cdot 3KCl$ $SnCl_4 \cdot KCl$	SO_3-C_5H_5N	C_5H_5N	$SO_3 \cdot C_5H_5N$ $SO_3 \cdot 2C_5H_5N$
$SnCl_4$-$CaCl_2$	$CaCl_2$	$2SnCl_4 \cdot 1CaCl_2$ $SnCl_4 \cdot CaCl_2$ $2SnCl_4 \cdot 3CaCl_2$	$AsCl_3$-C_5H_5N	C_5H_5N	$2AsCl_3 \cdot 1C_5H_5N$ $AsCl_3 \cdot C_5H_5N$ $AsCl_3 \cdot 2C_5H_5N$

[17] JACKSON and SMITH, *J. Am. Chem. Soc.*, **62**, 544 (1940).
[18] LENHER, *J. Am. Chem. Soc.*, **43**, 29 (1921).

7.45 "Neutralization" reactions have also been studied in selenium(IV) oxychloride by the potentiometric technique. Titration curves similar to those for acid-base reactions in water are obtained for interactions between nonprotonic acids and nonprotonic bases. Figure 7.3 shows the titration curves obtained for

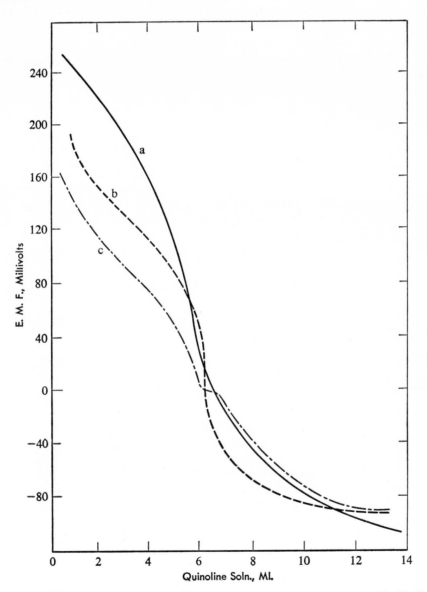

Fig. 7.3 Titration curves of (a) sulfur trioxide, (b) iron(III) chloride, and (c) tin(IV) chloride with quinoline in selenium(IV) oxychloride. (From PETERSON, HEIMERZHEIM, and SMITH, *J. Am. Chem. Soc.*, 65, 2403, 1943)

the acids sulfur trioxide, iron(III) chloride, and tin(IV) chloride with the base quinoline.[19] These curves indicate that the reactions are of the "weak acid — weak base" type.

7.46 It is evident from the material discussed in this section that the Solvent System concept has been of great value in interpreting many reactions in both protonic and nonprotonic solvents in terms of acid-base relationships. The limitations of the concept are two-fold: (1) the restriction of acid-base behavior to particular solvents, and (2) the emphasis upon ionization as the outstanding factor in acid-base properties. A more general concept based upon structural considerations and a definite set of experimental criteria is the *Lewis Electronic* concept of acids and bases.

The Lewis Electronic Concept [3,20,21]

7.47 According to Lewis there are four experimental criteria which serve to characterize acids and bases. These "phenomenological criteria" are the following:

1. *Neutralization.* Acids and bases combine more or less rapidly with each other. Reaction of one with the other neutralizes the characteristic properties of each.
2. *Reactions with indicators.* Acids and bases may be titrated against each other by the use of indicators.
3. *Displacement reactions.* An acid or base will generally displace a weaker acid or base from its compounds.
4. *Catalytic activity.* Acids and bases frequently act as catalytic agents in chemical reactions.

For a substance to be classified as an acid or a base it must exhibit all four of these characteristics.

7.48 Examination of acid-base equilibria in the light of the experimental criteria led to the following definitions. An acid molecule or ion is one in which the normal electron grouping surrounding some atom is incomplete, and thus the molecule or ion can accept an electron pair from some other atom; a base, on the other hand, has an electron pair it can share with an acid. Typical acids are: BF_3, SO_3, H^+, $SnCl_4$, $AlCl_3$; typical bases, OH^-, O^{2-}, CN^-, R_3N, R_2O. It is apparent that acids and bases are substances which are commonly referred to as "acceptor" and "donor" molecules, respectively. "Neutralization" involves the formation of a coordinate covalent bond between the acid and the base. In Table 7.5 there are listed examples of typical acid-base pairs and their neutralization products.

[19] PETERSON, HEIMERZHEIM, and SMITH, *J. Am. Chem. Soc.*, 65, 2403 (1943).
[20] LEWIS, *Valence and the Structure of Atoms and Molecules*, The Chemical Catalog Co., Inc., New York, 1923.
[21] LEWIS, *J. Franklin Inst.*, 226, 293 (1938).

TABLE 7.5

Acid-Base Pairs According to the Lewis Concept

Acid	Base	"Neutralization" Product	Acid	Base	"Neutralization" Product
HCl	R_3N	$R_3NH^+ + Cl^-$	$SnCl_4$	$SeOCl_2$	$2SeOCl^+ + SnCl_6^{2-}$
BCl_3	R_3N	$R_3N \cdot BCl_3$	$SeOCl_2$	C_5H_5N	$C_5H_5NSeOCl^+ + Cl^-$
SO_3	R_3N	$R_3N \cdot SO_3$	Ag^+	NH_3	$Ag(NH_3)_2^+$
HCl	H_2O	$H_3O^+ + Cl^-$	CO_2	O^{2-}	CO_3^{2-}
$AlCl_3$	$COCl_2$	$COCl^+ + AlCl_4^-$			

7.49 A discussion of the experimental behavior of acids and bases in terms of the Lewis definitions is in order. The definitions place emphasis on the structures of the reacting substances; there are no restrictions whatever with regard to solvent or ionization.

7.50 Inspection of the acid-base pairs of Table 7.5 shows that both the Brönsted-Lowry and the Solvent System concepts are merely specialized examples of the more general Lewis idea. The essential criterion for "neutralization" according to the Lewis concept is the formation of the coordinate covalent bond. This may take place either in the presence or absence of solvent and may frequently be accompanied by the ionization of the compound formed. In some instances the formation of the coordinate bond may be represented as taking place simultaneously with ionization, or as involving intermediate formation of a hydrogen bond, followed by proton transfer.

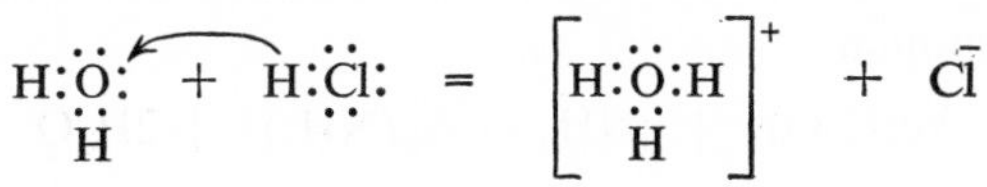

$$H:\overset{..}{\underset{..}{O}}: \; + \; H:\overset{..}{\underset{..}{Cl}}: \; = \; \left[H:\overset{..}{\underset{..}{O}}:H \right]^+ \; + \; \bar{Cl}$$
$$H H$$

The above reaction may also be regarded as a displacement of a weak base (Cl^-) by a stronger one (H_2O).

7.51 Acid-base titrations with the aid of indicators may be carried out in a variety of solvents. Bases such as pyridine and triethylamine have been titrated with such acids as boron trichloride and tin(IV) chloride dissolved in carbon tetrachloride, and silver perchlorate dissolved in benzene, the indicators used being thymol blue, butter yellow, and crystal violet. The latter is especially convenient to use, since it is soluble in a large number of solvents and usually gives the same color change in different solvents. The data of Table 7.6 summarize a few titrations which have been carried out to demonstrate the acidic and basic characteristics predicted for compounds on the basis of their structures.[22]

7.52 There are many examples of displacement, the third criterion which characterizes acid-base behavior. A familiar illustration of the displacement

[22] LUDER, MCGUIRE, and ZUFFANTI, *J. Chem. Educ.*, **20**, 344 (1943).

TABLE 7.6

Acid-Base Titrations in a Number of Solvents

Solvent	Acids	Bases
H_2O	HCl	NH_3
	H_2SO_4	C_5H_5N
	$HC_2H_3O_2$	C_2H_5OH
	HNO_3	![dioxane structure] $\begin{smallmatrix} CH_2CH_2 \\ O \qquad\quad O \\ CH_2CH_2 \end{smallmatrix}$
$C_6H_5^{\bullet}Cl$	HCl (gas)	Ethers
	BCl_3	Carboxylic acid anhydrides
	$SnCl_4$	Alcohols
CCl_4	BCl_3	C_5H_5N
	HCl (gas)	Amines
	$AlCl_3$	Esters

(Methyl violet indicator: yellow in acid solution, violet in basic solution.)

of a weaker acid by a stronger one is found in the liberation of carbon dioxide from carbonate solutions upon treatment with hydrogen chloride.

$$CO_3^{2-} + 2H^+ = CO_2 + H_2O$$
$$\text{acid} \qquad \text{acid}$$

The "neutralization" of silver ion by ammonia, listed in Table 7.5, in reality involves the displacement of the weaker base water from the aquated ion by the stronger base ammonia.

$$Ag(H_2O)_2^+ + 2NH_3 = Ag(NH_3)_2^+ + 2H_2O$$

Related to the case cited above are "neutralization" reactions in such ionizable nonaqueous solvents as sulfur dioxide, carbonyl chloride, and selenium(IV) oxychloride, and also in such nonionizable solvents as ether and pyridine. The reactions between boron trichloride and triethylamine in selenium(IV) oxychloride and in ether, respectively, are pertinent illustrations. Both acid and base undergo reaction with selenium(IV) oxychloride.

$$BCl_3 + SeOCl_2 = SeOCl^+ + BCl_4^-$$
$$(C_2H_5)_3N: + SeOCl_2 = (C_2H_5)_3N:SeOCl^+ + Cl^-$$
$$SeOCl^+, BCl_4^- + (C_2H_5)_3N:SeOCl^+, Cl^- = (C_2H_5)_3N:BCl_3 + 2SeOCl_2$$

When the reaction is carried out in ether, the latter, acting as a base, reacts with boron trichloride.

$$(C_2H_5)_2O: + BCl_3 = (C_2H_5)_2O:BCl_3$$

This reaction is followed by the displacement of ether by the stronger base triethylamine.

$$(C_2H_5)_2O:BCl_3 + (C_2H_5)_3N: = (C_2H_5)_3N:BCl_3 + (C_2H_5)_2O:$$

7.53 In addition to the examples of displacement described above, there are important reactions of this type which take place either between solids or in the fused state at high temperatures. These will be discussed in the next section.

7.54 The fourth experimental criterion of acid-base behavior is that of catalytic activity. Many believe that the most useful application of the Lewis concept is found in the catalytic activity of acids in the field of organic chemistry. Thus, the hydrogen acids, aluminum chloride, boron trifluoride, sulfur trioxide, and iron(III) bromide are all important acid catalysts and may be used interchangeably in many instances. A discussion of this phase of acid behavior is beyond the scope of this text.

Acid-Base Reactions at High Temperatures [4,23]

7.55 A great number of important reactions in metallurgical and ceramic processes take place at high temperatures. Many of these reactions, and others which occur in high temperature systems, may be regarded as acid-base phenomena.

7.56 Much experimental evidence has been accumulated which demonstrates that "onium" salts (*i.e.*, compounds formed by reaction of hydrogen acids with ammonia or amines and which have been characterized as acids in their respective parent solvents) behave as acids in the solid as well as in the fused state at elevated temperatures. Ammonium sulfate and ammonium fluoride have long been used as fluxes in the opening of ores. Anhydrous metal chlorides can be obtained from their hydrates by heating in the presence of ammonium chloride, the latter presumably acting as an acid to repress hydrolysis and the formation of basic salts. Fused ammonium nitrate is capable of dissolving a large number of metallic oxides, such as CuO, UO_3, MgO, CdO, NiO, ZnO, etc., with the formation of the corresponding nitrates, ammonia, and water.[24] Such carbonates as $BaCO_3$, $MnCO_3$, and $CaCO_3$ are similarly dissolved. The action of fused ammonium nitrate on metals is entirely analogous to that of aqueous nitric acid. A wide variety of metals react vigorously and dissolve with the evolution of nitrogen and ammonia, for example,

$$Cu + 3NH_4NO_3 = Cu(NO_3)_2 + N_2 + 2NH_3 + 3H_2O.$$

The fused nitrate effects numerous oxidations, *e.g.*, tin(II) chloride is converted to tin(IV) oxide. Rare earth chlorides, bromides,[25] and iodides [26] have been prepared in excellent yields by reaction at elevated temperatures between the oxides and an excess of the ammonium salt, followed by removal of the excess of the latter under reduced pressure.

7.57 Fused pyridinium chloride, $C_5H_5N \cdot HCl$, readily dissolves such metals as Al, Cd, Ca, Mg, and Zn with the evolution of hydrogen and the formation of metal chloride and pyridine. Other metals (Mn, Ni, Sn, Pb, Fe) react similarly

[23] AUDRIETH and MOELLER, *J. Chem. Educ.*, **20**, 219 (1943).
[24] AUDRIETH and SCHMIDT, *Proc. Nat. Acad. Sci.*, **20**, 221 (1934).
[25] REED, HOPKINS, and AUDRIETH, *J. Am. Chem. Soc.*, **57**, 1159 (1935).
[26] TAEBEL and HOPKINS, *Z. anorg. allgem. Chem.*, **235**, 62 (1937).

but less rapidly; As, Hg, Ag, and Pt are unattacked.[27]   Numerous metallic oxides and carbonates are also readily dissolved by molten pyridinium chloride.

7.58 The reactions cited above are readily interpreted in terms of the characteristic reactions of Brönsted-Lowry acids.   There are many high temperature changes, however, which are not explained by the application of the Brönsted-Lowry concept.   For interpretation of these phenomena we must turn to the Lewis electronic concept.

7.59 Reactions between ionic substances containing the donor ions $:\ddot{O}:^{2-}$, $:\ddot{S}:^{2-}$, and $:\ddot{F}:^-$ and coordinatively unsaturated substances containing covalently bound oxygen (*e.g.*, SiO_2, TiO_2, PO_3^-, BO_2^-) may be regarded as acid-base reactions in the Lewis sense.   In every case, reaction results in the formation of a covalent bond between the donor and acceptor, as in the formation of PO_4^{3-}.

$$:\ddot{O}:^{2-} + :\overset{\ddot{}}{\underset{\ddot{}}{O}}:\overset{}{P}:\ddot{O}:^- = :\overset{:\ddot{O}:}{\underset{:\ddot{O}:}{O}}:\overset{}{P}:\ddot{O}:^{3-}$$

Reactions between the substances listed above, and many others similar in type, are of importance in the manufacture of glass, cement, and ceramic products, in the formation of slag in the blast furnace, and in the preparation of certain electrolytic melts.   A number of these reactions are summarized in Table 7.7.

TABLE 7.7

The Lewis Concept and Acid-Base Reactions at Higher Temperatures

Bases	Acids	"Neutralization" Products	Applications
O^{2-} (from MO, MOH, MCO$_3$, MSO$_4$)	SiO_2, Al_2O_3, B_2O_3	SiO_3^{2-} or SiO_4^{4-} AlO_2^- or AlO_3^{3-} BO_2^- or BO_3^{3-}	Manufacture of glass, cement and ceramic products. Slag formation.
O^{2-} (from MO)	$BO_2^-(B_2O_3)$, PO_3^-	BO_3^{3-}, PO_4^{3-}	Borax bead tests. Metaphosphate bead tests.
O^{2-} (from MO)	$S_2O_7^{2-}$, $(SO_4^{2-} \cdot SO_3)$, HSO_4^-, $(H_2O + S_2O_7^{2-})$	SO_4^{2-}	Opening of ores.
S^{2-} (from Na$_2$S)	FeS, Cu$_2$S	FeS_2^{2-}, CuS^-	Orford process for nickel concentration.*
F^- (from alkali fluorides)	BeF_2, AlF_3, TaF_5	BeF_4^{2-}, AlF_6^{3-}, TaF_7^{2-}	Electrolytic melts.

AUDRIETH and MOELLER, *J. Chem. Educ.*, **20**, 219 (1943)

* Application now obsolete.

[27] AUDRIETH, LONG, and EDWARDS, *J. Am. Chem. Soc.*, **58**, 428 (1936).

7.60 Inasmuch as substances like silica exist in the form of large polymeric molecules, chemical combination with a base must be accompanied by depolymerization. This depolymerization is effected by the base in much the same manner that iso- and heteropoly anions are converted to simple ions in aqueous solution by the addition of base (*e.g.*, conversion of $Cr_2O_7^{2-}$ to CrO_4^{2-}). Similarly, since fused metaphosphate melts are polymeric in nature, their combination with base must involve degradation.

$$(PO_3^-)_x + xO^{2-} \rightleftharpoons xPO_4^{3-}$$

An interesting application of depolymerization of fused sodium metaphosphate by a Lewis base is found in the preparation of sodium monofluorophosphate, Na_2PO_3F. Treatment of the melt with sodium fluoride for a few minutes at 800° gives excellent yields of the fluorophosphate.[28]

[28] HILL and AUDRIETH, *J. Phys. Colloid Chem.*, **54**, 690 (1950).

PART

III

THE CHEMISTRY OF
THE ELEMENTS

SECTION A. *The Representative Elements*

Chapter 8. Perspective   291

9. Hydrogen   295

10. Group I — The Alkali Metals   301

11. Group II   314

12. Group III   325

13. Group IV   345

14. Group V   378

15. Group VI   422

16. Group VII — The Halogens   456

PERSPECTIVE

8.1 The representative (or regular) elements consist of the periods (or series) shown in the table.

I	II	III	IV	V	VI	VII	VIII
							$_2$He
$_1$H							
$_3$Li	$_4$Be	$_5$B	$_6$C	$_7$N	$_8$O	$_9$F	$_{10}$Ne
$_{11}$Na	$_{12}$Mg	$_{13}$Al	$_{14}$Si	$_{15}$P	$_{16}$S	$_{17}$Cl	$_{18}$Ar
$_{19}$K	$_{20}$Ca	$_{31}$Ga	$_{32}$Ge	$_{33}$As	$_{34}$Se	$_{35}$Br	$_{36}$Kr
$_{37}$Rb	$_{38}$Sr	$_{49}$In	$_{50}$Sn	$_{51}$Sb	$_{52}$Te	$_{53}$I	$_{54}$Xe
$_{55}$Cs	$_{56}$Ba	$_{81}$Tl	$_{82}$Pb	$_{83}$Bi	$_{84}$Po	$_{85}$At	$_{86}$Rn
$_{87}$Fr	$_{88}$Ra						

In each of the periods, with the exception of the H–He period, in which the $1s$ orbital is being filled, s and p orbitals are progressively filled and the number of electrons in the outer shell increases regularly from one to eight, e.g., Li $1s^22s^1$; Be $1s^22s^2$; B $1s^22s^22p^1$;... Ne $1s^22s^22p^6$. Underlying the outer shell is one which contains either two, eight, or eighteen electrons. For the periods Li–Ne and Na–Ar, there are respectively two and eight electrons in the underlying shell; for the remainder of the complete periods, the first and second elements have eight electrons in the next to the outer shell and the rest of the elements eighteen electrons. This change in configuration results from the intervention of transition series between the second and third elements, beginning with the third complete period. Thus, between calcium and gallium and between strontium and indium there occur the $3d$ (scandium-zinc) and the $4d$ (yttrium-cadmium) short transition series, respectively, and between barium and thallium both the $5d$ (lanthanum; hafnium-mercury) short transition series and the $4f$ (lanthanide) long transition series.

8.2 Examination of the elements which make up any one of the representative series shows that, in general, there is a definite transition from active metal to active nonmetal as the outer shell is progressively filled from s^1 to s^2p^5. It should be emphasized, however, that this transition becomes less marked with increasing period number, i.e., with increasing atomic complexity. Thus, whereas silicon is completely nonmetallic in character, germanium, the corresponding element

291

of the next series, has some distinctly metallic characteristics. The trend toward nonmetallic character is least pronounced in the last complete series; polonium, for example, a member of a family of which the first three members are com- pletely nonmetallic in character, has many of the attributes of a metal. Ele- ments having completed s and p orbitals, $i.e.$, an s^2p^6 configuration (for helium $1s^2$), are chemically stable, and elements having this configuration exist as monatomic gases, known as the inert gases. There is no conclusive evidence that these substances form bonds with other atoms in ordinary chemical reac- tions; in this sense the inert gases have no chemistry and are therefore not discussed in this text.

8.3 Similarities in chemical properties within a group of representative ele- ments are due to the identical configuration of valence electrons. Variations in behavior are attributable chiefly to differences in sizes of atoms (or ions), and to differences in the number of electrons in the penultimate shells of the atoms. One significant effect of the difference in size on properties is found in the marked difference in chemical behavior of the first members of the representative element families as compared with their congeners. Thus lithium, beryllium, and boron are in many respects more similar in properties to the elements falling diagonally below them in the next families ($i.e.$, Li–Mg, Be–Al, B–Si) than they are to the other members of their respective groups. The divergence in the behavior of carbon from that exhibited by its congeners is in large measure due to its inability to accommodate more than eight electrons in its valence shell. A similar consideration applies to nitrogen, oxygen, and fluorine; in addition, the extremely high electronegativity of these elements, as compared with that of their congeners, accounts for some of the observed differences in properties.

8.4 For the members of either representative group I or II, in which the electronic configuration underlying the outer shell is that of an inert gas, chem- ical reactivity of the gaseous atoms, as manifested by ionization potentials, becomes more pronounced with increasing atomic size. In general, reactivity in aqueous solution, as given by electrode potential values, follows the same order. However, one notable exception to the trend in reactivity in solution is found in group I (the alkali metals), and is directly attributable to size considera- tions. The potential of the lithium electrode, instead of being the lowest for the members of the group, is actually greater than that of cesium. This apparent anomaly results from the much greater tendency of the very small lithium ion, as compared with the other alkali metal ions, to coordinate water molecules. Thus, the energy liberated in the reaction

$$M^+(g) + xH_2O = M(H_2O)_x^+$$

is sufficiently great for the lithium ion to give this element the highest electrode potential of the alkali metals.

8.5 No simple generalization relating size and reactivity can be made for metals in groups in which there is a change from a penultimate shell of eight electrons to one of eighteen. Consideration of the metallic members of group III illustrates this point. The values of the third ionization potentials and of the electrode potentials (for the reaction $M + xH_2O = M(H_2O)_x^{3+} + 3e^-$) for these elements are shown in the table.

	Third ionization potential, volts	Electrode potential, volts
Al	28.3	+1.67
Ga	30.6	+0.52
In	27.9	+0.34
Tl	29.7	−0.72

The great drop in reactivity from aluminum to gallium, in spite of the increase in size, may reasonably be ascribed to the existence of the first short transition series between these elements. As a result of the almost steady decrease in size across this series, arising from the filling of the $3d$ orbitals, there occurs a regular increase in effective nuclear charge, which in gallium is manifested by a larger ionization potential and a smaller electrode potential than would be anticipated. The much lower reactivity of thallium as compared with indium is explained in a similar manner, except that in this case two series intervene, namely the third short ($5d$) transition series and the lanthanides, along each of which a relatively steady decrease in size occurs.

8.6 The change from a shell of eight electrons underlying the valence shell to one of eighteen, resulting from the intervention of a short transition series, also may affect basicity relationships. Thus, in either group I or II, the hydroxides (or normal oxides) become more basic with increasing cation size. On the other hand, in group III, aluminum hydroxide is a distinctly stronger base than the corresponding gallium compound, even though the calculated ionic radius of aluminum is significantly less than that of gallium (0.52 Å as compared with 0.60 Å). The apparent inversion in basicity may be explained by the fact that the hydroxide (or oxide) ion polarizes the gallium ion (which has 18 electrons in its outer shell) more than it does the aluminum ion (which has only 8 electrons). The higher degree of deformation is accompanied by increased covalent character of the metal-oxide bond and consequent decreased basicity of the hydroxide. Both aluminum hydroxide and gallium hydroxide exhibit acidic as well as basic characteristics, gallium hydroxide being the more acidic.

8.7 Reactivity of nonmetals, as measured by their tendency to acquire electrons and form negative ions, diminishes with increasing size within each group. The formation of simple anions involves the attainment of inert gas configurations, and the ability to form such ions is most pronounced for the nonmetals of groups VI and VII, which acquire two electrons and one electron, respectively, in their reactions with many metallic elements. Of course, these reactive nonmetals can also combine with other nonmetallic elements, as well as with some metals, with the formation of covalent bonds. Few monatomic anions with charge greater than −2 are known, the energy requirements for the acquisition of more than two electrons being extremely great. There appears to be little doubt, however, that nitrogen (and perhaps phosphorus) can form a trinegative ion in reactions with strongly electropositive metals. Generally, the nonmetals in the middle groups of the representative elements, *e.g.*, B, C, Si, N, P, enter into chemical combination through covalent union.

8.8 Metals of representative series of elements which have a shell of two or eight electrons adjacent to the valence shell (*i.e.*, the elements of groups I and II and aluminum) have only one stable oxidation state, corresponding to the number of valence electrons. On the other hand, representative metals with a penultimate shell of eighteen electrons commonly exhibit two oxidation states, with the lower one having an s^2 outer shell configuration which results from removal of the p electrons solely. Thus, states of $+1$ and $+3$ are known for thallium, $+2$ and $+4$ for tin and lead, and $+3$ and $+5$ for antimony and bismuth. The existence of variable oxidation states for these elements can be attributed to the distinct energy separation between the s and p valence electrons, which becomes more pronounced with an increasing number of electrons between the nucleus and the valence shell. In other words, the more penetrating s electrons are shielded less effectively from the nucleus than are the p electrons as the atomic size within a group increases. Thus, it is found that the lower of the two oxidation states becomes more stable toward the bottom of the group; conversely, the higher state becomes more difficult to attain.

8.9 Positive ions of charge greater than three are unknown for the representative metals. The alkali metals are invariably ionic in their simple compounds, as are calcium, strontium, barium, and radium, of group II. Metals (even those, such as beryllium and aluminum, exhibiting high electrode potentials in aqueous solution) which give rise to simple cations of high charge density, tend to form simple binary compounds possessing considerable covalent character, as a result of the great polarizing power of such cations. It is with these same elements that the less basic hydroxides and the more stable complexes of the representative metals are found.

8.10 Generally, representative metals are much inferior to those of the short transition series in ability to form complex compounds. In large part this may be due to the lack of available inner d orbitals for the formation of strong covalent bonds with potential ligands.

CHAPTER 9

HYDROGEN

9.1 The atoms of the various isotopes of hydrogen possess the simplest electronic configuration of all the elements, $1s^1$. Formally, the hydrogen atom may be considered to be related to both the alkali metal and the halogen atoms — to the former in that it has a single valence electron and to the latter in that it requires one electron to attain an inert gas (helium) structure. Chemically, however, hydrogen, unlike the alkali metals, does not lose its single valence electron and form a simple monopositive ion in ordinary chemical reactions, the energy requirement being too great; and the tendency of the hydrogen atom to gain an electron and form a mononegative ion is considerably smaller than that of the halogens. Much of the chemistry of hydrogen is so nearly unique as to warrant a brief special discussion.

Properties of Ordinary Hydrogen

9.2 Three isotopes of hydrogen exist: ordinary hydrogen, $_1H^1$; heavy hydrogen or deuterium, $_1H^2$ (or $_1D^2$); and tritium, $_1H^3$ (or $_1T^3$). The ratio of hydrogen to deuterium in nature is approximately 6000 : 1. Tritium, which occurs in extremely minute quantities, is obtained primarily by the bombardment of deuterium by deuterons (D^+); it is radioactive, having a half-life of approximately 12 years.

9.3 Although hydrogen constitutes less than 1 per cent by weight of the earth's crust, approximately 16 per cent of the atoms on the surface of the earth are those of hydrogen. In the latter respect, it is, next to oxygen, the most abundant element. Most of the earth's hydrogen is found in water; only minute quantities of elementary hydrogen are observed in nature.

GENERAL REFERENCES

EPHRAIM, *Inorganic Chemistry*, 4th Edition, Interscience Publishers, Inc., New York, 1943, pp. 79–80; 115–119; 159; 396–397; 869–878.

SIDGWICK, *The Chemical Elements and Their Compounds*, Oxford University Press, London, 1950, pp. 11–32; 33–56; 57–58; 338–348; 364–367.

WELLS, *Structural Inorganic Chemistry*, 2nd Edition, Oxford University Press, London, 1950, Ch. VII.

9.4 Molecular hydrogen is diatomic and exists in two forms which are called ortho and para. These forms differ in the direction of nuclear (proton) spins. In the ortho variety, the spins of the hydrogen nuclei are in the same direction, whereas in para hydrogen the nuclear spins are opposed. In ordinary hydrogen at room temperature and above, the ratio of the ortho to the para form in equilibrium mixture is 3 : 1. The equilibrium ratio varies with temperature, the percentage of the para form increasing with decreasing temperature. The conversion from one form to the other is extremely slow unless effected in the presence of certain catalysts. Thus, the para variety is obtained practically pure when ordinary hydrogen is adsorbed on charcoal at the temperature of liquid hydrogen (20.39° K). In the absence of catalysts, gaseous para hydrogen remains unchanged for weeks even at ordinary temperatures; the change from the para form to the equilibrium mixture is catalyzed by paramagnetic substances. The physical properties of the two varieties differ to a slight extent as indicated in the table.

	Ordinary H_2	Para	Ortho
M.p., °K	13.95	13.83	13.99
B.p., °K at 760 mm.	20.39	20.26	20.43

9.5 In its chemical reactions the hydrogen atom, having one valence electron and one stable orbital, achieves a stable helium configuration either by the formation of one covalent bond or by acquiring an additional electron, forming the hydride ion, H^-. Combination by covalence takes place with most of the nonmetals; with the more active nonmetals (*e.g.*, Cl_2, Br_2, etc.) large quantities of energy are liberated in the reaction. Reaction with strongly electropositive metals results in the formation of compounds containing the negative hydride ion. In either case, the binary compounds formed are known as hydrides. These compounds are discussed in some detail in the next section.

9.6 A word regarding the possibility of the existence of the hydrogen ion, H^+ (the proton), in ordinary chemical reactions is pertinent. Although this is the formula commonly written for the ion which possesses characteristic acid properties in aqueous solution, it must be emphasized that the hydrogen ion never exists as a free nucleus in solution. As a result of its very small radius (approximately 1/50,000 that of the lithium ion), this ion exerts a tremendous attraction upon the solvent water molecules and is converted to the covalent state by union with the latter. (A similar situation exists in other protonic solvents. See Chapter 7.) In aqueous solution the hydrogen ion is thus formulated H_3O^+ (the hydronium ion). It should be pointed out that although this is a convenient way of representing the nature of the hydrogen ion in water, this ion is undoubtedly attached to more than one water molecule. It has been estimated that the heat of hydration of the proton is approximately 250,000 calories larger than that of any other monopositive ion.

The Hydrides

9.7 On the basis of the nature of the binding of the hydrogen, three general classes of hydrides are recognized.

1. Saltlike hydrides containing H⁻.

2. Those involving covalently bound hydrogen. This class may be further subdivided into the following types:
   a. Volatile binary hydrides,
   b. Complex hydrides.

3. The interstitial or metal-like hydrides.

Saltlike Hydrides **9.8** Hydrogen can remove an electron from extremely electropositive elements and form white compounds containing the mononegative hydride ion, H^-. Thus by direct combination at elevated temperatures with alkali and alkaline earth metals (with the exception of beryllium and magnesium) substances of the respective formulas MH and MH_2 are formed. That these are true ionic compounds containing H^- is demonstrated by the fact that when they are electrolyzed in the molten state hydrogen is liberated at the anode. X-ray examination shows that the alkali metal hydrides possess the typical sodium chloride crystal lattice.

9.9 When heated in the absence of air, these hydrides decompose and yield the free metal and hydrogen. Their thermal stability decreases with increasing size of the cation as indicated.

$$LiH > NaH > KH > RbH > CsH$$
$$CaH_2 > SrH_2 > BaH_2$$

The dissociation temperatures of the hydrides of the alkaline earth metals and of lithium are considerably higher than those of the other alkali metals. They all react vigorously with water, yielding hydrogen and the corresponding metal hydroxides. The potential for the reaction

$$H^- = \tfrac{1}{2}H_2 + e^-$$

has been estimated to be 2.33 volts. At room temperature the saltlike hydrides are poor reducing agents; their reducing power at elevated temperatures is considerable, presumably due to dissociation and the liberation of active hydrogen. Thus, they are capable of reducing refractory metal oxides at high temperatures. The heated, solid alkali metal hydrides absorb carbon dioxide, yielding the corresponding formates.

$$MH + CO_2 = HCOO^-, \quad M^+$$

They convert sulfates to sulfides. In reactions with nonmetals (*e.g.*, phosphorus, oxygen, sulfur, and chlorine) the hydrides behave as mixtures of metal and hydrogen.

Hydrides Containing Covalently Bound Hydrogen **9.10** The representative elements of groups IV, V, VI, VII, and boron of group III form volatile, covalent binary hydrides. The formulas for the simplest hydrides for the members of groups IV–VII are given by EH_{8-N}, where N is the group number; in each case, therefore, E, the central atom, has attained an inert gas configuration as a result of covalent binding with the appropriate number of hydrogen atoms. The formulas for the simplest hydrides of boron and aluminum, B_2H_6 and $(AlH_3)_n$, indicate that in these cases the nature of the binding is not so straightforward.

9.11 The stability of the hydrides in any periodic group decreases markedly with increasing atomic number of the central atom; the covalent hydrides of elements which are predominantly metallic in character (*e.g.*, PbH_4, BiH_3) are particularly unstable. In the hydrides of all but the most electronegative elements (nitrogen, oxygen, and fluorine), only weak van der Waals forces exist between the molecules. Ammonia, water, and hydrogen fluoride are held together, especially in the solid and liquid states, largely by intermolecular hydrogen bonds. The effects of hydrogen bonding on the physical properties of these substances have already been discussed (see 5.128–131).

9.12 The role of carbon with respect to hydride formation is an exceptional one. This element is capable of forming a multiplicity of stable hydrides (hydrocarbons) by virtue of the ability of carbon atoms to share electron pairs with one another to form long chain and ring structures. This ability for "chaining" (catenation) is also possessed, but to a much smaller degree, by elements which are close to carbon in the periodic table. Thus, in the same group, silicon and germanium are known to form a limited number of hydrides of the general formula E_nH_{2n+2}, which are known as silanes and germanes, respectively. Silanes up to Si_6H_{14} have been prepared, and Ge_3H_8 has been characterized. Nitrogen also forms a number of hydrides which contain nitrogen chains. These chains are, however, of short length, and the compounds are exceedingly unstable. The only known hydride which contains an oxygen to oxygen link is hydrogen peroxide. The considerable stability of the carbon-carbon bond is probably largely due to the electronic configuration of the carbon. In its saturated compounds carbon (valence shell $2s^1 2p^3$) is 4-covalent and possesses eight completely shared electrons, the *maximum* number possible in the second shell. The carbon atom therefore possesses neither donor nor acceptor properties.

9.13 Boron forms two series of hydrides, B_nH_{n+4} and B_nH_{n+6}, the simplest boron hydride known being diborane, B_2H_6. These compounds are of considerable interest inasmuch as they do not have a sufficient number of valence electrons to allow the formation of electron-pair bonds between the atoms. These hydrides, together with the complex hydrides to be mentioned below, are discussed in some detail in the chapter dealing with the chemistry of group III representative elements (see 12.27–37). A number of complex hydrides of boron and aluminum have been prepared. Those which have been most extensively studied are lithium aluminum hydride, $LiAlH_4$, lithium borohydride, $LiBH_4$, and sodium borohydride, $NaBH_4$. These hydrides, unlike the saltlike binary hydrides of the alkali and alkaline earth metals, are powerful reducing agents at room temperature. X-ray examination indicates that lithium and sodium borohydrides are composed of the alkali metal ions and the borohydride ions (BH_4^-). The latter appears to be tetrahedral.

9.14 In addition to the complex hydrides mentioned above, others, *e.g.*, $Be(BH_4)_2$, $Al(BH_4)_3$, have also been prepared. The high volatility of the aluminum compound, b.p. 44.5°, and electron diffraction evidence point to its covalent character.

Interstitial or Metal-like Hydrides **9.15** Many of the transition elements are capable of absorbing hydrogen into the interstices of their lattices to give "compounds" which differ considerably from the hydrides already discussed. These "compounds" are hard, nonvolatile solids whose formulas usually vary with changes in temperature and hydrogen pressure and frequently do not show whole number stoichiometric compositions, *e.g.*, $PdH_{0.6}$, $TaH_{0.76}$. The transition metal hydrides are metallic in character in that the nature of the metal lattices and other properties of the parent metals such as type of conductivity are not changed fundamentally by the absorption of hydrogen. Considerable evidence indicates that in most instances free hydrogen atoms are absorbed and that these atoms occupy the holes which exist between the metal atoms; hence the name "interstitial hydrides." The metal lattice is expanded as a result of the entry of hydrogen, and so the hydrides are less dense than the metals from which they are derived.

Deuterium

9.16 The extent to which isotopes of any given element differ in properties is determined in large measure by the ratio of their masses. Isotopic differences are therefore greater the lighter the element. The mass-ratio for deuterium to hydrogen (2 : 1) is greater than for any other pair of isotopes except tritium to hydrogen, and deuterium is sufficiently different from ordinary hydrogen to be worthy of special mention.

9.17 The principal method for the production of deuterium is the fractional electrolysis of water in which the H : D ratio is approximately 6000. The cell generally employed consists of an electrolyte of dilute sodium hydroxide solution and electrodes of nickel. The success of the process is dependent upon the fact that ordinary hydrogen is preferentially evolved upon electrolysis, the gas liberated at the cathode ordinarily being $\frac{1}{5}$–$\frac{1}{8}$ as rich in deuterium as is the water undergoing electrolysis. During the later stages of the process, the cathodic gases, which are relatively rich in deuterium, are burned and returned to the cell at the appropriate time. Prolonged electrolysis results in a residue of "heavy water," D_2O. Gaseous deuterium may be obtained from the latter by continued electrolysis. A comparison of some properties of ordinary hydrogen and deuterium, and of ordinary water and deuterium oxide, is given below in Table 9.1.

9.18 The deuterium molecule, like that of ordinary hydrogen, exists in ortho and para forms, the ratio of the former to the latter at room temperature being 2 : 1. At low temperatures, in the presence of such catalysts as charcoal and nickel, the pure ortho form is obtained.

9.19 In general, deuterium and its compounds react more slowly than do ordinary hydrogen and its corresponding compounds. Thus, at 30° ordinary hydrogen combines with chlorine three times as rapidly as does deuterium.

TABLE 9.1

Properties of Ordinary Hydrogen and Deuterium and Their Oxides

Property	H	D	H_2O	D_2O
Atomic weight	1.0080	2.0015	——	——
Density$_{25}^{25}$	——	——	1.00000	1.10764
Temperature of maximum density	——	——	3.98° C	11.22° C
Boiling point (760 mm.)	20.38° K	23.6° K	100° C	101.42° C
Freezing point	13.95° K	18.65° K	0° C	3.802° C
Heat of fusion, cal./mole	28	47	1436	1520
Dielectric constant at 0°	——	——	80.7	81.5
$E°$ (volts) for $D_2 = 2D^+$ (in pure D_2O) $+ 2e^-$	——	0.0034	——	——
K_{D_2O} at 25°	——	——	——	0.3×10^{-14}

9.20 The exchange reactions of deuterium, *i.e.*, the replacement of ordinary hydrogen atoms by deuterium, have thrown considerable light on the conditions necessary for the breaking of the bonds between hydrogen and other atoms. A few inorganic exchange reactions will be briefly described here.

9.21 Exchange between elementary deuterium and ordinary hydrogen (free or combined) will not usually occur unless the deuterium has been converted into the atomic form by some agency such as heat, catalysis (with Pt or Ni usually), electrical discharge, or irradiation. For example, at temperatures above 600° deuterium will react with ordinary hydrogen to give HD, and with water and ammonia to give deuterated products. The rates of deuteration are primarily dependent on the strength of the X—H bond.

9.22 On the other hand, the exchange between ionizable hydrogen and ionizable deuterium is extremely rapid. Thus D_2O and H_2O react with the evolution of considerable heat. It has been shown that the deuterium in D_2O generally reacts immediately with hydrogen bound to nitrogen, oxygen, sulfur, or the halogens, whereas hydrogen attached to carbon is replaced only under special conditions.

CHAPTER 10

GROUP I—THE ALKALI METALS

General Properties

10.1 The alkali metals (Li, Na, K, Rb, Cs, Fr) comprise the first group of representative elements. The atoms of members of this group possess in common an inert gas kernel and a single electron in the outermost shell (Table 10.1). This single electron is loosely held (see Table 10.2 for values of ionization potentials) and, as a consequence, the alkali metals are characterized by their great tendency to form monopositive ions possessing stable inert gas configurations.

TABLE 10.1

Electronic Configurations of the Alkali Metals

	1	2	3	4	5	6	7
	s	$s\ p$	$s\ p\ d$	$s\ p\ d\ f$	$s\ p\ d$	$s\ p$	s
$_3$Li	2	1					
$_{11}$Na	2	2, 6	1				
$_{19}$K	2	2, 6	2, 6	1			
$_{37}$Rb	2	2, 6	2, 6, 10	2, 6	1		
$_{55}$Cs	2	2, 6	2, 6, 10	2, 6, 10	2, 6	1	
$_{87}$Fr	2	2, 6	2, 6, 10	2, 6, 10, 14	2, 6, 10	2, 6	1

10.2 The physical properties of the metals may be correlated in large measure with the single, loosely held valence electron. The elements are excellent conductors of electricity and readily emit electrons under the influence of light (photoelectric effect). With the exception of lithium they are ex-

GENERAL REFERENCES

LATIMER, *The Oxidation States of the Elements and Their Potentials in Aqueous Solutions*, 2nd Edition, Prentice-Hall, Inc., New York, 1952, Ch. 23.

PARTINGTON, *A Textbook of Inorganic Chem-* *istry*, 6th Edition, Macmillan and Company, Limited, London, 1950, Ch. XXXVI.

SIDGWICK, *The Chemical Elements and Their Compounds*, Oxford University Press, London, 1950, pp. 59–102.

TABLE 10.2

Some Properties of the Alkali Metals

	Li	Na	K	Rb	Cs	Fr
Natural isotopes	6, 7 *	23	39 *, 40 †, 41	85 *, 87 †	133	223 †
Density, g./cc.	0.53	0.97	0.86	1.53	1.90	
M.p., °C.	179	97.5	63.5	39.0	28.4	
B.p., °C.	1372	892	774	679	690	
Ionic radius in crystals, Å	0.71	0.95	1.33	1.47	1.74	
Ionization potential, volts						
1st electron	5.36	5.12	4.32	4.16	3.87	
2nd electron	75.28	47.06	31.66	——	——	
Electrode potential, $E°$, in volts, for M(s) = $M(H_2O)_x^+ + e^-$	3.045	2.714	2.925	2.925	2.923	
Heat of hydration of gaseous ion, kcal./mole	123	97	77	70	63	

* Most abundant isotope
† Radioactive

tremely soft and readily fused. When freshly cut they possess a bright luster which rapidly disappears because of reaction of the metals with the atmosphere.

10.3 The alkali metals are extremely reactive chemically; indeed, they are the most electropositive elements known. The ionization potentials decrease regularly from lithium to cesium, and, in general, the order of chemical reactivity increases in the same direction. However, the differences in sizes of the ions resulting from the loss of the single valence electron play an important role in determining relative reactivities and the nature of the products formed on reaction.

10.4 For the elements Na-Cs, the large sizes of their ions (and also the small charge) account for their slight ability to form stable hydrates and other complex ions. On the other hand, the small radius (0.71 Å) of the lithium ion permits it to attract water molecules strongly, thus accounting in large measure for the high electrode potential of lithium in water solution (see Table 10.2). On the basis of ionization potentials alone, one would predict that lithium would have the lowest electrode potential of the alkali metals. Because of the small size of the lithium ion (and the corresponding large ionization potential), this element in many respects resembles the elements of the second group of representative elements, particularly magnesium (see 10.5 ff.). In addition to the considerable differences in properties between lithium and the other alkali metals, there are some distinct differences in the chemical behavior of sodium as compared with that of potassium, rubidium, and cesium. This is particularly evident in the reactions of the metals with molecular oxygen. A summary of some of the important reactions of the alkali metals is given in Table 10.3.

TABLE 10.3
Reactions of the Alkali Metals

Reaction	Remarks
$4M + O_2^* = 2M_2O$	Li only
$2M + O_2^* = M_2O_2$	Na; Li slightly
$M + O_2^* = MO_2$	K, Rb, Cs; either by combustion of metals in oxygen, or by their rapid oxidation in liquid NH_3
$2M + H_2 = 2MH$	Heated metals; saltlike hydrides
$6M + N_2 = 2M_3N$	Li only; rapidly at elevated temperatures
$2M + X_2 = 2MX$	X = halogen
$2M + S = M_2S$	With Se and Te also
$3M + P = M_3P$	With As and Sb also
$2M + 2H_2O = 2MOH + H_2$	
$2M + 2NH_3 = 2MNH_2 + H_2$	With gaseous NH_3 at elevated temperatures; with liquid NH_3 in presence of catalyst

* Oxygen in excess

Special Aspects of the Chemistry of the Alkali Metals

The "Anomalous" Behavior of Lithium **10.5** It has been stated that lithium, primarily because of the small size of its ion, differs in many ways from the other alkali metals, and resembles magnesium to a large degree. This is not surprising, in view of the fact that the ionic radii of lithium and magnesium are very similar, the values being 0.71 and 0.66 Å, respectively. The similarity of these two elements and some differences between lithium and the other alkali metals are discussed below.

10.6 Reaction between lithium and excess oxygen at elevated temperatures (see Table 10.3) results chiefly in the formation of the monoxide; each of the other alkali metals gives a higher oxide. Lithium is the only alkali metal which combines directly with nitrogen to yield the nitride. The ready combination of the metal with carbon to give a carbide is analogous to the behavior of magnesium; the reactivity of the alkali metals toward carbon is greatest with lithium and least with cesium. Lithium is the only alkali metal capable of forming an ammoniate ($Li(NH_3)_4$) in liquid ammonia solution.

10.7 The solubilities of lithium salts in water show many similarities to those of the corresponding magnesium compounds. Thus, the chlorides, bromides, and iodides of these elements are extremely soluble; in fact, lithium chloride, like the magnesium compound, is deliquescent. The fluorides, carbonates, phosphates, and oxalates exhibit low solubility. Lithium (and to a lesser extent sodium) resembles magnesium in the remarkably great solubility of its perchlorate in organic solvents. This is illustrated by the solubility values in acetone (in moles of perchlorate per 100 moles of solvent at 25°), which are given below.

Li	Na	K	Rb	Cs	Mg
74.4	24.5	0.065	0.030	0.037	11.1

10.8 Another striking difference between lithium and the other alkali metals is shown by the relative instability of its carbonate. Thus, at 1200°, the alkali metal carbonates exhibit the following approximate dissociation pressures (in mm. of Hg).

Li_2CO_3	Na_2CO_3	K_2CO_3	Rb_2CO_3	Cs_2CO_3
300	41	27	60	95

Reactions of the Alkali Metals with Oxygen; the Superoxides.[1,2,3] **10.9** The reactions of the alkali metals with molecular oxygen demonstrate clearly that, although it is profitable to study these elements as members of a group which show many similarities, the smaller members, *i.e.*, lithium and sodium, differ markedly in some respects from the larger ones.

10.10 It has already been mentioned that only in the case of lithium is the monoxide, M_2O, obtained on combustion of the metal in an excess of oxygen. The monoxides of the elements beyond lithium may be prepared by direct oxidation in the presence of excess metal. Reaction of sodium with an excess of oxygen gives chiefly the peroxide; in the industrial process for the production of this compound a two-step method is employed, as shown in the following equations.

$$2Na + \tfrac{1}{2}O_2 = Na_2O$$
$$Na_2O + \tfrac{1}{2}O_2 = Na_2O_2$$

When the vapors of potassium, rubidium, and cesium are burned in air or oxygen, superoxides, MO_2, are obtained.

10.11 The superoxides, the least familiar of the common * oxides of the alkali metals, are yellow substances which have been shown by X-ray and magnetic studies to contain the O_2^- (superoxide) ion, with a structure in which both a single electron-pair bond and a three-electron bond between the two

$$:O\,\dot{\cdot}\dot{\cdot}\,O:^-$$

oxygen atoms may be involved. At 0°, the superoxides react with liquid water in accordance with the following equation.

---

[1] YOST and RUSSELL, *Systematic Inorganic Chemistry*, Prentice-Hall, Inc., New York, 1946, pp. 384–7.

[2] KLEINBERG, *Unfamiliar Oxidation States and Their Stabilization*, University of Kansas Press, Lawrence, Kansas, 1950, Ch. III.

[3] SCHECHTER and KLEINBERG, *J. Chem. Educ.*, **24**, 302 (1947).

* It has recently been shown that O_3^- the ozonide ion, is capable of existence. Alkali metal ozonides have been prepared by the action of ozone on the solid hydroxides. The ozonides are yellow to orange substances which have a paramagnetism corresponding to one unpaired electron; they decompose on contact with water to liberate oxygen. KAZARNOVSKII, NIKOLSKII, and ABLETSOVA, *Doklady Akad. Nauk, S.S.S.R.*, **64**, 69 (1949); WHALEY and KLEINBERG, *J. Am. Chem. Soc.*, **73**, 79 (1951).

$$2MO_2 + aq. = M_2O_2 \cdot aq. + O_2$$

At higher temperatures, reaction with water results in the formation of the metal hydroxide.

$$2MO_2 + H_2O = 2MOH + \tfrac{3}{2}O_2$$

Some properties of the superoxides are listed in Table 10.4.

TABLE 10.4

Some Properties of Alkali Metal Superoxides

Property	KO_2	RbO_2	CsO_2
Density (g./cc.)	2.14	3.06	3.80
Melting point, °C.	380	412	432
Dissociation temperature (p = 1 atm)	660	1157 (unstable)	1265 (unstable
ΔH (kcal.) for reaction $2M + 2O_2 = 2MO_2$	-133.7	-137.6	-141

10.12 Although sodium superoxide cannot be prepared by burning the metal in oxygen at atmospheric pressure,* it can be obtained in excellent yield by reaction between sodium peroxide and oxygen in a stainless steel bomb at temperatures in the neighborhood of 450° and at initial pressures of about 300 atmospheres.

$$Na_2O_2 + O_2 = 2NaO_2$$

The superoxide can also be produced by combustion of the metal under similar conditions, but it has not yet been possible to obtain an inert container for the molten metal under the conditions required for superoxide formation.

10.13 The reactions of solutions of the alkali metals in liquid ammonia with molecular oxygen bring out some interesting group relationships. The slow oxidation of liquid ammonia solutions of the metals at temperatures ranging from $-70°$ to $-33°$ results in the initial formation of peroxide which is reduced by the excess of metal to the monoxide. Ammonolysis of the latter yields amide, which is subsequently oxidized to nitrite.

$$2M + O_2 = M_2O_2$$
$$M_2O_2 + 2M = 2M_2O$$
$$M_2O + NH_3 = MOH + MNH_2$$
$$2MNH_2 + \tfrac{3}{2}O_2 = MOH + MNO_2 + NH_3$$

The rapid oxidation of potassium (and presumably rubidium and cesium) produces chiefly the peroxide, provided the process is stopped as soon as free metal

---

* The yellow color often found in samples of commercial sodium peroxide is probably due to the presence of small amounts of the superoxide. Whenever the peroxide is yellow in color it also possesses a small degree of paramagnetism.

disappears; the peroxide may be converted to superoxide by continued oxidation. There is practically no amide formation when potassium is rapidly oxidized at $-50°$. The rapid oxidation of sodium at temperatures from $-77°$ to $-33°$, under conditions which permit no amide formation, yields a yellow product of empirical formula $NaO_{1.67}$, which corresponds to a mixture of $1Na_2O_2$ to $4NaO_2$. The high degree of paramagnetism of the product lends credence to such a formulation.

10.14 The behavior of lithium is to a large extent analogous to that of the alkaline earth metals.[4] The rapid oxidation of liquid ammonia solutions of the metal at $-33°$, under conditions which inhibit amide formation in the case of sodium, results in a product which consists chiefly of monoxide and peroxide in addition to smaller amounts of nitrite and hydroxide. When the metal is oxidized at $-78°$, a bright lemon-yellow solution is formed, which gives an absorption spectrum very similar to the spectra of rapidly oxidized solutions of sodium and potassium. Since the latter elements form superoxides upon rapid oxidation in liquid ammonia, the similarity in absorption spectra supports the postulate that lithium forms a superoxide which is stable in liquid ammonia solution at $-78°$. The yellow color disappears when the solution is permitted to warm up to $-33°$.

10.15 Substances of the empirical formulas Cs_2O_3 (chocolate-brown) and Rb_2O_3 (black) have been characterized. The former has been obtained as a product intermediate between the peroxide and the superoxide by the rapid oxidation of cesium metal in liquid ammonia at -50 to $-70°$. The latter is formed when rubidium superoxide is thermally decomposed at $550°$. X-ray and magnetic evidence have demonstrated that these "sesquioxides" are best formulated as $M_2O_2 \cdot 2MO_2$, since they contain both peroxide and superoxide ions in the ratio indicated.

The Nature of Liquid Ammonia Solutions of the Alkali Metals [5] **10.16** The alkali metals exhibit remarkable behavior in liquid ammonia. They dissolve to give solutions which are blue in color when dilute, and of metallic, copperlike appearance when concentrated. Evaporation of the ammonia from a freshly prepared solution results in the recovery of the original metal. When the solutions are permitted to stand, the blue color slowly fades and a colorless solution, from which metal amide may be recovered, is obtained.

$$M + NH_3 = MNH_2 + \tfrac{1}{2}H_2$$

The stability of the metal-ammonia solutions decreases with increasing size of the metal atom. Sodium may be recovered largely unchanged from solutions which have stood for a week or two; potassium solutions begin to show appreciable decomposition after approximately eight hours. The amide reaction is catalyzed by the addition of such substances as platinum black, oxides of iron,

[4] THOMPSON and KLEINBERG, *J. Am. Chem. Soc.*, **73**, 1243 (1951).

[5] YOST and RUSSELL, *Systematic Inorganic Chemistry*, Prentice-Hall, Inc., New York, 1946, pp. 136–148.

iron(III) nitrate 9-hydrate, and others. Where compound catalysts are used, it is probable that their reduction products (the metals) are the active catalytic agents.[6]

10.17 The fact that the solubilities of the alkali metals do not change rapidly with temperature (Table 10.5) indicates that the heat of solution to form

TABLE 10.5

Solubilities of the Alkali Metals in Liquid Ammonia

(Moles NH_3 per mole alkali metal)

Metal	t, °C.	Solubility
Li	0	3.60
	−33.2	3.75
	−63.5	3.81
Na	0	5.79
	−33.8	5.48
	−50	5.39
K	0	4.68
	−33.5	4.95
	−50	5.05

saturated solutions is not large. Determinations of the molecular weight of sodium in liquid ammonia yield values which show that the metal is monatomic in this medium, and somewhat dissociated in some manner in the less concentrated solutions. The absorption spectra of dilute solutions of the metals are identical at the same concentrations, indicating that the blue color is due to the presence of the same species in each case.

10.18 The solutions are excellent conductors of electric current, the equivalent conductance at all concentrations being greater than that of any other known combination of solvent and electrolyte. For concentrated solutions, the conductance is of the same order of magnitude as that for metals. This strongly suggests that the conducting species are different from those responsible for the conductance of ordinary salt solutions. It has been shown that, in liquid ammonia solutions of the alkali metals, the negative carrier possesses a mobility from 7 to 280 times as great as the positive one.

10.19 The following equilibria have been proposed to account for the electrical behavior of the alkali metal solutions.

$$M \rightleftharpoons M^+ + e^-$$
$$e^- + nNH_3 \rightleftharpoons (NH_3)_n \cdot e^-$$

The high conductance in concentrated solutions has been attributed to the existence of free electrons in solution. The fact that the conductance falls to a minimum with dilution has been thought to be due to an increasing degree of solvation of the electrons, and the final increase in conductance in very dilute

[6] WATT, *Chem. Revs.*, **46**, 289 (1950).

solutions has been attributed to the increasing ionization of the metal atoms.

10.20 Although the proposed equilibria have been highly successful in explaining many of the properties of alkali metal-ammonia solutions, they do not appear to be correct in some important respects. They do not explain the fact that the paramagnetic susceptibility of sodium solutions is very low at a concentration (ca. $0.2N$) where a minimum in conductance is found. At this point, where the contribution of neutral atoms would be expected to be a maximum, according to the postulated equilibria, the paramagnetic susceptibility would be expected to be relatively high since the electrons would not be free but would be bound to metal atoms. Although optical evidence indicates that in dilute solutions the electrons are ammoniated, it is difficult to account for the high conductivities on this basis.

10.21 In summary, these points may be made: All available data show that concentrated alkali metal-ammonia solutions exhibit essentially metallic behavior. In dilute solutions it is probable that the metal ionizes. However, the exact state of the electrons in these solutions still is unknown.

Reactions of Alkali Metal-Ammonia Solutions [6] **10.22** Liquid ammonia solutions of the alkali metals are powerful reducing media. Although their use as such is still largely unexplored, a large quantity of interesting and useful information has been uncovered.

10.23 Liquid ammonia is in certain respects a more favorable solvent than water for the study of reactions involving powerful reducing agents. One important disadvantage in the use of water is the fact that reducing agents stronger than hydrogen may liberate this element from the solvent. In liquid ammonia, however, the alkali metals, which are the most powerful reducing agents known, can exist in solution for some time without reaction with the solvent, so long as catalysts for the amide reaction are absent. Moreover, the low degree of self-ionization of ammonia (the specific conductance is 5×10^{-11} at $-33°$) permits the preparation of many unusual compounds which are unstable in aqueous medium because of hydrolysis.

10.24 The active reducing agent in the alkali metal solutions is the electron, the metal ion in solution ordinarily * not influencing the course of the primary reduction reaction. Reductions of elemental substances, positive ions, and negative ions have been effected.

10.25 Of the elements, only a small number react with liquid ammonia solutions of the alkali metals. In general the elements which are capable of being reduced are those belonging to groups IV, V, and VI of the representative elements. There exists as yet no conclusive evidence for reductions involving the members of the short transition series or of the lanthanides.

10.26 Each representative element (with oxygen being a notable exception, see 10.13–14) that is reduced usually forms a white or slightly colored insoluble compound which has a composition corresponding to the normal oxidation

---

* The effect of alkali metal ion on the nature of the product formed on oxidation with molecular oxygen has already been discussed (see 10.13–14).

state of the element in question. Thus, sulfur yields sodium sulfide, Na_2S; bismuth, sodium bismuthide, Na_3Bi; etc. In addition to compounds of this type, most of the elements also form soluble salts containing homopolyatomic anions (e.g., Na_2S_{2-5}, Na_3Bi_3); liquid ammonia solutions of these compounds possess intense, characteristic colors. Among the elements which have been reduced in this fashion are germanium, tin, lead, nitrogen, phosphorus, arsenic, antimony, bismuth, sulfur, selenium, and tellurium.

10.27 The reduction of a large number of compounds has been investigated. Of the substances studied, only a few cases have involved reaction of the anion. Reduction of a negative ion generally results either in the formation of an ion of lower oxidation number,

$$Na^+ + NO_2^- + Na^+ + e^- = Na_2NO_2\downarrow,$$

or, more commonly, in the production of more than one anion,

$$2Na^+ + S_x^{2-} + 2Na^+ + 2e^- = Na_2S\downarrow + 2Na^+ + S_{(x-1)}^{2-}.$$

The behavior of the cyanonickelate(II) ion, $[Ni(CN)_4]^{2-}$, toward alkali metal solutions is of particular interest, since compounds in which nickel possesses the unusual oxidation states of 0 and $+1$ may be formed. With an excess of the cyanide complex, the following reaction takes place.

$$[Ni(CN)_4]^{2-} + e^- = [Ni(CN)_3]^{2-} + CN^-$$

When the reducing agent is present in excess, the cyanonickelate(0) ion is formed.

$$[Ni(CN)_4]^{2-} + 2e^- = [Ni(CN)_4]^{4-}$$

10.28 Reduction of a positive ion ordinarily results in the formation of a neutral atom or group as the primary product. Most widely studied compounds have been the metal halides and simple cyanides. In most cases, the reduction products are similar to those obtained by direct reaction with the corresponding alkali metal, i.e., the primary product is the free element.

$$MX_y + yNa = M\downarrow + yNaX$$

The free metal frequently reacts with any excess alkali metal present in solution to yield intermetallic compounds, e.g., the reduction of cadmium iodide by means of sodium gives $NaCd$ and $NaCd_{5-7}$. Because metal halides and cyanides tend to react at an appreciable rate with alkali metal amides (produced as a result of the catalytic action of the free element formed as the primary reduction product), competitive reactions frequently occur to a large extent. This is particularly the case in the reduction of the halide or cyanide of a transition metal, since most of the free transition metals are excellent catalysts for amide formation. This competitive effect is illustrated by the reduction of nickel(II) bromide at the boiling point of ammonia.

Primary reaction $\qquad\qquad NiBr_2 + 2K = Ni + 2KBr$

Secondary reactions $\qquad\quad 2K + 2NH_3 = 2KNH_2 + H_2$
$\qquad\qquad\qquad\qquad\qquad$ (Rapid in the presence of Ni)
$\qquad\qquad NiBr_2 + 2KNH_2 + 2NH_3 = 2KBr + Ni(NH_2)_2 \cdot 2NH_3$

The metals produced upon reduction of the halides or cyanides are usually very finely divided and pyrophoric.

10.29 The behavior of metal and metalloid oxides toward reduction by alkali metals in liquid ammonia solution is analogous to that of the halides, with one major exception. Competitive reactions of the type shown above are of little significance.

10.30 In addition to the categories of reactions already described, a variety of other reductions has been studied. Only one other class, which has already been mentioned in the section dealing with acid-base concepts (see 7.23), will be described here, namely the reaction of ammonium salts with solutions of alkali metals.

$$2NH_4^+ + 2e^- = 2NH_3 + H_2$$

This reaction is commonly used to oxidize excess alkali metal in reaction mixtures. It is also employed to bring ammonolytic reactions to completion by the neutralization of the ammonium salts formed during the course of such reactions.

10.31 Concentrated solutions of ammonium nitrate in ammonia are capable of dissolving sodium and potassium without evolution of hydrogen. It has been shown that in such solutions potassium and ammonium nitrate react in the approximate ratio of 3 : 1, a ratio required for the following reaction.

$$NH_4NO_3 + 3K = NH_3 + K_2NO_2 + KOH$$

Complex Compounds of the Alkali Metals [7,8,9,10,11]   **10.32** An outstanding property of the alkali metal ions is their slight tendency to form complex compounds. This is not surprising in view of the relatively large radii (except Li^+) and small charge of these ions.

10.33 The ability to form complexes is greatest with lithium ion and drops off markedly in passing to the heavier metals. An examination of the hydrates of the alkali metal salts of about thirty inorganic acids shows that 76 percent of the lithium salts, 74 percent of the sodium salts, and 23 percent of the potassium salts exist as solid hydrates. Of the rubidium and cesium compounds, only the ferrocyanide (cyanoferrate(II)) is hydrated. In the case of the compounds of the last three elements, there is some evidence which indicates that the water of crystallization is bound to the anion. The number of water molecules in the stable hydrates of the lithium salts never exceeds four.

10.34 Some of the ammoniates of alkali metal salts, particularly those of lithium, possess a considerable degree of stability. For example, $LiI \cdot 4NH_3$ exhibits a dissociation pressure of only 100 mm. at 60.5°. In general, as would

[7] SIDGWICK, *The Chemical Elements and Their Compounds*, Oxford University Press, London, 1950, pp. 97–100.

[8] SIDGWICK and PLANT, *J. Chem. Soc.*, **123**, 676 (1923).

[9] SIDGWICK and BREWER, *J. Chem. Soc.*, **127**, 2379 (1925).

[10] BREWER, *J. Chem. Soc.*, 361 (1931).

[11] *Ann. Repts. Chem. Soc.*, **30**, 88 (1933); **35**, 165 (1938).

be expected from cation size considerations, the stability of the ammines decreases in the order Li > Na > K. With the same alkali metal, the stabilities of the halide ammoniates decrease in the following order: I > Br > Cl.

10.35 A relatively large number of alkali metal complexes with organic molecules have been made. These complexes are of considerable interest with respect to their structures, and also because of the light they shed on the coordinating tendencies of the alkali metal ions.

10.36 The action of alkali metal hydroxides (Li, Na, K) on 4-indoxylspirocyclopentane (I) gives rise to a series of chelate complexes in which the metal

atom possesses a coordination number of four. The structure II has been assigned to these complexes.

10.37 These compounds are soluble in toluene, and the sodium and potassium derivatives may be crystallized from this medium without decomposition. In the presence of water, however, the complexes are decomposed. On heating, they lose one mole of 4-indoxylspirocyclopentane.

10.38 A large number of alkali metal compounds with other organic molecules containing two donor groups have been prepared. Among the organic substances which have been utilized are β-(*i.e.*, 1,3-)diketones * and ketonic

* The hydroxyl hydrogen of the enol form of these compounds is acidic and is readily replaced by alkali metal.

esters, o-hydroxy aromatic esters and aldehydes, and o-nitrophenols. The configurations which have been assigned to the various compounds prepared are shown in skeletal form (X = C or N).

10.39 Compounds of structure I are usually saltlike in behavior. They are insoluble in liquid hydrocarbons but dissolve in hydroxylic solvents; when heated they char without melting. Compounds of structure I may be converted to substances (II, III, and IV) which exhibit covalent behavior by the formation of addition compounds with water or with the original (or a similar) organic compound. For example, sodium benzoylacetone, which is saltlike, adds two

sodium benzoylacetone

molecules of water upon recrystallization from 96 per cent ethanol to yield a compound which is appreciably soluble in toluene. An interesting case of the

conversion of a compound of structure I to one of structure III involves the reaction of the salt sodium o-nitrophenoxide with an excess of salicylaldehyde to give the following compound.

10.40 The coordination number of lithium in its complexes never exceeds 4, whereas the other alkali metals show coordination numbers of both 4 and 6. The coordination numbers of the alkali metals in a variety of complexes with organic molecules containing two donor groups are shown in Table 10.6.

TABLE 10.6

Some Alkali Metal Chelates

Metal	Coordination No. 4	Coordination No. 6
Li	LiB · 2H$_2$O LiM · 2H$_2$O LiS · 2H$_2$O LiS · HS LiQ · HS LiIn · HIn	None
Na	NaB · 2H$_2$O NaE · 2H$_2$O NaA · 2H$_2$O NaS · HS NaNp · HS NaNc · HS NaIn · HIn	NaB · 4H$_2$O NaQ · 2HS
K	KA · 2H$_2$O KS · HS KNp · HS KIn · HIn	KQ · 2HS KS · 2HS
Rb	RbS · HS	RbS · 2HS
Cs	CsS · HS	CsS · 2HS

HB = benzoylacetone; HA = acetylacetone; HE = ethyl acetoacetate; HQ = ½ quinizarin (1,4-dihydroxyanthraquinone); HM = methyl salicylate; HS = salicylaldehyde; HNp = *o*-nitrophenol; HNc = *o*-nitrocresol; HIn = 4-indoxylspirocyclopentane

CHAPTER 11

GROUP II

Introduction

11.1 Electronically, the members of the second group of representative elements differ from the corresponding alkali metals in that their atoms contain two electrons in the outermost shell (Table 11.1). These two electrons, except

TABLE 11.1

Electronic Configurations of Group II Representative Elements

	1	2	3	4	5	6	7
	s	*s p*	*s p d*	*s p d f*	*s p d*	*s p*	*s*
$_4$Be	2	2					
$_{12}$Mg	2	2, 6	2				
$_{20}$Ca	2	2, 6	2, 6	2			
$_{38}$Sr	2	2, 6	2, 6, 10	2, 6	2		
$_{56}$Ba	2	2, 6	2, 6, 10	2, 6, 10	2, 6	2	
$_{88}$Ra	2	2, 6	2, 6, 10	2, 6, 10, 14	2, 6, 10	2, 6	2

in the case of gaseous beryllium, are readily lost, but less readily than the one valence electron of the alkali metals (compare values of ionization potentials). As a result of the lesser tendency to lose their valence electrons, the group II elements, although they are highly active, are much less active than the corresponding alkali metals. The tendency for ionization in aqueous solution increases from beryllium to radium. (See electrode potentials, Table 11.2.) The difference in reactivity is illustrated by the reactions of the metals with water; whereas calcium, strontium, and barium react vigorously with cold water, mag-

GENERAL REFERENCES

LATIMER, *The Oxidation States of the Elements and Their Potentials in Aqueous Solutions*, 2nd Edition, Prentice-Hall, Inc., New York, 1952, Ch. 22.

PARTINGTON, *A Textbook of Inorganic Chemistry*, 6th Edition, Macmillan and Company, Limited, London, 1950, Ch. XXXVII.

SIDGWICK, *The Chemical Elements and Their Compounds*, Oxford University Press, London, 1950, pp. 193–261.

TABLE 11.2

Some Properties of the Group II Metals

	Be	Mg	Ca	Sr	Ba	Ra
Natural isotopes	9	24 *, 25, 26	40 *, 42, 43, 44, 46, 48	84, 86, 87, 88 *	130, 132, 134, 135, 136, 137, 138 *	226 †
Density, g./cc.	1.84	1.75	1.55	2.6	3.75	(5.0)
Melting point, °C.	ca. 1300	650	851	757	850	(960)
Boiling point, °C.	——	1107	1487	1384	1640	(1140)
Ionic radius in crystals, Å	0.38	0.66	0.99	1.15	1.37	1.50
Ionization potential, volts						
1st electron	9.28	7.61	6.09	5.61	5.19	5.27
2nd electron	18.1	14.96	11.82	10.98	9.95	(10.10)
Electrode potential, $E°$, in volts, for $M(s) = M(H_2O)_x^{2+} + 2e^-$	+1.85	+2.37	+2.87	+2.89	+2.90	+2.92
Heat of hydration of gaseous ion, kcal./ mole (approx.)	——	460	395	355	305	

* Most abundant isotope
† Radioactive

nesium is attacked readily only by boiling water, and beryllium is inert toward this medium even at high temperatures.

11.2 Physically, the elements are highly metallic. They possess a grayish white luster when freshly cut or scraped. However, with the exception of beryllium and magnesium, which form thin, protective films of oxide, the group II metals tarnish readily on exposure to air. The elementary substances are good conductors of electric current. They are much harder than the corresponding alkali metals. The degree of hardness varies considerably; beryllium is capable of scratching glass, whereas barium is only slightly harder than lead.

11.3 As with the alkali metals, the first member of the group is sufficiently different from the other members to merit separate treatment. There are marked differences in chemical properties between beryllium and magnesium, and less marked, but distinct differences between magnesium and the remaining elements of the group. Calcium, strontium, barium, and radium, which are commonly known as the alkaline earth metals, are remarkably similar, and are best considered as a unit.

11.4 As in the case of lithium, the deviations in the behavior of beryllium are attributable to the small size and correspondingly intense electrical field of the ion. This element has a great tendency to form compounds which possess considerable covalent character, whereas corresponding compounds of the other members of the group are ionic in nature.   As an illustration of this, one may cite the extremely poor conductivity of the fused halides; the specific conductivity of beryllium chloride at 451° is 3.19×10^{-3}, which is about one-thousandth that of sodium chloride.   The ability of the members of the second group to form complex ions is greatest with beryllium — another result of the intense electrical field of the ion.   The diagonal relationship noted in the chemistry of lithium and magnesium is also apparent here in the striking resemblance between beryllium and aluminum.   The tendency for covalent compound formation, the amphoterism of the hydroxides, and reaction of the metals with alkali metal hydroxide solutions to yield hydrogen are examples of this similarity.   The chemistry of the other members of the group (and also the water chemistry of beryllium) is largely that of the dipositive ions.

11.5 A few additional group chemical relationships are worthy of mention. The reactivity toward hydrogen increases with increasing atomic weight of metal, beryllium and magnesium showing little ability to react.   The rate of combination with nitrogen increases in the same direction, whereas the stability of the nitride formed diminishes.   As would be expected, the thermal stability of the carbonates increases with size of the cation.   This is brought out by a tabulation of the approximate temperatures at which the dissociation pressures of the carbonates attain a value of one atmosphere.   Normal beryllium carbonate can

$BeCO_3^-$	$MgCO_3$	$CaCO_3^-$	$SrCO_3$	$BaCO_3$
very unstable	540°	900°	1290°	1360°

be prepared only in a carbon dioxide atmosphere; a basic carbonate is precipitated when sodium carbonate solution is added to a solution of a beryllium salt.   Except for that for calcium superoxide there is little evidence for the existence of any oxide higher than the peroxide for the group II elements. Beryllium does not appear to form even a peroxide.   The ability of the other elements to form peroxides increases with atomic number.

11.6 Although there are some exceptions, the aqueous solubility of the compounds of the three larger members of the group decreases in the order Ca^{2+} > Sr^{2+} > Ba^{2+}; the solubilities of relatively few beryllium compounds have been determined, and the solubilities of magnesium compounds fit no regular pattern within the group.   This order does not hold for the hydroxides, fluorides, and oxalates.   The sulfates and selenates of beryllium and magnesium are much more soluble than the corresponding compounds of the remaining elements. The aqueous solubilities of beryllium fluoride and oxalate are, respectively, about 3000 and 1000 times greater than those of the corresponding magnesium compounds.   In general, the solubilities of the halides of a particular element increase in order of increasing size of the halide ion, the fluorides, other than beryllium fluoride, being insoluble.

11.7 Table 11.3 summarizes some of the important reactions of the members of the group.   The elementary substances are ordinarily prepared by the electrolysis of mixtures of the fused chlorides or fluorides and alkali metal halides.

TABLE 11.3

Reactions of the Group II Elements

Reaction	Remarks
$2M + O_2 = 2MO$	Ba also gives the peroxide, BaO_2
$M + H_2 = MH_2$	At elevated temperatures with Ca, Sr, Ba; saltlike hydrides
$3M + N_2 = M_3N_2$	At high temperatures
$M + X_2 = MX_2$	X = halogen
$M + S = MS$	With Se and Te also
$3M + 2P = M_3P_2$	At high temperatures
$M + 2C = MC_2$	Ca, Sr, Ba at high temperatures; Be forms Be_2C
$M + 2H_2O = M(OH)_2 + H_2$	Rapid at room temperature only with Ca, Sr, Ba
$2M + 2NH_3 = 2M(NH_2)_2 + H_2$	Ca, Sr, Ba in liquid ammonia in presence of catalyst; or by action of gaseous ammonia on heated metals
$3M + 2NH_3 = M_3N_2 + 3H_2$	At high temperatures
$M + OH^- + H_2O = HMO_2^- + H_2$	Be only

Beryllium

General Characteristics **11.8** Elementary beryllium in a finely divided state burns readily in air to produce the oxide, BeO; the massive metal, when heated, forms a protective coating of oxide. The metal is unattacked by nitric acid, but dissolves readily in either concentrated hydrochloric or sulfuric acid. It is also soluble in aqueous alkali.

$$Be + OH^- + H_2O = HBeO_2^- + H_2$$

11.9 As would be expected from the above reaction, the relatively insoluble hydroxide is amphoteric; this is not surprising in view of the intense ionic field of the ion, Be^{2+}. The hydroxide is believed to exist in two forms; the unstable freshly precipitated α-form, presumably of the formula $Be_2O(OH)_2$, and the stable β-form, $Be(OH)_2$. Neither modification is capable of absorbing carbon dioxide. Both forms dissolve in concentrated sodium hydroxide solution to give beryllates, $NaHBeO_2$ or Na_2BeO_2. In acid medium there is formed $Be(H_2O)_4^{2+}$, which undergoes hydrolysis at higher pH values to give what is presumably $[BeOH(H_2O)_3]^+$. The oxide, which may be obtained by the thermal decomposition of the hydroxide, becomes refractory when heated to high temperatures, a behavior which is analogous to that of magnesium and aluminum oxides.

Beryllium Complexes **11.10** As has already been mentioned, the anhydrous halides of beryllium are largely covalent in character. They are extensively hydrolyzed in aqueous solution, from which basic salts may be obtained upon evaporation. The very high solubility of the beryllium halides in water is an indication of the great tendency of beryllium to form complex aquo ions. Thus from a solution of the chloride in water the complex $[Be(H_2O)_4]Cl_2$ may be crystallized. A maximum coordination number of 4 is attained by beryllium in its complex compounds.

11.11 Most of the complexes of beryllium are those with molecules containing oxygen as the donor atom. Practically all the inorganic salts form tetrahydrates, one example of which has been cited above. The tetrahydrates usually possess high stability; for example, $[Be(H_2O)_4](ClO_4)_2$ retains its water of hydration up to the temperature at which the anion decomposes.

11.12 Another manifestation of the propensity of the beryllium ion for forming complexes is offered by the appreciable solubility of the oxide in aqueous solutions of beryllium salts, the ratio of oxide dissolved to beryllium ion increasing with the concentration of the latter. The evidence available indicates that the oxide replaces water molecules from the hydrated ion to form complex ions of the formula $[Be(OBe)_x(OH_2)_{4-x}]^{2+}$.

11.13 Addition compounds of alcohols and phenols with beryllium halides are unknown, but these halides are capable of combining with ethers, aldehydes, and ketones. Thus the compound $BeCl_2 \cdot 2(C_2H_5)_2O$ is formed by direct combination. This compound and the complexes with aldehydes and ketones have the properties of covalent substances, showing relatively low melting points and high solubilities in organic solvents. The addition compounds are therefore formulated as shown.

11.14 The nonionized chelate compounds in which oxygen atoms serve as donors are of considerable interest. These complexes are of two types: (1) derivatives of β-(*i.e.*, 1,3-)diketones, β-ketoesters, hydroxyketo compounds, and hydroxyquinones; and (2) derivatives of carboxylic acids. Of compounds of the first type, only the complexes of the β-diketones are discussed briefly.

11.15 It has already been mentioned (see 10.32 *ff.*) that the hydrogen atom of the enol form of a β-diketone is acidic and may be replaced by metals. For example, on treatment of a mixture of acetylacetone and beryllium chloride with aqueous ammonia, the nonelectrolyte beryllium acetylacetonate shown is precipitated. This is a volatile substance (m.p., 108.5°; b.p., 270°), readily soluble in some organic solvents and insoluble in cold water, but decomposed by hot water as well as by acids and alkalies.

11.16 Proof that the bonds are tetrahedrally disposed about the beryllium atom in complexes of this type is offered by the fact that in some cases stereoisomers have been obtained. Thus, the beryllium derivative of benzoylpyruvic acid has been resolved. (See also 6.48.)

11.17 A large number of nonionic basic beryllium derivatives of monobasic carboxylic acids has been prepared. These compounds have the formula $Be_4O(OCR)_6$ and are volatile substances, soluble in most organic solvents and

$$\overset{\text{O}}{\underset{}{\parallel}}$$

insoluble in water. One general method for their production is by reaction between the metal chloride and a benzene solution of the acid which contains a trace of water. Presumably the complex forms as a result of the hydrolysis of the beryllium salt of the organic acid. The compounds are stable toward heat

$$4Be(OCR)_2 + H_2O = Be_4O(OCR)_6 + 2R\overset{\text{O}}{\underset{}{\overset{\parallel}{C}}}\!-\!OH$$

and toward all but drastic oxidations; they are hydrolyzed only slowly by boiling water, and are converted to the appropriate inorganic salt and the free organic acid upon treatment with mineral acid. The tendency for beryllium to form these complexes is so great that it is extremely difficult to prepare the corresponding normal salts.

11.18 The structure of the basic acetate, the best known of these compounds, has been studied by X-ray methods. These studies indicate that the molecule possesses tetrahedral symmetry, the central oxygen atom being surrounded tetrahedrally by the four beryllium atoms, and the six acetate groups forming the edges of the tetrahedron as shown below.

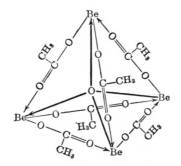

11.19 Stable anionic chelate complexes of beryllium have been prepared from dibasic acids. The interaction of beryllium hydroxide and alkaline solutions of catechol gives compounds of the formula $M_2[Be(C_6H_4O_2)_2] \cdot xH_2O$ (where $M = NH_4$, Na, K, or $\frac{1}{2}Ba$), containing the ion shown. Similar compounds of beryllium with salicylic and o-hydroxytoluic acids are known.

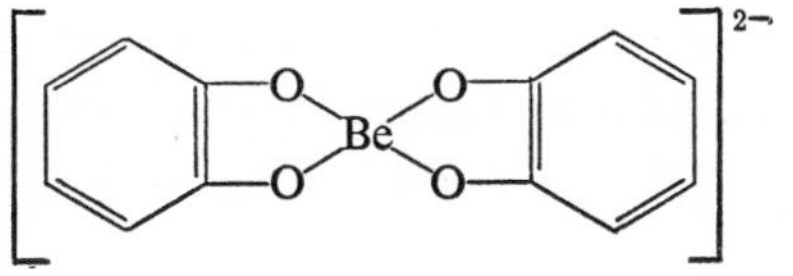

11.20 Malonic, $CH_2 \big\langle{}^{COOH}_{COOH}$, and oxalic, $\big|{}^{COOH}_{COOH}$, acids appear to form auto-

complexes with beryllium which possess the general formula $Be[BeA_2]$. The oxalate, of empirical composition $BeC_2O_4 \cdot 3H_2O$, is particularly noteworthy; it is the only oxalate of a dipositive metal which has an appreciable aqueous solubility. Its molecular conductivity is relatively low and constant over a wide range of concentration. Freezing point depression measurements in water also indicate a low degree of dissociation. It has been proposed that in aqueous solution the hydrated monochelate compound is in equilibrium with the highly dissociated dichelate autocomplex. It is presumed that one additional water molecule is attached to each oxalate group.

11.21 Beryllium halides, with the exception of the fluoride, readily combine with ammonia to give ammine complexes. Phase studies on the systems halide-ammonia indicate the formation of compounds containing 4, 6, and 12 molecules of ammonia, but of these only the tetrammines exhibit any high degree of stability; thus, $BeCl_2 \cdot 4NH_3$ has a dissociation pressure of only 6mm. at 156°. Although the tetrammines are thermally stable, they are readily decomposed by water.

11.22 In addition to the nitrogen complexes containing ammonia, compounds with amines (both aliphatic and aromatic) and nitriles have been characterized. In ether, beryllium chloride adds amines to give primarily the diammine complexes. The inability of beryllium to add four amine groups has been attributed to a combination of steric factors and the weaker coordinating power of the amines as compared with ammonia. Similarly, hydrogen cyanide forms the complex $BeCl_2 \cdot 4HCN$, whereas the nitriles, *i.e.*, organic cyanides, give only $BeCl_2 \cdot 2RCN$.

11.23 By the dissolution of beryllium oxide in an excess of alkali or alkaline earth acid fluoride, or by high temperature reaction between the oxide and metal fluorosilicate, fluoroberyllates, derivatives of fluoroberyllic acid, H_2BeF_4, can be prepared. The alkali metal salts are very soluble, whereas the alkaline earth metal derivatives possess low aqueous solubility. In this respect they resemble the sulfates. Although the reactions of the aqueous solutions indicate the presence of $Be(H_2O)_4^{2+}$ in solution, beryllium migrates toward the anode on electrolysis; the salts can be recrystallized unchanged from aqueous solutions. There is some evidence that similar but less stable chloro complexes exist,

Magnesium

General Characteristics **11.24** The tendency for covalent compound formation diminishes markedly from beryllium to magnesium. The chemistry of the simple magnesium compounds is primarily the chemistry of the Mg^{2+} ion. This ion forms complexes readily — much less so than the beryllium ion, but to a considerably greater degree than the alkaline earth metal ions.

11.25 The salts which are derived from strong acids undergo little hydrolysis at ordinary temperatures, but at high temperatures the hydrolytic reaction assumes some importance. It is impossible to prepare the anhydrous halides by the thermal decomposition of the hydrates; for example, when $MgCl_2 \cdot 6H_2O$ is heated, hydrogen chloride is evolved and basic chlorides (or mixtures of oxide and chloride) are formed.

11.26 The hydroxides of beryllium and magnesium are distinctly different. Whereas the hydroxide of beryllium is amphoteric and only slightly dissociated in water, that of magnesium is a strong electrolyte. Magnesium hydroxide, like beryllium hydroxide, exhibits only slight aqueous solubility, the solubility product constant being 8.9×10^{-12} at $25°$. The hydroxide can therefore be prepared by metathesis in aqueous medium. It can also be made by the hydration of the oxide; the reaction with water, however, is very slow. The chemical reactivity of the oxide varies according to the temperature at which it has been prepared, decreasing considerably if the oxide has been exposed to high temperatures.

Complex Compounds **11.27** These compounds are rather numerous, the majority and the most stable of them containing the magnesium ion linked to oxygen. The maximum coordination number of six is frequently attained by magnesium in its complexes.

11.28 In addition to the hydrates, complexes containing the magnesium-oxygen linkage are found with alcohols, aldehydes, ketones, ethers, and other organic compounds. The magnesium-oxygen bond is a strong one; indeed, in the case of the perchlorate, the affinity for water is so great that the substance serves as one of the most efficient drying agents. Water can be removed from the hydrates of magnesium perchlorate (containing 6-, 4-, or $2H_2O$) only at temperatures in the neighborhood of $250°$.

11.29 A variety of compounds with nitrogen-containing molecules as the complexing units are known. These are ordinarily less stable than the magnesium-oxygen compounds. Most magnesium salts readily absorb ammonia to give ammine complexes, some of which are fairly stable to heat. As examples, the ammoniates of magnesium chloride may be cited; the hexa-, tetra-, and diammine exist, the latter having a dissociation pressure of only 18 mm. at $181°$. Complexes containing pyridine, aromatic amines, and nitriles are also known. The nitrogen-containing complexes are decomposed in water.

11.30 There appear to be few if any complexes in which magnesium is coordinated to a halogen or to sulfur.

Calcium, Strontium, Barium, and Radium

General Characteristics **11.31** These elements, commonly known as the alkaline earth metals, are closely related in chemical character. The chief difference among them is to be found in the radioactive nature of radium and its compounds. Inasmuch as relatively little pure chemical work has been carried out with radium, the discussion which follows is concerned with the other three elements.

11.32 The reactivity of the metals increases with atomic number. Several reactions are worthy of special mention. Calcium, strontium, and barium combine readily with hydrogen at elevated temperatures to give saltlike hydrides, MH_2, which exhibit greater stability than do the hydrides of the alkali metals. This is indicated by the values (in kcal.) for the heats of formation of the solid hydrides from the solid metal and hydrogen gas:

MH	$-\Delta H$	MH_2	$-\Delta H$
LiH	21.6		
NaH	14		
KH	10	CaH_2	46
RbH	12	SrH_2	42
CsH	12	BaH_2	40.8

11.33 The metals react with carbon at high temperatures to yield carbides which apparently contain $[C{\equiv}C]^{2-}$; on hydrolysis these substances yield acetylene. This is to be contrasted with the behavior of beryllium which yields Be_2C, the hydrolysis of which produces methane. The most important carbide of the group is that of calcium, which is most efficiently made by the reaction of calcium oxide with carbon in an electric furnace. At red heat this substance is capable of fixing atmospheric nitrogen to yield the cyanamide CaNCN. The chief product formed when barium carbide absorbs nitrogen is the cyanide. The carbides melt at extremely high temperatures.

11.34 Calcium, strontium, and barium, like the alkali metals, dissolve in liquid ammonia to give colored solutions. However, in contrast to the alkali metals,* the alkaline earth metals form stable ammoniates of the formula $M(NH_3)_6$ at $-33°$, the boiling point of ammonia. The tendency for ammoniate formation decreases, as would be expected, with increasing size of the metal atom. The ammoniates are metallic in appearance and are good conductors of electric current. At higher temperatures these compounds decompose.

11.35 The reactions of the heated alkaline earth metals toward molecular oxygen are considerably different from those of the alkali metals; no evidence for superoxide formation is found with the alkaline earth metals. Calcium and strontium give the normal oxides, MO, whereas barium forms the peroxide BaO_2. The latter substance can also be prepared by heating the monoxide in air under pressure. At one time this reaction served as the basis for the commercial production of oxygen, since a decrease in pressure, once the peroxide is

---

* The anomalous behavior of lithium, which forms an unstable tetrammoniate in liquid ammonia solution, has been noted (see 10.5–8).

formed, results in a release of oxygen, which may be conveniently pumped off. Only the peroxide of barium has been prepared commercially in a high state of purity; the peroxides of calcium and strontium are obtained as the octahydrates, $MO_2 \cdot 8H_2O$, by the action of hydrogen peroxide or sodium peroxide on solutions of soluble compounds of the metals.

11.36 The hydroxides of the alkaline earth metals are strong bases, but are considerably less soluble than the corresponding alkali metal compounds. Their molar solubilities, as shown by the following data for 20°, increase markedly with increasing size of the metal ion:

$Ca(OH)_2$	$Sr(OH)_2$	$Ba(OH)_2$
0.022	0.065	0.22

The hydroxides may be obtained by the treatment of the oxides with water; the reaction is strongly exothermic. The stability of the hydroxides toward thermal decomposition to the oxide increases with atomic number of the metal, barium hydroxide being the only member of the group which is sufficiently stable to be heated to fusion.

Alkaline Earth Metal Complexes **11.37** The complexes of calcium, strontium, and barium resemble those of magnesium to a great extent. The alkaline earth metal ions form complexes chiefly with oxygen-containing compounds; their ability to coordinate with nitrogen is very weak, and with other elements practically nonexistent. Only a few observations regarding the complexes will be made here.

11.38 Water-insoluble acetylacetonates have been prepared by reaction of the diketone with the metal hydroxide or an aqueous solution of the cyanide. These differ from the magnesium chelate in that they crystallize as dihydrates from solvents containing a little water; the water of crystallization is readily removed by warming under reduced pressure. It appears, therefore, that in these chelates the alkaline earth metal may exhibit a coordination number of either 6 (in the dihydrate) or 4 (in the anhydrous compound).

11.39 Within recent years, a reagent capable of forming complexes of considerable stability with magnesium and alkaline earth metal ions has been discovered. This substance is ethylenediaminetetraacetic acid, which is often used in the form of its tetrasodium salt, known commercially as Versene or

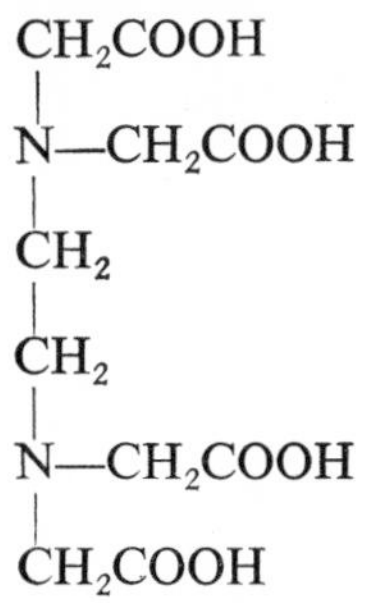

$$CH_2COOH$$
$$|$$
$$N—CH_2COOH$$
$$|$$
$$CH_2$$
$$|$$
$$CH_2$$
$$|$$
$$N—CH_2COOH$$
$$|$$
$$CH_2COOH$$

Sequestrene. It is potentially capable of acting either as a quadridentate or sexadentate group toward the metal ions. The following alkaline earth metal complexes have been characterized (ethylenediaminetetraacetic acid = H_4Y):

$$K_2[CaY] \qquad\qquad H_2[BaY] \cdot 4H_2O$$
$$H_2[SrY] \cdot 3\tfrac{1}{2}H_2O \qquad K_2[BaY] \cdot 8H_2O$$
$$Sr[SrY] \cdot 5H_2O \qquad\quad Ba[BaY] \cdot 2\tfrac{1}{2}H_2O$$

11.40 Ethylenediaminetetraacetic acid has proved of value in water-softening inasmuch as it forms stable soluble complexes with those metal ions responsible for water-hardness. It is capable of dissolving deposits of calcium sulfate and the alkaline earth metal carbonates and phosphates. The reagent is widely used for the quantitative determination of metal ions.*

* For an excellent discussion of ethylenediaminetetraacetic acid and its complexes see WELCHER, *The Analytical Uses of Ethylenediaminetetraacetic Acid*, D. Van Nostrand Company, Inc., Princeton, 1957.

CHAPTER 12

GROUP III

Introduction

12.1 The third group of representative elements, the aluminum family, is composed of the elements boron, aluminum, gallium, indium, and thallium, the electronic configurations of which are shown in Table 12.1. Electronically

TABLE 12.1

Electronic Configurations of Group III Representative Elements

	1	2	3	4	5	6
	s	*s p*	*s p d*	*s p d f*	*s p d*	*s p*
$_5$B	2	2, 1				
$_{13}$Al	2	2, 6	2, 1			
$_{31}$Ga	2	2, 6	2, 6, 10	2, 1		
$_{49}$In	2	2, 6	2, 6, 10	2, 6, 10	2, 1	
$_{81}$Tl	2	2, 6	2, 6, 10	2, 6, 10, 14	2, 6, 10	2, 1

these elements may be subdivided into two classes: one, consisting of boron and aluminum, which possesses an inert gas kernel, and the other (gallium, indium, and thallium) which has completed *s*, *p*, and *d* orbitals underlying the three (s^2p) valence electrons.

12.2 A number of important properties of these elements are summarized in Table 12.2. The elements exhibit a common oxidation state of $+3$. However, as the small calculated ionic radii (Table 12.2) of the tripositive ions would indicate, there exists little tendency for the formation of simple ions in this oxidation state. This fact is emphasized by the large values for the sums of the three ionization potentials. Thus we find that practically all of the simple com-

GENERAL REFERENCES

LATIMER, *The Oxidation States of the Elements and Their Potentials in Aqueous Solutions*, 2nd Edition, Prentice-Hall, Inc., New York, 1952, Ch. 9 and 19.

PARTINGTON, *A Textbook of Inorganic Chem-*istry, 6th Edition, Macmillan and Company, Limited, London, 1950, pp. 652–9, 803–18.

SIDGWICK, *The Chemical Elements and Their Compounds*, Oxford University Press, London, 1950, pp. 334–438, 458–87.

TABLE 12.2

Some Properties of the Group III Elements

	B	Al	Ga	In	Tl
Natural isotopes	10, 11 *	27	69 *, 71	113, 115 *	203, 205 *
Density, g./cc.	2.4	2.70	5.91	7.3	11.85
Melting point, °C.	2300	658	29.75	155	303.5
Boiling point, °C.	2550	1800	1700	>1450	1650
Ionic radius in crystals, M^{3+}, Å	——	0.52	0.60	0.81	Tl^+ 1.59 Tl^{3+} 0.95
Covalent radius, Å	0.80	1.248	1.245	1.497	1.549
Ionization potential, volts					
1st electron	8.33	5.96	5.97	5.76	6.07
2nd electron	23.98	18.75	20.43	18.79	20.32
3rd electron	37.75	28.32	30.6	27.9	29.71
Electrode potential, $E°$, in volts, for reaction $M(s) = M(H_2O)_x^{3+}$ $+ 3e^-$	——	+1.67	+0.52 $Tl = Tl^+ + e^-$	+0.34	−0.72 + 0.34
Heat of hydration of gaseous ion, kcal./mole	——	1121	1124	994	984

* More abundant isotope

pounds corresponding to the +3 state are largely covalent in nature. The melting points of the trichlorides (as compared to those of the group II chlorides) serve to illustrate this point:

$BeCl_2$	440° C	BCl_3	−107° C
$MgCl_2$	708	$AlCl_3$	192.6(1700 mm.)
$CaCl_2$	772	$GaCl_3$	77.9
$SrCl_2$	873	$InCl_3$	586
$BaCl_2$	962	$TlCl_3$	25(?)

12.3 Although it is exceedingly difficult to remove three electrons from the gaseous atoms, the elements of the aluminum family, with the notable exception of boron, which is completely nonmetallic in character, are fairly active metals in aqueous medium. This is borne out by the values for the electrode potentials (Table 12.2), which are much higher than would be expected from the ionization potential values. The high electrode potentials may be accounted for by the high polarizing power of the relatively small tripositive ions, as a result of which the ready hydration of the ions is accompanied by the liberation of considerable energy (Table 12.2). The great polarizing ability of the elements in their tripositive states is generally manifested in their strong tendency to form complex compounds, and in the character of their oxides.

12.4 Boron trioxide, B_2O_3, is acidic, being the anhydride of a series of weak acids, the most familiar of which is orthoboric acid, H_3BO_3. The hydrous oxides of aluminum and gallium are amphoteric in character. The situation with regard to the indium and thallium compounds is somewhat obscure, there being conflicting reports in the literature. Undoubtedly In_2O_3 is primarily basic in nature, being readily soluble in acids, and reputedly insoluble, or only slightly soluble, in strongly alkaline solutions. An indate of the formula $Mg[InO_2]_2$ has reportedly been obtained by reaction between magnesium oxide and a boiling solution of indium(III) chloride. Tl_2O_3 is apparently completely basic; the existence, however, of $Tl(OH)_3$ is doubtful. A report [1] dealing with physicochemical studies of the tripositive ions of gallium, indium, and thallium gives the following order of basicities:

$$In^{3+} > Ga^{3+} > Tl^{3+}.$$

The hydrolysis constants of the trichlorides at 25° for In(III), Ga(III), and Tl(III) are 1.2×10^{-5}, 4.1×10^{-4}, and 3.3×10^{-3}, respectively.

12.5 In contrast to the behavior of the alkali metals and that of the group II representative elements, at least some of the members of group III exhibit more than one oxidation state in their compounds. The case of thallium is unambiguous; this element shows an oxidation state of $+1$, which is considerably more stable than the $+3$ state. The situation with regard to gallium and indium is not so clear-cut. There is no question that compounds exist in which these elements show oxidation states less than $+3$; on the basis of the empirical formulas of the compounds isolated, these elements would appear to have oxidation states of $+1$ and $+2$. However, whether the $+2$ state really exists is a matter of some doubt. In addition, there is evidence, which appears to be conclusive, that aluminum possesses a very unstable $+1$ oxidation state. The whole question of lower oxidation states of the group III elements is specifically discussed in sections 12.56 *ff*.

12.6 It is worthwhile at this point, however, to examine the electronic configurations of these elements in terms of known, and also possible, oxidation states. The group III elements possess the electronic configuration ns^2np^1 in the valence shell. In general, less energy is required to remove p electrons than s electrons from the same shell; in the case of the elements under discussion this fact is borne out in the marked differences between the values for the first and second ionization potentials (Table 12.2). It is not surprising, therefore, that thallium, the element in which the valence shell is farthest removed from the nucleus, possesses a stable $+1$ oxidation state. One might expect that the monopositive state would also exist for gallium and indium, but that, in view of the smaller sizes of these atoms as compared with thallium, this state would be much less stable than the $+1$ state of thallium. By the same reasoning, it is not at all surprising that, although there is excellent evidence for the existence of monopositive aluminum in a number of reactions, there is only one report in the literature on the isolation of a compound containing aluminum(I).

12.7 Solely on the basis of electronic configuration, it would be predicted that

[1] MOELLER and KING, *Technical Information Pilot, ONR*, Dec. 8, 1950, p. 2131; *J. Phys. and Colloid Chem.*, **54**, 999 (1950).

there is little likelihood of the $+2$ oxidation state in any group III element. The possibility of dimerization must not be overlooked, however; dimerization would result in the pairing of the s electron through a metal-metal bond. Such a situation exists in the well-known case of mercury(I) chloride, which is correctly formulated as Hg_2Cl_2.

Boron

General Characteristics   **12.8** Inasmuch as boron is the only member of the group which is entirely nonmetallic and which thus differs markedly from the other members, its chemistry is worthy of separate emphasis.   In many respects the behavior of boron is similar to that of silicon.

12.9 Boron is a relatively rare element, constituting about 10^{-3} per cent of the earth's crust.   It occurs as orthoboric acid, H_3BO_3, and as borates.   The element can be obtained in the so-called amorphous form as an impure dark brown powder by the high temperature reaction of the oxide with magnesium or some other powerful reducing agent, or by the reduction of the fluoroborate, KBF_4, with potassium.   A pure crystalline variety has been prepared by passing a mixture of the tribromide and hydrogen over a tantalum filament heated to 1100–1300°.   Crystalline boron is harder than carborundum and possesses a low electrical conductivity.   In contrast to the high reactivity of the "amorphous" form (see Table 12.3), the crystalline variety is rather inert, being unaffected by

TABLE 12.3

Reactions of "Amorphous" Boron

Reaction	Remarks
$4B + 3O_2 = 2B_2O_3$	At elevated temperatures; high heat of reaction
$2B + N_2 = 2BN$	At white heat
$2B + 2NH_3 = 2BN + 3H_2$	At white heat
$2B + 3X_2 = 2BX_3$	With all the halogens
$2B + 3S = B_2S_3$	By passage of sulfur vapor over boron at 1200°
$nB + mM = M_mB_n$	With many metals; alkali metals do not combine directly; the compounds seldom have the simple compositions expected from valence considerations
$2B + 6KOH = 2K_3BO_3 + 3H_2$	Fusion with alkali

hot concentrated hydrohalic acids, and reacting only slowly with hot concentrated nitric or sulfuric acid.

Boron Trioxide and Its Derivatives   **12.10** Boron trioxide, commonly prepared by the dehydration of orthoboric acid at red heat, is entirely acidic in its properties.   It is capable of dissolving most metal oxides to form glasses, many of which possess characteristic colors.   It is a good dehydrating agent, reacting readily with water to form orthoboric acid, H_3BO_3, which is commonly known simply as boric acid. The trioxide is also the anhydride of two additional common boric acids, namely tetra- or pyroboric ($H_2B_4O_7$) and metaboric (HBO_2) acids. The latter substances are obtained by the controlled dehydration of the ortho acid.

$$4H_3BO_3 \xrightarrow{-4H_2O} 4HBO_2 \xrightarrow{-H_2O} H_2B_4O_7$$

12.11 The behavior of the ortho acid in aqueous solution is essentially that of a weak monobasic acid, the equilibrium constant for the reaction,

$$H_3BO_3 = H^+ + H_2BO_3^-,$$

being approximately 6×10^{-10} at 25°. The situation actually is more complicated than is indicated by this simple equilibrium, since there is reason to believe that the anions of the other boric acids (BO_2^- and $HB_4O_7^-$) also are present in solution in equilibrium with each other and with $H_2BO_3^-$. Polymerization of the ortho acid with the formation of tetraboric acid (and perhaps more complex polyacids) generally occurs at high concentrations.

12.12 Numerous metal borates have been made. The common methods of preparation involve metathesis in aqueous medium, or the fusion of boron trioxide with the appropriate metal oxide. Of the various metal borates known, the only ones which exhibit appreciable aqueous solubility are those containing metals in monovalent states.

12.13 Few orthoborates have been obtained; treatment of orthoboric acid solution with aqueous alkali results in the formation of the tetraborate ion, $B_4O_7^{2-}$. Orthoborates of certain trivalent metals, *e.g.*, $InBO_3$ and YBO_3, are known. The structure of the anions in these compounds has been shown to be plane triangular, as are the carbonate and nitrate anions.

12.14 Soluble salts of the meta- and tetraboric acids are common. In addition, a large number of complex polyborates of the empirical formula

$$(M_2O)_m(B_2O_3)_n$$

have been made, the most common values for the number of boron atoms per alkali metal atom being 1, 2, and 5. Thus from the system Na_2O, B_2O_3, H_2O, the following compounds have been isolated at 30°:

$$NaBO_2 \cdot 4H_2O; \quad Na_2B_4O_7 \cdot 10H_2O; \quad NaB_5O_8 \cdot 5H_2O$$

Complexes with Polyhydroxy Compounds **12.15** Although boric acid is a very weak acid, its acidity can be considerably enhanced by the addition of certain polyhydric alcohols such as glycerol and mannitol. In fact, boric acid can be titrated as a strong acid in the presence of these polyhydroxy alcohols. In addition, the electrical conductivity of the resulting solution is enormously greater than that of either additive, and if the alcohol is optically active, there is a marked change in its rotatory power. The above noted phenomena have been attributed to complex formation between the boric acid and the alcohol.[2] It must be pointed out that the phenomena described occur to the greatest degree only when the organic compound contains hydroxyl groups on adjacent carbon atoms, and then only when these groups are in the same plane, *i.e.*, occupy *cis* positions relative to the carbon atoms. Moreover, it is necessary to add to the solution a certain quantity of alkali before pronounced changes are observed. The latter fact indicates that the reaction involved is between molecules of the alcohol and the borate ion. In agreement with this, it has been found that sodium metaborate is much more effective in its action on the appropriate polyhydroxy alcohols than is boric acid.

12.16 The general structure I has been proposed for the complexes which are formed. In addition to dichelate structures of this type, there is some evi-

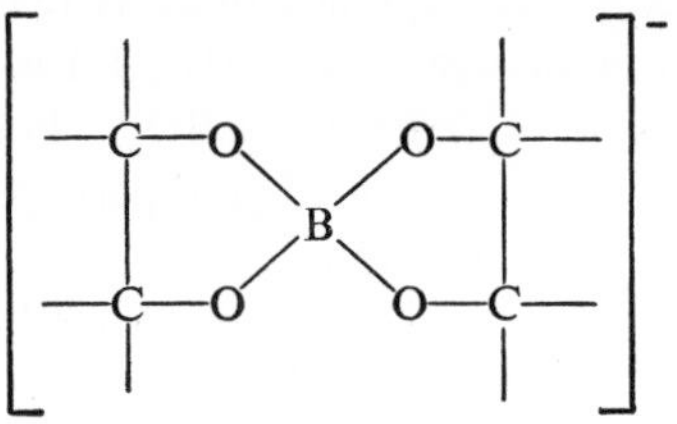

$$\left[\begin{array}{c} -C-O \diagup O-C- \\ B \\ -C-O \diagdown O-C- \end{array}\right]^{-} \qquad \left[\begin{array}{c} HO \diagup O \\ B \diagdown C_6H_{12}O_4 \\ HO \diagdown O \end{array}\right]^{-} H^{+}$$

I 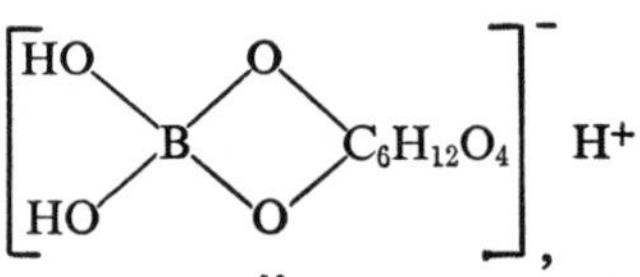   II

dence that monochelate structures may also be produced. Thus the mannitol–boric acid complex has been formulated as II.

12.17 Similar complexes are formed between polyhydroxy acids and free boric acid, and also between alkali metal borates and alkali metal salts of the polyhydroxy compounds. In the first case, complexes analogous to the one shown for tartaric acid are obtained. Alkali metal salts of such compounds have been isolated. For the second case, the following reaction has been proposed.

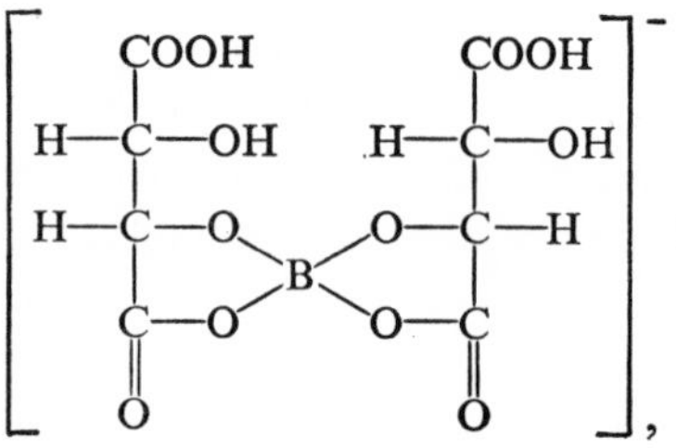

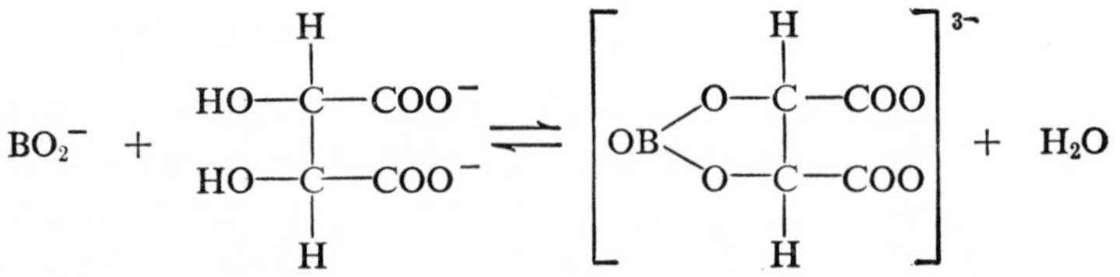

$$\left[\begin{array}{cc} COOH & COOH \\ H-C-OH & H-C-OH \\ H-C-O & O-C-H \\ C-O \diagup B \diagdown O-C \\ O & O \end{array}\right]^{-} H^{+}$$

$$BO_2^- + \begin{array}{c} H \\ HO-C-COO^- \\ HO-C-COO^- \\ H \end{array} \rightleftharpoons \left[\begin{array}{c} H \\ OB \diagup O-C-COO \\ \diagdown O-C-COO \\ H \end{array}\right]^{3-} + H_2O$$

[2] See SISTER MARY MARTINETTE, *Inorganic Seminar Abstracts*, University of Illinois, Mar. 23, 1948, pp. 85–89, for an excellent discussion of complex formation between boric acid and organic polyhydroxy compounds.

The Halides and Their Derivatives **12.18** Boron forms trihalides with all of the halogens. These are covalent compounds for which the melting and boiling points increase with increasing atomic weight of the halogen. With the excep-

	BF_3	BCl_3	BBr_3	BI_3
M.p., °C.	−126.8	−107	−45	43
B.p., °C.	−101	13(764 mm.)	90.6	210

tion of the fluoride, they are prepared from the oxide by treatment with the appropriate halogen and carbon at high temperatures.

$$B_2O_3 + 3C + 3X_2 = 2BX_3 + 3CO$$

The fluoride is obtained by reaction of hydrogen fluoride with the oxide; the former may be prepared *in situ* by the action of concentrated sulfuric acid on fluorspar, CaF_2.

$$CaF_2 + H_2SO_4 = 2HF + CaSO_4$$
$$B_2O_3 + 6HF = 2BF_3 + 3H_2O$$

12.19 The trihalides are readily hydrolyzed, the fluoride according to equation I and the others according to equation II, yielding the appropriate hydrohalic acids.

$$\text{I} \quad 4BF_3 + 3H_2O = H_3BO_3 + 3HBF_4$$
$$\text{II} \quad BX_3 + 3H_2O = H_3BO_3 + 3HX$$

12.20 In addition to the trifluoride, reaction of boron trioxide and hydrogen fluoride gives difluoroboric acid, $H[BF_2(OH)_2]$. This substance is also obtained to some extent in the reaction between the trifluoride and water. Difluoroboric acid is a strong, monobasic acid which boils at 160° and supercools to a glass at −20°. The pure liquid has an electrical conductivity of the same order of magnitude as that of anhydrous sulfuric acid, a fact which indicates that the liquid undergoes a high degree of autoionization.

12.21 Trifluoroboric acid can be prepared by reaction between boron trifluoride and water in the molar ratio of 1 : 2, or by treatment of the trioxide with 40% hydrofluoric acid. It is a low melting solid (6°), and a strong acid in aqueous solution. The empirical formula of the substance is $BF_3 \cdot 2H_2O$. It has been shown by X-ray analysis that trifluoroboric acid is isomorphous with ammonium perchlorate, and that its correct formulation must be

$$[H_3O^+][BF_3OH^-].$$

12.22 The trihalides, in which the boron atom has a sextet of valence electrons, have a great tendency to act as acceptor molecules in the formation of a variety of complex compounds. The most effective donor molecules are those containing nitrogen. The great majority of the nitrogen complexes are ammines, and the most stable of these contain boron trifluoride. As an example, one may cite $F_3B : NH_3$, which is readily made by the combination of ammonia and the trifluoride in anhydrous ether. It sublimes at 180° with some decomposition to $BF_2 \cdot NH_2$, owing to the tendency for an internal ammonolysis to take place. It is interesting that in the case of boron tribromide, combination with ammonia takes place only at temperatures where ammonolysis is extremely marked, and as a result no tribromide-ammonia addition compound has been isolated.

12.23 Boron trihalides form complexes with practically all oxygen-containing organic compounds. The behavior of alcohols and acids toward boron trifluoride is analogous to that of water, *i.e.*, the reactions yield fluoroboric acid derivatives. Thus the compound types with empirical formulas $BF_3 \cdot 2ROH$ and $BF_3 \cdot ROH$ are in reality derivatives of $H[BF_3OH]$ and may undoubtedly be more correctly formulated as $[H \cdot ROH^+][BF_3OR^-]$ and $H[BF_3OR]$, respectively. The methanol derivative, $BF_3 \cdot CH_3OH$, possesses a high electrical conductivity.

12.24 The compounds formed by the boron halides with ethers are of the true coordination type. Some comparative physical constants of the methyl and ethyl ether derivatives of boron trifluoride are listed in the table. It has been

	$F_3B:O(CH_3)_2$	$F_3B:O(C_2H_5)_2$
M.p., °C.	−14	−60.4
B.p., °C.	126.6	125.7
Heat of formation of gaseous molecule (from halide and ether), kcal./mole	13.9	12.5

shown, by electron diffraction investigation, that the valence bonds are tetrahedrally disposed about the boron atom in $F_3B : O(CH_3)_2$. The compound appears to be considerably dissociated in the vapor state. Compounds of the formula type $Cl_3B : OR_2$ may be sublimed *in vacuo* without decomposition. At temperatures above 50° at atmospheric pressure they decompose.

$$Cl_3B : OR_2 = RCl + Cl_2BOR$$

The etherates are extremely sensitive to the action of water or alcohol, being converted to boric acid or its ester.

12.25 The reactions of boron trifluoride and trichloride with β-diketones are of interest in that the nature of the product is apparently dependent on the relative strength of the boron-halogen bond. When the trifluoride reacts with a β-diketone (*e.g.*, acetylacetone, benzoylacetone) in benzene solution, hydrogen fluoride is evolved and structure I is produced. The compounds are low melting (acetylacetonate, 45°; benzoylacetonate, 155°) substances which are soluble in benzene. With the trichloride, in which the boron-halogen bond is weaker than in the trifluoride, two halogens are replaced and compounds of structure II are formed. These are known as boronium salts. The acetylacetone and benzoylacetone derivatives are readily made in ether as solvent. The chloride ion may be replaced by any one of a large number of complex anions (e.g., I_3^-, $AuCl_4^-$, $SnCl_6^{2-}$, $PtCl_6^{2-}$, etc.) to yield more stable salts. Boronium salts are low melting substances (acetylacetone $-PtCl_6$ salt, 180°; $-SnCl_6$ salt, 210°) which dissolve in chloroform but are decomposed by water.

12.26 Numerous stable compounds containing the fluoroborate ion, BF_4^-, exist; analogous complexes of the other halogens are virtually unknown. The parent of these complexes is fluoroboric acid, HBF_4, solutions of which may be obtained by the addition of a slight excess of orthoboric acid to a 40% aqueous solution of hydrogen fluoride.

$$H_3BO_3 + 4HF = HBF_4 + 3H_2O$$

It is also formed as a product of hydrolysis of boron trifluoride (see 12.19). Fluoroboric acid is a strong acid in aqueous solution. The fluoroborate ion, BF_4^-, is slowly hydrolyzed, with the liberation of fluoride ion.

$$BF_4^- + 3H_2O = H_3BO_3 + 3H^+ + 4F^-$$

The Boron Hydrides **12.27** A number of volatile binary compounds of boron and hydrogen, which contain boron atoms linked to each other, are known. The existence of these compounds presents an intriguing structural problem to the chemist, inasmuch as they do not possess a sufficient number of valence electrons for the formation of a complete series of electron-pair bonds. Thus in B_2H_6, the simplest of the borohydrides, there are twelve valence electrons; for complete electron-pair binding fourteen would be required.

12.28 The general formulas of the hydrides which are known are of two types, B_nH_{n+4} and B_nH_{n+6}, the former apparently being the more stable. A compilation of names, formulas, and some physical constants of the more common boron hydrides (or, as they are frequently called, boranes) is given in Table 12.4.

TABLE 12.4

Physical Constants of the Boron Hydrides *

Name	Formula	Melting Point, °C.	Boiling Point, °C.
Diborane	B_2H_6	−165.5	−92.5
Tetraborane	B_4H_{10}	−120	18
Stable pentaborane	B_5H_9	−46.6	48
Unstable pentaborane	B_5H_{11}	−123	−63
Hexaborane	B_6H_{10}	−65	(v.p. at 0°, 7.2 mm.)
Decaborane	$B_{10}H_{14}$	99.7	213

* BELL and EMELÉUS, *Quart. Revs.*, **2**, 132 (1948).

Of the various boron hydrides, the chemistry of diborane, B_2H_6, has been most extensively investigated; therefore the discussion which follows will be confined primarily to it.

12.29 Several methods are available for the preparation of diborane. Reaction of magnesium boride, Mg_3B_2, with hydrochloric or phosphoric acid gives a mixture of boranes, the chief component of which is tetraborane, B_4H_{10}. The thermal decomposition of the latter substance yields diborane. A second method involves the passage of a mixture of hydrogen and boron trichloride (or bromide) through an electrical discharge, and condensation of the products by means of liquid air. The process gives B_2H_5Cl as the main product. This substance rapidly undergoes disproportionation at 0° to yield diborane.

$$6B_2H_5Cl = 5B_2H_6 + 2BCl_3$$

Diborane is most readily and quantitatively prepared by the action of the trichloride on lithium aluminum hydride, $LiAlH_4$, in ether medium [3] — a type of

$$3LiAlH_4 + 4BCl_3 = 3LiCl + 3AlCl_3 + 2B_2H_6$$

reaction which is also useful for the preparation of aluminum hydride and the group IV hydrides.

12.30 The question of the structure of diborane and the other boron hydrides has attracted the attention of many investigators. There has been general agreement that the boron atoms in the boranes are joined to each other in some fashion, but the manner in which the valence electrons are distributed among the various boron and hydrogen atoms has been a matter of considerable speculation.

12.31 A theory regarding the structure of diborane, which appears to be concordant with the physical and chemical properties of the substance, is one

which postulates a bridged type of molecule (I) which may be written in the resonance forms II. An alternative manner of depicting the bridged structure involves what has been called the "protonated double bond" configuration, III,

[3] FINHOLT, BOND, and SCHLESINGER, *J. Am. Chem. Soc.*, **69**, 1199 (1947).

in which the two central hydrogens are believed to be disposed perpendicularly to the plane of the rest of the molecule.

12.32 A bridged configuration for diborane is apparently consistent with its properties. Such a structure contains only paired electrons, a fact which would account for the diamagnetism of the molecule. It is possible to replace a maximum of four hydrogens by methyl groups to yield compounds in which there are never more than two methyl groups on any one boron atom. The diborane molecule is readily converted to compounds which contain the BH_3 group; thus reaction with carbon monoxide gives $BH_3 : CO$. Moreover, a bridged configuration is concordant with the structural data obtained from electron diffraction and infrared and Raman spectra measurements. (See also 5.136–138.)

12.33 The boron hydrides undergo a number of interesting reactions. They all decompose at red heat to give elementary boron and hydrogen. All are hydrolyzed, but the ease with which hydrolysis takes place varies. For example, diborane is rapidly and completely decomposed by water at room temperature to yield orthoboric acid and hydrogen, whereas hydrolysis of hexaborane goes to completion only at elevated temperatures. Diborane is converted to $Na_2[B_2H_6]$ by the action of cold dilute sodium amalgam. The sodium derivative liberates hydrogen when brought in contact with water; when it is treated with gaseous hydrogen chloride, the original diborane is produced. Diborane combines reversibly with carbon monoxide to yield borine carbonyl, $H_3B : CO$. The carbonyl, which melts at $-137°$ and boils at $-64°$, is about 95 per cent dissociated at $100°$. The action of halogens, hydrogen halides, or boron trihalides on diborane yields halogenated derivatives. Thus chlorine reacts violently to give only boron trichloride, whereas bromine, which reacts slowly even at $100°$, yields boron tribromide and products which contain mainly the monobromide, B_2H_5Br. The monohalodiboranes are unstable, reverting relatively rapidly to diborane and the boron trihalides.

12.34 Diborane reacts with ammonia to give a white, nonvolatile, water-soluble substance of the empirical formula $B_2H_6 \cdot 2NH_3$. It has apparently been demonstrated that this compound is an ammonium salt; treatment of a liquid ammonia solution at $-77°$ with elementary sodium causes the evolution of one hydrogen atom for every two boron atoms in the compound. It has been suggested that the ammonia derivative of diborane has the structure NH_4^+,

triborine triamine

$[H_3B\!-\!NH_2\!-\!BH_3]^-$.* The "diammoniate" is readily converted into other compounds which contain the B—N—B grouping. For example, when heated to $200°$, it gives triborine triamine (also known as borazole and borazene), $B_3N_3H_6$, a substance which is the most stable compound containing a boron to

---

* This formulation has recently been questioned. Alternatives proposed are

$$[H_2B(NH_3)_2](BH_4) \quad \text{and} \quad NH_4 \cdot BH_2 \cdot NH_2 \cdot BH_4.$$

hydrogen linkage, and which is considered to be an inorganic analogue of benzene.

12.35 In addition to the simple boron hydrides, complexes containing the BH_4 group are known. Complex borohydrides of the alkali metals, magnesium, calcium, beryllium, aluminum, and a number of transition metals have been prepared. Sodium borohydride is the source, either direct or indirect, of most of the other complexes. This compound is best obtained by reaction between sodium hydride and methyl borate at 230–270°, the product being extracted from the reaction mixture with isopropylamine or liquid ammonia.[4]

$$4NaH + B(OCH_3)_3 = NaBH_4 + 3NaOCH_3$$

Other alkali metal borohydrides may be prepared from the sodium compound by the appropriate metathetical reactions,[5,6] e.g.,

$$KOH + NaBF_4 \overset{H_2O}{=} KBF_4\downarrow + NaOH$$

$$LiCl + NaBH_4 \overset{\underset{amine}{isopropyl}}{\underset{\Delta}{=}} LiBH_4 + NaCl\downarrow.$$

The alkali metal salts may in turn be used as sources of other complex borohydrides, e.g.,

$$AlCl_3 + 3NaBH_4 \underset{in\ vacuo}{\overset{130°}{=}} Al(BH_4)_3\uparrow + 3NaCl.$$

12.36 The alkali metal borohydrides are white, crystalline solids having a face-centered cubic structure, in which the components are M^+ and BH_4^-. The spacing is such as to permit free rotation of the tetrahedral BH_4^-. $Al(BH_4)_3$ has been shown by electron diffraction studies to be covalent in character. Each boron atom is attached to four hydrogen atoms and to one aluminum atom, thus giving boron a covalence of five, a most unusual situation for an element of the first period of eight. The exact electron distribution in the compound is unknown, although the interatomic distances indicate that the electron deficiency is confined to the B—H bonds. The Al—H distance, 2.14 Å, is normal, whereas the B—H distance, 1.27 Å, the same as in diborane, is larger than the theoretical (1.18 Å) for a boron-hydrogen single bond. Electron diffraction patterns of $Be(BH_4)_2$ vapor show that this substance has a structure similar to that of the aluminum compound. The change from ionic to covalent character from the alkali metal borohydrides to the aluminum compound is also indicated by a comparison of volatilities: $LiBH_4$, sublimes at 275°; $NaBH_4$, stable up to 400°; $Be(BH_4)_2$, b.p. 91.3°; $Al(BH_4)_3$, b.p. 44.5°.

12.37 The borohydride ion is unstable toward water.

$$BH_4^- + 2H_2O = BO_2^- + 4H_2$$

[4] SCHLESINGER, BROWN, and FINHOLT, *J. Am. Chem. Soc.*, **75**, 205 (1953).
[5] BANUS, BRAGDON, and HINCKLEY, *J. Am. Chem. Soc.*, **76**, 3848 (1954).
[6] SCHLESINGER, BROWN, and HYDE, *J. Am. Chem. Soc.*, **75**, 209 (1953).

The reactivity of the alkali metal compounds toward this reagent decreases with increasing weight of the metal atom. Thus, the lithium compound reacts violently, the sodium compound may be recrystallized from cold water with little decomposition, and potassium borohydride is quite stable. Beryllium and aluminum borohydrides are readily decomposed by water, the products of reaction being boric acid, hydrogen, and metal hydroxide. The beryllium and aluminum compounds are spontaneously inflammable. Alkali metal borohydrides are becoming increasingly valuable as reducing agents in both inorganic and organic chemistry.

Aluminum, Gallium, Indium, and Thallium

General Characteristics **12.38** Aluminum is the most common metal in the earth's crust, where it occurs to the extent of about 7.5 per cent by weight. On the other hand, gallium, indium, and thallium, although widely distributed in nature, are found in only small concentrations (Ga, 15; In, 0.1; and Tl, 0.3 p.p.m.). Although rare in occurrence, gallium, indium, and thallium are readily obtainable as by-products of processes utilizing certain sulfide ores. Thus gallium and indium are obtained from lead and zinc smelters, and thallium from the flue dust of chamber process sulfuric acid works. The metals of group III are readily obtained by electrolytic methods.

12.39 Some important physical constants of the metals are summarized in Table 12.2. Aluminum is an extremely light substance ($d = 2.7$) of great tensile strength; although of silvery appearance when freshly cut, it soon loses its luster as a result of the formation of a thin oxide film. Gallium is hard and brittle, and possesses a wide liquid range (ca. 30–1700°). Indium is a soft, silvery metal of rather high ductility and malleability. Thallium is soft and malleable, but of poor tensile strength.

The metals of group III are rather active elements. A summary of some of their important reactions is given in Table 12.5.

TABLE 12.5

Reactions of Group III Metals

Reaction	Remarks
$4M + 3O_2 = 2M_2O_3$	At high temperature; Ga only superficially oxidized; Tl also forms Tl_2O; $\Delta H_{Al_2O_3} = 402.9$ kcal./mole
$2M + N_2 = 2MN$	Al only
$2M + 3X_2 = 2MX_3$	With all the halogens; Tl also forms TlX; existence of thallium(III) iodide questionable
$2M + 2OH^- + 2H_2O = 3H_2 + 2MO_2^-$	With Al and Ga only
$2M + 3S = M_2S_3$	At high temperature; Tl gives Tl_2S
$2M + 6H^+ = 2M^{3+} + 3M_2$	Tl forms Tl^+

The +3 Oxidation State **12.40** The common oxidation state of the group III elements, and the most stable except in the case of thallium, is the +3 state. The basicity relationships of the oxides, the parents of the various compounds of these elements, have already been discussed (see 12.4). A more detailed description of oxide properties follows.

12.41 An anhydrous oxide of aluminum, Al_2O_3, is found in nature and is known as corundum. This is an extremely hard and unreactive substance, and is commonly used as an abrasive. In addition, the oxide bauxite, $Al_2O_3 \cdot nH_2O$, is found in nature, and is at present the industrial source of the metal. Aluminum oxide forms two definite hydrates: $AlO \cdot OH$ (or $Al_2O_3 \cdot H_2O$) and $Al(OH)_3$ (or $Al_2O_3 \cdot 3H_2O$). Aluminum hydroxide, $Al(OH)_3$, is an insoluble substance which exhibits amphoteric behavior in aqueous medium.

$$Al(OH)_3(s) = Al^{3+} + 3OH^- \qquad K = ca.\ 2 \times 10^{-33}$$
$$Al(OH)_3(s) = H^+ + AlO_2^- + H_2O \qquad K = ca.\ 4 \times 10^{-13}$$

As a base, aluminum hydroxide yields salts in aqueous solutions which contain $Al(H_2O)_6^{3+}$. Soluble aluminum salts of weak acids, *e.g.*, carbonates, acetates, etc., are incapable of existing in aqueous solution and undergo complete hydrolysis, resulting in the precipitation of aluminum hydroxide. As an acid, it gives rise to salts containing AlO_2^- or AlO_3^{3-} (aluminate ion). These ions are doubtless hydrated in solution and are probably more correctly formulated as $[Al(OH)_4]^-$ and $[Al(OH)_6]^{3-}$. Alkali metal aluminates, being salts of a weak acid (weaker than boric acid), are extensively hydrolyzed; the addition of carbon dioxide precipitates aluminum hydroxide from their solutions. There exist a large number of minerals, known as *spinels*, which have the composition $MO \cdot Al_2O_3$, where M may be Mg^{2+}, Zn^{2+}, etc.

12.42 Gallium sesquioxide, Ga_2O_3, may be obtained by the thermal decomposition of the nitrate, sulfate, or hydrated oxide. Like aluminum oxide, the gallium compound becomes refractory when ignited. Two forms of the oxide are known, the transition point for the conversion of the low temperature α-form to the β-variety being 380°. Two hydrated oxides, $GaO \cdot OH$ and $Ga(OH)_3$ are known to exist; it is believed that the former, which is the more stable form, is produced when an aqueous solution of Ga^{3+} is treated with alkali. Gallium hydroxide (hydrous gallium oxide) is amphoteric.

$$Ga(OH)_3 = Ga^{3+} + 3OH^- \qquad K = ca.\ 5 \times 10^{-37}$$
$$Ga(OH)_3 = H^+ + H_2GaO_3^- \qquad K = ca.\ 1 \times 10^{-15}$$

There is evidence that trisodium gallate(III), Na_3GaO_3, is formed when the hydroxide is dissolved in concentrated sodium hydroxide solution. Gallium(III) salts, like the corresponding aluminum compounds, are extensively hydrolyzed in aqueous solution; on boiling, basic salts are precipitated from such solutions.

12.43 Indium sesquioxide, In_2O_3, may be prepared by methods analogous to those employed for the gallium compound, and also by the combustion of the metal in air. The hydroxide, $In(OH)_3$, is obtained by precipitation from an

In(III) solution with alkali. It appears to be primarily basic in character, although the compound $Mg(InO_2)_2$ has been reported (see 12.4).

12.44 Thallium sesquioxide, Tl_2O_3, is prepared in the same manner as the indium compound. The sesquioxide, which is completely basic in character, appears to form no hydrates and so cannot be formulated as a hydroxide. It is thermally unstable, and begins to lose oxygen at 100° to give the monoxide Tl_2O.

12.45 All of the metallic elements of group III form trihalides of the general empirical formula MX_3. The trihalides of thallium are of relatively low thermal stability, owing to the strong tendency for this element to assume the monopositive condition. The stability of the thallium trihalides decreases markedly with increasing weight of the halogen. Thus the trifluoride decomposes at 500°, the trichloride begins to lose chlorine at 40°, and the tribromide loses halogen even more readily to become what is probably $Tl^I[Tl^{III}Br_4]$. Thallium(III) iodide probably does not exist; the compound of empirical formula TlI_3 is believed to contain I_3^-. All of the stable trihalides can be prepared by a method which is a standard one for the preparation of volatile anhydrous halides.

$$M_2O_3 + 3C + 3X_2 = 2MX_3 + 3CO$$

12.46 The melting and boiling points of the stable trihalides, which are shown in the table, indicate that, with the possible exception of the fluorides, these compounds are covalent in character. That the chlorides, bromides, and

	Melting Point, °C.	Boiling Point, °C.
AlF_3	1290	Sublimes at 1291
$AlCl_3$	192.6 (at 1700 mm.)	" at 180°
$AlBr_3$	97.5	255
AlI_3	179.5	381
GaF_3	950° (sublimes)	——
$GaCl_3$	77.9	201.3
$GaBr_3$	121.5	279
GaI_3	212	346
InF_3	1170	1200
$InCl_3$	586	——
$InBr_3$	436	——
InI_3	210	——

iodides of aluminum and gallium, at least in the liquid state, are indeed covalent is confirmed by the fact that these substances are extremely poor conductors of electric current at temperatures just above their melting points; thus the specific conductivity of aluminum chloride at 194° is 4.5×10^{-7} ohm^{-1} cm.$^{-1}$.*

12.47 Molecular weight determinations on aluminum trichloride in the vapor state, and in such noncoordinating solvents as benzene, show that this substance

* The conductivities of gallium(III) chloride, bromide, and iodide at temperatures just below the melting points have been interpreted as indicating that the solids are ionic. On the other hand, the low conductivities of the molten materials show them to be covalent. (GREENWOOD and WORRALL, *J. Inorg. Nucl. Chem.*, **3**, 357 (1957).)

is a dimeric molecule Al_2Cl_6. The electron diffraction patterns of chloride, bromide, and iodide show that in the vapor state all three compounds consist of two AlX_4 tetrahedra as shown, having one edge in common. It has similarly been demonstrated that the trichlorides of gallium and indium, and also the bromide and iodide of the latter, are dimeric in the vapor state. In aqueous solution, the trihalides, as a result of the high polarizing power of the relatively small tripositive ions, are readily hydrated and give solutions possessing a high electrical conductivity. From such solutions, the trihalides can be isolated as hydrates, e.g., $[Al(H_2O)_6]Cl_3$, $[In(H_2O)_4]Cl_3$. The aluminum halides also form complexes with alcohols, ethers, ketones, and aldehydes.

12.48 The trihalides of the group III metals form a variety of additional complex compounds, the most numerous being the complex halides. Aluminum fluoride has a great affinity for fluoride ion, giving rise to complexes of the types $M_3[AlF_6]$ and $MAlF_4$. The former are exceedingly stable, and by far the more numerous. The best known example is the naturally occurring cryolite, $Na_3[AlF_6]$. The ammonium derivative is thermally unstable and decomposes at 350° to give ammonium fluoride and NH_4AlF_4; at higher temperatures further decomposition occurs and aluminum fluoride is formed. In the solid state both types of fluoro complexes are built up of AlF_6 octahedra.

12.49 The stability of other aluminum complex halides, in which the maximum coordination number of the metal is four, is small. A few compounds of the type $M[AlCl_4]$ (e.g., M = Li, K, NH_4) have been prepared from melts consisting of aluminum chloride and the appropriate metal chloride, or from solutions of the trihalide in benzene. These complexes cannot be prepared in aqueous solution. Analogous bromo complexes, which can also be made by dry methods, are soluble in benzene and toluene. The chloride and bromide complexes are low melting materials, e.g., $Li[AlCl_4]$, 143.5°; $Na[AlBr_4]$, 201°. The affinity of the aluminum halides for halide ion falls off markedly with increasing weight of halogen; only one complex iodide, $K[AlI_4]$, has been reported.

12.50 Of the halides of the other three metals, gallium appears to form only fluoride complexes in aqueous medium; indium forms chlorides and bromides; and thallium forms chlorides, bromides, and iodides. The gallium fluoride complexes are mainly of the type $M_3[GaF_6]$, and are made by bringing together the trifluoride and alkali metal fluorides in dilute hydrofluoric acid. Water-soluble compounds of the type $M[GaF_5(OH_2)] \cdot 6H_2O$, where M = Mn, Co, Ni, Zn, and Cd, are also known. Among the indium and thallium complexes which have been prepared are $K_3[InCl_6] \cdot 1.5H_2O$, $(NH_4)_2[InCl_5(OH_2)]$, $H[TlCl_4] \cdot 3H_2O$, $K_2[TlCl_5] \cdot H_2O$, $Li_3[TlCl_6] \cdot 8H_2O$, $K[TlBr_4]$, and $Rb_3[TlBr_6]$.

12.51 The aluminum halides, with the exception of the trifluoride, readily form complexes with ammonia and organic amines. Stable monammines and triammines are formed with ammonia. The former are believed to be covalent in character. The ammines of the trichloride, bromide, and iodide of gallium and indium contain large numbers of ammonia molecules, whereas the ammines of the trifluorides have at most three moles of ammonia per mole of trihalide. The triammoniates cannot be made directly from the anhydrous fluorides; they can be prepared, however, by the treatment of the fluoride trihydrates with liquid ammonia. No ammoniates of trihalides of thallium have been characterized. Complexes with ethylenediamine, *e.g.*, $TlCl_3 \cdot en \cdot H_2O$, $TlBr_3 \cdot en_3$, etc., are obtained by reaction between aqueous solutions of the halides and the amine.

12.52 The chelate complexes of the group III tripositive ions are numerous and stable. The majority of these complexes are of the trichelate type, the metal ions exhibiting their maximum coordination number of six. With β-diketones, aluminum, gallium, and indium form compounds of the structure shown. These substances are covalent in character; thus aluminum acetylacetonate is low melting (192°) and boiling (315°), soluble in organic solvents, but practically insoluble in water.

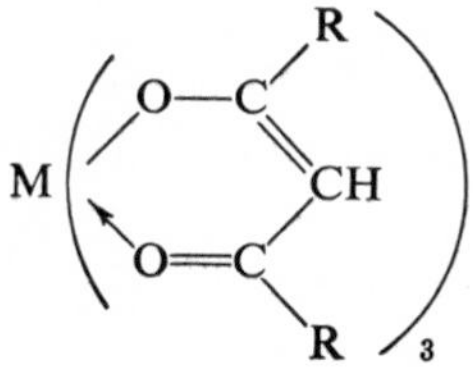

12.53 Oxalato complexes of all four metals have been obtained. For aluminum and thallium, oxalato derivatives of both the di- and trichelate types are known, for gallium only the trichelate type, and for indium only the dichelate.

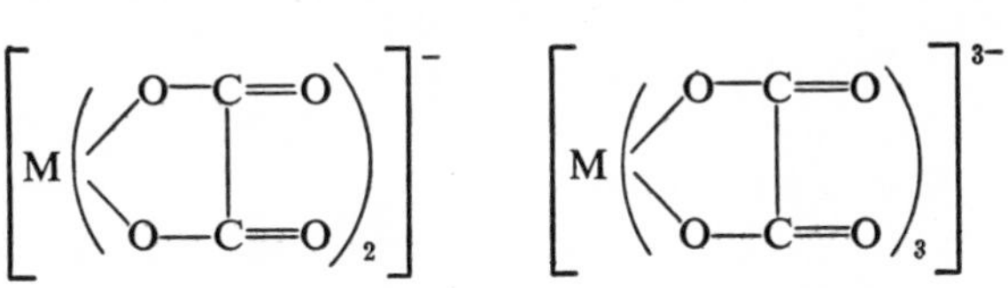

12.54 Of considerable importance in the analytical chemistry of the group III metals are the complexes with 8-hydroxyquinoline. These are of the trichelate type shown.

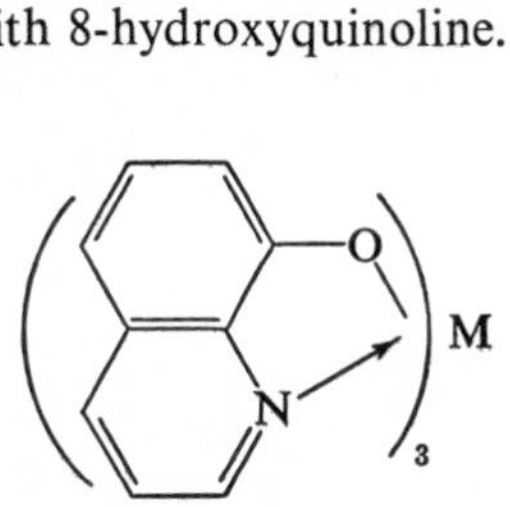

12.55 One complex compound worthy of special mention is lithium aluminum hydride, $Li[AlH_4]$. This substance is prepared by reaction between lithium hydride and aluminum chloride in anhydrous ether medium.

$$4LiH + AlCl_3 \overset{(C_2H_5)_2O}{=} Li[AlH_4] + 3LiCl$$

It is soluble in ether, but decomposes readily in water.

$$LiAlH_4 + 4H_2O = LiOH + Al(OH)_3 + 4H_2$$

It is a powerful and often specific reducing agent, and so finds considerable use in organic chemistry. It is also of great utility in the conversion of anhydrous halides to the corresponding hydrides (see 12.29 for its use in the preparation of diborane) and in the preparation of complex borohydrides.

Lower Oxidation States **12.56** The stability of monopositive thallium with respect to oxidation to the +3 state is brought out by the electrode potential for the reaction.

$$Tl^+ = Tl^{3+} + 2e^- \qquad E° = ca. -1.25 \text{ v.}$$

Thallium(I) ion is similar in some respects to both the alkali metal and silver or lead(II) ions. It resembles the latter primarily in the solubilities of some of its salts; thus the chloride, bromide, and iodide are sparingly soluble, and the fluoride exhibits appreciable aqueous solubility (3.59 moles per liter of water at 25°). Thallium(I) ion forms an insoluble chromate and sulfide. On the other hand, like the alkali metal ions, it shows comparatively little tendency to form complex ions in aqueous solution. Thallium(I) hydroxide, TlOH, is a strong, fairly soluble base.

12.57 The lower valence states of the other group III metals are unstable with respect to oxidation to the common tripositive state. Nevertheless, compounds containing these metals in lower states have been isolated, and considerable evidence points to the production of such states as unstable species in a variety of reactions.

12.58 There appears to be no doubt that aluminum(I) fluoride, AlF, is capable of existence at high temperatures. When elementary aluminum and the trifluoride are heated together in a high vacuum, the following equilibrium is established.

$$2Al + AlF_3 \rightleftharpoons 3AlF$$

At temperatures below 700° a negligible quantity of aluminum(I) is present; at 1000° aluminum(I) fluoride is believed to be the predominant species in the equilibrium mixture. Upon condensation of the gaseous species in the mixture, the sublimate consists of metallic aluminum in admixture with its trifluoride, the ratio of fluorine to total aluminum corresponding to AlF. This reaction has been proposed as the basis of a process for refining aluminum.

12.59 The preparation of solid aluminum(I) iodide has been achieved by the use of an electrodeless discharge in the vapor of the triiodide at a temperature below 50°.[7] This resulted in the decomposition of the triiodide, primarily into elementary iodine and aluminum monoiodide, the latter being deposited on the walls of the discharge tube. The monoiodide was not obtained pure, but was invariably contaminated with metallic aluminum, the best product having the empirical composition $Al_{1.22}I$ and being a buff-colored, rather nonvolatile material.

12.60 Additional evidence for the formation of monopositive aluminum comes from electrochemical studies in nonaqueous solvents. The anodic oxida-

[7] SCHUMB and ROGERS, *J. Am. Chem. Soc.*, **73**, 5806 (1951).

tion of aluminum in an electrolyte of sodium or ammonium acetate dissolved in anhydrous acetic acid [8] gives anodic current efficiencies considerably higher than can be explained by formation of Al^{3+}. In some cases, initial mean valence numbers for aluminum as low as 1.8, based upon loss in weight of the anode and Faraday's law, were obtained. No lower valent species of aluminum, however, was isolated. Analogous experiments in nitrate-bromide solutions in liquid ammonia have given similar results.[9] Here, although no monopositive aluminum was isolated, nitrate ion was reduced to elementary nitrogen in amount equivalent to the quantity of aluminum(I) oxidized to the tripositive state.

12.61 Compounds containing gallium and indium in lower valence states have been isolated. $GaCl_2$, a white substance melting at 170.5°, has been prepared by heating the trichloride with an excess of the metal at 175° *in vacuo*. Vapor density measurements on this substance between 400° and 470° show that a considerable number of $GaCl_2$ "molecules" are present, in addition to some polymers. Magnetic measurements, however, show that solid $GaCl_2$ is diamagnetic, indicating the absence of simple Ga^{2+}, with the structure

$$1s^2 2s^2 2p^6 3s^2 3p^6 3d^{10} 4s^1.$$

The suggestion that $GaCl_2$ is actually an autocomplex of the type $Ga^I[Ga^{III}Cl_4]$ has been confirmed by X-ray diffraction investigation of the crystalline material [10] and examination of the Raman spectrum of the fused compound.[11]

12.62 A substance of empirical formula Ga_2O has been prepared by heating a mixture of the calculated quantities of sesquioxide and metal *in vacuo*. It has been shown, however, that this "substance" gives no X-ray lines other than those of the metal and sesquioxide. Gallium(III) sulfide yields a substance of the formula GaS when treated with hydrogen at 800°. When GaS is thermally decomposed in a high vacuum, the sesquisulfide and a volatile gray-black material of the composition Ga_2S are formed. The latter substance may also be prepared by reaction of the sesquisulfide and the theoretical quantity of metal in a vacuum at 700–720°. The existence of the *three* sulfides has been reported to have been confirmed by means of characteristic X-ray diagrams.

12.63 Reaction of indium(III) fluoride with hydrogen at high temperatures gives a hygroscopic material of the empirical formula InF_2. Indium reacts at its melting point with dry hydrogen chloride to yield $InCl_2$. This material, like all other soluble substances containing indium in a lower oxidation state, disproportionates in water to give the metal and the tripositive ion. Reduction of $InCl_2$ by means of metallic indium results in the formation of the diamagnetic monochloride, InCl. This is a light-sensitive compound which exists in two modifications, one red and the other yellow. The high-temperature reaction of

[8] DAVIDSON and JIRIK, *J. Am. Chem. Soc.*, **72**, 1700 (1950).
[9] BENNETT, DAVIDSON, and KLEINBERG, *J. Am. Chem. Soc.*, **74**, 732 (1952).
[10] GARTON and POWELL, *J. Inorg. Nucl. Chem.*, **4**, 84 (1957).
[11] WOODWARD, GARTON, and ROBERTS, *J. Chem. Soc.*, 1956, p. 3723.

iodine with an excess of indium metal in a carbon dioxide atmosphere yields InI. This substance liberates hydrogen from dilute acids. In$_2$O has been obtained by reduction of the sesquioxide with hydrogen at temperatures below 400°, and subsequent sublimation *in vacuo* at 750°. The material possesses a characteristic X-ray pattern, indicating that it is a true compound rather than a mixture. It is unaffected by cold water, but is soluble in hydrochloric acid solution with the liberation of hydrogen.

CHAPTER 13

GROUP IV

Introduction

13.1 Carbon, silicon, germanium, tin, and lead comprise the fourth group of representative elements. Although these elements possess a common s^2p^2 valence shell configuration, only carbon and silicon are characterized by an inert gas kernel, the last three elements (as in the previous group and in all succeeding groups of representative elements) having an underlying shell of eighteen electrons (Table 13.1).

TABLE 13.1

Electronic Configurations of Group IV Representative Elements

	1	2	3	4	5	6
	s	$s\ p$	$s\ p\ d$	$s\ p\ d\ f$	$s\ p\ d$	$s\ p$
$_6$C	2	2, 2				
$_{14}$Si	2	2, 6	2, 2			
$_{32}$Ge	2	2, 6	2, 6, 10	2, 2		
$_{50}$Sn	2	2, 6	2, 6, 10	2, 6, 10	2, 2	
$_{82}$Pb	2	2, 6	2, 6, 10	2, 6, 10, 14	2, 6, 10	2, 2

13.2 A number of additional properties of the members of the group are listed in Table 13.2. Examination of the ionization potentials shows that the energy requirement for removal of all the valence electrons (compare with the preceding group, Table 12.2) is extremely high and indicates that there is little likelihood for the existence of simple tetrapositive ions for these elements. There

GENERAL REFERENCES

LATIMER, *The Oxidation States of the Elements and Their Potentials in Aqueous Solutions*, 2nd Edition, Prentice-Hall, Inc., New York, 1952, Ch. 8.

SIDGWICK, *The Chemical Elements and Their Compounds*, Oxford University Press, London, 1950, pp. 368–9, 487–550, 551–627, 667–71.

WELLS, *Structural Inorganic Chemistry*, 2nd Edition, Oxford University Press, London, 1950, pp. 508–53.

TABLE 13.2

Some Properties of Group IV Elements

	C	Si	Ge	Sn	Pb
Natural isotopes	12 *, 13, 14 †	28 *, 29, 30	70, 72, 73, 74 *, 76	112, 114, 115, 116, 117, 118, 119, 120 *, 122, 124	204, 206, 207, 208 *
Density, g./cc.	D 3.51 G 2.22	2.33	5.36	W 7.31 G 5.75	11.34
Melting point, °C.	3570	1414	958	231.9	327.5
Boiling point, °C.	3470 (subl.)	2355	2700	2362	1755
Covalent radius, Å	0.771	1.173	1.223	1.412	1.538
Ionic radius in crystals, Å					
M^{4+}	——	0.41	0.53	0.71	0.84
M^{2+}	——	——	——	1.10	1.27
Ionization potential, volts					
1st electron	11.22	8.12	8.09	7.30	7.38
2nd electron	24.28	16.27	15.86	14.5	14.96
3rd electron	47.6	33.3	34.1	30.5	31.9
4th electron	64.2	44.9	45.5	39.4	42.1
Electrode potential $E°$, in volts, for M(s) = $M(H_2O)_x^{2+} + 2e^-$	——	——	0.0 (estimate)	0.136	0.126
Electronegativity (F = 4.0)	2.5	1.8	1.7	1.7	

* Most abundant isotope
† Radioactive

is some evidence, however, for the existence of Si^{4+} in silicates. For example, all of the properties of glasses seem to be consistent with a random ionic network.

13.3 All the members of the group possess the ability to utilize the valence electrons for the formation of four tetrahedral (SP^3) covalent bonds, thereby attaining inert gas configurations. This property, which is extremely pronounced in carbon, and of considerable importance in silicon, germanium, and tin, is generally of little significance so far as lead is concerned. The great tendency for 4-covalency is the chief characteristic of the chemistry of carbon, which forms electron-pair bonds of great strength with hydrogen, the halogens, nitrogen, oxygen, sulfur, and with other carbon atoms. The compounds of tetracovalent carbon are characterized by their inertness toward reagents which attack by means of an electron donating mechanism. For example, the tetrahalides are incapable of forming complexes and they do not undergo solvolysis under ordinary conditions. Undoubtedly, such stability is primarily attributable to the fact that the carbon atom (in which the second quantum shell is being filled) is electronically saturated when it is 4-covalent. On the other hand, the tetrahalides of silicon, germanium, and tin, which are common tetracovalent compounds of these elements, are capable of forming complexes by union with donor groups, and are readily susceptible to hydrolysis. These elements can have more than eight electrons in the valence shell, and in the tetrahalides can act as electron-pair acceptors with the use of d orbitals to give substances in which the central atom has a covalency greater than four. Although a fair number of compounds of tetracovalent lead with alkyl and aryl groups are known, only a few strictly inorganic compounds have been characterized, PbH_4, PbF_4, and $PbCl_4$, and of these the hydride and chloride are extremely unstable, the latter with respect to decomposition to lead(II) chloride and elementary chlorine. Tetrapositive lead, in general, is a potent oxidizing agent. This is a manifestation of the increasing difficulty of attainment of the maximum oxidation state with increasing atomic number in groups of representative elements in which the latter members have an 18, s^2p^x configuration in the outer shells. This phenomenon was noted in the previous group and is apparent also in representative groups V and VI. Paralleling the decreased stability of the tetrapositive state is the enhanced stability of the dipositive state. The dipositive state first definitely appears with germanium in which it possesses strong reducing power, and is of considerable importance in the chemistry of tin and lead. In polar solvents, +2 tin and lead can exist as cationic species. It is noteworthy that the dipositive state appears with germanium which is the lightest element of the group in which metallic properties first become important, and that this state has its greatest stability in those members which are true metals.

13.4 Consistent with the relatively low electronegativities (Table 13.2), is the nonexistence, except perhaps for carbon, of simple negative ions for the members of the group. With the most electropositive metals, carbon forms binary compounds which are designated as saltlike carbides. Even in these compounds, however, it is probable that the binding is in large measure covalent in character.

13.5 The chemistry of carbon differs significantly from that of the other members of the group. An outstanding property of carbon is its pronounced ability for self-linkage (catenation). This ability, which is so marked in carbon, and which is responsible for the great multiplicity of organic compounds, diminishes sharply for silicon, germanium, and tin, and is practically nonexistent for lead. A number of factors undoubtedly contribute to this trend for self-linkage. One is the inability of carbon to attain a covalence greater than four, in contrast to the behavior of the heavier elements of the group (see above). The relative bond energies of the element-element single bonds would also appear to be of significance so far as the ability for catenation is concerned. Thus the energy of the carbon-carbon bond is considerably greater than that of the silicon-silicon bond, the values being 82 and 50 kcal. per mole, respectively. Moreover, the silicon-silicon bond is significantly less stable than bonds between silicon and other elements, as is illustrated by the data given in the table.

| Si—Si | 50 kcal./mole | Si—F | 136 | Si—Br | 73 | Si—O | 106 |
| Si—H | 81 | Si—Cl | 90 | Si—I | 53 | Si—S | 60 |

The high value for the energy of the Si—O bond, which is exceeded only by that of the Si—F bond, is worthy of emphasis. It is not surprising, therefore, to find that the chemistry of silicon as it occurs in nature, is almost entirely that of the oxide and its derivatives. In this regard there is a close resemblance between the chemistry of silicon and that of boron.

13.6 In comparison with the other members of its group, carbon is unique in its ability to form stable multiple bonds with other carbon atoms and also with other nonmetallic atoms such as nitrogen, oxygen, and sulfur. In each multiple bond situation the carbon atom completes its octet of valence electrons.

Thus the following linkages are among those encountered: $\diagdown \!\! \text{C}\!\!=\!\!\text{C} \diagup$,

$-\text{C}\!\!\equiv\!\!\text{C}-$, $-\text{C}\!\!\equiv\!\!\text{N}:$, $\diagdown \!\! \text{C}\!\!=\!\!\overset{..}{\text{O}}:$, and $\diagdown \!\! \text{C}\!\!=\!\!\overset{..}{\text{S}}:$. In compounds in which these

linkages exist, carbon exhibits a covalence of less than four. No similar situation is known for silicon or its homologs.

13.7 In view of the many differences in the chemistry of carbon and silicon, these elements are considered separately in the discussion which follows. Germanium, tin, and lead, the members of the group which are predominantly metallic in character, are discussed as a unit. No attempt is made to make the coverage exhaustive, but rather those aspects of the chemistry are described which serve to emphasize major areas of difference and similarity among the elements and their compounds.

Carbon

The Element

13.8 Carbon exists in two distinct crystalline modifications, diamond and graphite,* which differ widely in their properties. The differences can be well correlated in terms of the structures of these species.

13.9 Structurally, the diamond crystal is a giant molecule showing cubic

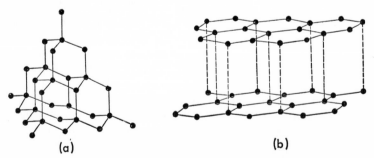

(a)   (b)

Fig. 13.1   Crystal structure of (a) diamond and (b) graphite.

* The so-called amorphous forms of carbon have been shown to have the graphite structure.

symmetry, with each carbon atom bound covalently to four others disposed at the corners of a regular tetrahedron at a distance of 1.54 Å, Figure 13.1(a). Since the breakdown of the diamond crystal involves the rupture of many strong carbon-carbon bonds, the diamond is the hardest natural substance known and has the highest melting point (about 3570°) of any element.   Moreover, since the valence electrons of each carbon atom are completely utilized for the formation of covalent bonds, the diamond is a nonconductor of electric current.   Its transparency and high index of refraction make it valuable as a jewel.

13.10 In contrast to diamond, graphite is a soft, black, much less dense (2.22 as compared with 3.51 g./cc.) solid, having an appreciable electrical conductivity.   These properties are consistent with the structure of graphite, which is a two-dimensional giant molecule made up of layers of hexagonal rings of carbon atoms, Figure 13.1(b), in which each carbon atom is joined to three others by covalent bonds at a distance of 1.42 Å.   The distance between layers (3.40 Å) is too great for the existence of normal covalent bonds between them.   Thus, carbon in graphite must be regarded as being essentially 3-covalent.   The weak binding forces operative between layers permit their ready separation and account for the softness of graphite.   The ability of graphite to act as an electrical conductor is in accord with the fact that more valence electrons are available than are required for the formation of single electron-pair bonds within a sheet.

13.11 Thermodynamically, graphite is the more stable form at 25° and one atmosphere pressure; the heat of combustion is -94.04 kcal. as compared to -94.49 kcal. for diamond.   It has been demonstrated that even at pressures from 15,000 to 30,000 kg./cm.^{2} and at a temperature of 2,000° graphite is still the more stable allotrope.   Calculations show that the two allotropic modifications are in equilibrium under about 15,000 atmospheres pressure at 300° K, and under about 40,000 atmospheres at 1,500° K.

13.12 Carbon is relatively inert at ordinary temperature, but when heated, it is capable of reaction with a number of elementary substances.   It combines with oxygen with the liberation of considerable heat to give a mixture of carbon monoxide and carbon dioxide, the relative yields of products being dependent upon the temperature and the proportions of reactants.   At high temperatures reaction with elementary sulfur yields the disulfide, and with fluorine the tetrafluoride.   A number of metals combine directly with carbon to give carbides (see below).

13.13 Graphite undergoes a number of unusual reactions which are attributable to its layer structure.   For example, oxidation by potassium chlorate in a mixture of nitric and sulfuric acids results in the swelling of the graphite and the insertion of oxygen between the carbon layers.   The carbon : oxygen ratio in the substance produced (which is known as "graphitic oxide") varies from 2.2 : 1 to 3.5 : 1.   Although the carbon sheets of the graphite remain unchanged, the distance between them is increased from 3.40 to more than 6 Å.   In addition to the entry of oxygen between the layers, oxidation of surface carbon atoms to carboxyl groups takes place; mellitic acid, $C_6(COOH)_6$, a derivative of benzene, is formed on more complete oxidation of graphite. When "graphitic oxide" is heated, large volumes of carbon monoxide and carbon dioxide are liberated.

13.14 Oxidation of graphite in the presence of a strong acid, such as sulfuric, nitric, perchloric, or phosphoric acid, is accompanied by the separation of layers and the entry of acid groups between them, the layers themselves being unaffected. Saltlike substances, *e.g.*, $(C_{24})^+(HSO_4)^- \cdot 2H_2SO_4$ (approximate formula), are produced. The degree of uptake of acid is dependent upon its concentration and also upon the extent of oxidation. The "graphitic salts" are decomposed by water, with the regeneration of graphite.

13.15 Other substances which have been shown to be capable of penetrating and expanding the graphite layers are the alkali metals potassium, rubidium, and cesium, the halogens fluorine and bromine, and iron(III) chloride. With the alkali metals, substances of stoichiometric composition, *e.g.*, KC_8 and KC_{16}, apparently are formed. Fluorine gives the "monofluoride" CF, and bromine vapor is absorbed to a maximum extent corresponding to the composition $CBr_{0.77}$. The maximum uptake of iron(III) chloride gives a substance of the formula $C_9(FeCl_3)$, in which the magnetic moment of the iron is unchanged from its original value, a fact which indicates that no iron-carbon bond has been produced.

Binary Compounds with Metals [1]

13.16 Binary compounds of carbon with metals, and also with certain nonmetals (*e.g.*, silicon and boron) are commonly known as carbides. The compounds with metals may be classified into three broad groups: (1) saltlike carbides, formed primarily by metals of representative groups I, II, and III, the members of the copper group, zinc and cadmium, and the lanthanides; (2) interstitial carbides, produced by transition metals with d^2s^2 and d^3s^2 outer configuration, and by molybdenum and tungsten; and (3) a class known for chromium, manganese, iron, cobalt, and nickel, and differing in properties from the interstitial carbides.

13.17 Three distinct varieties of saltlike carbides have been characterized; those apparently containing C^{4-}, those having C_2^{2-}, and a magnesium compound in which C_3^{4-} presumably is present. The saltlike carbides are colorless or faintly colored, transparent substances which do not conduct electric current at ordinary temperature and are decomposed by water or acids with the liberation of hydrocarbons.

13.18 Examples of the first type of saltlike substances are Be_2C and Al_4C_3. The beryllium compound is obtained by reaction between the metal and carbon or a hydrocarbon at temperatures above 1000°, or by the reduction of beryllium oxide with carbon at temperatures in the neighborhood of 2000°. Al_4C_3 is prepared by direct combination of the elements, the reaction proceeding rapidly at 2000°. These compounds liberate methane, CH_4, on hydrolysis, and are there-

[1] WELLS, *Structural Inorganic Chemistry*, 2nd Edition, Oxford University Press, London, 1950, pp. 550–53; 701–06.

fore occasionally referred to as methanides. Methanides are not formed with metal cations of large size.

13.19 The very great majority of the saltlike carbides contain C_2^{2-}. Typical examples of carbides of this type are Na_2C_2, K_2C_2, Cu_2C_2, BeC_2, MgC_2, CaC_2, ZnC_2, $Al_2(C_2)_3$, LaC_2, CeC_2, PrC_2, and UC_2. Members of this class are known as acetylides, since on hydrolysis they yield acetylene, C_2H_2. For many of the compounds acetylene is the only hydrocarbon produced in the hydrolytic reaction; for others, although acetylene is the main hydrocarbon product, smaller quantities of other hydrocarbons, *e.g.*, ethylene and methane, are also formed. It has been suggested that other hydrocarbons in addition to acetylene are liberated if the hydroxide which is formed on hydrolysis contains the metal in an oxidation state higher than in the carbide. In such a case, conversion of the metal in the carbide to the higher state it possesses in the hydroxide may be accompanied by evolution of hydrogen, which reacts with some of the liberated acetylene to give other hydrocarbons. This suggestion appears to be in accord with experimental facts. Thus CaC_2, K_2C_2, $Al_2(C_2)_3$, etc., which are converted to hydroxides without change in valence state of the metal, liberate only acetylene on hydrolysis. On the other hand, the rare-earth acetylides, *e.g.*, CeC_2, PrC_2, NdC_2, in which the metals are presumably in the dipositive state, and which on hydrolysis are converted to hydroxides containing the tripositive metals, give methane and ethylene as well as acetylene.

13.20 The acetylides have been prepared by a number of methods. Thus, the alkali metal compounds and BeC_2 and MgC_2 can be obtained by reaction between acetylene and the heated metals; lithium and sodium acetylides can also be prepared by direct union of the elements at elevated temperatures. The alkaline earth metal and rare-earth acetylides are commonly made by heating the oxides with carbon in an electric furnace. The compounds of the copper group elements are conveniently produced by treatment of acetylene with ammoniacal solution of the appropriate metal salts, and the corresponding carbides of zinc and cadmium are made by the interaction of the hydrocarbon and metal alkyls (*e.g.*, $Zn(C_2H_5)_2$) in a solvent such as petroleum ether.

13.21 The unique compound Mg_2C_3 may be prepared by the action of the metal on acetylene, but at a temperature higher than that required for the preparation of the acetylide MgC_2. It is best obtained, however, by heating magnesium with methane or pentane. Not only are the two magnesium carbides structurally different, as shown by X-ray investigation, but they show different hydrolytic behavior. Whereas MgC_2 yields only acetylene on treatment with water, Mg_2C_3 gives chiefly the hydrocarbon allylene, CH_3—$C\equiv CH$. On the basis of the formation of this hydrocarbon on hydrolysis it is inferred that C_3^{4-} is present in Mg_2C_3.

13.22 The interstitial carbides, like the corresponding hydrides (see 9.15), are formed by the entry of the small nonmetallic atom into interstices of the crystal lattices of transition elements. The structures of the transition metals are such that two types of carbides may be formed — the MC variety with a cubic close-packed lattice and the M_2C type with hexagonal close-packing. Moreover, the sizes of the interstices limit the formation of such carbides to transition metals with atomic radii greater than about 1.3 Å (Ti, Zr, Hf, V, Nb, Ta, Mo, and W).

13.23 The interstitial carbides are prepared either by direct union of the powdered metal with carbon at temperatures in the region of 2,200° or by heating the metal filament in an atmosphere of some hydrocarbon. The compounds are metal-like in a number of their properties; thus they possess opacity, luster, and a high electrical conductivity which decreases with increasing temperature. They are unusually hard (*e.g.*, TiC and W_2C have hardnesses of 8–9 and 9–10, respectively, on Moh's scale, compared to a value of 10 for diamond), have extremely high melting points (TiC, 3410°; W_2C, 3130°K), and are inert toward all chemicals with the exception of oxidizing agents.

13.24 The union of carbon with transition metals having atomic radii less than 1.3 Å (Cr, Mn, Fe, Co, and Ni) gives substances which differ from interstitial carbides, not only in composition but also in reactivity. The compounds which have been prepared are Cr_3C_2 and M_3C (M = Mn, Fe, Co, and Ni). In contrast to the inertness of the interstitial compounds, these carbides react readily with dilute acids, and in some instances with water, to give a variety of products. For example, Mn_3C gives a mixture of methane and hydrogen on treatment with water, whereas Fe_3C and Ni_3C are decomposed by hydrochloric acid with the formation of hydrogen, mixtures of hydrocarbons, and free carbon. The crystal structures of these carbides are rather complex and are not similar to those of the metals.

Binary Compounds with Boron and Silicon

13.25 The carbides of boron and silicon differ markedly in properties from all other binary compounds of carbon with nonmetals. They are covalent polymeric materials, extremely hard, high melting, and relatively inert chemically.

13.26 Although a number of boron carbides have been reported to have been prepared by direct union of the elements or by the reduction at high temperatures of boron trioxide with carbon, the one compound which has been characterized unequivocally is B_4C, or better, $B_{12}C_3$. The crystal unit consists of linear chains of three carbon atoms, with groups of twelve boron atoms at the vertices of a nearly regular icosahedron, each boron atom being linked to five others in the same unit and to either another boron atom or a carbon atom in the adjacent unit. Boron carbide is a fair conductor of electric current.

13.27 Silicon carbide (carborundum), SiC, is prepared commercially by reduction of silica with carbon at about 3500°. This substance is a black, iridescent material, almost as hard as diamond. It is known in three similar crystalline modifications, each consisting of tetrahedra in which carbon and silicon atoms occupy alternate positions. The C—Si bond distance is 1.90 Å, a value which is almost the arithmetic mean of the C—C and Si—Si distances in diamond and crystalline silicon.

4-Covalent Carbon

13.28 The great majority of the compounds of carbon contain the element in the 4-covalent state. Inasmuch as these compounds are regarded as lying in the province of organic chemistry they are not discussed in this text. However, a few remarks regarding the tetrahalides are pertinent, in view of the fact that compounds of this type will be discussed in some detail for the other members of the group.

13.29 All of the possible tetrahalides of carbon (except CAt_4) have been obtained. A summary of some of their physical constants is given in Table 13.3.

TABLE 13.3

Some Physical Constants of the Carbon Tetrahalides

Compound	Melting Point, °C.	Boiling Point, °C.
CF_4	−185	−128
CCl_4	−22.9	76.4
CBr_4	93.7	decomp.
CI_4	171.0	decomp.

The relative inertness of 4-covalent carbon toward attack by electron donating groups has been mentioned (see 13.3). One additional point is noteworthy, namely the thermal instability of the bromide and iodide. This is a deviation from the trend found for the thermal behavior of the tetrahalides of the other members of the group, where the stability in any one halide series decreases with increasing atomic weight of the central atom. The instability of these two carbon compounds is probably the result of steric factors, *i.e.*, the inability of the small carbon atom to accommodate readily the large halogen atoms.

Simple Compounds of Multiply-bonded Carbon

13.30 From the inorganic viewpoint the chemistry of multiply-bonded carbon is largely that of the oxides, their derivatives, and compounds containing the cyanide group. An important characteristic of groups containing multiply-bonded carbon is their ability to act as ligands in the formation of complex compounds. This section is concerned with aspects of the chemistry of some relatively simple compounds containing multiply-bonded carbon, and is followed by a discussion of a number of the more important complex types.

The Oxides of Carbon **13.31** Three oxides of carbon are known with certainty: carbon suboxide, C_3O_2, the anhydride of malonic acid ($CH_2(COOH)_2$); carbon monoxide, CO, which may formally be regarded as the anhydride of formic acid; and carbon dioxide, the anhydride of carbonic acid.

13.32 Carbon suboxide is prepared by the dehydration *in vacuo* of malonic acid by phosphoric anhydride at temperatures of 140–150°. The oxide is a gaseous substance (f.p. −6.8°.) with a vile odor. It is extremely soluble in water with the formation of the parent acid. Electron diffraction measurements show that the molecule possesses a linear structure, with the C—O distance being 1.20 Å (calculated for C=O, 1.22 Å) and the C—C bond length 1.30 Å (calculated for C=C, 1.33 Å). The actual state of the molecule may be regarded as a resonance hybrid to which the following structures make contributions:

$$:\overset{..}{\underset{..}{O}}::C::C::C::\overset{..}{\underset{..}{O}}: \qquad +:\overset{..}{O}:::C:C:::C:\overset{..}{\underset{..}{O}}:- \qquad -:\overset{..}{\underset{..}{O}}:C:::C:C:::O:+$$

13.33 Carbon monoxide (b.p., $-190°$; f.p., $-205.1°$) is formed almost quantitatively by the combustion of carbon in an insufficient supply of air at $1000°$; at temperatures in the neighborhood of $500°$ carbon dioxide is practically the sole product, even when the carbon is present in excess. Commercially, carbon monoxide is obtained largely by the oxidation of hot coke by steam.

$$H_2O(g) + C = H_2 + CO$$

The equilibrium constant for the reaction is about 1 at $600°$.

13.34 Structurally, carbon monoxide is probably best represented by three resonance configurations of approximately equal significance: [2]

$$+:C:\overset{..}{\underset{..}{O}}:- \qquad :C::\overset{..}{\underset{..}{O}}: \qquad -:C:::O:+$$

13.35 A number of properties of carbon monoxide are compatible with these structures. Thus the molecule has a very small dipole moment (0.1D) and the observed C—O bond distance is 1.13 Å (calculated for C—O, 1.51, for C=O, 1.22, and for C≡O, 1.10 Å)*.

13.36 Carbon monoxide is a relatively reactive substance. When heated, particularly in the presence of a catalyst such as platinum or nickel, the monoxide is reversibly decomposed as indicated.

$$2CO = C + CO_2$$

The equilibrium mixture contains about 95% of the dioxide at $500°$, but only 0.6% of this material at $1000°$. The monoxide burns in air with the formation of the dioxide ($\Delta H = -67.6$ kcal. per mole of CO oxidized), and combines directly with halogens (in the presence of light), sulfur, and selenium to give carbonyl compounds, e.g., $COCl_2$, COS. With certain transition metals and some of their salts carbon monoxide gives metal carbonyls, $M_x(CO)_y$, in which the oxide functions as a donor molecule via the carbon atom. These compounds are discussed in the next section. At elevated temperatures the monoxide is capable of reducing metal oxides, and as a result finds considerable use in metallurgy (for example, in the production of pig iron). The reduction of steam by carbon monoxide is a valuable reaction for the preparation of hydrogen.

$$CO + H_2O(g) = CO_2 + H_2$$

At $400°$ the reaction goes 94 per cent toward completion. The catalyzed reactions between carbon monoxide and hydrogen have become commercially significant, e.g., for the preparation of methanol and hydrocarbons. It is interesting

[2] PAULING, *The Nature of the Chemical Bond*, 2nd Ed., Cornell University Press, Ithaca, 1940, pp. 135–36, 195.

* These values are based on carbon having a completed valence shell. To calculate the carbon-oxygen bond distances in the first two structures shown above, suitable corrections to take into account the incomplete carbon valence shell would be necessary. These corrections would result in smaller values than those cited for these structures.

that although carbon monoxide may be obtained by the dehydration of formic acid, the gas is only slightly soluble in water. It is more soluble in alkaline solutions, with which it gives formates.

13.37 Carbon dioxide is the product of the complete oxidation of free or combined carbon. It is also produced by a number of other methods: the action of mineral acids on metal carbonates, the thermal decomposition of some carbonates (*e.g.*, $CaCO_3$, $MgCO_3$), and the alcoholic fermentation of glucose.

13.38 Solid carbon dioxide has a sublimation pressure of 1 atmosphere at $-78.5°$. Carbon dioxide is monomolecular in the vapor state, possesses a linear structure, and has a zero dipole moment. No single configuration adequately describes the molecule, and (see 5.107) it has been proposed that carbon dioxide is a resonance hybrid to which the following structures contribute significantly:

$$: \ddot{O} :: C :: \ddot{O} : \qquad -: \ddot{O} : C ::: O :+ \qquad +: O ::: C : \ddot{O} :-$$

The absence of a dipole moment and the C—O bond distance (1.15 Å) are consistent with such a formulation.

13.39 Carbon dioxide is rather stable thermally up to about 1000°. Above that temperature it decomposes appreciably to the monoxide and oxygen. As the thermal stability indicates, carbon dioxide is a weak oxidizing agent. However, at elevated temperatures, the more active metals (*e.g.*, sodium, potassium, and the alkaline earth metals) burn in carbon dioxide to yield elementary carbon and the appropriate metal oxide or carbonate.

13.40 Carbon dioxide is soluble in water to the extent of about 0.1% at 22.6° and 1 atmosphere pressure. Up to about 5 atmospheres the aqueous solubility is almost directly proportional to the pressure; above 5 atmospheres of carbon dioxide pressure the solubility is greater than that calculated by Henry's law. Aqueous solutions of carbon dioxide are slightly acidic as a result of the formation of carbonic acid which functions as a diprotic acid.

$$H_2CO_3 + H_2O = H_3O^+ + HCO_3^- \qquad K_1 = 4.2 \times 10^{-7}$$
$$HCO_3^- + H_2O = H_3O^+ + CO_3^{2-} \qquad K_2 = 4.8 \times 10^{-11}$$

The dissociation constants cited above are calculated on the assumption that all the carbon dioxide is present as H_2CO_3. As a matter of fact, however, less than 1% of the carbon dioxide in solution is present as carbonic acid.

13.41 Two types of salts, the hydrogen carbonates (bicarbonates), and the normal carbonates, containing, respectively, HCO_3^- and CO_3^{2-}, are derivable from carbonic acid. The alkali metal carbonates (including the ammonium salt, but not the lithium compound) possess considerable aqueous solubility; carbonates of other metals are generally insoluble. Bicarbonates are usually much more soluble than the normal salts, and insoluble carbonates, $CaCO_3$ for example, may be brought into solution by treating their aqueous suspensions with an excess of carbon dioxide.

$$CaCO_3\downarrow + CO_2 + H_2O = Ca(HCO_3)_2$$

13.42 Solutions of both carbonates and bicarbonates are alkaline as a result of hydrolysis.

$$CO_3^{2-} + H_2O = OH^- + HCO_3^-$$
$$HCO_3^- + H_2O = OH^- + H_2CO_3$$

Less important than the hydrolytic reaction is the protolysis of the bicarbonate ion.

$$HCO_3^- + H_2O = H_3O^+ + CO_3^=$$

The net result of the hydrolytic and protolytic reactions of the bicarbonate ion is the equilibrium,

$$2HCO_3^- = H_2CO_3 + CO_3^{2-} \qquad K = 1.1 \times 10^{-4},$$

which accounts for the ready conversion of carbonates to bicarbonates on passage of carbon dioxide into aqueous solutions (or suspensions) of the former.

13.43 The thermal stability of the carbonates and bicarbonates increases with the basic nature of metal oxides from which they are derived. Thus, magnesium carbonate exhibits a dissociation pressure of 1 atmosphere at approximately 540°, whereas the corresponding barium compound exerts the same dissociation pressure at 1360°. Bicarbonates yield normal carbonates on thermal decomposition.

$$2HCO_3^- = CO_3^{2-} + CO_2 + H_2O$$

The carbonate ion is coplanar, with bond angles of 120° and a C—O distance of 1.31 Å. The properties of the ion are in accord with the resonance formulations shown.

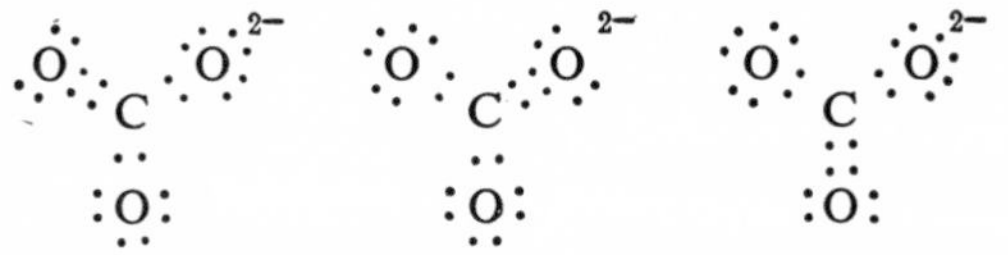

Compounds Containing the —CN Group **13.44** In terms of composition the simplest compound possessing the cyanide group is cyanogen, $(CN)_2$, an extremely poisonous gas (b.p., −21.1°; f.p., −27.8°) which resembles the halogens in most of its chemical properties. This substance is commonly prepared by the thermal decomposition of noble metal (Hg, Ag, Au) cyanides. Cyanogen is a nonpolar molecule apparently possessing a linear structure, the C—N and C—C bond distances being 1.16 Å and 1.37 Å, respectively. The molecule may be considered to be a resonance hybrid with the structure shown below making the greatest contribution.

$$: N ::: C : C ::: N :$$

13.45 Cyanogen is readily soluble in water, in which medium it slowly undergoes a number of rather complicated reactions. Among the hydrolytic products which have been identified are hydrocyanic and cyanic acids (halogen-like behavior); ammonium formate, cyanate, and oxalate; urea; and oxamide. The formation of the last-named substance definitely indicates the presence of a C—C bond in the cyanogen molecule. Cyanogen is extremely stable toward decomposition by heat, being characterized by a tendency to form a polymeric substance known as paracyanogen.

13.46 The parent substance of simple metal derivatives containing the —C≡N group is hydrogen cyanide, HCN, a low boiling liquid (b.p., 25.6°; m.p., −13.4°) of extremely high dielectric constant (116 at 20°). There is no doubt that hydrogen cyanide exists in an associated state, and it has been suggested (Pauling, *op. cit.*, pp. 294–5) that polymerization occurs as a result of hydrogen bonding, in the manner shown.

$$H—C≡N---H—C≡N---H—C≡N$$

It is noteworthy that although two isomeric series of esters, R—C≡N and R—N≡C, are derivable from hydrogen cyanide, the parent compound is known only in the one form.

13.47 Hydrogen cyanide is obtained by volatilization from solution when a metal cyanide is treated with dilute sulfuric acid; use of the concentrated acid results in the production of carbon monoxide. Aqueous solutions of hydrogen cyanide are weakly acidic, the ionization constant of hydrocyanic acid being 4.9×10^{-10}. The acid is slowly hydrolyzed to ammonia and formic acid.

13.48 Both ionic and covalent metallic derivatives of hydrogen cyanide are known. The cyanides of sodium, potassium, rubidium, cesium, and thallium(I) are ionic in nature, the first three possessing the sodium chloride lattice (face-centered cubic) and the last two having the cesium chloride structure (body-centered cubic). No structural data are available for the alkaline earth compounds. Aqueous solutions of ionic cyanides are basic as a result of the reaction

$$CN^- + H_2O = HCN + OH^-,$$

for which the equilibrium constant is about 5×10^{-6} at room temperature. Because of the hydrolytic reaction it is impossible to prepare in aqueous medium cyanides of elements such as aluminum and chromium, which give insoluble oxides or hydroxides instead.

13.49 Definitive structural information has been obtained for the covalent metal cyanides $Cu(CN)_2$, AgCN, and AuCN. For example, AgCN apparently consists of infinite chains of alternate silver atoms and cyanide groups arranged in a hexagonal structure. The value (5.26 Å) found for the distance between silver atoms in the chains is in accord with the picture of the cyanide group acting as a bridge between silver atoms. Undoubtedly other metal cyanides will be shown to be nonionic when more structural investigations have been carried out.

Complexes with Multiply-bonded Carbon as Donor Atom

13.50 The most important ligands containing multiply-bonded carbon capable of functioning as the donor atom in the formation of complex compounds are carbon monoxide, the cyanide ion, and olefinic substances. Coordination compounds with carbon monoxide as ligand are formed only by certain transition metals; these complexes are of considerable interest to the chemist because of their unusual properties and also because their structural nature has been a matter of considerable speculation. Cyano complexes which are stable with respect to dissociation are known for most transition metal ions and also for zinc, cadmium, and dipositive mercury. Ethylene and certain of its derivatives form coordination compounds with a number of metal ions, *e.g.*, dipositive platinum and unipositive copper and silver. Discussion of the olefin complexes is beyond the scope of this text.

The Metal Carbonyls.[3]   **13.51** A list of the volatile metal carbonyls which have been characterized and some of their properties are given in Table 13.4. It is

TABLE 13.4

The Metal Carbonyls

Chromium Group	Manganese Group	Iron Group	Cobalt Group	Nickel Group
$Cr(CO)_6$ Colorless; subl.	$[Mn(CO)_5]_2$ * Golden-yellow; m.p. 154–155°	$Fe(CO)_5$ Yellow; m.p. −20°; b.p. 103°	$[Co(CO)_4]_2$ Orange-red	$Ni(CO)_4$ Colorless; m.p. −25°; b.p. 43°
		$Fe_2(CO)_9$ Yellow; decomp. 100°		
		$[Fe(CO)_4]_3$ Green; decomp. 140°	$[Co(CO)_3]_4$ Black; decomp. 60°	
$Mo(CO)_6$ Colorless; subl.	$[Re(CO)_5]_2$ Colorless; m.p. 177°; subl.	$Ru(CO)_5$ Colorless; m.p. −22°		
		$Ru_2(CO)_9$ Orange	$[Rh(CO)_4]_2$ Orange; m.p. 76° (decomp.)	
		$[Ru(CO)_4]_3$ Green		
$W(CO)_6$ Colorless; subl.		$Os(CO)_5$ Colorless; m.p. −15°		
		$Os_2(CO)_9$ Yellow; m.p. 224°; subl.	$[Ir(CO)_4]_2$ Yellow-green; subl.	
			$[Ir(CO)_3]_x$ Yellow; decomp. 210°	

* Brimm, Lynch and Sesny, *J. Am. Chem. Soc.*, **76**, 3831 (1954). $[Mn(CO)_5]_2$ was obtained by the reduction of manganese(II) iodide with magnesium in ether under a pressure of 1000–3000 p.s.i.g. of carbon monoxide.

[3] Eméleus and Anderson, *Modern Aspects of Inorganic Chemistry*, 2nd Ed., D. Van Nostrand Company, Inc., New York, 1952, pp. 408–440.

seen that compounds of the type $M_x(CO)_y$ are formed by members of the transition triads (with the exception of palladium and platinum) and by the elements of the chromium and manganese groups, and that both mononuclear and polynuclear carbonyls are known.

13.52 A number of methods serve for the preparation of the metal carbonyls, there being no one mode of production which is suitable for all. Nickel tetracarbonyl and iron pentacarbonyl are produced commercially by direct combination of metal and carbon monoxide. The metal must be in an active state, and is ordinarily so obtained by low-temperature reduction. Reaction with nickel occurs at room temperature and atmospheric pressure; combination to give iron pentacarbonyl is effected at 180–200° and 50–200 atmospheres of carbon monoxide pressure. Cobalt, molybdenum, and tungsten carbonyls can also be formed by union of the metals with carbon monoxide under pressure and at elevated temperatures, especially in the presence of sulfur as catalyst.

13.53 Nickel tetracarbonyl may be produced in aqueous medium by the action of carbon monoxide on nickel(II) sulfide, cyanide, or the nickel salts of various organic thio acids (*e.g.*, thiosalicylic, thioacetic, thioglycollic) suspended in sodium hydroxide solution. It has been suggested that reaction occurs according to the equations shown.

$$2NiX_2 + 2nCO = 2Ni(CO)_nX + X_2$$
$$2Ni(CO)_nX + 4\text{-}2n(CO) = Ni(CO)_4 + NiX_2$$

The second step thus is believed to involve disproportionation of monopositive nickel.

$$2Ni(I) = Ni(0) + Ni(II)$$

13.54 With nickel(II) salts of certain thio acids, *e.g.*, $Ni(S\!-\!\underset{\displaystyle \|}{\overset{\displaystyle S}{C}}\!-\!C_6H_5)_2$, reaction with carbon monoxide in solutions containing OH^- or SH^- involves the following type of disproportionation.

$$2Ni(II) = Ni(0) + Ni(IV)$$

The specific reaction follows.*

13.55 Chromium, molybdenum, and tungsten hexacarbonyls may be obtained on a laboratory scale in relatively good yields by a Grignard method. For ex-

* HIEBER and BRUCK, *Z. anorg. u. allgem. Chem.*, **269**, 28 (1952).

ample, reaction in ether medium between a Grignard reagent, chromium(III) chloride, and carbon monoxide under pressure (35–70 atmospheres), followed by hydrolysis, gives about a 60% yield of $Cr(CO)_6$. Only covalent halides can be employed successfully in the Grignard reaction; for the preparation of the molybdenum and tungsten carbonyls, $MoCl_5$ and WCl_6 have been used as starting materials.

13.56 The carbonyls of ruthenium, osmium, rhodium, and iridium have been prepared by interaction of the halides of the metals with carbon monoxide in the presence of a halogen acceptor such as finely divided silver. Carbonyl halides are formed as intermediate products. Optimum conditions for reaction vary with metal halide employed; thus the preparation of ruthenium penta-carbonyl is best effected at 170° and a carbon monoxide pressure of 250 at-mospheres and that of the corresponding osmium compound at 120° and 200 atmospheres gas pressure. The process involving conversion of the inter-mediate carbonyl halide to the carbonyl is illustrated by the following equilibria.

$$2RuI_3 + 4CO = 2Ru(CO)_2I_2 + I_2$$

$$Ru(CO)_2I_2 \underset{I_2}{\overset{CO+Ag}{\rightleftharpoons}} Ru(CO)_nI \underset{I_2}{\overset{CO+Ag}{\rightleftharpoons}} Ru(CO)_5$$

13.57 Some of the polynuclear carbonyls can be obtained by the decomposi-tion of the simple compounds. For example, decomposition of iron penta-carbonyl takes the course shown.

$$Fe(CO)_5 \xrightarrow{light} Fe_2(CO)_9 \xrightarrow{heat} [Fe(CO)_4]_3$$

13.58 The properties of the metal carbonyls are those of typical covalent substances. They are characterized by their volatility, solubility in many non-polar solvents, and insolubility in polar media. The diamagnetism of the carbonyls shows that there are no unpaired electrons in the d orbitals of the metals. It is interesting that in the simple carbonyls (formed only by the metals of even atomic number) the metal atom has the *effective atomic number*, E.A.N., (see 6.16) of the next inert gas. Thus in $Ni(CO)_4$ the E.A.N. of nickel is 36 (krypton structure); molybdenum in $Mo(CO)_6$ has the E.A.N. of xenon (54); etc.

13.59 The structures of the simple carbonyls have been determined, but rela-tively little definite structural information is available for the polynuclear com-pounds. It is now generally accepted that in the carbonyls the CO groups exist as such and are joined to the metal through the carbon atom. That each carbon monoxide molecule occupies a single coordination position is evidenced by the fact that these groups may be replaced in a stepwise fashion by neutral molecules such as pyridine and phosphorus trifluoride.

13.60 Electron diffraction data (Pauling, *op. cit.*, pp. 251–4) for $Ni(CO)_4$ are best interpreted in terms of a tetrahedral structure (SP^3 binding) for this mole-cule, with the Ni—C—O grouping linear. The C—O bond length is 1.15 Å compared to 1.13 Å for the CO molecule, and the Ni—C distance of 1.82 Å is less by 0.18 Å than that calculated for a single bond between these atoms and greater by 0.03 Å than the distance for a metal-carbon double bond. It has been proposed that the tetracarbonyl is structurally a resonance hybrid to which configurations shown make major contributions.

$$—\overset{|}{\underset{|}{Ni}} : C ::: O : \qquad —\overset{|}{\underset{|}{Ni}} :: C :: \overset{..}{O} :$$

$$\text{(A)} \qquad\qquad\qquad \text{(B)}$$

In structure (B), one pair of electrons for the double bond between nickel and carbon comes from a $3d$ orbital of the nickel atom.

13.61 The hexacarbonyls of the chromium group elements possess octahedral configurations, a fact indicative of D^2SP^3 binding. In each of these compounds the metal-carbon distance is about 0.10 Å less than that required by a single bond, and this has been interpreted as showing that these bonds have some double-bond character.

13.62 A number of interesting types of derivatives of the metal carbonyls are known. In certain carbonyls carbon monoxide can be replaced by strongly coordinating groups, *e.g.*, pyridine, ethylenediamine, *o*-phenanthroline, ammonia, cyanide ion, phosphorus trihalides, or aromatic isonitriles. In general, monomeric carbonyls are less reactive toward substitution than the polynuclear compounds. When carbon monoxide is replaced by a neutral group, the product is a covalent material. Examples of products formed by substitution reactions are

$Ni_2(CO)_3py$ (py = pyridine), $Ni(PF_3)_4$, $Fe_2(CO)_4py_3$, and $Ni(CN \cdot C_6H_5)_4$.

13.63 Rather unusual derivatives of the carbonyls are the metal carbonyl hydrides. Only two of these compounds — $Fe(CO)_4H_2$ and $Co(CO)_4H$ — have been extensively investigated. Others which have been reported are $Re(CO)_5H$, $Os(CO)_4H$, $Rh(CO)_4H$, and $Ir(CO)_4H$. Iron and cobalt carbonyl hydrides are liberated when alkaline solutions of the parent carbonyls are acidified.

$$Fe(CO)_5 + 4OH^- = [Fe(CO)_4]^{2-} + CO_3^{2-} + 2H_2O$$
$$[Fe(CO)_4]^{2-} + 2H^+ = Fe(CO)_4H_2$$

Cobalt carbonyl hydride may also be obtained from aqueous cobalt(II) suspensions by reactions analogous to those which yield nickel carbonyl (see 13.53). In addition, a variety of high pressure syntheses can be used for its preparation, *e.g.*, reaction of dimeric cobalt carbonyl with hydrogen; union of cobalt, carbon monoxide, and hydrogen; direct combination of cobalt hydride and carbon monoxide; etc. Similar high pressure reactions serve for the production of the carbonyl hydrides of osmium, rhodium, and iridium, but cannot be employed for the iron compound.

13.64 Iron carbonyl hydride is a pale yellow liquid which solidifies at $-70°$ and possesses a nauseating odor. It is a powerful reducing agent. Above $-10°$, it yields hydrogen and products arising from the decomposition of the $Fe(CO)_4$ radical.

$$Fe(CO)_4H_2 = H_2 + Fe(CO)_4$$
$$2Fe(CO)_4 = Fe(CO)_5 + [Fe(CO)_3]$$
$$\text{polymeric}$$

Cobalt carbonyl hydride (yellow, f.p. $-26.2°$) decomposes at temperatures above its freezing point to give hydrogen and dimeric cobalt tetracarbonyl.

13.65 Iron and cobalt carbonyl hydrides behave as weak acids in aqueous medium and are thus capable of forming metal derivatives. Those of the alkali and alkaline earth metals, e.g., $[Fe(CO)_4H]Na$, $[Fe(CO)_4H]_2Ca$, and also of ammine cations, e.g., $[Fe(CO)_4H]_2[M^{II}(NH_3)_6]$ (where M^{II} = Mn, Fe, Co, or Ni), are saltlike materials, being decomposed by acids or water with the regeneration of the parent carbonyl hydrides. In addition, iron carbonyl hydride forms stable salts with amines, such as, for example, $[Fe(CO)_4][py \cdot H]_2$, a substance which behaves as a strong electrolyte when dissolved in pyridine or liquid ammonia. With salts of members of the copper and zinc families, the carbonyl hydrides undergo metathesis to yield insoluble metal derivatives, e.g., $[Fe(CO)_4]Hg$, which appear to be nonelectrolytes and which are more stable toward the action of acids than are the alkali metal salts.

13.66 Iron and cobalt carbonyl hydrides have been shown to be structurally similar to nickel tetracarbonyl, each having four CO groups arranged tetrahedrally about the metal atom, with the M—C—O grouping linear. There is some uncertainty concerning the mode of attachment of the hydrogen atoms.

13.67 There exists a third important derivative type of the metal carbonyls, namely, the carbonyl halides. Compounds of this type apparently are not formed by chromium, molybdenum, tungsten, and nickel, but are known for the other elements which give carbonyls, as well as for palladium, platinum, and the members of the copper group. Examples of carbonyl halides are $Re(CO)_5X$, $Fe(CO)_5X_2$, $Fe(CO)_4X_2$, $Co(CO)I_2$, $Pt(CO)_2Cl_2$, and $Cu(CO)X$ (where X = Cl, Br, I). No fluorides have been obtained. A general method for the preparation of these compounds involves the direct combination of anhydrous metal halides with carbon monoxide.

13.68 The properties of the iron carbonyl halides are well known and a few of them are noted below. They are readily obtained by the action of halogen on iron pentacarbonyl. $Fe(CO)_5X_2$ is first formed and this evolves carbon monoxide spontaneously to give $Fe(CO)_4X_2$. The latter, which can also be prepared directly from iron(II) halides and carbon monoxide under pressure, can be further decomposed to give $Fe(CO)_2X_2$. All the iron carbonyl halides are non-electrolytes and are soluble in inert organic solvents. Reaction with water results in the liberation of carbon monoxide and the formation of hydrated iron(II) halide. Both the stability and the volatility of the carbonyl halides of metals which form carbonyls decrease in the order I > Br > Cl. The reverse trend is shown for the carbonyl halides of palladium, platinum, and the copper group metals.

The Complex Cyanides **13.69** The cyanide ion forms stable complexes with many of the transition metal ions, including the members of the zinc family.

There appears to be little doubt that in these complexes union of the cyanide ion to the central metal atom occurs through the carbon atom. Examples of some common cyano complexes, along with their structures, are shown in Table 13.5.

TABLE 13.5
Some Complex Cyanides

Metal	Oxidation State	Compound Type	Structure
Cu, Ag, Au	+1	$[M(CN)_2]^-$	Linear
Ni, Pd, Pt	+2	$[M(CN)_4]^{2-}$	Square planar
Zn, Cd, Hg	+2	$[M(CN)_4]^{2-}$	Tetrahedral
Mn, Fe, Co	+2	$[M(CN)_6]^{4-}$	Octahedral
V, Cr, Mn, Fe, Co	+3	$[M(CN)_6]^{3-}$	Octahedral
Mo	+3, +4, +5	$[M(CN)_8]^{5-,4-,3-}$	Dodecahedral
W	+4, +5	$[M(CN)_8]^{4-,3-}$	Dodecahedral

13.70 Complexing with cyanide ion frequently results in a marked stabilization of one oxidation state for an element which can exhibit variable valence states. It must be pointed out, however, that no generalizations can be made at present with regard to which oxidation state of any particular element will be stabilized. One illustration of an extremely important stabilization of a particular valence state is found with the copper group metals where complexing with cyanide ion strongly favors the unipositive state. This is of considerable value in the metallurgy of silver and gold where these metals may be removed from their native ores by extraction with alkali metal cyanide solutions in the presence of air. The extent to which complexing with cyanide stabilizes the +1 state is brought out by the oxidation potential data for the reaction $M(0) = M(I) + e^-$, both in the absence and presence of cyanide ion.

$$Cu = Cu^+ + e^- \qquad E° = \quad -0.521 \text{ v.}$$
$$Cu + 2CN^- = Cu(CN)_2^- + e^- \qquad E° = \quad ca.\ 0.43$$
$$Ag = Ag^+ + e^- \qquad E° = \quad -0.799$$
$$Ag + 2CN^- = Ag(CN)_2^- + e^- \qquad E° = \quad 0.31$$
$$Au = Au^+ + e^- \qquad E° = ca.\ -1.68$$
$$Au + 2CN^- = Au(CN)_2^- + e^- \qquad E° = \quad 0.60$$

13.71 Cyano complexes of transition elements and of zinc, cadmium, and mercury are extremely stable with respect to dissociation in aqueous solution. This is illustrated by the instability constant data of Table 13.6.

13.72 Complex cyanides with alkali or alkaline earth metals as cations are generally water soluble. When aqueous solutions of cyanide complexes, particularly those containing $[M(CN)_6]^{x-}$ ions, are treated with simple salts of transition metals, insoluble compounds are frequently formed. These possess complicated structures.

TABLE 13.6

Instability Constants of Some Cyano Complex Ions

(Reaction: $[M^{x+}(CN)_y]^{+x-y} \rightleftharpoons M^{x+} + yCN^-$)

Complex Ion	Instability Constant, K	Complex Ion	Instability Constant, K
$[Fe(CN)_6]^{4-}$	1×10^{-35}	$[Au(CN)_2]^-$	5×10^{-39}
$[Fe(CN)_6]^{3-}$	1×10^{-42}	$[Zn(CN)_4]^{2-}$	1.3×10^{-17}
$[Ni(CN)_4]^{2-}$	1×10^{-22}	$[Cd(CN)_4]^{2-}$	1.4×10^{-19}
$[Cu(CN)_2]^-$	1×10^{-16}	$[Hg(CN)_4]^{2-}$	4×10^{-42}
$[Ag(CN)_2]^-$	1.8×10^{-19}		

Silicon

The Element

13.73 Silicon is second in abundance to oxygen in the earth's crust, about 87 per cent of which is composed of silica and silicates. The element may be obtained by high temperature reduction of silicon dioxide (silica) with carbon, of the tetrachloride with sodium, or of sodium fluorosilicate with aluminum. The first and last methods give a gray, lustrous product which is a fair conductor of electric current and is known as crystalline silicon; the other process yields the so-called amorphous silicon. Structurally, there is no difference in the two products; both exhibit the diamond structure.

13.74 At room temperature, silicon is rather inert toward all elemental substances except fluorine, in which it ignites spontaneously with the formation of the tetrafluoride. At higher temperatures, it reacts with the other halogens; with oxygen and with sulfur to give the dioxide and disulfide; with nitrogen to form the nitride Si_3N_4; and with many molten metals to yield silicides. It dissolves in solutions of alkali metal hydroxides, with the liberation of hydrogen.

$$Si + 2OH^- + H_2O = SiO_3^{2-} + 2H_2$$

The standard potential for the reaction below has been estimated to be 1.7 volts.

$$Si + 6OH^- = SiO_3^{2-} + 3H_2O + 4e^-$$

Silicon Dioxide and Derivatives

13.75 Silicon dioxide (silica), SiO_2, is the only oxide of silicon definitely known in the solid state. There appears to be little doubt that the monoxide, SiO, can exist in the vapor state. The brown solid product of this empirical composition, obtained by the reduction of silica with carbon or silicon at high temperatures and the subsequent slow cooling of the vapor, has been shown by X-ray analysis to be a mixture of silica and silicon, undoubtedly formed by the disproportionation of SiO vapor. Rapid cooling of the vapor yields a hard black glass, which may be a polymeric monoxide.

13.76 Silicon dioxide, in contrast to carbon dioxide, is a relatively infusible material (m.p., ca. 1700°). It exists in nature in three crystalline modifications, the most stable of which is the material known as quartz. All the allotropic forms are three dimensional polymeric materials, in which each silicon atom is joined tetrahedrally to four oxygen atoms, each of the latter being common to two tetrahedra. The polymeric nature of the substance and the great strength of the Si—O bonds account for the chemical properties of silica.

13.77 Silica melts to a highly viscous liquid having a great tendency to super-cool to a glass. The glass has proved to be of considerable utility as a result of its low coefficient of expansion, high softening temperature ($>1500°$), and transparency to ultraviolet radiation. Silica is extremely stable chemically. (This stability is reflected in its high heat of formation, which has a value of about 200 kcal. per mole.) It is inert toward hydrogen, all the halogens but fluorine, and to all acids with the exception of hydrofluoric, which converts the dioxide to the volatile tetrafluoride.

$$SiO_2 + 4HF = 2H_2O + SiF_4$$

At elevated temperatures silica is reduced by alkali and alkaline earth metals and also by carbon (see 13.73). Fusion with basic oxides or carbonates converts the dioxide to silicates.

13.78 Silicon dioxide is an acidic oxide, and potentially the anhydride of a series of silicic acids. However, no such acids have been isolated in pure condition; the reported preparation of mono- and hemihydrates, i.e., H_2SiO_3 and $H_2Si_2O_5$, has not been confirmed. Attempts to prepare solid silicic acids by treatment of a soluble silicate with strong acid have yielded only a gel of the hydrous dioxide.

13.79 Alkali metal silicates have been prepared, and a large number of silicates with complex structures (e.g., felspars, micas, zeolites, talc) are found in nature. The alkali silicates, the only ones exhibiting water solubility, are prepared by fusion of sand with the appropriate metal carbonate, the composition of the product being determined by the ratio of reactants. Products having $SiO_2 : M_2O$ formula weight ratios up to $2 : 1$ give true solutions in water; those with greater silica content form colloidal dispersions. Salts containing anions of the following empirical compositions have been characterized among the soluble silicates: SiO_3^{2-}, SiO_4^{4-}, $Si_2O_5^{2-}$, $Si_2O_7^{6-}$, and $Si_4O_9^{2-}$. The structures of naturally occurring silicates have been elucidated by X-ray analysis, but a discussion of the subject is beyond the range of this book. (See Pauling, op. cit., pp. 385–400, for an excellent discussion of the structures of silicates.) The most significant point with regard to all the silicates is that the basic structural unit is the tetrahedral SiO_4 group.

Silicon Hydrides (The Silanes)

13.80 Silicon forms volatile hydrides exclusively of the type Si_nH_{2n+2}, corresponding to the paraffinic hydrocarbons. The fact that the maximum number of silicon atoms which has thus far been found in the chain is six emphasizes the remarkable decrease from carbon to silicon in ability of the group IV representative elements to self-link. The known silanes and some of their physical properties are given in Table 13.7.

TABLE 13.7

The Silanes

Compound	Melting Point, °C.	Boiling Point, °C.
SiH_4	−185	−111.9
Si_2H_6	−132.5	−14.5
Si_3H_8	−117.4	52.9
Si_4H_{10}	−84.3	107.4
Si_5H_{12}		>100
Si_6H_{14}		>100

13.81 The action of 20 per cent hydrochloric acid on magnesium silicide, Mg_2Si, yields mainly hydrogen and relatively small quantities of all the silanes, the latter being separated and purified by fractionation. Decomposition of magnesium silicide by ammonium bromide in liquid ammonia gives mono- and disilane as the major products, in addition to hydrogen. These silanes are most readily obtained in high purity and in excellent yield by treatment of the corresponding chlorides, $SiCl_4$ and Si_2Cl_6, with lithium aluminum hydride in ethyl ether at 0°.[4] The same type of reaction is useful for the preparation of monogermane, GeH_4, and monostannane, SnH_4, as well as for alkyl and aryl derivatives of silicon, germanium, and tin hydrides. The general equation for this type of synthesis is shown below.

$$4ER_yX_{4-y} + (4-y)LiAlH_4 \xrightarrow[0°]{(C_2H_5)_2O} 4ER_yH_{4-y} + (4-y)LiX + (4-y)AlX_3$$

(E = Si, Ge, or Sn; X = halogen; R = alkyl or aryl group; y may vary from 0 to 3.)

13.82 All the silanes are spontaneously inflammable in air and react vigorously with water contained in glass vessels (as a result of the presence of traces of OH^- in such water) to give hydrogen and hydrous silicon dioxide. The high reactivity of the higher silanes is a manifestation of the relative weakness of the Si—Si bond as compared to the Si—O link.

The Silicon Halides

13.83 Silicon forms both simple and mixed tetrahalides, as well as catenated binary halides of the general formula type Si_nX_{2n+2}. A summary of the binary halides which have been characterized, along with their melting and boiling points, is given in Table 13.8.

Simple Tetrahalides　**13.84** The tetrahalides (where the halogen = Cl, Br, I)

---

[4] FINHOLT, BOND, WILZBACH and SCHLESINGER, *J. Am. Chem. Soc.*, **69**, 2692 (1947).

generally are obtained directly or indirectly by combination of the elements. An illustration of the latter method is the preparation of the tetrachloride by passage of chlorine over a heated mixture of silica and carbon.

$$SiO_2 + 2C + 2Cl_2 = SiCl_4 + 2CO$$

The tetrafluoride is conveniently prepared by reaction of concentrated sulfuric acid with a mixture of calcium fluoride and silica or by the thermal decomposition of barium fluorosilicate.

13.85 As can be seen from Table 13.8, the tetrahalides are all volatile substances, with boiling point increasing with atomic weight of the halogen. In

TABLE 13.8

Binary Halides of Silicon

Compound	Melting Point, °C.	Boiling Point, °C.	Compound	Melting Point, °C.	Boiling Point, °C.
SiF_4	−90.2	−95.7 (subl.)	Si_2I_6	250 (decomp.)	
$SiCl_4$	−70.4	57.0	Si_3Cl_8		216
$SiBr_4$	5.2	154.6	Si_4Cl_{10}		150 (15 mm.)
SiI_4	123.8	290	Si_5Cl_{12}		190 (15 mm.)
Si_2F_6	−19.0	−19.1	Si_6Cl_{14}		200 (subl. *in*
Si_2Cl_6	2.5	147	$Si_{10}Cl_{22}$		*vacuo*)
Si_2Br_6	95	265			

contrast to the behavior of carbon, silicon in the tetrahalides can function as an electron pair acceptor, with the use of available *d* orbitals. Thus the tetrahalides are readily hydrolyzed and also act as acceptor molecules in the formation of coordination compounds. The ability of the silicon halides to form coordination compounds is not so great as that of the corresponding germanium and tin compounds. The hydrolytic reaction is complete and irreversible, and for the chloride, bromide, and iodide proceeds as indicated.

$$SiX_4 + (y + 2)H_2O = SiO_2 \cdot yH_2O + 4H^+ + 4X^-$$

With the tetrafluoride, a secondary reaction occurs between this compound and the hydrofluoric acid formed initially.

$$SiF_4 + 2HF = 2H^+ + [SiF_6]^{2-}$$

13.86 Complex compounds derived from the tetrahalides are few in number and are formed primarily with the tetrafluoride as the acceptor molecule. Although there have been reports of the preparation of molecular addition compounds of silicon tetrachloride with nitrogen donors, the exact nature of these compounds is rather obscure.

13.87 Compounds formed by the union of the tetrafluoride with nitrogen bases and fluoride ion as donor groups are the only complexes of this halide which have been described. Direct combination of the halide with trimethylamine yields $SiF_4 \cdot N(CH_3)_3$ and $SiF_4 \cdot 2N(CH_3)_3$;[5] with ethylenediamine, $SiF_4 \cdot$ en is produced.[6] The latter compound is quite stable, subliming unchanged at 225° and 0.2 mm. pressure. No addition compounds are formed between silicon tetrahalides and ammonia; Si—X bonds are ruptured, with the replacement of halogen by —NH$_2$ or =NH. Silicon tetrafluoride has a great tendency to unite with fluoride ion to yield the hexafluorosilicate anion, $[SiF_6]^{2-}$ (see 13.85). A large number of metal fluorosilicates have been prepared, most of which are readily soluble in water. It is interesting and rather unusual that the alkali metal (Na, K, Rb, Cs) salts are relatively insoluble, as are the salts of barium, yttrium, and the rare earths. The acid from which the salts are derived, H_2SiF_6, can be isolated from aqueous solution as a dihydrate at temperatures above 0° and as a tetrahydrate below this temperature. Fluorosilicic acid is a strong, stable acid, and its salts are only slightly hydrolyzed.

Catenated Halides.[7] **13.88** As would be expected, few catenated halides of silicon are known (Table 13.8). For fluorine, bromine, and iodine, only the compounds of the formula Si_2X_6 have been prepared; for chlorine, all the members of the homologous series Si_nX_{2n+2} through Si_6Cl_{14} have been isolated, and in addition $Si_{10}Cl_{22}$ has been described.

13.89 Several methods have been employed for the preparation of catenated silicon halides. Only a few of the more useful ones will be mentioned. Hexabromodisilane, Si_2Br_6, is most conveniently made by the action of bromine on a calcium-silicon alloy at elevated temperatures.

$$2CaSi_x + (3x + 2)Br_2 \overset{180-200°}{=} 2CaBr_2 + xSi_2Br_6$$

A similar method yields the first six members of the chloro series, which are separated by fractional distillation. Hexafluorodisilane is obtained by halogen exchange between the hexachloro compound and zinc fluoride. Hexaiododisilane is formed when the tetraiodide is heated with finely divided silver. $Si_{10}Cl_{22}$ is one of the products of reaction between oxygen-free hydrogen and silicon tetrachloride in a quartz tube at 1000–1100°.

13.90 The catenated halides are covalent substances, easily soluble in a variety of organic solvents. They are sensitive toward moisture, and, except under special conditions, hydrolysis results in the removal of all the halogens, one of the main products of hydrolysis being "silico-oxalic acid," $H_2Si_2O_4$. The higher chlorides inflame in air at elevated temperatures.

Mixed Tetrahalides **13.91** A number of mixed tetrahalides of silicon have been characterized. These include complete series of fluorochloro (*i.e.*, SiF_3Cl, SiF_2Cl_2, $SiFCl_3$), fluorobromo, fluoroiodo, and chlorobromo derivatives, and also the compounds $SiFCl_2Br$ and $SiFClBr_2$.

13.92 Fluorochlorides [8] are best prepared by means of the Swartz reaction

[5] WILKINS and GRANT, *J. Chem. Soc.*, 1953, p. 927.
[6] SCHUMB and COOK, *J. Am. Chem. Soc.*, **75**, 5133 (1953).
[7] SCHUMB, *Chem. Revs.*, **31**, 587 (1942).
[8] BOOTH and SWINEHART, *J. Am. Chem. Soc.*, **54**, 4750 (1932).

between the tetrachloride and antimony(III) fluoride in the presence of chlorine or antimony(V) fluoride as catalyst. The reaction gives all the possible fluoro-chlorides as well as the tetrafluoride, the products being separated by fractionation. The fluorobromides are made by halogen exchange between the tetrabromide and antimony(III) fluoride at 100° in the absence of a catalyst.[9]

Fluoroiodides [10] and chlorobromides [11] are readily obtained by the "redistribution reaction" between equal volumes of the appropriate tetrahalides, followed by fractionation to separate and purify the products.

13.93 As would be supposed, the mixed tetrahalides are all volatile (*e.g.*, SiF_3Cl, b.p. $-70°$; SiF_2I_2, b.p. $84.5°$) and readily hydrolyzed. The products of hydrolysis are those expected for mixtures of the parent tetrahalides.

Oxyhalides [12,13]

13.94 Silicon forms oxyhalides which differ from the types known for carbon and the elements of representative groups V and VI. No simple silicon oxyhalides exist; rather, the compounds are in reality siloxanes and contain Si—O—Si linkages.

13.95 Most of the silicon oxyhalides are of the type $Si_nO_{n-1}X_{2n+2}$, of which in the homologous chloro series all the members up to n = 7 have been prepared, and in the bromo series all up to n = 6. In addition to these substances, the fluoro compounds Si_2OF_6, $Si_2OF_4Cl_2$, and $Si_2OF_3Cl_3$ have been isolated. The known compounds which do not fall into the type noted above are $(SiOCl_2)_4$, $(SiOBr_2)_4$, and Si_4OCl_{10}.

13.96 Members of both the oxychloro and oxybromo series may be prepared by heating silicon in a mixture of oxygen and halogen or by the action of oxygen on the tetrahalides. These reactions give mixtures of the members of the homologous series, as well as the tetramers $(SiOX_2)_4$, and the products are separated by fractional distillation. The chloro series may also be obtained by the partial hydrolysis of the tetrachloride in moist ether, no tetramer being formed. The oxyfluorides are produced by the fluorination of hexachlorodisiloxane, Si_2OCl_6, by means of antimony(III) fluoride in the presence of antimony(V) fluoride as catalyst.

13.97 The oxyhalides are oily liquids which are soluble without reaction in a variety of nonhydroxylic solvents. Their volatility decreases with increasing complexity in any one series, *e.g.*, b.p. of $Si_3O_2Cl_8$, $80.5°$ (15 mm.); of $Si_4O_3Cl_{10}$, $114.7°$ (15 mm.). They are rapidly hydrolyzed, the rate of attack by water diminishing with decrease in volatility of the oxyhalide. The chloro com-

[9] SCHUMB and ANDERSON, *J. Am. Chem. Soc.*, **58**, 994 (1936).

[10] ANDERSON, *J. Am. Chem. Soc.*, **72**, 2091 (1950).

[11] ANDERSON, *J. Am. Chem. Soc.*, **67**, 859 (1945).

[12] BOOTH and OSTER, *J. Am. Chem. Soc.*, **67**, 1092 (1945).

[13] SCHUMB, et al., *J. Am. Chem. Soc.*, **59**, 261 (1937); **63**, 2753 (1941); **72**, 3178 (1950); **75**, 1513 (1953).

pounds are transformed to the corresponding ethyl esters by treatment with absolute ethanol. The compounds of formula $Si_nO_{n-1}X_{2n+2}$ have the chain structures indicated.

$$X\left(\begin{array}{c} X \\ | \\ Si-O \\ | \\ X \end{array}\right)_{n-1}\begin{array}{c} X \\ | \\ Si-X \\ | \\ X \end{array}$$

13.98 Si_4OCl_{10} may be regarded as the first member of a $Si_{2n+2}O_nCl_{4n+6}$ series. This substance is made by the partial hydrolysis of Si_2Cl_6 in ether at $-78°$.

Germanium, Tin, and Lead

The Elements

13.99 Germanium, tin, and lead are relatively uncommon substances, making up about 10^{-11}, 10^{-6}, and 2×10^{-5} per cent, respectively, of the earth's crust. These elements are commonly referred to as the metals of group IV. However, metallic characteristics are most pronounced in tin and lead, there being no sharp change from nonmetallic to metallic character from silicon to germanium. As a matter of fact, elementary germanium possesses the diamond structure, although it is a semi-conductor. Tin exists in at least three allotropic modifications, with the transition temperatures shown.

$$\alpha\text{-Sn} \overset{13.2°}{=} \beta\text{-Sn} \overset{161°}{=} \gamma\text{-Sn} \overset{231.8°}{=} \text{liquid}$$
$$\text{(gray tin)} \quad \text{(white tin)} \quad \text{(rhombic tin)}$$

The transition from white tin to the brittle gray variety is slow and is catalyzed by the presence of the latter. The change is accompanied by an increase in volume. Gray tin has the diamond structure, whereas the white modification exhibits a metallic lattice. One crystalline form — with the cubic metallic lattice — is known for lead.

13.100 A number of significant chemical properties of the elements are illustrated by the reactions given in Table 13.9.

TABLE 13.9

Reactions of the Representative Group IV Metals

Reaction	Remarks
$M + O_2 = MO_2$	At elevated temperatures. Pb gives PbO or Pb_3O_4
$M + 2X_2 = MX_4$	X = halogen. Pb forms PbX_2
$M + 2S = MS_2$	At high temperatures. Pb yields PbS
$M + 2H^+ = M^{2+} + H_2$	No reaction with Ge
$M + 2OH^- = MO_2^{2-} + H_2$ (or HMO_2^-)	With Sn and Pb. Ge forms $HGeO_3^-$; $Ge + OH^- + 2H_2O = 2H_2 + HGeO_3^-$
$3M + 4HNO_3 = 3MO_2 + 4NO + 2H_2O$	With Ge and Sn. Pb gives $Pb(NO_3)_2$

13.101 These reactions serve to emphasize the increasing stability of the $+2$ oxidation state, as compared to the tetrapositive state, with increasing atomic number within the group. Quantitative oxidation state relationships are shown in the following potential diagrams.

Acidic Solution

$$Ge \xrightarrow{(0.0)} Ge^{2+} \xrightarrow{(0.3)} GeO_2$$
$$Ge \xrightarrow{0.1} GeO_2$$

$$Sn \xrightarrow{0.136} Sn^{2+} \xrightarrow{-0.15} Sn^{4+}$$

$$Pb \xrightarrow{0.126} Pb^{2+} \xrightarrow{-1.455} PbO_2$$

Basic Solution

$$Ge \xrightarrow{1.0} HGeO_3^-$$

$$Sn \xrightarrow{0.91} HSnO_2^- \xrightarrow{0.93} Sn(OH)_6^{2-}$$

$$Pb \xrightarrow{0.54} PbO \xrightarrow{-0.28} PbO_2$$

The Tetrapositive State

13.102 Examination of the tetrapositive state of germanium, tin, and lead clearly points up significant relationships existing among the elements of representative group IV. Pertinent information on these relationships may be obtained from consideration of the chemistry of the hydrides, halides, and oxides and related compounds corresponding to this oxidation state.

Hydrides **13.103** As with silicon, the hydrides of group IV representative metals all correspond to the formula M_nH_{2n+2} (Table 13.10). Consistent with

TABLE 13.10

The Hydrides of Ge, Sn, and Pb

Compound	Melting Point, °C.	Boiling Point, °C.
GeH_4	−165	−90
Ge_2H_6	−109	29
Ge_3H_8	−105.6	110.5
SnH_4	−150	−52
PbH_4		ca. −13

the decrease in ability of the elements to undergo self-linkage with increasing atomic number is the small number of compounds which have been isolated. Thus, the first three members of the homologous germane series are known, but tin and lead form only the hydrides SnH_4 and PbH_4.

13.104 The germanes are obtained by methods analogous to those used for the preparation of the silicon hydrides (see 13.81). The action of dilute hydrochloric acid on magnesium germanide, Mg_2Ge, yields, in addition to hydrogen, a mixture of the three germanes, which may be separated by fractional distillation. Monogermane and monostannane are conveniently prepared by reaction of lithium aluminum hydride on the tetrachlorides in ether. Small yields of monoplumbane are produced by interaction of a magnesium-lead alloy and hydrochloric acid or by the electrolytic reduction of lead(II) salts at a lead cathode.

13.105 The hydrides (MH_4) of the metallic members of representative group IV are considerably less stable thermally than the corresponding compounds of carbon and silicon, the stability decreasing with increasing atomic number of the central atom. Thus, decomposition to element and hydrogen occurs at the approximate temperatures given.

CH_4	SiH_4	GeH_4	SnH_4	PbH_4
800°	450°	285°	150°	0°

The germanes are less reactive than the silanes toward oxygen; whereas the silanes are spontaneously inflammable in air, monogermane is not attacked by oxygen below 230°. Di- and trigermane are more readily susceptible to oxidation than is the hydride GeH_4. The germanes and monostannane are much more resistant to hydrolysis than the silanes, monogermane and monostannane being unaffected by water and even by concentrated solutions of alkali.

Tetrahalides and Derivatives **13.106** All of the possible tetrahalides of germanium, tin, and lead, with the exception of $PbBr_4$ and PbI_4, have been isolated (Table 13.11). As might be expected, no catenated halides have been prepared for these elements. The nonexistence of $PbBr_4$ and PbI_4 is in accord with the strongly oxidizing properties of $+4$ lead and the reducing ability of bromide and iodide.

13.107 A number of mixed tetrahalides of germanium, including all the fluorochlorides, have been prepared. No mixed tetrahalides of tin or lead have been isolated.

13.108 The tetrachlorides, bromides, and iodides are readily obtained by direct union of the elements. Thermal decomposition of barium fluorogermanate yields germanium tetrafluoride. Tin(IV) fluoride is prepared by halogen exchange between the tetrachloride and hydrogen fluoride, and the lead compound has been made by reaction of lead(IV) oxide with bromine trifluoride.[14]

13.109 With the exception of tin(IV) fluoride, the tetrahalides of germanium and tin are readily volatile, the volatility for any one halide type decreasing from germanium to tin (Table 13.11). The fact that tin tetrafluoride is much less volatile than the other halides is presumed to be indicative of ionic binding in

TABLE 13.11

Tetrahalides of Ge, Sn, and Pb

Compound	Melting Point, °C.	Boiling Point, °C.	Compound	Melting Point, °C.	Boiling Point, °C.
GeF_4	−15 (4 atm.)	−37.4 (subl.)	$PbCl_4$	−15	decomp.
SnF_4		705 (subl.)	$GeBr_4$	26.1	186.5
PbF_4			$SnBr_4$	33.0	203.3
$GeCl_4$	−49.5	86.5	GeI_4	144	decomp.
$SnCl_4$	−36.2	114.1	SnI_4	144.5	348 (extrap.)

[14] GUTMANN, *Angew. Chem.*, **62A**, 312 (1950).

this compound. The other tetrahalides have been shown to have covalent tetrahedral structures.

13.110 The thermal stability of a series with a common central atom is in the order $MF_4 > MCl_4 > MBr_4 > MI_4$. In view of the oxidizing properties of tetrapositive lead, it is not surprising that the tetrachloride is unstable toward heat and is decomposed to the dichloride and elementary chlorine at temperatures in the neighborhood of 100°.

13.111 The tetrahalides of germanium and tin, like the corresponding silicon compounds, are readily hydrolyzed, the products of reaction for the chlorides, bromides, and iodides of germanium and tin, and the fluoride of the former, being analogous to those described for silicon tetrahalides (see 13.85). However, the ease of reaction with water diminishes from silicon to germanium to tin (*i.e.*, with increasing metallic character of the central atom). Whereas hydrolysis of silicon tetrahalides is complete and irreversible, the corresponding reaction for the germanium and tin compounds is incomplete and may be repressed by the addition of the appropriate hydrohalic acid. Hydrolysis of lead(IV) chloride is accompanied by some decomposition to dichloride.

13.112 The tendency for germanium and tin tetrahalides to function as acceptor molecules in the formation of coordination compounds is considerably greater than that of analogous silicon materials. The number of complex compounds derived from lead tetrahalides is limited by the ability of lead(IV) to act as a strong oxidizing agent. As is the situation with the silicon compound (see 13.87), germanium tetrachloride forms no addition compounds with ammonia, but rather is ammonolyzed. For tin(IV) chloride, however, there is some evidence for the existence of a diammoniate. Addition compounds of the 1 : 2 type, in which tin exhibits a coordination number of six, have been described for the tetrachloride with pyridine and such oxygen-containing organic molecules as alcohols, ethers, aldehydes, ketones, and carboxylic acids. The ability to form similar compounds is much less pronounced for tin(IV) bromide and is essentially nonexistent for the iodide.

13.113 In certain nonaqueous media germanium and tin tetrachlorides react with β-diketones (*e.g.*, acetylacetone) with the cleavage of two metal-halogen bonds and the formation of nonelectrolytes of structure (a). Silicon tetrachloride under similar conditions reacts with the rupture of three Si—Cl linkages to produce salts (b), which are rapidly hydrolyzed by water.

(a)   (b)

13.114 Whereas the only complex halo ion known for silicon is $[SiF_6]^{2-}$, germanium forms hexahalo complexes with fluorine and chlorine; and for tin, such complexes with all four halogens have been characterized. The fact that not all the halo complexes have been isolated for silicon and germanium is probably attributable to steric factors, *i.e.*, the inability for the smaller central atoms to accommodate the larger halogens.

13.115 The hexafluorogermanates are similar in structure and solubility to the corresponding silicon compounds (see 13.87). Alkali metal fluorogermanates are prepared by precipitation from solutions of germanium dioxide in hydrofluoric acid. The chlorogermanates are formed by reaction of the appropriate metal salt with solutions of germanium tetrachloride in hydrochloric acid. Whereas the $[GeF_6]^{2-}$ ion is rather stable in water, the analogous chloro ion is rapidly hydrolyzed with the precipitation of germanium dioxide.

13.116 Hexahalo complexes of tin are obtained by methods similar to those employed for the germanium compounds, *i.e.*, from solutions of the tetrahalides in the appropriate hydrohalic acids. The stability of the complexes toward hydrolysis decreases very markedly with increasing size of the halogen; the fluoro and chloro compounds are reasonably stable, but the bromo and iodo complexes give tin(IV) oxide almost immediately on treatment with water.

13.117 No hexafluoro complexes of lead(IV) have been prepared.* However, a compound with the formula K_3HPbF_8 has been described. This substance is extremely soluble in water and is easily hydrolyzed. No structural information for it is available. Hexachloroplumbates of the general formula $M_2[PbCl_6]$ are formed when solutions of chlorine and lead(II) chloride in hydrochloric acid are treated with the appropriate metal chlorides. These compounds are unstable in water, being immediately converted to lead(IV) oxide.

Dioxides and Derivatives **13.118** Dioxides are known for all three of the metallic elements of the group. Germanium dioxide is obtained by roasting the disulfide or by dehydration of the hydrous oxide. Tin(IV) oxide occurs in nature as *cassiterite* (see 13.119). Lead dioxide, which is dark-brown to black in contrast to the other dioxides, which are white, is prepared by the oxidation of lead(II) oxide or of lead(II) salts in dilute alkaline solution, *e.g.*, by means of hypochlorite.

13.119 Germanium dioxide is dimorphic, one modification possessing the quartz structure and the other the tetragonal rutile (TiO_2) lattice, the latter form being stable below the transition temperature of 1033°. Although tin(IV) oxide exists in three crystalline forms, only the rutile modification (cassiterite) is of any chemical significance. The only known modification of lead dioxide has the rutile lattice.

13.120 Germanium dioxide is amphoteric in character. On treatment with concentrated hydrofluoric or hydrochloric acid it is converted to the correspond-

---

* Very recently alkaline earth hexafluoroplumbates(IV), $M^{II}[PbF_6]$, have been obtained by the action of fluorine at elevated temperatures on, *e.g.*, $BaPbO_3$. (HOPPE and BLINNE, *Z. anorg. u. allgem. Chem.*, **293**, 251, 1957.)

ing volatile tetrahalide; dissolution in solutions of alkali yields germanates. Meta-, M_2GeO_3, and orthogermanates, M_4GeO_4, have been reported. Hydrous germanium(IV) oxide, which is prepared by hydrolysis of the tetrachloride, is soluble to some extent in water, giving an acidic solution. Cassiterite, SnO_2, is insoluble in aqueous medium and relatively inert toward acids and alkalies, unless these reagents are concentrated. The dioxide is, however, readily acted on by fused alkalies with the production of soluble stannates. Treatment of solutions of alkali stannates with acid gives the α-hydrous dioxide (commonly called α-stannic acid), a substance which is readily soluble in either strong acids or strong bases. On the other hand, the β-oxide ("metastannic acid"), pro-duced by the action of concentrated nitric acid on tin or by hydrolysis of tin(IV) compounds in hot water, is insoluble in acids but soluble in alkali solutions. Both the α- and the β-oxide have the same crystal structure as cassiterite and probably differ only in particle size. Alkali metal metastannates formerly be-lieved to be 3-hydrates, e.g., $K_2SnO_3 \cdot 3H_2O$, are now known to contain the octahedral $[Sn(OH)_6]^{2-}$. Lead dioxide possesses little solubility in water or in dilute acids or alkalies. Concentrated acids, which are capable of being reduced, dissolve the dioxide with the formation of lead(II) and the appropriate oxida-tion product of the acid employed, e.g., chlorine from hydrochloric acid. Fusion of lead dioxide with alkali or alkaline earth oxides gives rise to plum-bates, both meta- and orthoplumbates having been described. Alkali metal plumbates are isomorphous with the analogous stannates and thus contain $[Pb(OH)_6]^{2-}$. In contrast to germanium and tin dioxides, which are high melting, thermally stable substances, e.g., SnO_2 melts at 1127°, lead(IV) oxide begins to lose oxygen below 200° and forms Pb_3O_4. The latter substance is believed actually to be lead(II) orthoplumbate(IV), $Pb_2^{II}Pb^{IV}O_4$. Plumbates are more stable toward heat than is the dioxide.

The Dipositive State

Monoxides **13.121** The monoxides of germanium, tin, and lead are amphoteric substances, the basic properties becoming more pronounced from germanium to lead. The stability with respect to conversion to the dioxide increases in the same direction.

13.122 Germanium(II) oxide can be prepared by the hydrolysis of the di-chloride or by reduction of the dioxide by means of hypophosphorous acid (H_3PO_2). Obtained by the former method, the oxide is a yellow hydrated material which is acidic in character; the latter mode of formation yields a black powder which sublimes at 710°. Tin monoxide (blue-black crystals or brown powder) is obtained by the thermal decomposition of the oxalate or by dehydration at 100° of the hydrated oxide, $SnO \cdot \frac{1}{2}H_2O$, which is formed by treat-ment of tin(II) solutions with alkalies. Lead monoxide (litharge) is prepared by heating the metal in air or by decomposition of the dioxide or Pb_3O_4 at temperatures exceeding 500°.

13.123 Lead monoxide is known in two modifications, one a red, low-temperature (α) form of tetragonal structure, and the other a yellow, high-temperature, orthorhombic (β) variety. The temperature of transition between the two forms is not known with certainty; interconversion is slow. Tin monoxide and α-lead monoxide are identical in structure, being polymeric molecules, with each oxygen atom joined tetrahedrally to four metal atoms and each metal atom attached at one side to four oxygen atoms which are disposed in a square.

13.124 Germanium monoxide is easily converted to the dioxide by heating in air or by oxidation with nitric acid. It is soluble in acids and alkalies, reaction with the latter yielding solutions of germanites (germanates(II)). Solutions of the monoxide in hydrohalic acids, in which the germanium presumably is present in the form of halo complexes, are rather stable in the absence of oxidizing agents. On the other hand, hydrogen is evolved from highly alkaline solutions and the germanium is converted to the germanate (germanate(IV)) ion, $HGeO_3^-$. Both tin and lead monoxides are readily soluble in solutions of strong acids and strong bases. Solutions of tin(II) oxide in strong bases probably contain the stannite, *i.e.*, the stannate(II) ion, $[SnO_2]^{2-}$ or $[SnO \cdot OH]^-$, although salts corresponding to this ion have not been isolated. Alkaline solutions of tin(II) are powerful reducing agents (see 13.101 for oxidation potential), the tin being easily converted to the stannate(IV) ion. In contrast to this behavior, solutions containing the plumbite ion (plumbate(II)), $[PbO \cdot OH]^-$, are stable toward oxidation.

13.125 No compounds of the formula $M(OH)_2$ are definitely known for the metallic members of group IV.

Dihalides and Derivatives **13.126** All of the dihalides of germanium, tin, and lead are known. A summary of their melting and boiling points is given in Table 13.12. The dihalides are much less volatile than the corresponding

TABLE 13.12

Melting and Boiling Points of the Dihalides of Ge, Sn, and Pb

Compound	Melting Point, °C.	Boiling Point, °C.	Compound	Melting Point, °C.	Boiling Point, °C.
GeF_2			$GeBr_2$	122	
SnF_2			$SnBr_2$	215	619
PbF_2	818	1,285	$PbBr_2$	373	916
$GeCl_2$		subl.	GeI_2		
$SnCl_2$	247	603	SnI_2	320	720
$PbCl_2$	298	954	PbI_2	412	

tetrahalides (cf. Table 13.11), a fact consistent with the expected increase in ionic character in the compounds containing the elements in the lower oxidation state. The resistance of the dihalides against oxidation to the tetrapositive state increases from germanium to lead.

13.127 Germanium(II) halides are made by interaction of the tetrahalides and the free element. The temperature of reaction must be controlled in each case because of the tendency of the dihalides to disproportionate to metal and tetrahalides at elevated temperatures. Tin(II) halides can also be obtained from the tetrahalides by reduction with the metal. The dissolution of the metal in hydrohalic acids yields dihalides, which can be isolated from solution as hydrates, e.g., $SnCl_2 \cdot 2H_2O$. Dehydration to anhydrous halide must be effected under conditions which inhibit hydrolysis. Lead(II) halides, since they are relatively insoluble in water, may be made conveniently by metathetical reactions in this medium.

13.128 The germanium dihalides are not simple molecular compounds as are the tetrahalides, but appear to be polymeric molecules in which the germanium atoms are bridged by halogen. The structures of the solid tin(II) halides have not been determined; in the vapor state these compounds are covalent, the molecules being chiefly monomeric and triangular. Of the lead(II) halides, the fluoride, chloride, and bromide appear to be ionic in the solid state.

13.129 Germanium(II) halides are unstable both toward hydrolysis and oxidation. The standard potential for the reaction $Ge^{2+} + 2H_2O = GeO_2 + 4H^+ + 2e^-$ is about 0.3 volt. Chloro and iodo complexes with the formulas $MGeCl_3$ and $MGeI_3$ have been prepared. These are easily hydrolyzed and are also readily oxidized by air. Aqueous solutions of tin(II) halides contain the $[Sn(H_2O)_x]^{2+}$ ion. Such solutions undergo hydrolysis with the deposition of basic salts, e.g., $Sn(OH)Cl$. Halo complexes of tin(II) appear to be formed with all the halogens and compounds of the types $MSnX_3$ and M_2SnX_4 have been isolated. In the presence of excess hydrohalic acid these substances are considerably more stable toward hydrolysis and air oxidation than the parent dihalides. As a result of complex formation, the aqueous solubility of lead(II) chloride, bromide, or iodide increases in the presence of added halide ion after an initial decrease due to the common ion effect. Complex chlorides corresponding to the formulas $MPbCl_3$, M_2PbCl_4, and M_4PbCl_6 have been reported. Coordination compounds of lead dihalides with ammonia and amines have also been described, e.g., $PbX_2 \cdot 2NH_3(X = Cl, Br, I)$.

CHAPTER 14

GROUP V

Introduction

14.1 The members of the nitrogen family, the fifth group of representative elements, have the ns^2np^3 valence configuration (Table 14.1). As is the case in

TABLE 14.1

Electronic Configurations of Group V Representative Elements

	1	2	3	4	5	6
	s	s p	s p d	s p d f	s p d	s p
$_7$N	2	2, 3				
$_{15}$P	2	2, 6	2, 3			
$_{33}$As	2	2, 6	2, 6, 10	2, 3		
$_{51}$Sb	2	2, 6	2, 6, 10	2, 6, 10	2, 3	
$_{83}$Bi	2	2, 6	2, 6, 10	2, 6, 10, 14	2, 6, 10	2, 3

the two previous groups these elements fall into two classes on the basis of electronic configuration: one, comprising nitrogen and phosphorus, with an inert gas kernel, and the other, consisting of arsenic, antimony, and bismuth, with completed s, p, and d orbitals underlying the shell of valence electrons. Some important properties of the group members are listed in Table 14.2.

GENERAL REFERENCES

LATIMER, *The Oxidation States of the Elements and Their Potentials in Aqueous Solutions*, 2nd Edition, Prentice-Hall, Inc., New York, 1952, Ch. 7.

PARTINGTON, *A Textbook of Inorganic Chemistry*, 6th Edition, Macmillan and Company, Ltd., London, 1950, Ch. XXIX, XXX, XXXI, pp. 848–77.

REMY, *Treatise on Inorganic Chemistry*, (transl. and amended by Anderson), Elsevier Publishing Company, Amsterdam, 1956, Vol. I, Ch. 14.

SIDGWICK, *The Chemical Elements and Their Compounds*, Oxford University Press, London, 1950, pp. 654–803.

WELLS, *Structural Inorganic Chemistry*, 2nd Edition, Oxford University Press, London, 1950, Ch. XV and XVI.

YOST and RUSSELL, *Systematic Inorganic Chemistry*, Prentice-Hall, Inc., New York, 1946, Ch. 1–7.

TABLE 14.2

Some Properties of the Group V Elements

	N	P	As	Sb	Bi
Natural isotopes	14 *, 15	31	75	121 *, 123	209
Density, g./cc.	0.808 (of liquid)	W 1.82 V 2.34	M 5.72 Y 1.97	M 6.58 Y 5.3	9.8
Melting point, °C.	−210.0	W 44.1 V ca. 620	814 (36 atm.)	630.5	271
Boiling point, °C.	−195.8	W 280	633 (subl.)	1325	1560
Ionic radius in crystals, Å					
M^{3-}	1.4	1.85			
M^{3+}				0.92	1.08
Covalent radius, Å	0.74	1.10	1.21	1.41	1.52
Ionization potential, volts					
1st electron	14.54	11.0	10	8.64	8
2nd electron	29.60	19.65	20.1	18	16.6
3rd electron	47.42	30.15	28.0	24.7	25.42
4th electron	77.45	51.35	49.9	44.0	45.1
5th electron	97.86	65.00	62.5	55.5	55.7
Electrode potential, $E°$, in volts, for reaction $M + H_2O = MO^+ + 2H^+ + 3e^-$				−0.21	−0.32
Electronegativity (F = 4; H = 2.1)	3.0	2.1	2.0	1.8	

* More abundant isotope.
W = white and V = violet phosphorus
M = metallic and Y = yellow arsenic and antimony

14.2 As in the carbon family, there is a fairly regular transition down the group from an element which is completely nonmetallic in character to one which is almost entirely metallic. Metallic properties again first assume importance where the underlying shell of 18 electrons is first encountered, i.e., with arsenic. One again finds the first member of the family widely different in properties from its homologs.

14.3 Pertinent group trends are brought to light by consideration of the oxidation state relationships between the elements. The members of the group lack three electrons of attaining inert gas configurations; the energy necessary for acquiring these electrons and forming trinegative ions is extremely great, and this ionic state is formed only by nitrogen and perhaps phosphorus, and then only with the more electropositive metals. It should be noted that these two elements are the only ones of the group which are completely nonmetallic in behavior.

14.4 Attainment of inert or pseudo inert gas configurations by the loss of the five valence electrons is precluded by prohibitive energy requirements, and pentapositive ions are nonexistent. The tendency for the heavier members of representative groups III and IV to lose the p valence electrons and form cationic species possessing an ns^2 outer configuration (e.g., Tl^+, Pb^{2+}) is also observed in group V, where antimony and bismuth are sufficiently metallic to give tripositive cations. It should be pointed out, however, that simple cations of these elements are extremely rare. As a matter of fact, there appears to be only one anhydrous trihalide (BiF_3) which is essentially completely ionic in character; it is noteworthy that this substance consists of the most electropositive member of the group and the most electronegative element known. It is likely that tripositive cationic species are present in antimony and bismuth salts of strong oxy-acids, e.g., $Sb_2(SO_4)_3$, $Bi(ClO_4)_3 \cdot 5H_2O$, but the simple (or hydrated) cations appear to be incapable of existence in pure water in more than trace amounts, since these compounds are immediately hydrolyzed to give basic salts containing SbO^+ and BiO^+.

14.5 The elements of group V exhibit a variety of oxidation states which involve the sharing of the valence electrons. These states are attained by the use of either all five valence electrons or of the three p electrons. For nitrogen, all possible states from -3 (e.g., in NH_3) to $+5$ (e.g., in HNO_3 or NO_3^-) are known. It should be emphasized that nitrogen is incapable of forming more than four covalent bonds, inasmuch as the valence shell cannot be expanded beyond eight electrons. Phosphorus also shows a multiplicity of covalent oxidation states in its compounds: -3 (PH_3); -2 (P_2H_4); $+1$ (H_3PO_2); $+3$ (H_3PO_3, PCl_3); $+4$ ($H_4P_2O_6$); $+5$ (H_3PO_4, PCl_5, $POCl_3$, $[PF_6]^-$). It is apparent that phosphorus can use all five s and p electrons for the formation of simple covalent bonds, and, in addition, can employ a d orbital for accepting an electron-pair from a donor group (as in $[PF_6]^-$). The most common formal oxidation states of arsenic, antimony, and bismuth are $+3$ and $+5$, e.g., as in MX_3 and MX_5, respectively. As is the situation with phosphorus, these elements can exhibit covalences greater than five through the use of available d orbitals, e.g., in $[AsF_6]^-$, $[SbCl_6]^-$, and $[Sb(OH)_6]^-$.

14.6 Formally, the only class of covalent compounds exemplifying the trinegative oxidation state are the hydrides, MH_3, which are formed by all the members of the group. (It should be noted, however, that on the basis of electronegativity values, Table 14.2, nitrogen is the only member of the group that is more electronegative than hydrogen.) The thermal stability and the ease of formation of the hydrides decrease quite remarkably from NH_3 to BiH_3. The decreasing stability with increasing metallic character of the element bound to hydrogen is also manifested in increased ability to function as reducing agents. Moreover, basic character, i.e., the ability to act as a donor molecule, diminishes markedly in the same direction. Thus the ammonium ion is readily formed and is relatively stable, whereas the phosphonium ion, PH_4^+, easily gives up the proton, and the corresponding ions for the remaining elements of the group are practically nonexistent. The existence of a great number of ammine complexes is also in accord with the strong donor properties of ammonia.

14.7 With regard to the tripositive state, examination of a number of properties of the sesquioxides and trihalides reveals important group relationships. The sesquioxides correspond to the following formulas: N_2O_3, P_4O_6, As_4O_6, Sb_4O_6, and Bi_2O_3. The first two members of the series are completely acidic in character, and are the anhydrides of nitrous acid (HNO_2) and phosphorous acid (H_3PO_3), respectively. The last member exhibits only basic properties, whereas saturated aqueous solutions of arsenic and antimony sesquioxides undergo both acidic and basic dissociation. There is no regular trend within the group in the tendency for the oxides (or their aqueous solutions) to function as reducing agents. Whereas nitrous acid is converted to the nitrate ion only by powerful oxidizing agents such as permanganate, phosphorous acid is a strong reducing agent and is readily oxidized to H_3PO_4. Although the sesquioxides of the metallic members of the group are rather stable toward oxidation to the pentapositive condition, the stability of Bi_2O_3 is by far the most pronounced. This is consistent with the trends observed in groups III and IV for the relationships between the mono- and tripositive and the di- and tetrapositive oxidation states, respectively.

14.8 All the members of group V form complete series of trihalides. With the exception of bismuth trifluoride, these compounds are monomolecular, covalent substances, each possessing an unshared pair of s electrons. From the viewpoint of electronegativity differences, the trihalides, save for the trichloride, bromide, and iodide of nitrogen, may be regarded as containing the group V elements in a tripositive oxidation state. The nitrogen trihalides differ from the others in a number of important respects. These differences may be attributed largely to the inability of nitrogen to expand its valence shell beyond eight electrons. Nitrogen in the trihalides can therefore function solely as a donor atom in acid-base reactions (in the Lewis sense). On the other hand, the trihalides of the other members of the group are potentially either electron-pair donors, with the use of the unshared pair of s electrons, or acceptor molecules utilizing available d orbitals of the central atoms.

14.9 A particularly striking difference in chemical behavior is observed in the hydrolytic reaction. Nitrogen trichloride is completely decomposed by water with the formation of ammonia and hypochlorous acid. Since the trihalide is capable of acting only as a donor molecule toward water, the reaction presumably proceeds *via* the hydrogen bonding mechanism shown.*

$$Cl:\overset{\overset{\textstyle Cl}{\cdot\cdot}}{\underset{\underset{\textstyle Cl}{}}{N}}: + H:\overset{\cdot\cdot}{\underset{\cdot\cdot}{O}}: = \left[Cl:\overset{\overset{\textstyle Cl}{\cdot\cdot}}{\underset{\underset{\textstyle Cl}{}}{N}}:\text{---}H:\overset{\cdot\cdot}{\underset{\cdot\cdot}{O}}: \right] = [NHCl_2] + HOCl$$

$$[NHCl_2] \xrightarrow{H_2O} [NH_2Cl] \xrightarrow{H_2O} NH_3$$

The trihalides of the other group members, although they possess unshared electron pairs, contain central atoms much less electronegative than nitrogen

---

* It is noteworthy that nitrogen trifluoride is inert toward water. The inability to undergo hydrolysis may be explained by the deactivating effect of the highly electronegative fluorine atoms on the donor ability of the nitrogen atom.

and have little ability to react with water through a hydrogen bonding mechanism. Here the water apparently is the donor molecule and the reaction results in the production of the appropriate hydrohalic acid and the group V element hydroxide or basic salt.

$$
\begin{matrix} & X \\ & \ddots \\ X : M : \\ & \ddots \\ & X \end{matrix}
\ + \
\begin{matrix} \ddots \\ : O : H \\ \ddots \end{matrix}
\ = \
\left[\begin{matrix} & & H \\ & X & \ddots O : H \\ X : M : \ddots \\ & & X \end{matrix} \right]
\ = \ M(OH)X_2 + HX
$$

$$M(OH)X_2 \xrightarrow{H_2O} M(OH)_2X \xrightarrow{H_2O} M(OH)_3$$

For the trihalides of phosphorus, arsenic, antimony, and bismuth the ease and extent of hydrolysis generally decrease with decreasing covalent character of the compound type, *i.e.*, with increasing electronegativity of the halogen for a series with a common central atom, and with increasing metallic character (decreasing electronegativity) of the central atom for a series with a common halogen atom. Specific hydrolytic reactions are described in the appropriate sections in the text.

14.10 Trihalides of arsenic, antimony, and bismuth can also function as acceptor molecules toward halide ion and other bases to form coordination compounds of varying stability (see 14.151). The phosphorus trihalides appear unable to behave in a similar fashion.

14.11 However, the phosphorus compounds have considerable tendency to act as electron-pair donors toward such strongly receptive substances as the halogens (except for iodine), oxygen, sulfur, and others (see 14.100). This type of behavior becomes of greatly diminishing importance with increasing metallic character of the central atom in the trihalides, and is of practically no significance for the bismuth trihalides.

14.12 The pentahalides and the oxides may be regarded as representative compounds containing the group V elements in a +5 oxidation state. No complete series of pentahalides is known for any member of the group. Thus no such compounds exist for nitrogen (see 14.5); no pentaiodides have been isolated; arsenic and antimony pentabromides are unknown; and bismuth pentafluoride is the only pentahalide which has been prepared for this element. The absence of phosphorus pentaiodide from the list of known compounds would certainly appear to be attributable to steric factors, and the nonexistence of pentachloride, bromide, and iodide of bismuth to the strongly oxidizing properties of the pentapositive state of this element. The pentahalides act as electron-pair acceptors toward water molecules and other basic substances, particularly toward halide ion (see 14.107; 14.141–143). As with the trihalides (see above), the nature of the hydrolytic reaction is influenced greatly by the electronegativity of the central atom.

14.13 All the elements form oxides corresponding to the +5 state, and although these compounds are acidic, the acidic nature diminishes quite sharply with increasing size (decreasing electronegativity) of the group V element.

This is illustrated by the extent of dissociation of the acids derived from the oxides of the first three members of the group. (These oxides are readily soluble in water, in contrast to the relative insolubility of the pentoxides of antimony and bismuth.) One finds that nitric acid is essentially completely dissociated in water, whereas orthophosphoric (H_3PO_4) and arsenic (H_3AsO_4) acids are, respectively, moderately strong ($K_1 = 7.5 \times 10^{-3}$) and relatively weak ($K_1 = 2.5 \times 10^{-4}$) acids in their first stage dissociation.

14.14 Consistent with the greater stability of the tripositive state relative to the pentapositive state for the metallic members of the group is the fact that the oxides of +5 arsenic, antimony, and bismuth cannot be obtained by oxidation of the elements or of the sesquioxides with atmospheric oxygen. As might be expected, bismuth(V) oxide is the most difficult to prepare, and the least stable of these oxides, so far as transformation to the sesquioxide is concerned. There is no regular trend within the group in the ability of the +5 oxides to function as oxidizing agents. Thus in acid solution the bismuth compound is by far the strongest oxidizing agent, nitric acid ($N_2O_5 + H_2O$) is next, and the pentoxides of antimony and arsenic are moderately powerful oxidants. Phosphoric acids have little tendency to act as oxidizing agents.

14.15 A quantitative overall view of the relative stabilities of the various oxidation states of the group V elements is given in Table 14.3, in which are

TABLE 14.3

Group V Potentials in Acid Solution *

$$NH_3 \xrightarrow{-0.27} N_2 \xrightarrow{-1.45} HNO_2 \xrightarrow{-0.94} NO_3^-$$

$$PH_3 \xrightarrow{0.065} P \xrightarrow{0.50} H_3PO_3 \xrightarrow{0.276} H_3PO_4$$

$$AsH_3 \xrightarrow{0.60} As \xrightarrow{-0.247} HAsO_2 \xrightarrow{-0.559} H_3AsO_4$$

$$SbH_3 \xrightarrow{0.51} Sb \xrightarrow{-0.212} SbO^+ \xrightarrow{-0.581} Sb_2O_5$$

$$BiH_3 \xrightarrow{ca.0.8} Bi \xrightarrow{-0.32} BiO^+ \xrightarrow{ca.-1.6} Bi_2O_5$$

* Taken from LATIMER, *The Oxidation States of the Elements and Their Potentials in Aqueous Solutions*, 2nd Edition, Prentice-Hall, Inc., New York, 1952, p. 125.

listed the standard oxidation potentials for the more important couples in acid solution.

Nitrogen

The Element

14.16 Nitrogen is the only element of the group which is gaseous in the free state. Combined nitrogen occurs to only a small extent in the earth's crust, primarily as ammonium salts, nitrites, and nitrates, but the free element constitutes about 80 per cent by volume of the earth's atmosphere.

14.17 Molecular nitrogen is diatomic, the N—N distance being 1.095 Å, a value which corresponds to that expected for a triple bond between the two atoms, $:N:::N:$. Physically, molecular nitrogen is colorless and odorless, difficult to condense (critical temperature, $-147.1°$; critical pressure, 33.5 atm.), and less soluble in water than is oxygen. Chemically, the element is inert, particularly at ordinary temperature. This inertness is in accord with the large value (225.3 kcal. per mole) for the dissociation energy of the molecule. As a result of the stability of the nitrogen molecule, many nitrogen compounds are endothermic and tend to decompose to give the free element. At elevated temperatures nitrogen reacts with some compounds (*e.g.*, with CaC_2 to give $CaN \cdot CN$ and carbon); it also combines directly with certain metals and a few nonmetals (*e.g.*, boron) to form nonvolatile substances commonly known as nitrides. Under special experimental conditions, nitrogen is capable of uniting directly with hydrogen and with oxygen to give ammonia (see 14.26) and nitric oxide (see 14.64), respectively.

Nitrides [1]

14.18 In formulas and in properties, the nitrides resemble the hydrides (see 9.7 *ff.*) and the carbides (see 13.16 *ff.*). Thus the nitrides fall into three classes: ionic, covalent, and interstitial.

14.19 The ionic nitrides have compositions which are consistent with the presence of N^{3-}. Their formulation as ionic materials is supported by the results of X-ray analysis, and the nitride ion has been calculated to have a radius of 1.4 Å. Ionic nitrides are formed by lithium (Li_3N), by the elements of representative group II and members of the zinc family (M_3N_2), and by thorium (Th_3N_4). Alkali metal nitrides other than the lithium compound have not yet been obtained pure. The explosive mercury(II) nitride, Hg_3N_2, prepared by interaction of mercury(II) iodide and potassium amide in liquid ammonia, may differ structurally from other nitrides of the formula M_3N_2.

14.20 Nitrides of lithium and the elements of representative group II can be

TABLE 14.4

Reaction of Li and Group II Elements with Nitrogen

Metal	Minimum Temp. (°C.) for Reaction	Remarks	$\Delta F°_{298.1}$, kcal./mole
Li	Slow at room temp.; rapid at 250°		-37.33
Be	900°	Reversible at 2200°	-121.40
Mg	560°	MgO catalyst; P_{N_2} = 1 atm. at 1100°	-100.78
Ca	500°	Rapid	-70.55
Sr	300–400°	Rapid	-76.79
Ba	560°		-72.79

[1] WELLS, *op. cit.*, pp. 476–80; 701–06; YOST and RUSSELL, *op. cit.*, p. 10.

obtained readily by the direct union of nitrogen with the metals at elevated temperatures. Conditions of reaction are shown in Table 14.4, along with the free energy of formation of the nitrides. In some instances ionic nitrides can be prepared by thermal decomposition (deammonation) of the parent amides, *e.g.*, Ba_3N_2 and Zn_3N_2 from $Ba(NH_2)_2$ and $Zn(NH_2)_2$.

14.21 The ionic nitrides are generally high melting, colorless, transparent materials which readily react with water with the formation of metal hydroxides and the liberation of ammonia.

14.22 Nitrogen forms volatile covalent compounds with a number of elements, *e.g.*, hydrogen (see 14.26), carbon (see 13.44), fluorine and chlorine (see 14.49). In addition, nonvolatile covalent materials are known for the elements of the boron family (except thallium) and for silicon and phosphorus. The nonvolatile substances comprise the so-called covalent nitrides.

14.23 The nitrides of boron, aluminum, and silicon can be prepared by direct union of the elements at high temperatures. Gallium nitride is produced when the metal is heated in ammonia at 1200°; the indium compound is formed by the decomposition of $(NH_4)_3InF_6$ at 600°; and the nitride of phosphorus results when the addition compound $P_2S_5 \cdot 6NH_3$ is heated to redness in an atmosphere of ammonia. The covalent nitrides have formulas predicted from valence considerations, *e.g.*, BN, Si_3N_4, P_3N_5. They are white or gray powders having high melting points and considerable chemical stability. The nitrides of the elements of the boron family are giant molecules with lattices like those of the two forms of carbon (see 13.9). Thus BN has the graphite structure with alternate boron and nitrogen atoms in the hexagonal rings,* whereas the corresponding compounds of aluminum, gallium, and indium have lattices very similar to that of diamond.

14.24 Transition metals with the idealized valence electronic configurations d^1s^2, d^2s^2, and d^3s^2 (*i.e.*, members of the scandium, titanium, and vanadium families) and the rare-earth elements cerium and praseodymium give nitrides which approximate the composition MN. Transition metals of other families form nitrides of the formulas M_2N and M_4N (*e.g.*, W_2N, Mo_2N, Mn_4N, Fe_4N), as well as additional types, *e.g.*, Ni_3N, Mn_3N_2. Transition metal nitrides can be obtained by reaction between finely divided metal and ammonia at temperatures in the region of 1100–1200°, or by heating the metal filament in a nitrogen atmosphere. The "compounds" of types MN, M_2N, and M_4N are definitely interstitial in nature, *i.e.*, they contain nitrogen atoms in the interstices of the metal lattice. Most of the nitrides of the composition MN possess the sodium chloride structure. The interstitial nitrides, like the carbides, are chemically unreactive except toward oxidizing agents, and possess high melting points (*e.g.*, TiN, m.p. 2947°), great hardness (TiN, 8–9 on Moh's scale), and metallic conductivity.

* Recently, the hexagonal form of boron nitride has been converted to a cubic modification by treatment at high temperatures and pressures. The cubic form is hard enough to scratch diamond, and, in turn, the latter can scratch the cubic nitride.

The Hydronitrogens and Related Compounds

14.25 Three binary compounds of nitrogen with hydrogen are of significance: ammonia, NH_3; hydrazine, $H_2N—NH_2$; and hydrazoic acid, HN_3. Nitrogen, unlike carbon, shows little ability to form stable compounds containing chains of the atoms. Compounds with two or more nitrogen atoms linked together are invariably unstable and tend to decompose with the liberation of molecular nitrogen. This instability cannot be attributed to the weakness of single or double nitrogen-nitrogen bonds but rather to the very great strength of the triple bond.

Ammonia, NH_3   **14.26** Ammonia, the most stable of the hydronitrogens, is prepared on a large scale by the direct union of its elements (Haber process), the reaction attaining a state of equilibrium.

$$N_2 + 3H_2 \rightleftharpoons 2NH_3 + 22 \text{ kcal.}$$

It is evident that the synthesis is favored by high pressures and low temperatures. However, reaction at low temperatures is too slow to be economically feasible unless catalyzed. At temperatures below 400° the rate of formation of ammonia, even in the presence of a catalyst, is not sufficiently rapid for commercial utilization. Satisfactory conditions for reaction are pressures of 100–200 atmospheres, temperatures of 550–600°, and a catalyst consisting of finely divided iron and small amounts of Al_2O_3 and K_2O.

14.27 Ammonia is a colorless gas with a characteristic odor that is perceptible even at great dilutions. The molecule (dipole moment 1.47×10^{-18} e.s.u.) has a pyramidal structure, with nitrogen at the apex; the height of the pyramid is 0.360 Å, the N—H bond distance 1.016 Å (theoretical for the N—H single bond, 1.04 Å), and the H—N—H bond angle 108°. In the liquid state, ammonia is associated, as a result of hydrogen bonding, and therefore differs quite markedly in properties from the hydrides of the other elements of the group, in which the lower electronegativities of the central atoms preclude the possibility of hydrogen bonding. Thus the freezing point ($-77.7°$), boiling point ($-33.35°$), heat of vaporization (327 cal./g. at $-33°$), and dielectric constant (22 at $-33°$) are abnormally high in comparison with the values of the corresponding constants for phosphine, arsine, etc.

14.28 The close similarity in properties between ammonia and water, also an associated liquid, has already been noted with regard to the utilization of liquid ammonia as the parent substance of a system of acids and bases (see 7.19 *ff.*). In addition, the remarkable ability of liquid ammonia to dissolve alkali and alkaline earth metals and the use of the resulting solutions as reducing media have been described (see 10.16 *ff.*).

14.29 Ammonia, as a result of the presence of an unshared pair of *s* electrons, is a base in the Lewis sense, behaving as the most effective donor molecule of the hydrides of the group. The basic character of ammonia is only weakly manifested toward water, itself a relatively basic substance.

$$NH_3 + H_2O = NH_4^+ + OH^- \qquad K = 1.8 \times 10^{-5}$$

Although it has been proposed that undissociated ammonium hydroxide, NH_4OH, is present in ammonia-water solutions in equilibrium with NH_4^+ and OH^-, it appears to have been demonstrated unequivocally that this compound is not stable in the undissociated condition. However, the solid hydrates, $NH_3 \cdot H_2O$ (m.p. $-79.0°$) and $NH_3 \cdot \frac{1}{2}H_2O$ (m.p. $-78.8°$) have been isolated. Presumably, in these compounds the water is linked to ammonia by means of hydrogen bonding.

14.30 As would be expected, ammonia, either in the gaseous state or in solution, combines readily with hydrogen acids to yield salts containing the ammonium ion.

$$NH_3 + HX = NH_4^+ + X^-$$

Ammonium salts strongly resemble alkali metal salts, particularly those of potassium and rubidium, in their solubilities and structures. The similarity between ammonium and rubidium salts is not surprising in view of the nearly identical ionic radii of the cations, NH_4^+ 1.43 Å and Rb^+ 1.47 Å. Ammonium salts, like those of rubidium, are generally nonhydrated. They are thermally unstable, the products of decomposition being dependent upon the nature of the anion. When heated, salts with anions incapable of being reduced, e.g., NH_4Cl and $(NH_4)_2CO_3$, yield ammonia and the hydrogen acid or decomposition products of the acid (e.g., $(NH_4)_2CO_3 = 2NH_3 + CO_2 + H_2O$), whereas those with oxidizing anions, e.g., $Cr_2O_7^{2-}$ and NO_2^-, give rise to an oxidation product of NH_3.

$$NH_4NO_2 = N_2 + 2H_2O$$

14.31 Besides combining with protonic acids, ammonia forms addition compounds with nonprotonic electronically unsaturated molecules, e.g., BF_3 and SO_3, and with many metal ions. In both cases the reactions may be regarded as neutralizations in the Lewis sense. Interaction with electronically unsaturated molecules leads to the formation of molecular addition compounds, e.g., $H_3N \cdot BF_3$; reaction with metal ions gives ammoniated cations, e.g., $Cd(NH_3)_4^{2+}$, $Co(NH_3)_6^{3+}$.

14.32 Mention has already been made of ionic nitrides (see 14.19). These compounds, as well as the other nitrides which have formulas consistent with the usual valence considerations, e.g., AlN, Si_3N_4, P_3N_5, may be regarded as being derived from ammonia by replacement of all the hydrogens. Replacement of one and two hydrogen atoms by metals yields substances containing the amide, NH_2^-, and imide, NH^{2-}, ions, respectively. These compounds are ammono bases, i.e., they bear the same relationship to liquid ammonia as a solvent as hydroxides and oxides do to water (see 7.22).

14.33 Metal amides are formed primarily by the elements of representative groups I and II. They can be prepared by heating the metal in gaseous ammonia, by reaction between metal and liquid ammonia in the presence of a catalyst such as iron or an iron salt, or in some instances by metathesis between soluble potassium amide, KNH_2, and a metal salt in liquid ammonia. Metal imides are much less well known than are the amides. A typical example is lead imide, $PbNH$, which can be obtained by the following reaction.

$$PbI_2 + 2KNH_2 \underset{NH_3}{\overset{\text{liquid}}{=}} PbNH\downarrow + NH_3 + 2KI$$

Although stable in liquid ammonia, amides and imides are decomposed by water with the liberation of ammonia and the formation of the corresponding metal hydroxides.

14.34 Ammonia is relatively stable toward most oxidizing agents. Although it is inert toward oxygen at ordinary temperatures, its catalyzed reaction with atmospheric oxygen to yield nitric oxide is of considerable commercial importance in the production of nitric acid (see 14.64). High temperature oxidation in the absence of catalyst gives nitrogen. Nitrogen is also the product when gaseous ammonia is passed over heated metal oxides, *e.g.*, copper(II) oxide, or when gaseous or aqueous ammonia is treated with chlorine or bromine. The oxidation of ammonia in alkaline solution to chloramine by hypochlorite ion is of significance in the preparation of hydrazine (see 14.35 *ff.*).

Hydrazine[2], $H_2N—NH_2$ **14.35** In a formal sense, hydrazine is related to ammonia by the substitution of an amide group for a hydrogen atom. The compound is commonly prepared by treatment of a large excess of ammonia in sodium hydroxide solution with hypochlorite in the presence of glue or gelatin. Reaction occurs in two stages; chloramine, NH_2Cl, is formed initially and then is converted to hydrazine.

$$NH_3 + OCl^- = NH_2Cl + OH^-$$
$$NH_2Cl + NH_3 + OH^- = H_2N—NH_2 + Cl^- + H_2O$$

However, a third reaction decreases the yield of hydrazine.

$$2NH_2Cl + N_2H_4 = N_2 + 2NH_4Cl$$

This reaction is catalyzed by traces of heavy metal ions (particularly copper) which are ordinarily present in water, and is inhibited by glue or gelatin. These proteinlike materials presumably complex the heavy metal ion impurities.

14.36 The hydrazine synthesis is carried out at 80–90°, after an initial mixing of the reactants at low temperatures. In commercial practice, fractional distillation of the reaction mixture gives the hydrazine as an 85 per cent solution of the hydrate $N_2H_4 \cdot H_2O$. This can be converted to the anhydrous material by dehydration with barium oxide and distillation under reduced pressure in a hydrogen atmosphere.

14.37 Anhydrous hydrazine is a colorless liquid which boils at 113.5° and freezes at 1.8°. The high dipole moment, 1.35 *D*, and the Raman spectrum are consistent with an unsymmetrical structure for the molecule, as is the high dielectric constant (53 at 23°). Hydrazine is monomeric in the vapor state, and electron diffraction measurements show the N—N distance to be 1.47 Å (calculated for the N—N single bond, 1.48 Å). Although it is an endothermic

---

[2] AUDRIETH and OGG, *The Chemistry of Hydrazine*, John Wiley and Sons, Inc., New York, 1951.

compound (ΔH°_{298} for $N_2H_4(g) = 22.25$ kcal.), hydrazine shows little tendency to undergo thermal decomposition even at moderately high temperatures.

14.38 Hydrazine is extremely soluble in water, from which it is recovered as the monohydrate (f.p., -40°; b.p., 118.5°). The aqueous solutions are weakly alkaline, and although hydrazine is a diacidic base, only the first stage dissociation is of significance.

$$N_2H_4 + H_2O = N_2H_5^+ + OH^- \qquad K = 8.5 \times 10^{-7} \text{ at } 25^{\circ}$$

Whereas hydrazine is capable of forming two series of salts, $N_2H_5^+$, X^- and $N_2H_6^{2+}$, $2X^-$, only those of the first type are common. With the exception of the acid sulfate, $N_2H_5^+HSO_4^-$, these are water soluble. Use is made of the insolubility of the sulfate in recovery of hydrazine on the laboratory scale.

14.39 In aqueous solution hydrazine is both an oxidizing and a reducing agent as indicated.

$$N_2H_5^+ + 3H^+ + 2e^- = 2NH_4^+ \qquad\qquad E^0 = 1.275 \text{ v.}$$
$$N_2H_4 + 2H_2O + 2e^- = 2NH_3 + 2OH^- \qquad E_B^0 = -0.1$$
$$N_2H_5^+ = N_2 + 5H^+ + 4e^- \qquad\qquad E^0 = 0.23$$
$$N_2H_4 + 4OH^- = N_2 + 4H_2O + 4e^- \qquad E_B^0 = 1.16$$

Although, on the basis of potentials, hydrazine should be a powerful oxidizing agent in acid solution, the rate of reaction with many reducing agents is slow. With strong reducing agents, such as elementary zinc, tin(II), and titanium(III), quantitative conversion of hydrazinium ion to ammonium ion occurs. Oxidation of solutions of hydrazine ordinarily yields nitrogen as a product as in the example given.

$$N_2H_5^+ + 2Br_2 = N_2 + 5H^+ + 4Br^-$$

14.40 Anhydrous hydrazine burns in air and undergoes violent reaction with the halogens. Sparking of the vapor at 100° results in explosive decomposition with the formation of ammonia, nitrogen, and hydrogen.

Hydroxylamine, NH_2OH **14.41** Although it is not strictly a hydronitrogen, hydroxylamine is closely related to both ammonia and hydrazine. Hydroxylamine can be prepared by a variety of methods, the most practical one involving the electrolytic reduction of low concentrations of nitrate ion in 50 per cent sulfuric acid at an amalgamated lead cathode. Following electrolysis, sulfate is precipitated with barium chloride, the solution evaporated to dryness, and hydroxylamine extracted into alcohol as the hydrochloride (hydroxylammonium chloride), $NH_2OH \cdot HCl$. In a useful alternative method of preparation, a slightly acidic solution of alkali metal nitrite is reduced by sulfur dioxide or acid sulfite ion at temperatures between 0° and 5°. The main product formed is the hydroxylamine disulfonate ion.

$$NO_2^- + 2HSO_3^- + H^+ = HON(SO_3)_2^{2-} + H_2O$$

This is quantitatively converted to the hydroxylammonium ion by acid hydrolysis at 100°, an intermediate product being the hydroxylamine monosulfonate ion, $HONH(SO_3)^-$.

14.42 Anhydrous hydroxylamine can be obtained from the hydrochloride by treatment with sodium butoxide in butanol solution. After filtration of the sodium chloride formed, the solution is cooled to $-10°$, whereupon NH_2OH crystallizes. The free base (m.p., $33°$; b.p., $58°$ at 22 mm. pressure) is thermally unstable and begins to decompose above $15°$, with the formation of nitrogen, nitrous oxide, ammonia, and water. Hydroxylamine is extremely soluble in the polar solvents water and ethanol, but insoluble in hydrocarbons. Aqueous solutions are basic ($K_{NH_2OH} = 6.6 \times 10^{-9}$), but less so than corresponding solutions of ammonia or hydrazine. Aqueous solutions (both acidic and alkaline) possess oxidizing as well as reducing properties, as is shown by the following selection of half-reactions.

$$NH_3OH^+ + 2H^+ + 2e^- = H_2O + NH_4^+ \qquad E° = 1.35 \text{ v.}$$
$$NH_2OH + H_2O + 2e^- = NH_3 + 2OH^- \qquad E_B° = 0.42$$
$$2NH_3OH^+ = N_2 + 4H^+ + 2H_2O + 2e^- \qquad E° = 1.87$$
$$2NH_2OH + 2OH^- = N_2 + 4H_2O + 2e^- \qquad E_B° = 3.04$$
$$2NH_2OH + 4OH^- = N_2O + 5H_2O + 4e^- \qquad E_B° = 1.05$$

Although the potentials cited indicate that hydroxylamine is a very strong oxidizing agent in acid medium, the rate of reaction is slow with many powerful reducing agents. Thus tin(II) ion appears to be unaffected by hydroxylamine in acid solution. However, under the same conditions zinc, iron(II), and titanium(III) convert hydroxylamine to ammonium ion. In both alkaline and acid solutions, hydroxylamine is a strong reducing agent and reacts with many oxidizing agents, e.g., noble metal salts, permanganate, bromine, etc., the oxidation products usually being nitrogen, nitrous oxide, or mixtures of both. In alkaline solution hydroxylamine decomposes slowly, the principal products being ammonia and nitrogen.

Hydrazoic Acid, HN₃   **14.43** This compound and its salts have been made in a number of ways; the two most important methods involve the oxidation of either metal amides or hydrazine. The most suitable oxidizing agents for the conversion of metal amides to azides are the nitrate ion and nitrous oxide. Yields of sodium azide as high as 65 per cent may be obtained by reaction between molten sodium amide and powdered sodium nitrate at $175°$.

$$3NaNH_2 + NaNO_3 = NaN_3 + 3NaOH + NH_3$$

Yields up to 90 per cent are obtained if the oxidation is carried out with nitrous oxide at approximately $190°$.

$$2NaNH_2 + N_2O = NaN_3 + NaOH + NH_3$$

The acid itself may be obtained by distillation from acidified solutions of its salts or by reaction between hydrazine and oxidizing agents in acid solution. Although a variety of oxidizing agents may be employed, nitrous acid appears to give the best yields. The yield is determined largely by the acidity of the solutions.

$$N_2H_5^+ + HONO = HN_3 + H^+ + 2H_2O$$

If the acid concentration is too high the hydrazoic acid formed is rapidly oxidized by nitrous acid; if insufficient acid is present, nitrous oxide is formed in competition with hydrazoic acid.

14.44 Structural investigations show that the three nitrogen atoms are linear both in the azide ion and in covalent azides. However, in ionic compounds, e.g., NaN_3 and KN_3, the two N—N distances in the azide group are identical (ca. 1.15 Å), whereas in the covalent hydrazoic acid and methyl azide the two distances differ. For example, in HN_3 the N—N distances have values of 1.24 and 1.13 Å, which are in fair agreement with the values of 1.20 and 1.09 Å for double and triple bonds, respectively. The single value for the N—N bond distances in ionic substances has been interpreted in terms of the resonance structures shown, each of which contributes equally to the actual configuration of the ion.[3]

$$\overset{-}{:}\overset{..}{N}::\overset{+}{N}::\overset{..\,-}{N}: \qquad \overset{2-}{:}\overset{..}{N}:\overset{+}{N}:::N: \qquad :N:::\overset{+}{N}:\overset{..\,2-}{N}:$$

For covalent azides, the resonance structures shown below have been proposed to account for the observed interatomic distances.

$$R:\overset{..}{N}::\overset{+}{N}::\overset{..\,-}{N}: \qquad R:\overset{-}{N}:\overset{..}{N}:::\overset{+}{N}:$$

14.45 Hydrazoic acid (b.p., 37°; f.p., −80°) is a colorless liquid which is extremely explosive. Its vapor density corresponds to that of the simple molecular formula. At temperatures in the region of 290°, hydrazoic acid decomposes with the formation of ammonia, nitrogen, and hydrogen. It is infinitely soluble in water, the resulting solutions having approximately the same acid strength as corresponding solutions of acetic acid ($K_{HN_3} = 1.8 \times 10^{-5}$).

14.46 The salts of hydrazoic acid are similar to the halides in many respects, particularly with regard to aqueous solubility. Thus silver, mercury(I), and lead(II) azides are insoluble. Alkali and alkaline earth azides melt without decomposition, but when heated to temperatures above 300° they decompose quietly to the metal and nitrogen. Heavy metal azides (Pb, Tl, Hg(I) and (II), Ba) decompose explosively when heated or struck.

14.47 In aqueous solution, hydrazoic acid and the azide ion can function both as oxidizing and reducing agents.

$$HN_3 + 11H^+ + 8e^- = 3NH_4^+ \qquad\qquad E° = 0.69 \text{ v.}$$
$$HN_3 + 3H^+ + 2e^- = NH_4^+ + N_2 \qquad\qquad E° = 1.96$$
$$HN_3 = \tfrac{3}{2}N_2 + H^+ + e^- \qquad\qquad E° = 3.1$$
$$N_3^- + 7H_2O + 6e^- = 7OH^- + N_2H_4 + NH_3 \qquad E_B° = 0.62$$
$$N_3^- = \tfrac{3}{2}N_2 + e^- \qquad\qquad E_B° = 3.4$$

[3] PAULING, *The Nature of the Chemical Bond*, 2nd Edition, Cornell University Press, Ithaca, 1940, pp. 200–201.

Although the potentials are highly favorable, solutions of hydrazoic acid and azides are often rather unreactive toward reducing and oxidizing agents at ordinary temperature, and heating is frequently required to effect reaction. Metals of such widely differing reducing ability as aluminum and copper are slowly oxidized by hydrazoic acid, with ammonium ion, nitrogen, and hydrazine being formed as reduction products. In acid solution, titanium(III), chromium(II), and tin(II) readily reduce hydrazoic acid to ammonium ion and nitrogen. In basic medium sodium amalgam and iron(II) hydroxide convert the azide ion to hydrazine and ammonia. Among oxidizing agents, iron(III), iodic acid, and hydrogen peroxide have little effect on hydrazoic acid. Cerium(IV) and nitrous acid quantitatively oxidize hydrazoic acid to nitrogen, as does iodine if a trace of thiosulfate is present. Permanganate reacts rapidly with azide ion in acid solution, yielding variable oxidation products.

14.48 In addition to the ionic compounds, a number of covalent azides are known. Among these are the very unstable halogen azides, FN_3, ClN_3, BrN_3, and IN_3. Fluorine azide has been prepared by reaction between elementary fluorine and hydrazoic acid in a stream of nitrogen. It is a greenish yellow gas (b.p., ca. $-82°$; f.p., ca. $-154°$), which decomposes at room temperature to nitrogen and N_2F_2. Chlorine azide is formed when an aqueous mixture of sodium azide and hypochlorite is acidified with acetic or boric acid. The pure compound, obtained from solution by distillation, is a colorless, explosive gas which freezes to a yellow solid at about $-100°$. Bromine azide, a volatile orange-red liquid (f.p., ca. $-45°$) can be obtained by reaction between silver or sodium azide and bromine in ether or benzene. The iodine compound is produced by treatment of an aqueous suspension of silver azide with an ether or benzene solution of iodine. The compound is an unstable light-yellow solid.

Nitrogen Halides

The Simple Halides   **14.49** Included among these compounds are NF_3, N_2F_2, NCl_3, $NBr_3 \cdot 6NH_3$, and $NI_3 \cdot xNH_3$. The trihalides are obtained in a number of ways. Nitrogen trifluoride is formed as the main product of the electrolysis of fused ammonium acid fluoride, $NH_4F \cdot HF$, at $125°$ in a copper cell having a graphite rod as anode. Reaction between chlorine and an acidic aqueous solution of an ammonium salt is a convenient method for the preparation of the trichloride.

$$NH_4^+ + 3Cl_2 = NCl_3 + 4H^+ + 3Cl^-$$

The compound may be extracted from solution by means of carbon tetrachloride in which it is rather stable. Although the pure tribromide and triiodide have not been isolated, the ammoniates noted above have been obtained: the tribromide hexammoniate is formed by interaction of bromine and ammonia at low pressures and temperatures; and a variety of iodide ammoniates result from reaction of iodine with liquid ammonia. Dinitrogen difluoride (difluorodiazine), N_2F_2, is produced by the decomposition of fluorine azide in the gas phase at 200 mm. pressure.

14.50 On the basis of electronegativity differences, nitrogen trifluoride is the only true trihalide of nitrogen. This colorless compound (f.p., $-208.5°$; b.p., $-129°$) is an exothermic substance ($\Delta H°_f = -26$ kcal.) and differs from the other nitrogen trihalides in its extreme stability. At ordinary temperature it is unaffected by water (see footnote to 14.9), alkalies, and a number of strong reducing agents. It is thermally stable, but a gaseous mixture with water can be ignited by sparking.

$$2NF_3 + 3H_2O = 6HF + NO + NO_2$$

The trifluoride is attacked violently by alkali metals which have been heated above their melting points, the reaction products being nitrogen and metal fluorides. The trichloride, which is formed endothermically ($\Delta H°_f = 55.4$ kcal.), is an unstable yellow liquid (b.p., $71°$; f.p., $-27°$) which explodes on exposure to light or on contact with many organic substances or upon being heated above its boiling point. Its ease of hydrolysis to ammonia and hypochlorous acid has been noted (see 14.9). The tribromide and triiodide ammoniates are intensely colored explosive solids, which, like the trichloride, are very readily hydrolyzed. It has been reported that the triiodides give iodide ion and nitrogen(III) oxide (N_2O_3) when decomposed by water alone, and give ammonia and hypoiodite when hydrolyzed in alkaline medium.

14.51 Structural information is available for the nitrogen fluorides. The trifluoride is monomolecular in the vapor state and apparently the molecule is a trigonal pyramid with nitrogen at the apex.[4] The N—F bond distance has been calculated to be 1.37 Å and the F—N—F bond angle 102.5°. The pyramidal structure would appear to be inconsistent with the extremely low dielectric constant (1.001275 at 760 mm.) of the compound. In the vapor state difluorodiazine appears to be composed of an equal mixture of the *cis* and *trans* isomers of F—N=N—F.[5]

Oxyhalides of Nitrogen　**14.52** Two varieties of oxyhalides of nitrogen exist — the nitrosyl halides, NOX, and the nitryl halides, NO_2X. The latter type has no parallel in the remaining elements of the group, and although compounds of antimony and bismuth are known which are analogous in composition to nitrosyl halides, they differ markedly from the latter in properties. The nitrosyl halides may be regarded as acid halides of nitrous acid (HONO), whereas the antimony and bismuth compounds, SbOX and BiOX, are basic salts.

14.53 All the nitrosyl halides, with the exception of the iodide, are known. The compounds can be made by direct union of nitric oxide and the halogen. In the case of the fluoride this reaction is complete and irreversible; for the chloride and bromide the reaction is reversible and the products are not obtained pure. At room temperature nitrosyl chloride is about 0.5 per cent dissociated; the bromide is still less stable, being about 7 per cent dissociated at one atmosphere pressure of the compound.

[4] SCHOMAKER and LU, *J. Am. Chem. Soc.*, **72**, 1182 (1950).
[5] BAUER, *J. Am. Chem. Soc.*, **69**, 3104 (1947).

14.54 The nitrosyl halides are volatile substances (NOF, f.p. $-132.5°$, b.p. $-59.9°$; NOCl, f.p. $-64.5°$, b.p. $-6.4°$; NOBr, f.p. $-55.5°$, b.p. ca. $0°$) with colors similar to those of the free halogens. All are highly reactive. (Nitrosyl chloride and bromide are endothermic compounds, with $\Delta H°_f$ of the gaseous species being 12.5 and 15.8 kcal., respectively.) They are immediately hydrolyzed by water with the primary formation of nitrous acid and the appro-

$$NOX + H_2O = HONO + HX$$

priate hydrohalic acid. The nitrous acid undergoes some decomposition to yield nitric acid and nitric oxide. Nitrosyl fluoride resembles fluorine in its action on elementary substances; thus silicon, red phosphorus, arsenic, and other elements are spontaneously ignited in the gas. It is, however, unreactive toward iodine. Nitrosyl chloride acts as a donor molecule toward a number of metal chlorides, forming addition compounds having one or two moles of oxyhalide per formula weight of metal chloride (e.g., $FeCl_3 \cdot NOCl$, $AuCl_3 \cdot NOCl$, $ZnCl_2 \cdot NOCl$, $TiCl_4 \cdot 2NOCl$, $SnCl_4 \cdot 2NOCl$, $PtCl_4 \cdot 2NOCl$). These compounds probably are best formulated as complexes containing the nitrosyl ion, NO^+, e.g., $NO^+[FeCl_4]^-$, $(NO^+)_2[SnCl_6]^{2-}$. Indeed the addition compound with tin(IV) chloride has been shown to be similar in structure to $(NH_4)_2[SnCl_6]$.

14.55 The nitrosyl halides are polar compounds, the chloride and bromide having dipole moments of 1.83 and 1.87 D, respectively, in carbon tetrachloride solution. The Cl—N and Br—N bond distances in the vapors have been found to be 1.95 and 2.14 Å, respectively. These distances are much greater than the calculated single-bond values of 1.73 Å for Cl—N and 1.88 Å for Br—N, but less than those calculated for pure ionic bonds. The molecules are nonlinear, with the X—N—O bond angle in each case about 116°. The observed N—O bond distances (1.14 Å for NOCl and 1.15 Å for NOBr) are somewhat less than the value calculated for a double bond and larger than that for a triple bond. The observed bond distances are interpreted in terms of the resonance structures shown.[6]

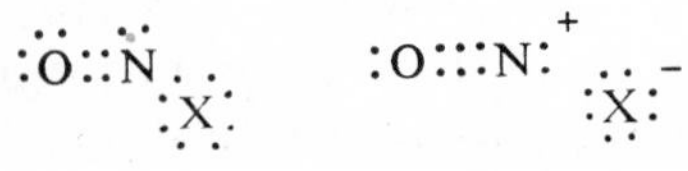

14.56 Only two nitryl halides, NO_2F and NO_2Cl, have been characterized definitely. The fluoride, a colorless gas (f.p., $-166°$; b.p., $-72.4°$), is obtained by combination of nitrogen dioxide and fluorine in a copper vessel or by the thermal decomposition of nitryl fluoroborate, $NO_2[BF_4]$. The latter is prepared by reaction between boron trioxide, potassium nitrate, and bromine trifluoride. Nitryl chloride (f.p., $-145°$; b.p., $-15.9°$) cannot be made by direct union of nitrogen dioxide and chlorine. It is formed in quantitative yield by the oxidation

[6] KETELAAR and PALMER, *J. Am. Chem. Soc.*, **59**, 2629 (1937).

of nitrosyl chloride with ozone; it can also be prepared by the action of chlorosulfonic acid, $ClSO_2OH$, on concentrated nitric acid.

$$NOCl + O_3 = NO_2Cl + O_2$$

14.57 Nitryl fluoride is a powerful fluorinating agent, being even more reactive than the nitrosyl compound. Thus it ignites even iodine, converting the latter to the pentafluoride. The nitryl halides are decomposed rapidly by water, with the production of nitric and hydrohalic acids. Nitryl chloride, like the fluoride, is a strong oxidizing agent. In the temperature range 100–150° the chloride decomposes into nitrogen dioxide and chlorine at a rate dependent on the total pressure, including the contribution of any added unreactive gas. Nitryl chloride, like the corresponding nitrosyl compound, is capable of forming addition compounds with certain metal chlorides, e.g., $SbCl_5 \cdot NO_2Cl$ or $NO_2[SbCl_6]$ (nitronium hexachloroantimonate(V)).

Oxides of Nitrogen and Related Compounds

14.58 Nitrogen forms oxides corresponding to all oxidation states from $+1$ to $+5$. A list of these compounds, along with some of their properties, is given in Table 14.5. In addition to the oxides cited, there is evidence for the existence of the extremely unstable compounds NO_3 and N_2O_6.

TABLE 14.5

Oxides of Nitrogen

Oxidation State of Nitrogen	Formula	Name	Melting Point, °C.	Boiling Point, °C.	Heat of Formation, ΔH°_{298}, kcal./mole
$+1$	N_2O	Nitrous oxide	-98.84	-88.51	19.6 (gas)
$+2$	NO	Nitric oxide	-163.61	-151.74	21.6 (gas)
$+3$	N_2O_3	Nitrogen sesquioxide	-103	3.5	20.0 (gas)
$+4$	NO_2	Nitrogen dioxide ⎫	-11.2	21.15	8.0 (gas)
$+4$	N_2O_4	Dinitrogen tetroxide ⎬			2.4 (gas)
$+5$	N_2O_5	Dinitrogen pentoxide	——	32.4 (subl.)	1.2 (gas)

14.59 It should be noted that the gaseous oxides are endothermic substances. This is a striking consequence of the great stability of the triple bond in the nitrogen molecule.

Nitrous Oxide (Nitrogen(I) Oxide), N_2O **14.60** This compound is commonly obtained by the thermal decomposition of ammonium nitrate at 170–260°. (At higher temperatures the decomposition may become explosive.) The small amount of nitric oxide, NO, produced in the reaction may be removed by passage of the gas through aqueous iron(II) sulfate, whereby the complex $[FeNO]^{2+}$ is formed.

14.61 The nitrous oxide molecule is linear but not symmetrical, the gas having a dipole moment of 0.17 D. The observed sum of the N—N and N—O distances in the gas is 3.32 ± 0.02 Å and is in excellent agreement with the value expected for the following significant resonance structures.

$$-:\overset{..}{\underset{..}{N}}::\overset{+}{N}::\overset{..}{\underset{..}{O}}: \qquad :N:::\overset{+}{N}:\overset{..}{\underset{..}{O}}:^-$$

14.62 At ordinary temperature nitrous oxide is stable toward both oxidizing and reducing agents. At high temperatures, however, where decomposition to the elements becomes appreciable, the compound is a rather strong oxidizing agent and is readily reduced to elementary nitrogen (*e.g.*, by alkali metals, organic compounds, hydrogen, ammonia).

14.63 Although it is formally the anhydride of hyponitrous acid,

$$\text{HON}=\text{NOH} *$$

(probable structure), and is produced in the decomposition of that acid, nitrous oxide is converted neither to the acid by dissolution in water nor to hyponitrite salts by reaction with solutions of alkali. The gas is appreciably soluble in water (about 130 cc. in 100 g. of H_2O at 0°); the solid hydrate $N_2O \cdot 6H_2O$ can be obtained from aqueous solution at low temperatures.

Nitric Oxide (Nitrogen(II) Oxide), NO **14.64** This substance is the important intermediate in the chief commercial process for the manufacture of nitric acid. It may be obtained by direct union of the elements at high temperatures (*e.g.*, in an electric arc). The reaction attains a state of equilibrium, and although the direct union of nitrogen and oxygen is an endothermic process, the yields of nitric oxide are extremely small even at very high temperatures. For example, at 2400° under equilibrium conditions, with air as the source of reactants, the yield of nitric oxide is only about 2.23 per cent by volume, and at 3200° about 4.4 per cent. Most of the nitric oxide used for the production of nitric acid is prepared by the atmospheric oxidation of ammonia on platinum gauze at temperatures above 500°. The reaction is strongly exothermic and the heat liberated helps maintain the catalyst at a high enough temperature to promote rapid oxidation of the ammonia. For laboratory use, nitric oxide is prepared conveniently by treatment of an aqueous mixture of potassium nitrite and

---

* This acid can be prepared by reaction between hydrogen chloride in ether solution and silver hyponitrite.

$$Ag_2N_2O_2(s) + 2HCl \text{ (in ether)} = 2AgCl(s) + H_2N_2O_2 \text{ (in ether)}$$

Evaporation of the solvent gives the free acid as a white, explosive solid. The silver salt is produced from the sodium salt by metathesis, and the latter is obtained in small yield in solution by the reduction of sodium nitrite or nitrate by means of sodium amalgam. In addition to sodium hyponitrite, hydroxylamine, ammonia, and hydrogen are also formed.

Hyponitrous acid is very soluble in water, but in solution decomposes readily to nitrous oxide and water. The free acid is a weak dibasic acid and the alkali metal salts are considerably hydrolyzed. Strong oxidizing agents convert hyponitrites to nitrates.

potassium iodide with concentrated sulfuric acid, the gas evolved being purified by passage through concentrated alkali and phosphoric anhydride.

$$2HNO_2 + 2I^- + 2H^+ = 2NO + I_2 + 2H_2O$$

14.65 Nitric oxide, with a total of eleven electrons in the valence shells of the nitrogen and oxygen atoms, is an "odd" molecule and exhibits the degree of paramagnetism expected for a substance with one unpaired electron. (μ at room temperature is approximately 1.8 Bohr magnetons.) It is the most stable of the known "odd" molecules and in the gaseous state shows no tendency for dimerization (*cf.* NO_2, sec. 14.74). The inability of gaseous nitric oxide to dimerize has been attributed [7] to almost complete resonance between the structures shown. The molecule thus effectively possesses the structure : N $\vdots\vdots$ O :,

$$: \overset{.}{N} :: \overset{..}{O} : \quad \text{and} \quad : \overset{-..}{N} :: \overset{.\ +}{O} :$$

with both a three-electron bond and a double bond between the atoms. Such a structure is consistent with the small dipole moment of the molecule (0.16 *D*) and also with the observed N—O distance of 1.14 Å, which lies between the calculated radius sum values of 1.18 and 1.06 Å for double and triple bonds, respectively. In the liquid state, nitric oxide, which is blue in color in contrast to the colorless gas, apparently exists as a dimer.

14.66 Nitric oxide is rather reactive chemically. It combines directly with all the halogens but iodine to yield the nitrosyl halides (see 14.53). At ordinary temperature it unites fairly rapidly and completely with oxygen to give nitrogen dioxide, a reaction of great significance in the manufacture of nitric acid (see 14.81). It is quantitatively oxidized to nitric acid by an acidified permanganate or dichromate solution. At high temperatures nitric oxide is capable of functioning as an oxidizing agent; such materials as ignited phosphorus, carbon, and magnesium, which have a high affinity for oxygen, continue to burn in the gas. An important characteristic of nitric oxide is its tendency to form complexes with many salts and with certain metals and to replace carbon monoxide in a number of metal carbonyls. In some of the compounds formed (*e.g.*, $NOAlCl_4$) nitric oxide functions as the cation, NO^+; in at least one simple compound (*e.g.*, NaNO) it apparently exists as the NO^- group; and in coordination compounds, where the nitric oxide is directly joined to a metal atom or ion, it appears to be present either as a neutral unit, *e.g.*, $Co(CO)_3NO$, or as the NO^+ group, *e.g.*, $[Fe(CN)_5NO]^{2-}$.*

Nitrogen Sesquioxide (Nitrogen(III) Oxide), N_2O_3 **14.67** This compound is extremely unstable and exists pure only as a solid (m.p. $-103°$). The sesquioxide may be obtained as a blue liquid (b.p. 3.5°) by condensation of an equimolar mixture of nitric oxide and nitrogen dioxide at $-20°$. Even in the liquid

---

[7] PAULING, *op. cit.*, pp. 266–68.

* For an excellent discussion of inorganic nitrosyl compounds consult MOELLER, *J. Chem. Educ.*, **23**, 441, 542 (1946); **24**, 149 (1947).

state it is partially dissociated into the component oxides, and at room temperature there is present only a small concentration of N_2O_3 (*e.g.*, 10.5 per cent at one atmosphere and 25°) in equilibrium with the oxides.

Nitrous Acid and Nitrites **14.68** Nitrogen sesquioxide is the anhydride of nitrous acid, $H : \overset{..}{\underset{..}{O}} : \overset{..}{N} :: \overset{..}{\underset{.}{O}}$. Thus the gas (*i.e.*, an equimolar mixture of NO and NO_2) is converted quantitatively to nitrite ion, NO_2^-, by reaction with solutions of alkalies. Combination of the sesquioxide directly with water yields nitrous acid, which is unstable and is partially decomposed to nitric oxide and nitrogen dioxide, the latter reacting to give nitric acid.

$$3HNO_2 = H^+ + NO_3^- + 2NO + H_2O$$

Aqueous solutions of nitrous acid are commonly prepared by the interaction of cold solutions of soluble nitrites and strong acids; under these conditions the decomposition reaction is minimized. Nitrous acid is a weak acid and solutions of its alkali and alkaline earth metal salts are alkaline.

$$HONO = H^+ + ONO^- \qquad K = 6.0 \times 10^{-4} \text{ at } 30°$$

14.69 These salts, which in addition to the silver salt constitute the simple nitrites, can be prepared by either of two methods: (1) the heating of the nitrate (or of a mixture of the nitrate with the corresponding hydroxide or carbonate) with a reducing agent such as iron, carbon, or lead; or (2) the reaction between an equimolar mixture of nitric oxide and nitrogen dioxide and either the solid metal hydroxide or its aqueous solution (see above). Although only the few simple salts noted above are known, the nitrite ion readily forms complexes with many transition metal ions. In the very great majority of these complexes the nitrite group is coordinated to the metal atom through the nitrogen, and the compounds are in reality nitro complexes. There is some evidence that union through oxygen may occur in some instances, with the formation of true nitrito complexes (see 6.32).

14.70 Structural investigations have demonstrated that the nitrite ion is triangular in nature. The N—O distance of 1.13 Å is approximately equal to that observed in the nitrosyl halides (see 14.55), indicating that the bonds are similar.

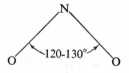

14.71 Nitrous acid and nitrites possess both oxidizing and reducing properties, being rather strong oxidizing agents in acid solution as indicated.

$$2HNO_2 + 4H^+ + 4e^- = N_2O + 3H_2O \qquad E° = 1.29 \text{ v.}$$
$$HNO_2 + H^+ + e^- = NO + H_2O \qquad E° = 1.00$$

Iron(II), titanium(III), and iodide ion, which are one-electron reducing agents, react with nitrous acid with the formation of nitric oxide. Tin(II), which in terms of potential is a better reducing agent in acid solution than either iron(II) or iodide ion but a poorer one than titanium(III), converts nitrous acid to hydroxylamine in the cold and to nitrous oxide when the solutions are hot. Reduction of $+3$ nitrogen in nitrous acid to the $+1$ state in nitrous oxide is understandable in that tin(II) is a two-electron reducing agent, *i.e.*, is converted to tin(IV). Formation of hydroxylamine in the cold solutions is believed to proceed through the intermediate formation of the nitroxyl radical, NOH, or dihydroxylammonia, $NH(OH)_2$, in each of which nitrogen possesses an oxidation state of $+1$.

14.72 Powerful oxidizing agents, *e.g.*, permanganate, chlorine, or bromine, are necessary for the oxidation of nitrous acid to nitric acid.

$$HNO_2 + H_2O = NO_3^- + 3H^+ + 2e^- \qquad E^\circ = -0.94 \text{ v.}$$

Reaction with the agents cited above is rapid, and is a quantitative process with permanganate. In basic medium, oxidation of nitrite ion to nitrate can be accomplished with comparatively weak oxidizing agents.

$$2OH^- + NO_2^- = NO_3^- + H_2O + 2e^- \qquad E_B^\circ = -0.01 \text{ v.}$$

Nitrogen(IV) Oxides, NO_2 and N_2O_4 **14.73** The essentially quantitative conversion at room temperature of nitric oxide to nitrogen dioxide by means of oxygen has been mentioned (see 14.66). On a laboratory scale, the dioxide is ordinarily prepared by heating lead nitrate.

$$2Pb(NO_3)_2 = 2PbO + 4NO_2 + O_2$$

14.74 The dioxide, a reddish-brown gas, is an "odd" molecule; it is less stable than nitric oxide, and exists in equilibrium with its colorless, diamagnetic dimer, dinitrogen tetroxide.

$$2NO_2 \rightleftharpoons N_2O_4 + 14.7 \text{ kcal. at } 25^\circ$$

The formation of the dimer is favored by low temperatures. At temperatures below -11.2° (the melting point), the equilibrium lies completely to the right; at the boiling point (21.15°), the vapor contains about 20 per cent dioxide, and at 135° the tetroxide is 99 per cent dissociated to the dioxide. The dioxide is thermally stable to about 150° and above this temperature begins to decompose into nitric oxide and oxygen. At 600° this decomposition is practically complete.

14.75 The dioxide molecule has a triangular structure, with an O—N—O bond angle of about 132° and an N—O bond distance of 1.20 Å. It has been proposed that the resonance configurations shown contribute to the actual structure of the molecule.

In contrast with the situation for nitric oxide (see 14.65), there is insufficient resonance stabilization in the dioxide to prevent dimerization. Although the structure of the tetroxide has not been determined with certainty, there appears to be little doubt that this substance is symmetrical. There is some question as to whether the two nitrogen atoms are directly linked to each other or are bridged by two oxygen atoms.

14.76 In its chemical properties nitrogen dioxide (or the tetroxide) behaves like the mixed anhydride of nitrous and nitric acids. Small concentrations of dioxide react with cold water to give a mixture of these acids in accordance with the following equilibrium.

$$2NO_2 + H_2O \rightleftharpoons HNO_2 + H^+ + NO_3^- \qquad K = 10^5$$

In warm water the nitrous acid formed is unstable in the presence of nitric acid, and with large concentrations of the dioxide the reaction takes mainly the course shown.

$$3NO_2 + H_2O \rightleftharpoons 2NO_3^- + 2H^+ + NO \qquad K = 2 \times 10^8$$

This reaction is of considerable significance in the manufacture of nitric acid. Nitrogen dioxide reacts with alkaline solutions, as might be expected, to give only nitrite and nitrate.

14.77 The nitrogen(IV) oxides are potent oxidizing agents, being comparable to bromine. When ignited, such nonmetals as carbon, phosphorus, and sulfur continue to burn in an atmosphere of nitrogen dioxide. The gas is reduced catalytically by hydrogen, with the formation of ammonia and water. Alkali metals are rapidly corroded on contact with the dioxide. In view of the oxidation state of nitrogen in the nitrogen(IV) oxides it is to be expected that these substances may function as reducing agents also. However, only strong oxidizing agents, *e.g.*, permanganate ion in acid medium, are capable of converting them to nitric acid.

Dinitrogen Pentoxide (Nitrogen(V) Oxide), N_2O_5 **14.78** This white solid is the anhydride of nitric acid and can be obtained readily by the dehydration of the acid by means of phosphoric anhydride.

$$4HNO_3 + P_4O_{10} = 4HPO_3 + 2N_2O_5$$

The pentoxide is removed from the reaction mixture by sublimation at 35–40°. An alternative method of preparation involves the oxidation of nitric oxide or nitrogen dioxide with ozone.

14.79 Optical and X-ray evidence shows that the solid pentoxide consists of nitronium, NO_2^+, and nitrate, NO_3^-, ions. However, the vapor obtained by sublimation of the solid is composed of simple molecules with the structure $O_2N-O-NO_2$.

14.80 The oxide is thermally unstable and decomposes readily and irreversibly into oxygen and the dioxide. It dissolves readily in water to form nitric acid.

$$\tfrac{1}{2}N_2O_5 + \tfrac{1}{2}H_2O = HONO_2 + 10.4 \text{ kcal. } (20°)$$
$$HONO_2 + aq. = H^+, ONO_2^- \ aq. + 7.5 \text{ kcal.}$$

Nitric Acid and Nitrates **14.81** Most of the nitric acid produced industrially is made from ammonia.

$$NH_3 \xrightarrow[\substack{catalyst \\ 500-1000°}]{air} NO \xrightarrow[air]{cool} NO_2 \xrightarrow{H_2O} HNO_3 + NO$$

Smaller quantities are obtained by distillation from mixtures of sodium nitrate (Chile saltpeter) and concentrated sulfuric acid.

14.82 Absolute nitric acid is a colorless liquid having the following physical properties: d_4^{25} 1.503; b.p. 83°; f.p. −41.59°; v.p. 57 mm. (25°). It is light and heat sensitive and decomposes into nitrogen dioxide, oxygen, and water. Structural investigations of the vapor indicate that the $HONO_2$ molecule is planar and has the configuration shown.

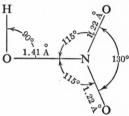

14.83 Nitric acid is infinitely soluble in water and is a strong acid in this solvent. Aqueous solutions of the acid find considerable use as oxidizing media. The nature of the reduction products obtained is dependent largely upon the concentration of the nitric acid employed. Although the potentials are highly favorable for the conversion of nitrogen in nitric acid to all possible lower oxidation states, in actuality only a few of these states are realized. It is believed that in many instances nitric acid is reduced initially to nitrous acid. However, in solutions of low hydrogen ion concentration the latter decomposes to yield nitric oxide and the net reduction reaction is usually the following.

$$NO_3^- + 4H^+ + 3e^- = NO + 2H_2O \qquad E° = 0.96 \text{ v.}$$

At high acid concentrations an equilibrium mixture of nitrogen(IV) oxides is ordinarily formed.

$$2NO_3^- + 4H^+ + 2e^- = 2NO_2 + 2H_2O \qquad E° = 0.80 \text{ v.}$$

Generally, the reaction between nitric acid and any specific reducing agent cannot be represented by a single equation, since mixtures of reduction products are obtained.* It should be emphasized that from the practical viewpoint concentrated nitric acid is a much more powerful and rapid oxidizing agent than is the dilute acid.

14.84 The reaction of concentrated nitric acid with concentrated hydrochloric acid and also the behavior of 100 per cent nitric acid in absolute sulfuric acid deserve special mention. A mixture of concentrated nitric and hydrochloric acids in the volume ratio 1 : 3 is commonly known as *aqua regia* and is useful for dissolving the noble metals gold and platinum. Reaction between the acids occurs in accordance with the equation given. The solvent action of aqua regia

$$4H^+ + NO_3^- + 3Cl^- = NOCl + Cl_2 + 2H_2O$$

on the noble metals does not arise from an increase in the reduction potential of nitric acid in the presence of chloride ion, but rather is attributed to an increase

* Although nitric oxide and nitrogen(IV) oxides are the common reduction products of nitric acid, reactions are known (*e.g.*, zinc and dilute nitric acid) in which reduction all the way to ammonia occurs.

in the oxidation potentials of the metals resulting from the formation of chloro complexes.

14.85 There is considerable evidence that in absolute sulfuric acid anhydrous nitric acid undergoes a complex ionization to yield the nitronium ion, NO_2^+.

$$HONO_2 + 2H_2SO_4 = NO_2^+ + H_3O^+ + 2HSO_4^-$$

Such solutions are powerful nitrating agents for aromatic compounds; nitration in these solutions, as well as in those of nitric acid in concentrated aqueous sulfuric acid, is believed to proceed through attack of the aromatic nucleus by the nitronium ion.

14.86 The inorganic salts of nitric acid generally have high solubility in water (*e.g.*, $NaNO_3$, 88.0 g. and $Ca(NO_3)_2$, 132.6 g. in 100 g. of H_2O at 20°). The salts of strong bases are neutral to litmus; those of weak insoluble bases (*e.g.*, $Hg(NO_3)_2$) are frequently hydrolyzed by water with the precipitation of basic nitrates or oxides. In contrast to its behavior in acid solutions, the nitrate ion in basic medium is a poor oxidizing agent.

$$NO_3^- + H_2O + 2e^- = NO_2^- + 2OH^- \qquad E_B^0 = 0.01 \text{ v.}$$

The nitrate ion has the configuration of an equilateral triangle, with the nitrogen atom occupying the center. The N—O bond length of 1.21 Å is very close to that expected for the basic resonance structure[8] shown.

Phosphorus

The Element

14.87 Phosphorus is the twelfth most abundant element in the earth's crust, where it occurs to the extent of 0.142 per cent, almost exclusively in the form of salts of orthophosphoric acid, H_3PO_4. The chief minerals of phosphorus are *phosphorite*, $3Ca_3(PO_4)_2 \cdot Ca(OH)_2$, and *apatite*, $3Ca_3(PO_4)_2 \cdot Ca(F, Cl)_2$. Industrially, the element is obtained from phosphate minerals by heating them with sand and coke in an electric furnace at temperatures in the range of 1150–1450°. Conversion to the element occurs in two stages.

$$2Ca_3(PO_4)_2 + 6SiO_2 = P_4O_{10} + 6CaSiO_3$$
$$P_4O_{10} + 10C = P_4 + 10CO$$

The phosphorus vaporizes from the furnace and is condensed under water as a white waxy solid.

14.88 Elementary phosphorus exists in at least three allotropic forms. The modification obtained commercially by the condensation of the vapor is known as *white* or *yellow* phosphorus. It is a toxic, low melting (44.1°), low boiling

---

[8] PAULING, *op. cit.*, p. 209.

(280°) material of density 1.82. White phosphorus is dimorphic, and is known in the ordinary α or cubic form obtained by crystallization from solution or from its vapor and in the β or hexagonal form prepared by cooling the cubic variety to $-76.9°$. White phosphorus is soluble in such solvents as benzene, ethyl ether, carbon disulfide, sulfur monochloride, and phosphorus trichloride. The molecular weight in solution and in the vapor state up to 800° corresponds to P_4. Structural investigation of the vapor has shown that the molecule is tetrahedral, with a P—P distance of 2.21 Å and valence bond angles of 60°.

14.89 White phosphorus is an extremely reactive substance, igniting spontaneously in air with the formation of phosphoric anhydride and the liberation of much heat and light.

$$P_4 + 5O_2 = P_4O_{10} + 740 \text{ kcal.}$$

It combines energetically with the halogens to yield tri- and pentahalides. Combination with sulfur yields sulfides, the nature of the compound obtained (*e.g.*, P_4S_3, P_4S_{10}) being determined by the molecular ratio of reactants. It unites directly and vigorously with many metals to yield phosphides (*e.g.*, Ca_3P_2), substances which are analogous to the nitrides as to type, but which have not been so well characterized structurally. White phosphorus is a fair reducing agent and is converted to orthophosphoric acid by the action of moderately strong oxidizing agents.

$$\tfrac{1}{4}P_4 + 4H_2O = H_3PO_4 + 5H^+ + 5e^- \qquad E° = 0.3 \text{ v.}$$

Reaction with warm solutions of alkalies results in the liberation of phosphine and the formation of the hypophosphite ion, $H_2PO_2^-$.

$$P_4 + 3OH^- + 3H_2O = PH_3 + 3H_2PO_2^-$$

14.90 When heated to about 250° in the absence of air or when exposed to light, white phosphorus is slowly transformed to a *red* modification. This transformation is catalyzed by iodine, a trace of which makes the transition almost violent at 200°. By prolonged heating of phosphorus in molten lead at 800°, followed by chilling in a freezing mixture, a *violet* form of the element is obtained. Although the physical properties of the red variety are to a large extent dependent upon conditions of preparation, there appears to be little doubt that the red material, after appropriate heat treatment, possesses a structure identical to that of the violet form. It has been suggested that red phosphorus consists of a number of allotropic forms, the principal one being that known in the pure state as violet phosphorus.

14.91 Violet (or red) phosphorus differs markedly in properties from the white modification. The density (2.2) is somewhat greater than that of the white variety; it is relatively nontoxic; and it is insoluble in carbon disulfide. Moreover, the violet form is considerably less active chemically. Thus it does not react with solutions of alkalies, and union with nonmetals occurs at much higher temperatures than required for analogous reactions with white phosphorus.

14.92 Another form of the element which has been characterized unequivo-cally is *black* phosphorus. This can be obtained by subjecting the white modi-fication to a pressure of 12,000 kg. per sq. cm. This substance is iron gray in color and possesses a metallic luster. Not only does it resemble graphite in appearance, but like the latter, it possesses a layer structure, with the distance between adjacent layers (3.68 Å) much greater than that (2.18 Å) between any one phosphorus atom and each of its three nearest neighbors in a layer. In con-trast to the white and violet modifications, black phosphorus is a conductor of electric current. It is less readily acted on by oxidizing agents than is the violet form. At about 550° black phosphorus is transformed to the violet modification.

The Phosphorus Hydrides

14.93 Only two phosphorus hydrides, phosphine, PH_3 (f.p., $-133°$; b.p., $-87.4°$), and diphosphine, P_2H_4 (f.p., $-99°$; b.p., $51.7°$), are known definitely. These substances are extremely poisonous. The preparation of phosphine by reaction between white phosphorus and aqueous alkali has already been noted (see 14.89). This hydride can be obtained more conveniently by the hydrolysis of metal phosphides, as in the example given.

$$Ca_3P_2 + 6H_2O = 2PH_3 + 3Ca(OH)_2$$

Both methods of preparation give some diphosphine as impurity, and it is be-lieved that the presence of this substance is responsible for the spontaneous ignition of the gas produced. Diphosphine can be removed from the gas by freezing. Pure phosphine is made by the action of alkali on phosphonium iodide.

$$PH_4I + OH^- = PH_3 + I^- + H_2O$$

The phosphine molecule, like ammonia, possesses a pyramidal structure. The P—H bond distance is 1.42 Å (calculated for a single bond is 1.40 Å) and the H—P—H bond angle 93°. Unlike ammonia, phosphine is not associated in the liquid state.

14.94 Phosphine ignites in air at about 150° to yield orthophosphoric acid. The gas is considerably less soluble in water than is ammonia, the maximum solubility being about 0.01M. Aqueous solutions decompose, giving among other products phosphorus and hydrogen. In alkaline solution, phosphine is a fairly strong reducing agent.

$$PH_3 + 3OH^- = \tfrac{1}{4}P_4 + 3H_2O + 3e^- \qquad E_B^\circ = 0.89 \text{ v.}$$

14.95 Phosphine is much less basic than ammonia, and the phosphonium salts, PH_4X, even of strong acids, are largely dissociated into the component compounds at low temperatures. For example, the dissociation pressure of phosphonium chloride reaches a value of 1 atmosphere at a temperature be-low 0°, whereas the corresponding ammonium salt attains this pressure at 340°. The extremely weak basic character of phosphine is illustrated by the ready decomposition of phosphonium halides into the parent compounds merely on treatment with water. The most stable phosphonium salt is the iodide. This can be prepared by the union of phosphine and anhydrous hydrogen iodide but is best made by the careful addition of water to the residue obtained from the evaporation in an inert atmosphere of a solution of white phosphorus and iodine in carbon disulfide. The colorless phosphonium iodide sublimes from the reaction mixture at 80°. The exact nature of the reactions occurring in the process has not been established.

14.96 Diphosphine is a highly unstable substance. It is spontaneously inflammable and on standing in the absence of air decomposes into phosphine and "solid phosphorus hydride." The latter is a yellow insoluble material of the empirical formula P_2H; its exact character is unknown. Diphosphine, in contrast to hydrazine, its nitrogen analog, is completely without basic properties.

The Phosphorus Halides and Related Compounds

14.97 In addition to simple and mixed tri- and pentahalides, phosphorus forms tetrahalides (P_2X_4) and oxy- and thiohalides of the compositions POX_3 and PSX_3. All of these are molecular compounds. For the group V elements, the mixed trihalides, the tetrahalides, and the oxy- and thiohalides appear to be entirely restricted to phosphorus.

Simple Trihalides **14.98** These compounds, all of which are known, can be obtained by direct union of the elements, phosphorus being present in excess of the amount required by the stoichiometry of the reaction. Even under these conditions, pentahalides (except the iodide) may be formed. Purification of trihalide is readily accomplished by fractional distillation (*e.g.*, b.p.: PCl_3, 74.2°; PCl_5, 160° (subl.)). Phosphorus trifluoride is most conveniently prepared by halogen exchange reactions involving the trichloride or bromide, *e.g.*, between PCl_3 and AsF_3, PCl_3 and PbF_2, or PBr_3 and ZnF_2.

14.99 The trihalides are volatile materials, with the volatility decreasing, as expected, with increasing halogen weight (*e.g.*, b.p.: PF_3, $-101.15°$; PBr_3, 175.3°). They are monomolecular in the vapor state, and electron diffraction data show them to have the structure of a trigonal pyramid, with phosphorus at the apex and halogen atoms at the base. Such a structure may be regarded as being derived from a tetrahedron in which the unshared pair of electrons on the phosphorus atom occupies one of the corners. The experimentally determined P—X bond distances for the trifluoride and chloride, particularly for the former, are less than the sums of the single-bond radii, *e.g.*, P—F, observed 1.52 Å, calculated radius sum 1.82 Å; P—Cl, observed 2.00 Å, radius sum 2.09 Å. The short distances have been attributed to partial double-bond character of the phosphorus-halogen bond.[9]

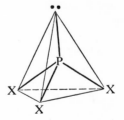

---

[9] PAULING, *op. cit.*, Ch. VII.

14.100 The phosphorus trihalides act as donor molecules toward strong acceptors. The trihalides (except the iodide) are capable of adding oxygen, sulfur, and additional halogen to give POX_3, PSX_3, and PX_5, respectively. The trichloride combines with platinum(II) chloride to give the compound $PtCl_2 \cdot 2PCl_3$, which is known in *cis* and *trans* forms. With boron tribromide, the addition compounds $BBr_3 \cdot PCl_3$ and $BBr_3 \cdot PBr_3$ are formed. The trifluoride and tribromide readily replace carbon monoxide in nickel tetracarbonyl, $Ni(CO)_4$, with the formation of $Ni(PX_3)_4$.[10]

14.101 Phosphorus trichloride, bromide, and iodide are completely and irreversibly hydrolyzed on contact with water to yield phosphorous acid and the appropriate hydrohalic acid.

$$PX_3 + 3H_2O = H_2(HPO_3) + 3H^+ + 3X^-$$

14.102 The trifluoride is little affected by cold water, but is hydrolytically decomposed by steam at 100°. The hydrolysis of the trihalides has been interpreted in terms of their functioning as acceptor molecules toward water (see 14.9). It should be emphasized that no compounds of the trihalides with donor molecules have been isolated.

Mixed Trihalides **14.103** These compounds are all related to the trifluoride, and only fluorochlorides (PF_2Cl, $PFCl_2$) and fluorobromides (PF_2Br, $PFBr_2$) have been prepared. They are obtained by halogen exchange reactions like those given.

$$2PF_3 + PCl_3 = 3PF_2Cl$$
$$PCl_3 + CaF_2 = PF_2Cl + CaCl_2$$

As would be supposed, the mixed trihalides are volatile (b.p.: PF_2Cl, $-47.3°$; $PFCl_2$, 13.85°; PF_2Br, $-16.1°$; $PFBr_2$, 78.4°) and readily hydrolyzed. Moreover, they tend to decompose into mixtures of the simple compounds. Like the simple trihalides, they have a trigonal pyramid structure.

Pentahalides **14.104** The simple pentahalides, all of which save the iodide are known (see 14.12), can be prepared by reaction of phosphorus with an excess of halogen. The pentafluoride can also be made by exchange of halogen between the pentachloride and arsenic trifluoride.

$$3PCl_5 + 5AsF_3 = 3PF_5 + 5AsCl_3$$

14.105 The pentafluoride is a gaseous substance (b.p. $-84.6°$) of great thermal stability, whereas the chloride and bromide are solid materials which when heated decompose reversibly into trihalide and halogen. The stability of the bromide in the vapor state is quite small.

14.106 Two mixed pentahalides, PF_3Cl_2 and PF_3Br_2, have been obtained by combination between the trifluoride and the appropriate halogen at room

[10] IRVINE and WILKINSON, *Science*, **113**, 742 (1951); WILKINSON, *J. Am. Chem. Soc.*, **73**, 5501 (1951).

temperature. When heated, the mixed halides decompose into the simple pentahalides. Structural studies show that in the vapor state the pentafluoride and pentachloride have the trigonal bipyramid configuration expected for molecules with SP^3D binding. However, whereas in the penta-fluoride only a single P—F bond distance (1.56 Å) is observed, in the pentachloride two P—Cl lengths (2.04 Å equatorial, 2.11 Å axial) are found. X-ray examination of the solid penta-chloride strongly indicates that it is a salt consisting of tet-rahedral $[PCl_4]^+$ and octahedral $[PCl_6]^-$. It is of interest to note that this compound is a fairly good conductor of electric current in such solvents as nitrobenzene. The solid penta-bromide appears to be composed of $[PBr_4]^+$ and Br^-.

14.107 Inasmuch as phosphorus in the pentahalides is capable of expanding its valence shell beyond ten electrons, these compounds can react with electron-pair donors. Reaction with water as the donor molecule proceeds ener-getically, the halide being hydrolyzed in two stages.

$$PX_5 + H_2O = POX_3 + 2H^+ + 2X^-$$
$$POX_3 + 3H_2O = H_3PO_4 + 3H^+ + 3X^-$$

Decomposition by means of ammonia occurs with the formation of ammonium salts and ammono derivatives of phosphoric acid. The reaction, however, is complex, and the nature of products is dependent upon experimental conditions. It is noteworthy that except for compounds containing the hexafluorophosphate ion, $[PF_6]^-$, no stable complexes formed by the union of the pentahalides with donor groups have been isolated. (The existence of $[PCl_6]^-$ in the solid penta-chloride has been noted above.)

14.108 The parent of the hexafluorophosphates is the strong acid $H[PF_6]$, which is prepared either by reaction between ammonium fluoride and phosphoric anhydride at 135° or by the addition of the anhydride to 40 per cent hydro-fluoric acid. Alkali and ammonium salts can be obtained in good yield when phosphorus pentachloride and the appropriate simple fluoride salt are heated together. It is interesting that if the fluoride of a dipositive cation is used no complex is isolated, but rather the pentachloride is converted quantitatively to the fluoride. In their solubilities alkali metal fluorophosphates bear a close resemblance to the perchlorates, e.g., the rubidium and cesium salts are only slightly soluble in water. Aqueous solutions are neutral to phenolphthalein and are not hydrolyzed even on long heating with alkali. Hydrolysis occurs in strongly acidic media.

Tetrahalides **14.109** Two tetrahalides, P_2Cl_4 and P_2I_4, have been character-ized. The tetrachloride is obtained when an electric discharge is passed through a mixture of hydrogen and phosphorus trichloride. The tetraiodide is prepared by the union of the elements in carbon disulfide in the presence of traces of water as catalyst. The colorless tetrachloride (f.p., −28°; b.p., 180°) is sensitive to air oxidation and hydrolysis. On standing, it decomposes to the trichloride and phosphorus. The red tetraiodide (m.p., 124.5°) decomposes in a similar fashion and is also readily hydrolyzed. Products of hydrolysis include phosphine and hydriodic, hypophosphorous, phosphorous, and phosphoric acids. The fact that in alkaline solution hydrogen peroxide converts the tetraiodide to the hypophosphate ion, $P_2O_6^{4-}$, is indicative of P—P binding.

Oxy- and Thiohalides   **14.110** These are all derived from the pentahalides and are limited to the types POX_3 (phosphoryl halides) and PSX_3 (thiophosphoryl halides). No iodides have been isolated, but both simple and mixed compounds, *e.g.*, POF_2Cl, $POCl_2Br$, PSF_2Br, are known for the other halogens.

14.111 Although formed by the partial hydrolysis of the pentahalides (see 14.107), phosphoryl halides are most conveniently obtained by other methods. The fluoride can be prepared in a number of ways: reaction between phosphoric anhydride (P_4O_{10}) and such solid fluorides as cryolite (Na_3AlF_6) and calcium fluoride at elevated temperatures; halogen exchange between phosphoryl chloride (see below) and a metal fluoride, *e.g.*, ZnF_2, PbF_2, BiF_3, or SbF_3. (Use of antimony(III) fluoride also yields mixed phosphoryl fluorohalides.) Thiophosphoryl fluoride and mixed halides may be obtained by similar methods. Phosphoryl chloride and bromide are best prepared by heating the appropriate pentahalide with oxalic acid.

$$PX_5 + (COOH)_2 = POX_3 + 2H^+ + 2X^- + CO + CO_2$$

They can also be made by reaction between pentahalide and phosphoric anhydride. The thiophosphoryl compounds are formed from the pentasulfide in a corresponding manner.

14.112 The phosphoryl and thiophosphoryl halides are low melting, low boiling, covalent substances possessing tetrahedral structures in the vapor state. They are soluble without reaction in nonhydroxylic organic solvents. The oxyhalides are rapidly decomposed by water, the products of reaction being orthophosphoric acid and hydrohalic acids. The corresponding reaction of thiophosphoryl halides proceeds somewhat more slowly, suggesting the possibility that the larger sulfur atom offers steric hindrance to attack of the phosphorus atom by the electron-pair donor, water. Both phosphoryl and thiophosphoryl fluoride are converted by alkaline hydrolysis to fluorophosphate ions, *e.g.*, $PO_2F_2^-$, PO_3F^{2-}, $PSOF_2^-$.

14.113 As a result of the presence of the sulfur atom, the thiophosphoryl halides possess some properties not observed in the oxygen compounds. Thus thiophosphoryl fluoride is spontaneously inflammable in air, whereas the corresponding oxygen compound is stable. Phosphoryl chloride is thermally stable, but the thio compound loses sulfur irreversibly when heated strongly in the absence of air. Hydrolysis of thiophosphoryl fluoride results in the removal of a small amount of sulfur as sulfide, a process which can be enhanced by the presence of a silver salt.

Oxides of Phosphorus

14.114 The compounds which have been described are P_4O_6, P_4O_{10}, P_4O_8 or $(PO_2)_n$, and PO_3. Of these, only the first two are of considerable importance and therefore are discussed in some detail. $(PO_2)_n$ is formed when the sesqui-oxide, phosphorus(III) oxide, is heated *in vacuo* to temperatures above $210°$. It is a solid material which sublimes at $180°$ and appears to have the composition P_4O_8 in the vapor state at $500°$. Although formally the anhydride of hypo-phosphoric acid $H_4P_2O_6$, $(PO_2)_n$ dissolves in water to yield equivalent quantities of phosphorous and phosphoric acids. The oxide corresponding to the com-position PO_3 is produced in small yield as a deep-violet material by the sparking of a mixture of phosphoric anhydride (phosphorus(V) oxide) vapor and oxygen. Aqueous solutions of PO_3 possess powerful oxidizing ability. It has been sug-gested that the compound is a peroxide of the composition

$$O_2\text{—P—O—O—P—}O_2.$$

Phosphorus(III) Oxide **14.115** This compound (m.p., $23.8°$; b.p., $175.4°$) is obtained as the chief product in the combustion of white phosphorus in a limited supply of air. Unreacted phosphorus may be removed by conversion to the insoluble red form on exposure of a carbon disulfide solution of the crude prod-uct to a mercury arc. The molecular weight of the sesquioxide both in solution (in organic solvents) and in the vapor state corresponds to the formula P_4O_6. Structural investigations of the vapor show that in the molecule the four phosphorus atoms occupy the corners of a tetrahedron, with the oxygen atoms being just outside the mid-points of the six edges (P—O bond length 1.65 Å).

14.116 Above $210°$ the compound decomposes into elementary phosphorus and $(PO_2)_n$. It reacts vigorously with chlorine and bromine; when heated with iodine in carbon disulfide solution in a closed tube, reaction occurs to yield the tetraiodide.

$$5P_4O_6 + 8I_2 = 4P_2I_4 + 3P_4O_{10}$$

Combination of the sesquioxide with oxygen is slow at ordinary temperature. Phosphorus(III) oxide is the anhydride of phosphorous acid and is converted to this substance on shaking with cold water. In hot water decomposition occurs and elementary phosphorus, phosphine, and phosphoric acid are found among the products.

Phosphorus(V) Oxide **14.117** This substance, known also as phosphorus pentoxide and phosphoric anhydride, is formed as the main product in the burn-ing of white phosphorus in an excess of air. It can be freed from lower oxide contaminants by sublimation in oxygen. Pure phosphorus(V) oxide as obtained commercially sublimes at about $358°$ at 1 atm. pressure. The compound is known in three crystalline modifications and one amorphous form. In the vapor state and in the most stable crystalline modification phosphorus(V) oxide exists as the dimer P_4O_{10}. This has the same structure as P_4O_6, with an extra oxygen on each phosphorus atom at a distance of 1.39 Å, which is much shorter than the value (1.62 Å) found for the other P—O bond distances in the molecule.

14.118 Phosphorus(V) oxide is quite stable thermally.   Its outstanding chemical characteristic is the great avidity with which it absorbs water to yield phosphoric acids; reaction with a limited supply of water gives polymeric metaphosphoric acids, $(HPO_3)_x$; with additional quantities of water pyrophosphoric acid, $H_4P_2O_7$, and finally orthophosphoric acid, H_3PO_4, are formed. The heat of solution of the oxide to give the latter acid is about 35 kcal. per mole.

Oxyacids and Their Salts

14.119 The more common oxyacids, which are known either in the free state or in the form of salts, are listed in Table 14.6 in order of increasing oxidation state of phosphorus.   Only the acids of the tri- and pentapositive states are derived from known anhydrides, namely, P_4O_6 and P_4O_{10}, respectively.   In all the oxyacids, phosphorus exhibits a coordination number of four and is tetrahedral. The acids containing phosphorus in the $+1$ and $+3$ states are strong reducing agents; those derived from pentapositive phosphorus possess little oxidizing power.   In addition to the compounds shown in Table 14.6, pyrophosphorous acid, $H_4P_2O_5$, and metaphosphorous acid, HPO_2, are known; also two peroxy

TABLE 14.6

Some Oxyacids of Phosphorus

Oxidation State of Phosphorus	Compound	Name	Characteristics *
$+1$	$H(H_2PO_2)$	Hypophosphorous acid	Monoprotic; $K = 1 \times 10^{-2}$; strong reducing agent.
$+3$	$H_2(HPO_3)$	(ortho) Phosphorous acid	Diprotic; $K_1 = 1.6 \times 10^{-2}$; $K_2 = 7 \times 10^{-7}$; strong reducing agent in alkaline solution.
$+4$	$H_4P_2O_6$	Hypophosphoric acid	Tetraprotic; $K_1 = 6.4 \times 10^{-3}$; $K_2 = 1.5 \times 10^{-3}$; $K_3 = 5.4 \times 10^{-8}$; $K_4 = 9.4 \times 10^{-11}$
$+5$	$(HPO_3)_n$	Metaphosphoric acids	Polymeric; n = 3 and 4 for salts; pure acids have not been isolated.
	$H_5P_3O_{10}$	Triphosphoric acid	Known in the form of its salts.
	$H_4P_2O_7$	Pyrophosphoric acid	Tetraprotic; $K_1 = 1.4 \times 10^{-1}$; $K_2 = 1.2 \times 10^{-2}$; $K_3 = 2.9 \times 10^{-7}$; $K_4 = 3.6 \times 10^{-9}$
	H_3PO_4	Orthophosphoric acid	Triprotic; $K_1 = 7.5 \times 10^{-3}$; $K_2 = 6.2 \times 10^{-8}$; 1.2×10^{-12}

* Values for dissociation constants for the acids vary slightly depending upon the source.

acids, H_3PO_5 and $H_4P_2O_8$, derived from orthophosphoric, H_3PO_4, and pyrophosphoric acid, $H_4P_2O_7$, respectively, have been characterized.

Hypophosphorous Acid   **14.120** Hypophosphorous acid, $H(H_2PO_2)$, containing monopositive phosphorus is ordinarily prepared in the form of its barium salt by reaction of white phosphorus with aqueous barium hydroxide (see 14.89). The free acid is obtained from the barium salt as a colorless substance (m.p., 26.5°) by metathesis. It is a strong monoprotic acid for which the structural formula * shown may be written. Although they are unaffected by oxygen, both acidic and alkaline hypophosphite solutions are strong reducing agents; reaction with oxidizing agents is frequently slow, however.

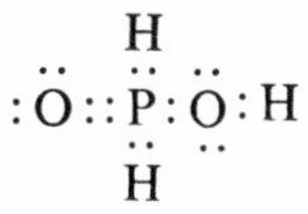

$$H_2O + H_3PO_2 = H_3PO_3 + 2H^+ + 2e^- \qquad E° = 0.50 \text{ v.}$$
$$3OH^- + H_2PO_2^- = HPO_3^{2-} + 2H_2O + 2e^- \qquad E_B° = 1.57$$

Solutions of the acid are stable at room temperature but decompose when heated above 140° to give phosphine, phosphoric acid, and hydrogen.

Phosphorous Acid **14.121** The common oxyacid corresponding to the +3 state of phosphorus is (ortho)phosphorous acid, $H_2(HPO_3)$. Although it may be obtained by reaction of phosphorus(III) oxide with ice water (see 14.116), it is more conveniently prepared by the hydrolysis of the trichloride (see 14.101). The pure acid is a deliquescent, low melting (m.p., 71.7–73.6°), colorless solid. Only two of the hydrogen atoms are replaceable, and on this basis the formula shown may be assigned to the acid. Phosphite salts containing the $H_2PO_3^-$ and HPO_3^{2-} ions can be prepared.

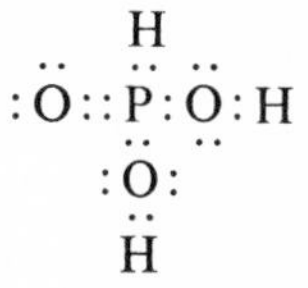

14.122 In aqueous medium phosphorous acid is a fairly strong acid ($K_1 = 1.6 \times 10^{-2}$); concentrated solutions (and also the free acid) are unstable when heated and decompose into phosphine and orthophosphoric acid.

$$4H_3PO_3 = PH_3 + 3H_3PO_4$$

As indicated by the oxidation potentials, acidic and alkaline phosphite solutions possess strong reducing power.

$$H_2O + H_3PO_3 = H_3PO_4 + 2H^+ + 2e^- \qquad E° = 0.276 \text{ v.}$$
$$3OH^- + HPO_3^{2-} = PO_4^{3-} + 2H_2O + 2e^- \qquad E_B° = 1.12$$

Although the potential is highly favorable, reaction between molecular oxygen and phosphorous acid solutions is slow at room temperature.

Hypophosphoric Acid **14.123** Hypophosphoric acid, in which phosphorus formally exhibits the +4 oxidation state, has the composition $H_4P_2O_6$. It is com-

---

* There is strong evidence that in oxyacids, ionizable (replaceable) hydrogen is bound to oxygen; those hydrogen atoms which are not replaceable are joined directly to the central atom of the acid. The electronic formulas for the oxyacids of phosphorus and the various phosphate ions commonly are written so that the phosphorus atoms are surrounded by octets of electrons. Since phosphorus can expand its valence shell beyond eight electrons, a structure such as the one shown above does not appear to be unreasonable. Indeed, in the orthophosphate ion the P—O bond distance is considerably shorter than that expected for a single bond.

monly obtained as the rather insoluble sodium salt $Na_2H_2P_2O_6 \cdot 6H_2O$ by the action of aqueous sodium acetate on white phosphorus which has been partially submerged in water and exposed to air. Other products of reaction are soluble acid salts of phosphorous and phosphoric acids. The sodium salt of hypophosphoric acid can be converted to the less soluble lead salt, which in turn can be transformed to a solution of the acid by treatment with hydrogen sulfide. From the solution the free acid is obtained as the dihydrate $H_4P_2O_6 \cdot 2H_2O$ by evaporation in a vacuum.

14.124 The hydrated acid (m.p., 70°) is a colorless, deliquescent material, which on thermal decomposition yields phosphorous and orthophosphoric acids. Aqueous solutions are stable toward molecular oxygen but hydrolyze to yield the same acids as are obtained on decomposition of the solid. Although the acid is tetraprotic (see Table 14.6), the more common salts are of the types $M^IH_3P_2O_6$ and $M^I_2H_2P_2O_6$.

14.125 Evidence that the formula of hypophosphoric acid is $H_4P_2O_6$ rather than H_2PO_3 comes from molecular weight determinations in aqueous solution and from the diamagnetism of a number of its salts. The properties of the acid make it highly likely that the two phosphorus atoms are linked together in the molecule by a single covalent bond.

```
        H     H
        ..    ..
       :O:   :O:
    ..  ..    ..  ..
   H:O:P  :  P:O:H
    ..  ::    ::  ..
       :O:   :O:
        ..    ..
```

The Phosphoric Acids and Their Salts   **14.126** The most important of the various acids and salts containing phosphorus in its maximum oxidation state of $+5$ is orthophosphoric acid, H_3PO_4. In addition to orthophosphoric acid and its salts, other phosphoric acids and /or their salts are known, which may be considered to be derived from orthophosphoric acid or its salts by condensation reactions involving the elimination of water. Condensation products possessing ring structures are called metaphosphates; those with simple P—O—P chains are commonly known as polyphosphates. The structural unit common to all phosphoric acids and phosphates is the PO_4 tetrahedron. Inasmuch as the subject of condensed phosphates is an extremely complicated one, and one concerning which there are many aspects still not clear, only a few facets of this topic will be discussed.

14.127 Orthophosphoric acid is the product of reaction of phosphorus(V) oxide with an excess of water. The pure material is a white, crystalline, low melting (42.4°) solid having a strong tendency to supercool. It is completely miscible with water. Although it is a triprotic acid, only the first stage dissociation occurs to any significant extent ($K_1 = 7.5 \times 10^{-3}$; $K_2 = 6.2 \times 10^{-8}$; $K_3 = 1.2 \times 10^{-12}$). On the basis of its triprotic character, the structure of the acid may be formulated as shown. Chemically, aside from its functions as an acid, orthophosphoric acid is rather unreactive at room temperature. The same may be said for the other phosphoric acids.

```
        H
        ..
       :O:
        ..
   :O::P:O:H
        ..
       :O:
        ..
        H
```

14.128 Salts derived by the successive replacement of all three hydrogen atoms are known — $M^IH_2PO_4$, $M^I_2HPO_4$, and $M^I_3PO_4$ — and are commonly designated as primary, secondary, and tertiary orthophosphates, respectively. The latter are most difficult to obtain because of the weakly acidic nature of the third hydrogen atom. Of the secondary and tertiary phosphates only the alkali metal salts possess considerable aqueous solubility; the primary phosphates are generally the most soluble of the three types of salts. Aqueous solutions of tertiary orthophosphates are strongly alkaline, as a result of hydrolysis. Primary and secondary phosphates are thermally unstable and decompose when heated.

$$xNaH_2PO_4 = (NaPO_3)_x + xH_2O$$
$$2Na_2HPO_4 = Na_4P_2O_7 + H_2O$$

The orthophosphate ion, PO_4^{3-}, is tetrahedral, with a P—O bond distance much shorter than that calculated for a single bond. For example, in Ag_3PO_4 this distance, as determined by X-ray analysis, is 1.61 Å (calculated for P—O, 1.70; for P=O, 1.55 Å).

14.129 Of the condensed acids, only one, pyrophosphoric (diphosphoric) acid, $H_4P_2O_7$, has been definitely isolated in the crystalline state, although there appears to be no question that triphosphoric acid, $H_5P_3O_{10}$, exists. Pyrophosphoric acid can be obtained by prolonged heating of the ortho acid at 200–300°; the solid acid (m.p., 61°, with decomposition) slowly crystallizes from the cooled melt. Although pyrophosphoric acid is a tetraprotic acid containing two strongly acidic hydrogen atoms ($K_1 = 1.4 \times 10^{-1}$; $K_2 = 1.2 \times 10^{-2}$),* it appears to form only two series of salts — $M^I_2H_2P_2O_7$ and $M^I_4P_2O_7$ or $M^{IV}P_2O_7$ (M^{IV} = Ti, Sn, Zr, Hf). Of the normal pyrophosphates, only the alkali metal salts are water soluble, their solutions being alkaline through hydrolysis. In solution they are slowly converted to orthophosphates. The acid salts are soluble and most give a weakly acidic reaction in water. Electronically, pyrophosphoric acid may be represented as shown. On the basis of X-ray evidence, the neutral pyrophosphate ion appears to consist of two PO_4 tetrahedra having one oxygen atom in common.

14.130 Pyrophosphoric acid may be regarded as the first member of a polyphosphoric acid series of the general formula $H_{n+2}P_nO_{3n+1}$. Although no other members of the series have been isolated, the next higher homolog, triphosphoric acid, $H_5P_3O_{10}$, has been prepared in the form of salts of the types $M^I_5P_3O_{10}$ and $M^IM^{II}_2P_3O_{10}$, e.g., $Na_5P_3O_{10}$, $NaZn_2P_3O_{10}$. The former of the two specific examples cited is obtained by reaction between aqueous sodium hydroxide and sodium trimetaphosphate, $(NaPO_3)_3$ (see below). Hydrolysis of the tri-

---

* It should be noted that pyrophosphoric acid is considerably stronger than the ortho acid. In general, the more highly condensed the acid is, the stronger it is.

phosphate ion yields orthophosphate and pyrophosphate. The triphosphate ion is a linear polymer composed of PO_4 tetrahedra. In addition to pyro- and triphosphates, there appear to exist high linear polymeric phosphates of the type $M^I_n[P_nO_{3n-1}(OH)_2]$, in which n has values of 16 to 90.

14.131 If the condensation of orthophosphoric acid molecules is carried beyond the stage which gives the pyro- acid, a substance of the composition $(HPO_3)_n$, known as metaphosphoric acid, is ultimately produced. Triphosphoric acid and other linear acids of higher molecular weight appear to be formed as intermediates between the pyro- acid and $(HPO_3)_n$. Metaphosphoric acid is in reality a mixture of polymeric substances, and no individual species appears to have been isolated. However, alkali metal salts of metaphosphoric acid in which the condensed phosphate ions are trimeric and tetrameric have been prepared. These anions possess cyclic structures. Sodium trimetaphosphate is obtained by the thermal decomposition of the primary orthophosphate (see above) or of the dihydrogen pyrophosphate.

$$3Na_2H_2P_2O_7 = 3H_2O + 2(NaPO_3)_3$$

Sodium trimetaphosphate exists in three crystalline forms. Hydrolysis of tri- and tetrametaphosphates ultimately yields the orthophosphate ion.

Arsenic, Antimony, and Bismuth

The Elements

14.132 Although arsenic and antimony occasionally occur uncombined in nature, their principal minerals are sulfides. Bismuth is commonly found in the native state. Elementary arsenic and antimony are obtained from their sulfide ores by conversion to the oxides by roasting and reduction of the latter with carbon.

14.133 Both arsenic and antimony exist in a number of allotropic modifications. The most stable form of each element possesses a metallic crystal lattice. Metallic arsenic is a gray, brittle, and rather soft substance which sublimes at 633° at one atmosphere pressure. In the vapor state arsenic exists as tetrahedral tetratomic molecules up to 800°. Metallic antimony is a relatively soft, silver-white, brittle material (m.p., 630.5°; b.p., 1325°). The molecular weight in the vapor state at 1572° corresponds to the formula Sb_3, and it is likely that at lower temperatures this element is also tetratomic. The best characterized of the unstable modifications of arsenic, and also antimony, is a yellow form; in each case the yellow modification resembles white phosphorus in general behavior but is even more reactive. Bismuth appears to occur only in a metallic form (m.p., 271; b.p., ca. 1560°). It is a reddish-white, brittle substance which is somewhat softer than arsenic and antimony. In the vapor state it exists as a mixture of Bi_2 and Bi molecules.

14.134 Chemically, arsenic, antimony, and bismuth are stable toward air at room temperature, but burn when heated to yield the oxides As_4O_6, Sb_4O_6, and Bi_2O_3, respectively. At elevated temperatures the elements also combine directly with the halogens, sulfur, and a variety of metals. Arsenic, antimony, and bismuth fall below hydrogen in the electromotive series and are thus unreactive toward nonoxidizing acids.

$$As + 3H_2O = H_3AsO_3 + 3H^+ + 3e^- \qquad E° = -0.247 \text{ v.}$$
$$Sb + H_2O = SbO^+ + 2H^+ + 3e^- \qquad E° = -0.212$$
$$Bi + H_2O = BiO^+ + 2H^+ + 3e^- \qquad E° = -0.32$$

The increase in metallic character from arsenic to bismuth is pointed up by the reactions of the elements with oxidizing acids. Arsenic dissolves in dilute nitric acid or in concentrated sulfuric acid to yield arsenious acid, H_3AsO_3, and in concentrated nitric acid to give arsenic acid, H_3AsO_4. Antimony reacts with nitric acid to give either Sb_4O_6 or Sb_2O_5, depending upon the concentration of the acid. With concentrated sulfuric acid, $Sb_2(SO_4)_3$ is formed. Hot concentrated nitric or sulfuric acid dissolves bismuth with the production of aquated Bi^{3+}; thus from the nitric acid solution the salt $Bi(NO_3)_3 \cdot 5H_2O$ can be isolated.

14.135 Arsenic and antimony dissolve in hot concentrated alkali with the formation of arsenite (arsenate(III)) and antimonite (antimonate(III)) ions, respectively. The standard potentials for the half-reactions in alkaline solution are given.

$$As + 4OH^- = AsO_2^- + 2H_2O + 3e^- \qquad E_B° = 0.68 \text{ v.}$$
$$Sb + 4OH^- = SbO_2^- + 2H_2O + 3e^- \qquad E_B° = 0.66$$

The Pentapositive State

Pentahalides and Derivatives **14.136** Only four of the twelve possible simple pentahalides of arsenic, antimony, and bismuth are known with certainty. All the fluorides and antimony pentachloride have definitely been obtained, and in addition, there is some reason to believe that arsenic(V) chloride may exist at low temperatures. The absence of pentahalides other than the fluoride for bismuth is not surprising in view of the very great tendency of this element to assume the tripositive condition. The nonexistence for arsenic and antimony of the other possible members of the series is probably the result of a combination of steric factors and the oxidizing ability of these elements in the pentapositive state.

14.137 Arsenic pentafluoride and antimony pentachloride are readily obtained by direct union of the elements. The most convenient method for the production of antimony(V) fluoride utilizes halogen exchange between the pentachloride and hydrogen fluoride. Bismuth(V) fluoride is prepared by combination between elementary fluorine and the trifluoride at 460–500°.

14.138 A number of mixed antimony(V) chlorofluorides have been identified, *e.g.*, SbF_3Cl_2. It is believed that a compound of the type SbF_3X_2 is the fluorine carrier in the so-called Swarts reaction involving fluorination by means of antimony(III) fluoride in the presence of chlorine or bromine as catalyst.

14.139 The pentafluorides of arsenic, antimony, and bismuth are volatile materials (b.p.: AsF_5, $-52.3°$; SbF_5, $150°$; BiF_5, $550°$ [subl.]) and resemble the corresponding phosphorus compound in their considerable thermal stability. When heated, antimony(V) chloride decomposes to the trichloride and chlorine. As one might suppose, bismuth(V) fluoride is a potent oxidizing agent, reacting explosively with hydrogen and with liquid aliphatic hydrocarbons at temperatures well below $100°$. The antimony compound acts as a direct fluorinating agent toward such inorganic compounds as $MoCl_5$, WCl_5, P_4O_{10}, and CrO_2Cl_2.

14.140 The pentahalides function as acceptor molecules toward water and other donor groups. The nature of the hydrolytic reaction for the antimony and bismuth compounds is markedly different from that of the phosphorus pentahalides (see 14.107). Bismuth(V) fluoride appears to exert a powerful oxidizing action on water, reaction being accompanied by fire and by the liberation of a gaseous substance with properties very much like those of ozone. Hydrolysis of antimony pentahalides, unlike the corresponding reaction for the phosphorus compounds, does not appear to go to completion. This is not unexpected in view of the considerable decrease in electronegativity on passing from phosphorus to antimony. Water combines with antimony pentafluoride to give a substance of the composition $SbF_5 \cdot 2H_2O$. Although the structure of this compound has not been determined, its reactions clearly indicate that it is, in reality, an oxyfluoro complex. Under suitable conditions water reacts with the pentachloride to give the "hydrates" $SbCl_5 \cdot H_2O$ and $SbCl_5 \cdot 4H_2O$. It is probable that these substances also are oxyhalo complexes.

14.141 Arsenic and antimony pentahalides form halo complexes of the type $[EX_6]^-$, *e.g.*, $[AsF_6]^-$, $[SbF_6]^-$, and $[SbCl_6]^-$. No analogous complex is obtained from bismuth(V) fluoride. Although antimony pentabromide is unknown, a complex ion of the composition $[SbBr_6]^-$ has been identified. However, the available evidence indicates that this ion probably is a polybromide of tripositive antimony. The hexafluoro complexes are prepared by the addition of an alkali metal fluoride to a solution of the appropriate pentoxide in concentrated hydrofluoric acid. The hexafluoroantimonates are much more readily decomposed by water than are the hexafluorophosphate complexes (see 14.108). The hydrolysis reaction in pure water is rapid and results in the replacement of a maximum of three fluorine atoms by hydroxide; in alkaline solution, the hexafluoroantimonate(V) ion is transformed into $[Sb(OH)_6]^-$. $[SbF_6]^-$ has been shown to be octahedral in structure.

14.142 In addition to alkali metal hexachloroantimonates and the strong acid $HSbCl_6 \cdot 4.5H_2O$, chloro complexes with di- and tripositive cations are known. The latter substances contain large numbers of water molecules of crystallization and a chlorine content which would appear to indicate that the antimony exhibits a coordination number greater than six, *e.g.*, $FeSbCl_8 \cdot 8H_2O$. However, precipitation reactions with aqueous silver nitrate definitely demonstrate that these substances contain $[SbCl_6]^-$. Thus, only two chlorine atoms are immediately precipitated from solutions of the iron compound cited above.

14.143 Aside from the halo complexes, the only other stable coordination compounds of the pentahalides appear to be the 1 : 1 addition compounds of antimony(V) chloride with ethers, alcohols, aldehydes, esters, and nitriles.

Oxides and Oxyacids **14.144** The chemistry of the pentoxides emphasizes the decreasing tendency of the group V elements to attain the pentapositive state as they become more metallic in nature. Unlike phosphorus pentoxide, the corresponding compound of arsenic, antimony, or bismuth cannot be prepared by atmospheric oxidation of the element or of the sesquioxide. Arsenic pentoxide, As_2O_5,* is commonly obtained by the dehydration of arsenic acid, H_3AsO_4, which is formed by the oxidation of the sesquioxide with a strong oxidizing agent such as concentrated nitric acid. The antimony compound, Sb_2O_5,* is produced in a hydrated condition by reaction between concentrated nitric acid and the metal. The anhydrous oxide, which readily loses oxygen at temperatures in the neighborhood of 700°, to give Sb_2O_4 (see 14.159), is obtained by careful heating of the hydrate. Bismuth(V) oxide does not appear to have been prepared in the pure condition, a not surprising fact in view of the powerful oxidizing properties of the pentapositive state of this element. Treatment of alkali metal bismuthates, $MBiO_3$, (see below) with nitric acid gives red-brown substances approximating Bi_2O_5 in composition. These materials undergo extensive loss of oxygen, even at temperatures below 100°.

14.145 Arsenic pentoxide is extremely soluble in water and gives solutions containing orthoarsenic acid, H_3AsO_4. From solution, hydrated forms of this acid can be isolated, and these yield the anhydrous acid, as well as the pyro-, $H_4As_2O_7$, and meta-, $HAsO_3$, acids on thermal decomposition. In its first stage dissociation orthoarsenic acid is a somewhat weaker acid than is orthophosphoric. In acid solutions it is a rather strong oxidizing agent.

$$H_3AsO_4 + 2H^+ + 2e^- = HAsO_2 + 2H_2O \qquad E° = 0.559 \text{ v.}$$

The salts (arsenates) derived from the acid resemble the phosphates in their characteristics.

14.146 No simple acid derived from Sb_2O_5 has been isolated. Solid products obtained by complete hydrolysis of antimony(V) chloride, which were at one time called antimonic acid, are antimony(V) oxide hydrates of variable water content. These substances, the saturated solutions of which are fairly acid, are soluble both in acids and in alkalies. The acid solutions probably contain the compound $H[Sb(OH)_6]$. An insoluble potassium or sodium salt may be precipitated in the cold from such solutions, and X-ray analysis of the sodium salt has shown it to possess the hexahydroxoantimonate(V) ion, $[Sb(OH)_6]^-$.

---

* Empirical formula; structure unknown.

In addition to compounds containing this ion, antimonates formally related to the hypothetical antimonic acids H_3SbO_4, $H_4Sb_2O_7$, and $HSbO_3$ can be prepared by fusion of antimony(V) oxide with the appropriate quantities of, *e.g.*, alkaline earth metal oxide. Acid solutions of antimonates are relatively strong oxidizing agents.

14.147 The fact that $+5$ bismuth is a very strong oxidizing agent in acid medium

$$Bi_2O_5^{\cdot} + 6H^+ + 4e^- = 2BiO^+ + 3H_2O \qquad E° = ca.\ 1.6\ v.$$

precludes the isolation of an acid derived from the pentoxide. However, alkali metal metabismuthates, $MBiO_3$, have been prepared by the oxidation (*e.g.*, with chlorine, peroxydisulfate ion, permanganate ion) of bismuth(III) oxide suspended in concentrated alkali hydroxide solutions. Orthobismuthates, M_3BiO_4, can be obtained readily by heating the sesquioxide with the appropriate quantity of alkali metal oxide (or peroxide) in air.

$$Bi_2O_3 + 3Na_2O + O_2 = 2Na_3BiO_4$$

The Tripositive State

Trihalides and Derivatives   **14.148** In contrast to the situation with the pentahalides, the complete series of trihalides is known for arsenic, antimony, and bismuth. The melting and boiling points of these compounds are listed in Table 14.7.

TABLE 14.7

Melting and Boiling Points of As, Sb, and Bi Trihalides

Compound	Melting Point, °C.	Boiling Point, °C.	Compound	Melting Point, °C.	Boiling Point, °C.
AsF_3	-5.95	62.8	$AsBr_3$	31	220
SbF_3	ca. 290	319	$SbBr_3$	96	228
BiF_3	725	Saltlike	$BiBr_3$	218	453
$AsCl_3$	-13	130	AsI_3	141	ca. 400
$SbCl_3$	72.9	221	SbI_3	170.3	ca. 410
$BiCl_3$	230	447	BiI_3	408	500(decomp.)

14.149 All the trihalides can be prepared by direct union of the elements, the group V element being present in excess in order to keep to a minimum the formation of pentahalide where that is possible. The fluorides, however, are ordinarily formed by other methods. Thus arsenic(III) and bismuth(III) fluorides are obtained by reaction between the sesquioxides and hydrofluoric acid, and the antimony compound by halogen exchange between the trichloride and hydrogen fluoride.

14.150 The trihalides behave as acceptor molecules toward water and other Lewis bases. The nature of the hydrolytic products is consistent with the increasingly metallic character in passing from arsenic to bismuth. Reaction of arsenic trihalides with water goes nearly to completion to yield arsenious and hydrohalic acids; the reaction may be reversed by addition of hydrohalic acid. Antimony and bismuth trihalides (with the exception of the fluorides) are partially and reversibly decomposed with the formation of insoluble compounds containing the SbO^+ (antimonyl) and BiO^+ (bismuthyl) cations.

$$BiX_3 + H_2O \rightleftharpoons BiO^+, X^- + 2H^+ + 2X^-$$

With antimony trifluoride, hydrolysis occurs to a very limited extent only. The corresponding bismuth compound, the only trihalide of the group which appears to be a true salt, does not undergo hydrolysis.

14.151 The trihalides form complexes with halide ion, their tendency to act as acceptor molecules increasing from arsenic to bismuth. For arsenic, salts of the types $M[AsCl_4]$, $M[AsBr_4]$, and M_2AsBr_5 (M = alkylammonium ion) have been prepared. These salts are not very stable and are immediately decomposed by water or alcohol, but can be recrystallized without change from a concentrated solution of the appropriate hydrohalic acid. Compounds of the composition $M[SbF_4]$, M_2SbCl_5 and $M_3[SbCl_6]$ have been isolated for antimony. Bismuth trihalides give complex salts of the types $M[BiX_4]$, M_2BiX_5, and $M_3[BiX_6]$, with fluoro compounds being limited to the first class and all three types being formed by the other halides. The fluoro compounds appear to be the least stable of these complexes. Since no structural information is available for the halo complexes, it is not known whether the central atom actually exhibits a coordination number of five in the compounds with five halogen atoms.

14.152 Addition compounds, chiefly of the 1 : 1 variety, are formed by certain of the antimony and bismuth trihalides with organic donor molecules. Thus antimony(III) chloride and bromide give such compounds with a number of ethers, aldehydes, and mercaptans, and bismuth(III) chloride with tertiary amines. Particularly interesting are the addition compounds produced by interaction of antimony(III) chloride with aromatic hydrocarbons such as benzene, toluene, and mesitylene. These mainly have the composition $SbCl_3 \cdot Ar$, but a few are of the type $2SbCl_3 \cdot Ar$. The compounds are unstable, low melting substances which have not been characterized structurally.

14.153 Arsenic, antimony, and bismuth trihalides have very little tendency to utilize their unshared pairs of electrons in donor-acceptor reactions. One example in which an antimony(III) halide serves as a donor molecule in the formation of a complex compound is worthy of citation. Reaction of nickel tetracarbonyl with the trichloride in cyclohexane yields $[Ni(CO)_3(SbCl_3)]$, a compound which is rapidly decomposed by acids and alkalies.[11] The replacement of only a single carbon monoxide is in contrast to the complete replacement of this group by phosphorus trichloride under similar conditions (see 14.100).

[11] WILKINSON, *J. Am. Chem. Soc.*, **73**, 5502 (1951).

Oxides and Related Compounds **14.154** The formulas for the sesquioxides of arsenic, antimony, and bismuth are commonly written as As_4O_6, Sb_4O_6, and Bi_2O_3. It has been shown that in both the solid and vapor (up to at least 800°) arsenic(III) oxide is composed of tetrahedral molecules of As_4O_6 (see P_4O_6, 14.115). Moreover, molecular weight determinations in nitrobenzene also give the doubled formula. Antimony sesquioxide exists in two crystalline modifications, one of which is composed of tetrahedral Sb_4O_6 molecules and the other of infinite double chains of the type shown.

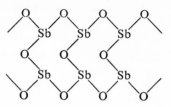

14.155 At least two crystalline forms of bismuth(III) oxide also are known, but in none have discrete molecules been distinguished.

14.156 Arsenic(III) oxide is prepared commercially by the roasting of arsenopyrite, FeAsS. The corresponding antimony and bismuth compounds are formed when the metals are burned in air.

14.157 Arsenic(III) oxide is a white, fairly volatile (b.p., 465°) substance which is moderately soluble in water. The aqueous solutions contain arsenious acid and it is not known whether this acid is present in the meta form, $HAsO_2$, or as some hydrate of this form. However, it is commonly written as the ortho acid, H_3AsO_3. Arsenious acid dissociates both as a weak acid and a weak base.

$$H_3AsO_3 = H^+ + H_2AsO_3^- \ (AsO_2^- + H_2O) \qquad K = 6 \times 10^{-10}$$
$$HAsO_2 = AsO^+ + OH^- \qquad K = 5.0 \times 10^{-15}$$

It is apparent from the basic dissociation constant that the concentration of AsO^+ is extremely small except in solutions of high hydrogen ion concentration. There is no evidence that As^{3+} is formed. Arsenious acid is converted to arsenic acid only by strong oxidizing agents.

$$HAsO_2 + 2H_2O = H_3AsO_4 + 2H^+ + 2e^- \qquad E° = -0.559 \text{ v.}$$

14.158 The majority of the salts of arsenious acid are metaarsenites, *e.g.*, M^IAsO_2. The alkali metal salts are extremely soluble, the alkaline earth derivatives possess smaller solubility, and heavy metal salts are generally insoluble. In alkaline medium the arsenite ion is a powerful reducing agent.

$$AsO_2^- + 4OH^- = AsO_4^{3-} + 2H_2O + 2e^- \qquad E_B° = 0.67 \text{ v.}$$

14.159 Antimony(III) oxide is a white, relatively insoluble, thermally stable substance. Ignition of the compound in air at temperatures below 900° gives the so-called tetroxide, Sb_2O_4. This material is probably a mixed sesqui- and pentoxide. Although saturated solutions of antimony(III) oxide undergo both acidic and basic dissociation, the latter type of dissociation apparently gives little Sb^{3+} and probably occurs as shown.

$$Sb_4O_6 + 2H_2O = 4SbO^+ + 4OH^- \qquad K = ca.\ 10^{-17}$$

The sesquioxide is inert toward dilute acids, but dissolves in concentrated acids (see 14.161). Reaction with solutions of alkalies results in the formation of antimonites (antimonate(III) salts), M^ISbO_2. The sodium salt appears to be the only alkali metal compound which has been isolated and this is obtained as slightly soluble hydrates, *e.g.*, $NaSbO_2 \cdot 3H_2O$. Solutions of antimonites are extensively hydrolyzed, and when alkaline they possess strong reducing properties.

14.160 Bismuth(III) oxide (m.p., 820°), a yellow substance at room temperature and red-brown when hot, exhibits no acidic characteristics. It is insoluble in solutions of alkalies but dissolves readily in acids to form bismuth(III) salts (see 14.161). The addition of hydroxide ions to solutions of bismuth salts gives bismuth(III) hydroxide, $Bi(OH)_3$. Although this substance is difficult to obtain in the pure condition, it has been shown to be a definite chemical compound. No analogous compound is known for arsenic or antimony. Bismuth(III) hydroxide, like the oxide from which it is derived, is completely basic in nature. If the hydroxide is heated to 100°, it is converted to a material of the approximate formula $BiO(OH)$.

Antimony(III) and Bismuth(III) Salts **14.161** The saltlike character of anhydrous bismuth(III) fluoride has already been noted (see 14.150). There is little doubt that the hydrated cationic species $Sb(H_2O)_x^{3+}$ and $Bi(H_2O)_x^{3+}$ are present in solution when the sesquioxides of antimony and bismuth are dissolved in concentrated solutions of strong oxyacids. It is possible to crystallize normal salts, *e.g.*, $Sb_2(SO_4)_3$, $Bi_2(SO_4)_3$, $Bi(NO_3)_3 \cdot 5H_2O$, from such solutions. However, these salts have a great tendency to hydrolyze, and in water or even in dilute solutions of the oxyacids they are largely converted to materials containing the basic SbO^+ and BiO^+ ions.

CHAPTER 15

GROUP VI

Introduction

15.1 As might be expected from their s^2p^4 valence shell configuration (Table 15.1), the elements of representative group VI (O, S, Se, Te, and Po)

TABLE 15.1

Electronic Configurations of Group VI Representative Elements

	1	2	3	4	5	6
	s	$s\ p$	$s\ p\ d$	$s\ p\ d\ f$	$s\ p\ d$	$s\ p$
$_8$O	2	2, 4				
$_{16}$S	2	2, 6	2, 4			
$_{34}$Se	2	2, 6	2, 6, 10	2, 4		
$_{52}$Te	2	2, 6	2, 6, 10	2, 6, 10	2, 4	
$_{84}$Po	2	2, 6	2, 6, 10	2, 6, 10, 14	2, 6, 10	2, 4

---

mainly exhibit nonmetallic chemical behavior. The increasing metallic character with increasing atomic number, so marked in the two previous groups of representative elements, is observed less clearly in group VI. It might be sup-

LATIMER, *The Oxidation States of the Elements and Their Potentials in Aqueous Solutions*, 2nd Edition, Prentice-Hall, Inc., New York, 1952, Ch. 3, 4, and 6.

PARTINGTON, *A Textbook of Inorganic Chemistry*, 6th Edition, Macmillan and Company, Ltd., London, 1950, Ch. XI, XIII, XXVI, XXVII, and XXVIII.

REMY, *Treatise on Inorganic Chemistry* (translated and amended by Anderson), Elsevier Publishing Company, Amsterdam, 1956, Vol. I, Ch. 15.

SIDGWICK, *The Chemical Elements and Their Compounds*, Oxford University Press, London, 1950, pp. 855–997.

WELLS, *Structural Inorganic Chemistry*, 2nd Edition, Oxford University Press, London, 1950, Ch. X–XIV.

YOST and RUSSELL, *Systematic Inorganic Chemistry*, Prentice-Hall, Inc., New York, 1946, Ch. 8–11.

TABLE 15.2
Some Properties of the Group VI Elements

	O	S	Se	Te	Po
Natural isotopes	16 *, 17, 18	32 *, 33, 34, 36	74, 76, 77, 78, 80 *, 82	120, 122, 123, 124, 125, 126, 128, 130 *	210 *†, 211 †, 212 †, 214 †, 215 †, 216 †, 218 †
Density	1.27 (for solid at m.p.)	2.06 (rhombic)	4.82 (gray)	6.25	
Melting point, °C.	−218.9	119.0 (monoclinic)	217.4 (gray)	449.8	
Boiling point, °C.	−182.96	444.60	684.8	1390	
Ionic radius in crystals, Å, for E^{2-}	1.40	1.84	1.98	2.21	
Covalent radius, Å	0.74	1.04	1.17	1.37	1.53
Ionization potential, volts					
1st electron	13.614	10.357	9.750	9.01	
2nd electron	35.146	23.4	21.3	————	
3rd electron	54.934	35.0	33.9	30.5	
4th electron	77.394	47.29	42.72	37.7	
5th electron	113.873	72.5	72.8	60.0	
6th electron	138.080	88.03	81.4	72.0	
Electronegativity (F = 4; H = 2.1)	3.5	2.5	2.4	2.1	
Electrode potential, $E°$, volts					
$O_2 + 2H_2O$ $+ 2e^- = 4OH^-$	0.401				
$E + 2e^- = E^{2-}$ (basic solution)		−0.48	−0.92	−1.14	

* Most abundant isotope
† Radioactive

posed, from the behavior of the elements of the two previous groups, that metallic characteristics would assume some importance where a shell of 18 electrons underlying the valence shell is first encountered. However, selenium, although it exists in a metallic as well as in a nonmetallic crystalline modification, is typically nonmetallic in its reactions. The ordinary form of tellurium is metallic, yet this element is also essentially nonmetallic in chemical behavior. It is true that tellurium appears to be able to form salts with the anions of strong acids, e.g., $Te(SO_4)_2$, but these compounds are so unstable that they have not been well characterized and it is uncertain that they contain simple tellurium ions. The last member of the group, polonium, is the most metallic. In its chemical properties it resembles its homolog tellurium and also its group V neighbor bismuth. Polonium is a radioactive disintegration product of radium. Since its most abundant isotope (^{210}Po) possesses a short half-life (138.7 days), little natural polonium has been available for study, and our knowledge of its chemistry is scanty.

15.2 Some important properties of the group VI elements are shown in Table 15.2.

15.3 All the elements of the group (apparently even polonium) exhibit a tendency to attain inert gas (s^2p^6) configurations by accepting two electrons from metals and forming dinegative ions, e.g., O^{2-}, S^{2-}, Se^{2-}, Te^{2-}. However, the processes whereby the atoms acquire two electrons are endothermic; for example, the energy requirement for conversion of one gram atom of atomic oxygen to oxide ion (gas) has been estimated to be 150 kcal. (Compare with the energetics for the formation of halide ions from halogen atoms, sec. 16.2.) In the formation of solid compounds, the work expended for the production of the dinegative ion, and also for the cation, is supplied by the lattice energy (see 5.21–22) of the resulting solid. Consistent with the relative electronegativities of the elements (Table 15.2), is the fact that ionic oxides are found for practically all the metals, whereas sulfur, selenium, and tellurium form binary ionic compounds only with the most electropositive metals, e.g., Na_2S, CaS.

15.4 In aqueous solution the conversion of oxygen to the dinegative state takes place with a decrease in free energy, the potential for the reaction, $O_2 + 2H_2O + 2e^- = 4OH^-$, being $+0.401$ v. The situation in solution differs from that described above for the formation of gaseous O^{2-} in that the reaction of the latter with water to form the hydroxide ion is a strongly exothermic process. As the potential values of Table 15.2 show, the stability of the dinegative state with respect to oxidation to the free element decreases rather significantly from oxygen to tellurium, i.e., the ability of the free elements to function as oxidizing agents decreases markedly with increasing atomic number.

15.5 The formation of ions of the type EH^- illustrates another manner in which the elements of representative group VI can acquire inert gas configurations. The stability of this ion for oxygen is reflected in the electrode potential value cited above. The corresponding ion for sulfur, SH^-, is a fairly strong reducing agent, and is readily oxidized to the free element. The apparent lack of compounds containing SeH^- and TeH^- appears to attest to the instability of these species.

15.6 Additional ways in which the members of the group can reach octet configurations are through the formation of two single electron-pair bonds, one double bond, or a single electron-pair bond in which both electrons come from another atom. Molecules in which the elements exhibit 2-covalence are common and include binary compounds with hydrogen, e.g., H_2O, H_2Se, etc., and the halogens, e.g., OF_2, SCl_2, $TeBr_2$, as well as numerous organic compounds, e.g., R_2O, R_2Te, etc. The ability to form double bonds appears to be limited to oxygen and sulfur, and such bonds are found most frequently when these elements are joined with carbon — for example, as in carbonyl halides, urea, thiourea, and carboxylic and thiocarboxylic acids. Situations in which a group VI element attains the octet by accepting a share in a pair of electrons contributed by another atom are relatively few in number. The amine oxides, $R_3N{\rightarrow}O$, sulfoxides, $R_2S{\rightarrow}O$, and sulfones, $R_2S{\Large\substack{{\nearrow}O\\{\searrow}O}}$, afford illustrations of cases in which the oxygen atom acts as an electron-pair acceptor. The polysulfides, polyselenides, and polytellurides (see 15.57 ff.) may be given as examples in which the heavier elements of the group apparently attain inert gas configurations by accepting electron-pairs from like atoms already having completed octets.

15.7 Oxygen can exhibit a covalence greater than two (see above) and the cases in which a higher covalence is shown are worthy of citation. In oxonium compounds, the most common of which are formed by the union of organic compounds (alcohols, ethers, aldehydes, and ketones) with metallic salts or hydrogen acids, oxygen is 3-covalent. The oxonium compounds are usually ionic in character — $[R_2O \cdot M]^+X^-$*, $[R_2O \cdot H]^+X^-$. (See also the hydronium ion, H_3O^+, sec. 9.6.) In these substances oxygen may be regarded as utilizing an unshared pair of electrons in the valence shell for the formation of a coordinate covalent bond with the positive entity of the added compound.† 4-Covalent oxygen exists but is extremely rare. One example is found in basic beryllium acetate, $Be_4O(OCOCH_3)_6$ (see 11.18). Oxygen cannot have a covalence greater than four in its compounds since its valence shell ($n = 2$) can hold a maximum of only eight electrons.

15.8 In all its covalent compounds, except those with fluorine, oxygen is considered to be in a negative oxidation state. Sulfur, selenium, and tellurium, elements of considerably lower electronegativity than oxygen, commonly exhibit positive oxidation states. In line with the nonmetallic behavior of these elements the bonding in the positive oxidation states is predominantly covalent in nature.

15.9 Positive oxidation states of four and six are most frequently displayed, and in addition a small number of relatively unstable compounds are found in which the +1 and +2 states are shown. The higher oxidation states are most commonly found in compounds in which sulfur, selenium, tellurium, or polonium is bound to oxygen. Inasmuch as the valence shell for sulfur, selenium, and tellurium in each case has a principal quantum number greater than two, these elements, unlike oxygen, are not limited to a maximum covalence of four. Thus compounds are encountered in which the elements are 6-covalent (e.g., the hexafluorides, sec. 15.65); in these, d orbitals of the valence shell of the group VI element are utilized for the formation of octahedral SP^3D^2 bonds. As might be expected, the tendency for sulfur, selenium, and tellurium to attain 6-covalence is greatest for tellurium, the largest element.

15.10 As is the situation in representative groups III, IV, and V, the maximum oxidation state (+6) becomes increasingly difficult to attain (at least in solution)

---

* More than one molecule of the oxygen compound may be attached to the metal atom.

† To the extent that the bonding between the oxygen and the metal ions is covalent in character, hydrated metal ions may be regarded as oxonium derivatives.

with increasing atomic number. This is illustrated herewith by a summary of the potential relationships existing between the +4 and +6 states in acid solution. It is to be noted that in terms of available potential values the trend is not altogether uniform.

$$H_2SO_3 \rightarrow SO_4^{2-} \qquad E^\circ = -0.17 \text{ v.}$$
$$H_2SeO_3 \rightarrow SeO_4^{2-} \qquad E^\circ = -1.15$$
$$TeO_2 \quad \rightarrow H_6TeO_6 \qquad E^\circ = -1.02$$
$$PoO_2 \quad \rightarrow PoO_3(?) \qquad E^\circ = -1.5(?)$$

15.11 A number of important differences in chemical behavior between oxygen and the remaining elements of the group have been revealed in the foregoing introduction. In view of these differences, and of many others which exist, oxygen and its compounds are treated separately in the discussion which follows. Sulfur, selenium, and tellurium, although differing in many respects, are sufficiently similar to warrant treatment as a unit. Finally, brief mention is made of some aspects of polonium chemistry.

Oxygen

The Element

15.12 Oxygen, the most abundant chemical element, comprises in compound form about one half of the earth's crust by weight. In the uncombined state it makes up 23 per cent by weight (and 20.8 per cent by volume) of the atmosphere. Three isotopes of the element, with masses 16, 17, and 18, occur in nature, ^{16}O having a relative abundance of about 99.8 per cent.

15.13 Ordinary oxygen is a diatomic gas, and although the molecule possesses an even number of electrons, it exhibits a paramagnetism corresponding to the presence of two unpaired electrons. The molecule may be represented by the structure :O⋮⋮O: in which the oxygen atoms are united by a single electron-pair bond and two three-electron bonds (5.112–113).[1] The oxygen molecule possesses high thermal stability and is only about one per cent dissociated into its atoms at 2300°.

15.14 Chemically, molecular oxygen is characterized by its ability to combine directly with most of the elements, notable exceptions being the inert gases, the halogens, gold, and platinum. It is frequently necessary to heat the reactants to initiate combination, but once reaction starts, it is accompanied by the evolution of considerable heat, and often the products become incandescent. As might be predicted from the value of the potential for its conversion to hydroxide ion (see 15.4), molecular oxygen is a fairly good oxidizing agent in aqueous solution. Among the ions which are directly oxidized by oxygen are Cr^{2+},

---

[1] PAULING, *The Nature of the Chemical Bond*, 2nd Edition, Cornell University Press, Ithaca, 1940, pp. 272–74.

Fe^{2+}, SO_3^{2-}, V^{2+}, and Ti^{3+}. It has been shown that with Ti^{3+} the formation of peroxide (peroxytitanic acid) is an intermediate stage in the oxidation.

15.15 In addition to the ordinary diatomic modification, oxygen exists in an extremely unstable, diamagnetic, triatomic form, O_3, known as ozone. No analogous substance is known for the other members of the group. Ozone is ordinarily prepared in low yields by the passage of a silent electric discharge through oxygen or air, the reaction being strongly endothermic.

$$3O_2 = 2O_3 - 34.2 \text{ kcal.}$$

15.16 Ozone is a light blue gas (f.p., $-249.6°$; b.p., $-111.5°$) exhibiting low water solubility. It is characterized by its great reactivity. Consistent with the endothermic nature of its formation is the instability of ozone with respect to reversion to ordinary oxygen. As a result of this, the substance, in high concentrations, can be highly explosive. Ozone is an extremely powerful oxidizing agent, its reduction potential in acid solution being exceeded by that of only one common substance, fluorine. Ordinarily only one of the oxygen atoms of the molecule is reduced.

$$O_3 + 2H^+ + 2e^- = O_2 + H_2O \qquad E° = 2.07 \text{ v.}$$
$$O_3 + H_2O + 2e^- = O_2 + 2OH^- \qquad E_B° = 1.24$$
$$(F_2 + 2e^- = 2F^- \qquad E° = 2.87)$$

15.17 Electron diffraction and infrared data indicate that the ozone molecule is triangular in structure. On the basis of the electron diffraction evidence, the configuration shown has been proposed. The fact that the oxygen to oxygen bond distance is intermediate between the theoretical values of 1.48 Å for a single bond and 1.10 Å for a double bond has been interpreted to indicate that the actual structure is a resonance hybrid of the following forms.

Compounds with Hydrogen

15.18 Oxygen forms two binary compounds with hydrogen: water, H_2O, and hydrogen peroxide, H_2O_2.* The former is the most common of all oxygen compounds.

Water **15.19** The water molecule is highly polar. As a consequence of the high electronegativity of oxygen, water (both liquid and solid) exists as a substance in which individual molecules are associated through hydrogen bonding. A similar situation does not prevail for the binary hydrogen compounds of the

---

* It has been assumed that the unstable intermediate HO_2 is produced in certain reactions of ozone and also of hydrogen peroxide in aqueous solution. This substance may be regarded as the parent of alkali metal superoxides (see 10.9 *ff.*).

other elements of group VI, and these exist as discrete molecules in the liquid state. The effect of hydrogen bonding is manifested in the abnormal physical properties of water as compared with corresponding properties of the other binary hydrogen compounds of the group. For example, from extrapolation of the melting points of the other hydrides (H_2S, H_2Se, H_2Te) it would be predicted that water would melt at $-100°$ rather than at $0°$.

15.20 The strongly polar nature of water, as manifested by the high value (ca. 80) of the dielectric constant, is responsible for its excellence as an ionizing solvent. Water is without a peer as a solvent for inorganic ionic substances. Not only are the forces between the oppositely charged ions in the crystal weakened considerably as a result of the high dielectric constant of water but, in addition, the great tendency of water molecules to solvate with the ions supplies energy for the solution process. In some instances the energy of solvation is sufficiently large to break bonds between metal and nonmetal which are primarily covalent in character. For example, although aluminum chloride exists as the dimeric molecule Al_2Cl_6, it readily dissolves in water to give solutions possessing high electrical conductivity. The process of solvation converts the covalently bound aluminum to the hydrated ionic form.

15.21 Solvated water molecules frequently remain bound to salts when they are removed from solution by crystallization or by evaporation of the solvent. The resulting compounds, known as hydrates, usually contain stoichiometric amounts of water, e.g., $AlCl_3 \cdot 6H_2O$, and are characterized by a different crystal structure (and often different color) from the anhydrous salt. Although in these substances the water of hydration is most commonly attached to the cation, cases in which it is bound to the anion are apparently not rare. In addition to the compounds in which water molecules are solvated directly to the ions, substances containing water of hydration are known which do not differ markedly in structure from the anhydrous materials. In these compounds the water occupies holes or tunnels existing in the crystal lattice. Such substances, e.g., the zeolites, readily undergo reversible hydration and dehydration.

15.22 When water molecules are joined to cations which have no inner d orbitals available for binding (i.e., cations of the representative group elements and Zn^{2+}, Cd^{2+}, and Hg^{2+}), it is probable that solvation occurs through ion-dipole interaction. In general, the tendency of such cations to hydrate is greater the smaller the size and the larger the charge. Thus salts of large unipositive ions such as rubidium, cesium, ammonium, and silver are practically never hydrated. With ions of transition elements which have available inner d orbitals, it is conceivable that the bonds between metal ion and water may be essentially covalent in character, although it is more likely that with these ions, also, the bonding is of the ion-dipole type. At least one example is known in which a transition metal ion is joined to water molecules by primarily covalent bonds. Thus it has been shown that the hydrated cobalt(III) ion, Co^{3+} aq., is essentially diamagnetic, a fact consistent with a formulation of D^2SP^3 (inner orbital) binding for the ion.[2]

    [2] FRIEDMAN, HUNT, PLANE and TAUBE, *J. Am. Chem. Soc.*, **73**, 4028 (1951).

15.23 The presence in the crystal of anion water has been proposed to account for the sulfate hydrates which contain odd numbers of water molecules, *e.g.*, $NiSO_4 \cdot 7H_2O$, $CuSO_4 \cdot 5H_2O$, $Li_2SO_4 \cdot H_2O$, $MgSO_4 \cdot 7H_2O$, $Na_2SO_4 \cdot 7H_2O$. It has been shown by X-ray analysis that in $CuSO_4 \cdot 5H_2O$ and $NiSO_4 \cdot 7H_2O$ one of the water molecules is bound to the sulfate ion, presumably through two hydrogen bonds. In each case, the water linked to the anion is also joined to two of the water molecules attached to the cation.

15.24 Water is a poor conductor of electric current; the specific conductance is about 4×10^{-8} ohm^{-1} at 18° and is explained in terms of the following equilibrium.

$$2H_2O \rightleftharpoons H_3O^+ + OH^- \qquad K = 1 \times 10^{-14} \text{ (at 25°)}$$

Although the value for the dissociation constant is small, this equilibrium is significant in accounting for the amphiprotic nature of water as a solvent.

15.25 Water is capable of acting both as an oxidizing and a reducing agent, although it is weak in each of these respects.

$$2H_2O + 2e^- = H_2 + 2OH^-(10^{-7} \text{ M}) \qquad E = -0.414 \text{ v.}$$
$$2H_2O = O_2 + 4H^+(10^{-7} \text{ M}) + 4e^- \qquad E = -0.815$$

From the potential values it is seen that reducing agents with oxidation potentials more positive than 0.414 volt should be able to liberate hydrogen from pure water, whereas oxidizing agents with reduction potentials more positive than 0.815 v. should tend to liberate oxygen. With increasing alkalinity of the solutions elementary hydrogen becomes more difficult to obtain, and a similar situation with regard to oxygen evolution is observed as the aqueous solutions become more acid. These facts are reflected in the values for the standard potentials.

$$2H_2O + 2e^- = H_2 + 2OH^- \qquad E_B^\circ = -0.828 \text{ v.}$$
$$2H_2O = O_2 + 4H^+ + 4e^- \qquad E^\circ = -1.229$$

15.26 The rate at which equilibrium is attained for the hydrogen couple (H_2, H^+) is ordinarily slow, and even under extremely favorable potential conditions, *e.g.*, in the reaction of *pure* zinc with cold dilute acids, reduction of hydrogen ion frequently does not occur at an appreciable speed. The oxygen couple (OH^-, O_2) is highly irreversible and rather high overvoltages are necessary for the oxidation of water to elementary oxygen.

Hydrogen Peroxide and Derivatives **15.27** Aqueous solutions of hydrogen peroxide [3] are prepared on a commercial scale by the hydrolysis of organic peroxides or of the peroxydisulfate ion ($S_2O_8^{2-}$). The latter is obtained by the low temperature (5–10°) anodic oxidation at a platinum anode of concentrated solutions of sulfuric acid or ammonium or potassium acid sulfate, ordinarily containing hydrofluoric acid.

$$2HSO_4^- = S_2O_8^{2-} + 2H^+ + 2e^-$$

[3] SHANLEY, *J. Chem. Educ.*, **28**, 260 (1951). An excellent summary of the technology of hydrogen peroxide.

Fractional distillation of the solutions at atmospheric pressure yields a distillate containing about 30 per cent H_2O_2, the hydrolysis of persulfate occurring during this process.

$$S_2O_8^{2-} + 2H_2O = H_2O_2 + 2HSO_4^-$$

Fractionation of the 30 per cent product under reduced pressure and at relatively low temperatures (about 60°) gives solutions containing at least 90 per cent hydrogen peroxide. Further purification can be effected by fractional crystallization.

15.28 An older mode of preparation involves metathesis between barium peroxide, BaO_2, and sulfuric acid. This method is still utilized industrially for the production of dilute solutions of the compound.

15.29 Pure hydrogen peroxide (f.p., −0.89°; b.p., 151° (extrapolated); density, 1.4442 at 18°) is a pale blue, oily liquid. Like water, it is a highly associated, polar substance. Its dielectric constant (89.2 at 0°) is higher than that of water (84.4 at 0°). The pure substance has a specific conductance of 2×10^{-6} at 0° and the ion product, $(H^+)(OOH^-)$, is about 1.55×10^{-12} at 20°. Thus the hydrogen ion concentration is about twelve times that in pure water. Hydrogen peroxide is completely miscible with water and the resulting solutions are weakly acidic.

$$H_2O + H_2O_2 = H_3O^+ + OOH^- \qquad K = 2.4 \times 10^{-12}$$

15.30 Structural investigations show that the hydrogen peroxide molecule is nonlinear and that one hydrogen atom is attached to each oxygen, the O—O—H bond angle being about 100°. The oxygen-oxygen distance is about 1.47 Å, which is used as a standard for the calculation of the oxygen single bond radius.

15.31 Hydrogen peroxide is thermodynamically unstable and has a great tendency to decompose into water and elementary oxygen.

$$2H_2O_2(\text{liq.}) = 2H_2O(\text{liq.}) + O_2(g) + 46.9 \text{ kcal.}$$

At high temperatures decomposition occurs with explosive violence; at ordinary temperatures the break-down is quite slow in the absence of catalysts, e.g., most heavy metals and their ions, dust, and the enzyme catalase. Aqueous solutions of hydrogen peroxide are stabilized by such substances as fluorides, pyrophosphates, and 8-hydroxyquinoline, which complex heavy metal ions. Alkaline solutions are generally more susceptible than acidic ones to catalytic decomposition.

15.32 In aqueous solution hydrogen peroxide can function both as an oxidizing and as a reducing agent.

$$
\begin{aligned}
H_2O_2 + 2H^+ + 2e^- &= 2H_2O & E^\circ &= 1.77 \text{ v.} \\
OOH^- + H_2O + 2e^- &= 3OH^- & E_B^\circ &= 0.88 \\
H_2O_2 &= O_2 + 2H^+ + 2e^- & E^\circ &= -0.682 \\
OOH^- + OH^- &= O_2 + H_2O + 2e^- & E_B^\circ &= 0.076
\end{aligned}
$$

As the potential values indicate, hydrogen peroxide is an extremely strong oxidizing agent in both acidic and alkaline media, but a rather poor reducing agent. Hydrogen peroxide exhibits reducing properties only toward powerful oxidants, *e.g.*, MnO_4^- in acid solution. It should be noted that molecular oxygen is always released in reactions in which the compound acts as a reducing agent. Although the potential is more favorable in acid solution, oxidation by means of hydrogen peroxide is frequently slow in this medium, but rapid in alkaline solution.

15.33 Two classes of simple salts are derived from hydrogen peroxide, namely the hydroperoxides and the normal peroxides, containing, respectively, OOH^- and O_2^{2-}. There is available little definitive information on hydroperoxides; in large measure this is attributable to the difficulty in establishing unequivocally the presence of the hydroperoxide ion in solid compounds. The preparation of the normal peroxides Na_2O_2 and BaO_2 has already been described (see 10.10; 11.35). Although these are the only simple peroxides which have been prepared industrially in a high state of purity, analogous compounds are known for the other members of representative groups I and II (except beryllium), as well as for zinc, cadmium, and mercury. The normal peroxides are frequently obtained in a hydrated condition, *e.g.*, $Na_2O_2 \cdot 8H_2O$, $SrO_2 \cdot 8H_2O$, by the action of hydrogen peroxide on solutions of the metal salts or hydroxides. Normal peroxides are thermally unstable and when heated, decompose with the liberation of oxygen. In aqueous solution they are hydrolyzed with the formation of hydrogen peroxide.

15.34 Peroxy acids, *i.e.*, acids containing oxygen-oxygen links, are known. One such acid, peroxydisulfuric acid, has been noted in connection with the preparation of hydrogen peroxide and is discussed in more detail in the section dealing with the peroxy acids of sulfur (see 15.101 *ff.*). Although there is little definite knowledge of their structure, the peroxy acids may be considered to be derived from oxy acids by replacement of oxide oxygens by peroxy groups. Alternatively, they may be looked upon as the products of reaction between acid anhydrides and hydrogen peroxide, and indeed, this type of reaction serves as one of the common methods for their preparation. The formation of the peroxydisulfate ion, $S_2O_8^{2-}$, by the electrolytic oxidation of acid sulfates has been described. Other salts of peroxy acids have been obtained by anodic oxidation, *e.g.*, $K_2C_2O_6$ (potassium peroxydicarbonate) from potassium hydrogen carbonate. In a number of instances peroxy derivatives have been made by the action of concentrated hydrogen peroxide on oxy salts. For example, reaction between 30 per cent hydrogen peroxide and cold solutions of ammonium dichromate in the presence of a potassium salt yields the insoluble compound $K_2Cr_2O_{12}$, which is believed to contain the anion shown.

15.35 Peroxy acids or their salts are formed by the following elements: B, C, Ti, Zr, Sn, N, P, S, V, Nb, Ta, Cr, Mo, W, and U. Frequently the composition of the peroxy compound obtained from a particular element will vary with the mode of preparation. In relatively few cases have the compounds been obtained in a pure condition. Peroxy acids are slowly decomposed by water with the formation of hydrogen peroxide and the parent oxy acid.

15.36 Compounds with hydrogen peroxide of crystallization have been obtained and are known as peroxy hydrates. These substances give hydrogen peroxide immediately when brought in contact with water and in this manner differ from peroxy acids or their salts.

Compounds of Oxygen with Other Nonmetals

15.37 The inert gases are the only nonmetals which are incapable of forming binary compounds with oxygen. The chemistry of the oxides of the nonmetals of representative groups III, IV, and V has already been discussed; the oxides of sulfur, selenium, and tellurium are considered in the present chapter and the halogen oxides in Chapter 16. A few general observations on the properties of nonmetallic oxides are pertinent here.

15.38 All the binary compounds of oxygen with nonmetals are essentially covalent in character and most occur as simple or relatively simple molecules, e.g., CO, CO_2, N_2O_5, P_4O_{10}. Two notable exceptions which have already been described are boron trioxide and silicon dioxide; although the bonding is predominantly covalent in these substances, they exist as large polymeric materials. In all nonmetallic oxides, with the exception of the oxygen fluorides, OF_2 and O_2F_2, oxygen is the more electronegative constituent. Many of the oxides are acid anhydrides, and where a number of such oxides are known for a particular element the relative strengths of the resulting acids can be correlated with the oxidation state of the element. Thus H_2SO_4, derived from SO_3, is a stronger acid than H_2SO_3, formed from the anhydride SO_2, and similarly, HNO_3 (from N_2O_5) is stronger than HNO_2 (from N_2O_3). In each of the acids cited, the hydrogen atoms are ionizable, i.e., they are bound to oxygen atoms, which are in turn joined to the central atom. In a crude way it may be pictured that the higher the oxidation state of the central atom (sulfur or nitrogen) the more strongly does it tend to attract the electrons of the attached oxygen atoms, thus facilitating the release of protons. An apparent exception to this is found in the fact that orthophosphorous acid, H_3PO_3, the anhydride of which is P_4O_6, is a stronger acid than orthophosphoric acid, H_3PO_4, formed from P_4O_{10}, the first stage dissociation constants being 1.6×10^{-2} and 7.5×10^{-3}, respectively. The phosphorus acids, however, are not strictly comparable to the pairs cited above. In the nitrogen and sulfur acids the members have the same number of ionizable hydrogens, whereas H_3PO_3 and H_3PO_4 differ in this respect, the former being diprotic and the latter triprotic.

Compounds of Oxygen with Metals

15.39 The vast majority of the metallic oxides are ionic in nature, and most of them contain the simple oxide ion, O^{2-}. A relatively small number of compounds with polyatomic oxygen anions are known. The anions of this type which have been characterized are the peroxide ion, O_2^{2-}; the superoxide ion, O_2^-; and the ozonide ion, O_3^-. Compounds in which these anions are present have already been discussed (see 10.9 ff.) and only a few remarks regarding them will be made.

15.40 Union with polyatomic anions of oxygen appears to occur most easily for metals which yield ions of relatively low charge density, i.e., ions of small ratio of charge to radius. Thus simple peroxides are formed most readily by the alkali and alkaline earth (Ca, Sr, Ba) metals and zinc, cadmium, and mercury. It is noteworthy that there is no evidence for the existence of a peroxide for beryllium, the smallest member of representative group II, and that among the alkaline earth metals it is just with barium that the peroxide can be made by direct union. The ability to form superoxides seems restricted to alkali and alkaline earth metals, and ozonides have been isolated only for the former. The importance of the role of cationic size in the formation of superoxides is indicated by the fact that of the alkali metal compounds only those of potassium, rubidium, and cesium can be made by direct reaction between metal and oxygen at atmospheric pressure. Moreover, lithium superoxide appears to be stable only in liquid ammonia and at temperatures well below the boiling point ($-33.35°$) of the medium. Polyatomic oxygen anions are characterized by the readiness with which they give up molecular oxygen when heated or when decomposed in aqueous solution. It is interesting that peroxides are products of the thermal decomposition of alkali metal ozonides.

15.41 All the metals form oxides having formulas corresponding to the presence of the normal oxide ion, O^{2-}. However, not all these oxides are truly ionic, as their chemical behavior shows. As might be supposed, the normal oxides of the most electropositive metals, e.g., the alkali and alkaline earth elements and the lanthanides, are ionic. These compounds are completely basic and readily react with water, the oxide ion being converted to the hydroxide ion. In addition, there are oxides of the types M_2O_3 and MO_2, e.g., Tl_2O_3, Bi_2O_3, ThO_2, which, although they are not converted to hydroxides by water, are nevertheless ionic. These substances readily form salts by reaction with acids, but are unaffected by solutions of strong bases. A large number of metals yield oxides which are amphoteric (e.g., BeO, Al_2O_3, Ga_2O_3, SnO, PbO) and react with both strong acids and strong bases. Saturated aqueous solutions of these oxides undergo both acidic and basic dissociation according to the example.

$$Pb^{2+} + 2OH^- \rightleftharpoons PbO(s) + H_2O \rightleftharpoons H^+ + HPbO_2^-$$

The binding in these amphoteric oxides may be regarded as possessing both ionic and covalent character. It is worth noting that, although according to potentials beryllium and aluminum are strongly electropositive elements, they yield amphoteric oxides. This can be attributed to the high polarizing ability (see 5.122–123) exhibited by cations of high charge density. Where a metal can form more than one oxide, e.g., Sb_4O_6, Sb_2O_5; PbO, PbO_2, the ionic or covalent character of the compounds is related to the oxidation state of the metal. The most ionic (basic) oxide will be the one containing the metal in the lowest oxidation state. Not infrequently, a transition element has oxides which vary in character from distinctly basic (ionic) to completely acidic, *e.g.*, CrO (basic); Cr_2O_3 (amphoteric); CrO_3 (acidic).

Sulfur, Selenium, and Tellurium

The Elements

15.42 Sulfur occurs to the extent of about 0.05 per cent in the earth's crust, mainly in the free state, as sulfide, and as sulfate. Selenium and tellurium are less common than sulfur (relative abundance: S, 50000; Se, 60; Te, 1) and ordinarily occur as impurities in heavy metal sulfide ores, from which they are recovered as dioxides in the metallurgical processes. The free elements are obtained by reduction (*e.g.*, with sulfur dioxide) of aqueous solutions of the dioxides.

15.43 A number of modifications are known for sulfur in each of the three physical states, and, although the subject of the various forms of the element has received considerable attention, the problem is extremely complex and not entirely resolved. Therefore, only a few of the more definite conclusions will be mentioned. The allotropic form stable at room temperature is rhombic (α) sulfur. This variety is insoluble in water but is readily soluble in carbon disulfide (50.4 g. in 100 g. of solvent at 25°), from which it can be recrystallized unchanged. Rhombic sulfur undergoes transformation into the enantiomorphic monoclinic (β) modification at 95.6°, the process being weakly endothermic. Transition between the two forms is slow, and, as a matter of fact, rhombic sulfur can be heated (rapidly) to its melting point of 112.8° without suffering any appreciable conversion to the monoclinic modification. Monoclinic sulfur is even more soluble in carbon disulfide and other organic solvents than is the rhombic form. The true melting point of monoclinic sulfur is 119.0°, but the substance ordinarily melts in the neighborhood of 115° to give a liquid probably containing at equilibrium three molecular species, S_8, S_6, and S_4. Equilibrium between these species is attained slowly, and both rhombic and monoclinic sulfur, if they are heated rapidly, yield a liquid consisting solely of S_8 molecules. At 120° liquid sulfur is a yellow transparent, mobile liquid; above 160° it becomes brown and increasingly viscous as the temperature is raised to 200°. Beyond this temperature the viscosity decreases and at the boiling point, 444.60°, the liquid is once again mobile. The viscosity changes appear to be related to the proportions of S_8, S_6,* and S_4 in the liquid.

15.44 Studies on the vapor density of sulfur and its change with temperature show that the molecular species S_8, S_6, S_4, and S_2 can be present simultaneously.

---

* Some investigators believe that the species in liquid sulfur which has been assigned the formula S_6 is in reality a high chain polymer.

For example, at 450° and 500 mm. pressure, the relative amounts of these molecules have been found to be: S_8, 53.9%; S_6, 37.0%; S_4, 4.9%; and S_2, 4.2%. At 750° and the same pressure, the corresponding percentages are 0.1, 0.8, 7.2, and 91.9, respectively. Above 2000°, dissociation of S_2 into atomic sulfur becomes important. Whereas both solid and liquid sulfur are diamagnetic, the vapor over a wide temperature range is paramagnetic. The paramagnetism, although somewhat less than that expected for a molecule with two unpaired electrons, has been attributed to S_2, which is believed to have a structure analogous to that of the oxygen molecule (see 15.13).

15.45 Molecular weight determinations in carbon disulfide reveal that both rhombic and monoclinic sulfur have a molecular complexity corresponding to S_8. X-ray investigation has shown that the rhombic modification consists of isolated, puckered 8-membered rings, with the S—S bond distance of 2.12 Å (calculated for a single covalent bond, 2.08 Å) and a S—S—S bond angle of about 105°. S_8 molecules in the liquid and vapor states appear to have the same

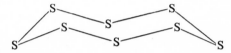

ring structure. There is some evidence that S_6 and S_4 are open chain molecules. (Solids containing S_6 rings have also been reported.) In the S_2 molecule the interatomic distance (1.88 Å) is that expected for a double bond between the atoms.

15.46 The existence of polyatomic molecules such as S_8 is a manifestation of the ease with which this element undergoes self-linkage by single covalent bond formation. In this respect sulfur differs from oxygen quite markedly. The great difference in the ability of these elements to self-link is reflected in single bond energy values: O—O, 34.9; S—S, 63.8 kcal. per mole. Compounds containing S—S bonds (*e.g.*, polysulfides, polythionic acids) are discussed in sections 15.57–59 and 15.114–117.

15.47 Selenium, like sulfur, exists in a variety of forms, but only the solid modifications have been well characterized. Two kinds of crystalline selenium are known: the gray, metallic, hexagonal form and the red, monoclinic modifications. There are, in addition, a red amorphous variety and a black vitreous form which differ from each other only in their state of subdivision. The black variety is commonly obtained by the rapid cooling of the molten element, and the red amorphous form is produced when selenite is reduced by sulfur dioxide in acid solution. Extraction of amorphous or vitreous selenium with carbon disulfide yields amber to dark red solutions. Slow evaporation of these solutions below 72° gives the so-called alpha monoclinic form; rapid removal of carbon disulfide yields the beta monoclinic modification. Evaporation of the solvent above 75° produces gray hexagonal selenium, which may also be obtained by heating the monoclinic forms. Gray selenium is the more stable of the two crystalline modifications at ordinary temperatures. In contrast to monoclinic selenium, the gray form is relatively insoluble in carbon disulfide. It possesses a metallic luster but is a relatively poor conductor of electric current, the conductivity being considerably greater in the light than in the dark.

15.48 In carbon disulfide and in other inert solvents monoclinic selenium has a molecular weight corresponding to Se_8, the molecule presumably having the same structure as that of sulfur. In the vapor state Se_8 decomposes to a considerable degree into Se_6 and Se_2, the vapor density at 900° being that of the diatomic molecule. Above 2000° selenium exists in the monatomic form. The interatomic distance in the Se_2 molecule is 2.19 Å (calculated for Se=Se, 2.14 Å). Selenium vapor, like gaseous oxygen and sulfur, is paramagnetic, probably as the result of the presence of the Se_2 species.

15.49 The only well-defined crystalline form of tellurium is a metallic form isomorphic with gray or metallic selenium. Tellurium is a silver-white, brittle substance having an electrical conductivity at 500° about one per cent of that of mercury at room temperature. It is insoluble in practically all solvents with which it does not react chemically. It has been shown that in the temperature range 1400 to 2100° tellurium vapor is diatomic, the interatomic distance (ca. 2.6 Å) corresponding fairly closely to the theoretical value for double bonding between the atoms.

15.50 In reactions with other elements sulfur, selenium, and tellurium for the most part resemble oxygen. Unlike oxygen, however, they are able to combine directly with the halogens, tellurium forming compounds with all the halogens, and sulfur and selenium with all but iodine. They burn in air with the production of dioxides, but are unable to unite directly with nitrogen. A characteristic property of sulfur and selenium, and to a lesser extent of tellurium, is the formation of homopolyatomic anions, e.g., S_x^{2-}, Se_x^{2-}, by combination of the free element with the appropriate anion. All three elements dissolve in concentrated nitric acid.

$$3X + 4HNO_3 = 3XO_2 + 2H_2O + 4NO \qquad (X = S, Se, Te)$$

Sulfur, but apparently not selenium or tellurium, reacts with concentrated solutions of alkali.

$$3S + 6OH^- = SO_3^{2-} + 2S^{2-} + 3H_2O$$

Binary Compounds with Hydrogen and their Derivatives

15.51 In addition to the hydrides expected from valence considerations, i.e., H_2S, H_2Se, and H_2Te, the "poly" compounds H_2S_2 and H_2S_3 have definitely been prepared and there is some evidence for the existence of H_2Se_2. Some properties of the normal hydrides are listed in Table 15.3, along with corresponding data for water. The effect of hydrogen bonding on the properties of the latter is apparent.

15.52 The normal hydrides are commonly obtained by reaction between acids and metal sulfides, selenides, and tellurides; the sulfur and selenium compounds are also prepared by heating mixtures of the element and paraffin.

TABLE 15.3

Some Properties of the Group VI Hydrides

	H_2O	H_2S	H_2Se	H_2Te
Melting point, °C.	0.00	−85.60	−60.4	−51
Heat of fusion, kcal./mole	1.435	0.568		
Boiling point, °C.	100	−60.75	−41.5	−1.8
Heat of vaporization, kcal./mole	9.715	4.463	4.75	5.7
Density at boiling point, g./ml.	0.958	0.993	2.004	2.650
Heat of formation at 20°, kcal./mole	−68.35	−4.80	18.5	34.2
Free energy of formation at 25°, kcal./mole	−56.72	−7.86	2.37	31.0

15.53 As the data of Table 15.3 show, hydrogen sulfide is formed exothermically from its elements, whereas the selenium and tellurium compounds are endothermic. It is not surprising, therefore, that hydrogen selenide and telluride are unstable at room temperature and slowly decompose into the elements.

15.54 All three hydrides dissolve to a moderate extent in water to give acidic solutions, the solubility in each case approximating 0.1 mole per liter at atmospheric pressure. The acid strength increases from H_2S to H_2Te, the values for the first stage dissociation constants being 8.7×10^{-8}, 1.9×10^{-4}, and 2.3×10^{-3}, respectively, at 18°. The hydrides react with varying ease with oxygen to give water and the free elements. Reaction of oxygen with hydrogen sulfide occurs readily at ignition temperatures. With hydrogen selenide and telluride oxidation takes place at room temperature, but with the former only in the presence of moisture. In aqueous solution the compounds are converted to the free elements by relatively weak oxidizing agents, e.g., I_2, Fe^{3+}.

15.55 The hydrides form two classes of metal derivatives, corresponding to M^IEH and M^I_2E. These may be regarded as being the analogs of the hydroxides and normal oxides, respectively. However, in contrast to the normal metal oxides, the great majority of which are ionic in character, compounds containing E^{2-} (sulfide, selenide, and telluride) are found only with the most electropositive (e.g., alkali and alkaline earth) metals. There appear to be only a few ionic sulfides containing tripositive ions and none of tetrapositive ions.

15.56 Only the alkali and alkaline earth metal sulfides, selenides, and tellurides are water soluble. Solutions of both the acid and normal derivatives are alkaline as a result of hydrolysis; the extent of this reaction decreases from sulfide to telluride, as would be expected from the relative acid strengths of the parent compounds. Sulfides of metals which give weakly basic or amphoteric hydroxides, e.g., Cr_2S_3, Al_2S_3, are completely decomposed by water with the liberation of hydrogen sulfide. Alkaline solutions of sulfides, selenides, and tellurides are oxidized by air, the ease of oxidation increasing quite markedly in the listed order. (See Table 15.2 for potentials for the reaction $E + 2e^- = E^{2-}$.)

15.57 The hydrogen polysulfides, H_2S_2 and H_2S_3, are produced when a concentrated aqueous solution of sodium polysulfide (see below) is decomposed by hydrochloric acid. Best results are obtained when the metal polysulfide has the empirical composition $Na_2S_{2.5}$. The hydrogen polysulfides are found in admixture with free sulfur in a yellow oil which forms during the course of reaction, and are separated and purified by fractional distillation at low pressures. In addition to H_2S_2 and H_2S_3, higher polysulfides, e.g., H_2S_5, H_2S_6, probably exist. The hydrogen polysulfides are readily soluble in common organic solvents. They have a great tendency to decompose with release of sulfur, a reaction which is accelerated by the presence of hydroxide ion.

15.58 Dihydrogen disulfide, H_2S_2, (m.p., $-89°$; b.p., $71°$) not only resembles hydrogen peroxide in mode of preparation and in chemical properties, but it is also similar in structure. The molecule has two structurally equivalent sulfur atoms, with the S—S distance of 2.05 Å, the calculated value for a single bond being 2.08 Å. Experimental evidence indicates that the higher polysulfides also contain chains of sulfur atoms terminated at each end by a hydrogen atom.

15.59 Although no hydrogen polyselenides and polytellurides have definitely been isolated, alkali metal salts containing polyatomic selenium and tellurium anions, as well as those of sulfur, are well known. These substances are commonly formed in solution by reaction between the appropriate free element and sulfides, selenides, or tellurides in water or in liquid ammonia. The nature of the products isolated is determined largely by the quantity of the element employed. For sulfur, compounds varying in composition from $M^I_2S_2$ to $M^I_2S_6$ have been prepared containing potassium, rubidium, and cesium; no lithium polysulfides appear to have been characterized. Polyselenides up to $M^I_2Se_5$ and tellurides to $M^I_2Te_6$ have been obtained in liquid ammonia. Alkaline earth metal polysulfides and polytellurides have also been prepared, but these have been less studied than the alkali metal compounds. It should be emphasized that in all these compounds the anion is dinegative, e.g., S_6^{2-}, Se_4^{2-}, Te_3^{2-}, and probably possesses a chain structure.

15.60 The poly salts are all highly colored, the depth of color of the sulfides increasing from orange to red with increasing anion size. Upon acidification the polysulfides give free sulfur, H_2S, H_2S_2, and H_2S_3; the polyselenides and tellurides react analogously, except that they yield no compounds corresponding to H_2S_2 and H_2S_3. In aqueous solution polysulfides are slowly converted to free sulfur and thiosulfate ($S_2O_3^{2-}$) by reaction with oxygen.

Binary Halides and Derivatives

15.61 A summary of the binary compounds of the halogens with sulfur, selenium, and tellurium is given in Table 15.4. Inasmuch as the halogen is the more electronegative component, these compounds may be regarded as true halides. It appears significant that no compounds of sulfur or selenium with iodine have been described; these elements have approximately equal electronegativities.

15.62 Halides of the types E_2X_2, EX_2, EX_4, and EX_6 have been characterized for sulfur, selenium, and tellurium, and in addition, S_2F_{10} is known. The compounds can all be obtained by direct combination of the elements; in a few instances other methods are utilized more conveniently. It is noteworthy that the maximum oxidation state for the group is attained only with fluorine, e.g., SF_6, SeF_6, and TeF_6. The hexafluorides are more volatile (Table 15.4)

TABLE 15.4

Binary Compounds of the Halogens with Sulfur, Selenium, and Tellurium
(With boiling points in °C.)

Compound Type	F	Cl	Br	I
E_2X_2	S_2F_2 (?)	S_2Cl_2 (138) Se_2Cl_2 (decomp.)	S_2Br_2 (90, decomp.) Se_2Br_2 (decomp.)	
EX_2	SF_2 (?)	SCl_2 (59, decomp.) $SeCl_2$ (exists only as vapor) $TeCl_2$ (324)	$SeBr_2$ (exists only as vapor) $TeBr_2$ (339)	
EX_4	SF_4 (-40) SeF_4 (93) TeF_4 (m.p. 129.6°)	SCl_4 (exists only as solid) $SeCl_4$ (exists only as solid) $TeCl_4$ (390)	$SeBr_4$ (exists only as solid) $TeBr_4$ (414, decomp.)	TeI_4 (decomp.)
EX_6	SF_6 (-63.8, subl.) SeF_6(-46.6, subl.) TeF_6(-38.9, subl.)			
E_2X_{10}	S_2F_{10} (29)			

and generally less reactive than the lower fluorides. This is explained by the greater degree of shielding of the central atom in the hexafluorides, with the result that this atom is less readily available for interaction with other groups.

The Lower Halides **15.63** The only monohalides, i.e., compounds of the type E_2X_2, which have been definitely isolated are the chlorides and bromides of sulfur and selenium. It is interesting that S_2Br_2 is the only known binary compound of sulfur and bromine. The monohalides are formed by direct union of the elements; selenium monobromide can also be prepared by reduction of the tetrabromide with selenium.

$$SeBr_4 + 3Se = 2Se_2Br_2$$

All the compounds except sulfur monochloride are unstable at their boiling points and cannot be distilled without extensive decomposition. In the vapor state selenium monobromide is completely dissociated into the dibromide ($SeBr_2$) and selenium. Sulfur monochloride is decomposed into the elements above 300°. The monohalides are all immediately decomposed by water; with S_2Cl_2 the principal products are free sulfur, hydrogen sulfide, sulfite, and thiosulfate. The monohalides are soluble in a variety of nonaqueous solvents, and in these media exhibit normal molecular weights. The S_2Cl_2 molecule in the vapor state has the structure shown (calculated for S—S single bond, 2.08 Å; for S—Cl single bond, 2.03 Å).

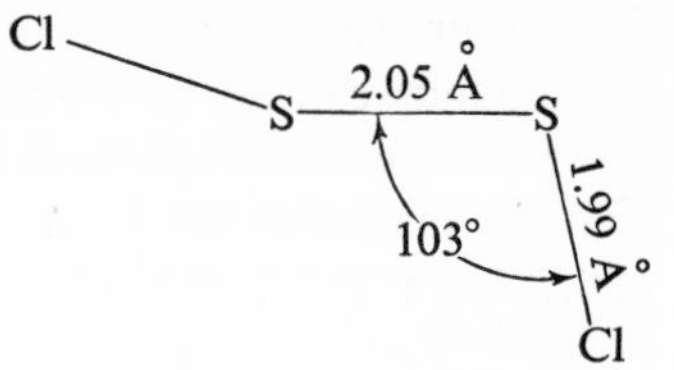

Cl — S — 2.05 Å — S — Cl, 1.99 Å, 103°

15.64 Five dihalides, SCl_2, $SeCl_2$, $TeCl_2$, $SeBr_2$, and $TeBr_2$, have been characterized unequivocally. Sulfur dichloride is prepared by reaction between chlorine and the monochloride. Selenium dichloride and dibromide exist only in the vapor state and are formed by the thermal decomposition of other selenium halides, e.g., $SeCl_4$, Se_2Br_2 (see above). Tellurium dichloride is made either by direct combination or by reaction between the tetrachloride and elementary tellurium, and the dibromide is formed when the tetrabromide is heated. Those dihalides which exist as solids, SCl_2, $TeCl_2$, and $TeBr_2$, are readily hydrolyzed. The products of reaction of sulfur dichloride with water are similar to those obtained from the monochloride (see above), and the tellurium compounds react as shown in the equation. Selenium dichloride

$$2TeX_2 + 3H_2O = Te + H_2TeO_3 + 4HX$$

vapor is stable at least in the range from 190° to 600°, and the dibromide from 250° to 500°. Condensation of the vapor gives free halogen and monohalide in each case.

15.65 All possible tetrahalides, except SBr_4, SI_4, and SeI_4, are known. The tetrachlorides, tetrabromides, and tellurium tetraiodide are readily made by union of the elements, but this method is unsuitable for the preparation of the tetrafluorides because of the ready conversion of these to the hexafluorides by reaction with fluorine. The tetrafluorides have been obtained by the reactions shown below.[4]

$$S + 4CoF_3 \overset{CaF_2}{=} SF_4 + 4CoF_2$$

$$SeCl_4 + 4AgF \overset{50°}{=} SeF_4 + 4AgCl$$

$$2TeF_6 + Te \overset{180°}{=} 3TeF_4$$

The tetrahalides, with the exception of tellurium tetrachloride which gives no indication of decomposition up to 500°, are thermally unstable. Sulfur and selenium tetrachlorides and selenium tetrabromide are stable only in the solid state. Fusion of the sulfur compound appears to yield an equimolar mixture of dichloride and elementary chlorine. The vapor obtained from subliming selenium tetrachloride is similarly constituted, and the tetrabromide gives selenium monobromide and bromine at 70–80°. Tellurium tetrabromide is almost completely dissociated above its boiling point (414°) into the dibromide and bromine, and above 100° the tetraiodide begins to decompose into the elements, whereas the tetrafluoride undergoes disproportionation above 193.8° with the formation of elementary tellurium and the hexafluoride. Each of the

[4] JUNKINS, BERNHARDT, and BARBER, *J. Am. Chem. Soc.*, **74**, 5749 (1952).

tetrahalides is reactive toward water, giving ultimately the appropriate dioxide (or corresponding acid) and the hydrohalic acid. The ease of hydrolysis for the tetrafluorides increases with size of the central atom, and therefore with increasing polarity of the E—F bond. Both the increasing size of the central atom and the increasing bond polarity tend to make the central atom more accessible to attack by the electron-pair donor, water.

The Hexafluorides [5] **15.66** These compounds are prepared by direct combination of the elements. The reactions are strongly exothermic, the heats of formation of the gaseous substances being -262, -246, and -315 kcal. per mole, respectively, for SF_6, SeF_6, and TeF_6.

15.67 In comparison with the lower halides, the hexafluorides are relatively unreactive. The sulfur compound is especially inert and does not appear to react under conditions less severe than red heat. Even at red heat, however, it is not attacked by oxygen, ammonia, or many other substances. Selenium hexafluoride, although a rather stable substance, is definitely more reactive than the sulfur compound. Thus, in contrast to the inertness of the latter toward ammonia, selenium hexafluoride reacts with ammonia at temperatures above 200°.

$$SeF_6 + 2NH_3 = N_2 + Se + 6HF + 116 \text{ kcal.}$$

The tellurium compound is the most active of the hexafluorides. Whereas both sulfur and selenium hexafluorides are inert toward water at room temperature, tellurium hexafluoride is completely decomposed in this medium within one day.

$$TeF_6 + 6H_2O = H_6TeO_6 + 6HF$$

The trend in reactivity observed for the hexafluorides can be attributed, as in the case of the tetrafluorides, to the increasing size of the central atom and the successively greater polar character of the bonds from sulfur to tellurium (see above).

15.68 The hexafluorides have been shown to be octahedral in structure. Such a structure is consistent with the utilization of outer d orbitals of the central atoms for SP^3D^2 binding.[6] The bond distances of 1.58, 1.70, and 1.84 Å, respectively, for S—F, Se—F, and Te—F are much shorter than the values of 1.76, 1.89, and 2.09 Å for the sums of the normal covalent radii. The shortened S—F bond distance cannot be accounted for in terms of the polarity of the bond alone and perhaps the additional possibility of decrease in bond length as a result of contributions from double-bonded resonance structures must also be considered. (See sections 4.26–28 for a discussion of the additivity of covalent bond radii.)

Disulfur Decafluoride **15.69** In very small amounts S_2F_{10} (f.p., $-92°$; b.p., 29°) is formed as a by-product when sulfur hexafluoride is prepared. The

[5] BURG, *Fluorine Chemistry*, Academic Press, Inc., New York, 1950, Vol. I, Ch. 2.
[6] BROCKWAY and PAULING, *Proc. Nat. Acad. Sci.*, **19**, 68 (1933).

decafluoride is a rather stable substance but less stable than the hexafluoride. Although inert toward water and cold solutions of alkali, it is attacked by molten potassium hydroxide and by iron, copper, and platinum at elevated temperatures. Structurally, S_2F_{10} appears to consist of two SF_5 groups united through the sulfur atoms, the bonds from each sulfur atom being directed toward the corners of an octahedron.[7] The S—S bond distance is 2.21 Å (calculated for a single bond, 2.08 Å) and the S—F distance is 1.56 Å (calculated, 1.76 Å).

Complex Halides **15.70** Certain tetrahalides of selenium and tellurium are capable of acting as acceptor molecules toward the corresponding halide ions in aqueous solution with the formation of ions mainly of the composition $[EX_6]^{2-}$. In all cases the complex salts which can be isolated contain large, univalent cations, *e.g.*, K^+, NH_4^+, alkylammonium. Tellurium tetrahalides also give hydrated complexes containing only five halogens, and the anion in these compounds is probably best formulated as $[TeX_5H_2O]^-$. No fluoro or iodo complexes have been prepared for selenium and no complex fluorides for tellurium.

15.71 Anhydrous hexachloro- and hexabromoselenates(IV) can be crystallized from concentrated hydrohalic acid solutions of the tetrahalides and the appropriate metal halides at 0°. The chloro complexes are unstable in water and decompose to yield selenious acid, H_2SeO_3; in the absence of air, solutions of the bromo compounds seem to be more stable. Dark red crystals of the free acid $H_2[SeBr_6]$ have been isolated from solutions of selenium tetrabromide in concentrated hydrobromic acid. Highly colored, readily hydrolyzable salts of the type $M_2[TeX_6]$ (X = Cl, Br, or I) are prepared by the action of the appropriate halide salts on solutions of tellurium dioxide in hydrohalic acids. Pentahalo hydrated complexes in the form of free acids, *e.g.*,

$$HTeCl_5 \cdot H_2O, \quad HTeBr_5 \cdot 5H_2O, \quad HTeI_5 \cdot 8H_2O,$$

can also be obtained. The acids are low-melting materials which readily evolve hydrogen halide in air. The hexahalo salts of selenium(IV) and tellurium(IV) are isomorphous with analogous complexes of lead, platinum, and tin, an indication that the $[SeX_6]^{2-}$ and $[TeX_6]^{2-}$ types are octahedral.

Oxides and Oxyhalides

Oxides **15.72** The common binary compounds of sulfur, selenium, and tellurium with oxygen are the dioxides (EO_2) and trioxides (EO_3). All the dioxides are obtained readily; of the trioxides, the selenium compound is the most difficult to prepare, and has not yet been made in the pure form.

15.73 The dioxides can be made merely by burning the elements in air. The reactions are strongly exothermic, the heats of formation at 18° being −70.92, −56.36, and −77.58 kcal. per mole, respectively, for SO_2, SeO_2, and TeO_2. Sulfur dioxide is also obtained in large quantities as a product of the roasting of sulfide ores in air. The common method for the preparation of selenium

[7] HARVEY and BAUER, *J. Am. Chem. Soc.*, **75**, 2840 (1953).

dioxide utilizes the reaction of gray selenium with hot nitric acid to form selenious acid, which is then dehydrated. Tellurium dioxide is ordinarily obtained in a similar manner; however, the product of reaction of tellurium with nitric acid is not tellurous acid, but rather a basic nitrate which is formulated as $2TeO_2 \cdot HNO_3$.

15.74 Physically, sulfur dioxide is a colorless gas (m.p., $-75.46°$; b.p., $-10.02°$); selenium and tellurium dioxides are white solids, the former subliming readily (the vapor pressure equals 1 atm. at 315°) and the latter first showing an appreciable vapor pressure at about 450°. Sulfur dioxide is easily condensed to a liquid which has been studied as a medium for inorganic reactions (see 7.35 ff.). In the vapor state sulfur and selenium dioxides exist as discrete SO_2 and SeO_2 molecules. These molecules have been shown to be angular, with O—E—O bond angles of about 120°. The S—O and Se—O bond distances have been estimated to be 1.43 Å and 1.61 Å, respectively. It has been proposed that the SO_2 molecule has a structure involving important contributions from the resonance forms shown.

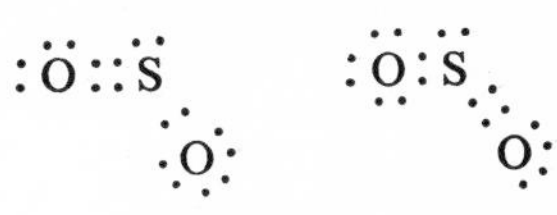

15.75 The dioxides of sulfur and selenium are readily soluble in water, whereas the tellurium compound has only limited solubility (ca. 7 mg. per liter). The resulting solutions are acidic (see sections 15.90–91).

15.76 As the large heats of formation indicate, the dioxides possess high thermal stability. Thus sulfur dioxide is essentially undecomposed up to about 2000°. Gaseous sulfur dioxide is stable toward most reducing agents and ordinarily is converted to free sulfur only with difficulty. Although it does not burn or support combustion, it does combine with oxygen in the presence of catalysts to give the trioxide, a reaction of great importance in the manufacture of sulfuric acid (see below). Selenium dioxide, in contrast to the sulfur compound, is readily reduced and as a result finds considerable use as an oxidizing agent in organic chemistry. Both selenium dioxide and tellurium dioxide form addition compounds with strong acids, e.g., $SeO_2 \cdot 2HCl$, $TeO_2 \cdot 2HCl$, $2TeO_2 \cdot HClO_4$. Although tellurium dioxide is relatively insoluble in water, it dissolves in solutions of alkali hydroxides to form tellurites (M_2TeO_3).

15.77 The combination of sulfur dioxide with molecular oxygen to give the trioxide is extremely slow at ordinary temperature, and, commercially, the synthesis is carried out at elevated temperatures (400–700°) in the presence of a catalyst (e.g., spongy platinum, vanadium(V) oxide). The reaction is strongly exothermic

$$SO_2(g) + \tfrac{1}{2}O_2(g) = SO_3(g) + 23 \text{ kcal.}$$

and is characterized by the free energy relationship $\Delta F° = -22.6 + 0.02136\,T$ (kcal. per mole). Excessively high temperatures must be avoided since the trioxide undergoes extensive decomposition above 900°. For example, the equilibrium constant for the above reaction is 34.5 at 526.9° and 0.25 at 926.9°.

15.78 Selenium trioxide has been made in admixture with the dioxide by reaction of the free element with oxygen in a high-frequency glow discharge. It is of interest that the trioxide cannot be obtained by the dehydration of selenic acid, H_2SeO_4; the dioxide and oxygen are formed when the acid is heated or is treated with phosphoric anhydride. Tellurium trioxide is prepared by the dehydration of telluric acid, H_6TeO_6, at temperatures between 300° and 360°.

15.79 Sulfur trioxide exists in at least three crystalline modifications, the relationships between the various forms being rather complex. When the vapor is condensed at −80° it forms icelike crystals (γ-SO_3) which melt at 16.85°. This modification, if kept below 25°, slowly changes over to the β form, consisting of long feathery asbestoslike crystals which melt at 32.5°. In addition there is another asbestoslike (α) modification which melts at 62.3° and which is formed when sulfur trioxide vapor is condensed at liquid air temperatures. Both the γ and β forms are unstable with respect to transition to the α variety. The α and β forms consist of large polymeric molecules. The commercial product consists of a mixture of the α and β modifications and has a melting point in the neighborhood of 40°, depending on the proportions of these forms present. Sulfur trioxide is volatile, the boiling point of the liquid being 44.8°. The vapor is monomeric and has a zero dipole moment; the SO_3 molecule has been shown to have the configuration of an equilateral triangle with the sulfur atom at the center; the S—O bond distance (1.43 Å) is identical to that in sulfur dioxide. Both selenium trioxide and tellurium trioxide are solid materials which are much less volatile and stable than the corresponding sulfur compound. Thus, whereas sulfur trioxide is only slightly decomposed at 400°, both the selenium and tellurium compounds are significantly dissociated to dioxide and oxygen in the neighborhood of 200°.

15.80 Sulfur trioxide is an exceedingly reactive substance. It combines vigorously with water to form sulfuric acid and with basic oxides to yield sulfates.

$$SO_3 + H_2O = H_2SO_4 + 21.3 \text{ kcal. (at 20°)}$$

It is a powerful oxidizing agent, particularly at high temperatures, and reacts with many metallic and nonmetallic halides, with the exception of fluorides, to give the free halogens. With hydrogen chloride it forms chlorosulfonic acid, HSO_3Cl. Its action on organic compounds results in the formation of sulfonic acids (especially with aromatic hydrocarbons) or in the removal of the elements of water and the liberation of carbon.

15.81 Both selenium and tellurium trioxides are also potent oxidizing agents, but their behavior in this regard has not been studied extensively. Selenium trioxide is hygroscopic, forming solutions of selenic acid. On the other hand, tellurium trioxide reacts quite slowly with water but dissolves readily in hot solutions of alkalies to give tellurates.

Oxyhalides **15.82** Only sulfur and selenium appear to be able to form oxyhalides. The compounds are of the types EOX_2 and EO_2X_2, with none of the latter being known for selenium. Substances of the EOX_2 type are commonly called thionyl and selenyl halides, or sulfur(IV) and selenium(IV) oxyhalides, whereas the SO_2X_2 compounds are known as sulfuryl halides or sulfur(VI) oxyhalides. A summary of the known oxyhalides, along with their melting and boiling points, is given in Table 15.5. As is indicated by the low values of the

TABLE 15.5

Oxyhalides of Sulfur and Selenium

Compound	Melting Point, °C.	Boiling Point, °C.	Compound	Melting Point, °C.	Boiling Point, °C.
SOF_2	−129.5	−43.8	$SeOCl_2$	10.9	176
SOFCl	−139.5	12.2	$SeOBr_2$	41.6	ca. 200
$SOCl_2$	−104.5	78.8	SO_2F_2	−136.7	−55.4
$SOBr_2$	−49.5	137	SO_2FCl	−124.7	7.1
$SeOF_2$	4.6	124 ± 3	SO_2Cl_2	−54.1	69.1

melting and boiling points, the oxyhalides exist as simple covalent molecular species.

15.83 Thionyl and selenyl halides are obtained in a number of ways. Thionyl fluoride is best prepared by halogen exchange between antimony(III) fluoride and thionyl chloride in the presence of antimony(V) chloride, the compound SOFCl being formed as a by-product in the reaction. The chloride is ordinarily made by reaction between phosphorus pentachloride and sulfur dioxide, and the bromide

$$PCl_5 + SO_2 = SOCl_2 + POCl_3$$

by treatment of the chloride with hydrogen bromide at low temperatures. Selenyl fluoride (also called selenium oxyfluoride) is obtained by halogen exchange at 140° between selenyl chloride and silver fluoride, the reaction being carried out in a platinum or Monel metal apparatus, since the product attacks glass at elevated temperatures. The preparation of selenyl chloride is effected by the dehydrative distillation of $SeO_2 \cdot 2HCl$ (see 15.76) from phosphoric anhydride. Reaction of bromine on a mixture of selenium and selenium dioxide yields selenyl bromide.

15.84 Thionyl and selenyl halides are characterized by their high reactivity, the latter compounds being generally less stable. Both types are hydrolyzed completely by water, giving the corresponding dioxide or acid derived from the dioxide and the appropriate hydrohalic acid according to the reaction given.

$$SOCl_2 + 2H_2O = H_2SO_3 + 2HCl$$

Except for thionyl fluoride, the hydrolytic rate is rapid. Both the thionyl and selenyl halides are thermally unstable and when strongly heated decompose to yield dioxide, free halogen and lower halide, e.g., S_2Cl_2, Se_2Cl_2.

15.85 The thionyl and selenyl halides have been shown to possess pyramidal structures. For the former the S—O bond distance is about 1.45 Å in each

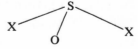

halide, a value considerably shorter than that (1.78 Å) calculated for single covalent bonding. The short distance may be interpreted to indicate that resonance structures involving sulfur to oxygen double bonding make a significant contribution to the actual structure of the molecule. The EOX_2 compounds are highly polar molecules; for example, thionyl chloride has a dipole moment of 1.58 D in benzene at 25°.

15.86 Some aspects of the use of selenium(IV) oxychloride as a medium for chemical reactions have been discussed (see 7.41 *ff*.).

15.87 Three sulfuryl halides have been characterized — SO_2F_2, SO_2Cl_2, and SO_2FCl. Sulfuryl fluoride is obtained in the pure condition by the thermal decomposition of barium fluorosulfonate.

$$Ba(SO_3F)_2 \overset{500°}{=} SO_2F_2 + BaSO_4$$

The chloride is prepared by direct union of sulfur dioxide and chlorine in the presence of a catalyst, *e.g.*, camphor, ethylene, activated charcoal. The mixed halide SO_2FCl is formed at 300° and 6 atmospheres pressure by the reaction shown.

$$3SO_2Cl_2 + SbF_3 \overset{SbCl_5}{=} SbCl_3 + 3SO_2FCl$$

15.88 Sulfuryl fluoride is much less reactive than the corresponding thionyl compound. In contrast to the slow but complete hydrolysis of the latter compound at room temperature, sulfuryl fluoride is unaffected by water even in a sealed tube at 150°. The relative inertness of the sulfuryl compound can be attributed in large part to the higher degree of shielding of the central sulfur atom by oxygen and fluorine atoms, which prevents penetration by water, a relatively weak Lewis base. Sulfuryl fluoride is attacked, however, by stronger bases; thus hydroxide ion reacts slowly to give fluoride and fluorosulfonate ions, the latter being converted ultimately to sulfate. Aqueous ammonia de-

$$SO_2F_2 + 2OH^- = F^- + SO_3F^- + H_2O$$

composes the sulfuryl compound, yielding sulfamide, $SO_2(NH_2)_2$, and related compounds. Sulfuryl chloride is much less stable than the fluoride, particularly at higher temperatures. At 300° the chloride is entirely decomposed into sulfur dioxide and chlorine; sulfuryl fluoride, however, is stable to at least 500°. An interesting difference is encountered in the hydrolytic behavior of the two compounds. Whereas the fluoride is inert toward water at room temperature, the chloride is completely hydrolyzed to yield sulfuric and hydrochloric acids.

15.89 The sulfuryl halides have distorted tetrahedral structures, with the S—O bond distance being approximately equivalent to that in the thionyl compounds.

Oxyacids and Related Compounds

Sulfurous, Selenious, and Tellurous Acids   **15.90** These acids are derived from the dioxides and have the composition H_2EO_3. Solutions of sulfurous and selenious acids are formed when the extremely soluble dioxides are dissolved in water. Free sulfurous acid, H_2SO_3, has never been prepared, although the hydrate $SO_2 \cdot 7H_2O$ can be crystallized from cold, concentrated solutions of the acid. H_2SeO_3, the only known hydrated form of the dioxide, is obtained as a white hygroscopic solid from solutions of the dioxide in water. In a dry atmosphere solid selenious acid readily reverts to the dioxide by the loss of water. Since tellurium dioxide is but slightly soluble in water, only dilute solutions of tellurous acid can be made. No solid compound corresponding to H_2TeO_3 has been isolated. Acidification of an aqueous solution of potassium tellurite, K_2TeO_3, with nitric acid gives a white, flocculent, hydrated dioxide having no definite composition.

15.91 Each of the acids is diprotic and the following dissociation constants (at 25°) have been reported. H_2SO_3: $K_1 = 1.25 \times 10^{-2}$, $K_2 = 5.6 \times 10^{-8}$; H_2SeO_3: $K_1 = 2.7 \times 10^{-3}$, $K_2 = 2.5 \times 10^{-7}$; H_2TeO_3: $K_1 = 2 \times 10^{-3}$, $K_2 = 1 \times 10^{-8}$. There is some evidence that tellurous acid can also undergo basic dissociation.

$$H_2TeO_3 = TeO(OH)^+ + OH^- \qquad K = 1 \times 10^{-12}$$

$TeO(OH)^+$ is formed when the dioxide is dissolved in strong acids.

$$TeO_2 + H^+ = TeO(OH)^+ \qquad K = 8.9 \times 10^{-3}$$

15.92 Both normal ($M^I_2EO_3$) and acid (M^IHEO_3) salts are known for all three acids. In general, the acid salts are more soluble than the normal compounds, and of the latter only the alkali metal derivatives exhibit appreciable water-solubility. As might be expected from second stage dissociation constants of the acids, the normal salts all give alkaline aqueous solutions as a result of hydrolysis. When alkali metal acid sulfites are heated the corresponding pyrosulfites, $M^I_2S_2O_5$, are formed.

$$2MHSO_3 = H_2O + M_2S_2O_5$$

These salts can also be made by reaction between sulfur dioxide and solutions of normal metal sulfites. In the pyrosulfite ion the two sulfur atoms are linked to each other. (Compare with the pyrosulfate ion, see 15.99.) The normal sulfite and selenite ions have a strong tendency to form complexes with transition metal ions, coordination occurring through oxygen atoms. The sulfite ion appears to be able to occupy either one or two coordination positions; in all cationic complexes containing the SeO_3^{2-} group the latter is unidentate. The acid tellurites are unstable in water and break down to normal tellurites and tellurium dioxide. In addition to the compounds derived from the simple acid, salts corresponding to polytellurous acids, e.g., $M^I_2Te_2O_5$, $M^I_2Te_4O_9$, $M^I_2Te_6O_{13}$, have been prepared.

15.93 Solutions of sulfurous acid and its salts possess reducing properties.

$$H_2O + H_2SO_3 = SO_4^{2-} + 4H^+ + 2e^- \qquad E° = -0.17 \text{ v.}$$
$$2OH^- + SO_3^{2-} = SO_4^{2-} + H_2O + 2e^- \qquad E°_B = 0.93$$

They are oxidized slowly by air to sulfate, the reaction being accelerated by the presence of such reducing agents as iron(II) or arsenite ion. Halogens convert sulfurous acid and sulfite solutions rapidly and quantitatively to sulfate. With other oxidizing agents, dithionate ion, $S_2O_6^{2-}$, in addition to sulfate is often formed. Toward strong reducing agents, such as iodide and hydrogen sulfide, sulfurous acid functions as an oxidizing agent. Although elementary sulfur is a common product of the reduction of sulfurous acid, other substances, *e.g.*, thiosulfate and polythionate, are often formed as a result of the occurrence of side reactions.

15.94 Selenious and tellurous acids, although not strong oxidizing agents, are more powerful than sulfurous acid and are much more readily reduced to the free elements.

$$H_2SO_3 + 4H^+ + 4e^- = S + 3H_2O \qquad E° = 0.45 \text{ v.}$$
$$H_2SeO_3 + 4H^+ + 4e^- = Se + 3H_2O \qquad E° = 0.740$$
$$TeO_2(s) + 4H^+ + 4e^- = Te + 2H_2O \qquad E° = 0.529$$

On the other hand, selenious and tellurous acids are extremely weak reducing agents in comparison with sulfurous acid, and their conversion to selenic and telluric acids is effected only by very strong oxidants (see below).

Simple Acids Derived from the Trioxides **15.95** The simple oxyacids related to the trioxides are H_2SO_4, H_2SeO_4, and H_6TeO_6. Sulfuric acid, the most widely used synthetic inorganic chemical, is prepared by two methods. In the contact process, sulfur trioxide, obtained by the union of the dioxide with molecular oxygen (see 15.77), is dissolved in 98 per cent sulfuric acid to form either the 99.5 per cent acid or the fuming acid $H_2SO_4 \cdot SO_3$. In the second commercial mode of preparation, the lead chamber process, sulfur dioxide, oxygen, and water vapor combine in the presence of nitric oxide to yield a solution containing 62 to 77 per cent H_2SO_4. The reactions occurring in this process are complex, but the formation of the sulfuric acid is believed to take place by way of the intermediate production of nitrosyl sulfuric acid, $HOSO_2ONO$.

$$NO + \tfrac{1}{2}O_2 = NO_2$$
$$NO_2 + NO + O_2 + 2SO_2 + H_2O = 2HOSO_2ONO$$
$$2HOSO_2ONO + H_2O = 2H_2SO_4 + NO + NO_2$$

15.96 Selenic acid can be obtained by the oxidation of selenious acid with chlorine or bromine. The reactions are reversible and equilibrium is attained slowly.

$$X_2 + H_2SeO_3 + H_2O = 3H^+ + HSeO_4^- + 2X^-$$
$$K_{25°} = 1.42 \times 10^9 \text{ when } X = Cl, \text{ and } 0.88 \text{ when } X = Br$$

The preparation of the acid is better accomplished by the action of aqueous bromine on a suspension of silver selenite or by the oxidation of selenious acid

$$Ag_2SeO_3 + Br_2 + H_2O = H_2SeO_4 + 2AgBr$$

with chloric acid at temperatures in the neighborhood of 100°. Telluric acid is made by the oxidation of elementary tellurium or the dioxide by means of 30 per cent hydrogen peroxide in concentrated sulfuric acid, or by chromium trioxide (CrO_3) in nitric acid.

15.97 Anhydrous sulfuric acid is a colorless liquid which freezes at 10.37°. It begins to boil at 290°, the process being accompanied by the evolution of the trioxide. The acid has a tremendous affinity for water and forms several hydrates, e.g., $H_2SO_4 \cdot H_2O$ (m.p., 8.47°); $H_2SO_4 \cdot 2H_2O$ (m.p., −39.46°); $H_2SO_4 \cdot 4H_2O$ (m.p., −28.25°). Aqueous solutions are strongly acidic; the first stage dissociation of the acid is practically complete in dilute solution and the dissociation constant for the second stage ($HSO_4^- = H^+ + SO_4^{2-}$) is about 10^{-2} at 25°. Anhydrous selenic acid (m.p., 57–8°) is much less stable than sulfuric acid and begins to evolve oxygen when heated above 210°. It also has a strong affinity for water and forms two hydrates, $H_2SeO_4 \cdot H_2O$ (m.p., 26°) and $H_2SeO_4 \cdot 4H_2O$ (m.p., −51.7°). In its acid properties selenic acid is quite similar to sulfuric acid, the first stage dissociation being complete in dilute aqueous solution and the second stage ionization constant having a value of 1.15×10^{-2} at 25°. Telluric acid differs considerably from sulfuric and selenic acids. The common form is the ortho acid H_6TeO_6, and no compound of the formula H_2TeO_4 is known. Orthotelluric acid exists in two crystalline modifications, one a cubic form and the other monoclinic, the latter being the more stable. X-ray analysis has shown that in the acid six hydroxide groups are disposed octahedrally about tellurium. The acid is soluble to the extent of about 34 g. per 100 g. of water at 18° and when crystallized from solution below 10° it is isolated as the 4-hydrate. Orthotelluric acid exhibits the behavior of an extremely weak dibasic acid in aqueous solution, the first stage dissociation constant being of the order of 6×10^{-7}. When the pure acid is heated to 140° in a sealed tube, it is converted to a syrupy mass known as allotelluric acid. The latter is completely miscible with water and the solutions are considerably more acidic than those of the ortho acid. Allotelluric acid is believed to be a mixture of polymeric acids containing mainly $(H_2TeO_4)_n$; on standing, it reverts to the ortho acid. Above 300° orthotelluric acid is converted to tellurium trioxide.

15.98 As would be expected from their two-stage dissociation, sulfuric and selenic acids form normal and acid salts. The salts of selenic acid are similar in many respects to the sulfates and in most cases corresponding salts are isomorphous. In general, the normal selenates are more soluble than the sulfates. The most marked difference between the two types of salts is found in the ease with which selenates lose oxygen when they are heated. The normal sulfate and selenate ions are tetrahedral in structure, with S—O and Se—O bond distances of 1.51 and 1.61 Å, respectively. These values are much shorter than those (1.78 and 1.88 Å) required for single bonds between the atoms and have been interpreted to indicate a large degree of double bond character.

15.99 Thermal decomposition of acid sulfate salts (M^IHSO_4) results first in the evolution of water vapor and the formation of pyrosulfates $M^I_2S_2O_7$, derivatives of fuming sulfuric acid (oleum) (see 15.93); further heating is accompanied by the liberation of sulfur trioxide, the normal sulfate being produced. The pyrosulfate ion consists of two SO_4 tetrahedra having one oxygen atom in common. It is immediately converted to normal sulfate by water. In line with its dibasic character in aqueous solution telluric acid readily forms alkali metal salts of the types $M^IH_5TeO_6$ and $M^I_2H_4TeO_6$. The latter can be dehydrated to give neutral salts of the composition $M^I_2TeO_4$. The normal orthotellurate Na_6TeO_6 has been prepared by heating Na_2TeO_4 with Na_2O. Other normal tellurates which have been characterized are Hg_3TeO_6 and Zn_3TeO_6.

15.100 In contrast to the behavior of sulfuric acid, selenic and telluric acids are strong oxidizing agents, although their reactions are frequently not rapid.

$$SeO_4^{2-} + 4H^+ + 2e^- = H_2O + H_2SeO_3 \qquad E° = 1.15 \text{ v.}$$
$$H_6TeO_6 + 2H^+ + 2e^- = 4H_2O + TeO_2 \qquad E° = 1.02$$

Selenic acid acts slowly on chloride and bromide ions, the free halogens and selenious acid being formed. Reaction with sulfurous acid, which is a stronger reducing agent than either chloride or bromide, is even slower, the products being elementary selenium and sulfuric acid. The free element is also obtained quantitatively by reduction of selenic acid with hydrazine in hydrochloric acid solution at 60°. Telluric acid undergoes similar reactions; and here also sulfurous acid acts more slowly than either chloride or bromide.

Peroxysulfuric Acids **15.101** Two peroxy acids derived from sulfuric acid are known — peroxymonosulfuric acid (Caro's acid), H_2SO_5, and peroxydisulfuric acid, $H_2S_2O_8$. The latter has been briefly mentioned in the section in hydrogen peroxide and derivatives (see 15.27). Little appears to be known of analogous selenic and telluric acids.

15.102 Peroxymonosulfuric acid is obtained by the action of 30 per cent hydrogen peroxide on concentrated sulfuric acid at room temperature. The reaction is reversible, but the reformation of reactants occurs slowly. It is also

$$H_2O_2 + H_2SO_4 = H_2SO_5 + H_2O$$

a product of the hydrolytic decomposition of solutions of peroxydisulfuric acid prepared by the electrolysis of acid sulfates or concentrated sulfuric acid. Anhydrous peroxydisulfuric acid (m.p. 65°) and peroxymonosulfuric acid (m.p. 45°) are formed by reaction between chlorosulfonic acid and anhydrous hydrogen peroxide, the product obtained being determined by the ratio of reactants.

$$2HSO_3Cl + H_2O_2 = H_2S_2O_8 + 2HCl$$
$$HSO_3Cl + H_2O_2 = H_2SO_5 + HCl$$

15.103 Salts of peroxymonosulfuric acid are unstable and have not been isolated in the pure condition. Alkali metal salts of peroxydisulfuric acid ($M^I_2S_2O_8$), particularly the potassium and ammonium compounds, are well known and are prepared by the electrolytic oxidation of concentrated solutions of sulfates at low temperature. The peroxydisulfate ion is one of the most potent oxidizing agents known and is capable of converting Cr(III) to $Cr_2O_7^{2-}$,

$$S_2O_8^{2-} + 2e^- = 2SO_4^{2-} \qquad E° = 2.01 \text{ v.}$$

Mn^{2+} to MnO_2, etc. The oxidations are frequently slow at room temperature, but are catalyzed by monopositive silver. The mechanism of the catalysis involves the reaction shown as the rate-determining step, oxidation of the re-

$$S_2O_8^{2-} + Ag^+ = 2SO_4^{2-} + Ag^{3+}$$

ductant then being effected by tripositive silver.

15.104 X-ray analysis of ammonium and cesium peroxydisulfates shows that $S_2O_8^{2-}$ consists of two SO_4 tetrahedra joined through two oxygen atoms, with S—O and O—O bond distances of 1.50 and 1.31 Å, respectively, and the O—O—S bond angle of 128°. The short S—O distance (cf. SO_4^{2-}, sec. 15.98) can be considered to indicate a high measure of double bond character. Thus the structure shown can be considered to represent closely the actual state of the parent acid. Peroxymonosulfuric acid can be formulated similarly.

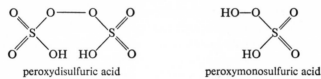

peroxydisulfuric acid   peroxymonosulfuric acid

The Thio Oxyacids

15.105 The pronounced ability of sulfur to self-link gives rise to thio oxyacids and derivatives which appear to have no parallel so far as selenium and tellurium are concerned. The thio oxyacids which have been characterized, either as the free acids or in the form of salts, are dithionous (hyposulfurous), $H_2S_2O_4$, thiosulfuric, $H_2S_2O_3$, dithionic, $H_2S_2O_6$, and a series of polythionic acids, $H_2S_xO_6$ (x = 3–6).

Dithionous (Hyposulfurous) Acid, $H_2S_2O_4$ **15.106** Normal salts of this acid are prepared by the reduction of acid sulfite solutions by means of zinc, or by the action of sodium or potassium amalgam on dry sulfur dioxide. Solutions of dithionites are unstable and decompose in the following manner.

$$2S_2O_4^{2-} + H_2O = S_2O_3^{2-} + 2HSO_3^-$$

The rate of decomposition is increased by acidification, the end products of reaction being sulfurous acid and elementary sulfur. The solid salts, e.g., $Na_2S_2O_4$, are relatively stable. Dithionites, in basic solution, are strong and rapid reducing agents.

$$4OH^- + S_2O_4^{2-} = 2SO_3^{2-} + 2H_2O + 2e^- \qquad E_B° = 1.12 \text{ v.}$$

In its first stage dissociation the free acid is strong; K_1 has been calculated to be 0.45 and K_2 3.5×10^{-3} at 25°.

15.107 The formulation of the dithionite ion as $S_2O_4^{2-}$ rather than SO_2^- is in accord with cryoscopic and conductivity measurements and also with the diamagnetism of the sodium salt. The properties of the ion leave little doubt that the sulfur atoms are bound to each other and that each is attached to two oxygen atoms.

Thiosulfuric Acid, $H_2S_2O_3$ **15.108** Only the normal salts (thiosulfates) of this acid have been characterized. They are ordinarily made by the union of elementary sulfur with a sulfite in aqueous solution. They may also be obtained by the oxidation of sulfides or from the decomposition of dithionites (see above).

The two sulfur atoms in $S_2O_3^{2-}$ are not equivalent. This is demonstrated by the fact that when the ion is prepared by the union of sulfite and radioactive sulfur (^{35}S) and is then decomposed by acid, all the activity is found in the free sulfur.

$$SO_3^{2-} + S^* = S^*SO_3^{2-} \text{ (S*, radioactive)}$$
$$S^*SO_3^{2-} + 2H^+ = H_2SO_3 + S^*$$

If the two sulfur atoms were equivalent, half of the radioactivity would have appeared in the elementary sulfur and half in the sulfite ion. The thiosulfate ion must thus be regarded as being formally derived from the sulfate ion (see section 15.98) by replacement of one oxygen atom by sulfur.

15.109 The alkali and alkaline earth thiosulfates are very soluble in water (*e.g.*, $Na_2S_2O_3 \cdot 5H_2O$, 74.7 g. per 100 g. of water at 0°); the lead, silver, and thallium(I) salts are only slightly soluble. Aqueous thiosulfate solutions are stable toward alkali but are decomposed by acids, the rate of decomposition and the nature of the products being dependent upon the hydrogen ion concentration. With dilute strong acid, decomposition is rapid and sulfurous acid and sulfur are formed; this reaction is accompanied by the less rapid production of pentathionic acid.

$$5S_2O_3^{2-} + 6H^+ = 2S_5O_6^{2-} + 3H_2O$$

When thiosulfate solutions are treated with concentrated strong acid, the deposition of free sulfur occurs more slowly, and hydrogen sulfide and the polysulfide H_2S_2 are found among the products.

15.110 Mild oxidizing agents (*e.g.*, I_2) and even powerful oxidizing agents which react slowly (*e.g.*, $S_2O_8^{2-}$, section 15.103) convert the thiosulfate ion to tetrathionate, $S_4O_6^{2-}$. Strong, rapidly acting oxidizing agents yield sulfate ion.

$$2S_2O_3^{2-} = S_4O_6^{2-} + 2e^- \qquad E° = -0.08 \text{ v.}$$

15.111 The thiosulfate ion forms fairly stable complexes with a number of heavy metal ions, *e.g.*, Cu^+, Ag^+, Cd^{2+}, Sb^{3+}, Bi^{3+}. Thus the instability constant of the complex ion $Ag(S_2O_3)_2^{3-}$ has been calculated to be 6×10^{-14}, a value which accounts for the usefulness of "hypo" ($Na_2S_2O_3 \cdot 5H_2O$) as a fixing agent in the photographic process. The thiosulfate ion is capable of functioning as either a unidentate or bidentate ligand. In the former case, coordination to the metal ion apparently occurs through sulfur, $M \leftarrow S—SO_3$, and in the latter instance, through both sulfur and oxygen.

Dithionic Acid, $H_2S_2O_6$ **15.112** Aqueous solutions of normal salts of this acid are obtained by the oxidation of aqueous sulfur dioxide or sulfites by means of such reagents as manganese dioxide, iron(III), cerium(IV), or permanganate, with the first oxidant being most commonly employed. Some sulfate is always

$$MnO_2 + 2SO_2 = MnS_2O_6$$

produced in a side reaction. The solution of manganese(II) dithionate is ordinarily treated with barium hydroxide to effect precipitation of manganese and sulfate ions, and the compound $BaS_2O_6 \cdot 2H_2O$ is crystallized from the resulting solution after the removal of excess barium hydroxide with sulfuric acid. Barium dithionate is used as source material for the preparation of other dithionates and also for the free acid. Solutions of the latter are formed by treatment of the barium salt with an equivalent quantity of sulfuric acid. All the known salts are water soluble.

15.113 X-ray investigation of the structure of the cesium salt has shown conclusively that the dithionate ion is correctly formulated as $S_2O_6^{2-}$; the sulfur atoms are linked together and each is bound to three oxygen atoms. The S—S distance of 2.08 Å corresponds to the calculated value for a single bond; the S—O bond distance is 1.50 Å. (See SO_4^{2-}, sec. 15.98.)

15.114 Dithionic acid is a strong acid. Dilute solutions are stable at room temperature but begin to decompose to a measurable extent at temperatures above 50°; concentrated solutions are unstable.

$$H_2S_2O_6 = H_2SO_4 + SO_2$$

The salts of dithionic acid decompose in a similar fashion when heated to about 250°; aqueous solutions are stable even when boiled.

15.115 The acid and its salts are relatively inert toward even strong oxidizing agents. Thus at room temperature dilute solutions of the salts are unaffected by permanganate or chlorine. At higher temperatures, if reaction occurs it is a result of the decomposition reaction noted above. Reducing agents such as arsenite and tin(II) are without action on dithionates; zinc or sodium amalgam converts dithionate ultimately to dithionite, sulfite being first formed.

Polythionic Acids, $H_2S_nO_6$ (n = 3–6) **15.116** With few exceptions, only normal salts of these acids have been characterized, the sodium and potassium compounds being best known. The polythionates differ from the dithionates in a number of important respects. The polythionates are prepared by the reduction of sulfites rather than by oxidation. Unlike the dithionates, the polythionates are attacked by oxidizing agents.

15.117 X-ray analysis of potassium trithionate, $K_2S_3O_6$, has shown that in the trithionate ion the three sulfur atoms are in a chain, with an S—S—S bond angle of about 100°. Each of the end sulfur atoms is in the center of a tetrahedron at the corners of which are three oxygen atoms and one sulfur atom, the latter being common to both tetrahedra. Structures of the higher polythionates have not been elucidated; there is little doubt, however, that the sulfur atoms in these substances are linked together.

15.118 Mixtures of polythionates are produced when thiosulfate solutions are treated with·sulfur dioxide in the presence of arsenic(III) oxide; the quantity of the latter substance and also the hydrogen ion concentration of the solution determine the relative proportions of the individual polythionates formed. Modifications of the thiosulfate-sulfur dioxide reaction can be utilized for the preparation of each class of polythionate, but individual compounds are sometimes also obtained conveniently by other methods. Thus sodium trithionate can be made by the action of hydrogen peroxide on a cold saturated solution of sodium thiosulfate.

$$2Na_2S_2O_3 + 4H_2O_2 = Na_2S_3O_6 + Na_2SO_4 + 4H_2O$$

Sodium and potassium tetrathionates are commonly prepared by reaction between iodine and the appropriate thiosulfate.

$$2S_2O_3^{2-} + I_2 = S_4O_6^{2-} + 2I^-$$

Potassium pentathionate, $K_2S_5O_6$, can be obtained from Wackenroder's liquid * by the addition of potassium acetate. Potassium hexathionate, $K_2S_6O_6$, can be made by reaction between potassium nitrite and potassium thiosulfate in concentrated hydrochloric acid at temperatures in the neighborhood of $-10°$.

15.119 All the polythionates are water soluble. In strongly acidic solution, the salts undergo rapid decomposition, the tri- and tetrathionates being converted mainly to elementary sulfur, sulfur dioxide, and sulfate ion, and the penta- and hexathionates chiefly to sulfur and sulfur dioxide. In weakly acidic solution the trithionate ion is slowly hydrolyzed as follows.

$$S_3O_6^{2-} + H_2O = S_2O_3^{2-} + SO_4^{2-} + 2H^+$$

The thiosulfate formed then reacts rapidly with trithionate.

$$S_2O_3^{2-} + S_3O_6^{2-} + H^+ = S_4O_6^{2-} + HSO_3^-$$

In strongly alkaline solutions, trithionate is converted chiefly to sulfite and thiosulfate. In neutral and weakly acidic solutions, the tetrathionate ion undergoes slow decomposition to tri- and pentathionate, the pentathionate ion to tetrathionate and elementary sulfur, and the hexathionate to pentathionate and sulfur. All the higher polythionates ($n = 4$–6) are ultimately transformed by alkali to sulfite and thiosulfate, trithionate being an intermediate product.

---

* Wackenroder's liquid is formed by passage of hydrogen sulfide into aqueous sulfur dioxide and contains a mixture of polythionic acids.

Polonium

15.120 Polonium, a radioactive disintegration product of radium, was first isolated from pitchblende (an ore containing mainly U_3O_8), where it is present to the extent of about one gram in 25,000 tons of ore. (One part of polonium is found for every 5000 parts of radium.) After removal of the radium from pitchblende, the residue can be worked for bismuth, an element very similar to polonium in its analytical chemistry. Polonium is carried along with bismuth in the operations utilized for the separation of the latter element, and being considerably more noble than bismuth, can be separated from this element by electrolytic reduction in acid solution. Polonium has been obtained recently by the bombardment of bismuth with neutrons.

$$^{209}_{83}Bi + ^{1}_{0}n = ^{210}_{83}Bi = e^- + ^{210}_{84}Po$$

Polonium is an alpha-emitter and disintegrates to form lead.

15.121 The scarcity of polonium (the most abundant isotope, ^{210}Po, has a half-life of 138.7 days) has necessitated the use of carrier techniques * for the study of its chemistry. In addition to its similarity to bismuth (see above), polonium resembles its homolog tellurium, and many of our ideas on the chemistry of polonium have been inferred from experiments in which tellurium has been used as a carrier for the polonium activity.

15.122 Oxidation states of -2, $+2$, $+4$, and $+6$ appear to exist for polonium. Polonium forms a volatile hydride, presumably of the composition PoH_2, when a solution of the element in hydrochloric acid is treated with magnesium. As would be expected from the position of polonium in group VI, the hydride is extremely unstable, and even at $-180°$ it is largely dissociated into the elements. A polonide of the composition Na_2Po has been prepared; this substance forms mixed crystals with Na_2Te. The $+4$ state is the most common oxidation state in aqueous solution; on the basis of electrochemical behavior, the polonium seems to be capable of existing in either a cationic (Po^{4+} or PoO^{2+}) or anionic (PoO_3^{2-}) form. The $+4$ state is found in the dioxide PoO_2 and also probably in a chelate with acetylacetone. Evidence for the tetrapositive nature of polonium in the acetylacetonate comes from the fact that when the substance is recrystallized from benzene along with the corresponding aluminum and thorium(IV) complexes, the activity follows the thorium and not the aluminum. The $+6$ state of polonium is said to be formed from the dioxide by oxidation with chromium(VI) in acid solution. There is some indication that Po^{2+} ion can be formed in aqueous solution.

* The chemistry of the radioactive substance is studied in the presence of a well-known element (carrier) which is likely to have a similar chemistry. By permitting the carrier to undergo characteristic reactions and determining whether the activity of the radioactive substance "follows" the carrier, inference may be made regarding the properties of the radioactive material. Thus if the well-known species is converted to a certain oxidation state and then precipitated and the activity is found in the precipitate, it is assumed that the radioactive substance exhibits the same oxidation state.

CHAPTER 16

GROUP VII—THE HALOGENS

Introduction

16.1 Fluorine, chlorine, bromine, iodine, and astatine constitute the halogens, the seventh group of representative elements. These elements are characterized by ns^2np^5 valence shell configurations (Table 16.1). A number of important properties of the group members are summarized in Table 16.2.

TABLE 16.1

Electronic Configurations of the Halogens

	1	2	3	4	5	6
	s	$s\ p$	$s\ p\ d$	$s\ p\ d\ f$	$s\ p\ d$	$s\ p$
$_9$F	2	2, 5				
$_{17}$Cl	2	2, 6	2, 5			
$_{35}$Br	2	2, 6	2, 6, 10	2, 5		
$_{53}$I	2	2, 6	2, 6, 10	2, 6, 10	2, 5	
$_{85}$At	2	2, 6	2, 6, 10	2, 6, 10, 14	2, 6, 10	2, 5

16.2 As would be expected from their electronic arrangements, the elements are nonmetallic and in their reactions have a great tendency to attain the appropriate inert gas configurations by the acquisition of an additional electron.

GENERAL REFERENCES

EMELÉUS and ANDERSON, *Modern Aspects of Inorganic Chemistry*, 2nd Edition, D. Van Nostrand Company, Inc., New York, 1952, pp. 301–09.

LATIMER, *The Oxidation States of the Elements and Their Potentials in Aqueous Solutions*, 2nd Edition, Prentice-Hall, Inc., New York, 1952, Ch. 5.

PARTINGTON, *A Textbook of Inorganic Chemistry*, 6th Edition, Macmillan and Company, Ltd., London, 1950, Ch. XIV, XVII, and XX.

REMY, *Treatise on Inorganic Chemistry* (translated and amended by Anderson), Elsevier Publishing Company, Amsterdam, 1956, Vol. I., Ch. 17.

SIDGWICK, *The Chemical Elements and Their Compounds*, Oxford University Press, London, 1950, pp. 1097–1261.

WELLS, *Structural Inorganic Chemistry*, 2nd Edition, Oxford University Press, London, 1950, Ch. VIII and IX.

TABLE 16.2

Some Properties of the Halogens

	F	Cl	Br	I	At
Natural isotopes	19	35 *, 37	79 *, 81	127	215 †, 216 †, 218 †
Melting point, °C.	−223	−102.1	−7.3	113	
Boiling point, °C.	−188.3	−34.7	58.0	183	
Color	Pale yellow	Yellow-green	Red-brown	Gray-black	
Ionic radius in crystals, Å, for X⁻	1.34	1.80	1.90	2.23	
Covalent radius, Å	0.72	0.99	1.14	1.33	
1st ionization potential, volts	17.42	13.01	11.84	10.44	
Electronegativity (H = 2.1; O = 3.5)	4.0	3.0	2.8	2.5	
Heat of dissociation for reaction $X_2 = 2X$, kcal./mole	38 ± 3	57.2	45.4	35.5	
Dissociation constant at 1000° C.	——	10^{-8}	8×10^{-3}	10^{-1}	
Electrode potential, $E°$, in volts for $X_2 + 2e^- = 2X^-$	2.87	1.359	1.065	0.535	

* More abundant isotope
† Radioactive

The halogens can acquire this electron by the formation of simple mononegative (halide) ions or by the establishment of single covalent bonds. The ease with which halide ions are produced is reflected in the high electronegativities of the halogens (Table 16.2), in the large quantities of energy released when a gaseous halogen atom takes on an electron (F, 83 ± 3; Cl, 86.5; Br, 81.5; I, 74.2 kcal. per g. atom), and in the large values for the standard reduction potentials (Table 16.2). It is seen that, in general, the ability to form mononegative ions decreases with increasing size of the halogen atom. Anhydrous ionic halides commonly result from the union of the halogens with strongly electropositive metals which give rise to cations of relatively large size (*e.g.*, the alkali and alkaline earth metals and the lanthanides).

16.3 Simple covalent bonds are usually formed when halogens are joined together, to other nonmetals, and to metals which would yield ions of large charge and small calculated radii. In the latter connection, the covalent nature of beryllium chloride and aluminum and gallium trichlorides, bromides, and iodides has been cited. It should be emphasized that, in contrast to the chlorides, bromides, and iodides, the fluorides of metals giving ions of high charge density (*e.g.*, BiF_3) are frequently ionic in character. This is not surprising in view of the strongly electronegative character of fluorine. The great tendency of the halogens to attain inert gas configurations by electron-pair sharing is reflected in the diatomic nature of the simple molecules and their considerable stability toward thermal dissociation (Table 16.2). It should be noted that the stability of the halogen-halogen bond falls off quite significantly from chlorine to iodine.

16.4 Although a covalence of one is most common, the halogens, with the notable exception of fluorine, are capable of exhibiting higher covalencies. In at least some instances, covalencies greater than one undoubtedly occur through the utilization of outer d orbitals and the expansion of the valence shell beyond an octet of electrons. For example, among the interhalogens, which are discussed later in the chapter (see 16.16 ff.), chlorine in ClF_3 has ten electrons in the valence shell, bromine in BrF_5 has twelve, and iodine fourteen in IF_7.

16.5 On covalent union with more electronegative elements, chlorine, bromine, and iodine can be considered to exhibit positive oxidation states. Thus, in nitrogen tribromide and triiodide (see 14.50), in the interhalogens and polyhalides, and in various oxy compounds, halogens may be regarded as possessing electropositive character. The common positive oxidation states are $+1$, $+3$, $+5$, and $+7$.

16.6 A striking facet of the chemical behavior of iodine, the least electronegative of the common halogens, is the ability to form compounds in which it apparently functions as a cationic species. Thus there have been prepared a rather large number of complexes in which the unipositive iodine ion is stabilized by coordination with pyridine and other nitrogen bases, e.g., Ipy_2NO_3. (Bromine gives similar but less stable compounds.) There is evidence also that iodine may play a metallic role even in the tripositive state as in such compounds as $I(ClO_4)_3 \cdot 2H_2O$ and $I(C_2H_3O_2)_3$.

16.7 In many respects the chemistry of fluorine differs from that of its homologs. A few differences in behavior have been brought out in the foregoing discussion and others will become apparent in the sections which follow. In large measure, the "anomalous" properties of fluorine are due to its small atomic size, extremely high electronegativity, and great oxidizing power.

The Elements

16.8 The common halogens are fairly abundant elements, their estimated per cent by weight in the earth's crust (including the hydrosphere and lithosphere) being fluorine, 0.072, chlorine, 0.14, bromine, 2.5×10^{-4}, and iodine, 3×10^{-5}. The main minerals of fluorine are *fluorspar*, CaF_2; *cryolite*, Na_3AlF_6; and *apatite*, $3Ca_3(PO_4) \cdot Ca(F, Cl)_2$. Chlorine and bromine are found associated with each other in sea water, dry salt lakes, and brine wells, largely as sodium and other alkali and alkaline earth metal salts; iodine occurs mainly as sodium iodate and periodate impurities in the nitrate deposits of Chile. Astatine, essentially unknown until 1942, is an exceedingly rare, radioactive element, occurring to the extent of about 4×10^{-23} per cent by weight in the earth's crust in the form of the short-lived isotopes of mass numbers 215, 216, and 218.

Most of our scanty knowledge of this element comes from tracer studies with the isotope of mass 211 which is prepared by the bombardment of bismuth with high-energy alpha particles. The chemistry of astatine is discussed briefly at the end of the chapter.

16.9 The elementary halogens can all be obtained by processes which involve oxidation of halide ion, either electrolytically or by means of oxidizing agents. Inasmuch as fluorine is the most powerful common oxidizing agent known, it is prepared by electrolytic means. Commercial processes utilize either molten $KF \cdot 2HF$ or $KF \cdot HF$ as electrolyte in nickel, copper, or Monel metal cells, electrolyses being carried out at about $100°$ with the former electrolyte and at about $250°$ with the latter. Nickel and carbon have been employed successfully as anodes, the latter element being more suitable for electrolyses at $250°$ than at $100°$. On an industrial scale chlorine is chiefly prepared by the electrolysis of concentrated solutions of sodium chloride. In the laboratory, the element is obtained by the oxidation of chloride ion in acid medium by means of a strong oxidizing agent, e.g., permanganate; similar methods serve for the preparation of small quantities of bromine and iodine. Large quantities of bromine are obtained from sea water by the oxidation of the bromide ion with chlorine. The bromine is blown out of solution by a stream of air and is ordinarily absorbed in sodium carbonate solution, by which it is converted to a mixture of bromide and bromate. Acidification of the carbonate solution gives the free element in the main technical process for its production.

$$BrO_3^- + 5Br^- + 6H^+ = 3Br_2 + H_2O$$

Iodine is obtained from the sodium iodate in the Chilean nitrate deposits by reduction with acid sulfite ion.

16.10 Examination of the data of Table 16.2 shows that the halogens are volatile substances, with fluorine and chlorine being gaseous at room temperature, bromine liquid, and iodine solid. Iodine sublimes readily. The halogens dissolve in water with reaction (see below), the solubility of chlorine, bromine, and iodine in moles per liter at $20°$ and 1 atmosphere pressure being 9×10^{-2}, 2.1×10^{-1}, and 1.33×10^{-3}, respectively. Solutions of iodine in various solvents are of considerable interest. In solvents incapable of acting as donor molecules, e.g., carbon tetrachloride, chloroform, and hexane, iodine gives violet solutions, whereas in solvents which can function as electron-pair donors, e.g., water, ethers, and alcohols, the color is brown. Iodine is diatomic in both the violet and brown solutions; however, it has been demonstrated that whereas in the violet solutions iodine does not interact with the solvent, in the brown an equilibrium exists between free iodine and the halogen bonded to the solvent.

$$I_2 + \text{solvent} \rightleftharpoons I_2 \cdot \text{solvent}$$

16.11 The general chemical properties of the common halogens as related to their electronic configurations have been discussed in the introduction to the chapter. Specific inorganic reactions of importance are summarized in

TABLE 16.3

Reactions of the Common Halogens

Reaction	Remarks
$nX_2 + 2M = 2MX_n$	With most metals; most vigorous with F_2.
$X_2 + nX_2' = 2XX_n'$	Formation of interhalogens.
$nX_2 + X^- = X_{2n+1}^-$	With Cl_2, Br_2, and I_2, particularly I_2; $n = 1$ for Cl_2 and Br_2.
$X_2 + H_2 = 2HX$	With all the halogens.
$3X_2 + 2P = 2PX_3$	With all the halogens; As, Sb, and Bi also yield trihalides.
$5X_2 + 2P = 2PX_5$	Not with I_2; Sb gives pentafluoride and pentachloride; As and Bi form pentafluoride; existence of $AsCl_5$ questionable.
$X_2 + 2S = S_2X_2$	With Cl_2 and Br_2; Cl_2 also forms SCl_4; S gives SF_6 with F_2.
$X_2 + CO = COX_2$	With Cl_2 and Br_2.
$X_2 + SO_2 = SO_2X_2$	With F_2 and Cl_2.
$X_2 + H_2S = S + 2HX$	
$3X_2 + 8NH_3 = N_2 + 6NH_4X$	With F_2, Cl_2, and Br_2.
$X_2 + 2X'^- = 2X^- + X_2'$	F_2 with Cl^-, Br^-, and I^-; Cl_2 with Br^- and I^-; Br_2 with I^-. See reduction potentials, Table 16.2.
$\left. \begin{array}{l} 2X_2 + 2H_2O = 4H^+ + 4X^- + O_2 \\ X_2 + H_2O = H^+ + X^- + HOX \end{array} \right\}$	X = Cl, Br, I. See discussion below.

Table 16.3. A number of the reactions listed have already been noted in previous chapters, and of the remainder, only those of the halogens with water will be discussed at this time, since they bring out significant group relationships.

16.12 It is seen that the halogens can react with water in two important ways.

$$(1)\quad 2X_2 + 2H_2O = 4H^+ + 4X^- + O_2$$
$$(2)\quad X_2 + H_2O = H^+ + X^- + HOX$$

The standard potentials for the first reaction have been estimated to be approximately 2.0, 0.54, 0.25, and -0.28 volts, when X is fluorine, chlorine, bromine, and iodine, respectively. In line with these potentials, fluorine reacts energetically and completely with water to liberate oxygen, whereas chlorine and bromine react much less vigorously, oxygen being evolved only slowly. Reaction with iodine does not occur, but rather oxygen liberates the halogen from solutions of hydriodic acid.

16.13 In view of the great reactivity of fluorine, hydrolysis (reaction 2) is not observed with this element. With the other halogens the extent of hydrolysis falls off significantly from chlorine to iodine, the equilibrium constants at 25° being 4.66×10^{-4} for chlorine, 5.8×10^{-9} for bromine, and 3×10^{-13} for iodine.

16.14 Mention has been made of the brown solutions iodine forms in donor solvents. There is considerable evidence that in these solutions the iodine bound to solvent molecules exists in a highly polarized condition and that equilibria of the following type involving cationic iodine may occur.

$$I_2 \cdot \text{solvent} \rightleftharpoons I^+ \cdot \text{solvent} + I^-$$

Estimates have been made of the equilibrium constants for the reaction $X_2(\text{aq.}) + H_2O(\text{l.}) \rightleftharpoons H_2OX^+(\text{aq.}) + X^-(\text{aq.})$. At 25° the following approximate constants have been found[1,2]: Cl_2, 10^{-30}; Br_2, 10^{-20}; I_2, 10^{-10}. These values indicate that of the halogens only the hydrated I^+ should be sufficiently stable to exist in detectable quantities in aqueous solution.

Compounds of the Halogens

16.15 Numerous references have been made to binary halides and halo complexes in the discussion of the previous groups of representative elements, and others will be encountered in the treatment of the elements of the various transition series. In the present chapter compounds of the halogens with each other, with hydrogen, and with oxygen are considered, and in addition, the compounds which presumably contain cationic iodine are described.

The Interhalogens [3,4,5]

16.16 Molecular compounds of the halogens with each other are known as interhalogens. Interhalogens of the types XX', XX'_3, XX'_5 and XX'_7 have been characterized, and the specific compounds known, their colors and melting and boiling points are listed in Table 16.4. These extremely volatile compounds

TABLE 16.4
Melting and Boiling Points of the Interhalogens

Type	Compound	Color	Melting Point, °C.	Boiling Point, °C.
XX'	ClF	Colorless gas	−155.6	−100.1
	BrF	Pale brown gas	ca. −33 (decomp.)	ca. 20
	BrCl	——		
	ICl	α Ruby-red solid	27.2	97–100
		β Brown-red solid	13.9	——
	IBr	Gray-violet solid	42	ca. 116
XX'_3	ClF_3	Colorless gas	−82.6	12.0
	BrF_3	Light yellow-green liquid	8.8	127.6
	ICl_3	Orange solid	101 (decomp.)	——
XX'_5	BrF_5	Colorless liquid	−61.3	40.5
	IF_5	Colorless liquid	9.6	98
XX'_7	IF_7	Colorless gas	5 (2 atm.)	4.5

[1] BELL and GELLES, *J. Chem. Soc.*, 1950, p. 2734.
[2] ALLEN and KEEFER, *J. Am. Chem. Soc.*, **77**, 2957 (1955).
[3] SHARPE, *Quart. Revs.*, **4**, No. 2, 115 (1950).
[4] GREENWOOD, *Revs. Pure Applied Chem.* (Australia), **1**, 84 (1951).
[5] BOOTH and PINKSTON, *Chem. Revs.*, **41**, 421 (1947).

are named as halides of the more electropositive element, *e.g.*, BrF, bromine monofluoride; and ICl_3, iodine trichloride.

16.17 With the exception of iodine heptafluoride, the interhalogen molecules possess unshared pairs of electrons. Structurally, an unshared electron pair ordinarily appears to occupy one of the corners of a polyhedron, thus exhibiting directional characteristics of a shared electron pair bond.[6] In the interhalogens, the larger halogen is the central atom, the number of other halogens which can be accommodated by covalent bonds being related to the relative sizes of the atoms in the compound. The highest degree of covalence is thus found when fluorine is combined with iodine. The interhalogens are characterized by very great reactivity, a fact which has made the determination of their structures a difficult matter.

Compounds of the XX′ Type   **16.18** Substances of this type are prepared by direct union of the elements, and all the possible compounds have been characterized, with the exception of iodine monofluoride. Two of the known compounds, bromine monofluoride and bromine monochloride, have not been obtained in the pure condition. The former, the least stable of the bromine fluorides, disproportionates spontaneously to elementary fluorine and the higher fluorides BrF_3 and BrF_5. Evidence for the existence of bromine monochloride comes mainly from absorption spectra measurements on bromine-chlorine mixtures either in the gaseous state or in carbon tetrachloride solution. The compound is extensively dissociated into the elements at room temperature.

$$2BrCl \rightleftharpoons Br_2 + Cl_2$$

One of the XX′ compounds, iodine monochloride, exists in two crystalline modifications, known as the α and β forms (Table 16.4); the latter is the less stable form and readily reverts to the α modification.

16.19 Interatomic distances have been determined for chlorine and bromine monofluorides and for iodine monochloride. For the latter the I—Cl bond distance is 2.32 Å, a value equal to the sum of the single covalent radii. For chlorine monofluoride and bromine monofluoride the respective bond distances of 1.63 and 1.76 Å are significantly shorter than the calculated radius sums of 1.71 and 1.86 Å. The shortening has been ascribed to the marked differences in electronegativity of the halogens in these compounds.

16.20 Molten iodine monochloride and monobromide have been shown to be fairly good conductors of electric current, the compounds exhibiting specific conductances of 4.42×10^{-3} and 4.0×10^{-4} ohm^{-1} cm^{-1}, respectively, at their melting points. On passage of direct current through the melts, iodine is transported to the cathode. The electrochemical behavior of the molten chloride has been interpreted in terms of the following mode of self-ionization.

$$2ICl \rightleftharpoons I^+ + ICl_2^-$$

---

[6] PAULING, *The Nature of the Chemical Bond*, 2nd Edition, Cornell University Press, Ithaca, 1940, pp. 110–111.

The equilibria $XX' \rightleftharpoons \frac{1}{2}X_2 + \frac{1}{2}X_2'$ have been studied by spectroscopic means, and the values obtained for the heats and free energies of dissociation and for the dissociation constants for the various 1–1 interhalogens at 298.16° K are

TABLE 16.5
Some Thermodynamic Properties of XX′ Interhalogens
for the Reaction $XX' \rightleftharpoons \frac{1}{2}X_2 + \frac{1}{2}X_2'$ at 298.16° K

Compound	$\dfrac{\Delta H°}{T}$, cal./mole deg.	$\dfrac{\Delta F°}{T}$, cal./mole deg.	$K = \dfrac{(p_{X_2}^{\frac{1}{2}})(p_{X_2'}^{\frac{1}{2}})}{(p_{XX'})}$
ClF	47.012	48.183	2.950×10^{-11}
BrF	65.703	66.821	2.491×10^{-15}
BrCl	0.80286	2.1578	0.3376
ICl	11.186	12.507	1.848×10^{-3}
IBr	5.673	5.9719	4.953×10^{-2}

listed in Table 16.5.[7] The data show the following order of stability with respect to dissociation to the parent molecular halogens at room temperature.

$$BrCl < IBr < ICl < ClF < BrF$$

It should be pointed out that, although bromine monofluoride is the most stable 1–1 interhalogen toward dissociation, it nevertheless is an extremely unstable molecule with respect to disproportionation. (See above.)

16.21 In their chemical reactions the XX′ compounds closely resemble the free halogens. With many metals and nonmetals they form mixtures of the corresponding halides. They combine with alkali metal halides to give polyhalide complexes (see 16.32 ff.). Reaction with water often occurs in a manner similar to that of the free halogens.

$$XX' + H_2O = H^+ + X' + HOX$$
$$(X = \text{the more electropositive halogen})$$

Compounds of the XX′₃ Type **16.22** The three interhalogens of this class, ClF_3, BrF_3, and ICl_3, can be prepared by direct combination of the elements, the monohalides being intermediate products. Physical data for these compounds are given in Table 16.4.

16.23 Detailed structural information is available on chlorine trifluoride. Low temperature X-ray diffraction [8] and microwave spectrum [9] analysis lead to a planar structure for the molecule (Fig. 16.1), with the chlorine bonded to one fluorine atom (F) at a distance of 1.62 Å and to two fluorine atoms (F′) at 1.72 Å, the F—Cl—F′ bond angle being about 87°. As a crude approximation, the planar configuration may be considered to be derived from the use of

[7] COLE and ELVERUM, *J. Chem. Phys.*, **20**, 1543 (1952).
[8] BURBANK and BENSEY, *J. Chem. Phys.*, **21**, 602 (1953).
[9] SMITH, *J. Chem. Phys.*, **21**, 609 (1953).

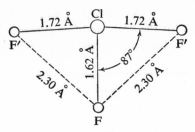

Fig. 16.1   The structure of the ClF₃ molecule. (From BURBANK and BENSEY, *J. Chem. Phys.*, **21**, 602, 1953)

hybridized SP^3D orbitals on the chlorine atom, with three of these orbitals used in binding the fluorine atoms and two containing the unshared pairs of electrons. Theoretically, SP^3D hybridization should result in bonds directed toward the apices of a trigonal bipyramid.[10]   In the ClF₃ molecule the fluorine atoms may be regarded as occupying one equatorial and two axial positions of a slightly distorted trigonal bipyramid.

16.24 In the fused state bromine trifluoride and iodine trichloride exhibit fairly high electrical conductivities, the specific conductance values being 8.1×10^{-3} and 8.5×10^{-3} ohm^{-1} cm^{-1} at the respective melting points of 8.8° and 101°.   Molten chlorine trifluoride is a poor conductor of electric current, having a specific conductance of 3×10^{-9} ohm^{-1} cm^{-1} at 0°.   It has been proposed that liquid bromine trifluoride undergoes the following self-ionization.

$$2BrF_3 \rightleftharpoons BrF_2^+ + BrF_4^-$$

16.25 Chlorine trifluoride and bromine trifluoride are rather stable thermally. At 25°, the vapor of the latter is dissociated only to a slight extent to monofluoride and fluorine, whereas chlorine trifluoride appears actually to exist in a somewhat associated condition.   Dissociation of chlorine trifluoride into its elements is extensive above 280°.   Iodine trichloride is almost completely dissociated in the vapor state into the monochloride and chlorine.

16.26 The trifluorides are very reactive substances and behave as powerful fluorinating agents toward both inorganic and organic substances, reaction with the latter often being accompanied by inflammation.   All the elements, except for a few metals, nitrogen and the inert gases, are energetically attacked by chlorine trifluoride.   Bromine trifluoride acts on a large number of oxides and oxyanions converting them to fluorides and complex fluorides, respectively. In many of these reactions molecular oxygen is liberated in quantitative yield. Metal chlorides, bromides, and iodides are converted to fluorides by chlorine and bromine trifluorides.   Iodine trichloride is much less reactive than chlorine and bromine trifluorides, and it is likely that its reactions are essentially those of the monochloride resulting from thermal decomposition.

16.27 Bromine trifluoride has been investigated as a parent solvent for a

---

[10] KIMBALL, *J. Chem. Phys.*, **8**, 188 (1940).

system of acids and bases. In accordance with the proposed mode of self-ionization (see 16.24), substances giving rise to $[BrF_2]^+$ may be regarded as acids in bromine trifluoride and those yielding $[BrF_4]^-$ as bases. (See Solvent System concept of acids and bases, section 7.27.) Thus alkali metal fluorides are bases in the bromine trifluoride system.

$$K^+F^- + BrF_3 = K^+[BrF_4]^-$$

Similarly, fluoride ion acceptors like SnF_4, VF_5, NbF_5, and TaF_5 are acids.

$$SbF_5 + BrF_3 = [BrF_2]^+ + [SbF_6]^-$$

Compounds containing $[BrF_2]^+$ and $[BrF_4]^-$ ions have been prepared in bromine trifluoride by reactions like those depicted above, *e.g.*,

$$[BrF_2]^+[SbF_6]^-, \quad [BrF_2]^+[NbF_6]^-, \quad K^+[BrF_4]^-, \quad Ag^+[BrF_4]^-.$$

Substances such as those listed are good conductors of the electric current when dissolved in bromine trifluoride. A typical neutralization reaction in bromine trifluoride is shown in the following equation.

$$K^+[BrF_4]^- + [BrF_2]^+[SbF_6]^- = K^+[SbF_6]^- + 2BrF_3$$

Compounds of the Types XX'_5 and XX'_7 **16.28** The only such compounds known are the fluorides BrF_5, IF_5, and IF_7. The pentafluorides are prepared by direct combination of the elements, the purification of the bromine compound involving separation from the less volatile trifluoride. Iodine heptafluoride is obtained in quantitative yield by heating the pentafluoride in fluorine. It is not surprising that a high order of covalency is attained by the larger halogens when they are united to fluorine, the most powerful oxidizing agent and the smallest of the halogens.

16.29 Vapor density measurements on the higher fluorides lead to molecular weights which are concordant with the simple formulas. The structures of the compounds seem to have been fairly well established.[11,12] The pentafluoride molecules appear to be of the tetragonal pyramidal type, with four fluorine atoms at the corners of a square base and the iodine or bromine atom and the

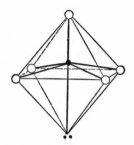

Fig. 16.2 The Structure of BrF_5 and IF_5.

[11] LORD, LYNCH, SCHUMB, and SLOWINSKI, *J. Am. Chem. Soc.*, **72**, 522 (1950).
[12] STEPHENSON and JONES, *J. Chem. Phys.*, **20**, 1830 (1952).

fifth fluorine atom on the fourfold axis perpendicular to the base. This model is consistent with the expected P^3D^2 bond hybridization; it is also in accord with a tetragonal bipyramid structure in which the unshared electron pair on the central halogen atom occupies one of the apices (Fig. 16.2). Iodine heptafluoride apparently possesses a pentagonal bipyramidal structure, with the iodine atom situated at the center of a regular pentagon of fluorine atoms and the other two fluorine atoms being disposed at equal distances above and below the fivefold axis through the iodine atom.

16.30 The higher fluorides are remarkably stable toward thermal decomposition. Bromine pentafluoride remains unaltered up to at least 460°, and iodine pentafluoride is stable at temperatures up to 400°. Above 500° the iodine compound disproportionates into molecular iodine and the heptafluoride. The latter gives no evidence of decomposition up to 460°.

16.31 Bromine pentafluoride is by far the most reactive of the three higher fluorides and resembles chlorine trifluoride in chemical behavior. The pentafluoride reacts readily with many oxides, halides, and hydrides and with all the elements except nitrogen, oxygen, and the inert gases, fluorides being formed in all cases. Iodine pentafluoride is the least active of the higher fluorides. It is inert toward many elements, and even some of the more active ones, such as the alkali metals, chlorine, and sulfur, are attacked only at elevated temperatures to give fluorides. Iodine pentafluoride is readily hydrolyzed, iodic and hydrofluoric acids being produced. The heptafluoride is similar to bromine pentafluoride in its reactions.

The Polyhalide Complexes

General Considerations **16.32** Complex salts containing mononegative anions consisting of a central halogen joined to other halogen atoms are known as polyhalides. Polyhalide anions of the types X_n^-, $XX_n'^-$, and $XX'X_n''^-$ have been identified, and the great majority of the complexes have iodine as the central atom. It is of interest that relatively few polyhalides containing fluorine have been obtained.

16.33 It is noteworthy that the nonsolvated polyhalides which have been isolated commonly contain large cations, *e.g.*, Rb^+, Cs^+, quaternary ammonium ions, and such coordination complexes as $[Co(NH_3)_6]^{3+}$ and $[Ni(NH_3)_6]^{2+}$. In fact, the stability of the members of any one series of polyhalides (with the exception of salts containing BrF_4^-, sec. 16.43) is greater the larger the cationic size. Polyhalide salts having smaller cations have been obtained in the solid condition, but these are invariably solvated, *e.g.*, $NaI_3 \cdot 2H_2O$, $KI_3 \cdot H_2O$, $NH_4I_3 \cdot 3H_2O$, $LiI_3 \cdot 4C_6H_5CN$.

16.34 The heaviest halogen of a polyhalide anion serves as the central atom and the other halogens are ordinarily arranged symmetrically around it. Extensive structural investigations have been made on polyhalides containing iodine as the central atom and the evidence indicates that the binding in these complexes is usually covalent, with the central iodine atom utilizing d orbitals of the valence shell for the formation of bonds. It is seen in Table 16.6, where bond

TABLE 16.6

Bond Lengths in Some Polyhalide Ions

Ion	Bond	Bond Length (exptl.), $\overset{\circ}{A}$	Sum of Covalent Radii, $\overset{\circ}{A}$
ICl_2^-	I—Cl	2.34	2.32
$IClBr^-$	I—Cl	2.38	2.32
	I—Br	2.50	2.47
ICl_4^-	I—Cl	2.34	2.32
I_3^-	I—I	2.82, 3.10	2.67
I_5^-	I—I	2.93, 3.14	2.67

lengths in some polyhalide ions are tabulated, that the I—X distances in most instances are very nearly the sums of the covalent radii. Notable exceptions are found in the I—I distances in the tri- and pentaiodide ions and these are discussed later (see 16.38).

16.35 Most of the polyhalides are low-melting materials having colors ranging from yellow to black. They are soluble in solvents of high dielectric constant; solution in water is often accompanied by hydrolysis. Both in the solid state and in solution, the polyhalides tend to dissociate into a halogen (or interhalogen) and a simple halide. The simple halide formed when dissociation occurs in the absence of solvent contains the most electronegative halogen present in the polyhalide.

Compounds with Anion Type X_n^- **16.36** The ions of this class which have been identified include Cl_3^-, Br_3^-, I_3^-, I_5^-, I_7^-, and I_9^-, with salts of the triiodide ion being by far the most common and the most stable. No trichloride compound containing an inorganic cation has been isolated, the existence of the trichloride ion having been established from studies on the effect of hydrogen chloride on the solubility of elementary chlorine in water. The stability of the trihalides in aqueous solution toward dissociation to free halogen and halide ion follows the order $I_3^- > Br_3^- > Cl_3^-$, the equilibrium constants at 25° for the reaction

$$X_2 + X^- \rightleftharpoons X_3^-$$

being 725, 17.8, and 10^{-2}, respectively. The same order of stability holds for solid trihalides containing a common cation; for salts having the same trihalide anion the stability increases with cationic size. The stability patterns are illustrated by the following data on the temperatures at which the tribromides and triiodides of rubidium and cesium exhibit dissociation pressures of one atmosphere: RbI_3, 192°; CsI_3, 250°; $RbBr_3$, 105.5°; $CsBr_3$, 147.5°.

16.37 With very large cations (*e.g.*, quaternary ammonium ions, solvated alkali metal ions) polyiodides of higher order than triiodide have been obtained in the solid state. The polyiodide anions of higher order which have been characterized include penta-, hepta-, and enneaiodides, e.g., $NH_4I_5 \cdot H_2O$, $KI_7 \cdot H_2O$, $(C_2H_5)_4NI_7$, $KI_9 \cdot 3C_6H_6$, $(CH_3)_4NI_9$, $RbI_9 \cdot 3C_6H_6$. These compounds are prepared by reaction between the iodide salt and the stoichiometric quantity of iodine in the appropriate solvent; methanol or ethanol is commonly utilized for the production of the nonsolvated quaternary ammonium salts. The higher order polyiodides are much less stable than the triiodides with respect to dissociation. For example, on the basis of the absorption spectra of tetramethylammonium penta- and enneaiodides in ethylene chloride,[13] the conclusion was reached that these polyiodides are essentially completely dissociated into the triiodide ion and iodine in this solvent.

16.38 The structures of the triiodide and pentaiodide ions have been elucidated by X-ray analysis. The triiodide[14] has been found to be linear and asymmetric and to have two different I—I bond distances, each considerably greater than twice the calculated covalent radius of the iodine atom (Table 16.6). The pentaiodide in $(CH_3)_4NI_5$ has been shown to consist of nearly square iodine nets within which V-shaped I_5^- can be distinguished; in this ion also (Table 16.6) there are two different I—I distances.[15] It has been suggested that, in the pentaiodide ion, iodine does not use d orbitals in the valence shell for the formation of bonds, but that the complex ion results from interaction of an iodide ion with polarizable iodine molecules. This is accompanied by a weakening of the interatomic bonds in the latter. The resonance structures shown below have been proposed for I_5^-.

A similar type of interaction has been postulated to account for the observed I—I distances in the triiodide ion.

Compounds with Anion Type $XX'_n{}^-$ **16.39** Included in this class of anions are I_2Br^-, ICl_2^-, IBr_2^-, $BrCl_2^-$, Br_2Cl^-, ICl_4^-, BrF_4^-, and IF_6^-. Salts containing the $XX'_n{}^-$ type of anion are the most common of the polyhalides and next to the triiodides are the most stable in the nonsolvated condition. It is worth noting that no salts containing I_2Cl^- have been prepared, and only the cesium compound with I_2Br^- is known.

16.40 Compounds containing anions of the $XX'_2{}^-$ class are best made by reaction between finely powdered halide and the appropriate halogen or halogen halide in the absence of solvent.[16]

[13] BUCKLES, YUK, and POPOV, *J. Am. Chem. Soc.*, **74**, 4369 (1952).
[14] MOONEY, *Z. Krist.*, **90**, 143 (1935).
[15] HACH and RUNDLE, *J. Am. Chem. Soc.*, **73**, 4321 (1951).
[16] CREMER and DUNCAN, *J. Chem. Soc.*, 1931, p. 1857.

$$RbI + Br_2 = RbIBr_2$$
$$CsCl + ICl = CsICl_2$$
$$CsBr + 2ICl = CsICl_2 + IBr$$

This dry method of preparation is slow, but essentially quantitative yield of polyhalide is often obtained. Moreover, the product is free from water and hydrolysis products.

16.41 The thermal stability for XX'_2^- compounds with a common cation follows the order $IBr_2^- > ICl_2^- > I_2Br^- > BrCl_2^- > Br_2Cl^-$. This is illustrated by the temperatures at which the cesium compounds have a dissociation pressure of 1 atmosphere: $CsIBr_2$, 242.5°; $CsICl_2$, 209°; CsI_2Br, 201.5°; $CsBrCl_2$, 138°; $CsBr_2Cl$, 124°.

16.42 ICl_2^- and IBr_2^- have been shown by X-ray analysis to be linear, with the iodine being the central atom.[17,18,19,20] The I—Cl and I—Br distances are approximately equal to the sums of the covalent radii (Table 16.6). The linear structure of the ions is in accord with the hypothesis that a d orbital of the valence shell of the iodine atom is used in bond formation and that the chlorine and bromine atoms lie at the two apices of a trigonal bipyramid and the three unshared pairs of electrons in the equatorial plane.[6]

16.43 Two ions of the composition XX'_4^- are known: ICl_4^- and BrF_4^-. The latter has already been referred to in connection with the use of bromine trifluoride as a solvent (see 16.27). It is interesting that, in contrast to the situation existing with the other polyhalides, the order of increasing thermal stability of compounds containing BrF_4^- is not that of increasing cationic size. Thus the following order of thermal stability *in vacuo* has been found for the alkali metal tetrafluorobromates: $K > Na > Rb > Cs$. Potassium tetrafluorobromate, the most extensively studied compound of this group, is a white crystalline substance, inert toward common organic solvents but immediately decomposed by water with the formation of oxygen, bromine, and hydrofluoric and bromic acids. Above 200° thermal decomposition is extensive, bromine trifluoride and potassium fluoride being formed.

16.44 Tetrachloroiodates are prepared by the addition of iodine to solutions of metal chlorides in hydrochloric acid, followed by saturation with chlorine. The tetrachloroiodate ion differs from the other polyhalides in forming a series of salts with dipositive cations, *e.g.*, Be^{2+}, Mg^{2+}, Ca^{2+}, Mn^{2+}, Co^{2+}, Ni^{2+}. These salts are all octahydrates and a number of them are rather stable. Salts of the larger alkali metals, *e.g.*, K, Rb, Cs, are obtained anhydrous, but the lithium and sodium salts are generally hydrated, *e.g.*, $LiICl_4 \cdot 4H_2O$, $NaICl_4 \cdot 4H_2O$. In aqueous solution the tetrachloroiodates dissociate to varying extents to give the metal chloride and iodine trichloride, the latter then being hydrolyzed to iodate. ICl_4^- is planar, with the chlorine atoms at the corners of a square sur-

[17] WYCKOFF, *J. Am. Chem. Soc.*, **42**, 1100 (1920).
[18] MOONEY, *Z. Krist*, **100**, 519 (1939).
[19] CLARK, *Proc. Natl. Acad. Sci.*, **9**, 117 (1923).
[20] BOSWORTH and PAULING, *J. Am. Chem. Soc.*, **47**, 1561 (1925).

rounding the central iodine atom.[21] The two unshared pairs of electrons on the iodine atom can be considered to be directed in space one above and one below the ICl_4 plane in such a manner as to complete an octahedron.[6] The I—Cl bond distance is close to that required for a single covalent bond (Table 16.6).

16.45 One compound (KIF_6) containing an ion of the $XX_6'^-$ type has been characterized. This is obtained by reaction between potassium fluoride and iodine pentafluoride. It is unstable in water and toward heat. Reaction with water yields hydrofluoric and iodic acids, as well as other products. At its melting point (about 200°), KIF_6 is extensively decomposed into its parent compounds.

Compounds with Anion Type $XX'X_n''^-$ **16.46** This is the least common polyhalide type and only three anions of this class are known: $FIBr^-$, $ClIBr^-$, and $FICl_3^-$. Compounds containing either of the first two ions are made by combination of metal (or ammonium) halide and the appropriate interhalogen as in the example.

$$CsF + IBr = CsFIBr$$

Salts of the type $MFICl_3$ can be prepared by the action of chlorine and iodine on alkali metal fluorides, either in the dry state or in aqueous solution. An alternative mode of preparation involves reaction between an acidic solution of metal fluoride and an excess of iodine trichloride. Salts of organic amines can be prepared similarly. The $MFICl_3$ compounds are sufficiently stable so that they may be recrystallized from water. On exposure to air they evolve iodine trichloride.

16.47 $ClIBr^-$, like ICl_2^-, is linear;[22] iodine is the central atom and the interhalogen distances (Table 16.6) are very nearly the sums of the covalent radii. Presumably, $FICl_3^-$ has a planar structure, like that of ICl_4^-.

The Hydrogen Halides

The Anhydrous Compounds **16.48** The hydrogen halides can be formed by direct combination of the elements. For fluorine, chlorine, and bromine, the reaction given is exothermic, the heats of formation of the hydrogen halides

$$\tfrac{1}{2}X_2 + \tfrac{1}{2}H_2 = HX$$

being −64.0, −22.0, and −13.5 kcal. per mole, respectively. Hydrogen iodide, however, is an endothermic compound ($\Delta H° = 0.8$ kcal. per mole). Union between fluorine and hydrogen takes place instantly, even with the solid halogen and liquid hydrogen. Reaction between hydrogen and chlorine, although slow in the dark, occurs explosively in the sunlight or at temperatures in the neighborhood of 250°. Bromine and iodine combine extremely slowly with hydrogen at room temperature, but reaction can be catalyzed at elevated temperatures. Thus hydrogen bromide can be synthesized at a fairly rapid rate at 375° in the presence of platinized silica gel as catalyst.

[21] MOONEY, *Z. Krist.*, **98**, 377 (1938).
[22] MOONEY, *Z. Krist.*, **98**, 324 (1938).

16.49 Hydrogen fluoride and hydrogen chloride are commonly made by heating appropriate salts, *e.g.*, NaCl and CaF_2, with concentrated sulfuric acid, the volatile hydrogen halides distilling from solution. Alternative methods to direct union of the elements for the preparation of hydrogen bromide involve the hydrolysis of phosphorus tribromide (see 14.101) and the bromination of such aromatic hydrocarbons as tetrahydronaphthalene. Because of the thermal instability of the gas (see 16.50), hydrogen iodide is ordinarily prepared in aqueous solution, conveniently by reaction between hydrogen sulfide and a suspension of iodine.

16.50 The hydrogen halides are all colorless gases possessing disagreeable odors. As might be expected from their heats of formation (see 16.48), the thermal stability of the compounds decreases with increasing halogen weight. Thus at 1000° the per cent of dissociation into parent molecules is for HCl, 0.0014; HBr, 0.5; and HI, 33. The decreasing stability is reflected in the values for the bond (dissociation) energies of the molecules: H—F, 132; H—Cl, 103; H—Br, 87; H—I, 71 kcal. per mole.

16.51 Whereas the other hydrogen halides exist essentially as monomolecular species, hydrogen fluoride is an associated substance as a result of hydrogen bonding between individual molecules. The physical properties (*e.g.*, melting point, boiling point, heat of vaporization) of hydrogen fluoride are therefore abnormally high in relation to the trends observed for the other hydrogen halides (Table 16.7). Electron diffraction evidence indicates that hydrogen

TABLE 16.7

Some Physical Properties of the Hydrogen Halides

Property	HF	HCl	HBr	HI
Melting point, °C.	−83.1	−114.8	−86.9	−50.7
Boiling point, °C.	19.5	−84.9	−66.8	−35.4
Heat of fusion at melting point, kcal. per mole	1.094	0.505	0.575	0.686
Heat of vaporization at boiling point, kcal. per mole	7.24	3.85	4.21	4.72

fluoride consists of polymeric aggregates even in the vapor state at moderate temperatures. A number of polymers up to $(HF)_5$ appear to exist in the vapor. These have a zigzag chain configuration with an F—H---F distance of about 2.55 Å and an H---F—H bond angle of approximately 140°.

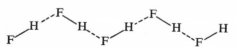

Solutions of the Hydrogen Halides (*The Hydrohalic Acids*) **16.52** The hydrogen halides exhibit high solubility in water: HF, 35.3; HCl, 42; HBr, 49; HI, 57 g.

per 100 g. of solution at 20° and 1 atmosphere pressure. Solution is accompanied by reaction yielding hydronium and halide ions.

$$H_2O + HX \rightleftharpoons H_3O^+ + X^-$$

This reaction goes essentially to completion for dilute solutions of HCl, HBr, and HI, and these substances behave as typical strong acids in water. (See 7.12 for the behavior of water as a leveling solvent.) In dilute solution HF is a rather weak acid, the equilibrium constant for the above reaction being 7.2×10^{-4}. In fairly concentrated solutions, however, HF behaves as a much stronger acid. In dilute solutions HF is believed to be present largely in the form of species in which it is joined to water through hydrogen bonds, e.g., H

$$\begin{array}{cc} H & \quad\quad H. \\ & \diagdown \quad\quad\quad\quad \diagup \\ & O-H---F \end{array}$$

The more concentrated solutions presumably contain the more strongly acidic species H   which reacts with water to give hydronium ions and

$$\begin{array}{c} H \\ \diagdown \\ \quad F---H-F \end{array}$$

HF_2^-. The latter is a rather stable ion, the equilibrium constant for the reaction $F^- + HF \rightleftharpoons HF_2^-$ being about 5 in water solution.

16.53 Although HCl, HBr, and HI are all essentially completely ionized in dilute aqueous solution, in less basic solvents, e.g., acetic acid (see 7.12), and in poorer ionizing solvents such as methanol, there is a distinct difference in the acid strengths of these substances, with HI being the strongest and HCl the weakest acid. Presumably, HF would be still weaker than HCl. It is to be noted that the order of acid strengths is the inverse of that for the bond (dissociation) energies of the hydrogen halide molecules (see 16.50). The relationships between the dissociation of the gaseous hydrogen halide molecules and the release of a proton in solution are shown in the following cycle.

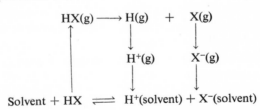

$$\begin{array}{ccccc} HX(g) & \longrightarrow & H(g) & + & X(g) \\ \uparrow & & \downarrow & & \downarrow \\ & & H^+(g) & & X^-(g) \\ \uparrow & & \downarrow & & \downarrow \\ Solvent + HX & \rightleftharpoons & H^+(solvent) & + & X^-(solvent) \end{array}$$

Binary Compounds with Oxygen

16.54 The known compounds of oxygen with the halogens are listed in Table 16.8. The oxygen-halogen compounds, with the exception of those of fluorine which have little resemblance to the oxygen derivatives of the other halogens, are truly oxides rather than halides. In all but the fluorine compounds, the oxygen is more electronegative than the halogen.

16.55 Two oxygen compounds of iodine, I_2O_4 and I_4O_9, have been omitted from Table 16.8. These substances are believed not to be true oxides, but are rather the basic, $IO(IO_3)$, and normal, $I(IO_3)_3$, iodates of tripositive iodine.

TABLE 16.8

**Melting and Boiling Points of Binary Compounds
of the Halogens with Oxygen**

Type	F	Cl	Br	I
X_2O	OF_2 m.p. $-223.8°$ b.p. $-144.8°$	Cl_2O m.p. $-11.6°$ b.p. $2°$	Br_2O m.p. $-17.5°$ b.p. (decomp.)	——
X_2O_2	O_2F_2 m.p. $-160°$ b.p. (decomp.)	——	——	——
XO_2	——	ClO_2 m.p. $-59°$ b.p. $11°$	BrO_2 (decomp.)	——
X_2O_5	——	——	——	I_2O_5 (nonvolatile)
X_3O_8	——	——	Br_3O_8* (decomp.)	——
XO_3	——	$Cl_2O_6(ClO_3)$ m.p. $3.5°$ b.p. $203°$ (calc.)	——	——
X_2O_7	——	Cl_2O_7 m.p. $-91.5°$ b.p. $80°$	——	——

* See footnote to sec. 16.66.

The Oxygen Fluorides **16.56** Oxygen difluoride, OF_2, a colorless gas, is obtained in low yield by reaction between elementary fluorine and dilute sodium hydroxide solution.

$$2F_2 + 2NaOH = 2NaF + OF_2 + H_2O$$

The second binary oxygen-fluorine compound, oxygen monofluoride, O_2F_2, is formed as a yellow-orange solid by the passage of an electric discharge through a mixture of the elements at a pressure of 15–20 mm. and at liquid air temperatures. Melting and boiling points of the oxygen fluorides are given in Table 16.8.

16.57 Oxygen difluoride is an angular molecule, with the F—O—F bond angle about 100° and the F—O bond distance 1.4 Å (calculated for a single covalent bond 1.46 Å). The difluoride is an endothermic compound, the heat of formation from gaseous oxygen and fluorine having been estimated to be 4.6 ± 2 kcal. per mole. Oxygen difluoride is a highly reactive substance, particularly at elevated temperatures, where it undergoes decomposition to the constituent elements. When heated it reacts strongly with both metals and nonmetals to give mixtures of oxides and fluorides. It dissolves in water to the extent of 68 cc. per liter with apparent reaction, yielding a solution which has no acidic properties. The aqueous solutions possess strongly oxidizing properties, being capable, for example, of converting tripositive chromium to chromate. In concentrated solutions of alkali the difluoride is rapidly and completely decomposed with the formation of fluoride and oxygen.

16.58 Oxygen monofluoride begins to decompose into the elements in the neighborhood of $-100°$. Below this temperature, the brown vapor in equilibrium with the red liquid has a density corresponding to the formula O_2F_2. No information is available regarding the structure of the monofluoride or its chemical properties, except for the decomposition noted above.

The Chlorine Oxides **16.59** These compounds are characterized by their great instability, all of them being explosive. Two of the oxides, chlorine monoxide, Cl_2O, and chlorine heptoxide, Cl_2O_7, are the anhydrides of acids — hypochlorous, $HClO$, and perchloric acid, $HClO_4$, respectively.

16.60 Chlorine monoxide is most commonly obtained by passage of elementary chlorine over dry mercury(II) oxide at $0°$.

$$2Cl_2 + HgO = Cl_2O + HgCl_2$$

Chlorine dioxide, ClO_2, can be prepared by the action of concentrated sulfuric acid on potassium chlorate, under carefully controlled conditions, or more safely, by the action of dilute sulfuric acid on a mixture of the chlorate and oxalic acid.

$$KClO_3 + H_2SO_4 = HClO_3 + KHSO_4$$
$$3HClO_3 = HClO_4 + 2ClO_2 + H_2O$$
$$2KClO_3 + H_2C_2O_4 + H_2SO_4 = K_2SO_4 + 2H_2O + 2CO_2 + 2ClO_2$$

In the latter mode of preparation, the carbon dioxide liberated serves as a diluent for the chlorine dioxide, thus reducing danger of explosion. Dichlorine hexoxide, Cl_2O_6, is best made by the direct oxidation of the dioxide by means of ozonized oxygen, the product being frozen out at $0°$ and freed from dioxide impurity by careful fractionation at low pressures. Chlorine heptoxide is prepared by the dehydration of perchloric acid with phosphorus(V) oxide.

16.61 Chlorine monoxide is an endothermic compound, ΔH_f° being 18.2 kcal. The yellow-red gas decomposes explosively into the elements when heated, and the liquid is still more unstable. The compound is an extremely powerful oxidizing agent and reacts with most metals to give mixtures of oxides and chlorides. It is extremely soluble in water, with which it reacts to give hypochlorous acid. The molecule in the gaseous state has an angular structure

Cl—Cl, the bond angle being about $110.8°$ and the Cl—O bond distance 1.70 Å (calculated for a single bond 1.73 Å).[23]

16.62 Chlorine dioxide, an orange-yellow gas, is also an endothermic compound (ΔH_f° 19.7 kcal.) and appears to be even more reactive and explosive than the monoxide, often decomposing violently with little provocation. Although it is an "odd molecule" (see 5.79), it shows no tendency to dimerize in the liquid state or in solution in carbon tetrachloride. The gas is extremely soluble in water, forming what appears to be an octahydrate which is stable up to $18°$.

[23] DUNITZ and HEDBERG, *J. Am. Chem. Soc.*, **72**, 3108 (1950).

Aqueous solutions are stable in the dark, but in the light, reaction yielding chloric, $HClO_3$, and hydrochloric acids occurs slowly. In alkaline solution reaction takes place somewhat more rapidly, chlorite and chlorate being formed.

$$2ClO_2 + 2OH^- = ClO_2^- + ClO_3^- + H_2O$$

In acid solution chlorine dioxide is readily reduced to chlorous acid, $HClO_2$, which then decomposes to hydrochloric and chloric acids.

$$ClO_2 + H^+ + e^- = HClO_2 \qquad E° = 1.275 \text{ v.}$$

In the vapor state the compound has an angular configuration [23]; the O—Cl—O bond angle is 116.5° and the Cl—O bond distance 1.49 Å, the latter being much shorter than in Cl_2O (see 16.61). It is proposed that the short bond distance can best be interpreted in terms of structures for the dioxide involving resonance of a three-electron bond between chlorine and oxygen.

16.63 Dichlorine hexoxide is the least volatile of the chlorine oxides, existing as a dark-red liquid at room temperature. Magnetic susceptibility measurements indicate that in both the liquid and solid state this oxide exists as an equilibrium mixture of Cl_2O_6 and ClO_3. In the gaseous state the dimer appears to be completely dissociated into the paramagnetic monomer; the latter is thermally unstable and even at 0° is significantly decomposed into chlorine dioxide and oxygen. The hexoxide reacts explosively with many reducing agents and even with liquid water under certain conditions. When the hexoxide and water are brought together in the vapor state and the mixture is cooled, reaction appears to occur mainly as follows.

$$2ClO_3 + H_2O = HClO_3 + HClO_4$$

No definitive structural information is available for either Cl_2O_6 or ClO_3.

16.64 Chlorine heptoxide, a colorless volatile oil, is a highly endothermic substance ($\Delta H_f°$ 63.4 kcal.). Although it is the most stable of the binary compounds of oxygen and chlorine, it is still a rather explosive substance and detonates on shock or on heating. In contrast with the other chlorine oxides, it does not react at room temperature with organic substances such as paper and wood or with sulfur or phosphorus. It combines slowly with water to yield perchloric acid. Spectroscopic data indicate that the molecule consists of two ClO_3 groups bridged by an oxygen atom, with the Cl—O—Cl bond angle being 128°.

The Bromine Oxides **16.65** Three compounds of this class, Br_2O, BrO_2, and Br_3O_8, appear to be known with certainty. These substances are difficult to prepare and are very unstable.

16.66 Bromine monoxide, Br_2O, a brown liquid, is formed in a variety of ways: by reaction of bromine vapor with mercury(II) oxide at 50–100°; by interaction of the same substances in carbon tetrachloride medium, in which the monoxide is soluble; and by the decomposition of BrO_2 in a high vacuum, a method which yields a product of high purity. The dioxide is prepared by the action of an electric discharge on a mixture of the elements at low pressures and liquid air temperatures. Br_3O_8 is obtained by the interaction of an excess of ozone with bromine at temperatures from $-5°$ to $10°$.*

16.67 Bromine monoxide is unstable at temperatures above $-40°$, decomposing into the constituent elements. It is a powerful oxidizing agent, capable of converting iodine to I_2O_5. Reaction with solutions of alkali at low temperatures gives hypobromite, OBr^-. Bromine dioxide is a yellow solid, stable below $-40°$ but decomposing above that temperature to form elementary bromine and oxygen. Decomposition appears to be complete at $0°$. The dioxide is converted by strongly alkaline solutions to bromide and bromate. Br_3O_8 is a white crystalline solid, stable below $-80°$. Above this temperature it evolves oxygen unless kept in contact with ozone. It is readily soluble in water, forming an acidic solution with oxidizing properties. The structures of the bromine oxides have not been determined, but it is probable that Br_2O and BrO_2 have configurations analogous to those of the corresponding chlorine compounds.

Binary Iodine-Oxygen Compounds   **16.68** The pentoxide, I_2O_5, is apparently the only true oxide of iodine to have been characterized. This nonvolatile white substance is the anhydride of iodic acid, HIO_3, from which it can be obtained by dehydration at $195°$. It can also be prepared by the action of concentrated nitric acid on iodine. Despite the fact that it is an exothermic compound (ΔH_f° -48 kcal.), the pentoxide cannot be made by direct union of the elements. The compound is thermally unstable, decomposition to iodine and oxygen occurring when it is heated above $300°$. It is a strong oxidizing agent; the reaction whereby it rapidly converts carbon monoxide to the dioxide at temperatures above $65°$ and is itself reduced to elementary iodine is of analytical significance. It is extremely soluble in water (187.4 g. in 100 g. at $13°$), forming solutions of iodic acid.

16.69 Mention has been made of two compounds — I_2O_4 and I_4O_9 — which, although they contain only iodine and oxygen, are not regarded as really being oxides. I_2O_4, commonly known as iodine tetroxide, is a yellow solid obtained by the action of water on the products of reaction between iodic acid and warm concentrated sulfuric acid, probably $I_2O_3 \cdot H_2SO_4$ and $I_2O_4 \cdot H_2SO_4$. I_2O_4 is unstable toward heat, decomposing rapidly above $130°$ to yield the pentoxide and elementary iodine. It is slightly soluble in cold water, but dissolves with reaction in hot water, forming iodic acid and iodine. It is slowly converted by alkali to a mixture of iodate and iodide. The actual structure of the "tetroxide" is unknown, the formula I_2O_4 being assigned to the compound on the presumption that it is an iodyl iodate, $(IO)IO_3$. There is no conclusive proof for such a formulation.

* Recent evidence [PFLUGMACHER, RABBEN, and DAHMEN, *Z. anorg. Chem.*, **279**, 313 (1955)] indicates rather strongly that the substance actually obtained is BrO_3.

16.70 The compound I_4O_9, a light yellow solid, is obtained when iodine, either in the vapor state or in solution in chloroform, is treated with an ozone-oxygen mixture. The compound is more conveniently prepared by reaction between iodic acid and warm concentrated phosphoric acid. When heated above 75°, I_4O_9 decomposes in the following manner.

$$4I_4O_9 = 6I_2O_5 + 2I_2 + 3O_2$$

It is an extremely hygroscopic substance, reacting with water to give iodine and iodic acid as end products. It has been proposed that I_4O_9 is the normal iodate of tripositive iodine, $I(IO_3)_3$.

Oxygen Acids of the Halogens and Their Salts

16.71 No oxygen acids of fluorine are known. For the other halogens the list given in Table 16.9 summarizes the oxyacid types which exist.

TABLE 16.9

The Oxyacids of the Halogens

Oxidation State of the Halogen	Acid Type	Name	Nature of the Halogen
+1	HXO	Hypohalous acids	X = Cl, Br, I
+3	HXO_2	Halous acids	X = Cl, Br?
+5	HXO_3	Halic acids	X = Cl, Br, I
+7	HXO_4	Perhalic acids	X = Cl, I
	$H_4X_2O_9$	Mesodiperiodic acid	X = I
	H_5XO_6	Paraperiodic acid	X = I

16.72 The outstanding characteristic of the halogen oxyacids is their great power as oxidizing agents in acid medium. This fact is revealed in the potential diagrams shown in Table 16.10, where the oxidation potential data for oxyhalo anions in basic solution are also included. It is seen that, so far as reduction to the free halogen in aqueous acid solution is concerned, the ability of the oxyhalogen acids to function as oxidizing agents decreases with increase in oxidation state for chlorine or bromine. A similar situation exists for reduction to halide in basic solution. In general, the oxyhalogen acids are much stronger oxidizing agents in acid solution than are the corresponding anions in basic medium. The potentials of the oxyacids with respect to reduction to the free halogen are, with the exception of the value for perchloric acid, considerably greater than those for reduction of corresponding free halogens to halide ion. (See Table 16.2 for X_2, X^- potentials.) As a consequence, the oxyacids, except perchloric acid, are reduced to free halogen by halide ion.

16.73 A few additional generalizations can be made regarding the oxychloro compounds specifically. The acid strength increases with increasing oxidation state of chlorine. The thermal stability of both the acids and their salts increases in the same direction. Thus, a hypochlorite decomposes on heating to give

TABLE 16.10

Potential Diagrams for Oxyhalogen Acids and Anions

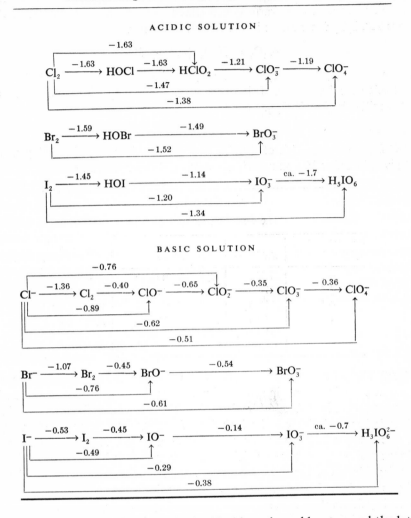

ACIDIC SOLUTION

BASIC SOLUTION

chlorate and chloride; chlorate yields chloride and perchlorate; and the latter on strong heating forms chloride and molecular oxygen. The same general trend in thermal stability holds for bromine and iodine compounds.

Hypohalous Acids and Hypohalites **16.74** Hypohalous acids are known for chlorine, bromine, and iodine, but only in aqueous solution. Solutions of the acids are obtained by hydrolysis of the halogens, a reaction which has already been discussed (see 16.13). An alternative method of preparation, and one which increases the yield of desired product by removing the hydrohalic acid formed in the hydrolysis reaction, utilizes the addition to the aqueous solution of an insoluble oxide, *e.g.*, mercury(II) oxide, which gives an insoluble or slightly ionized halide with the hydrohalic acid.

$$2Cl_2 + HgO + H_2O = HgCl_2 + 2HOCl$$

Hypohalite salts are formed by interaction of the free halogens and solutions of cold, dilute alkali.

$$X_2 + 2OH^- = XO^- + X^- + H_2O$$

16.75 The hypohalous acids are weak and the acid strength diminishes from chlorine to iodine, the approximate dissociation constants being HOCl, 10^{-8}; HOBr, 10^{-9}; HOI, 10^{-13}. There is some evidence that hypoiodous acid also undergoes basic dissociation.

$$HOI(aq.) + H_2O \rightleftharpoons H_2OI^+(aq.) + OH^-$$

The equilibrium constant for this reaction has been estimated to be of the order of 10^{-10}. An indication that hypoiodous acid possesses some basic character is afforded by the fact that it is transformed to iodine monochloride on treatment with hydrochloric acid. Both hypobromous acid and hypoiodous acid are extremely unstable, decomposing very rapidly into halate and halide mainly. Hypochlorous acid is considerably more stable, decomposition occurring slowly in the following ways.

$$2HOCl = 2HCl + O_2$$
$$3HOCl = 2HCl + HClO_3$$

Both reactions are markedly accelerated by light; the first one is also subject to catalysis by such substances as cobalt(II) and nickel(II) hydroxides.

16.76 Of the hypohalite salts, only a few derived from hypochlorous acid and hypobromous acid have been isolated in the solid condition. These include sodium and potassium hypochlorites and hypobromites and calcium, strontium, and barium hypochlorites. Hypobromite and hypochlorite solutions, like those of their parent acids, rapidly revert to mixtures of halate and halide. The main chemical characteristic of the hypochlorites is their strong oxidizing power.

Halous Acids and Halites   **16.77** The only acid of this class of unquestionable existence is chlorous acid, $HClO_2$. This very unstable substance is an initial product of reaction between chlorine dioxide and water.

$$2ClO_2 + H_2O = HClO_2 + HClO_3$$

However, it disproportionates rapidly in the following manner.

$$8HClO_2 = 6ClO_2 + Cl_2 + 4H_2O$$

Solutions of the acid are ordinarily made by the addition of sulfuric acid to aqueous barium chlorite. Chlorous acid is a moderately weak acid, having a dissociation constant of about 10^{-2}, and a strong oxidizing agent. Salts of the acid, the chlorites, are obtained by reaction between chlorine dioxide and metal hydroxides or peroxides, the latter reagent giving a product free from chlorate.

$$Na_2O_2 + 2ClO_2 = 2NaClO_2 + O_2$$

In oxidations, although alkaline solutions of the chlorite ion are strong oxidizing agents (Table 16.10), their action is much slower than acidified solutions. The chlorite ion is relatively stable with respect to disproportionation in alkaline solution. In the solid state, the chlorites, particularly those of heavy metals, explode when heated or struck.

16.78 Although no salts have been isolated, there is some evidence that the bromite ion is formed as a very unstable intermediate in certain reactions. For example, it appears likely that the thermal conversion of hypobromite to bromate takes the course indicated.

$$2BrO^- = BrO_2^- + Br^-$$
$$BrO_2^- + BrO^- = BrO_3^- + Br^-$$

Halic Acids and Halates **16.79** Halic acids and halates have been characterized for all the halogens, but of the acids only the iodine compound, the most stable halic acid, has been isolated in the solid condition. Chloric and bromic acids are generally obtained in solution by treatment of their salts, *e.g.*, $Ba(ClO_3)_2$, $Ba(BrO_3)_2$, with sulfuric acid. Iodic acid can be made in a similar fashion, as well as by other methods, *e.g.*, the oxidation of iodine with concentrated nitric acid or aqueous chlorine.

$$3I_2 + 10HNO_3 = 6HIO_3 + 10NO + 2H_2O$$
$$I_2 + 5Cl_2 + 6H_2O = 2HIO_3 + 10HCl$$

When the latter agent is employed as oxidant the hydrochloric acid formed is removed by means of silver(I) oxide.

16.80 Chloric and bromic acids are stable only in dilute solution; concentrated solutions, *e.g.*, containing about 50 per cent acid, undergo violent and often explosive decomposition. Iodic acid is considerably more stable. The white solid melts at 110° with partial dehydration to HI_3O_8 ($3I_2O_5 \cdot H_2O$). Conversion to pentoxide is complete at 195°. The halic acids are all fairly strong acids and powerful oxidizing agents (Table 16.10).

16.81 Halate salts are conveniently prepared by reaction of free halogen with solutions of hot alkali.

$$3X_2 + 6OH^- = XO_3^- + 5X^- + 3H_2O$$

Whereas only normal chlorates and bromates are known, acid salts of iodic acid have been prepared, *e.g.*, $M^I_2H(IO_3)_3$ and $M^IH_2(IO_3)_3$. These are much less common than the normal compounds and exist only in the solid state; in solution they form the normal salts and iodic acid. With a few exceptions, metal chlorates and bromates are appreciably soluble in water. Heavy metal iodates are generally insoluble. All the halates decompose when heated. Decomposition of chlorates usually leads first to chloride and perchlorate, and the latter on strong heating evolves oxygen with the formation of chloride. Most bromates decompose to bromide and oxygen, but some, particularly those of the less active metals, give chiefly oxygen, bromine, and oxide. Iodates are much more stable thermally than chlorates or bromates; however, they explode when heated with combustible substances, e.g., carbon and organic compounds.

16.82 The halate ions have been shown to have a pyramidal structure, the halogen atom lying above the plane of the three oxygen atoms.

Perhalic Acids and Perhalates **16.83** Perhalic acids and their salts contain the halogens in their maximum oxidation state of $+7$. Only chlorine and iodine exhibit this oxidation state, no perbromates having yet been isolated. There are a number of striking differences between the perchlorates and the periodates. This is largely attributable to the great difference in size between chlorine and iodine, a factor which permits the latter element to surround itself with six oxygen atoms, chlorine being limited to a maximum of four. Thus only one perchloric acid, $HClO_4$, is known, whereas at least three periodic acids, HIO_4, $H_4I_2O_9$, and H_5IO_6, have been characterized, with the last being by far the most important form. A somewhat similar situation has been encountered in representative group VI in the oxy acids corresponding to the maximum oxidation state for sulfur, selenium, and tellurium (see 15.97).

16.84 Alkali metal salts of perchloric acid are commonly prepared from chlorates, either by careful thermal decomposition or by electrolytic oxidation in solution. Other perchlorates are usually made by reaction of metal, metal oxide, or carbonate with aqueous perchloric acid. Anhydrous perchloric acid is obtained by treatment of potassium perchlorate with concentrated sulfuric acid, followed by vacuum distillation, or better, by reaction of ammonium perchlorate with a dilute mixture of nitric and hydrochloric acids, the perchloric acid being distilled under reduced pressure after concentration of the reaction mixture to remove excess nitric and hydrochloric acids.

16.85 The anhydrous acid (m.p., $-112°$) is an extremely unstable, colorless liquid and can be distilled only under reduced pressure without decomposition occurring, often explosively. It can be converted to the anhydride, chlorine heptoxide, by treatment with phosphorus(V) oxide at low temperatures. It is a very potent oxidant, reacting violently with most organic substances. Perchloric acid is completely miscible with water and forms several hydrates, of which the monohydrate is particularly interesting. This substance is a hygroscopic solid (m.p., $50°$) which has essentially the same crystal structure as ammonium perchlorate, and thus is correctly formulated as hydronium perchlorate, $(H_3O)^+ClO_4^-$. Perchloric acid is the strongest protonic acid known and the properties of cold dilute solutions are primarily those of the hydronium ion, the perchlorate ion being remarkably stable in such solutions. In hot concentrated aqueous solution, however, perchloric acid is a powerful oxidizing agent, although somewhat weaker in this respect than the other oxychloro acids, and reacts explosively with strong reducing agents.

16.86 Metal salts of the acid, the perchlorates, are the most stable of all the oxychloro compounds; they are much weaker oxidizing agents than the free acid and are decomposed (to give chloride and oxygen) only at high temperatures. Except for the potassium, rubidium, and cesium compounds, which are sparingly soluble, metal perchlorates are very soluble in water. It is interesting that the perchlorates of limited solubility are obtained solely in the nonhydrated condition. In the perchlorate ion the four oxygen atoms are tetrahedrally disposed about the central chlorine atom.

16.87 Paraperiodic acid, H_5IO_6 (sometimes called orthoperiodic acid), is commonly obtained from its salts, e.g., by metathesis between $Ba_5[IO_6]_2$ and sulfuric acid. Paraperiodates, the commonest of the periodate salts (see below), are often prepared from iodates, either by heating or oxidation with chlorine in alkaline solution as indicated by the equations. The first is not suitable for

$$5Ba[IO_3]_2 = Ba_5[IO_6]_2 + 4I_2 + 9O_2 \text{ (for alkaline earth and many}$$
$$\text{heavy metal periodates)}$$
$$2Na^+ + IO_3^- + Cl_2 + 3OH^- = Na_2H_3IO_6 + 2Cl^-$$

the preparation of some paraperiodates which decompose to iodates when heated.

16.88 Paraperiodic acid is a colorless, deliquescent solid which melts a little above 130° and decomposes at slightly higher temperatures with the formation of iodic acid, oxygen, and water. Under a vacuum it can be dehydrated in stages by heating, giving first mesodiperiodic acid, $H_4I_2O_9$, and then the meta acid, HIO_4. The latter is converted on further heating to iodic acid and oxygen; no anhydride, I_2O_7, is obtained. Paraperiodic acid is a weak acid, the first-stage dissociation constant being about 5×10^{-4} and the second-stage 2×10^{-7}. The concentration of $H_2IO_6^{3-}$ ion is very small in aqueous solution ($K_3 = 10^{-15}$). There is evidence that species other than those derived from the simple dissociation of paraperiodic acid are also present in aqueous solution. Thus the addition of potassium ion to a solution of the acid results in the precipitation of KIO_4, and the salt $K_4I_2O_9 \cdot 9H_2O$ can be crystallized from solution. In strongly acid solution paraperiodic acid is a very potent oxidizing agent (Table 16.10) and can convert manganese(II) to permanganate.

16.89 In addition to salts related to the three periodic acids described above, other metal periodates have been characterized, the most important being $M^I_3IO_5$ (meso) and $M^I_8I_2O_{11}$ (dipara or diortho). All periodates are extensively hydrolyzed in aqueous solution. The metaperiodate ion, like the perchlorate ion, possesses a tetrahedral structure. Paraperiodates have been shown by X-ray analysis to contain octahedral IO_6 groups.

The Cationic Behavior of Bromine and Iodine [24]

Coordination Compounds of Monopositive Iodine and Bromine **16.90** It has already been pointed out that hydrated I^+ should be sufficiently stable for existence in detectable quantities in aqueous solution (see 16.14) and that there

[24] KLEINBERG, *J. Chem. Educ.*, **23**, 559 (1946).

is evidence that hypiodous acid undergoes both acidic and basic dissociation, in the latter case yielding the hydrated monopositive iodine cation (see 16.75). More conclusive proof that iodine can exhibit cationic behavior is found in the preparation and characterization of complex compounds in which monopositive iodine is stabilized by coordination with pyridine and related compounds.

16.91 These compounds are made by treatment of the silver or mercury(I) salt of the appropriate acid with the calculated quantity of iodine and an excess of the organic amine in a nonaqueous solvent such as chloroform. Reaction occurs immediately as illustrated for the formation of specific compounds con-

$$AgNO_3 + I_2 + 2py = Ipy_2NO_3 + AgI$$

taining pyridine as ligand. Most of the complexes which have been prepared contain organic acid anions, *e.g.*, acetate, benzoate, succinate, p-nitrobenzoate, phthalate. Each of these compounds has one pyridine molecule for each iodine. The few complexes which have been prepared containing inorganic anions are obtained as dipyridine derivatives, *e.g.*, Ipy_2NO_3, Ipy_2ClO_4. It is interesting that the nitrate can readily be converted to the monopyridine derivative by removal of pyridine under reduced pressure.

16.92 The chemical reactions of these compounds leave no doubt that the iodine is positive and monovalent. They react with iodide ion to give free iodine; this reaction is utilized for the determination of iodine in the com-

$$I^+ + I^- = I_2$$

pounds. In water they undergo slow hydrolysis to give iodate and free iodine. With potassium chloride and potassium bromide metathesis occurs with the formation of ICl · py and IBr · py, respectively. Treatment of Ipy_2NO_3 with an equivalent quantity of sodium hydroxide solution results in the production of the oxide $(Ipy_2)_2O$, which in turn loses pyridine to give $(Ipy)_2O$. Electrolysis of Ipy_2NO_3 in chloroform solution yields free iodine at the cathode while the solution around the anode remains colorless. The iodine in the nitrate complex in chloroform solution can be replaced by such metals as zinc, iron, copper, gold, and mercury. It has been proposed that cationic monovalent iodine has a coordination number of two and that the dipyridine derivatives are therefore salts of the type [Ipy₂]X, whereas the monopyridine compounds are nonelectrolytes of the structure [IpyX]. Conductance data in acetone and methanol give some support, but not conclusive support, to such a formulation.

16.93 The monopositive bromine complexes $Brpy_2NO_3$ and $Brpy_2ClO_4$ have been obtained by procedures analogous to those used for the iodine compounds. Reaction of these complexes with potassium iodide in sodium hydroxide solution, followed by acidification with sulfuric acid, results in the liberation of iodine.

$$Br^+ + 2I^- = Br^- + I_2$$

Compounds of Tripositive Iodine   **16.94** There is evidence that iodine in union with the anions of certain oxyacids can exist as a cation or in a highly polar condition in the tripositive state.   Mention has been made of I_4O_9 (see 16.70), which can be regarded as the normal iodate of iodine(III), $I(IO_3)_3$.   Oxidation of iodine by perchloric acid or by ozone and perchloric acid gives iodine(III) perchlorate, $I(ClO_4)_3 \cdot 2H_2O$.   The acetate, $I(OCOCH_3)_3$, has been obtained by the oxidation of iodine with fuming nitric acid in the presence of acetic anhydride.   In the presence of chloro- and bromoacetic acids this reaction gives compounds such as $I(OCOCCl_3)_3$, $I(OCOCHCl_2)_3$, $I(OCOCH_2Cl)_3$, and $I(OCOCH_2Br)_3 \cdot I(IO_3)_3$; and with orthophosphoric acid present IPO_4 is produced.

16.95 The compounds are unstable toward heat and are rapidly hydrolyzed in the manner shown.

$$5IPO_4 + 9H_2O = I_2 + 3HIO_3 + 5H_3PO_4$$

The presence of tripositive iodine in these substances is shown by the fact that electrolysis of a saturated solution of the triacetate in acetic anhydride yields iodine at the cathode in amount demanded by Faraday's law.

Astatine [25,26]

16.96 Astatine, element 85, the last member of the halogen family, exists in nature to a minute extent as short-lived isotopes of mass numbers 215, 216, and 218.   The little information available regarding the chemistry of this element has been obtained from tracer experiments with the isotope 211, which is produced by reaction of high energy alpha particles (21–28 mev.) with an elementary

$$^{209}_{83}Bi + ^4_2He = ^{211}_{85}At + 2^1_0n$$

bismuth target.   With higher energy alpha particles the isotope 210 can be obtained.   Astatine 211 (half-life 7.5 hr.) undergoes two modes of nuclear change: one by k-electron capture to yield $^{211}_{84}Po$, and the other by alpha emission to give $^{207}_{83}Bi$.   For most of the chemical experiments described in the literature, astatine 211 was separated from the bismuth target by high vacuum distillation at the melting point of the latter element and was then dissolved in nitric acid, to give solutions 10^{-11} to 10^{-15} molar in astatine.   Because of the extreme dilution of the astatine solutions, interpretation of some of the experimental data has proved difficult.   However, there appears to be little doubt regarding the following properties of astatine.

16.97 The element can be obtained in the free state from solution in cold

[25] CORSON, MACKENZIE and SEGRÈ, *Phys. Rev.*, **57**, 459 (1940); SEGRÈ, MACKENZIE and CORSON, *ibid.*, **57**, 1087 (1940); CORSON, MACKENZIE and SEGRÈ, *ibid.*, **58**, 672 (1940).
[26] JOHNSON, LEININGER, and SEGRÈ, *J. Chem. Phys.*, **17**, 1 (1949).

concentrated nitric acid by reduction with iron(II). Elemental astatine, like the other halogens, is extractable into such organic solvents as carbon tetrachloride and benzene. The free element appears to disproportionate (to give At^- and some oxy-astatine anion) in basic solutions (pH = 13). It is reduced to the mononegative state by sulfur dioxide or zinc. At least two positive oxidation states of astatine exist in aqueous solution. Astatine is oxidized completely by cold bromine to yield an oxidation state that is carried poorly on silver iodate. More powerful oxidation (by hypochlorous acid or hot peroxydisulfate solution) gives a state which is carried essentially completely by silver iodate (AtO_3^-?).

SECTION B. *The Short Transition Series*

Chapter 17. Perspective   487

18. The Titanium Family   491

19. The Vanadium Family   499

20. The Chromium Family   513

21. The Manganese Family   530

22. The Transition Triads. I — Iron, Cobalt, and Nickel   545

23. The Transition Triads. II — The Platinum Metals   565

24. The Copper Family   589

25. The Zinc Family   607

PERSPECTIVE

17.1 The elements of the short transition series exist in periods in which the number of electrons in the outer shell remains for the most part constant at s^2 while the next to the outer shell is being built up from eight to eighteen electrons, *i.e.*, the (n − 1)d orbitals are being filled. The elements comprising these series are shown below, along with the idealized (n − 1)d ns configurations in their ground states.

	d^1s^2	d^2s^2	d^3s^2	d^4s^2	d^5s^2	d^6s^2	d^7s^2	d^8s^2	d^9s^2	$d^{10}s^2$
3d	$_{21}$Sc	$_{22}$Ti	$_{23}$V	$_{24}$Cr	$_{25}$Mn	$_{26}$Fe	$_{27}$Co	$_{28}$Ni	$_{29}$Cu	$_{30}$Zn
4d	$_{39}$Y	$_{40}$Zr	$_{41}$Nb	$_{42}$Mo	$_{43}$Tc	$_{44}$Ru	$_{45}$Rh	$_{46}$Pd	$_{47}$Ag	$_{48}$Cd
5d	$_{57}$La	$_{72}$Hf	$_{73}$Ta	$_{74}$W	$_{75}$Re	$_{76}$Os	$_{77}$Ir	$_{78}$Pt	$_{79}$Au	$_{80}$Hg

17.2 In actuality, the inner d levels are complete at copper, palladium, and gold in their respective series: Cu $3d^{10} 4s^1$; Pd $4d^{10} 5s^0$; Au $5d^{10} 6s^1$. However, in these elements d electrons are available for chemical reaction and it is at zinc, cadmium, and mercury that the d levels can be regarded as being filled and unavailable from the chemical viewpoint. Zinc, cadmium, and mercury do not exhibit the chemical characteristics common to most transition elements (see below) and may be considered at least equally well as representative elements.

17.3 In the 3d series (scandium through copper) there appears to be little doubt that each available d orbital is occupied singly before electron pairing occurs. That a similar situation prevails in the 4d and 5d series is very much open to question.

17.4 All elements of the short transition series are metals and there is a general (but not regular) decrease in electropositive character across any one series (*e.g.*, from scandium to copper). Many of the ions formed by the transition elements are colored and paramagnetic as a result of the presence of unpaired electrons. Most of the series members have a great tendency to form stable complex ions, a fact attributable not only to the favorable (high) charge density of most of the ions, but also, and more importantly, to the availability of the inner d orbitals for entry by electron pairs of ligands. Inasmuch as there is little total energy difference between $(n-1)d$ and ns electrons, electrons of both levels are available for chemical reaction, and most of the elements exhibit variable oxidation states. Indeed, variability of oxidation states is observed for all the elements save those of the scandium family and zinc and cadmium.

17.5 For the first six groups (scandium through the iron group), the maximum oxidation state exhibited corresponds to the sum of the outer s and inner d electrons. Beyond the iron group, except for zinc, cadmium, and mercury, there appears to be no correlation between electronic configuration and the maximum oxidation state. A maximum oxidation state of eight, the highest attained by any element, is reached in the iron group. Only two of the members of this group, ruthenium and osmium, form compounds in which this oxidation state is found, *e.g.*, RuO_4, OsO_4. It should be emphasized that the highest oxidation state is not always the most characteristic one of the element; moreover, the most stable state in simple compounds may not correspond to the most stable state in complex compounds. In general, within a transition group in which the elements exhibit variable oxidation states, the highest state becomes more stable with increasing atomic number and the lower states less stable. Thus the dichromate and permanganate ions in acid medium are much more powerful oxidizing agents than their respective analogs the tungstate and perrhenate ions. In any series of compounds (*e.g.*, halides, oxides) formed by a transition element, the ionic (basic) character decreases with increasing oxidation state of the element. This can be illustrated by a consideration of some of the properties of the common oxides of chromium.

Oxidation state of chromium	Oxide	Character	Ions formed
+2	CrO	basic	Cr^{2+}
+3	Cr_2O_3	amphoteric	Cr^{3+}
			CrO_2^-
			$[Cr(OH)_4]^-$
+6	CrO_3	acidic	CrO_4^{2-}
			$Cr_2O_7^{2-}$

17.6 Transition elements show both vertical (group) and horizontal resemblances. Horizontal likenesses are generally marked in adjacent elements having the same oxidation state. This is attributable to the very small change in radius across any one series for ions of constant charge.

V^{3+}	Cr^{3+}	Mn^{3+}	Fe^{3+}	Co^{3+}
0.69	0.62	0.66	0.64	0.63 Å

The most striking horizontal similarities are found among the elements commonly referred to as the "transition triads." Thus, iron, cobalt, and nickel are metals possessing similar physical properties, and, with the exception of iron which exhibits a +6 state also, analogous well-defined oxidation states of 2, 3, and 4. The second and third triads (Ru, Rh, Pd, and Os, Ir, Pt) are so like each other in chemical properties both in a horizontal and vertical direction that they are classified as the "platinum metals" and their chemistry is ordinarily discussed as a unit. The vertical similarities between the various pairs of platinum metals result from the *lanthanide contraction* (see 17.7), a phenomenon which has important consequences so far as the chemistry of short transition elements, as well as of the rare-earths, is concerned.

17.7 In the rare-earth, or lanthanide, elements (58–71) electrons are added progressively to the $4f$ level, whereas the electron distribution in the overlying $5s$, $5p$, $5d$, and $6s$ orbitals is not changed significantly. The filling of this level deep within the atom is accompanied by a monotonic decrease in size for ions of comparable charge, which is known as the *lanthanide contraction*. Largely as the result of this contraction, significant effects are observed on the properties of the $5d$ elements following the lanthanides, *i.e.*, on hafnium to gold.

17.8 Within a group of representative elements, *e.g.*, the alkali metals, the radius of the characteristic ion increases regularly and significantly with increasing atomic number. No such increase is found in the transition groups in which the last element follows the lanthanide series. In fact, the atomic (covalent) radius of the third member of the group corresponds quite closely to that of the second member (Fig. 17.1) and a similar situation prevails for the radii of ions of like charge.

Ti^{4+}, 0.68 Å	V^{5+}, 0.59 Å	Cr^{6+}, 0.52 Å
Zr^{4+}, 0.80	Nb^{5+}, 0.70	Mo^{6+}, 0.62
Hf^{4+}, ca. 8	Ta^{5+}, 0.73	W^{6+}, ca. 65

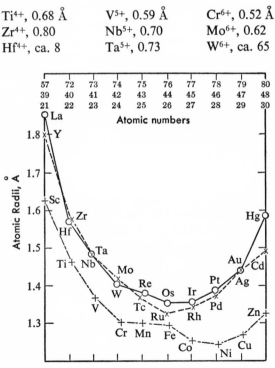

Fig. 17.1 Atomic radii of elements of short transition series. Values are for coordination number 12. (Taken from REMY, *Treatise on Inorganic Chemistry*, Vol. II, Elsevier Publishing Company, Amsterdam, 1956, p. XXVII)

17.9 Inasmuch as chemical properties within a group are in large measure related to the size of the atoms, it is not surprising to find that in the titanium to nickel families analogous compounds of the second and third members are much more closely related to each other than to corresponding compounds of the first member. Mention has already been made of the remarkable similarity of the platinum metals. Zirconium and hafnium are so analogous chemically that their separation until recently has proved to be an exceedingly difficult task, and the pairs niobium and tantalum, and molybdenum and tungsten, are much more similar to each other than to vanadium and chromium, respectively.

17.10 Also as a result of the lanthanide contraction, the last member of a transition group (provided it follows the lanthanide elements) is with few exceptions (*e.g.*, hafnium as compared to titanium and zirconium) the least electropositive of the family. This effect is most pronounced in the triad and copper families. The large increase in nuclear charge in passing from the second to the third member of the family is not accompanied by a corresponding increase in atomic size, and thus the valence electrons are more firmly bound by the nucleus.

17.11 In the detailed discussion of the chemistry of the short transition series elements in the following chapters, the scandium family is omitted. Two members of this group, yttrium and lanthanum, are closely related to the lanthanides both in occurrence and chemical characteristics, and are therefore considered briefly in Chapter 26. Actinium, the last member of the scandium family, is discussed in Chapter 27 as the prototype of the actinide series. The elements of the scandium group, with their $(n - 1)d^1 ns^2$ valence configuration, exhibit very simple chemistry, in contrast to the behavior of most of the other short transition series elements. They are very active metals, readily losing all three valence electrons * to form ions possessing inert gas configurations; no oxidation state other than $+3$ appears to exist. The simple compounds are all ionic in nature. Thus, the oxides, which are all insoluble, are completely basic, the basic character increasing with increasing cationic size from scandium to actinium. Although relatively little is known about their complexes, the scandium family elements are definitely much poorer complex formers than most of the other short transition series members. Indeed, they do not appear to be able to utilize inner d orbitals in complex formation. As expected, the ability to complex decreases markedly from scandium to actinium, that is, with increasing cationic size.

* The electrode potentials for the reaction $M = M(H_2O)_x^+ + 3e^-$ are as follows: for Sc, 2.08; Y, 2.37; La, 2.52; and Ac, ca. 2.6 volts.

CHAPTER 18

THE TITANIUM FAMILY

Introduction

18.1 The second group of short transition series elements is made up of titanium, zirconium, and hafnium, each possessing $(n-1)d^2ns^2$ valence shell configurations overlying a shell of eight electrons: $_{22}$Ti, $3d^24s^2$; $_{40}$Zr, $4d^25s^2$; $_{72}$Hf, $5d^26s^2$. Some properties of these elements are listed in Table 18.1. The melting and boiling point data cited are to be regarded as approximate values, since it is doubtful that they were obtained on the metals in their highest state of purity.

18.2 The titanium family is the first group of transition elements in which variable oxidation states are encountered. As would be predicted from the electronic configurations, the maximum oxidation state is $+4$. This is also by far the most stable state for these elements. All three also exhibit tri- and dipositive states, but these possess strong reducing properties and readily revert to the $+4$ condition. Titanium(III) is the only one of the lower oxidation states which has sufficient stability to exist extensively in aqueous solutions.

18.3 As the ionization potentials (Table 18.1) indicate, the energy required for the removal of the four valence electrons is extremely large, and there is little doubt that in anhydrous binary compounds of the type MX_4, in which the elements are in the tetrapositive condition, the binding is essentially covalent. Even in acidic aqueous solutions it is questionable that hydrated M^{4+}, with its strong tendency to undergo hydrolysis, exists to any considerable degree.

GENERAL REFERENCES

LATIMER, *The Oxidation States of the Elements and Their Potentials in Aqueous Solutions*, 2nd Edition, Prentice-Hall, Inc., New York, 1952, Ch. 18.

REMY, *Treatise on Inorganic Chemistry* (translated and amended by Anderson), Elsevier Publishing Company, Amsterdam, 1956, Vol. II, Ch. 3.

SIDGWICK, *The Chemical Elements and Their Compounds*, Oxford University Press, London, 1950, pp. 628–53.

TABLE 18.1

Some Properties of the Titanium Family Elements

	Ti	Zr	Hf
Natural isotopes	46, 47, 48 *, 49, 50	90 *, 91, 92, 94, 96	174, 176, 177, 178, 179, 180 *
Density, g/cc.	4.49	6.52	13.31
Melting point, °C.	1725	2100	2300
Boiling point, °C.	3260	ca. 3600	ca. 5200
Ionic radius in crystals, M^{4+}, Å	0.68	0.80	ca. 0.8
Covalent radius, Å	1.324	1.454	1.442
Ionization potential, volts			
1st electron	6.83	6.835	ca. 5.5
2nd electron	13.57	12.916	ca. 14.9
3rd electron	28.14	24.00	
4th electron	43.24	33.8	
Electrode potential, $E°$, in volts, for			
$M(s) + 2H_2O = MO_2 + 4H^+ + 4e^-$	0.86	1.43	1.57
$M(s) = M(H_2O)_x^{4+} + 4e^-$	——	1.53	1.70
$Ti + H_2O = TiO^{2+} + 2H^+ + 4e^-$	ca. 0.88		

* Most abundant isotope

18.4 Although the bonds between metal and oxygen in the dioxides (TiO_2, ZrO_2, HfO_2) are considered to be largely ionic,[1] these substances do not behave as completely basic oxides. Rather, the dioxides (unless they have been rendered refractory by strong ignition) have amphoteric characteristics, the basic nature increasing as expected from the titanium to the zirconium compound.

18.5 The extraordinary resemblance between zirconium and hafnium has been noted (see 17.9). In view of the fact that the latter has been known for only a relatively short time, there is much less information available regarding its chemistry than there is for that of zirconium. However, it seems a reasonable assumption that much of what is said about zirconium will apply equally well to hafnium. One main difference in chemical behavior between zirconium and hafnium is found in the generally greater dissociative stability of the complexes of zirconium. This has been utilized in procedures for the separation of the elements.

The Elements

18.6 Titanium and zirconium are relatively abundant elements, making up 0.42 and 0.020 per cent of the earth's crust, respectively. Hafnium constitutes only 4.5×10^{-4} per cent of the earth's crust and invariably is found in zirconium-containing minerals. The principal titanium minerals are the dioxide known as *rutile* and a substance having the composition $FeTiO_3$ and known as *ilmenite*.* Zirconium occurs primarily as the dioxide *baddeleyite* and as the silicate *zircon*, $ZrSiO_4$.

[1] WELLS, *Structural Inorganic Chemistry*, 2nd Edition, Oxford University Press, London, 1950, p. 360.

* Ilmenite is isomorphous with hematite, Fe_2O_3, and is undoubtedly a mixed oxide rather than a true titanate.

18.7 Inasmuch as pure titanium has properties resembling those of stainless steel, the element is rapidly assuming a position of considerable industrial significance. The metal is obtained commercially in the form of a sponge by the reduction of the tetrachloride vapor with molten magnesium in an inert atmosphere. The sponge can be converted to compact form by melting it under argon in an electric arc. Elemental zirconium can be produced in a similar fashion.

18.8 The metals are rather unreactive at ordinary temperatures. At elevated temperatures, however, they combine readily with the halogens to yield tetrahalides, with oxygen to give the dioxides, and with nitrogen and carbon to form interstitial nitrides and carbides with formulas MN and MC (see 13.22; 14.24). Reaction with oxygen is strongly exothermic, ΔH_f° being about -215, -255, and -290 kcal. per g. atom of metal, respectively, for TiO_2, ZrO_2, and HfO_2. The powdered metals are capable of absorbing hydrogen to give interstitial hydrides (see 9.15), the limiting composition attained approximating MH_2.

18.9 The free elements are essentially passive toward acids at room temperature and toward aqueous alkali even at higher temperatures. Titanium dissolves in hot hydrochloric acid, forming the trichloride; hot nitric acid converts the metal to a form of the hydrous oxide which is relatively inert toward acids and bases. Zirconium is attacked by neither of these acids, but is soluble in hot concentrated sulfuric acid and in aqua regia. The best solvent for the metals (and their compounds) is hydrofluoric acid. The solvent power of this acid undoubtedly is related to the strong tendency of the elements in their tetrapositive state to form fluoro complexes (see 18.18–19). Thus, the potential for the reaction

$$Ti + 6F^- = TiF_6^{2-} + 4e^-$$

has been estimated to be 1.19 volts.

The Tetrapositive State

Oxides and Related Compounds **18.10** Brief mention has been made of the occurrence of the dioxides in nature and of their amphoteric character. Titanium dioxide is more acidic than basic in behavior, whereas the corresponding zirconium and hafnium compounds are more basic than acidic. Titanium dioxide is unaffected by dilute acids, but is attacked by concentrated sulfuric acid and by molten acid sulfates, hydroxides, or carbonates of the alkali metals. It is worth noting that the product obtained from reaction with concentrated sulfuric acid is not a normal sulfate but rather a basic sulfate containing the titanyl ion, TiO^{2+}. Alkaline fusion yields titanates (see 18.12). Zirconium dioxide and presumably the hafnium compound, unless they have been strongly ignited, are dissolved rather readily by mineral acids, but not by solutions of hydroxides. Fusion with alkalies gives zirconates and hafniates, *e.g.*, $M^I_2ZrO_3$ (meta) and $M^I_4ZrO_4$ (ortho).

18.11 Above its melting point (ca. 1800°) titanium dioxide begins to evolve oxygen with the formation of Ti_2O_3. The dioxide has a dissociation pressure of 1 atmosphere at 2230°. Zirconium and hafnium dioxides appear to be thermally stable.

18.12 No hydroxides corresponding to the formula $M(OH)_4$ appear to exist. Complete hydrolysis of aqueous solutions of the elements in their tetrapositive state or treatment with alkali yields white, insoluble hydrous oxides, $MO_2 \cdot xH_2O$. The hydrous titanium dioxide obtained from cold solutions is readily soluble in aqueous alkali and from the resulting solutions titanates of the compositions $M^I_2TiO_3$ and $M^I_2Ti_2O_5$ (plus water of crystallization) can be isolated. Anhydrous titanates can be prepared by fusion of the dioxide with metal carbonates, oxides, or hydroxides. The alkali metal salts are of the types $M^I_4TiO_4$, $M^I_2TiO_3$, as well as polytitanates containing more than one TiO_2 to one M^I_2O. Alkaline earth titanates having the compositions $M^{II}TiO_3$, $M^{II}_2TiO_4$, and $M^{II}_3TiO_5$ have been made by fusion methods. Hydrous zirconium dioxide, obtained by precipitation from cold solutions, is practically insoluble in solutions of alkalies, but is easily soluble in acids. The hydrous oxide has, however, a tremendous adsorptive capacity for alkalies and is readily converted to colloidal dispersions by solutions of such substances.

Halides and Their Derivatives   **18.13** Titanium and zirconium form complete series of tetrahalides. A summary of the melting and boiling points of these compounds is given in Table 18.2.

TABLE 18.2

Melting and Boiling Points of Titanium and Zirconium Tetrahalides

Compound	Melting Point, °C.	Boiling Point, °C.	Compound	Melting Point, °C.	Boiling Point, °C.
TiF_4	—	284 subl.	$TiBr_4$	38.2	230
ZrF_4	—	subl.	$ZrBr_4$	450 (15 atm.)	357 (subl.)
$TiCl_4$	−23	136.4	TiI_4	150	377.2
$ZrCl_4$	437 (25 atm.)	331 (subl.)	ZrI_4	499 (6.3 atm.)	431 (subl.)

18.14 The titanium tetrahalides can all be prepared by direct union of the elements. The fluoride is best made by halogen exchange between the tetrachloride and hydrogen fluoride. The chloride and bromide are readily obtained by reaction of the appropriate gaseous halogen with a heated mixture of titanium dioxide and carbon. Similar methods are useful for the production of zirconium and hafnium tetrahalides.

18.15 X-ray investigation of titanium tetrabromide and iodide and of zirconium tetrachloride shows these substances to exist as molecular crystals with tetrahedral structure. Titanium tetrachloride exhibits a similar structure in the vapor state, and although no structural data are available for the fluoride, this substance has a vapor density at 444° corresponding to the simple molecular formula.

18.16 The chlorides, bromides, and iodides of titanium and zirconium, as would be expected for simple covalent substances, are soluble in a variety of organic media. In the presence of an excess of water the titanium compounds are completely hydrolyzed, hydrous titanium dioxide and the appropriate hydrohalic acid being formed. (*Cf.* the hydrolytic behavior of silicon tetrahalides, sec. 13.85.) With the tetrachloride, the hydrolytic reaction can be reversed by hydrochloric acid, an excess of this reagent giving the acid $H_2[TiCl_6]$. With small amounts of water, titanyl halides, $TiOX_2$, are produced. The reaction of titanium tetrafluoride with water is strongly exothermic, and under the appropriate conditions a hydrate of the composition $TiF_4 \cdot 2H_2O$ can be isolated. In contrast to the complete hydrolysis noted for titanium tetrachloride, the corresponding compounds of zirconium and hafnium are only partially hydrolyzed by an excess of water.

$$ZrCl_4 + H_2O = ZrOCl_2 + 2H^+ + 2\overline{Cl}$$

The reaction is only slightly repressed by the addition of hydrochloric acid; in fact, zirconyl chloride octahydrate, $ZrOCl_2 \cdot 8H_2O$, can be isolated from solutions of the tetrachloride in concentrated hydrochloric acid. There is good evidence that polymeric species, *e.g.*, $Zr_2O_3^{2+}$, are also formed in the course of hydrolysis.

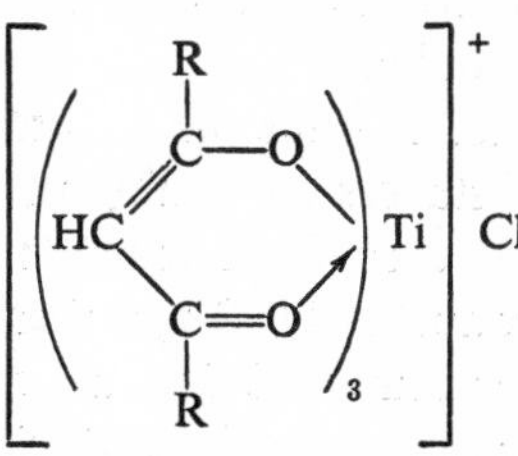

18.17 Titanium tetrahalides are capable of forming relatively stable complexes, particularly with oxygen donors and halide ion. Little information is available regarding complexes formed with nitrogen donors. All the halides combine with ammonia, but there is evidence that the addition reaction is often accompanied by ammonolysis. Thus, among the products isolated from reaction of the tetrachloride and tetrabromide with ammonia are $N{\equiv}Ti{-}Cl$ and $N{\equiv}Ti{-}Br$. Titanium tetrachloride and tetrabromide form addition compounds with such oxygen donor molecules as ethers, simple ketones, esters, and phosphoryl chloride; the complexes are usually of the 1 : 2 variety, *e.g.*, $TiCl_4 \cdot 2R_2CO$, in which titanium exhibits a coordination number of six. In general, the stability of these compounds toward hydrolysis is considerably less than that of analogous tin(IV) addition compounds. The behavior of zirconium tetrachloride toward esters and ketones is similar to that of the titanium compound. The addition compounds formed, however, are ordinarily stable only at low temperatures; at room temperature hydrogen chloride is evolved. The reaction of titanium and zirconium tetrachlorides with β-diketones is particularly interesting. The titanium compound reacts with β-diketones with the elimination of three chlorine atoms as hydrogen chloride and the formation of an ionic compound of the constitution shown (see analogous behavior of silicon tetrachloride, sec. 13.113). Combination of zirconium tetrachloride with acetylacetone at 0° yields $ZrCl_2(AA)_2$ (AA=acetylacetone), which when boiled with the diketone in benzene forms $ZrCl(AA)_3$, analogous to the titanium compound shown above. The last chlorine atom can be replaced by further reaction with acetylacetone in the presence of ammonia with the formation of the nonelectrolyte $Zr(AA)_4$, in which the metal atom exhibits a coordination number of eight.

18.18 All of the titanium tetrahalides appear to combine with halide ion to produce complex compounds of the type $M^I_2[TiX_6]$. Only the hexafluorotitanates possess a high degree of stability. Corresponding iodides have not been isolated, but they apparently can be formed in solution. Although hydrogen fluoride and titanium tetrafluoride do not combine under anhydrous conditions, in water these substances react to give a strongly acidic solution from which various metal hexafluorotitanates can be obtained by metathetical reactions. A large number of such complex salts have been obtained. Like the corresponding fluorosilicates (see 13.87), the titanium complexes are only very slightly hydrolyzed by water. However, they are much more stable than the fluorosilicates toward alkaline solutions, which precipitate hydrous titanium dioxide only very slowly. Hexachloro- and hexabromotitanates have been prepared, but they are unstable and difficult to isolate.

18.19 The halo complexes of zirconium are similar in many respects to the analogous titanium compounds, the fluorides being the only ones of any considerable stability. The chlorides cannot be obtained from aqueous medium, and no iodides are known. The fluoro complexes are somewhat less stable than their titanium analogs and most of them are readily decomposed at elevated temperatures. A number of types of fluoro complexes have been recognized, containing from five to eight fluorine atoms per atom of zirconium. The pentafluorides invariably are hydrated and probably should be formulated as $M^I[ZrF_5(H_2O)]$. The hexafluoro salts undoubtedly contain the octahedral ion, $[ZrF_6]^{2-}$. The heptafluorides, $M^I_3[ZrF_7]$, are of interest in that the central zirconium atom has the unusual coordination number of seven. (See sec. 6.108 for a discussion of the structure of $[ZrF_7]^{3-}$.) A number of octafluoro zirconium complexes with dipositive ions (Zn^{2+}, Cd^{2+}, Mn^{2+}, Ni^{2+}, Cu^{2+}) have been described. No information is available regarding their structures, but it is likely that they contain 8-coordinate zirconium.

Salts of Oxyacids   **18.20** No normal salts of tetrapositive titanium with oxyacid anions are known, and only a few such compounds have been reported for zirconium.

18.21 Attempts to prepare oxyacid salts of +4 titanium invariably yield substances containing the TiO^{2+} ion. It has already been noted, for example, that even from reaction of the dioxide with concentrated sulfuric acid the product is $TiOSO_4$ rather than the normal salt. It is interesting that, although the normal salt does not exist, anionic complexes derived from it have been prepared, *e.g.*, $M^I_2[Ti(SO_4)_3]$. The great majority of the complexes of titanium(IV) with oxyacid anions contain the titanyl group, *e.g.*, $M^I_2[TiO(SO_4)_2]$, $M^I_2[TiO(C_2O_4)_2]$.

18.22 In view of the increase in basic character from titanium to zirconium, it is not surprising to find that the latter element, in its tetrapositive state, can give normal salts with oxyacid anions. However, such compounds are few in number compared to basic salts containing the zirconyl ion and apparently can be obtained only in the absence of water. Thus evaporation of a solution of the dioxide or zirconyl chloride in concentrated sulfuric acid yields anhydrous $Zr(SO_4)_2$, and the normal acetate, $Zr(C_2H_3O_2)_4$, is the product of reaction between the tetrachloride and glacial acetic acid. These compounds are extremely water-sensitive, being readily converted to basic salts. Anionic complexes derived from both normal and basic salts have been characterized, *e.g.*, $H_2[ZrO(SO_4)_2] \cdot 3H_2O$, $(NH_4)_2[Zr(SO_4)_3] \cdot 3H_2O$, $K_4[Zr(SO_4)_4] \cdot xH_2O$, $Na_4[Zr(C_2O_4)_4] \cdot 4H_2O$, $H_4[ZrO(C_2O_4)_3] \cdot 7H_2O$. The first compound shown, which is isolated from aqueous solutions of the normal sulfate containing a large excess of sulfuric acid, undergoes hydrolytic decomposition in neutral aqueous solution to yield polynuclear complexes, *e.g.*, $H_4[Zr_4(OH)_8(SO_4)_6] \cdot 4H_2O$.

Lower Oxidation States

18.23 All three members of the group have oxidation states of $+3$ and $+2$, these lower states becoming progressively less stable from titanium to hafnium. The lower states of zirconium and hafnium, and also the dipositive state of titanium, are known only in solid compounds. Tripositive titanium is well-known both in solid compounds and in aqueous solution.

18.24 The reduction of aqueous titanium(IV), either electrolytically or by means of zinc and acids, gives violet solutions containing tripositive titanium. These solutions are relatively rapid reducing agents and find considerable use in analytical chemistry.

$$Ti^{3+} + H_2O = TiO^{2+} + 2H^+ + e^- \qquad E° = ca. - 0.1 \text{ v.}$$

Titanium(III), either in acidic or alkaline medium, is oxidized by atmospheric oxygen. The presence of tripositive titanium may help bring about the oxidation by air of substances not normally oxidized by this reagent. For example, in alkaline medium water is converted to hydrogen peroxide.

$$Ti_2O_3 \cdot xH_2O + O_2 + (x + 1)H_2O = 2TiO_2 \cdot xH_2O + H_2O_2$$

18.25 In its $+3$ state titanium is considerably more basic than in the tetrapositive state. In contrast to titanium(IV), $+3$ titanium can yield normal salts of oxyacids in aqueous solution, *e.g.*, formate, acetate, oxalate, and sulfate. Titanium(III) sulfate forms alums, $M^I Ti^{III}(SO_4)_2 \cdot 12H_2O(M^I = Rb, Cs)$. It would therefore appear that $Ti(H_2O)_x^{3+}$ can exist in water solution.

18.26 Among the solid binary compounds of tripositive titanium which have been prepared are the oxide and the halides. The oxide, Ti_2O_3, is obtained from the dioxide, either by thermal decomposition at about $2000°$ (see 18.11) or by reduction with carbon or hydrogen at elevated temperatures. Titanium(III) oxide is a stable substance, being inert toward all acids but sulfuric acid. It is noteworthy that the hydrous oxide, $Ti_2O_3 \cdot xH_2O$, which is precipitated from titanium(III) solutions by alkali, possesses no acidic characteristics.

18.27 Anhydrous titanium trifluoride, a purple solid, is obtained by the high temperature reduction of potassium hexafluorotitanate(IV) by means of elementary hydrogen. The magnetic moment of TiF_3 (1.75 Bohr magnetons) corresponds to the presence of one unpaired electron. The other anhydrous trihalides can be prepared by reduction of the tetrahalides with hydrogen at high temperatures, e.g., 650° for $TiCl_3$. The compounds are violet to black solids which are thermally unstable. Thus, at red heat the trichloride disproportionates to tetrachloride and dichloride. With water the trihalides yield hexahydrates, the chloride hydrate existing in violet and green forms, which presumably are hydrate isomers —

$$[Ti(H_2O)_6]Cl_3 \text{ (violet)} \quad \text{and} \quad [Ti(H_2O)_5Cl]Cl_2 \cdot H_2O(?) \text{ (green)}.$$

Anionic halo complexes derived from the trifluoride and trichloride have been described, e.g., K_2TiF_5, $(NH_4)_3TiF_6$, $Rb_2[TiCl_5(H_2O)]$. The trichloride, unlike the tetrachloride (see 18.17), reacts with ammonia without ammonolysis, the product being the hexammine.

18.28 The only compounds of dipositive titanium known with certainty are the oxide, chloride, and iodide. The oxide, TiO, has been obtained by reduction of the dioxide with elementary titanium in a vacuum at about 1600°. It is a high-melting substance (m.p. 1750°) which dissolves in dilute hydrochloric acid to yield hydrogen and +3 titanium. The dichloride and diiodide are prepared from the trihalides either by thermal decomposition (see above) or by reduction at elevated temperatures, e.g., $TiCl_3$ with hydrogen and TiI_3 with mercury. When heated, both halides decompose to give the metal and the tetrahalides. They are readily oxidized by air and react with acids with the liberation of hydrogen.

18.29 Only halides have been characterized for tri- and dipositive zirconium and hafnium. Zirconium trichloride and the tribromides of zirconium and hafnium can be obtained by the reduction of the appropriate tetrahalides with aluminum at elevated temperatures in a hydrogen atmosphere. The corresponding dihalides result when the trihalides are heated *in vacuo*.

$$2ZrBr_3 \overset{390°}{=} ZrBr_2 + ZrBr_4$$

Tetrahalides which are formed are removed readily by sublimation. The lower halides are dark, nonvolatile solids, closely resembling the analogous titanium compounds. Thus they decompose on heating and are easily oxidized by the air. That they are more powerful reducing agents than their titanium analogs is shown by the fact that they liberate hydrogen from water.

CHAPTER 19

THE VANADIUM FAMILY

Introduction

19.1 Vanadium, niobium, and tantalum, with the respective atomic numbers 23, 41, and 73 and valence shell configurations of $3d^34s^2$, $4d^45s^1$, and $5d^36s^2$, comprise the third group of the short transition series. Some properties of the elements are given in Table 19.1.

19.2 These elements exhibit a maximum oxidation state of $+5$, which for vanadium in acidic solution is a moderately strong oxidizing state, and for niobium and tantalum is rather stable. The oxides corresponding to the pentapositive state (M_2O_5) have both acidic and basic character, with the former being by far the more predominant. The acidic nature of the pentoxides diminishes from vanadium to niobium. No simple $+5$ ions exist; pentapositive vanadium frequently is found in a cationic form, but the positive species are invariably oxy ions, *e.g.*, VO^{3+} and $V(OH)_4^+$ (or VO_2^+). The latter species is commonly called *pervanadyl* ion.

19.3 Lower oxidation states of $+2$, $+3$, and $+4$ are well-defined for vanadium, both in solid compounds and in aqueous solution. The oxides corresponding to the $+2$ and $+3$ states are completely basic and simple (hydrated) vanadium cations are known for these states. Dipositive vanadium is somewhat similar to $+2$ iron, but is a considerably stronger reducing agent. The oxide derived from the tetrapositive state is amphoteric, but the salts formed with acids contain no simple $+4$ ion, but rather the VO^{2+} species.

GENERAL REFERENCES

LATIMER, *The Oxidation States of the Elements and Their Potentials in Aqueous Solutions*, 2nd Edition, Prentice-Hall, Inc., New York, 1952, Ch. 17.

REMY, *Treatise on Inorganic Chemistry* (translated and amended by Anderson), Elsevier Publishing Company, Amsterdam, 1956, Vol. II, Ch. 4.

SIDGWICK, *The Chemical Elements and Their Compounds*, Oxford University Press, London, 1950, pp. 804–51.

TABLE 19.1

Some Properties of the Vanadium Family Elements

	V	Nb	Ta
Natural isotopes	50, 51 *	93	180, 181 *
Density, g./cc.	5.98	8.58	16.69
Melting point, °C.	1715	1950	3010
Boiling point, °C.	ca. 3500	ca. 5100	ca. 6000
Ionic radius in crystals, M^{5+}, Å	0.59	0.70	ca. 0.7
Covalent radius, Å	1.224	1.342	1.343
Ionization potential, volts			
1st electron	6.74	6.88	7.7
2nd electron	14.65	13.895	
3rd electron	29.7	24.2	
4th electron	48		
5th electron	65.2		
Electrode potential, $E°$, in volts, for			
$V + 4H_2O$ $= V(OH)_4^+ + 4H^+ + 5e^-$	0.253		
$2M + 5H_2O$ $= M_2O_5 + 10H^+ + 10e^-$		0.65	0.81
$V = V^{2+} + 2e^-$	ca. 1.2		
$Nb = Nb^{3+} + 3e^-$		ca. 1.1	

* More abundant isotope

19.4 Lower oxidation states become increasingly difficult to obtain from vanadium to tantalum. Thus, for example, reduction with zinc and acid converts aqueous +5 vanadium to the dipositive state and +5 niobium to the +3 state, whereas pentapositive tantalum is unaffected. Relatively few compounds containing niobium and tantalum in lower states have been characterized and these are confined almost exclusively to oxides and halides.

19.5 Oxidation state relationships existing among the vanadium family elements in acid solution are summarized below.

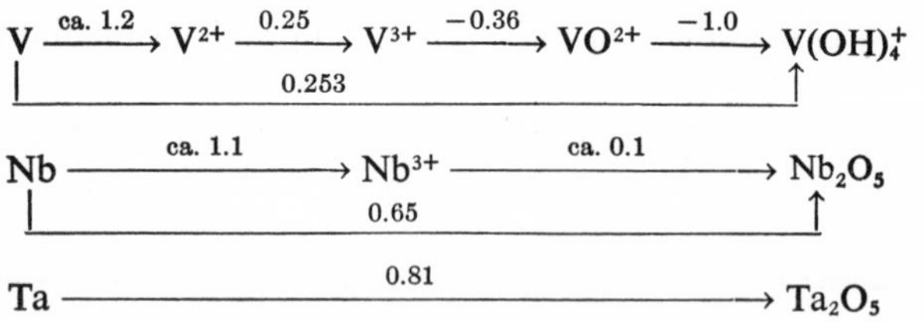

$$V \xrightarrow{\text{ca. 1.2}} V^{2+} \xrightarrow{0.25} V^{3+} \xrightarrow{-0.36} VO^{2+} \xrightarrow{-1.0} V(OH)_4^+$$
$$\text{(0.253)}$$

$$Nb \xrightarrow{\text{ca. 1.1}} Nb^{3+} \xrightarrow{\text{ca. 0.1}} Nb_2O_5$$
$$\text{(0.65)}$$

$$Ta \xrightarrow{0.81} Ta_2O_5$$

19.6 As a result of the lanthanide contraction, the ionic and covalent radii of niobium and tantalum are practically identical (Table 19.1). Consequently, there is a striking similarity in the chemistry of these elements.

The Elements

19.7 Vanadium, niobium, and tantalum are relatively rare elements, occurring in the earth's crust to the extent of 1.5×10^{-2}, 2×10^{-3}, and 2×10^{-4} per cent, respectively. The main vanadium-containing minerals are *patronite* (a complex sulfide), *vanadinite* $(3Pb_3(VO_4)_2 \cdot PbCl_2)$, *carnotite* $(K(UO_2)VO_4 \cdot \frac{3}{2}H_2O)$, and *roscoelite* (a complex silicate). Niobium and tantalum almost always are found together in nature, the most important minerals being *niobite* and *tantalite*, which are mainly iron(II) metaniobate and metatantalate, $Fe(NbO_3)_2$ and $Fe(TaO_3)_2$, with manganese often replacing some of the iron.

19.8 Vanadium, because of its high reactivity at elevated temperatures, is difficult to obtain pure. Inasmuch as the chief use of the metal is as an alloying agent in steels, the element is commonly prepared as an alloy with iron by reduction of a mixture of the pentoxide and iron(III) oxide with coke in an arc furnace. The preparation of elemental niobium and tantalum has as a prerequisite the separation of these two very similar elements from their minerals. The latter are best brought into solution by fusion with potassium acid sulfate, followed by treatment of the cooled melt with hydrofluoric acid. By addition of potassium fluoride to the solution containing the appropriate concentration of hydrofluoric acid, niobium is converted to $K_2[NbOF_5]$ and tantalum to $K_2[TaF_7]$. The latter is much less soluble than the niobium compound and separation can be effected by fractional crystallization. Recently, solvent extraction procedures have been utilized for the separation of the fluoro complexes. The free metals are obtained most conveniently as powders by electrolysis of the molten fluoro complexes $K_2[NbF_7]$ and $K_2[TaF_7]$. The powders are converted to bars by heat treatment at high pressures in the absence of air.

19.9 Vanadium, niobium, and tantalum, although unaffected at ordinary temperatures, react with most of the nonmetals when heated. A summary of a number of these reactions is given in Table 19.2.

TABLE 19.2

Reactions of Vanadium, Niobium, and Tantalum with Nonmetals

Nonmetals	*Products*
Oxygen	M_2O_5; V also forms VO_2.
Halogens	Nb and Ta give MX_5; V forms VF_5 with F_2, VCl_4 with Cl_2, VBr_3 and VI_3 with Br_2 and I_2.
Nitrogen	MN; interstitial compounds.
Carbon	MC; also M_2C; interstitial compounds.
Hydrogen	Quantity of hydrogen absorbed varies with temperature and pressure; interstitial substances formed.

19.10 Vanadium is resistant to the action of alkalies and all nonoxidizing acids (*e.g.*, hydrochloric, dilute sulfuric, etc.) with the exception of hydrofluoric acid. It is soluble in nitric acid, concentrated sulfuric acid, and aqua regia, the resulting solutions containing pentapositive vanadium in the form of VO^{3+} or $V(OH)_4^+$. Niobium and tantalum are considerably more inert than vanadium to the action of acids, being attacked only by hydrofluoric acid, undoubtedly with the formation of fluoro complexes. Both niobium and tantalum are slowly corroded by fused alkalies.

The Pentapositive State

Oxides and Related Compounds   **19.11** The pentoxides can be obtained by union of the metals with oxygen at elevated temperatures (Table 19.2), or by thermal dehydration of the hydrated oxides formed on appropriate treatment with acids of alkaline solutions of the elements in their +5 state. Vanadium pentoxide is most commonly prepared by ignition of ammonium metavanadate, NH_4VO_3.

19.12 The pentoxides are only slightly soluble in water, the resulting solutions being acidic. The vanadium compound dissolves in solutions of either strong bases or strong acids, reaction with the former yielding vanadates (see below) and with the latter, oxy salts which contain VO^{3+} or $V(OH)_4^+$.* Niobium and tantalum pentoxides are more resistant to the action of acids than is the corresponding vanadium compound, but can be brought into solution by treatment with hydrofluoric acid or by fusion with potassium acid sulfate. Fusion with alkali metal hydroxides or carbonates gives rise to niobates and tantalates.

19.13 The chemistry of the vanadates, niobates, and tantalates is complicated by the existence of a variety of polymeric anionic species. The vanadates have been studied in some detail and a number of significant facts concerning them follows. The alkali metal salts which have been isolated from solution can be grouped into classes: (1) colorless substances having an alkali metal to vanadium ratio of at least one; and (2) colored (usually red or brown) compounds in which the alkali metal-vanadium ratio is less than one. The former are obtained from alkaline or neutral solutions and are usually hydrated. The most common of these vanadates resemble the phosphates in their composition, *e.g.*, $M^I_3VO_4$(ortho), $M^I_4V_2O_7$(pyro), and M^IVO_3(meta).† These compounds come out of solution at definite pH ranges and their compositions are related to the tendency of the more simple vanadate ions to undergo condensation polymerization, this tendency becoming more pronounced with increasing acidity of the solution.

$$VO_4^{3-} \underset{\xleftarrow{\hspace{1cm}}}{\overset{pH\ 12–10.6}{\rightleftharpoons}} V_2O_7^{4-} \underset{\xleftarrow{\hspace{1cm}}}{\overset{pH\ 9.0–8.9}{\rightleftharpoons}} H_2V_4O_{13}^{4-}$$

19.14 The colored vanadates are obtained from acidic solutions and contain anions more highly polymerized than those noted above. Thus, for example, in the pH range 7.0 to 6.8 the change $H_2V_4O_{13}^{4-} \rightleftharpoons H_4V_5O_{16}^{3-}$ occurs and pentavanadates (*e.g.*, $M^I_3V_5O_{14}$, $M^I_4HV_5O_{15}$) can be isolated. With an increase in acidity beyond this point hydrated vanadium pentoxide begins to precipitate.

---

* Solution in hydrochloric acid is accompanied by the liberation of chlorine and the partial reduction of vanadium to the tetrapositive condition.

† From the ensuing discussion it is seen that the metavanadates are more correctly regarded as tetravanadates, $M^I_4V_4O_{12}$. Other tetravanadates, *e.g.*, $M^I_6V_4O_{13}$, can also be obtained.

Two definite hydrates, $V_2O_5 \cdot H_2O$ and $2V_2O_5 \cdot H_2O$ appear to have been characterized. These may be regarded as metavanadic, HVO_3, and tetravanadic, $H_2V_4O_{11}$, acids, respectively. At pH values below 2 the pentoxide dissolves to give a yellow solution containing oxovanadium ions (see 19.12).

19.15 Fusion of niobium pentoxide with an excess of sodium carbonate yields a melt of the orthoniobate, Na_3NbO_4; the orthotantalate is formed similarly from tantalum pentoxide. It is interesting that extraction of the melt with water yields a residue of sodium metaniobate, $NaNbO_3 \cdot 3H_2O$. Relatively little is definitely known about the polyniobates and polytantalates. Pyroniobates, $M^I_4Nb_2O_7$, and hexaniobates, $M^I_8Nb_6O_{19}$, appear to have been isolated, and the tantalate ions present in strongly alkaline solutions apparently are derived solely from the hypothetical pentatantalic acid $H_7Ta_5O_{16}$. Solutions of alkali metal niobates and tantalates are extensively hydrolyzed and are decomposed completely with the deposition of hydrated pentoxides when made even weakly acidic.

Binary Halides and Their Derivatives **19.16** The pentahalides of the elements of the vanadium family which have been obtained pure are listed in Table 19.3,

TABLE 19.3

Melting and Boiling Points of the Vanadium Family Pentahalides

Compound	Melting Point, °C.	Boiling Point, °C.	Compound	Melting Point, °C.	Boiling Point, °C.
VF_5	>200	111 (subl.)	$NbCl_5$	194	241
NbF_5	75.5	217–220	$TaCl_5$	211	241.6
TaF_5	96.8	229.4	$NbBr_5$	150	270

along with their melting and boiling points. As is indicated by the melting and boiling point data, the pentahalides exist as simple molecular compounds. The existence for vanadium of only one pentahalide, VF_5, should be noted. Oxyhalide compounds, both simple and complex, are more readily formed by this element in the pentapositive state than are completely halogenated derivatives.

19.17 Vanadium pentafluoride is obtained as a white sublimate from the disproportionation of the tetrafluoride (see 19.34), the reaction being carried out in a platinum vessel at 600° in an inert atmosphere.

$$2VF_4 = VF_5 + VF_3$$

The pentafluoride is soluble, probably with reaction, in a variety of organic solvents, *e.g.*, ethanol, toluene, ether, acetone. It is extremely sensitive to moisture, first giving vanadyl fluoride, VOF_3, and then the hydrated pentoxide.

19.18 Niobium pentafluoride is most conveniently prepared by exchange of halogen between hydrogen fluoride and the pentachloride, the latter being best obtained by chlorination of the pentasulfide at 250°. The pentabromide can be made by direct combination of the metal with bromine vapor. Analogous methods serve for the preparation of tantalum pentahalides. The pentahalides of both niobium and tantalum are readily attacked by water, yielding the hydrated pentoxides as ultimate products. Niobium pentafluoride appears to be somewhat more reactive than the corresponding tantalum compound. For example, alkaline hydrolysis of the niobium compound results in complete removal of fluorine and the formation of a niobate, whereas similar treatment of tantalum pentafluoride gives fluorotantalate complexes.

19.19 Electron diffraction investigation has shown that niobium pentachloride and pentabromide molecules in the vapor state possess trigonal bipyramid structures, with the metal-halogen distances (Nb—Cl, 2.29; Nb—Br, 2.46 Å) being very close to the calculated covalent radii sums.

19.20 The pentafluorides of all three metals combine with fluoride ion to form anionic complexes. There is an interesting trend from vanadium to tantalum with regard to the nature of the complex fluorides obtained in aqueous solution. The vanadium compounds are all oxyfluorides; for niobium, both oxyfluorides and completely fluorinated complexes are formed, with the former being the more stable; tantalum also forms complexes of both types, with the completely fluorinated compounds being more numerous and more stable. Only the completely fluorinated derivatives are described in this section.

19.21 Although unobtainable in aqueous medium, compounds containing the hexafluorovanadate(V) ion, $[VF_6]^-$, can be prepared in the solvent bromine trifluoride (see 16.27 [1]). Thus, $K[VF_6]$ is produced when vanadium trichloride (see 19.43) and potassium chloride are carefully brought together in the solvent. Other salts can be made similarly. The hexafluorovanadates fume in moist air, with the formation of hydrogen fluoride and vanadium pentoxide.

19.22 Niobium compounds of the types M^INbF_6 and $M^I_2NbF_7$ (M = alkali metal) can be obtained from oxyfluoro complexes (see 19.30) by reaction with hydrofluoric acid. A better method of preparation, since it avoids contamination with oxy compounds, involves the union of alkali metal fluoride with niobium pentafluoride in anhydrous hydrogen fluoride, the nature of the product formed being determined by the ratio of reactants. X-ray examination [2] reveals that in compounds of the type M_2NbF_7, niobium has a coordination number of seven. The heptafluoroniobate(V) ion has a structure derived from a trigonal prism, with the seventh fluorine atom added beyond the center of one of the rectangular faces (cf. the structure of $[ZrF_7]^{3-}$, sec. 6.108).

19.23 Three types of completely fluorinated complexes have been characterized for tantalum — M^ITaF_6, $M^I_2TaF_7$, and $M^I_3TaF_8$. The heptafluorotantalates are the most common. The compounds are ordinarily prepared by combination of the parent fluorides in hydrofluoric acid medium. The type of compound isolated appears to depend both upon the nature of the alkali metal employed and in some instances upon the ratio of reactants.[3] For example,

[1] EMELÉUS and GUTMANN, *J. Chem. Soc.*, 1949, p. 2979.
[2] HOARD, *J. Am. Chem. Soc.*, **61**, 1252 (1939).
[3] BALKE, *J. Am. Chem. Soc.*, **27**, 1140 (1905).

with lithium fluoride, only $LiTaF_6 \cdot 2H_2O$ is produced. Reaction between sodium fluoride and excess tantalum pentafluoride yields $Na_2TaF_7 \cdot H_2O$; however, when the alkali metal fluoride is present in excess, Na_3TaF_8 is formed. The only product isolated from combination of potassium fluoride and tantalum pentafluoride in dilute hydrofluoric acid is K_2TaF_7. In general, the fluoro complexes of tantalum are considerably more stable toward hydrolysis than the niobium compounds. The structure of the heptafluorotantalate ion is the same as that of the corresponding niobium ion. For the structure of an octafluorotantalate, see sec. 6.110.

19.24 Completely chlorinated complexes of niobium(V), although unattainable in water, have been prepared in iodine monochloride as solvent.[4] Thus, $KNbCl_6$ is formed by reaction between potassium chloride and niobium pentachloride. According to the Solvent System concept of acids and bases, the pentachloride functions as an acid in iodine monochloride (which is presumed to undergo self-ionization to yield I^+ and ICl_2^-).

$$ICl + NbCl_5 \rightleftharpoons I^+NbCl_6^-$$

Potassium chloride is a base in this solvent.

$$ICl + KCl \rightleftharpoons K^+ICl_2^-$$

Reaction between potassium chloride and niobium pentachloride to give $KNbCl_6$ is therefore a neutralization in iodine monochloride.

Oxyhalide Compounds **19.25** Simple oxyhalides of vanadium and niobium of the general formula $MOX_3(X = F, Cl, Br)$ have been prepared. No analogous compounds of tantalum appear to exist.

19.26 Vanadium(V) oxytrifluoride (m.p., 300°; b.p., ca. 480°) is obtained by reaction of the oxytrichloride with concentrated hydrofluoric acid in the cold, or by the oxidation of vanadium(III) fluoride (see 19.43) with molecular oxygen at red heat. The oxytrichloride (m.p., −79.5°; b.p., 127°) and tribromide (b.p., 130–136° at 100 mm.) can be prepared by the halogenation of vanadium(III) oxide; the chloride is also formed by the action of chlorine on vanadium pentoxide at elevated temperatures.

$$2V_2O_5 + 6Cl_2 = 4VOCl_3 + 3O_2$$

The oxyhalides are rapidly hydrolyzed by water, with the formation of pentoxide. The chloride, although miscible with most organic solvents, frequently acts as an oxidizing agent toward them. The bromide is thermally unstable and readily evolves elementary bromine.

$$2VOBr_3 = 2VOBr_2 + Br_2$$

19.27 On the basis of their relatively low boiling points, the vanadium(V) oxytrihalides would appear to be simple molecular compounds. This is certainly true of the chloride in the vapor state, in which the molecule has been

[4] GUTMANN, *Z. anorg. allgem. Chem.*, **264**, 151 (1951).

shown to have the configuration of a distorted tetrahedron,[5] with V—O and V—Cl bond distances of 1.56 and 2.12 Å, respectively. The V—O distance is considerably shorter than the sum of the single bond radii, and this has been taken to indicate the existence of some multiple bond character between these two atoms.

19.28 Niobium(V) oxytrifluoride is said to be formed when a fused mixture of the pentoxide and calcium fluoride is treated with gaseous hydrogen fluoride. The oxychloride and oxybromide can be obtained by reaction of the appropriate halogen on a heated mixture of the pentoxide and carbon. Like the corresponding vanadium compounds, the oxytrihalides of niobium are converted readily to the pentoxide by hydrolysis.

19.29 A variety of anionic oxyhalo complexes of pentapositive vanadium, niobium, and tantalum have been described.* Particularly numerous are the oxyfluoride compounds. Vanadium forms compounds of the types $MVOF_4$, M_2VOF_5, and $M_2VO_2F_3$. These substances are obtained by reaction between vanadium pentoxide and metal fluoride, ordinarily in hydrofluoric acid solution. They are relatively unstable substances; not only are they readily interconvertible, but they also undergo extensive hydrolysis, frequently with the formation of more complicated substances.

19.30 For niobium, the principal oxyfluoride complexes have the compositions M_2NbOF_5, M_3NbOF_6, and M_4NbOF_7. Substances containing $[NbOF_5]^{2-}$ are prepared by the addition of the appropriate quantities of metal fluoride to solutions of the pentoxide in hydrofluoric acid. The other types, obtained when the reaction is carried out in the presence of a large excess of metal fluoride, are relatively unstable and revert to the more stable M_2NbOF_5 form on recrystallization from water. Recrystallization of the oxy compounds from concentrated hydrofluoric acid results in removal of oxygen and the formation of completely fluorinated products, e.g.,

$$K_2NbOF_5 \cdot H_2O + 2HF = K_2NbF_7 + 2H_2O.$$

X-ray analysis of $K_2NbOF_5 \cdot H_2O$ shows this compound to contain octahedral $[NbOF_5]^{2-}$. Similar examination of K_3NbOF_6, prepared by the isothermal evaporation of an aqueous solution of $K_2NbOF_5 \cdot H_2O$ and potassium fluoride in the molar ratio of one to four, demonstrates the presence of $[NbOF_6]^{3-}$ with a structure of the same type as that of $[ZrF_7]^{3-}$ (see 6.108).

19.31 Oxyfluoride complexes of $+5$ tantalum appear to be derived solely from the hypothetical compound $TaOF_3$, and most of them are of the M_3TaOF_6 type, which is isomorphous with $M_3[ZrF_7]$. Inasmuch as the oxygen is easily replaced by fluorine, these compounds cannot be prepared in hydrofluoric acid medium and are obtained by direct reaction between tantalum pentoxide and alkali metal fluoride in the absence of solvent. The oxyfluorides decompose in

---

[5] PALMER, *J. Am. Chem. Soc.*, **60**, 2360 (1938).

* All the known complexes of $+5$ vanadium and niobium with acid radicals other than the halogens are oxo compounds, e.g., $M_3[VO_2(C_2O_4)_2]$, $M[VO_2(SO_4)]$, $M_3[NbO(C_2O_4)_3]$.

aqueous solution with the formation of pentoxide and a completely fluorinated complex.

19.32 A small number of oxychloro complexes of vanadium have been made. They are extremely soluble in water and therefore difficult to isolate and characterize. Two series of oxychloro complexes of niobium, M^INbOCl_4 and $M^I_2NbOCl_5$, have been obtained by interaction of metal chlorides and niobium pentoxide or pentachloride in concentrated hydrochloric acid. These substances are very susceptible to hydrolysis, being immediately converted to the pentoxide. Oxybromides of niobium which are similar to but less stable than the chloro compounds have been described. A few oxychloro complexes of tantalum, e.g., $(pyH)_2TaOCl_5 \cdot 2C_2H_5OH$ (py = pyridine), have been prepared from the pentachloride and the appropriate chloride in ethanol solution.

Lower Oxidation States

The Tetrapositive State **19.33** This oxidation state is well-known for vanadium and is readily formed by mild reduction of the +5 state. The dioxide, VO_2, which may be regarded as the parent compound of the +4 state, can be obtained from the pentoxide in a variety of ways, the most common being by fusion with oxalic acid. It is a dark-blue substance, soluble in both acids and alkalies. Reaction with aqueous acids gives blue solutions containing VO^{2+}. From alkaline solutions there can be isolated vanadate(IV) compounds which are mainly of the composition $M^I_2V_4O_9$. Other types of vanadates derived from the +4 state, e.g., $M^{II}VO_3$, $M^{II}_2VO_4$, and $M^{II}_3VO_5$, can be formed by reaction between the dioxide and alkaline earth oxides at high temperatures in a vacuum.

19.34 The fluoride and chloride of +4 vanadium are known. The tetrafluoride is obtained from the chloride by reaction with hydrogen fluoride at ordinary temperature. The tetrachloride can be prepared in a number of ways: e.g., the interaction of the pentoxide with carbon tetrachloride at 500–600°; the chlorination of ferrovanadium and separation of the desired product from the less volatile iron(III) chloride by fractionation. The tetrafluoride is a hygroscopic brown powder which begins to disproportionate into the penta- and trifluoride at 325° (see 19.17). The tetrachloride (a dark red liquid, f.p., 25.7°; b.p., 154°) is also unstable thermally and even at room temperature dissociates to the trichloride and elementary chlorine. Its vapor density corresponds to that expected for the simple molecular formula, but soon decreases as a result of dissociation. Electron diffraction data show the vapor to have a regular tetrahedral structure with a V—Cl bond distance of 2.03 Å (sum of single bond radii is 2.21 Å). The tetrachloride is immediately hydrolyzed to yield solutions of vanadium(IV) oxydichloride.

$$VCl_4 + H_2O = VOCl_2 + 2HCl$$

19.35 All vanadium(IV) oxydihalides with the exception of the iodide are known. The fluoride, VOF_2, is obtained as a yellow, relatively nonvolatile powder by heating the bromide with hydrogen fluoride. The oxydichloride can be made by the reduction of vanadium(V) oxytrichloride by means of hydrogen at elevated temperatures, and the bromide results from the action of a mixture of bromine and sulfur monobromide vapors on vanadium pentoxide at 700–800° (see also sec. 19.26). Vanadium(IV) oxydifluoride is insoluble in water and the common organic solvents. The chloride is a bright green deliquescent substance; treatment of an aqueous solution with sodium carbonate results in the precipitation of a gray, hydrated dioxide of the composition $2VO_2 \cdot 7H_2O$. Vanadium(IV) oxydibromide is a pale yellow material which begins to sublime in a vacuum at 330°, with extensive decomposition into bromine and the non-volatile vanadium(III) oxybromide, VOBr.

19.36 Although the nature of the binding in the vanadium(IV) oxydihalides has not been elucidated, there is no question that aqueous solutions of the chloride contain VO^{2+} (commonly known as the *vanadyl* ion). One simple vanadyl compound which is undoubtedly ionic in character is the sulfate, $VOSO_4$. This substance exists in two forms. One, a greenish, water-insoluble form, is prepared by heating the acid sulfate, $2VOSO_4 \cdot H_2SO_4$,* to 260° with concentrated sulfuric acid. The insoluble form is converted to a blue soluble modification on heating with water to 130°. The soluble form undergoes slow hydrolysis, with the deposition of a hydrated dioxide.

19.37 Practically all of the complexes of tetrapositive vanadium are vanadyl derivatives. A great majority of these are anionic in character and a few are nonelectrolytes. A number of examples of these compounds are noted below. Halo complexes are known only with fluorine and chlorine. Complex vanadyl fluorides are mainly of the composition $M^I_2VOF_4 \cdot 2H_2O$ and are formed by reaction between vanadium tetrafluoride and aqueous solutions of alkali metal fluorides. Chloro complexes with pyridinium or quinolinium ion as cation have been described and are of two types — e.g., $(pyH)_2VOCl_4 \cdot xH_2O$ and $(pyH)_4VOCl_6$. Among other anionic complexes which have been reported are those with thiocyanate, sulfate, and oxalate. The thiocyanato compounds all have the formula $M^I_2VO(NCS)_4 \cdot xH_2O$, whereas the sulfato and oxalato complexes are of two varieties, e.g., $M^I_2VO(SO_4)_2$ and $M^I_2(VO)_2(SO_4)_3$. There is no information available on the structures of the various anionic complexes. Illustrations of nonelectrolytes are the complexes with β-diketones, which are readily obtained from vanadium(IV) oxydichloride by precipitation of the hydrated dioxide and reaction of the latter with diketone in warm ethanol. The compounds all have the composition indicated, and are soluble in a variety of organic solvents but insoluble in water. The acetylacetone derivative has also been isolated as a monohydrate.

19.38 The only example of a relatively stable complex of vanadium(IV) which is not a vanadyl compound is K_2VCl_6, formed by reaction of potassium chloride

* The acid sulfate is obtained by crystallization from a solution of the dioxide in an excess of sulfuric acid.

and vanadium tetrachloride in iodine monochloride.[4] This compound cannot be made in water because of the ease with which vanadium(IV) is hydrolyzed.

19.39 The only compounds of tetrapositive niobium and tantalum which appear to have been characterized unequivocally are the dioxides and tetrachlorides. Niobium dioxide is obtained from the pentoxide by reduction with hydrogen at temperatures not exceeding 1300°. The analogous tantalum compound is also formed from the pentoxide, but by reduction with carbon at high temperatures. Both dioxides are dark gray to black substances which are insoluble in water and acids but dissolve with oxidation in hot solutions of alkali.

19.40 The tetrachlorides can be prepared from the corresponding pentachlorides by reduction with aluminum at elevated temperatures and low pressures. The compounds are thermally unstable and disproportionate into tri- and pentahalide as in the equation given.

$$2NbCl_4(s) \rightleftharpoons NbCl_3(s) + NbCl_5(g)$$

The tantalum trichloride formed in the decomposition of the tetrachloride is also unstable and when heated breaks down into dichloride and pentachloride.

The Tripositive State   **19.41** The tripositive state is of some significance for vanadium. The oxide, V_2O_3, corresponding to the +3 state, is entirely basic in nature and dissolves in acids to form salts containing tripositive vanadium (hydrated) as cation. Characteristically green aqueous solutions of +3 vanadium can be prepared by electrolytic reduction of acidic solutions containing the element in the +4 or +5 state. In chemical behavior tripositive vanadium bears some resemblance to iron(III), one notable difference being the relative ease with which the former can be converted to higher oxidation states.

19.42 Vanadium(III) oxide (vanadium sesquioxide), a black, extremely high-melting substance, is prepared by reduction of the pentoxide by hydrogen or carbon monoxide. When heated, it unites with oxygen to yield the dioxide. Hydrated forms of the sesquioxide can be precipitated by treatment of aqueous solutions of the trichloride with ammonia or alkali metal hydroxides. These are extremely sensitive to atmospheric oxidation, even at ordinary temperature.

19.43 The complete series of trihalides of vanadium is known. The yellow-green trifluoride can be obtained by the thermal decomposition of the tetrafluoride (see 19.34) or by halogen exchange between hydrogen fluoride and the trichloride at 600°. The latter compound (a violet substance) is best made by heating the tetrachloride (see 19.34). Vanadium tribromide can be prepared by the action of bromine vapor on the metal or its carbide(VC), the product coming off as a black sublimate in the neighborhood of 600°. The brown-black triiodide is obtained by direct combination of the elements at temperatures above 150°.

19.44 The trichloride, bromide, and iodide are hygroscopic and their solutions are extensively hydrolyzed. They crystallize from aqueous solutions as hexahydrates. The trifluoride, although it forms a trihydrate with water, is only slightly soluble in this medium. The trifluoride and tribromide are thermally stable and can be sublimed (at high temperatures) unchanged. On the other hand the trichloride and triiodide decompose when heated, the former to give the di- and tetrachloride and the latter the diiodide and elementary iodine. The character of the binding in the trihalides has not been determined.

19.45 Two oxyhalides of vanadium(III) — VOCl and VOBr — have been characterized. These compounds can be obtained by heating the corresponding vanadium(IV) oxydihalides in a vacuum. The vanadium(III) oxyhalides are sparingly soluble in water but dissolve readily in acids.

19.46 The compounds of tripositive vanadium with sulfate ion are of some interest. Electrolytic reduction of vanadium(IV) oxysulfate, $VOSO_4$, in sulfuric acid solution yields normal sulfates, $V_2(SO_4)_3$ (hydrated), and the acid sulfate $VH(SO_4)_2$ (hydrated). The normal sulfates are capable of forming alums with alkali metal sulfates and there is little doubt that they contain hydrated tripositive vanadium cations. An anhydrous normal sulfate has also been isolated. The evidence indicates that this sulfate, which is insoluble in water and sulfuric acid, is not a simple salt but is complex in nature.

19.47 Tripositive vanadium has a relatively large tendency to form complexes. Although the great majority of the complexes are anionic, some cationic and uncharged complexes have been characterized. The common coordination number for vanadium in these compounds is six, the ligands being octahedrally disposed about the vanadium.

19.48 Cationic complexes appear to be formed only with oxygen or nitrogen donors. Included among this type are the hydrates and the ammines. Mention has already been made of the trihalide hexahydrates; these very likely contain $[V(H_2O)_6]^{3+}$. Reaction of liquid ammonia on the anhydrous trichloride or tribromide gives the hexammine, e.g., $[V(NH_3)_6]Cl_3$.* The ammonia is loosely held and is removed quantitatively by solutions of alkali and at least partially by reaction with hot water.

19.49 Nonelectrolytic complexes of vanadium(III) with acetylacetone have been prepared and have the composition shown. In contact with air these are converted to vanadium(IV) derivatives (see 19.37).

19.50 A variety of anionic complexes is known. Among the more common compounds are the cyanides, thiocyanates, oxalates, and fluorides. In the first three types the anions occupy all six coordination positions; the fluoride compounds are of three classes — $M^I_3[VF_6]$, $M^I_2[VF_5(H_2O)]$, and $M^I[VF_4(H_2O)_2]$. In general, the ligands are labile and are readily and rapidly replaced, e.g., by OH^-.

The 6-coordinate complexes of vanadium(III) undoubtedly are "inner orbital" complexes with

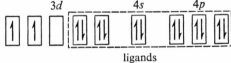

* With gaseous ammonia the trichloride undergoes ammonolysis with the formation of the nitride (VN) and ammonium chloride.

D^2SP^3 binding, in which the central atom has the electronic configuration shown. This is one of the characteristic configurations of labile complexes [6] (see 6.139 *ff.*).

19.51 Three compounds of tripositive niobium and tantalum are known definitely: $NbCl_3$, $TaCl_3$, and $TaBr_3$. It has already been noted that the trichlorides are products of the disproportionation of the tetrachlorides. The niobium compound can be obtained also by the reduction of the pentachloride by hydrogen at 400–450°; a similar reaction with the pentabromide of tantalum carried out at 700° gives the tribromide of that element.

19.52 Niobium trichloride is a black, nonvolatile substance which is unaffected by water. When heated in air it is converted to niobium(V) oxytrichloride. Oxidation with nitric acid yields the hydrated pentoxide. Tantalum trichloride is a green solid which dissolves in cold water without apparent change; in hot solutions or in the presence of alkali it is converted to the pentoxide with the liberation of hydrogen. Evaporation at low pressures of a solution of the trichloride containing hydrochloric acid leaves a compound with the formula $Ta_3Cl_7O \cdot 3H_2O$. The thermal instability of tantalum trichloride has been mentioned (see 19.40).

19.53 Blue aqueous solutions of tripositive niobium are formed by reduction of compounds containing the element in the pentapositive state by means of zinc and acid or by electrolysis. The niobium in these solutions is readily oxidized.

The Dipositive State **19.54** This is the least stable of the oxidation states of the elements of the vanadium family. As with the other lower oxidation states, it is best known for vanadium.

19.55 Aqueous solutions of violet dipositive vanadium result from the reduction of acidic solutions of the element in the +5 state by means of zinc. There is no doubt that $V(H_2O)_x^{2+}$ is present in the reduced solutions. This ion is a strong reducing agent and is slowly oxidized by water with the liberation of

$$V^{2+} = V^{3+} + e^- \qquad E° = 0.25 \text{ v.}$$

hydrogen. From sulfuric acid solutions the compound $VSO_4 \cdot 7H_2O$ can be obtained, which is isomorphous with the corresponding chromium(II) and iron(II) salts. Vanadium(II) sulfate forms double salts of the composition $M^I_2SO_4 \cdot VSO_4 \cdot 6H_2O$ with alkali metal sulfates.

19.56 Other simple compounds of vanadium(II) which have been prepared are the oxide and halides. The oxide is obtained as a nonstoichiometric compound (with oxygen content ranging from 47 to 56 atom per cent) by reduction of the pentoxide with hydrogen at 1700°. It is soluble in acids, but not in alkalies. Vanadium dichloride and diiodide are formed by the thermal decomposition of the corresponding vanadium(III) compounds (see 19.43). The dibromide is produced from the tribromide by reduction with hydrogen at elevated temperatures, and the anhydrous difluoride apparently has not yet

[6] TAUBE, *Chem. Revs.*, **50**, 69 (1952).

been isolated. The dihalides are relatively nonvolatile substances which dissolve in water to give the violet solutions characteristic of the +2 state.

19.57 Only two compounds of +2 niobium and tantalum have been reported — NbO and $TaCl_2$. Reference to the latter has already been made (see 19.40). It is a greenish-black, nonvolatile substance, which, although insoluble, is slowly attacked by water with the evolution of hydrogen and the formation of +3 tantalum. Niobium(II) oxide reputedly is formed by decomposition of the dioxide at 1750° in an argon atmosphere.

CHAPTER 20

THE CHROMIUM FAMILY

Introduction

20.1 The fourth group of elements of the short transition series consists of chromium, molybdenum, and tungsten, with the respective atomic numbers 24, 42, and 74 and valence shell configurations $3d^54s^1$, $4d^55s^1$, and $5d^46s^2$. A number of important properties of these elements are listed in Table 20.1.

20.2 The maximum oxidation state for the group is $+6$. The oxides corresponding to this state (MO_3) are completely acidic and no cationic species containing the elements in this state exist. There is a strong tendency, especially pronounced for molybdenum and tungsten, for the elements in the hexapositive condition to form polymeric anions. Molybdenum and tungsten in their maximum oxidation states are rather stable; $+6$ chromium in acidic solution is a potent oxidizing agent.

20.3 The most important of the lower oxidation states of chromium are $+2$ and $+3$.* Less well-known states which have been identified for this element are $+4$ and $+5$. The oxides derived from dipositive and tripositive chromium are, respectively, completely basic and amphoteric; and simple (hydrated) cations corresponding to these states exist. Dipositive chromium is a strong and rapid reducing agent both in acidic and alkaline medium. In acidic solution the element is most stable in its $+3$ state. An outstanding characteristic of tripositive chromium is its ability to form an extraordinarily large variety of stable cationic and anionic complexes.

GENERAL REFERENCES

LATIMER, *The Oxidation States of the Elements and Their Potentials in Aqueous Solutions*, 2nd Edition, Prentice-Hall, Inc., New York, 1952, Ch. 16.

REMY, *Treatise on Inorganic Chemistry* (translated and amended by Anderson), Elsevier Publishing Company, Amsterdam, 1956, Vol. II, pp. 119–86.

SIDGWICK, *The Chemical Elements and Their Compounds*, Oxford University Press, London, 1950, pp. 998–1068.

---

* The zero oxidation state as found in $Cr(CO)_6$ is not considered here. Reference to chromium hexacarbonyl can be found in sec. 13.55.

20.4 Lower oxidation states known for molybdenum and tungsten include +2, +3, +4, +5. It is interesting that, with the questionable exception of $Mo(H_2O)_x^{3+}$, no simple cationic species have been found for these elements.

20.5 As would be expected, molybdenum and tungsten are much more similar to each other than either one is to chromium. The tripositive oxidation state is the only one in which molybdenum and tungsten show little resemblance.

20.6 The oxidation potential relationships which exist among the elements of the chromium family are given below.*

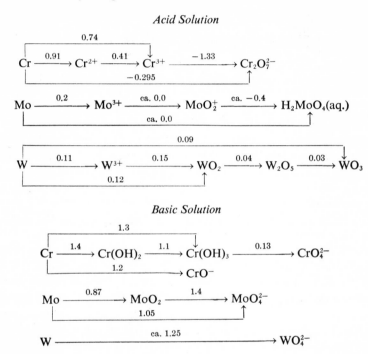

Acid Solution

Basic Solution

The Elements

20.7 Chromium, molybdenum, and tungsten are found in the earth's crust to the extent of approximately 1.8×10^{-2}, 7.5×10^{-4}, and 1×10^{-3} per cent, respectively. The most important minerals of these elements are *chromite* (a double oxide of the composition $FeO \cdot Cr_2O_3$), *molybdenite* (MoS_2), *wolframite* (a mixture of the isomorphous tungstates $FeWO_4$ and $MnWO_4$), and *scheelite* ($CaWO_4$).

20.8 Elementary chromium is commonly produced as an alloy with iron by reduction of chromite with carbon in an electric furnace. The pure metal can be obtained by reduction of chromium(III) oxide by means of aluminum at

* It should be emphasized that many of the potential values shown have not been determined experimentally, but rather have been calculated from free energy data. The existence of a number of the species listed, *e.g.*, simple tripositive molybdenum and tungsten cations and W_2O_5, is highly questionable.

TABLE 20.1
Some Properties of the Chromium Family Elements

	Cr	Mo	W
Natural isotopes	50, 52 *, 53, 54	92, 94, 95, 96, 97, 98 *	180, 182, 183, 184 *, 186
Density, g./cc.	7.2	10.2	19.1
Melting point, °C.	1830	2600	3400
Boiling point, °C.	ca. 2300	ca. 4800	ca. 5700
Ionic radius in crystals M^{6+}, Å	0.52	0.62	ca. 0.65
Covalent radius, Å	1.172	1.291	1.299
Ionization potential, volts			
1st electron	6.764	7.131	7.98
2nd electron	16.49	15.72	
3rd electron	ca. 31		
4th electron	ca. 50		
5th electron	ca. 73		
6th electron			
Electrode potential, $E°$, in volts, for			
$Cr = Cr^{2+} + 2e^-$	0.91		
$M = M^{3+} + 3e-$	0.74	0.2	0.11
$2Cr + 7H_2O = Cr_2O_7^{2-} + 14H^+ + 12e^-$	−0.295		
$Mo + 4H_2O = H_2MoO_4 + 6H^+ + 6e^-$		ca. 0	
$W + 2H_2O = WO_2 + 4H^+ + 4e^-$			0.12
$W + 3H_2O = WO + 6H^+ + 6e^-$			0.09

* Most abundant isotope

elevated temperatures. The most important process for the metallurgy of molybdenum has the following steps: (1) concentration of MoS_2 in the ore by flotation; (2) roasting of the sulfide to MoO_3; (3) extraction of the oxide with aqueous ammonia and isolation of $(NH_4)_2MoO_4$ from the resulting solution; (4) ignition of the ammonium molybdate to MoO_3; (5) reduction of the oxide with hydrogen at high temperatures. This procedure yields the metal in the form of a powder, which is converted to the massive metal by heat treatment at high pressures in an inert atmosphere. The common method for the separation of tungsten from its ores consists of fusion with sodium carbonate and extraction of the sodium tungstate formed by means of water. The tungstate is then converted to the hydrous trioxide, $WO_3 \cdot xH_2O$, by acidification. Ignition of the latter yields the anhydrous compound, which is reduced by hydrogen to give the pure metal in powdered form. Appropriate heat treatment of the powder yields the ductile metal.

20.9 Like the elements of the vanadium family, chromium, molybdenum, and tungsten are unreactive toward most nonmetals at ordinary temperatures. Reaction usually occurs readily at high temperatures, and a summary of a number of these reactions is given in Table 20.2.

TABLE 20.2

Reactions of the Chromium Family Elements with Nonmetals

Nonmetals	Products
Oxygen	Cr_2O_3; MoO_3; WO_3
Halogens *	CrF_3; $CrCl_3$; $CrBr_3$; CrI_2; MoF_6; $MoCl_5$; $MoBr_4$; WF_6; WCl_6; WBr_6; WI_2. No reaction between Mo and I_2 at 500°.
Sulfur	CrS; Mo_2S_3 and MoS_2; WS_2
Nitrogen	CrN; no reaction with Mo below 1000°, or with W below 2000°.
Carbon	Cr_3C_2; Mo_2C and MoC; W_2C and WC
Hydrogen	Cr absorbs hydrogen with no change in metal lattice; Mo and W absorb very little hydrogen.

* The products shown for molybdenum and tungsten, particularly with chlorine and bromine, are for very definite temperature conditions. The chlorides and bromides listed are thermally unstable.

20.10 Although in terms of oxidation potentials they must be regarded as active metals, the members of the chromium family readily assume a state of passivity. Chromium dissolves in dilute hydrochloric or sulfuric acid with the attainment of the dipositive state, but nitric acid, and even aqua regia, are without effect on it. Both molybdenum and tungsten are extremely resistant to the action of acids, although moderately concentrated nitric acid and hot concentrated sulfuric acid are reported to oxidize molybdenum.

20.11 Solutions of strong bases react slowly with chromium to form chromate(III) (chromite) solutions. Molybdenum and tungsten are unaffected by solutions of alkalies, but are rapidly attacked by alkaline melts containing oxidizing agents, e.g., potassium nitrate.

The Hexapositive State

Oxides and Related Compounds **20.12** Chromium(VI) oxide is obtained as a bright red precipitate (m.p. 197°) by the action of concentrated sulfuric acid on a concentrated aqueous solution of sodium or potassium dichromate. The corresponding molybdenum and tungsten compounds, respectively white (m.p. 791°) and lemon-yellow (m.p. 1473°) are the ultimate products of combustion of the metals or their compounds.

20.13 The chromium oxide, in contrast to the molybdenum and tungsten compounds, is thermally unstable. It begins to lose oxygen above its melting point, decomposition occurring in a number of stages.

$$CrO_3 \rightarrow Cr_3O_8 \rightarrow Cr_2O_5 \rightarrow CrO_2 \rightarrow Cr_2O_3$$

The oxide is a powerful oxidant, particularly toward organic materials. Unlike the insoluble molybdenum(VI) and tungsten(VI) oxides, it dissolves readily in water to give solutions containing chromic (H_2CrO_4) and dichromic ($H_2Cr_2O_7$)

acids. These diprotic acids, not isolable in the solid state, are strong acids in their first stage dissociation. All the trioxides are easily soluble in solutions of alkalies (MoO_3 also dissolves in ammonia-water). It is noteworthy that addition of excess strong acid to alkaline solutions of molybdenum and tungsten oxides precipitates molybdic and tungstic acids of definite compositions. Molybdic acid has the formula $H_2MoO_4 \cdot H_2O$ and is readily converted to the anhydrous acid H_2MoO_4 on gentle heating. So-called yellow tungstic acid, H_2WO_4, is obtained by precipitation from hot solutions of normal and paratungstates but not from solutions of metatungstates (see below). Precipitation in the cold gives *white tungstic acid*, a WO_3 gel of variable water content; this is readily converted to the yellow form.

20.14 From the yellow solutions of chromium(VI) oxide to which base has been added, salts containing the *chromate*(VI) ion, CrO_4^{2-}, can be isolated. Only the alkali metal and magnesium chromates exhibit high solubility in water. Acidification of chromate solutions gives orange solutions containing the *dichromate* ion, $Cr_2O_7^{2-}$.

$$2CrO_4^{2-} + 2H^+ \rightleftharpoons Cr_2O_7^{2-} + H_2O$$

With the notable exception of the silver compound, the dichromates which have been prepared, *e.g.*, those of sodium, potassium, magnesium, calcium, strontium, and barium, are very soluble in water. As might be expected from the equilibrium shown above, chromates are precipitated from weakly acidic solutions of dichromates by ions that give insoluble chromates but soluble dichromates. *Trichromates*, $M^I_2Cr_3O_{10}$, and *tetrachromates*, $M^I_2Cr_4O_{13}$, are also known. These substances are, respectively, deep red and red-brown in color and are obtained from highly acidic solutions containing an excess of chromium(VI) oxide.

20.15 From highly alkaline solutions of molybdenum(VI) oxide, salts containing the "normal" molybdate(VI) ion, MoO_4^{2-}, can be obtained. As with the vanadates (see 19.13–14), increases in acidity of molybdate solutions promote the tendency for the formation of polymeric anions. Thus, salts have been isolated with ratios of $M^I_2O : MoO_3$ of $1 : 2$, $1 : 2.33$, $1 : 3$, $1 : 4$, $1 : 8$, and $1 : 10$. Most of these appear to be normal or acidic salts of either the *paramolybdate* series, $M^I_6[Mo_7O_{24}]$, or of the *octamolybdate* series, $M^I_4[Mo_8O_{26}]$. Definitive data regarding the nature of the polymolybdate species in solution and also the structures of most of the solids which have been isolated are still lacking. The same applies to the polytungstates, which are discussed briefly below.

20.16 There is some evidence (not entirely conclusive) that the following changes occur on the addition of acids to alkaline solutions of tungsten(VI) oxide. Down to a pH of 8, "normal" tungstate(VI) ions, WO_4^{2-}, are present. Between pH 8 and 6, hexatungstate ions are formed, and these are present almost

$$6[WO_4]^{2-} + 7H^+ \rightleftharpoons [HW_6O_{21}]^{5-} + 3H_2O$$

exclusively between pH 6 and 4. With further increase in acidity the hydrogen hexatungstate ion is believed to be converted either to hexatungstate ions containing more hydrogen, *e.g.*, $[H_3W_6O_{21}]^{3-}$, or to dodecatungstate ions by the condensation

$$2[HW_6O_{21}]^{5-} + 4H^+ \rightleftharpoons [H_2W_{12}O_{40}]^{6-} + 2H_2O.$$

The transformation to $[H_3W_6O_{21}]^{3-}$ is favored in dilute solutions and that to $[H_2W_{12}O_{40}]^{6-}$ in concentrated solutions.

20.17 Three types of tungstate salts appear definitely to have been obtained. These are the "normal" tungstates with a composition $M^I_2O \cdot WO_3$, the *metatungstates*, having an $M^I_2O : WO_3$ ratio of 1 : 4, and the *paratungstates*, which have $12WO_3$ for every $5M^I_2O$. The latter two classes always contain water, which is believed to be bound in the anion, *e.g.*, $M^I_{10}[H_2W_{12}O_{42}]$ (for a paratungstate).

20.18 The chemistry of $+6$ molybdenum and tungsten is also characterized by the pronounced tendency to form *heteropoly* anionic species (see 6.114). These species differ from the (iso) polyanionic species considered above in that, whereas the iso species contain (in the formal sense) a single type of acid anhydride, *e.g.*, MoO_3 or WO_3, the heteropoly species commonly possess two different types of acid anhydrides, *e.g.*, $3(NH_4)_2O \cdot P_2O_5 \cdot 24MoO_3$. Heteropoly anions are found as constituents of both acids and salts.

20.19 A wide variety of acidic oxides are found associated with MoO_3 or WO_3 in heteropoly compounds, the most common being P_4O_{10}, SiO_2, and B_2O_3. The materials are invariably hydrated and commonly have an MoO_3 (or WO_3) : E (E = P, Si, B, etc.) ratio of six or twelve, although ratios between these limits are known. The heteropoly compounds are generally named in accordance with this ratio. Thus, the substance of the empirical formula $H_2SiW_{12}O_{40}$ is known as 12-tungstosilicic acid. The heteropoly acids and salts are obtained by direct union of their components in acid solution. For example, a hot solution of potassium polytungstate is capable of dissolving hydrous silicon dioxide; from the resulting solution there can be crystallized a tungstosilicate of the empirical formula $SiO_2 \cdot 12WO_3 \cdot 8KOH \cdot 10H_2O$. Treatment of this substance with excess acid removes the alkali to give a tungstosilicic acid with the $SiO_2 : WO_3$ ratio unchanged.

20.20 The structures of heteropoly acids and their salts are extremely complicated (see 6.114 *ff.*).

Binary Halides **20.21** Hexahalides are unknown for chromium. Molybdenum forms only the hexafluoride, whereas the fluoride, chloride, and bromide are known for tungsten. It is obvious that since molybdenum and tungsten have very similar covalent radii (Table 20.1) the nonexistence of molybdenum hexachloride and bromide cannot be explained on steric grounds.

20.22 All of the hexahalides can be prepared by direct union of the elements. Tungsten(VI) fluoride has also been obtained by reaction of arsenic(III) or antimony(III) fluoride and tungsten hexachloride, the latter being made most conveniently by the chlorination of the trioxide.

20.23 The hexafluorides are colorless, extremely volatile (b.p.: MoF_6, 35°; WF_6, 19.5°) substances possessing normal vapor densities. They are highly reactive, attacking (by fluorination) all but the most noble metals at room temperature. They are attacked violently by water to yield oxyfluorides or hydrous trioxides. Although the hydrolytic reaction demonstrates that the hexafluorides are coordinatively unsaturated, no stable complex compounds involving coordination of these halides with donor molecules have been prepared. Compounds of the compositions $M^I_2[MoF_8]$ and $M^I_2[WF_8]$ (M = K, Rb, Cs) have been obtained by condensing molybdenum or tungsten hexafluoride on the solid alkali metal fluorides.[1] Molybdenum hexafluoride differs from the tungsten compound in one major respect. The latter reacts by halogen exchange with such volatile chlorides as antimony(V) chloride and phosphoryl chloride to yield the hexachloride; a similar reaction with molybdenum hexafluoride gives the pentachloride.

20.24 Tungsten hexachloride (b.p. 347°) and hexabromide (subl.) are intensely colored, the solids being dark violet and black, respectively. These compounds are considerably less stable thermally than the fluoride, the chloride being slightly dissociated at the boiling point and the bromide so unstable toward even gentle warming that its vapor density cannot be determined. Both are readily soluble in common nonhydroxylic organic solvents. The bromide is readily hydrolyzed, but the chloride is more resistant than the fluoride to hydrolysis, apparently being attacked by water only at temperatures above 60°. Investigations of the gaseous and solid forms of the hexachloride show this substance to possess an octahedral structure, with a W—Cl distance in the vapor of 2.26 Å (calculated for a simple covalent bond, 2.29 Å).

Oxyhalides and Derivatives **20.25** In their maximum oxidation state the elements of the chromium family form simple oxyhalides which are molecular in character. The types of compounds which have been isolated include CrO_2X_2, MoO_2X_2, WO_2X_2, $MoOX_4$, and WOX_4. The specific compounds which definitely have been prepared are listed in Table 20.3, along with their reported melting and boiling points. The absence of iodides is worthy of note.

TABLE 20.3

Melting and Boiling Points of Chromium Family Oxyhalides

Compound	Melting Point, °C.	Boiling Point, °C.	Compound	Melting Point, °C.	Boiling Point, °C.
CrO_2F_2	31.6	29.6 (subl.)	WO_2Br_2		
MoO_2F_2			$MoOF_4$	98	ca. 180
CrO_2Cl_2	−96.5	116.7	WOF_4	110	190
MoO_2Cl_2			$WOCl_4$	209	233
WO_2Cl_2			$WOBr_4$	277	327

[1] COX, SHARP, and SHARPE, *J. Chem. Soc.*, 1956, p. 1242.

20.26 Chromyl fluoride, CrO_2F_2, can be obtained in the pure condition as violet crystals by reaction between chromium(VI) oxide and anhydrous hydrogen fluoride in an apparatus constructed from copper, silica-free glass, and Kel-F tubing.[2] The corresponding molybdenum compound is best made by the action of hydrogen fluoride on molybdenyl chloride, MoO_2Cl_2. Little is known specifically regarding reactions of chromyl fluoride, but it would be expected to have powerful oxidizing properties. The molybdenum compound is a colorless hygroscopic substance, insoluble in toluene and ether but readily soluble in arsenic(III) and silicon chlorides. Compared to the hexafluoride, molybdenyl fluoride is relatively inert.

20.27 Chromyl chloride (a deep red liquid) is formed in good yield by the action of a dichromate or chromium(VI) oxide on hydrochloric acid in concentrated sulfuric acid medium.

$$Na_2Cr_2O_7 + 6HCl \overset{H_2SO_4}{=} 2CrO_2Cl_2 + 2NaCl + 3H_2O$$

The analogous molybdenum and tungsten compounds (as well as WO_2Br_2) are formed by direct combination of the halogen with the dioxides (see 20.38) at elevated temperatures. Tungsten oxytetrahalides (WOX_4) are invariably produced along with the less volatile WO_2X_2 compounds and separation is readily effected by fractionation. Chromyl chloride is not only more volatile than the molybdenum and tungsten compounds but is also much more reactive, being a very powerful oxidizing agent. Chromyl and molybdenyl chlorides are readily decomposed by water (*e.g.*, $CrO_2Cl_2 + 2H_2O = H_2CrO_4 + 2HCl$), whereas tungstenyl chloride and bromide are only slowly hydrolyzed. In the vapor state, chromyl chloride has a tetrahedral structure which is considerably distorted, the following dimensions having been reported:[3] Cr—Cl distance, 2.12 Å; Cr—O distance, 1.57 Å; Cl—Cr—Cl angle, $113 \pm 3°$; Cl—Cr—O angle, $109 \pm 3°$; O—Cr—O angle, $105 \pm 4°$.

20.28 Oxytetrahalides are formed by molybdenum and tungsten; for the former element only the fluoride appears to have been definitely characterized, whereas for tungsten all but the iodide are known. The colorless fluorides, $MoOF_4$ and WOF_4, can be prepared by the partial hydrolysis of the hexafluorides; the tungsten compound can also be obtained by halogen exchange between hydrogen fluoride and the oxytetrachloride. The formation of tungsten oxytetrachloride and bromide in admixture with the WO_2X_2 compounds has already been mentioned; it is probable that the oxytetrahalides result from the decomposition of the tungstenyl compounds.

$$2WO_2X_2 = WO_3 + WOX_4$$

The oxytetrahalides are all fairly volatile substances (Table 20.3) and are extremely hygroscopic, being converted to trioxides by water. The oxytetrafluorides, like the hexafluorides, are fluorinating agents, but ordinarily their

[2] ENGELBRICHT and GROSSE, *J. Am. Chem. Soc.*, **74**, 5262 (1952).
[3] PALMER, *J. Am. Chem. Soc.*, **60**, 2360 (1938).

action is milder. Tungsten oxytetrafluoride has been shown to be relatively stable toward heat, the vapor density between 350 and 440° being normal.

20.29 Oxyhalide complexes of the elements of the chromium family in their maximum oxidation state are known. For chromium, only halochromates of the type $M^I[CrO_3X]$ appear to exist; fluoro and chloro compounds have definitely been prepared, but there is some question regarding the existence of the bromo and iodo derivatives. In view of the strong oxidizing power of chromium(VI), it would appear most unlikely that iodo compounds can be made. Alkali metal fluoro and chlorochromates are prepared by boiling a solution of metal dichromate with an excess of the halogen acid. The halochromates are readily decomposed by water, but can be recrystallized from the dilute halogen acid. $[CrO_3F]^-$ has been shown to have a tetrahedral configuration.

20.30 For hexapositive molybdenum and tungsten only oxyfluoride complexes have been prepared. For molybdenum three types of compounds have been reported: $M^I_2[MoO_3F_2]$, $M^I_2[MoO_2F_4]$, and $M^I_3[MoO_2F_5]$. $[MoO_2F_4]^{2-}$ is octahedral. The principal types of fluorotungstates are $M^I[WO_2F_3(H_2O)]$, $M^I_2[WO_2F_4]$, and $M^I_3[WO_3F_3]$, with the first being the most common. The oxyfluoro complexes of molybdenum or tungsten are obtained from solutions of molybdates or tungstates in hydrofluoric acid.

The Pentapositive State

20.31 Although +5 chromium is uncommon, a number of compounds containing the element in this oxidation state have been prepared.[4] The formation of Cr_2O_5 as an intermediate stage in the thermal decomposition of CrO_3 has been mentioned (see 20.13). Chromium(V) fluoride is produced in small yield as a sublimate on reaction of fluorine with a 3 : 1 molar mixture of potassium chloride and chromium(III) chloride, the main product being K_2CrF_6. The oxofluorochromates(V), $KCrOF_4$ and $AgCrOF_4$, are obtained by the action of bromine trifluoride on mixtures of metal chloride with chromium(VI) oxide. These substances are extremely sensitive to water, undergoing immediate decomposition to tri- and hexapositive chromium. Oxychloro complexes of the types $M^I_2[CrOCl_5]$ (M = K, Rb, Cs, NH$_4$) and M^ICrOCl_4 (M = pyridinium, quinolinium) have been reported to be formed by reduction of the trioxide by very concentrated hydrochloric acid in the presence of metal chloride at 0°. The compound $Cs_2[CrOCl_5]$ forms mixed crystals with the corresponding niobium(V) complex. Oxochromates(V) of the compositions $M^{II}_3(CrO_4)_2$ and $M^{II}_5(CrO_4)_3OH$ (M = Ba, Sr) have been characterized. The first type is made by reaction between alkaline earth metal carbonate and chromate at elevated temperatures in a nitrogen atmosphere. The barium compound is

$$4BaCrO_4 + 2BaCO_3 = 2Ba_3(CrO_4)_2 + 2CO_2 + O_2$$

a green-black substance which disproportionates into chromium(III) and chromium(VI) in dilute acids. Evidence that it contains pentapositive chromium

---

[4] KLEINBERG, *J. Chem. Educ.*, **29**, 324 (1952); **33**, 73 (1956).

consists in the great similarity in its X-ray pattern to that of $Ba_3(PO_4)_2$, and also in the fact that the molar susceptibility is 1.71 Bohr magnetons, corresponding to the one unpaired electron expected for an outer orbital complex of chromium(V). Compounds of the type $M^{II}_5(CrO_4)_3OH$ are obtained by heating a mixture of equivalent quantities of metal chromate(VI) and hydroxide in a nitrogen atmosphere and then extracting excess hydroxide with methanol. The X-ray patterns of these compounds are very like that of hydroxyl-apatite (phosphorite), $3Ca_3(PO_4)_2 \cdot Ca(OH)_2$.

20.32 Various types of compounds of pentapositive molybdenum and tungsten have been obtained, the anionic complexes being the most numerous. Among simple compounds, the existence of the oxides, E_2O_5, appears doubtful, although Mo_2O_5 has been reported to have been prepared by the reduction of the trioxide with the metal at high temperatures. Only one pentahalide, $MoCl_5$, is known for molybdenum. This is formed as a dark green substance (m.p., 194°; b.p., 268°) by direct combination of the elements at elevated temperatures. The pentachloride is thermally stable at least to 350°, at which temperature the dark red vapor exhibits a normal density. In the vapor state the pentachloride has the structure of a trigonal bipyramid, with a Mo—Cl distance of 2.27 Å (calculated for a simple covalent bond, 2.29 Å). In the fused state, as well as in the solid, the pentachloride is essentially a nonconductor of the electric current. It reacts violently with water, and solvolytic reactions also occur with hydroxylic organic liquids. Toward ether, the chloride acts as an acceptor molecule to give $MoCl_5 \cdot 2(C_2H_5)_2O$. When heated in air, the pentachloride is converted to molybdenyl chloride, MoO_2Cl_2. For tungsten, both the pentachloride and bromide have been prepared. The former is readily obtained as dark green needles from the thermal decomposition of the hexachloride, and the black pentabromide can be made by direct union of the elements at red heat, or by reaction between the hexachloride and hydrogen bromide at 250–300°, the hexabromide which is first formed being unstable in this temperature range. Both halides are extremely poor conductors of electric current and are soluble in a variety of organic solvents. They are easily hydrolyzed by water, but the products of hydrolysis have not been characterized.

20.33 A fairly large number of complexes containing pentapositive molybdenum and tungsten have been prepared, but only the oxyhalide and cyanide compounds are discussed here. Although no completely halogenated derivatives are known, complex oxyhalides have been obtained for +5 molybdenum with fluorine, chlorine, and bromine, and for tungsten only with chlorine and bromine. The most common type of mononuclear oxyfluoro complex of pentapositive molybdenum has the formula $M^I_2[MoOF_5]$; at least one polynuclear complex type, $M^I_5[Mo_3O_3F_{14}]$, has been made. The main classes of chloro and bromo complexes of +5 molybdenum and tungsten have the compositions $M^I_2[EOX_5]$ and M^IEOX_4, where M is usually an alkali metal or substituted ammonium derivative. The complexes are conveniently obtained by reaction of metal halide with a solution of molybdenum(V) or tungsten(V) in the appropriate hydrohalic acid; the pentapositive state of the element can be produced

by electrolytic reduction of molybdate or tungstate in hydrohalic acid solution.*
With molybdenum, the halo compounds of the class M^IMoOX_4 are usually
hydrated and are presumed to contain $[MoOX_4(H_2O)]^-$. The corresponding
tungsten compounds are known in anhydrous as well as in hydrated forms. All
of the halo complexes dissolve in water with extensive solvolysis. Solutions of
the tungsten complexes are readily oxidized by air. Chloro compounds of the
type $M^I_2[MoOCl_5]$ are paramagnetic, having moments corresponding to the
presence of one unpaired electron.

20.34 The cyano complexes are of interest in that in them molybdenum and
tungsten exhibit a coordination number of eight — $M^I_3[E(CN)_8]$. The compounds are obtained as yellow to orange materials from the cyano complexes
of the elements in the tetrapositive state (*e.g.*, $K_4[Mo(CN)_8]$) by oxidation with
permanganate ion. This is an unusual reaction since permanganate oxidizes
lower oxidation states of both molybdenum and tungsten in all other compounds
to the hexapositive condition. The octacyano complexes have been isolated as
free acids — $H_3Mo(CN)_8 \cdot 3H_2O$ and $H_3W(CN)_8 \cdot 6H_2O$ — as well as in the
form of salts. The compounds are readily converted to the cyano complexes
containing the elements in the +4 state (see below).

The Tetrapositive State

20.35 Very few compounds of chromium(IV) have been made. The simple
fluoride CrF_4 is the main product of reaction between elementary fluorine and
anhydrous chromium(III) fluoride or chloride. The tetrafluoride is a brown
solid which sublimes readily (without decomposition) and gives an appreciable
concentration of blue-gray vapor at 150°. It is immediately decomposed by
water to give chromium(III) and (VI). The preparation of the completely
fluorinated complex K_2CrF_6 has been described (see 20.31). It is a flesh-colored
solid which rapidly turns yellow on standing, and on heating disproportionates
to give chromium(V) fluoride and an unidentified chromium(III) compound.
K_2CrF_6 gives an X-ray pattern very similar to that of K_2MnF_6; this would
appear to leave little doubt that chromium is in the tetrapositive state.

20.36 Although a substance of the empirical formula CrO_2 is an intermediate
in the thermal decomposition of CrO_3 (see 20.13), there is some question that it
contains tetrapositive chromium. However, alkaline earth metal salts derived
from a chromium(IV) oxide have definitely been obtained by reactions such as
those shown below.[3]

$$\text{(a)} \quad Ba_3[Cr(OH)_6]_2 + Ba(OH)_2 \underset{N_2 \text{ atm.}}{\overset{1000°}{=}} 2Ba_2CrO_4 + 6H_2O + H_2$$

$$\text{(b)} \quad BaCrO_4 + Cr_2O_3 + 5Ba(OH)_2 \underset{N_2 \text{ atm.}}{\overset{900-1000°}{=}} 3Ba_2CrO_4 + 5H_2O$$

If the reactants in (a) are brought together in the proportion to give an atomic

* Although the addition of excess strong acid to molybdate and tungstate solutions causes
molybdic and tungstic acids to precipitate (see 20.13), under appropriate conditions metastable
solutions can be obtained.

ratio Ba : Cr $\geq$ 3, the product is barium pentoxochromate(IV), Ba_3CrO_5. The oxochromate(IV) compounds are green substances which decompose slowly in water and in dilute hydrochloric acid to give chromium(III) and (VI). Proof that the chromium is in the tetrapositive state is offered by magnetic and X-ray data. Thus Ba_2CrO_4 has a molar susceptibility of 2.82 Bohr magnetons (theoretical is 2.83 for an outer orbital complex with two unpaired electrons) and gives an X-ray pattern which corresponds well with that of Ba_2TiO_4.

20.37 A number of simple compounds and anionic complexes of +4 molybdenum and tungsten have been described. The simple compounds include tetrahalides and the dioxides. Of the possible tetrahalides, only molybdenum tetrachloride and the tetrachloride and iodide of tungsten have definitely been identified. All the tetrahalides are hydrolyzed by water. The tungsten compounds are nonvolatile and infusible, the chloride when heated disproportionating to the pentachloride and "dichloride," and the iodide being thermally stable. Molybdenum tetrachloride is a volatile brown powder which when heated tends to decompose into the trichloride and pentachloride. The tetrachloride can be formed by reaction between the dioxide and a solution of chlorine in carbon tetrachloride at 250°. It is also a product of the thermal decomposition of the trichloride (see 20.49). Both tungsten tetrachloride and tetraiodide are produced from the hexachloride, the former by reduction with hydrogen at high temperatures and the latter by heating with liquid hydrogen iodide under pressure.

20.38 The dioxides of molybdenum and tungsten can be prepared in a variety of ways, a common method being the carefully controlled reduction of the trioxides by means of hydrogen at temperatures not so high that the elementary substances are formed. Both dioxides are brown substances which are readily oxidized, e.g., by concentrated nitric acid to EO_3 and by elementary chlorine to EO_2Cl_2. They are unaffected by solutions of alkalies and hydrochloric and sulfuric acids.

20.39 A relatively small number of complex compounds of +4 molybdenum and tungsten are known, and in all but certain of the cyano complexes the elements exhibit a coordination number of six, e.g., $K_2[W(OH)Cl_5]$, $K_2[Mo(SCN)_6]$. The hydroxopentachlorotungstate(IV) complex is formed on reduction (by tin) of a solution of tungsten(VI) oxide in concentrated hydrochloric acid in the presence of potassium chloride. The red aqueous solution is stable toward air and the potassium salt is obtained from the solution as dark green crystals. No analogous molybdenum compound has been reported. Two series of cyano complexes, e.g., $M^I_4[E(CN)_8]$ and $M^I_4[EO_2(CN)_4]$, have been identified. It is remarkable that these can be obtained from solutions of the elements in either the tripositive or pentapositive state merely by addition of an excess of cyanide ion. The cyano complexes are extremely stable toward hydrolysis. $[Mo(CN)_8]^{4-}$ has been shown to have a dodecahedral structure. This fact, coupled with the diamagnetism of the octacyano compounds, demonstrates that the binding in the anion is of the D^4SP^3 inner orbital type.

The Tripositive State

20.40 There are two striking differences in the chemistry of +3 chromium as compared with the corresponding state for molybdenum and tungsten: (1) simple cations exist for chromium, but not for tungsten and probably not for molybdenum; (2) tripositive chromium is stable toward oxidation in acidic solution, whereas +3 molybdenum and tungsten are readily converted to the hexapositive condition. Tripositive molybdenum and tungsten are not at all similar; the former can exist in simple compounds such as halides and a sulfide as well as in a variety of complex compounds, but the latter is known only in the form of salts of the acid $H_3W_2Cl_9$.

20.41 Probably the foremost characteristic of tripositive chromium is its extraordinarily great tendency to form complex compounds, a tendency exceeded by no element and equalled perhaps by only +3 cobalt and +4 platinum. Although the vast majority of +3 chromium compounds are complex in character, a large number of simple compounds are known and the more important of these are described briefly below.

20.42 Chromium(III) oxide (green) is formed by the thermal decomposition of ammonium dichromate or the hydrous oxide, $Cr_2O_3 \cdot xH_2O$, the latter being obtained by the careful addition of alkali to a solution of a chromium(III) salt. The anhydrous oxide (if it has not been too strongly ignited) and the hydrous oxide are soluble in solutions of strong acids and bases, reaction with the former yielding solutions containing the $Cr(H_2O)_6^{3+}$ cation and with the latter the so-called chromite ion, CrO_2^- (better $Cr(OH)_4^-$).

20.43 Among the trihalides of chromium, the fluoride, chloride, and bromide are known both in the anhydrous condition and also in the form of hydrates, whereas the iodide has been obtained pure only as the 9-hydrate. The anhydrous compounds can be prepared by the usual methods, e.g., $Cr_2O_3 + C + X_2$; $Cr + X_2$. They are highly colored substances of low volatility. The chloride and bromide are definitely not ionic but consist of crystals containing two-dimensional $(CrX_3)_n$ layers, with van der Waals forces holding the layers together.[5] A number of hydrated forms of the fluoride exist, of which those with 6 and 3 water molecules are best known. There is little doubt that in the 6-hydrate the $[Cr(H_2O)_6]^{3+}$ ion is present; the 3-hydrate is probably best formulated as $[Cr(H_2O)_6][CrF_6]$. It is a curious fact that although the anhydrous trichloride is insoluble in water, it can be readily solubilized by the addition of trace amounts of reducing agents, e.g., $CrCl_2$, $SnCl_2$, $FeCl_2$. Three different compounds of the composition $CrCl_3 \cdot 6H_2O$ can be obtained from aqueous solution; these have been shown to be the hydrate isomers $[Cr(H_2O)_6]Cl_3$ (violet), $[Cr(H_2O)_5Cl]Cl_2 \cdot H_2O$ (pale green), and $[Cr(H_2O)_4Cl_2]Cl \cdot 2H_2O$ (dark green). There are two isomeric hexahydrates of the tribromide: $[Cr(H_2O)_6]Br_3$ (violet) and $[Cr(H_2O)_4Br_2]Br \cdot 2H_2O$ (green).

[5] WELLS, *Structural Inorganic Chemistry*, 2nd Edition, Oxford University Press, London, 1950, pp. 116, 278, 279.

20.44 An anhydrous compound as well as a variety of hydrated sulfates of tripositive chromium have been characterized. From aqueous solutions of the sulfate a number of alums have been obtained, the most common one being *chrome alum*, $K_2SO_4 \cdot Cr_2(SO_4)_3 \cdot 24H_2O$.

20.45 Aqueous solutions containing cationic chromium(III) are acidic as a result of hydrolysis.

$$[Cr(H_2O)_6]^{3+} + H_2O \rightleftharpoons [Cr(H_2O)_5OH]^{2+} + H_3O^+$$

20.46 An enormous number of complexes of tripositive chromium have been prepared. In the very great majority of these compounds the element exhibits its maximum coordination number of six. Among the cationic complexes, hydrates have already been mentioned. The most numerous of the cationic complexes are mononuclear and contain nitrogen donors, *e.g.*, $[Cr(NH_3)_6]Cl_3$ and $[Cr\,en_3]Cl_3$. The six coordination positions in these complexes can be taken up by two (or more) different ligands, *e.g.*, $[Cr(NH_3)_3(H_2O)Cl_2]Cl$ and $[Cr(NH_3)_5H_2O]Cl_3$. Polynuclear, particularly binuclear, chromium(III) ammines are also of importance; in these compounds the central chromium atoms are usually bridged by the hydroxo, oxo, or amido group, *e.g.*,

$$[(NH_3)_5Cr \overset{\displaystyle H}{\underset{\displaystyle \diagup \; \diagdown}{\overset{\displaystyle O}{}}} Cr(NH_3)_5]X_5.$$

20.47 In addition to the cationic species, neutral and anionic complexes are known. The neutral (*i.e.*, nonelectrolytic) complexes are relatively few in number; for example, they form as shown when chromium(III) combines with β-diketones. Anionic complexes are numerous, the best defined type being $M^I_3[CrX_6]$, where X is, *e.g.*, CN^-, SCN^-, or $\frac{1}{2}C_2O_4^{2-}$. Halo complexes are rare; among those which have been reported are $M^I_3[CrF_6]$, $M^I_2[CrX_5(H_2O)]$ (X = F, Cl, Br) and $M^I_3[CrCl_6]$. One of the most common anionic complexes is Reinecke's salt: $NH_4[Cr(NH_3)_2(NCS)_4]$.

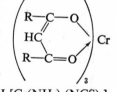

20.48 There appears to be little question that most of the complexes of chromium(III) are of the inner orbital variety, with D^2SP^3 binding. The complexes of this type, *e.g.*, $K_3[Cr(CN)_6]$, are relatively inert toward substitution.

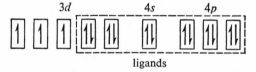

ligands

20.49 The simple compounds of tripositive molybdenum which are definite are almost exclusively halides and oxyhalides. Of the trihalides, the slightly volatile chloride and bromide have been obtained, the former by reduction of the pentachloride with hydrogen at 250° and the latter by direct combination of the elements at about 400°. The trihalides are inert toward water and most organic solvents but form addition compounds with pyridine, *e.g.*, $MoBr_3 \cdot 3py$. The trichloride on strong heating disproportionates into the di- and tetrachloride. It has been reported that strongly reducing, purple-red aqueous solutions of the trichloride are formed by the reduction of molybdenum(VI) in concentrated hydrochloric acid medium at a mercury cathode, but the exact nature of the molybdenum(III) species present is unknown. Addition of alkali metal chloride to such solutions results in the precipitation of chloro complexes of the types $M^I_3[MoCl_6]$ and $M^I_2[MoCl_5(H_2O)]$. Treatment of solutions of molybdenum(III) with alkali gives a black material approximating $Mo(OH)_3$ in composition and possessing powerful reducing properties.

20.50 The oxyhalides of tripositive molybdenum have the general formula $MoOX \cdot 4H_2O$ (X = F, Cl, Br). The chloro compound exists in brown and green forms, both of which are obtained from solutions of molybdenum(III) in hydrochloric acid by precipitation with acetone. Both forms dissolve in water to give solutions which initially are nonconducting, but which on hydrolysis give ionic species. The bromo compound is made in a manner similar to that employed for the chloro compound, and the oxyfluoride is formed from the latter substance by reaction with ammonium fluoride.

20.51 In addition to the chloro complexes noted above, complexes of +3 molybdenum with fluorine ($M^IMoF_4 \cdot H_2O$), with thiocyanate ($M^I_3Mo[SCN]_6$), and with cyanide (*e.g.*, $K_4[Mo(CN)_7 \cdot H_2O]$) have been obtained by methods related to that for the preparation of the chloro complexes. These compounds are all potent reducing agents.

20.52 No simple compounds of tripositive tungsten have been identified. Indeed, only one compound type, that containing the $W_2Cl_9^{3-}$ ion, is known for tungsten in this oxidation state. Aqueous solutions of this ion are produced by the electrolytic reduction of tungsten(VI) in concentrated hydrochloric acid. From solution a number of salts have been obtained, *e.g.*, $M^I_3[W_2Cl_9]$ (M = K, NH_4, Rb, Cs, Tl(I)), $[Co(NH_3)_6][W_2Cl_9]$, $[Cr(NH_3)_6][W_2Cl_9]$. When dry, the compounds are stable toward atmospheric oxidation. Their solubility in water diminishes with increasing cationic size; thus the thallium(I) compound is practically insoluble. In solution, they undergo slow hydrolysis and air oxidation at room temperature. X-ray examination has disclosed that the $W_2Cl_9^{3-}$ ion consists of two octahedra having one face in common. The ion is diamagnetic.

The Dipositive State

20.53 As with the elements in the tripositive state, there are notable differences in the chemistry of +2 chromium as compared with dipositive molybdenum and tungsten. A variety of simple and complex compounds of chromium are known and the great majority are strong and rapid reducing agents in both acidic and alkaline media. On the other hand there are no simple compounds of +2 molybdenum and tungsten, the only substances known being complex "dihalides" and their derivatives. The molybdenum compounds are extremely stable toward oxidation, the tungsten compounds much less so.

20.54 Tripositive chromium (particularly the violet ion, $Cr(H_2O)_6^{3+}$) is reduced electrolytically or by means of zinc and dilute acids to blue solutions containing hydrated Cr^{2+}. The +2 cation is a potent reducing agent, being readily oxidized by air, and even capable, under suitable conditions, *e.g.*, in the

$$Cr^{2+} = Cr^{3+} + e^- \qquad E^\circ = 0.41 \text{ v.}$$

presence of a platinum catalyst, of liberating hydrogen from solution. From the blue solutions a number of chromium(II) compounds, *e.g.*, $CrSO_4 \cdot 5H_2O$, $Cr(C_2H_3O_2)_2$, $CrCl_2 \cdot 4H_2O$, have been isolated. Addition of strong base gives an unstable yellow precipitate ($Cr(OH)_2$?) which liberates hydrogen from water.

20.55 All of the anhydrous dihalides have been prepared by conventional methods. They are substances of slight volatility. It has been shown that

$$CrCl_2 + 2HF(aq.) = CrF_2 + 2HCl$$
$$2CrCl_3 + H_2 \overset{\text{heat}}{=} 2CrCl_2 + 2HCl$$
$$Cr + I_2 \overset{800^\circ}{=} CrI_2$$

the vapor of the dichloride at about 1500° consists largely of Cr_2Cl_4 molecules.

20.56 As expected, the ability of dipositive chromium to form complex compounds is much weaker than for the element in the tripositive condition. Included among such compounds which have been described are a variety of ammines (*e.g.*, $CrCl_2 \cdot 6NH_3$, $5NH_3$, $3NH_3$, and $2NH_3$; complexes with ethylenediamine, pyridine, hydrazine, etc.), thiocyanato complexes ($Na_4[Cr(CNS)_6]$), cyanides ($K_4[Cr(CN)_6]$), and others. Magnetic measurements indicate that complexes with ammonia, ethylenediamine, and thiocyanate ion are of the outer orbital type, with four unpaired electrons, whereas that with cyanide ion is of the inner orbital (D^2SP^3) type, with two unpaired electrons. The various complexes, with the exception of those with hydrazine, are more or less unstable in water and air. The hydrazine complexes which have been prepared (*e.g.*, $CrCl_2 \cdot 2N_2H_4$, $CrI_2 \cdot 2N_2H_4$) are relatively insoluble in water and unusually stable toward atmospheric oxidation.

20.57 The "dihalides" of molybdenum and tungsten which have been prepared include the chloride and bromide of the former and the chloride, bromide, and iodide of the latter. Molybdenum "dichloride" and "dibromide" can be obtained by direct union of the elements at appropriate high temperatures or by thermal decomposition of higher halides, *e.g.*, of $MoCl_3$. The corresponding tungsten "dihalides" are formed by reduction of the pentahalides with hydrogen at elevated temperatures. The "diiodide" is the product of union of the elements at red heat.

20.58 The "dihalides" are colored solids which are infusible and nonvolatile. The molybdenum compounds are insoluble in water and stable toward acids.

They exhibit little reducing power. The tungsten compounds, however, liberate hydrogen from water and possess strong reducing power. Thus, the heated "dichloride" converts nitric acid vapor to ammonium nitrate.

20.59 It has been demonstrated that the "dihalides" have a molecular complexity corresponding to Mo_6X_{12}. One third of the halogen is attached much more loosely than the remainder. For example, treatment of Mo_6Cl_{12} with silver nitrate results in the precipitation of four chlorine atoms and the formation of $[Mo_6Cl_8](NO_3)_4$, and reaction with strong base gives $[Mo_6Cl_8](OH)_4$, which can be isolated from solution as the 14-hydrate. Moreover, the action of concentrated hydrobromic and hydriodic acids gives $[Mo_6Cl_8]Br_4$ and $[Mo_6Cl_8]I_4$, respectively, which are obtained from solution as the 6-hydrates. X-ray study of $[Mo_6Cl_8]^{4+}$ (*e.g.*, in $[Mo_6Cl_8](OH)_4 \cdot 14H_2O$) shows it to consist of eight chlorine atoms at the corners of a cube, with one molybdenum atom lying above the center of each of the six faces.

CHAPTER 21

THE MANGANESE FAMILY

Introduction

21.1 The manganese family, the fifth group of short transition series elements, consists of manganese, technetium, and rhenium, with the respective atomic numbers 25, 43, and 75 and ground state valence shell configurations corresponding to $(n - 1)d^5 ns^2$. Of these elements, the first and last occur in nature, manganese having been known as a distinct element since 1774 and rhenium first having been isolated in 1924. Technetium, discovered in 1937, is produced only in nuclear transmutations. A number of properties of the elements of the family are listed in Table 21.1.

TABLE 21.1

Some Properties of the Manganese Family Elements

	Mn	Tc	Re
Natural isotopes	55	None	185, 187 *†
Density, g./cc.	7.21	11.5	20.9
Melting point, °C.	1247	——	3150
Boiling point, °C.	2030	——	——
Ionic radius, in crystals, M^{7+}, Å	0.46	——	——
Covalent radius, Å	1.168	——	1.278
Ionization potential, volts 1st electron	7.432	7.23	7.87
Electrode potential, $E°$, in volts, for $Mn = Mn^{2+} + 2e^-$ $Re + 2H_2O = ReO_2 + 4H^+ + 4e^-$ $M + 4H_2O = MO_4^- + 8H^+ + 7e^-$	1.18	 −0.472	 −0.260 −0.367

* More abundant isotope
† Radioactive; β^- emitter

21.2 As would be expected, much less is known of the chemistry of technetium and rhenium than of manganese. Our knowledge of the low oxidation states of rhenium is particularly sketchy, and information on the chemistry of technetium is just beginning to be accumulated, weighable amounts of this element having become available only within the past few years.

21.3 The maximum oxidation state for the group is $+7$, which for manganese is a strong oxidizing state in both acidic and basic solution. Heptapositive technetium and rhenium are considerably more stable. The oxides, M_2O_7, corresponding to the maximum oxidation state, are completely acidic.

21.4 The elements exhibit a wide multiplicity of lower oxidation states. As is the general situation within a transition group, the lower oxidation states are formed most readily by the first member and become less stable with increasing atomic number of the element. Moreover, the tendency of the elements in the lower oxidation states to exist as simple cationic species diminishes in the same direction. This point has been strikingly exemplified in the chemistry of the chromium family (Ch. 20).

21.5 All the possible lower oxidation states from $+6$ to $+1$ have been found for both manganese and rhenium, and, in addition, for the latter element a most unusual state for a metal, namely -1, has been characterized. Although there is little doubt that technetium is capable of exhibiting the same wide variety of lower oxidation states as manganese and rhenium, up to the present only the preparation of tetrapositive technetium compounds has been described, *e.g.*, TcO_2, K_2TcCl_6.

21.6 Of the lower oxidation states of manganese, the $+4$ and $+2$ are the most common. The oxide corresponding to the former state, MnO_2, is almost entirely acidic in character and no simple cationic species derived from this oxide exist. Aside from the dioxide, all the known compounds of tetrapositive manganese contain the element as part of an anionic complex, *e.g.*, MnO_3^{2-}, MnF_6^{2-}. Manganese in the $+4$ condition is a strong oxidant in acid solution. In its dipositive state, manganese forms an oxide, MnO, which is almost completely basic in character and which dissolves in aqueous solutions of acids to give hydrated Mn^{2+}. It is interesting that although in solution the $+2$ state is the most stable form of the element and is oxidized only by powerful oxidants, manganese(II) oxide and hydroxide are readily oxidized, *e.g.*, by atmospheric oxygen.

21.7 Compounds of $+6$ manganese are limited to the manganate(VI) salts, $M^I_2MnO_4$, which are stable only in alkaline solution. Only one species of pentapositive manganese, MnO_4^{3-} (manganate(V)), is known and, like manganate(VI), this possesses stability only in the presence of an excess of alkali.

GENERAL REFERENCES_____

HACKNEY, *J. Chem. Educ.*, **28**, 186 (1951).

LATIMER, *The Oxidation States of the Elements and Their Potentials in Aqueous Solutions*, 2nd Edition, Prentice-Hall, Inc., New York, 1952, Ch. 15.

REMY, *Treatise on Inorganic Chemistry* (translated and amended by Anderson), Elsevier Publishing Company, Amsterdam, 1956, Vol. II, Ch. 6.

SIDGWICK, *The Chemical Elements and Their Compounds*, Oxford University Press, London, 1950, pp. 1262–1315.

In neutral and acidic media, decomposition of both manganate(VI) and (V) occurs, yielding manganese(IV) and (VII) as products. The only compounds of tripositive manganese exhibiting even a fair degree of stability are anionic complexes. The oxide, Mn_2O_3, is basic in character and dissolves in mineral acids under the appropriate conditions, with the initial formation of the highly unstable $+3$ cation. One compound of $+1$ manganese, $K_5[Mn(CN)_6]$, has been unequivocally characterized.

21.8 Of the lower oxidation states of rhenium the $+4$ state is by far the most common and the most stable and ranks second in importance to the $+7$ state in the chemistry of the element. Only a few binary compounds of tetra-positive rhenium have been isolated (*e.g.*, ReO_2, ReF_4, ReS_2, $ReSe_2$), and they are definitely covalent in nature. In the majority of its compounds $+4$ rhenium appears as part of an anionic complex, *e.g.*, ReO_3^{2-}, ReX_6^{2-} (X = F, Cl, Br, I).

21.9 Hexapositive and pentapositive rhenium, like the corresponding states of manganese, have a very strong tendency to disproportionate into the tetra- and heptapositive states. The number of rhenium(VI) compounds reported is small, *e.g.*, ReO_3, ReF_6, and a few oxyhalides. Rhenium(V) compounds include $NaReO_3$, $ReCl_5$, a few complex fluorides and oxychlorides, and a cyano complex. The only "simple" substances which have been obtained pure for tripositive rhenium are the chloride and bromide. These are covalent compounds which apparently are dimeric in character. In addition to the simple halides, rhenium(III) forms complexes of the type $M^I[ReX_4]$ (X = Cl, Br). Compounds containing rhenium in oxidation states lower than $+3$ are extremely rare. Among those which have been reported are: for Re(II), $(NH_4)_2ReCl_4$ and $RepyCl_2$; for Re(I), $Re(CO)_5X$ (X = Cl, Br, I); and for Re($-$I), $KRe \cdot 4H_2O$. In aqueous solution the states below $+3$ are extremely unstable toward oxidation and therefore, little is known with certainty about them in this medium.

21.10 Oxidation potential diagrams for the elements of the manganese family in acid solution are given below.

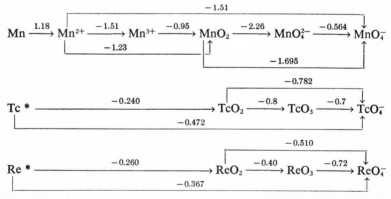

* These data are taken from an article by COBBLE, SMITH and BOYD, *J. Am. Chem. Soc.*, **75**, 5777 (1953). Potentials for changes involving TcO_3 are calculated values; there is no report of the preparation of this compound.

The Elements

21.11 Manganese is a relatively abundant element, constituting 0.085 per cent of the earth's crust. On the other hand, technetium has not been found in nature, and rhenium is an extremely rare element, occurring in the earth's crust only to the extent of about 1×10^{-7} per cent.

21.12 The most important manganese mineral is *pyrolusite* (MnO_2), from which the free metal can be obtained by reduction with aluminum. The reaction is, however, so highly exothermic that the dioxide is ordinarily converted to Mn_3O_4 by strong heating prior to reduction.

Technetium can be prepared in the form of radioactive isotopes by the bombardment of molybdenum(VI) oxide with neutrons.

$$_{42}^{98}\text{Mo} \xrightarrow{_0^1\text{n}} {}_{42}^{99}\text{Mo} \xrightarrow{-\beta^-} {}_{43}^{99}\text{Tc}$$

The technetium can be separated from the molybdenum target by sublimation as the volatile oxide Tc_2O_7. Technetium is found to the extent of about six per cent among the products of uranium-235 fission. The element can be recovered from fission-product solutions which have been acidified with hydrochloric acid by precipitation as the (black) sulfide Tc_2S_7. Reaction of the sulfide with ammoniacal hydrogen peroxide yields ammonium pertechnetate, NH_4TcO_4, which can be reduced to the metal at 600° by means of hydrogen.

21.13 Probably the main sources of rhenium are molybdenite (see 20.7) and the smelter residues from certain copper sulfide ores. The former may contain from 6×10^{-5} to 2×10^{-3} per cent rhenium. After appropriate oxidation, rhenium is isolated from its natural sources as the slightly soluble potassium perrhenate, $KReO_4$. The metal can be obtained by reduction of potassium or ammonium perrhenate with hydrogen at elevated temperatures.

21.14 Manganese is an active metal, displacing hydrogen from dilute solutions of strong, nonoxidizing acids and being converted to the dipositive state.

$$\text{Mn} = \text{Mn}^{2+} + 2e^- \qquad E° = 1.18 \text{ v.}$$

It is also brought into solution as Mn^{2+} by treatment with concentrated nitric or sulfuric acid. Union with oxygen at high temperatures gives Mn_3O_4 (*i.e.*, $MnO \cdot Mn_2O_3$) and with sulfur MnS. Combination with chlorine yields the dichloride and with fluorine a mixture of difluoride and trifluoride. At temperatures above 1200° the metal unites vigorously with nitrogen to form Mn_3N_2. The carbide Mn_3C is produced by heating the elements together. Elementary manganese appears to be unreactive toward hydrogen.

21.15 Technetium and rhenium are very much alike in chemical properties. Neither is affected by hydrochloric acid, but both dissolve rapidly in nitric acid with conversion to the +7 state ($HTcO_4$ and $HReO_4$). Air oxidation (*i.e.*, combustion) of the elemental substances produces volatile heptoxides (M_2O_7) (*cf.* manganese, above). Reaction of rhenium with excess fluorine and chlorine yields as main products the volatile halides ReF_6 and $ReCl_5$, respectively;

combination with bromine gives $ReBr_3$. Fusion of rhenium metal with sulfur results in the formation of the disulfide ReS_2. The metal is inert to hydrogen and nitrogen.

The Heptapositive State

21.16 The known compounds of the elements of the manganese family in the heptapositive state are the oxides and substances derived from them. It is interesting that no simple binary halides corresponding to this state have been obtained, although a few oxyhalides of rhenium(VII) and one of manganese(VII) have been described.

21.17 The heptoxides, M_2O_7, of all three elements have been prepared. The manganese compound is formed as a dense green-brown oil by reaction between potassium permanganate and concentrated sulfuric acid.

$$2KMnO_4 + H_2SO_4 = Mn_2O_7 + K_2SO_4 + H_2O$$

The analogous technetium [1] and rhenium oxides are produced by heating the elements in oxygen, a method not suitable for the preparation of manganese(VII) oxide in view of its thermal instability.

21.18 Manganese heptoxide begins to lose oxygen at $0°$ and decomposes with explosive violence when warmed. On the other hand, Tc_2O_7 (yellow, m.p. $119.5°$) and Re_2O_7 (yellow [stable form], m.p. $220°$) sublime without loss of oxygen, the rhenium compound exhibiting a normal vapor density in the neighborhood of $500°$.

21.19 The oxides all dissolve readily in water, giving solutions which are strongly acidic. Although no acids have been isolated from the manganese and rhenium solutions, evaporation of aqueous solutions of Tc_2O_7 yields dark red crystals of the composition $Tc_2O_7 \cdot H_2O$ (*i.e.*, $HTcO_4$).

21.20 The elements in their heptapositive state appear in salts as constituents of oxyanions: MnO_4^- (permanganate); TcO_4^- (pertechnetate); ReO_4^- (perrhenate) and ReO_5^{3-} (meso-perrhenate).* Permanganates can be obtained by the oxidation of manganese(II) or manganese dioxide by relatively strong oxidants.

$$MnO_2 + 4OH^- = MnO_4^- + 2H_2O + 3e^- \qquad E_B^\circ = -0.588 \text{ v.}$$

The medium must be alkaline but too large an excess of hydroxide ion must be avoided, inasmuch as it favors the formation of manganate, MnO_4^{2-} (manganate(VI)). Solutions of permanganate are also formed when manganese(II) is treated with very powerful oxidants, *e.g.*, PbO_2, in strongly acidic medium.

$$Mn^{2+} + 4H_2O = MnO_4^- + 8H^+ + 5e^- \qquad E^\circ = -1.51 \text{ v.}$$

21.21 Colorless normal perrhenates, *e.g.*, M^IReO_4, are made by neutralization of the acidic solutions of the heptoxide. Fusion of elemental rhenium or its lower oxides with oxidizing agents, *e.g.*, oxygen or nitrate ion, in the presence

---

[1] BOYD, et al., *J. Am. Chem. Soc.*, **74**, 556 (1952).

* These are better named as manganate(VII), etc.

of alkali gives the yellow or red meso-perrhenates, $M^I{}_3ReO_5$, rather than the normal compounds. The meso-perrhenates can also be obtained by addition of alkali to solutions of the normal compounds. In neutral aqueous solution the meso compounds are immediately hydrolyzed to the normal salts. The only pertechnetate reported is the ammonium salt, NH_4TcO_4, formed by evaporation to dryness of an aqueous solution of the heptoxide which has been neutralized with ammonia.[1]

21.22 Permanganates are deep purple in color, and for the alkali metal salts there is a progressive decrease in water solubility with increasing cationic size. The lithium and sodium compounds are extremely soluble. The outstanding property of the permanganate ion is the strong oxidizing power both in alkaline and acid solution. When it functions as an oxidant in the former medium it is converted to the dioxide, but in acid solution it is reduced to manganese(II).* (See 21.20 for potentials for these changes.) In very strongly alkaline medium, permanganate is transformed to manganate(VI), MnO_4^{2-}, with loss of oxygen. Ignition of anhydrous salts is also accompanied by evolution of oxygen.

21.23 The alkali metal normal perrhenates exhibit solubility behavior similar to that of the corresponding permanganates. In contrast to the powerful oxidizing ability of permanganate in alkaline solution, the perrhenate ion is stable in this medium. It is also a much weaker oxidant than permanganate

$$ReO_4^- + 2H_2O + 3e^- = ReO_2 + 4OH^- \qquad E_B^\circ = -0.594 \text{ v.}$$

in acid solution. Solid perrhenates, unlike permanganates, possess high thermal stability; thus, whereas potassium permanganate begins to evolve molecular oxygen at 200°, the corresponding rhenium compound distills without decomposition at 1370° and 1 atmosphere pressure.

21.24 The MO_4^- ions are tetrahedral in structure and generally slightly paramagnetic.[2]

21.25 Sulfides of the composition M_2S_7 exist for technetium and rhenium, but an analogous compound is apparently unknown for manganese. These sulfides can be obtained as black precipitates by the action of hydrogen sulfide on acidified solutions containing the elements in their heptapositive state. The rhenium sulfide is formed as the 1-hydrate, $Re_2S_7 \cdot H_2O$, and is insoluble in hydrochloric acid and in alkaline sulfide solutions. The anhydrous sulfide is formed by reaction of hydrogen sulfide with rhenium heptoxide. The heptasulfide decomposes when heated to yield sulfur and the disulfide. The existence of the heptasulfides of technetium and rhenium and their mode of preparation emphasize the high degree of stability of these elements in the +7 state.

21.26 No halo compounds of heptapositive technetium have yet been described. For +7 manganese and rhenium the following oxyhalides definitely have been prepared: MnO_3F, ReO_2F_3, $ReOF_5$, ReO_3Cl, and ReO_3Br. MnO_3F is formed when elementary manganese is treated with potassium nitrate in

---

[2] NELSON, BOYD and SMITH, *J. Am. Chem. Soc.*, **76**, 348 (1954).

* An exception to this occurs when MnO_4^- is reduced in acid solution in the presence of a large excess of fluoride ion, when MnF_3 is formed.

anhydrous (liquid) hydrogen fluoride, or by reaction between hydrogen fluoride and potassium permanganate.[3] The compound is an extremely unstable green gas, which begins to decompose in the neighborhood of 40°. The rhenium(VII) oxyfluorides are produced when rhenium(IV) oxide or potassium perrhenate is acted on by free fluorine diluted with nitrogen.[4] $ReOF_5$ (m.p., 34.5°; b.p., 55°) attacks organic matter rapidly; ReO_2F_3 (b.p. 200°) does so much more slowly. Both compounds undergo immediate hydrolysis to yield perrhenic and hydrofluoric acids. ReO_3Cl (m.p., 4.5°; b.p., 131°) is formed by reaction between the heptoxide and a mixture of rhenium(III) and (V) chlorides at elevated temperatures. The corresponding oxybromide (m.p., 39.5°; b.p., 163°) is produced when the product of reaction between heated elemental rhenium and a mixture of oxygen and bromine vapor is distilled over rhenium heptoxide. Both the chloride and bromide are extremely susceptible to hydrolysis.

The Hexapositive State

21.27 Although the oxide corresponding to the +6 state of manganese does not appear to exist, salts related to it are well known. These are the so-called manganates, $M^I_2MnO_4$, and are prepared by fusion of a mixture of manganese dioxide and a large excess of alkali in the presence of an oxidizing agent such as potassium nitrate or even atmospheric oxygen. Use of the latter reagent also gives some manganate(V) or (IV). The manganate(VI) compounds are dark green in color and stable in solution only in the presence of excess hydroxide ion. In neutral or acidic solution they disproportionate in accordance with the following equation.

$$3MnO_4^{2-} + 2H_2O = MnO_2 + 2MnO^- + 4OH^-$$

Only alkali metal salts (*e.g.*, K_2MnO_4; $Na_2MnO_4 \cdot 4H_2O$, $6H_2O$, $10H_2O$) have been obtained in a reasonable state of purity. The potassium compound is stable to about 500°, decomposing above this temperature with the evolution of oxygen.

$$2K_2MnO_4 = 2K_2MnO_3 + O_2$$

21.28 Rhenium(VI) oxide, ReO_3, has been obtained as a red material by reduction of the heptoxide with the free metal at 300°. The compound is inert toward water, hydrochloric acid, and dilute alkalies. It is oxidized by nitric acid to perrhenic acid. When heated *in vacuo* to 400° or boiled with concentrated alkali it decomposes to dioxide and heptoxide.

21.29 Green salts of rhenium(VI), apparently analogous to the manganate(VI) compounds, have been prepared, but none has been isolated in the pure state because of the strong tendency to disproportionate. Fusion of the appropriate mixture of perrhenate, rhenium dioxide, and alkali in the absence of air gives a green melt presumably containing ReO_4^{2-}. Treatment of the melt with water converts the +6 rhenium to Re(VII) and Re(IV).

[3] WIECHERT, *Z. anorg. Chem.*, **261**, 310 (1950).
[4] AYNSLEY, PEACOCK and ROBINSON, *J. Chem. Soc.*, 1950, p. 1622.

21.30 The only binary halide known for the +6 state of the elements of the group is ReF_6. This substance is obtained as a colorless gas (f.p., 18.8°; b.p., 47.6°) by the interaction of powdered rhenium and elementary fluorine at 125°. The hexafluoride is extremely unstable, functioning as a powerful fluorinating agent toward organic compounds and being immediately decomposed by water with the formation of perrhenic acid and the dioxide hydrate. Reduction of the hexafluoride under appropriate conditions by any of a variety of reducing agents, *e.g.*, H_2, CO, SO_2, Re, initially yields the tetrafluoride.

21.31 Three oxyhalides of rhenium(VI), $ReOF_4$, ReO_2F_2, and $ReOCl_4$, have been reported; no similar manganese compounds are known. The oxyfluorides reputedly are formed by reaction between metallic rhenium and a mixture of oxygen and fluorine at 125°–300°, but this reaction has not been confirmed.[4] It has also been claimed that $ReOF_4$ is a product of the action of the hexafluoride on quartz. $ReOCl_4$ is produced when a mixture of rhenium(V) and (III) chlorides is heated in oxygen to 150°. The oxytetrachloride is a dark brown solid (m.p. 28°) which, like all rhenium(VI) compounds, immediately disproportionates in water to give the +7 and +4 states of the element.

The Pentapositive State

21.32 It has been only in recent years that the +5 state of manganese has been characterized and well-defined methods developed for its preparation [5] as $[MnO_4]^{3-}$. The common preparative methods, one of which is similar to that for the production of manganate(VI) (see 21.27) but differs in the proportions of reactants, include: (a) reduction of an alkaline permanganate solution with iodide ion; (b) oxidation of a manganese(II) compound by means of potassium nitrate in an alkaline melt; (c) atmospheric oxidation of a fused mixture of manganese dioxide and metal hydroxide; (d) reaction between permanganate ion and metal hydroxide, either in aqueous solution or in the anhydrous state at high temperatures; and (e) the interaction at elevated temperatures between a manganate(VI) compound and the appropriate metal hydroxide.

21.33 Anhydrous alkali metal manganate(V) compounds are dark, blue-green substances, soluble in concentrated alkali solutions. From these solutions, hydrated salts can be recovered. Anhydrous potassium manganate(V) is stable in an oxygen atmosphere up to about 1000°. Magnetic analysis of $Na_3MnO_4 \cdot 10H_2O$ gives a Bohr magneton number in concordance with that expected for Mn(V), *i.e.*, corresponding to two unpaired electrons.

21.34 The scarcity of rhenium(V) compounds has already been noted (see 21.9). Sodium rhenate(V) ("hyporhenate"), $NaReO_3$, can be obtained by fusion of sodium perrhenate with rhenium dioxide and sodium hydroxide in the absence of air. (A similar reaction, but with different proportions of reactants, apparently gives rhenate(VI), see 21.29.) Sodium rhenate(V) is a yellow substance, which even in the anhydrous state is stable only in the pres-

[5] KLEINBERG, *J. Chem. Educ.*, **33**, 73 (1956).

ence of excess alkali. In neutral or acidic solution it immediately disproportionates to perrhenate and rhenium dioxide. Oxidation to perrhenate is readily
effected by air.

21.35 Rhenium pentachloride, $ReCl_5$, is the only binary halide known for
the +5 state of the elements of the manganese family. This compound is
produced by direct union of the elements, the less volatile trichloride also
being formed in small quantity. The pentachloride is a brown-black solid
which can be sublimed in a high vacuum. When heated in an atmosphere of
nitrogen, it decomposes to elementary chlorine and the trichloride. It burns
in oxygen with the formation of ReO_3Cl and $ReOCl_4$. Reaction with water
occurs instantaneously, the products being the hydrous dioxide, chlorine,
perrhenic acid, and the complex acid $H_2[ReCl_6]$. The last compound is also
formed by reaction with concentrated hydrochloric acid.

$$2ReCl_5 + 4HCl = 2H_2[ReCl_6] + Cl_2$$

21.36 Whereas no completely halogenated complex derivatives of rhenium
pentachloride are known, a number of oxychloride complexes containing
$[ReOCl_5]^{2-}$ have been isolated. The potassium salt $K_2[ReOCl_5] \cdot H_2O$ is
obtained as a yellow-green precipitate by the addition of potassium chloride
to a solution of Re(V) prepared by the electrolytic reduction of perrhenate
in hydrochloric acid solution. The complex is stable in dry air, but, like all
other rhenium(V) compounds, it undergoes immediate disproportionation in
contact with moisture. On treatment with such oxidizing agents as hydrogen
peroxide and nitric acid the complex is readily converted to perrhenate.

21.37 Although rhenium pentafluoride does not exist, complexes formally
derived from this compound have been made and have the composition
$M^I[ReF_6]$ (M = Na, K, Rb, Cs).[6] These substances are obtained by the
interaction of rhenium hexafluoride and alkali metal iodides in liquid sulfur
dioxide at $-65°$.

$$2ReF_6 + 2MI \overset{SO_2 \text{ (liq.)}}{=} 2M[ReF_6] + I_2$$

The hexafluororhenate(V) salts are white crystalline powders which attack
glass at 300° and are rapidly decomposed by moisture.

21.38 One complex cyanide of +5 rhenium, namely $K_3[ReO_2(CN)_4]$, has
been characterized. This orange substance is obtained when a solution containing potassium hexachlororhenate(IV) and excess potassium cyanide is
treated with hydrogen peroxide. The compound is readily soluble in water and
apparently unaffected by strong bases.

The Tetrapositive State

21.39 The +4 state for manganese and rhenium is a well-defined one, and
there is little question that this oxidation state is relatively stable for technetium,
even though only a few compounds corresponding to it have been prepared.

21.40 The dioxides of all three elements are known. Manganese dioxide,

[6] PEACOCK, *J. Chem. Soc.*, 1957, p. 467.

which is found in nature as the most common mineral of the element (see 21.12), can be prepared in the anhydrous state by the ignition of manganese(II) nitrate. Technetium dioxide is produced as a hydrate by reduction of aqueous pertechnetate with zinc and hydrochloric acid, and in the anhydrous form by thermal decomposition of ammonium pertechnetate.[2] The corresponding rhenium oxide is obtained as the 2-hydrate by the electrolytic reduction of perrhenate solutions; reduction of the heptoxide with hydrogen at 300° gives the anhydrous compound.

21.41 All three dioxides are black, water-insoluble substances. They exhibit widely different behavior toward strong heating; thus, MnO_2 decomposes first to Mn_2O_3 and then to Mn_3O_4,* whereas TcO_2 apparently sublimes *in vacuo* unchanged at temperatures above 1000°, and ReO_2 disproportionates to the metal and heptoxide when strongly heated in a vacuum. Manganese dioxide is a strong oxidizing agent and is readily converted to +2 manganese by reducing agents in acid solution (see 21.10 for the $MnO_2 - Mn^{2+}$ potential). On the other hand the dioxides of technetium and rhenium are much more stable toward reduction, but both are more easily oxidized to give the +7 state of the elements. In contrast to the behavior of manganese dioxide, which reacts with concentrated hydrohalic acids (HCl, HBr, and HI) with the liberation of halogen, the rhenium compound dissolves in these acids (and also in concentrated solutions of their salts) to form hexahalorhenate(IV) complexes, $[ReX_6]^{2-}$.

21.42 The acidic nature of manganese dioxide is brought out by its reactivity toward strongly basic oxides. Fusion of the latter with the dioxide, or even reaction in aqueous medium, gives rise to the so-called manganite, *i.e.*, manganate(IV), salts. Only from the melt can well-defined brownish compounds be isolated, and these contain the two components in varying proportions, *e.g.*, $CaO \cdot MnO_2$ ($CaMnO_3$); $CaO \cdot 2MnO_2$ ($CaMn_2O_5$); $CaO \cdot 3MnO_2$ ($CaMn_3O_7$); $CaO \cdot 5MnO_2$ ($CaMn_5O_{11}$); $2CaO \cdot MnO_2$. These compounds are extensively hydrolyzed in aqueous solution and in alkaline medium are easily oxidized, *e.g.*, to MnO_4^{2-}.

21.43 Rhenites, *i.e.*, rhenate(IV) compounds, are formed by a fusion reaction analogous to that described above, carried out in the absence of air. Very few of these substances have been isolated, since they are sensitive to the action of a variety of agents. Thus they are attacked by water and acids with the formation of rhenium dioxide; oxidizing agents convert them to perrhenates. The sodium and potassium salts, which have been shown to have the composition M_2ReO_3, are brown, insoluble, diamagnetic substances.

21.44 In addition to the anionic oxy complexes of manganese(IV), halo complexes with fluorine and chlorine of the type $M^I_2[MnX_6]$ (M = alkali metal) have been prepared. The hexafluoro compounds are obtained by the action of concentrated hydrofluoric acid on manganate(IV) or manganate(VI) salts.

---

* There is some question as to whether Mn_3O_4 contains Mn(III) and Mn(II) or whether it should be formulated as $2MnO \cdot MnO_2$. X-ray evidence favors the latter formulation.

Reaction with the latter gives permanganate as an additional product. The fluoro complexes are golden-yellow substances which are rapidly decomposed by water with the formation of manganese dioxide. Although the ultimate products of reaction of manganese dioxide with concentrated hydrochloric acid are chlorine, manganese(II) chloride, and water, there is reason to believe that manganese(IV) chloride is formed as an unstable intermediate. This chloride can be stabilized by coordination with chloride ion supplied by alkali metal chlorides. Thus potassium hexachloromanganate(IV) is formed by treatment of the permanganate with cold, concentrated hydrochloric acid.

$$2KMnO_4 + 16HCl = K_2[MnCl_6] + MnCl_2 + 4Cl_2 + 8H_2O$$

The chloro complex is a deep red solid which is rapidly hydrolyzed by water.

21.45 The only binary tetrahalide of the group which has been isolated is ReF_4. This compound is most conveniently made by reduction of the hexa-fluoride by means of hydrogen at 200°. The tetrafluoride is a dark green material (m.p. 124.5°) of low volatility. It is soluble in water, in which medium it undergoes decomposition with the production of the dioxide.

21.46 The formation of $[ReX_6]^{2-}$ by reaction between rhenium dioxide and hydrohalic acids has been noted above. Rather stable salts containing this ion type have been obtained. The existence of bromo and iodo complexes for rhenium, in contrast to their absence for manganese, testifies to markedly greater stability of the tetrapositive state for rhenium as compared with manganese.

21.47 Hexafluororhenate(IV) salts have been prepared by two methods: (1) by reduction of perrhenates by iodide ion in hydrofluoric acid solution, e.g.,

$$2KReO_4 + 16HF + 6KI = 2K_2ReF_6 + 4KF + 3I_2 + 8H_2O$$

and (2) by treatment of a solution of the tetrafluoride in concentrated hydro-fluoric acid with metal fluoride. The corresponding chloro, bromo, and iodo complexes can also be obtained by modifications of the reduction method noted above.

21.48 In aqueous solution, alkali metal hexachlororhenate(IV) salts are relatively stable, decomposing with the deposition of rhenium dioxide only on long standing or on boiling. In solution in the presence of strong bases the chloro complexes disproportionate in a complex fashion, yielding in the cold Re(III) and Re(VII) as ultimate products and in boiling solutions Re(II) and Re(VII).

21.49 Potassium hexachlorotechnetate(IV), isomorphous with the analogous rhenium compound and prepared in a similar fashion, i.e., by reduction of pertechnetate with potassium iodide in concentrated hydrochloric acid solution, has been described.[2]

The Tripositive State

21.50 The tripositive state is one of relatively little stability for both manganese and rhenium. No compounds of technetium in this oxidation state have been reported.

21.51 Manganese(III) oxide, Mn_2O_3, is found in nature along with other manganese minerals as a brown-black substance known as *braunite*. It can be prepared by ignition of the dioxide in air at temperatures between 530 and 940°; above the latter temperature Mn_3O_4 (see 21.41) is formed. The hydrated form of the oxide, $Mn_2O_3 \cdot H_2O$ or $MnO(OH)$, which occurs in nature (as the mineral *manganite*), is obtained synthetically when the precipitate formed by air oxidation of manganese(II) chloride solutions in the presence of excess ammonium chloride is dried at 100°.

21.52 Manganese(III) oxide appears to be entirely basic in properties. Treatment with acids undoubtedly gives rise to the unstable tripositive manganese cation (hydrated), which has a large tendency to disproportionate into the dipositive and tetrapositive states. Moreover, it is easily reduced.

$$Mn^{3+} + e^- = Mn^{2+} \qquad E° = 1.51 \text{ v.}$$

From solutions of the sesquioxide in concentrated hydrochloric or hydrofluoric acid anionic halo complexes of manganese(III) (see below) can be isolated upon addition of alkali metal chloride. Only a few simple manganese(III) salts have been isolated from solution. Among these is $MnF_3 \cdot 2H_2O$, which is obtained by crystallization from a solution of the sesquioxide in hydrofluoric acid or from the reaction between permanganate ion with dipositive manganese in hydrofluoric acid.

$$MnO_4^- + 4Mn^{2+} + 15HF = 5MnF_3 + 4H_2O + 7H^+$$

The anhydrous trifluoride is produced as a red solid by the action of fluorine on manganese(II) iodide. The anhydrous compound is unstable at high temperatures, breaking down into the difluoride and fluorine. Perhaps the best known simple salt is the acetate, which can be isolated from solution as the 2-hydrate after oxidation of manganese(II) acetate with chlorine. Manganese(III) acetate is a convenient source of other tripositive manganese compounds. In general, the simple salts are extensively hydrolyzed in neutral solution, yielding the hydrated sesquioxide.

21.53 In the majority of its compounds, tripositive manganese is found as part of an anionic complex. Illustrative of complexes which have been characterized are the following: $M^I_2MnF_5$ (often hydrated); $M^I_2MnCl_5$ (usually anhydrous; the ammonium salt crystallizes with one molecule of water); $M^I_3[Mn(C_2O_4)_3]$; $M^I[Mn(C_2O_4)_2(H_2O)_2]$; $M^I_3[Mn(CN)_6]$. It is interesting that although dipositive manganese is much more stable than the tripositive element in simple salts, the cyano complex noted above is formed on air oxidation of the analogous complex ($M^I_4[Mn(CN)_6]$) of +2 manganese.

21.54 Anhydrous rhenium(III) oxide has not been prepared. An unstable black hydrate is precipitated upon addition of strong base to a solution of +3 rhenium; this hydrate is rapidly oxidized to perrhenate by the air.

21.55 A chloride and bromide of rhenium of the composition ReX_3 are known. The chloride is formed by reduction of the pentachloride with rhenium metal at 500°, and is also one of the products (see 21.15) of direct union of the elements. The tribromide is readily produced by reaction between hydrated rhenium(III) oxide and hydrobromic acid or by direct combination of the elements.

21.56 The trichloride is a reddish-black substance which is soluble in water. Fresh aqueous solutions give no test for ionic chlorine. Molecular weight determinations in glacial acetic acid give values corresponding to a dimeric formula; presumably the structure of the compound is analogous to that of Al_2Cl_6, in which aluminum is tetrahedral. Neutral and alkaline solutions of the chloride are easily oxidized in the air, the rhenium being converted primarily to the tetrapositive state. In hydrochloric acid solution the compound is much more stable and is not affected by even so strong an oxidizing agent as permanganate ion. This increase in stability is doubtless due to the formation of the complex acid $H[ReCl_4]$. Salts of the composition $M^I[ReCl_4]$ can be crystallized from hydrochloric acid solutions to which alkali metal chlorides have been added. The tetrachlororhenate(III) salts are decomposed by strong heating to the metal, the trichloride and hexachlororhenate(IV) compounds. The chemical behavior of the green-black tribromide is generally similar to that of the chloride.

The Dipositive State

21.57 There is a striking contrast between the chemistry of $+2$ manganese and that of the corresponding state for rhenium. Whereas dipositive manganese represents, on the whole, the most stable oxidation state of this element and a great many compounds are known for it, $+2$ rhenium is extremely unstable and only a few compounds of this state have definitely been isolated.

21.58 Dipositive manganese is found in nature both as the oxide and hydroxide, the former being known as *manganosite* and the latter as *pyrochroite*. The dark green oxide can be obtained in the laboratory by reduction of higher oxides, *e.g.*, MnO_2, with hydrogen or carbon monoxide. The hydroxide, $Mn(OH)_2$, is obtained as a white precipitate ($K_{SP} = 2 \times 10^{-13}$) when strong base is added to solutions of manganese(II). Both the anhydrous oxide and the hydroxide are easily oxidized. Thus, the latter compound is converted by air first to the sesquioxide and ultimately to the dioxide. The potentials for these changes in alkaline medium are given below.

$$Mn(OH)_2 \xrightarrow{-0.1} Mn_2O_3 \cdot H_2O(MnOOH) \xrightarrow{-0.2} MnO_2$$

Both the oxide and hydroxide dissolve in acids to give solutions containing the hydrated Mn^{2+} cation. This ion is quite stable and in acid solution is oxidized only by very strong oxidants (see 21.10).

21.59 A large number of simple salts of dipositive manganese are known. Most of these are pink in color and, when derived from strong acids, give solutions that are initially neutral to litmus. From such solutions the hydroxide is slowly precipitated. The majority of the salts exhibit high solubility in water;

among those which are insoluble are the phosphate, carbonate, oxalate, and sulfide. The soluble salts generally crystallize from solution as hydrates, *e.g.*, $MnSO_4$ with 7, 5, 4, 2, or 1 H_2O, depending upon conditions of crystallization; $Mn(ClO_4)_2$ with 6 or 4 H_2O.

21.60 A variety of complexes of dipositive manganese have been prepared. Mention has already been made of the hexacyano complex (see above) and its instability toward oxidation. This compound type, and indeed the other anionic complexes definitely known, *e.g.*, $M^I_4[Mn(SCN)_6]$, M^IMnF_3, M^IMnCl_3, $M^I_2MnCl_4$, $M^I_4MnCl_6$, are all easily hydrolyzed. Among other complexes worth noting are $MnCl_2py_2$ (py = pyridine) and those with β-diketones. The pyridine compound is a nonelectrolyte and has a planar structure. The complexes with β-diketones are also nonelectrolytes and contain two organic molecules per manganese atom. They can be made by the interaction of manganese(II) oxide or carbonate with diketone in an inert atmosphere; if the reaction is carried out in air, the manganese is oxidized and the chelate derived from the +3 state, [Mn dik$_3$], is formed.

21.61 The formation of rhenium(II) by the decomposition of hexachlororhenate(IV) salts in boiling alkaline solutions has been described (see 21.48). There is evidence that dipositive rhenium (in addition to Re(IV) and (VII)) can also be obtained by boiling the hydrated sesquioxide with sodium hydroxide solutions, and also by reduction of the trichloride with zinc and sulfuric acid. No compound of rhenium in this oxidation state has, however, been isolated from aqueous solution.

21.62 The only compounds of +2 rhenium which appear to have been characterized unequivocally are some complexes which have been prepared in nonaqueous solutions.[7] Ammonium tetrachlororhenate(II), $(NH_4)_2[ReCl_4]$, is the product of reduction of $(NH_4)_2[ReCl_6]$ in acetone solution. Treatment of the rhenium(II) complex with the calculated quantity of pyridine yields what is apparently *cis*-$ReCl_2py_2$ (*cf.* $MnCl_2py_2$ above) as a gray-green precipitate. By the action of excess pyridine, the *cis* isomer is converted to $ReCl_2py_4$, which on heating goes over to the light green *trans* form of $ReCl_2py_2$.

Oxidation States Lower Than +2

21.63 Only a few compounds with manganese and rhenium in oxidation states lower than +2 have been described.*

21.64 The reduction of $[Mn(CN)_6]^{4-}$ in aqueous solutions containing an excess of cyanide ion, either electrolytically or by means of sodium amalgam or aluminum, gives high yields of the cyanomanganate(I) ion, $[Mn(CN)_6]^{5-}$. The potassium compound has been isolated as a diamagnetic, white precipitate and its solubility product determined to be about 2.4×10^{-11}. The compound

---

[7] TRONEV and BONDIN, *Doklady Akad. Nauk S.S.S.R.*, **86**, 87 (1952); *Chem. Abstracts*, **47**, 1527 (1953).

* The carbonyls in which the elements may be regarded as being in a zero oxidation state have already been noted (see 13.51 *ff.*).

is unstable in water, reacting with the evolution of hydrogen.   In $[Mn(CN)_6]^{5-}$ the diamagnetism is indicative of inner orbital D^2SP^3 binding.[8] A yellow substance possessing strong reducing power and apparently containing both manganese(I) and manganese(0), $K_5Mn(CN)_6 \cdot K_6Mn(CN)_6 \cdot 2NH_3$, is formed on reduction of potassium hexacyanomanganate(III) by potassium in liquid ammonia.[9]

21.65 Substances which may be regarded as rhenium(I) compounds are the carbonyl halides, $Re(CO)_5X$ (X = Cl, Br, I) (see 13.67). These can be made by reaction of the halogens with the carbonyl $[Re(CO)_5]_2$. The carbonyl halides are stable in air and soluble in such organic solvents as benzene and petroleum ether.

21.66 A most unusual phenomenon is the existence of mononegative rhenium, which can be produced in aqueous solution by the reduction of dilute, acidified solutions of potassium perrhenate in a Jones reductor.[10]

$$ReO_4^- + 8H^+ + 8e^- = Re^- + 4H_2O$$

A solid compound containing rhenide ion (-1 rhenium) has been obtained by reduction of potassium perrhenate in ethylenediamine-water solutions by means of potassium metal.[11] Extraction of the potassium hydroxide which is formed in the reaction permits the isolation of potassium rhenide tetrahydrate, $KRe \cdot 4H_2O$. This compound is slightly paramagnetic, the degree of paramagnetism being considerably less than that required for a substance with even one unpaired electron.   The magnetic behavior and energy considerations indicate that the rhenium exists in a hydrated complex having four water molecules coordinated at the corners of a square.

[8] TREADWELL and RATHS, *Helv. Chim. Acta*, **35**, 2259, 2275 (1952).
[9] CHRISTENSEN, KLEINBERG, and DAVIDSON, *J. Am. Chem. Soc.*, **75**, 2495 (1953).
[10] LUNDELL and KNOWLES, *J. Research Natl. Bur. Standards*, **18**, 629 (1937).
[11] BRAVO, GRISWOLD, and KLEINBERG, *J. Phys. Chem.*, **58**, 18 (1954).

CHAPTER 22

THE TRANSITION TRIADS
I — IRON, COBALT, AND NICKEL

Introduction

22.1 The so-called transition triads are made up of the following nine elements.

$_{26}$Fe	$_{27}$Co	$_{28}$Ni
$_{44}$Ru	$_{45}$Rh	$_{46}$Pd
$_{76}$Os	$_{77}$Ir	$_{78}$Pt

Nowhere in the periodic system, except among the lanthanide elements, are the resemblances between horizontally adjacent elements so marked as in these triads. Vertical resemblances are also of consequence, but they are of greatest significance in the second and third triads. It is convenient, therefore, to discuss the chemistry of the elements of the transition triads in two units, one dealing with the $3d$ triad (Fe, Co, Ni) and the other with the $4d$ and $5d$ triads, the elements of which are commonly called the platinum metals (see Chap. 23).

22.2 The elements of the $3d$ triad have the following valence shell configurations: Fe, $3d^6 4s^2$; Co, $3d^7 4s^2$; Ni, $3d^8 4s^2$. Some properties of the elements are shown in Table 22.1. It is apparent from the data cited that iron, cobalt, and nickel are very much alike in the orders of magnitude of their melting and boiling points, in the sizes of their dipositive ions and covalent radii, and in their values for first ionization potential.

GENERAL REFERENCES

LATIMER, *The Oxidation States of the Elements and Their Potentials in Aqueous Solutions*, 2nd Edition, Prentice-Hall, Inc., New York, 1952, Ch. 12, 13, and 14.

NYHOLM, *Chem. Revs.*, **53**, 263 (1953) (an excellent discussion of the stereochemistry and valence states of nickel).

REMY, *Treatise on Inorganic Chemistry* (translated and amended by Anderson), Elsevier Publishing Company, Amsterdam, 1956, Vol. II, Ch. 7, pp. 242–319.

SIDGWICK, *The Chemical Elements and Their Compounds*, Oxford University Press, London, 1950, pp. 1316–1453.

TABLE 22.1

Some Properties of Iron, Cobalt, and Nickel

	Fe	Co	Ni
Natural isotopes	54, 56 *, 57, 58	59	58 *, 60, 61, 62, 64
Density, g./cc.	7.86	8.83	8.90
Melting point, °C.	1528	1490	1452
Boiling point, °C.	2735	3100	2840
Ionic radius, in crystals			
M^{2+}, Å	0.76	0.74	0.73
M^{3+}, Å	0.64	0.63	——
Covalent radius, Å	1.165	1.157	1.149
Ionization potential, volts			
1st electron	7.83	7.8	7.61
Electrode potential, $E°$, in volts for $M = M^{2+} + 2e^-$	0.440	0.277	0.250

* Most abundant isotope

22.3 The most commonly encountered oxidation states of the elements are +2 and +3 for iron and cobalt, and +2 for nickel. Among other states which have been characterized definitely are the following: Fe +6 *, +5, +4, and 0; Co +4, +1, and 0; Ni +4, +3, +1, and 0. In addition, compounds in which iron and cobalt may be regarded as being in negative oxidation states have been reported.

22.4 A large number of simple (or hydrated) salts are known for iron, cobalt, and nickel in the +2 condition. In acidic aqueous solution the dipositive cations are rather stable, and their tendency to be oxidized decreases very strikingly from iron to nickel, as is evidenced by the values for the $Fe^{2+} - Fe^{3+}$ and $Co^{2+} - Co^{3+}$ potentials shown below and by the nonexistence of a tripositive nickel cation.

$$Fe^{2+} = Fe^{3+} + e^- \qquad E° = -0.771 \text{ v.}$$
$$Co^{2+} = Co^{3+} + e^- \qquad E° = -1.82$$

In contrast to its stability in acidic solution, the dipositive state (in the form of the hydroxides) is fairly readily oxidized in neutral or basic medium.

$$Fe(OH)_2 + OH^- = Fe(OH)_3 + e^- \qquad E°_B = 0.56 \text{ v.}$$
$$Co(OH)_2 + OH^- = Co(OH)_3 + e^- \qquad E°_B = -0.17$$
$$Ni(OH)_2 + 2OH^- = NiO_2 + 2H_2O + 2e^- \qquad E°_B = -0.49$$

It is apparent that the order of increasing stability in basic medium parallels that found in acidic solution, *i.e.*, Fe(II) < Co(II) < Ni(II).

22.5 Both iron(II) and nickel(II) form a wide variety of relatively stable

* Ruthenium and osmium, the congeners of iron in the 3*d* and 4*d* triads, exhibit a maximum oxidation state of +8. As is the general situation among transition elements, in the transition triads there is a considerable increase in the stability of higher valence states in passing from the 3*d* to the 4*d* and 5*d* series.

complexes. On the other hand, in the presence of many complexing agents dipositive cobalt is generally very readily oxidized and gives rise to stable (with respect to reduction) coordination compounds of cobalt(III). Thus one finds a great many complex compounds of tripositive cobalt, whereas, because of the powerful oxidizing power of the Co^{3+} ion (see above), only a few simple compounds are known.

22.6 Many compounds, both simple and complex, exist for tripositive iron. Those simple compounds which are water-soluble undoubtedly give the Fe^{3+} (hydrated) in solution. The increase in charge and decrease in cationic size from Fe^{2+} to Fe^{3+} (Table 22.1) have significant chemical consequences. Iron(III) salts are more extensively hydrolyzed than are the corresponding iron(II) compounds. Also, tripositive iron has a greater tendency to form simple compounds having appreciable covalent character, e.g., iron(III) chloride (see 22.38).

22.7 No simple salts of nickel(III) have been prepared. This oxidation state has definitely been obtained in a small number of complexes, and probably also in hydrated oxides.

22.8 Iron(VI) and iron(V) have been characterized only in the form of the anionic oxy complexes, FeO_4^{2-} and FeO_4^{3-}, respectively. The existence of the corresponding valence states for cobalt and nickel has not yet been established, although it is highly likely that cobalt(V) (as $KCoO_3$) has been prepared (see 22.20).

22.9 The tetrapositive state is now a well-defined one for all the elements of the 3d triad. Among the iron compounds which have been isolated are salts of oxyanions, e.g., FeO_3^{2-} and FeO_4^{4-}, and a few complexes containing the cation $[Fe^{IV}X_2diarsine_2]^{2+}$, where $X = Cl$ or Br, and diarsine = o-bis(dimethylarsino) benzene. For cobalt (IV) and nickel(IV) there appears to be little question of the existence of the oxides, CoO_2 and NiO_2, although these have never been obtained pure. In addition, a number of complex compounds containing the elements in this valence state have been characterized, e.g., $3K_2O \cdot CoO_2 \cdot 9MoO_3 \cdot 6\frac{1}{2}H_2O$, $3BaO \cdot NiO_2 \cdot 9MoO_3 \cdot 12H_2O$, Ba_2CoO_4, $BaNiO_3$, K_2NiF_6 (see 22.23 ff.).

22.10 For oxidation states lower than $+2$, the carbonyls (13.51 ff.) containing the elements in a zero state are well known. Other compounds of cobalt(0) and nickel(0) which have been characterized are $K_4[Co(CN)_4]$, $[Co(CO)_3A]_2$ (A = $P(OR)_3$), $K_4[Ni(CN)_4]$, $K_4[Ni(C\equiv CH)_4]$, $Ni(PX_3)_4$ (X = F, Cl, Br, NCO, NCS), and $Ni(CNR)_4$ (R = C_6H_5, p-$CH_3C_6H_4$, etc.). A number of interesting complexes of $+1$ cobalt and nickel have been prepared; these include $[Co(CNR)_5]X$ (CNR = aromatic isonitrile), $[Fe^{II}o$-phen$_3][Co(CN)_3CO] \cdot 3\frac{1}{2}H_2O$, and $K_4Ni_2(CN)_6$. Unusual compounds of iron and cobalt have been described, in which these elements may be regarded as being formally in the dinegative and mononegative states, respectively, e.g., $Na_2[Fe(CO)_4]$ and $Na[Co(CO)_4]$.

The Elements

22.11 Iron constitutes 4.75% of the earth's crust and ranks second in abundance to aluminum among the metals. Cobalt and nickel are much less common, their relative abundances being 4×10^{-3} and $1 \times 10^{-2}\%$, respectively.

22.12 The most important minerals of iron are *hematite* (Fe_2O_3), *limonite* ($Fe_2O_3 \cdot H_2O$), *magnetite* (Fe_3O_4), and *siderite* ($FeCO_3$), with the *taconites* (siliceous materials containing about 27% Fe_2O_3 and 50% SiO_2) beginning to assume a position of significance as sources of the metal. Cobalt is invariably found in nature associated with nickel, the principal minerals being *smaltite* ($CoAs_2$) and *cobaltite* ($CoAsS$). The chief sources of nickel are *pentlandite* ($NiS \cdot 2FeS$) and *garnierite* (a magnesium-nickel silicate of variable composition), minerals which are commonly found along with iron and copper sulfides.

22.13 The production of iron and its alloys on a technical scale is discussed adequately in many texts and will not be considered here. The preparation of the chemically pure metal can be accomplished in a number of ways: *e.g.*, by the thermal decomposition of the pentacarbonyl; by reduction of pure iron(III) oxide with hydrogen; or by cathodic deposition from solutions of iron(II) salts. The preparation of pure cobalt is complicated by the difficulties encountered in its separation from the metals, principally nickel, with which it occurs. In most separation procedures the cobalt is finally removed as the oxide, which is then reduced by means of carbon at elevated temperatures. The metallurgy of nickel, like that of cobalt, varies with the nature of the ore. A widely used process involves the ultimate separation of nickel as the volatile carbonyl $Ni(CO)_4$. Thermal decomposition of this substance (at about 200° and atmospheric pressure) gives a metal of 99.9–99.99% purity.

22.14 The elements of the 3d triad are all fairly active metals. Reaction with dilute nonoxidizing acids (*e.g.*, hydrochloric acid) results in the liberation of hydrogen and conversion of the metals to the dipositive state. (See Table 22.1 for the potentials for the reactions $M = M^{2+} + 2e^-$.) In the presence of strong

TABLE 22.2

Some Products of Reaction of Iron, Cobalt, and Nickel at Elevated Temperatures

Reagents	Products	Reagents	Products
Oxygen	Fe_3O_4 at 500°, Fe_2O_3 at higher temperatures; Co_3O_4; NiO	Silicon	FeSi and Fe_2Si; Co_2Si, Ni_2Si, and others
Sulfur	MS	Carbon monoxide	$Fe(CO)_5$; $[Co(CO)_4]_2$; $Ni(CO)_4$; iron and cobalt compounds obtained under pressure
Halogens (in excess)	FeX_3 (X = F, Cl, Br), FeI_2; CoX_2 (X = Cl, Br, I), CoF_2 and CoF_3; NiX_2		
Carbon	Fe_3C above 1200°; Co_3C and Ni_3C, stable only at temperatures of the molten metals	Carbon dioxide	FeO + CO; no reactions reported for Co and Ni
		Water (g)	$Fe_3O_4 + H_2$; CoO $+ H_2$; NiO $+ H_2$

oxidizing agents such as concentrated nitric acid, dichromate ion, or hydrogen peroxide the metals become passive. Warm dilute nitric acid dissolves the metals, iron being changed at least in part to the tripositive state and cobalt and nickel to the dipositive state. Massive iron is readily attacked by moist air at ordinary temperatures, with the formation of a surface coating of rust, a hydrated iron(III) oxide; cobalt and nickel do not undergo a similar atmospheric oxidation.

22.15 At elevated temperatures the metals are reactive toward a variety of reagents. A summary of a number of reactions is given in Table 22.2.

The Hexa- and Pentapositive States

22.16 The ferrates (ferrate(VI) compounds) are substances containing FeO_4^{2-} in which iron exhibits its known maximum oxidation state. They can best be obtained by the chlorine oxidation of suspensions of hydrous iron(III) oxide in concentrated alkaline solutions. Anodic oxidation of iron in alkaline medium also yields the ferrate(VI) ion. The iron(VI) compounds are deep red to purple in color, the sodium and potassium salts being very soluble in water and the barium compound relatively insoluble.

22.17 In alkaline solution the ferrate(VI) ion is relatively stable toward decomposition; in neutral medium or in the presence of a nonoxidizable acid it is converted to iron(III) with the liberation of oxygen. The ferrate(VI) ion is a more potent oxidant than permanganate. In alkaline medium it converts chromium(III) quantitatively to the $+6$ state and arsenite to arsenate; it is capable of oxidizing aqueous ammonia to nitrogen in the cold. The solid compounds decompose when heated, oxygen and iron(III) compounds being among the products of reaction.

22.18 X-ray examination shows marked similarities between FeO_4^{2-}, SO_4^{2-}, and CrO_4^{2-}; the potassium salts of these ions form mixed crystals. The ferrate(VI) ion is paramagnetic, the molar susceptibility of the potassium salt being 3.06 ± 0.02 Bohr magnetons. This value is in concordance with the theoretical moment (2.83 Bohr magnetons) expected for hexapositive iron with two unpaired $3d$ electrons.

22.19 Iron(V) has been obtained only recently.[1] Reaction at 450° between potassium superoxide, KO_2 (see 10.9 *ff.*), and iron(II) oxide in the molar ratio 3K : 1Fe gives quantitative yields of a black substance of the composition K_3FeO_4. This compound has been characterized as a true Fe(V) material by its X-ray diagram and also by magnetic susceptibility measurements. It exhibits a molar susceptibility of 3.6–3.7 Bohr magnetons (theoretical for Fe^{5+}, 3.87). In aqueous solution the ferrate(V) disproportionates into ferrate(VI) and hydrous iron(III) oxide.

22.20 Interaction between potassium superoxide and cobalt(II) oxide at 300° and 50 atm. oxygen pressure gives a substance having essentially the composition $KCoO_3$.[1] Although it has not been characterized definitely, this substance presumably contains pentapositive cobalt.

[1] KLEMM, *Angew. Chem.*, **66**, 468 (1954).

The Tetrapositive State

22.21 There appears to be little question that cobalt and nickel can form dioxides (probably hydrated), although the corresponding compound for iron is unknown. The oxidation of cobalt(II) solutions by iodine dissolved in concentrated solutions of alkali yields a black precipitate in which, according to studies on its oxidizing power, at least part of the metal is in the tetrapositive condition.[2] Similarly, the action of a variety of strong oxidizing agents, *e.g.*, chlorine, on dipositive nickel in alkaline medium gives precipitates containing as much as 1.9 atoms of oxygen per atom of nickel.[3] In neither the cobalt nor nickel case is there evidence of peroxide formation. Nickel(IV) oxide is a powerful oxidizing agent, capable of converting dipositive manganese to permanganate ion in acid solution.

22.22 Barium and strontium oxy salts of iron(IV) can be prepared from the hexahydroxoferrates(III) of these elements.[4] At elevated temperatures (300° for the barium compound and 400–500° for the strontium salt), the hexahydroxoferrates(III) are converted practically quantitatively to ferrate(IV) salts by molecular oxygen.

$$Ba_3[Fe(OH)_6]_2 + \tfrac{1}{2}O_2 = 2BaFeO_3 + Ba(OH)_2 + 5H_2O$$

In the products, the alkaline earth hydroxide appears to be bound chemically to the ferrate(IV); attempts to extract it result in extensive decomposition of the ferrate(IV) compound. Orthoferrates(IV) of barium and strontium, $M^{II}_2FeO_4$, are obtained by reaction at high temperatures (800–900°) of 1 to 1 molar mixtures of the hexahydroxoferrate(III) compounds and the metal hydroxides with oxygen.

$$Sr_3[Fe(OH)_6]_2 + Sr(OH)_2 + \tfrac{1}{2}O_2 = 2Sr_2FeO_4 + 7H_2O$$

Ferrate(IV) compounds are decomposed slowly by water and dissolve in acids with the liberation of oxygen and the formation of iron(III). (*Cf.* the analogous behavior of ferrates(VI).)

22.23 A barium cobaltate(IV) of the composition Ba_2CoO_4 has been prepared by the high temperature (1050°) oxidation of $Ba_2[Co(OH)_6]$ or of a 2 to 1 molar mixture of barium hydroxide and cobalt(II) hydroxide. It is a red-brown material which undergoes slow decomposition when in contact with water.

22.24 One type of cationic complex of iron(IV) is known [5]: $[FeX_2diarsine_2]^{2+}$. Treatment of a nitrobenzene solution of $[FeCl_2(o\text{-}C_6H_4(As(CH_3)_2)_2)_2][FeCl_4]$ with concentrated nitric acid gives an intensely dark solution. Addition of iron(III) chloride to this solution yields a black moisture-sensitive precipitate of the composition $[FeCl_2(o\text{-}C_6H_4(As(CH_3)_2)_2)_2][FeCl_4]_2$. The following evidence demonstrates the presence of iron(IV) in the cation. The molecular conductivity

[2] METZL, *Z. anorg. Chem.*, **86**, 358 (1914).

[3] BELLUCCI and CLAVARI, *Atti accad. Lincei* [5], **14**, II, 234 (1905); **16**, I, 647 (1907); *Gazz. chim. ital.*, **36**, I, 58 (1906); BOSWELL and ILER, *J. Am. Chem. Soc.*, **58**, 924 (1936).

[4] SCHOLDER, *Angew. Chem.*, **65**, 240 (1953); **66**, 461 (1954).

[5] NYHOLM and PARISH, *Chemistry and Industry*, 1956, p. 470.

of the compound is of the order of magnitude expected for a bi-univalent electrolyte. The molar susceptibility of the cation is 2.98 Bohr magnetons, a value in good agreement with that (2.83) expected for a D^2SP^3 Fe(IV) inner orbital complex,* in which there would be two unpaired electrons (see below).

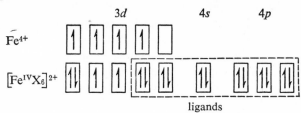

Conductimetric titration of the complex with iodide ion in nitrobenzene solution results in the liberation of iodine and a sharp end point after the addition of one equivalent of iodine per mole of compound. Reducing agents such as sulfur dioxide convert the complex to the original iron(III) compound.

22.25 Heteropolymolybdates of cobalt(IV) and nickel(IV) of the compositions $3K_2O \cdot CoO_2 \cdot 9MoO_3 \cdot 6\frac{1}{2}H_2O$ and $3BaO \cdot NiO_2 \cdot 9MoO_3 \cdot 12H_2O$ have been known for many years.[6] These substances are made by oxidation of dipositive cobalt and nickel in alkaline medium by ammonium peroxydisulfate in the presence of ammonium molybdate. The compounds are intensely colored and are strong oxidizing agents. The nickel compound is diamagnetic,[7] indicating that the tetrapositive nickel acts as the central atom of an anionic inner orbital complex with octahedral D^2SP^3 bonds.

22.26 A number of other complexes of nickel(IV) have been reported and are described briefly below. Oxidation of nickel(II) sulfate by sodium or potassium peroxydisulfate in the presence of periodate ion gives dark purple, insoluble crystals of the composition $Na(K)NiIO_6 \cdot xH_2O$.[7] No definite information regarding the structure of this complex is available. Barium nickelate(IV), $BaNiO_3$, is produced as a black powder by reaction at 700° between oxygen and an equimolar mixture of barium hydroxide and nickel(II) oxide.[8] The compound is insoluble in alkaline solutions but reacts readily with acids, the nickel being reduced to the dipositive state. Potassium hexafluoronickelate(IV), $K_2[NiF_6]$, has been obtained by the fluorination at 275° of a 2 : 1 molar mixture of potassium and nickel(II) chlorides.[9] The red compound is decomposed by water. X-ray measurements, which show that the complex exhibits a cubic structure like that of $K_2[PtCl_6]$, substantiate the presence of tetrapositive nickel. Moreover, the compound is diamagnetic,[10]

[6] HALL, *J. Am. Chem. Soc.*, **29**, 692 (1907).
[7] RÂY and SARMA, *J. Indian Chem. Soc.*, **25**, 205 (1948).
[8] LANDER and WOOTEN, *J. Am. Chem. Soc.*, **73**, 2452 (1951).
[9] KLEMM and HUSS, *Z. anorg. Chem.*, **258**, 221 (1949).
[10] HOPPE, *Angew. Chem.*, **62**, 339 (1950); NYHOLM and SHARPE, *J. Chem. Soc.*, 1952, p. 3579.

* Each molecule of diarsine occupies two coordination positions, coordination occurring through the tertiary arsenic atoms.

indicating D^2SP^3 binding in the anion. The formation of nickel(IV) complexes with salts of organic thio acids functioning as chelating groups has been mentioned in connection with the preparation of nickel tetracarbonyl (see 13.54). A cationic complex of nickel(IV), analogous to that of tetrapositive iron described above, has been prepared. Oxidation of $[NiCl_2(o\text{-}C_6H_4(As(CH_3)_2)_2)_2]Cl$ (see 22.52) by means of concentrated nitric acid in the presence of perchloric acid gives the deep-blue insoluble substance $[NiCl_2(o\text{-}C_6H_4(As(CH_3)_2)_2)_2](ClO_4)_2$ which possesses an oxidizing capacity consistent with the presence of tetrapositive nickel.[11] The compound is essentially diamagnetic, a fact in concordance with the expected octahedral (D^2SP^3) binding of the nickel(IV).

22.27 It is evident from the preceding discussion that the tetrapositive state of iron, cobalt, and nickel can be stabilized by complexing with the very electronegative oxygen ligand, and $+4$ nickel also by complexing with the even more electronegative fluoride ligand. This is not unexpected in view of the great resistance of these ligands toward oxidation. It is, however, surprising to find that nickel(IV) can also be stabilized by ligands of low electronegativity as exemplified by salts of certain organic thio acids and the diarsine, which also stabilizes iron(IV), noted above. Stabilization by these groups of low electronegativity (groups which can function as reducing agents toward metals in high oxidation states) can be effected when the method of preparation of the desired compound is indirect, *i.e.*, by oxidation of a complex containing the ligand already strongly bound to the metal in a lower oxidation state.

The Tripositive State

Oxides and Related Compounds   **22.28** Of the three possible anhydrous oxides of the elements in the $+3$ state only Fe_2O_3 is known. Hydrated oxides for both cobalt(III) and nickel(III) exist, and in addition, it has been claimed that the oxide Co_3O_4 contains both di- and tripositive cobalt.*

22.29 Iron(III) oxide is known in two forms, one (the α-form) paramagnetic and the other (the γ-modification) ferromagnetic. The former occurs in nature as *hematite* (see 22.12) and can also be obtained by the dehydration of the so-called α-form of $Fe_2O_3 \cdot H_2O$ (*limonite*, see 22.12), or by decomposition of iron(III) nitrate or oxalate. The γ-modification is produced when the γ-form of $Fe_2O_3 \cdot H_2O$ (which is found in nature as *lepidocrocite*) is heated. The γ-oxide is transformed into the α-form at temperatures above $400°$.

22.30 The oxide Fe_3O_4, which occurs in nature as *magnetite*, can be synthesized by burning iron filings in air at $500°$ (Table 22.2). This compound has been shown to be composed of both iron(II) and iron(III) oxides and possesses a spinel structure (see 12.41). The oxide is a black, acid-insoluble, strongly ferromagnetic substance. Ignition in air at temperatures above $500°$ gives Fe_2O_3.

---

[11] NYHOLM, *J. Chem. Soc.*, 1951, p. 2602.

* As in the case of Mn_3O_4 (see 21.41), there is considerable question as to the correct formulation of Co_3O_4. Both $CoO \cdot Co_2O_3$ and $2CoO \cdot CoO_2$ have been proposed, with the latter apparently being favored by X-ray evidence.

22.31 Iron(III) hydroxide of the composition $Fe(OH)_3$ has not been made. The gelatinous red-brown precipitate formed on addition of ammonia water to solutions of iron(III) salts is a hydrous oxide, $Fe_2O_3 \cdot xH_2O$, which when freshly prepared is amorphous to X-rays.

22.32 Fresh hydrous iron(III) oxide and also the anhydrous oxide, unless it has been strongly heated, are soluble in strong acids and to some extent in hot solutions of strong bases. Solution in strong acid yields hydrated Fe^{3+}; from these solutions (which vary in color depending upon the quantity and nature of the acid present), hydrated, water-soluble salts can be obtained by crystallization, *e.g.*, $FeCl_3 \cdot 6H_2O$, $Fe(NO_3)_3 \cdot 6H_2O$. Soluble salts of strong acids are moderately hydrolyzed in water, giving distinctly acidic solutions.

$$Fe(H_2O)_6^{3+} + H_2O \rightleftharpoons [Fe(H_2O)_5OH]^{2+} + H_3O^+$$

22.33 From hot solutions of the hydrous oxide in aqueous alkali metal hydroxides, ferrate(III) salts (commonly known as ferrites) can be isolated, *e.g.*, $NaFeO_2$. These compounds are more easily made by fusion of iron(III) oxide with alkali metal hydroxides or carbonates in the appropriate stoichiometric proportions. The alkali metal ferrate(III) salts are stable in solution only in the presence of a large excess of hydroxide ion; in neutral solution they immediately decompose, yielding the hydrous oxide. Structural analysis of potassium ferrate(III) has shown it to consist of a continuous network of FeO_4 tetrahedra, with potassium ions enmeshed in the network. It is interesting that many oxides of the MO type, *e.g.*, MgO, ZnO, CdO, unite with iron(III) oxide at elevated temperatures to give spinel-type compounds (see 12.41) rather than ferrate(III) salts. Hexahydroxoferrate(III) salts of strontium and barium, $M^{II}_3[Fe(OH)_6]_2$, have been obtained as white, microcrystalline powders by reaction at boiling temperatures of concentrated solutions of the alkaline earth metal hydroxides with solutions of iron(III) perchlorate.[4]

22.34 The monohydrate of cobalt(III) oxide, $Co_2O_3 \cdot H_2O$, occurs in nature as the mineral *stainierite*. The compound can be prepared as a brown or black powder by the drying at 150° of the hydrous oxide formed by atmospheric oxidation of cobalt(II) hydroxide suspended in potassium hydroxide solution. When the monohydrate is heated to 300° it begins to lose oxygen as well as water, yielding black Co_3O_4 (see 22.28).

22.35 No simple salts of tripositive cobalt appear to have been made by reaction of the sesquioxide hydrate with acids. This is not surprising in view of the strong oxidizing power of the tripositive cobalt cation in aqueous solution (see 22.4 for the Co^{2+}–Co^{3+} potential). The "simple" salts which have been isolated from water solution, *e.g.*, $CoF_3 \cdot 3\frac{1}{2}H_2O$ and $Co_2(SO_4)_3 \cdot 18H_2O$, are obtained by oxidation, usually electrolytic, of dipositive cobalt in the presence of a large excess of the appropriate acid. These substances are immediately decomposed by water with the evolution of oxygen. It should be pointed out that the hydrated salts noted above are probably not simple in the sense that the water molecules are bound to the tripositive cobalt by ion-dipole forces. It has been demonstrated that the hydrated cobalt(III) ion, $Co^{3+} \cdot$ aq., is diamagnetic, a fact which is indicative of inner orbital D^2SP^3 binding in the ion (see 22.46).

22.36 Although its existence has been disputed in the past, there is little doubt that nickel(III) oxide can be made, but in hydrated form. Reaction of bromine water with a suspension of nickel(II) hydroxide in potassium hydroxide solution at 25° gives a black product the analysis of which, after drying *in vacuo*, corresponds essentially to $Ni_2O_3 \cdot 2H_2O$.[12] Thermal decomposition of the hydrate is accompanied by the loss of oxygen and water and the formation of nickel(II) oxide. There is evidence that the monohydrate can be formed also under appropriate experimental conditions. Investigation of the X-ray absorption spectrum of the dihydrate shows that it does not consist of both nickel(II) and nickel(IV) and therefore must contain tripositive nickel.

Anhydrous Halides   **22.37** The anhydrous trihalides of the $3d$ transition triad elements are limited to the complete series for iron and to the fluoride for cobalt, no such compounds being known for nickel. The lack of simple halides of tripositive cobalt and nickel is consistent with the powerful oxidizing properties of these valence states. Of the trihalides of iron only the iodide has not been isolated in the pure condition; the compound decomposes (even at ordinary temperature) in accordance with the following equilibrium.

$$2FeI_3 \rightleftharpoons 2FeI_2 + I_2$$

The fluoride, chloride, and bromide of iron(III) can be made by direct union of the elements. Union of fluorine with elementary cobalt gives a mixture of di- and trifluoride, and the latter is obtained pure by reaction of fluorine with cobalt(II) chloride at 150°.

22.38 Iron trifluoride is a greenish, relatively nonvolatile substance, which is slightly soluble in water. The aqueous solutions, which are essentially neutral, have a low electrical conductivity and give practically no test for free fluoride or iron(III) ions. The trichloride is a red, deliquescent solid which melts and sublimes at 300°. When heated in a vacuum to temperatures above 500°, it undergoes dissociation into the dichloride and chlorine. The vapor of the trichloride at temperatures up to at least 400° is in the form of Fe_2Cl_6 molecules. The compound in the vapor state possesses a structure similar to that of aluminum chloride (see 12.47), that is, it is made up of two $FeCl_4$ tetrahedra with two halogen atoms being held in common. The Fe—Cl bond distance of 2.17 Å is very close to the value expected for a single covalent bond between these atoms. Above 750°, the vapor consists almost entirely of $FeCl_3$ molecules. Iron(III) chloride is soluble in a variety of organic solvents and solvates can be isolated from those solvents which possess donor properties, *e.g.*, $FeCl_3 \cdot (C_2H_5)_2O$. The compound is monomeric in most donor solvents.

22.39 The tribromide is very similar to the chloride in properties. It does, however, decompose more readily to dihalide and free halogen.

[12] CAIRNS and OTT, *J. Am. Chem. Soc.*, **55**, 534 (1933); **56**, 1094 (1934).

Complex Compounds **22.40** Tripositive iron has a considerable tendency to form coordination compounds. All three possible types of complexes — cationic, anionic, and nonelectrolytic — have been characterized. In all the solid complexes which have been isolated the iron exhibits a coordination number of six, and union of iron to its ligands by both inner orbital and outer orbital bonds is known. The ability of tripositive iron to form complexes with halogens, oxygen donors, and cyanide ion is particularly great; the affinity for nitrogen donors appears somewhat smaller, although some rather stable complexes with such donors which are capable of chelation have been prepared. A number of observations regarding some of the more common complexes are given below.

22.41 Cationic complexes which have been isolated appear to be almost entirely limited to those with nitrogen donors. Compounds with monodentate donor molecules such as ammonia, pyridine, and quinoline possess little stability; they exhibit high vapor pressures of the nitrogen compound (*e.g.*, $[Fe(NH_3)_6]Cl_3$ has a dissociation pressure of 324 mm. at 49°) and are immediately decomposed by water with the precipitation of hydrous iron(III) oxide. Chelates with such donors as dipyridyl and *o*-phenanthroline, *e.g.*, $[Fe\ dipy_3]^{3+}$, are more stable toward reaction with water and in general more inert toward substitution of the coordinated molecules by other ligands.

22.42 Among the anionic complexes, compounds with halide ion and oxygen donors as ligands are numerous. Compounds in which iron trihalides act as acceptors toward halide ion are found for the fluoride, chloride, and bromide, the dissociative stability decreasing with increasing size of the halogen. Fluoro complexes which have been isolated from aqueous solution include M^IFeF_4, $M^I_2FeF_5$, and $M^I_3FeF_6$, with the pentafluoro derivatives being the most common. Inasmuch as the pentafluoro complexes are invariably hydrated, it is probable that they contain $[FeF_5(H_2O)]^{2-}$. Both $[NH_4]_3[FeF_6]$ and $[NH_4]_2[FeF_5(H_2O)]$ have magnetic moments of 5.9 Bohr magnetons, corresponding to the presence of five unpaired electrons and indicating that the complexes are of the outer orbital SP^3D^2 type. A large number of chloro complex salts similar in composition to the fluorides, and also of the type $M^I_4FeCl_7$, have been prepared. Here again, the most common complexes are ordinarily of the pentahalic variety, and these are usually monohydrates. X-ray investigation of ammonium pentachloroferrate(III) 1-hydrate shows that this substance contains the octahedral $[FeCl_5(H_2O)]^{2-}$ anion. Relatively few bromide complexes have been isolated and those which have are of two types, M^IFeBr_4 and $M^I_2FeBr_5 \cdot xH_2O$. These salts are unstable green-black substances which cannot be recrystallized from water without decomposition.

22.43 Common anionic complexes with oxygen donors include those with carbonate, oxalate, tartrate, and phosphate. Some of these complexes are known only in solution and their compositions have not been determined. The oxalato complexes are relatively stable and have been well characterized. They are of the types $M^I_3[Fe(C_2O_4)_3]$ (hydrated) and $M^IFe(C_2O_4)_2$. The latter are also hydrated and probably contain $[Fe(C_2O_4)_2(H_2O)_2]^-$ as the anion.

22.44 Particularly inert with respect to substitution by other ligands are the anionic complexes containing cyanide ion. The main classes of such compounds are the hexacyanoferrates(III), $M^I_3[Fe(CN)_6]$, and the pentacyano or prusside complexes, e.g., $M^I_2[Fe(CN)_5H_2O]$, with the former being by far the more abundant. The hexacyano compounds are formed by oxidation of hexacyanoferrates(II) by means of strong oxidizing agents.

$$Cl_2 + 2[Fe(CN)_6]^{4-} = 2Cl^- + 2[Fe(CN)_6]^{3-}$$

Hexacyanoferrate(III) complexes are generally dark red in color when anhydrous and yellow or brown when hydrated. They give yellow aqueous solutions, in which, under the influence of light, the hexacyanoferrate(III) ion is transformed slowly into $[Fe(CN)_5H_2O]^{2-}$. The hexacyanoferrate(III) ion has a magnetic moment corresponding to the presence of one unpaired electron, suggesting that the complex is of the inner orbital D^2SP^3 type. The octahedral structure has been confirmed by X-ray analysis.

22.45 Examples of nonelectrolyte complexes of iron(III) are the chelates formed with β-diketones and salicylic acid. Thus the acetylacetone derivative has the constitution shown. It is readily soluble in organic solvents, stable to acids, and decomposed by alkalies.

22.46 Tripositive cobalt has an extraordinarily strong tendency to form complex compounds (see 22.35). In these substances cobalt is invariably 6-coordinate and in almost every case it is bound to its ligands by inner orbital D^2SP^3 bonds, as is indicated by the diamagnetism of the compounds. At least one complex, $K_3[CoF_6]$, appears to be of the outer orbital type, having a magnetic moment of 5.3 Bohr magnetons, a value very close to the theoretical (4.90) for four unpaired electrons. Configurations for inner and outer orbital complexes of Co(III) are given below.

Inner orbital complexes of tripositive cobalt are generally relatively inert toward substitution reactions and toward reduction.

22.47 Cobalt(III) forms particularly strong complexes with nitrogen donors, and the great majority of the known coordination compounds are ammines.

The hexamminecobalt(III) ion, $[Co(NH_3)_6]^{3+}$, may be regarded as the parent ion of the ammine compounds. The six coordination positions may be occupied by polydentate amines, e.g., $H_2NCH_2CH_2NH_2$ or $H_2NCH_2CH(NH_2)CH_2NH_2$; by mixtures of monodentate and polydentate amines; by combinations of ammine groups and water, e.g., $[Co(NH_3)_4(H_2O)_2]^{3+}$; by mixtures of ammine and negative groups, e.g., $[Co(NH_3)_4Cl_2]^+$; or by combinations of ammine, water, and negative groups, e.g., $[Co(NH_3)_2(H_2O)_2Cl_2]^+$.

22.48 Among other complexes of significance are those with cyanide ion and with oxygen donors. The cyano compounds are primarily of the type $M^I_3[Co(CN)_6]$. One type of pentacyano complex, $M^I_2[Co(CN)_5CO]$, has been isolated in the solid state, and there is evidence for the existence in solution of $[Co(CN)_5(H_2O)]^{2-}$. It is interesting that the free acid $H_3[Co(CN)_6] \cdot H_2O$ can be obtained by evaporation of acidified aqueous solutions of the hexacyano salts.

22.49 Examples of complexes with oxygen donors are the nonelectrolyte chelates with β-diketones, analogous to those formed with iron(III), mixed ammine-carbonato derivatives such as $[Co(NH_3)_5(CO_3)]^+$, oxalates of the type $M^I_3[Co(C_2O_4)_3]$, and mixed derivatives with ammines, e.g., $[Co(NH_3)_5(C_2O_4)]^+$.

22.50 In addition to the mononuclear complex types noted above, tripositive cobalt forms polynuclear complexes in which such groups as amido (NH_2^-), hydroxo (OH^-), and peroxo (O_2^{2-}) act as bridges for the cobalt atoms. Examples of such complexes are given.

Ion (a), decammine-μ-peroxodicobalt(III), is obtained as one of the products of oxidation of ammoniacal solutions of cobalt(II) with atmospheric oxygen.

22.51 A number of complexes of nickel(III) have been characterized unequivocally, and these are described below. Oxidation of the red, planar bis(triethylphosphine)dibromonickel(II), $[NiBr_2 \cdot 2(C_2H_5)_3P]$, by bromine yields a violet substance of the composition $NiBr_3 \cdot 2(C_2H_5)_3P$. In view of the monomeric character of the compound in benzene solution, the nickel is assumed to be 5-coordinate. The presence of tripositive nickel is indicated by the magnetic moment of the compound, $1.7 - 1.9$ Bohr magnetons, which corresponds to one unpaired electron. On the basis of the dipole moment, $2.5\ D$, it has been proposed that the complex has the square pyramid structure shown. Two alternative electronic configurations are possible for the square pyramid structure: $3D4S4P^3$, with the unpaired electron in a $3d$ orbital; and $3D^24S4P^2$, with the unpaired electron promoted to a $4p$ orbital.

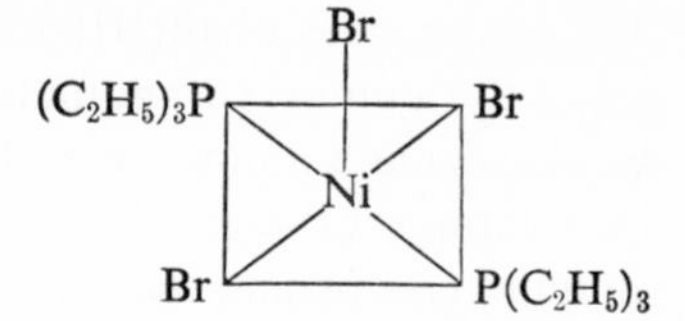

22.52 A series of stable nickel(III) complexes has been obtained with the strongly coordinating o-bis(dimethylarsino)benzene as one of the ligands. (See 22.24–26 for the use of this chelating agent for the preparation of Fe(IV) and Ni(IV) complexes.) Oxidation of complex $[Ni(C_6H_4(As(CH_3)_2)_2)_2]Cl_2$ by air in the presence of hydrochloric acid gives a greenish yellow precipitate of the constitution $[NiCl_2(C_6H_4(As(CH_3)_2)_2)_2]Cl$. Proof for this octahedral formulation comes from conductivity studies, titration of ionic chlorine with silver ion, and magnetic measurements, the latter showing the presence of one unpaired electron in the molecule. The anionic chloride can be replaced by such anions as ClO_4^- or $[PtCl_6]^{2-}$. The tripositive nickel complex is stable in air, but can be reduced by such agents as sulfur dioxide or tin(II) chloride to the complex containing $+2$ nickel. Analogous nickel(III) complexes containing coordinated bromide and thiocyanate in place of chloride have been prepared. It has been suggested that the bonding in the nickel(III) complexes is $3D^24S4P^3$, with promotion of the unpaired electron to a $5s$ orbital. This formulation is supported by the fact that the chloro complex (see 22.26) as well as the bromo compound can be oxidized to Ni(IV) compounds.

22.53 Nickelate(III) compounds of the type M^INiO_2 (M = Li, Na) have been prepared by bubbling oxygen through melts of the alkali metal hydroxides contained in nickel tubes at about $800°$.[13] The sodium derivative can also be obtained by reaction of a 1 : 3 molar mixture of sodium peroxide and hydroxide in a nickel tube. $LiNiO_2$ is rhombohedral; the sodium salt exists in two crystalline modifications, with a transition temperature at $220°$, the low temperature form being a monoclinic distortion of the $LiNiO_2$ structure. The compounds are strong oxidizing agents.

The Dipositive State

Oxides and Related Compounds **22.54** Oxides and hydroxides are known for all the $3d$ transition triad elements in the dipositive state. The anhydrous oxides are commonly obtained by ignition of appropriate oxygen-containing salts, e.g., FeC_2O_4, $CoCO_3$, $Ni(NO_3)_2$, or $NiCO_3$, in the absence of air. The hydroxides are formed as the initial products of precipitation when oxygen-free aqueous solutions of the dipositive cations are treated with hydroxide ion.

22.55 If formed at not too high a temperature, FeO is a black, pyrophoric substance, capable of decomposing water. The oxide, which possesses the

---

[13] DYER, BORIE and SMITH, *J. Am. Chem. Soc.*, **76**, 1499 (1954).

sodium chloride structure, invariably contains less oxygen than corresponds to the ideal formulation. The oxide as well as the hydroxide, $Fe(OH)_2$, are predominantly basic in character and dissolve in acids to give pale green solutions containing hydrated Fe^{2+}. The freshly precipitated hydroxide is white in color, but rapidly darkens on exposure to air, combination with oxygen ultimately yielding hydrous iron(III) oxide. (See 22.4 for the potential of the $Fe(OH)_2$–$Fe(OH)_3$ couple.) Fresh iron(II) hydroxide is somewhat soluble in concentrated aqueous sodium hydroxide; from the resulting solution sodium hexahydroxoferrate(II), $Na_4[Fe(OH)_6]$, can be isolated in the form of blue-green crystals. The corresponding strontium and barium salts can be obtained from the solution by appropriate metathetical reactions.

22.56 Cobalt(II) oxide, prepared as described above, is an olive-green solid, which on ignition in air is converted to Co_3O_4. The oxide, like FeO and NiO, exhibits the sodium chloride crystal lattice. Cobalt(II) hydroxide exists in two forms; the blue form first obtained by adding alkali to an aqueous solution of a cobalt(II) salt changes to a pink modification on standing. The exact nature of the change is not definitely known, but it appears that both forms have essentially the same crystal structure and it is likely that the forms differ only in particle size. On standing in air, cobalt(II) hydroxide is oxidized, but less easily than the corresponding iron(II) compound, to yield hydrated cobalt(III) oxide (see 22.4). Cobalt(II) hydroxide is readily soluble in dilute acids, yielding the pink hydrated Co^{2+}. The hydroxide, like $Fe(OH)_2$ (see above), is also appreciably soluble in concentrated alkali, and from such solutions red-violet salts containing the hexahydroxocobaltate(II) ion, e.g., $Na_4[Co(OH)_6]$, $Sr_2[Co(OH)_6]$, have been obtained. These salts are readily air oxidized and are immediately decomposed by water with precipitation of the original hydroxide.

22.57 Nickel(II) oxide and hydroxide are green substances which dissolve readily in acids to give green solutions containing hydrated Ni^{2+}. When strongly heated the oxide is transformed into a gray material inert toward the action of acids. The hydroxide is also soluble in ammonia-water forming the blue-violet $[Ni(NH_3)_4]^{2+}$ and probably other mixed ammine complexes, e.g., $[Ni(NH_3)_4(H_2O)_2]^{2+}$, $[Ni(NH_3)_6]^{2+}$.

Other Simple Compounds **22.58** Soluble salts of the metals are conveniently produced by reaction of the metals or oxides (or hydroxides) with the appropriate acids. Among the common soluble salts of iron(II) are the chloride, bromide, iodide, nitrate, sulfate, and acetate. On crystallization from solution these are isolated in hydrated form; thus from solution at room temperature the following hydrates are obtained: $FeCl_2 \cdot 4H_2O$, $FeBr_2 \cdot 6H_2O$, $FeI_2 \cdot 4H_2O$, $Fe(NO_3)_2 \cdot 6H_2O$, $FeSO_4 \cdot 7H_2O$, and $Fe(C_2H_3O_2)_2 \cdot 4H_2O$. Insoluble salts obtained by metathetical reactions include the oxalate, carbonate, phosphate, and sulfide. The fluoride is slightly soluble and separates from solution as the 8-hydrate. The anhydrous halides can be prepared in the following ways: the fluoride and chloride by reduction of the trihalides by means of hydrogen at elevated temperatures or by heating metal and hydrogen halide; the bromide by direct union of the elements, provided the metal is in excess; and the iodide also by direct combination of the elements, even with the halogen in excess.

22.59 Soluble salts of cobalt(II) and nickel(II) also include the halides (the fluorides being somewhat less than moderately soluble), the nitrate, sulfate, and acetate. As with the analogous iron(II) compounds, the soluble salts of dipositive cobalt and nickel are obtained from solution as hydrates, *e.g.*, $CoBr_2 \cdot 6H_2O$, $NiSO_4 \cdot 7H_2O$. The insoluble salts also correspond with those of dipositive iron. Complete series of dihalides are known for cobalt and nickel and these can be obtained by union of the elements at high temperatures. The dihalides of cobalt and nickel, as well as those of iron, are nonvolatile substances.

Complex Compounds **22.60** Iron(II) and particularly nickel(II) form a large number of stable complexes. On the other hand, as has been already noted (see 22.5), many complex compounds of dipositive cobalt are extremely unstable with respect to oxidation.

22.61 Inasmuch as there is a close resemblance between the important types of iron(III) complexes (see 22.40 *ff.*) and those of dipositive iron, only a few observations regarding the latter will be made. As with the iron(III) compounds, complexes of dipositive iron with chelating ligands, *e.g.*, [Fe *o*-phen$_3$]$^{2+}$, are generally considerably more inert toward substitution than those with simple ligands. However, chelation does not invariably lead to inertness; such complexes as [Fe en$_3$]$^{2+}$ and [Fe(C$_2$O$_4$)$_3$]$^{4-}$ are labile toward substitution. Paralleling the situation existing with the iron(III) compounds, the only relatively inert complexes of iron(II) with simple ligands are those with cyanide ion, *e.g.*, [Fe(CN)$_6$]$^{4-}$. Although in the majority of its complexes dipositive iron exhibits a coordination number of six, a coordination number of four is not uncommon, *e.g.*, [Fe dik$_2$] (dik = a β-diketone).

22.62 In view of the instability of cobalt(II) complexes and the difficulty in isolating them in the pure condition, the discussion which follows is concerned primarily with a number of the compound types which have been definitely identified. In these substances cobalt exhibits coordination numbers of four and six.

22.63 Dipositive cobalt has a relatively strong tendency to unite with nitrogen donors. Thus, for example, most simple salts can take up ammonia in varying amounts, the common compositions of the products being $CoX_2 \cdot 6NH_3$, $CoX_2 \cdot 4NH_3$, and $CoX_2 \cdot 2NH_3$. The hexammines undoubtedly contain the octahedral [Co(NH$_3$)$_6$]$^{2+}$. The tetrammines are usually nonelectrolytes and the cobalt is therefore 6-coordinate. The diammines also appear to be nonionic substances and presumably have planar structures. In general, the ammoniates are readily decomposed by water. Complexes with alkyl and aryl amines, pyridine, and quinoline have also been characterized.

22.64 The tendency for +2 cobalt to combine with oxygen donors is less pronounced than with nitrogen-containing ligands. Examples of some of the compound types which have been isolated (exclusive of hydrates) are carbonato derivatives, *e.g.*, $K_2Co(CO_3)_2 \cdot 4H_2O$, oxalato salts like $M^I_2Co(C_2O_4)_2 \cdot xH_2O$, and nonelectrolytic β-diketone complexes. The carbonato and oxalato salt types undergo extensive decomposition in water. The acetylacetonate of cobalt(II) has the composition $Co(C_5H_7O_2)_2$, the metal having a coordination of four. The coordination number can be raised to six by further union with such molecules as ammonia or pyridine.

22.65 Complexes with all the halide ions, thiocyanate, cyanide, and other ions are known. The cyanide complexes deserve special mention. Addition of excess cyanide ion to solutions of cobalt(II) gives not a hexacyano complex but rather a pentacyano ion,[14] which has been formulated as $[Co(CN)_5H_2O]^{2-}$. From such solutions, also containing potassium ion, addition of ethanol produces a violet precipitate of the composition $K_3Co(CN)_5$.[15] The solid is diamagnetic, but paramagnetic in solution of aqueous cyanide, the susceptibility in this medium corresponding to one unpaired electron per cobalt atom. The diamagnetism of the solid suggests dimer formation, since an inner orbital complex of cobalt(II) would have one unpaired electron. It is worth noting that magnetic data show that in complexes in which +2 cobalt has coordination numbers of 4 and 6 it usually tends to exhibit outer orbital binding.[16]

22.66 It should be emphasized that experimentation with most cobalt(II) complexes must be performed in the absence of air.

22.67 The most stable coordination compounds of nickel are those formed by the element in the dipositive state, and in these compounds nickel is ordinarily 4- or 6-coordinate. The complexes of nickel(II) are most conveniently discussed in terms of their magnetic behavior.

22.68 The paramagnetic 4-coordinate complexes are usually green or blue in color and have magnetic moments generally of the order of 3.2–3.4 Bohr magnetons, indicating the presence of two unpaired electrons and the formation of outer orbital tetrahedral SP^3 bonds, as shown below. Examples of such paramagnetic complexes are $[Ni(NH_3)_4]SO_3$, $[Ni\ en_2](SCN)_2 \cdot H_2O$, and

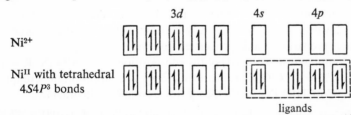

$[Ni(C_5H_7O_2)_2]$ (nickel(II) acetylacetonate). Recently, X-ray investigations of some of the 4-coordinate paramagnetic complexes have yielded evidence to support the tetrahedral structure.

22.69 Diamagnetic 4-coordinate complexes are ordinarily red, brown, or

[14] HUME and KOLTHOFF, *J. Am. Chem. Soc.*, **71**, 867 (1949).

[15] ADAMSON, *J. Am. Chem. Soc.*, **73**, 5710 (1951).

[16] SELWOOD, *Magnetochemistry*, 2nd Edition, Interscience Publishers, Inc., New York, 1956, pp. 225–226.

yellow in color. Representative of this class are $Na_2[Ni(CN)_4] \cdot 3H_2O$ and the nickel-dimethylglyoxime nonelectrolyte. The absence of unpaired electrons suggests that the binding in these complexes is of the planar (inner orbital) DSP^2 type, and this is supported by the available X-ray data.

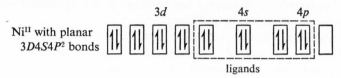

$$3d \qquad\qquad 4s \qquad\qquad 4p$$

Ni^{II} with planar
$3D4S4P^2$ bonds

ligands

22.70 Complexes in which nickel(II) is 6-coordinate are more numerous than the 4-coordinate compounds. Among the paramagnetic complexes of the former type are many hexammines, e.g., $[Ni(NH_3)_6]^{2+}$, $[Ni\ en_3]^{2+}$, $[Ni\ dipy_3]^{2+}$. The 6-coordinate compounds are usually blue or green in color, occasionally pink. Magnetic moment data are consistent with the presence of two unpaired electrons and therefore indicative of outer orbital SP^3D^2 binding. X-ray crystallographic analysis shows that the ligands are bound to the nickel in an octahedral fashion.

22.71 Only one diamagnetic 6-coordinate complex has definitely been isolated: $[Ni(C_6H_4(As(CH_3)_2)_2)_3](ClO_4)_2$. Presumably, in this complex the binding is of the $3D^24S4P^3$ type, with the two unpaired electrons originally in Ni^{2+} being promoted to an outer (5s) orbital.

22.72 In general, nickel(II) complexes with ammonia, ethylenediamine, oxalate, tartrate, and cyanide are relatively labile to substitution by other ligands. On the other hand complexes with a number of other chelating agents as ligands, e.g., $[Ni\ dipy_3]^{2+}$ and $[Ni\ o\text{-}phen_3]^{2+}$, are fairly inert. Thus, nickel is precipitated from these ions only on repeated treatment with hot ammonium sulfide solution.[17]

Oxidation States Lower Than $+ 2$[18]

22.73 Compound types in which iron, cobalt, and nickel are found in oxidation states lower than $+2$ have already been noted (see 22.10). A brief description of their preparation and properties follows.

22.74 Compounds of cobalt(I) of the composition $[Co(CNR)_5]X$ (R = phenyl, tolyl, etc.; X = I, ClO$_4$) are formed when the appropriate complexes of cobalt(II), $[Co(CNR)_4]X_2$, are reduced, for example by hydrazine.

$$5[Co(CNR)_4]I_2 + N_2H_4 = CoI_2 + 4[Co(CNR)_5]I + 4HI + N_2$$

The $+1$ cobalt complexes are soluble in polar organic solvents, but insoluble in such media as ether and petroleum ether. All the compounds are diamagnetic, a fact which is consistent with a formulation of inner orbital binding, with the cobalt having a true coordination number of five and the electronic configuration of krypton.

[17] TAUBE, Chem. Revs., **50**, 69 (1952).
[18] KLEINBERG, J. Chem. Educ., **29**, 324 (1952); **33**, 73 (1956).

22.75 Reaction between isonitriles and dimeric cobalt tetracarbonyl (see Table 13.4) proceeds in the following manner to yield complexes containing both cobalt(I) and cobalt(–I).

$$[Co(CO)_4]_2 + 5RNC \overset{benzene}{=} [Co(CNR)_5][Co(CO)_4] + 4CO$$

The same substances can also be obtained metathetically from $Na[Co(CO)_4]$ the preparation of which is described later (see 22.82).

$$Na[Co(CO)_4] + [Co(CNR)_5]ClO_4 \overset{organic}{\underset{solvent}{=}} [Co(CNR)_5][Co(CO)_4] + NaClO_4$$

22.76 An anionic complex of cobalt(I), $K_2[Co(CN)_3CO]$, can be prepared in solution by reaction in a carbon monoxide atmosphere between cobalt(II) in strongly alkaline medium and excess potassium cyanide.

$$2Co^{2+} + 3CO + 4OH^- + 6CN^- = 2[Co(CN)_3CO]^{2-} + CO_3^{2-} + 2H_2O$$

The presence of $+1$ cobalt in solution is established by titration with potassium hexacyanoferrate(III). Treatment of the solution with $[Fe\ o\text{-phen}_3]^{2+}$ gives a precipitate of $[Fe\ o\text{-phen}_3][Co(CN)_3CO] \cdot 3\frac{1}{2}H_2O$. Aqueous solutions of the Co(I) complex possess powerful reducing properties.

22.77 The only compound of nickel(I) which appears to have been characterized is a cyano complex of the composition $K_2Ni(CN)_3$. This deep red substance is obtained by reduction of $K_2[Ni(CN)_4]$ either in aqueous solution, e.g., by tin(II) chloride in alkaline solution, or in liquid ammonia, by potassium metal. X-ray analysis of the nickel(I) complex shows that the anion is dimeric and it has been proposed that the nickel atoms are bridged by cyanide groups. The compound must therefore be formulated as $K_4Ni_2(CN)_6$. It should be noted that the complex is diamagnetic. Since $+1$ nickel has an odd number of electrons and should exhibit paramagnetism, the diamagnetism indicates that the possibility of nickel-nickel bonding must not be overlooked.

22.78 Compounds, other than the carbonyls (see 13.51), in which cobalt and nickel exhibit an oxidation state of zero have only recently been synthesized. Reduction of potassium hexacyanocobaltate(III), $K_3[Co(CN)_6]$, with potassium in liquid ammonia yields a brown-violet, air-sensitive, pyrophoric cobalt(0) compound of the empirical formula $K_4Co(CN)_4$. The complex has a slight degree of paramagnetism, considerably less than that required for a single cobalt(0) atom with one unpaired electron. On this basis $Co(CN)_4^{4-}$ is assumed to be dimeric. The compound is decomposed by water with the evolution of hydrogen.

22.79 Compounds of the general type $[Co(CO)_3A]_2$, where $A = P(OC_6H_5)_3$, $P(OC_6H_4Cl-p)_3$, $P(OC_6H_4F-p)_3$, and $P(C_6H_5)_3$, have been obtained from dimeric cobalt tetracarbonyl by direct replacement of carbon monoxide. These compounds are highly colored and relatively low melting.

22.80 Reduction of $K_2[Ni(CN)_4]$ by means of an excess of potassium in liquid ammonia (see $K_4Ni_2(CN)_6$, above) gives the copper-colored nickel(0) complex, $K_4[Ni(CN)_4]$. The compound is extremely unstable in air and evolves hydrogen from water. Reduction of the acetylide nickel(II) complex $K_2[Ni(C \equiv CH)_4]$, also by potassium in liquid ammonia, yields the corresponding nickel(0) compound, $K_4[Ni(C \equiv CH)_4]$. This compound is an orange-brown, highly pyrophoric substance.

22.81 The carbon monoxide in nickel tetracarbonyl can be completely replaced by other neutral ligands by reaction in an organic solvent such as ether or benzene. In this manner, compounds of the types $Ni(PX_3)_4$ and $Ni(CNR)_4$ (22.10) have been prepared. These substances are all diamagnetic materials, and presumably, they, like their parent $Ni(CO)_4$, exhibit tetrahedral SP^3 binding.

22.82 Salts of the carbonyl hydrides $Fe(CO)_4H_2$ and $Co(CO)_4H$ (see 13.63), in which iron and cobalt may be regarded as being in the respective oxidation states of -2 and -1, are obtained from the parent carbonyls. The action of sodium in liquid ammonia on $[Fe(CO)_4]_3$, $Fe(CO)_5$, or $Fe_2(CO)_9$ gives $Na_2[Fe(CO)_4]$, and $[Co(CO)_4]_2$ forms $Na[Co(CO)_4]$. Reaction of a variety of Lewis bases (amines and alcohols) with dimeric cobalt tetracarbonyl results in a disproportionation of the carbon monoxide-bonded metal.

$$3Co^0 = Co^{2+} + 2Co^-$$

Thus, with aqueous ammonia the following reaction occurs.

$$3[Co(CO)_4]_2 + 12NH_3 = 2[Co(NH_3)_6][Co(CO)_4]_2 + 8CO$$

In a similar fashion, the complex $[Co\ en_3][Co(CO)_4]_2$ is formed. This compound can be converted to $[Co\ o\text{-}phen_3][Co(CO)_4]_2$ by replacement of ethylenediamine by o-phenanthroline or to $[Ni\ o\text{-}phen_3][Co(CO)_4]_2$ by metathesis with $[Ni\ o\text{-}phen_3]Cl_2$. Reaction of $[Co\ en_3][Co(CO)_4]_2$ with sodium sulfide results in the precipitation of cobalt(II) sulfide and the formation of $Na[Co(CO)_4]$; treatment with acids yields the carbonyl hydride, $Co(CO)_4H$. These reactions, as well as the high conductivity in acetone of a variety of compounds containing the $Co(CO)_4$ group, demonstrate that the latter should be formulated as a mononegative species.

CHAPTER 23

THE TRANSITION TRIADS
II — THE PLATINUM METALS

Introduction

23.1 The elements of the $4d$ and $5d$ triads, commonly known as the platinum metals, have the following valence shell configurations: $_{44}$Ru, $4d^75s^1$; $_{45}$Rh, $4d^85s^1$; $_{46}$Pd, $4d^{10}$; $_{76}$Os, $5d^66s^2$; $_{77}$Ir, $5d^9$; $_{78}$Pt, $5d^96s^1$. A number of properties of these elements are shown in Table 23.1.

23.2 Probably the most striking characteristic of the platinum metals is their nobility, in contrast to the much greater reactivity of the members of the $3d$ triad. (For example, compare electrode potentials in Table 23.1 with those in Table 22.1.) Another significant difference between the platinum metals and the iron triad elements is found in the scarcity of simple compounds of the platinum metals. Simple cations of the platinum metals are rare, and perhaps exist only in some of the compounds of dipositive palladium.

23.3 The platinum metals exhibit a wide multiplicity of oxidation states. As with the iron triad, the tendency to attain higher states diminishes with increasing atomic number across both the $4d$ and $5d$ triads. Thus the highest oxidation state encountered, namely $+8$, is found only for ruthenium and osmium. A summary of valence states which appear to have been definitely characterized, exclusive of the zero state in carbonyls, is given below.

Ru, 2, 3, 4, 5, 6, 7, 8;   Rh, 1, 2, 3, 4;   Pd, 0, 2, 3, 4

Os, 2, 3, 4, 6, 8;   Ir, 0, 1, 2, 3, 4, 6;   Pt, 0, 2, 3, 4, 6

GENERAL REFERENCES

LATIMER, *The Oxidation States of the Elements and Their Potentials in Aqueous Solutions*, 2nd Edition, Prentice-Hall, Inc., New York, 1952, Ch. 12, 13, and 14.

REMY, *Treatise on Inorganic Chemistry* (translated and amended by Anderson), Elsevier Publishing Company, Amsterdam, 1956, Vol. II, Ch. 7, pp. 319–59.

SIDGWICK, *The Chemical Elements and Their Compounds*, Oxford University Press, London, 1950, pp. 1454–1628.

TABLE 23.1

Some Properties of the Platinum Metals

	Ru	Rh	Pd	Os	Ir	Pt
Natural isotopes	96, 98, 99, 100, 101, 102 *, 104	103	102, 104, 105, 106 *, 108, 110	184, 186, 187, 188, 189, 190, 192 *	191, 193 *	190, 192, 194, 195 *, 196, 198
Density, g./cc.	12.30	12.42	12.03	22.7	22.65	21.45
Melting point, °C.	ca. 2400	1966	1555	ca. 2700	2454	1774
Boiling point, °C.	ca. 4200	ca. 3900	3170	ca. 4600	ca. 4500	ca. 3800
Ionic radius, in crystals						
M^{2+}, Å	0.81	0.80	0.85	0.88	0.92	0.96
M^{3+}, Å	0.72	0.72	0.74	0.78	0.80	0.83
Covalent radius, Å	1.241	1.247	1.278	1.255	1.260	1.290
Ionization potential, volts						
1st electron	7.5	7.7	8.3(?)	8.7	9.2	8.8
Electrode potential, $E°$, in volts for						
$M = M^{2+} + 2e^-$				−0.987		ca. −1.2
$M = M^{3+} + 3e^-$		ca. −0.8			ca. −1.15	

* Most abundant isotope

The most important oxidation states, in the sense that they are most common, are the following.

Ru, 2, 3; Rh, 3; Pd, 2, 4
Os, 4, 6, 8; Ir, 3, 4; Pt, 2, 4

23.4 In the description of the chemistry of the platinum metals which follows, the properties of the elemental substances are first described. Then, since on the whole the vertical resemblances among the platinum metals are somewhat more pronounced than those in a horizontal direction, the compounds are discussed from the viewpoint that these elements can be subdivided conveniently into the ruthenium-osmium, rhodium-iridium, and palladium-platinum dyads. Emphasis is given to the preferred oxidation states noted above, and in addition, some aspects of the chemistry of the less common oxidation states are considered.

The Elements

23.5 The platinum metals occur in extremely small amounts in nature, the relative abundance in the earth's crust being $5 \times 10^{-7}\%$ for platinum, $1 \times 10^{-6}\%$ for palladium, and about $1 \times 10^{-7}\%$ for each of the remaining elements. The elements are found associated with one another, usually as the free metals, which often occur in alloy form. Moreover, the metals are commonly found mixed with ores of such metals as copper, silver, gold, iron, and nickel. A few well-defined compounds are also encountered, examples being *sperrylite*, $PtAs_2$, and *braggite*, PdS.

23.6 The separation of the platinum metals from the other metals with which they are associated and from each other requires tedious and complicated procedures which will not be considered here. The methods of separation and purification which have been developed give metals of purity ranging from 99.7 to over 99.9%.

23.7 The densities and melting and boiling points of the platinum metals are listed in Table 23.1. In the massive form ruthenium and osmium are gray, brittle metals possessing considerable hardness. Rhodium and iridium are hard, white metals; rhodium is ductile and iridium is brittle and of low ductility. Compact palladium and platinum are white, lustrous substances, considerably softer than the other platinum metals and very malleable. All the metals can be obtained in a black finely divided ("spongy") condition by reduction of their compounds, either in solution or in the solid state. In the finely divided state, the elements, and especially palladium and platinum, have high adsorptive

TABLE 23.2

Some Products of Reactions of the Platinum Metals

Reagent	Ru	Os	Rh	Ir	Pd	Pt
Oxygen	RuO_2 at 500° with powdered metal	OsO_4 at 200° with powdered metal	Rh_2O_3 slowly at red heat with powdered metal	IrO_2 at 1070° with powdered metal	PdO at red heat with powdered metal	PtO at 420–440° and 8 atm pressure
Fluorine	RuF_5 at 300° with powdered metal	OsF_8(?) and OsF_6 at 250°	RhF_3 slowly at 500–600°	IrF_6 gentle heating with powdered metal	PdF_3 at 500°	PtF_4 (mainly) at red heat
Chlorine	$RuCl_3$ at red heat with powdered metal	$OsCl_4$ at 650–700°	$RhCl_3$ below 440°	$IrCl_3$ at 600–620° with powdered metal	$PdCl_2$ at red heat	$PtCl_2$ above 250°
Nitric acid (hot)	No reaction	OsO_4 with conc'd acid and powdered metal	No reaction	No reaction	$Pd(NO_3)_2$ rapidly with conc'd acid	No reaction
Aqua regia	No reaction	OsO_4 with powdered metal	No reaction with massive metal	No reaction	$H_2[PdCl_6]$	$H_2[PtCl_6]$
KOH + KNO_3 (molten)	K_2RuO_4	K_2OsO_4	RhO_2(?)	Ir_2O_3	PdO	$K_2PtO_3 \cdot xH_2O$
$KHSO_4$ (molten)	No reaction	Reaction(?)	$Rh_2(SO_4)_3$	$Ir_2(SO_4)_3$	$PdSO_4$	Basic sulfate

power for many gases, particularly hydrogen.   Thus at ordinary temperatures palladium can take up 350–850 times its own volume of hydrogen.

23.8 Although chemically they are all noble in character, the platinum metals differ considerably among themselves in reactivity.   For example, in the massive condition only osmium and palladium dissolve in nitric acid, and osmium, palladium, and platinum are the only ones attacked by aqua regia. Moreover, reaction with a specific reagent frequently requires different conditions and more importantly often gives products corresponding to different oxidation states.   These points are brought out in Table 23.2 where the products of reactions of the platinum metals with a variety of reagents are listed.

Compounds of the Platinum Metals

Ruthenium and Osmium

Common Oxidation States   **23.9** The most commonly encountered oxidation states of ruthenium are +2 and +3.   Few simple compounds corresponding to the former state have been isolated,* and little is known of its chemistry in solution.   There appears to be little doubt that ruthenium(II) can be obtained in aqueous solution by reduction of the trichloride (see below).   The blue solutions so formed are extremely unstable and are readily oxidized, *e.g.*, by permanganate to ruthenate(VI), RuO_4^{2-}.

23.10 Complex compounds of dipositive ruthenium are fairly numerous and generally reasonably stable toward oxidation.   They are all diamagnetic, 6-coordinate, and relatively inert toward substitution.   They undoubtedly have the configuration shown below.

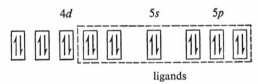

ligands

It is worth noting that in its complexes ruthenium(II) exhibits an effective atomic number of 54, corresponding to that of xenon.

23.11 Although the number of complexes is relatively large, only a few types have been obtained.   These include ammines, cyano derivatives, and nitrosyl compounds.

23.12 Ammine complexes with dipyridyl or tripyridyl molecules as ligands can be formed by reaction of ruthenium trichloride and the ammine, the latter functioning both as ligand and reducing agent.   The compounds are trichelate, *e.g.*, [Ru dipy₃]Cl₂, generally red in color, and extremely stable to the action of acids and bases.   Complexes containing ammonia as ligand are interesting

---

* The disulfide, diselenide, and ditelluride, which can be made by direct union of the elements at high temperatures, have the pyrite (FeS₂) structure and presumably contain dipositive ruthenium.

compounds. In these substances ammonia molecules occupy two, four, or five coordination positions, a coordination number of six being attained by the presence of sulfite or acid sulfite ions or neutral sulfur dioxide molecules, *e.g.*, $[Ru(NH_3)_4(SO_3H)_2]$, $Na_4[Ru(NH_3)_2(SO_3)_2(SO_3H)_2] \cdot 6H_2O$, $[Ru(NH_3)_5(SO_2)]Cl_2$, $[Ru(NH_3)_5(SO_3)] \cdot 2H_2O$. There appear to be no other complex compounds known which have the neutral sulfur dioxide molecule within the coordination sphere. The complexes are obtained by the action of bisulfite ion on appropriate ruthenium(III) compounds; for example, reaction of sodium bisulfite with $[Ru(NH_3)_5Cl]Cl$ gives $Na_4[Ru(NH_3)_2(SO_3)_2(SO_3H)_2]$ and $[Ru(NH_3)_4(SO_3H)_2]$.

23.13 The cyano complexes are primarily of the $[Ru(CN)_6]^{4-}$ type and are prepared by reduction of either tetroxoruthenate(VI) ion (see 23.39) or ruthenium trichloride by cyanide ion in hot aqueous solution. The alkali and alkaline earth metal salts are colorless materials, for the most part readily soluble in water. The free acid $H_4[Ru(CN)_6]$ has been isolated.

23.14 Ruthenium(II) nitrosyl complexes contain only one NO group in the molecule, the group functioning as a positive entity. Some examples of complexes of this type are $Ru(NO)X_3$ (X = Cl, Br, I), $M^I_2[Ru(CN)_5(NO)]$, and $M^I_2[Ru(NO)X_5]$. The chloride corresponding to the first type noted is a red substance which can be obtained in the form of a pentahydrate in a number of ways, one method being by evaporation of a solution of the tetroxide, *i.e.*, ruthenium(VIII) oxide (see 23.40), in hydrochloric acid with a large excess of nitric acid. The compound is readily soluble in water; treatment of the aqueous solution with alkali metal chloride gives $M^I_2[Ru(NO)Cl_5]$. The nitrosyl-cyanide complexes are formed when solutions of hexacyanoruthenate(II) salts in concentrated nitric acid are evaporated to dryness.

23.15 In terms of the number of compounds described, tripositive ruthenium is the most important oxidation state of the element. This is the lowest state for which binary compounds of the element have been characterized definitely.

23.16 Although no oxide of ruthenium(III) has yet been prepared, a hydroxide (or hydrous oxide) is apparently produced in an impure form when strong base is added to an aqueous solution of the trichloride. The black precipitate obtained is readily converted by air to the dioxide, RuO_2.

23.17 All the trihalides of ruthenium are known. The trifluoride has been obtained by the interaction of the pentafluoride (see 23.38) with a large excess of iodine at 150°.[1] It is a dark brown substance, insoluble in water and dilute

$$5RuF_5 + I_2 = 5RuF_3 + 2IF_5$$

acids and alkalies. The trichloride is commonly made by direct union of the elements at red heat in the presence of carbon monoxide. (Presumably carbonyl halides (see 13.67) are formed as intermediates.) Prepared in this fashion the trichloride is a black, water-insoluble substance, for which no structural

---

[1] AYNSLEY, PEACOCK, and ROBINSON, *Chem. Industry*, 1952, p. 1002.

information is available. A water-soluble monohydrate, $RuCl_3 \cdot H_2O$, can be obtained by evaporation of a solution of ruthenium(VIII) oxide (see 23.40) in hydrochloric acid in a stream of hydrogen chloride gas. The monohydrate is hygroscopic, giving brown-red solutions, which when freshly prepared give no test for ionic chlorine. Thus there is little doubt that the chloride is complex in nature. The tribromide is conveniently made, but not in a pure condition, by reaction between the hydroxide (see above) and hydrobromic acid. It is also a dark hygroscopic substance. The black, relatively insoluble triiodide is best prepared by the action of hydriodic acid on the tetroxide.

23.18 The most common coordination compounds of tripositive ruthenium are ammines and complex halides. The very great majority of the ammine complexes which have been prepared contain ammonia as ligand and they consist of the following types: $[Ru(NH_3)_6]^{3+}$, $[Ru(NH_3)_5X]^{2+}$, $[Ru(NH_3)_4X_2]^+$, and $[Ru(NH_3)_3X_3]$ (X = Cl, Br, etc.). The hexammines are formed as the ultimate products of reaction between ammonia and ruthenium trihalides. They are colorless substances which give neutral aqueous solutions and are relatively inert to substitution of ammonia molecules by other ligands. Thus treatment of the hexammine complexes with boiling concentrated hydrochloric acid results in the loss of only one ammonia molecule and the formation of the pentammine $[Ru(NH_3)_5Cl]^{2+}$. They are more sensitive to the action of alkalies, reacting to give as yet undetermined products. Tetrammines are obtained from appropriate ruthenium(II) ammine complexes; for example, reaction between $[Ru(NH_3)_4(SO_2)Br]Br$ with bromine yields the violet-red *trans*-$[Ru(NH_3)_4Br_2]Br$. The tetrammines, like the hexammines, are rather stable to attack by cold acids. The nonelectrolyte triammines (X = Cl or Br) are produced when the tetrammines are boiled with the appropriate hydrohalic acid. The ammine complexes are paramagnetic substances having magnetic moments of about 2 Bohr magnetons (theoretical spin-only value for one unpaired electron, 1.73).

23.19 Halo complexes of ruthenium(III) are formed only with chlorine and bromine as ligands and have compositions ranging from M^IRuX_4 to $M^I_4RuX_7$, with many of the compounds existing as hydrates. The complexes are generally made by reduction of compounds of ruthenium in higher oxidation states, *e.g.*, $RuCl_4 \cdot 5H_2O$, in appropriate media. The tetrahalo salts are red materials having at least two molecules of water of crystallization, and presumably the actual complex is best formulated as $M^I[RuX_4(H_2O)_2]$. Evidence for such formulation is afforded by the fact that the water cannot be removed without destruction of the complex. The best known pentachloro complex is the red 1-hydrate potassium salt, $K_2[RuCl_5(H_2O)]$. This can be dehydrated at 180–200° to give the black K_2RuCl_5. Alkali metal pentabromo complexes are known only in the form of the monohydrates. Hexahalo complexes have been obtained only with chloride as ligand; these are isolated as hydrates when solutions of pentachloro derivatives are saturated with hydrogen chloride. Heptachloro and heptabromo complexes are formed only as salts of organic amines.

23.20 The preferred oxidation states of osmium are $+4$, $+6$, and $+8$, with the first being the most stable. Binary compounds are known for all three oxidation states, but they are few in number, the majority of the compounds identified being complex in nature.

23.21 Binary compounds of tetrapositive osmium include the oxide, the fluoride, the chloride, and the iodide. Osmium(IV) oxide, OsO_2, is the lowest oxide of the element which has been characterized. It can be obtained in a number of ways, the best being by reaction between metal and osmium tetroxide (osmium(VIII) oxide). The compound is generally obtained as a black or brown powder, inert toward water and acids and easily reduced to the metal, *e.g.*, by hydrogen; it is converted to the tetroxide by heating in air. A hydrate of the composition $OsO_2 \cdot 2H_2O$ is formed when a solution of the tetroxide is reduced or when potassium hexachloroosmate(IV), $K_2[OsCl_6]$, (see below) is treated with alkali.

23.22 Osmium tetrafluoride, OsF_4, is formed in admixture with the hexa-fluoride by the incomplete fluorination of the powdered metal. It is a black, nonvolatile material, soluble in water with some hydrolysis. The tetrachloride is obtained as a black volatile substance by union of the elements at 650–700°. It dissolves slowly in water to give a yellow solution from which osmium(IV) oxide is rapidly deposited. The tetraiodide is formed as a violet-black hygroscopic material on evaporation of a solution of the hydrated dioxide with hydriodic acid.

23.23 Osmium(IV) forms many complexes, most of which are anionic. In these compounds, which are relatively stable to substitution, osmium is probably always 6-coordinate, with the configuration shown.

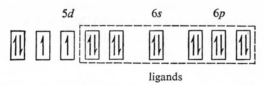

ligands

23.24 The great majority of the complexes which have been described contain the sulfito group, or halogen atoms, or both. Illustrative of the types of sulfito and mixed halogen-sulfito complexes are the following compounds: $M^I{}_8Os(SO_3)_6$, $M^I{}_6Os(SO_3)_5$, $M^I{}_7OsCl(SO_3)_5$, $M^I{}_6OsCl_2(SO_3)_4$, and $M^I{}_8OsCl_4(SO_3)_4$. Complexes with only sulfito groups as ligands have been obtained by the prolonged action of sodium bisulfite on $Na_6[OsO_2(SO_3)_4] \cdot 5H_2O$. The mixed chlorosulfito complexes have been produced by reaction between sulfites or bisulfites and hexachloroosmate(IV) salts. A large number of halo complexes have been made. These include the pure hexahalo derivatives $M^I{}_2[OsX_6]$ (X = F, Cl, Br, I); mixed hexahalo compounds, *e.g.*, $M^I{}_2[OsCl_5Br]$, $M^I{}_2[OsCl_3Br_3]$; and compounds containing five halogen atoms within the coordination sphere, *e.g.*, $M^I{}_2[Os(OH)Cl_5]$, $M^I{}_2[Os(OH)Cl_3Br_2]$, $M^I{}_2[Os(NH_2)Cl_5]$. Since the pure hexahalo derivatives are the most common of these compounds, only they are discussed briefly. Potassium hexafluoroosmate(IV) is obtained as a yellow crystalline material by neutralization of a solution of the tetrafluoride in hydrofluoric acid with potassium hydroxide, followed by evaporation of the resulting solution. Hexachloro and hexabromo complexes are formed by reduction by means of ethanol of aqueous solutions of osmium tetroxide containing the appropriate alkali metal salts. The hexachloro salts are brownish-red in color and the bromo compounds black. Both types of compounds are isomorphous with hexachloroplatinates(IV), $M^I_2[PtCl_6]$, which are octahedral. Hexaiodoosmates(IV) are produced by reaction of hydriodic acid on salts of $[OsO_3(NO_2)_2]^{2-}$ (see below). The compounds are dark violet in color and decompose in warm aqueous solution.

23.25 Only two binary compounds of osmium(VI) have been prepared — OsF_6 and OsP_2; all other compounds corresponding to this oxidation state are complex. The hexafluoride, a volatile yellow solid, is apparently the highest fluoride formed on direct combination of the elements at 200–250°, according to a recent report.[2] Contrary to a report [3] long accepted, no octafluoride is formed in this reaction. Formulation of the highest fluorination product of osmium as a hexafluoride is substantiated by vapor density measurements and infrared and Raman spectra. The physical properties of the hexafluoride (m.p., 34.4°; b.p., 47.5°) are identical with those which had been reported for the "octafluoride." Above 500°, osmium and elementary phosphorus begin to combine to yield the diphosphide, OsP_2, as the only product. The phosphide is a nonvolatile gray-black substance, inert to acid and alkaline solutions. At 1000° in a vacuum it decomposes into its elements.

23.26 Complex compounds of hexapositive osmium are numerous and include the following types: the osmates (tetroxoosmate(VI) salts), $M^I_2OsO_4$; the so-called osmyl derivatives, mainly of the anionic class $M^I_2[OsO_2X_4]$; the oxy-osmyl salts (trioxoosmate(VI) compounds), $M^I_2[OsO_3X_2]$; and remarkable salts containing nitrogen, $M^I[OsNX_4]$ and $M^I_2[OsNX_5]$, which are called nitrilohalides. The last two types appear to be unique for osmium among the platinum metals.

23.27 Tetroxoosmate(VI) salts are obtained by fusion of metallic osmium with mixtures of alkali metal hydroxide and nitrate, or by reduction, *e.g.*, with ethanol or nitrite ion, of osmium tetroxide in alkaline solution. When dry, the red or brown compounds are stable, but on ignition in air or in solution in contact with air the osmium is converted to the octapositive state. The highly colored osmyl complexes, $M^I_2[OsO_2X_4]$ (X = Cl, CN, NO_2, $\frac{1}{2}SO_3$, $\frac{1}{2}C_2O_4$), generally can be prepared from the tetroxide by reaction with materials containing the appropriate ligand as in the examples given. The cyano complexes are

$$OsO_4 + 4HCl + 2KCl = K_2[OsO_2Cl_4] + Cl_2 + 2H_2O$$
$$OsO_4 + 3H_2C_2O_4 + 2KOH = K_2[OsO_2(C_2O_4)_2] + 2CO_2 + 4H_2O$$
$$OsO_4 + 2NO + 2KNO_2 = K_2[OsO_2(NO_2)_4]$$

[2] MALM and WEINSTOCK, Abstract of Papers Presented at Miami, Fla. before the Division of Physical and Inorganic Chemistry of the American Chemical Society, April 7–12, 1957, p. 54R.

[3] RUFF and TSCHIRCH, *Ber.*, **46**, 929 (1913).

very resistant to the action of acids. Compounds containing chloro, nitro, sulfito, or oxalato groups as ligands are labile toward substitution by other groups; thus these complexes undergo fairly rapid decomposition in water. Few oxy-osmyl complexes, $M^I_2[OsO_3X_2]$, have been made, compounds with X corresponding to Cl, Br, NO_2, and $\frac{1}{2}C_2O_4$ being known. Of these, the nitro complexes appear to be the most stable and can be prepared by reaction between aqueous osmium tetroxide and alkali metal nitrite. The nitro complexes can be converted to chloro or bromo compounds by treatment with the appropriate hydrohalic acid. With excess of the acid, osmium is reduced to the tetrapositive state with the formation of $M^I_2[OsX_6]$. The very unusual nitrilohalides, $K[OsNBr_4]$ and $M^I_2[OsNX_5]$ (X = Cl, Br), are obtained by the action of hydrohalic acid on the equally unusual salts of osmium(VIII) of the composition $M^I[OsO_3N]$ (see below), free halogen being evolved in the reaction. The potassium salt shown above is the only tetrahalo compound known. This has been isolated as a deep red dihydrate which dissolves readily in water with rapid decomposition. Addition of an excess of alkali metal bromide to the aqueous solution gives the red pentabromo derivatives. Both the pentachloro and pentabromo salts also decompose in aqueous solution, the decomposition being more rapid in neutral and alkaline solutions than in the presence of excess hydrohalic acid.

23.28 The only definite binary compound corresponding to the maximum oxidation state of +8 for osmium is the tetroxide, OsO_4. In addition, there exist a number of complex salts which are derived from the tetroxide.

23.29 Osmium tetroxide (osmium(VIII) oxide), the ultimate product of oxidation of osmium and its compounds by air and other oxidizing agents, *e.g.*, hot concentrated nitric or sulfuric acid, is most conveniently made by heating the powdered metal in air to about 200°. The oxide is a colorless, volatile, poisonous substance (m.p., 40°; b.p., ca. 130°), the vapor density of which corresponds to the simple formula. In the vapor state the molecule has a tetrahedral structure, with a metal-oxygen distance of 1.66 ± 0.05 Å (calculated for Os—O single bond, 2.00 Å).

23.30 The tetroxide is extremely soluble in such nonassociated organic solvents as chloroform. It is only moderately soluble in water, and although the resulting solutions are neutral to litmus, they exhibit weakly acidic chemical behavior. Thus the addition of saturated solutions of alkali gives rise to salts such as $K_2[OsO_4(OH)_2]$. The tetroxide is a strong oxidizing agent and finds considerable use in specific organic oxidations.

23.31 Reaction of saturated solutions of alkali metal fluoride with osmium tetroxide at low temperatures (ca. $-10°$) permits the isolation of complexes of the composition $M^I_2[OsO_4F_2]$. The fluoro compounds, as well as the hydroxo complexes noted above, are yellow or brown materials which dissolve in water and which decompose in the air with the liberation of tetroxide.

23.32 The action of concentrated ammonia on warm, strongly alkaline solutions of tetroxide leads to the formation of the unusual complexes known as osmiamates, $M^I[OsO_3N]$.

$$OsO_4 + MOH + NH_3 = M[OsO_3N] + 2H_2O$$

The aqueous solubility of alkali metal osmiamates diminishes with increasing cationic size, and the potassium, rubidium, and cesium salts precipitate from solution when the above reaction is carried out. Nitrogen is evolved, as in the equation given, when the dry salts are heated *in vacuo*. Reaction with hydro-

$$2K[OsO_3N] = N_2 + K_2OsO_4 + OsO_2$$

chloric or hydrobromic acid yields the nitrilohalide complexes of osmium(VI) described above.

Less Common Oxidation States **23.33** Among the less frequently encountered oxidation states of ruthenium are +4, +5, +6, +7, and +8. Compounds of the element in these states are described briefly below.

23.34 The tetrapositive state is a fairly stable one though relatively few compounds are known for it. Simple compounds which have been isolated include the oxide, the chloride, and a basic chloride; the complexes are mainly of the halo type.

23.35 Ruthenium dioxide (ruthenium(IV) oxide) is the only oxide formed when the powdered metal is heated in oxygen. It is a black substance and is inert to acids. At elevated temperatures it is reduced to the powdered metal by hydrogen (*cf.* OsO_2, sec. 23.21).

23.36 Ruthenium tetrachloride 5-hydrate, $RuCl_4 \cdot 5H_2O$, and ruthenium hydroxotrichloride, $Ru(OH)Cl_3$, are formed along with $RuCl_3 \cdot H_2O$ (see 23.17) by the action of hydrochloric acid on ruthenium tetroxide, RuO_4. Both the tetrachloride and the hydroxotrichloride are red substances and extremely soluble in water.

23.37 The halo complexes of ruthenium(IV) are mainly of the types $M^I_2[RuX_6]$ and $M^I_2[RuX_5(OH)]$ (X = Cl, Br). The dark brown alkali metal hexahalo-ruthenates(IV) can be obtained by the oxidation of the ruthenium(III) complexes $M^I_2[RuX_5(H_2O)]$ (see 23.19) by the appropriate halogen. The aqueous solubility of the salts decreases with increasing size of the cation, the potassium salt being very soluble and the cesium compound practically insoluble in cold water. The solutions are extensively hydrolyzed. The pentahalohydroxo complexes can be made by the reduction of alkali metal ruthenates(VI) (see below) with ethanol and hydrohalic acid. In aqueous solution the compounds undergo decomposition; concentrated hydrohalic acid converts them to the hexahalo complexes.

23.38 The only known compounds of +5 ruthenium are the fluoride, RuF_5, and complexes formally derived from it. The pentafluoride is the only definite product of the direct union of the elements at elevated temperatures. It is a dark green material (m.p., 101°; b.p., 270–275°) which immediately undergoes hydrolytic disproportionation in water, the tetroxide being among the products. Complexes of the composition $M^I[RuF_6]$ (M = K, Rb, Cs) are formed by the action of fluorine at 350° on mixtures of ruthenium trichloride and alkali metal chloride in a 1 : 1 molar ratio.

23.39 The best characterized compounds of hexapositive ruthenium are the tetroxoruthenate(VI) complexes, $M^I_2[RuO_4]$, commonly called ruthenates. These substances are produced when the powdered metal or ruthenium dioxide is fused with a mixture of metal hydroxide and nitrate (or chlorate). (*Cf.* corresponding osmium compounds, section 23.27.) The alkali metal salts are dark green in color and soluble with decomposition in water and dilute acids. Reaction with the latter yields the dioxide and the "perruthenate" ion, RuO_4^-. (Compare the behavior of manganate(VI) salts, sec. 21.27.) Another type of ruthenium(VI) complex is the dioxotetrachlororuthenate(VI) ion, $[RuO_2Cl_4]^{2-}$, which is known both as the free acid $H_2[RuO_2Cl_4] \cdot 3H_2O$ and as alkali metal salts. The acid is obtained as a brown hygroscopic substance, unstable above 120°, by reaction between ruthenium tetroxide (see below), chlorine, and hydrochloric acid. The salts are formed when this reaction is carried out in the presence of metal chloride. They are readily reduced; for example, treatment with concentrated hydrochloric acids converts the ruthenium to hexachlororuthenate(IV) ion, $[RuCl_6]^{2-}$.

23.40 The only examples of $+7$ and $+8$ ruthenium which are definitely known are the perruthenates (*i.e.*, tetroxoruthenates(VII)), and the tetroxide, RuO_4, respectively. Perruthenates are best made by the oxidation of concentrated alkaline solutions of tetroxoruthenate(VI) salts by chlorine. The potassium compound is a black material which is stable in air, but decomposes to give the tetroxoruthenate(VI), the dioxide, and oxygen when heated in a vacuum. Similarly, decomposition to ruthenium(IV) and (VI) occurs in aqueous solution. Ruthenium tetroxide (ruthenium(VIII) oxide) is ordinarily prepared by passage of chlorine through a solution of an alkali metal tetroxoruthenate(VI) or by the action of periodic acid on such a solution, the volatile oxide being collected by distillation. The tetroxide is a yellow poisonous solid (m.p. 25°) which decomposes (frequently with explosive violence) above 100° to yield oxygen and the dioxide. Its vapor density (*e.g.*, at 100° and 106 mm. pressure) corresponds to the monomeric formula. The tetroxide is an extremely potent oxidant, reacting violently with many organic substances.

23.41 Less common oxidation states of osmium include $+2$ and $+3$. The majority of compounds corresponding to these states are complexes.

23.42 Among the dipositive osmium binary compounds which have been characterized are the sulfide, selenide, telluride, and chloride. The first three can be made by direct combination of the elements at high temperatures. They have the composition OsE_2 (E = S, Se, Te) and a pyrite structure (see footnote, sec. 23.9). They are relatively inert to alkalies and to most acids, but are converted to the tetroxide by hot concentrated nitric acid. The dichloride, $OsCl_2$, is obtained as a dark brown material when the trichloride (see below) is heated in a vacuum to 500°. It is highly probable that the dichloride is not a simple substance. The compound is insoluble in water and inert to hydrochloric and sulfuric acids. Hot concentrated nitric acid and aqua regia attack it slowly with the formation of osmium tetroxide.

23.43 The best known types of complexes formed by osmium(II) are the cyanides $M^I_4[Os(CN)_6]$ (cf. $M^I_4[Ru(CN)_6]$, section 23.13), nitrosyl derivatives of the composition $M^I_2[Os(NO)X_5]$ (X = Cl, Br, I) in which the NO group functions as a positive entity, and sulfito compounds of the formula $M^I_4[Os(SO_3)_3]$. These undoubtedly exhibit inner orbital D^2SP^3 binding and have electronic configurations similar to those of the complexes of ruthenium(II) (see 23.10). In general, like the latter, they are relatively inert toward substitution and are prepared by reduction of compounds of the element in higher oxidation states in the presence of the appropriate ligands. For example, the hexacyano derivatives can be obtained by the addition of potassium cyanide to a solution of osmium tetroxide.

23.44 Few compounds of tripositive osmium have been identified. The only binary compound reported is the chloride $OsCl_3$; complex types include $M^I_3[OsX_6]$ (X = Cl, Br), $M^I_2[Os(NO_2)_5(H_2O)]$, and a number of ammines.

23.45 Osmium trichloride is formed by chlorination of the powdered metal at temperatures above 700° (see $OsCl_4$, 23.22) or by the thermal decomposition of ammonium hexachloroosmate(IV) at 350° in an atmosphere of chlorine. It is a dark brown, hygroscopic substance which dissolves readily in water to yield weakly acidic solutions. It is noteworthy that freshly prepared solutions give practically no test for chloride ion. In solution at room temperature it is stable to alkalies and reducing agents such as sulfur dioxide and iron(II) sulfate. Hot concentrated nitric acid slowly transforms the trichloride to the tetroxide. At 500° in a vacuum disproportionation to dichloride and tetrachloride occurs.

23.46 Of the hexahalocomplexes of osmium(III) only the chloro derivatives have been obtained pure. These can be prepared by reaction of chlorine with a mixture of elementary osmium and appropriate alkali metal chloride at high temperatures, hexachloroosmates(IV) being intermediates in the reaction. The compounds are dark red substances which give unstable aqueous solutions. The nitro complexes are formed when hexachloroosmates(IV) are treated with alkali metal nitrites in excess. They are yellow to orange materials which are usually isolated as hydrates, e.g., $Na_2Os(NO_2)_5 \cdot 2H_2O$. Their aqueous solutions are fairly stable in the cold.

23.47 Ammine complexes which have been reported [4, 5, 6] are $[Os(NH_3)_6]^{3+}$, $[Os\ dipy_3]^{3+}$ (dipy = 2,2′-dipyridyl), and $[Os\ en_3]^{3+}$ (en = ethylenediamine). The first complex is formed by reaction of ammonium hexabromoosmate(IV) with ammonia at elevated temperatures and under pressure. Tris(ethylenediamine) osmium(III) ion is prepared from an ethylenediamine-osmium(IV) complex by reduction with sodium hydrosulfite. The dipyridyl complex is produced when the corresponding osmium(II) ion is oxidized by chlorine. The tris(2,2′-dipyridyl) osmium(III) ion has been obtained in enantiomorphic forms.

Rhodium and Iridium

Common Oxidation States **23.48** Of the variety of oxidation states exhibited

[4] DWYER and HOGARTH, *J. Proc. Roy. Soc. N. S. Wales*, **85**, 113 (1952).

[5] DWYER and GYARFAS, *J. Am. Chem. Soc.*, **73**, 2322 (1951).

[6] DWYER and HOGARTH, *J. Am. Chem. Soc.*, **75**, 1008 (1953).

by rhodium (see 23.3), the tripositive state stands out far above the others in its stability. This point is emphasized in the data of Table 23.2 where the products of reaction of the element with a number of reagents are given.

23.49 Examples of apparently simple compounds of rhodium(III) are the oxide, halides, and sulfates. The halo and cyano compounds and the ammines are important classes of complexes.

23.50 Rhodium(III) oxide, Rh_2O_3, is formed when the powdered metal is heated in air above 600°. It is a gray-black substance, inert to acids. Slow addition of alkali to solutions of tripositive rhodium results in the precipitation of the yellow hydrate $Rh_2O_3 \cdot 5H_2O$, which is soluble in acids.

23.51 The anhydrous trihalides are all known and can be obtained by appropriate direct union of the elements. (See Table 23.2 for conditions of preparation of RhF_3 and $RhCl_3$.) The iodide can also be prepared by precipitation from aqueous solution. The trifluoride is a dark red substance, practically inert to water, acids, and bases. The trichloride, as prepared by direct union, is also red and is insoluble in water and acids. Magnetic measurements [7] show that the substance is essentially diamagnetic. If the principle of maximum multiplicity (see 3.8) holds for rhodium and the chloride is ionic, the Rh^{3+} ion (with a $4d^6$ configuration) should be strongly paramagnetic. The diamagnetic character of the trichloride suggests an inner orbital D^2SP^3 complex in which rhodium is coordinated octahedrally to six chlorine atoms in some sort of an infinite three-dimensional complex. Other forms of rhodium trichloride exist. Evaporation of a solution of rhodium(III) oxide hydrate (see above) in hydrochloric acid yields $RhCl_3 \cdot 4H_2O$. This red substance is very soluble in water but gives no immediate test for chloride ions, demonstrating that the latter are complexed with rhodium. Removal of the water of crystallization at 180° in a hydrogen chloride atmosphere gives an anhydrous trichloride which is water-soluble; heating of this latter material to higher temperatures converts it to the water-insoluble form.

23.52 The sulfates which have been identified also appear to be complex substances. A number of sulfate hydrates have been obtained, the best known being $Rh_2(SO_4)_3 \cdot 14H_2O$ and $Rh_2(SO_4)_3 \cdot 6H_2O$. The former is a yellow material obtained by dissolving the oxide hydrate in cold dilute sulfuric acid and crystallizing by evaporation *in vacuo* at 0°; the red hexahydrate is prepared by evaporating an aqueous solution of the 14-hydrate to dryness at 100°.[7] From aqueous solutions of the 14-hydrate all the sulfate is immediately precipitated by addition of barium ion; fresh solutions of the red 6-hydrate give no test for sulfate ion and have a low electrical conductivity. Both hydrates are essentially diamagnetic.[7] Presumably, therefore, in the 14-hydrate rhodium is present as $[Rh(H_2O)_6]^{3+}$ in which the six water molecules are joined to rhodium by inner orbital D^2SP^3 bonds, whereas in the 6-hydrate at least part of the rhodium is in the form of sulfate complexes in which all of the sulfate groups are united to rhodium by inner orbital bonding.

[7] GAVIS and SIENKO, *J. Am. Chem. Soc.*, **77**, 4983 (1955).

23.53 In the very great majority of its complexes tripositive rhodium is 6-coordinate. In general these compounds are relatively inert to substitution, which is not surprising in view of their probable electronic configuration (*cf.* Ru(II) complexes, sec. 23.10).

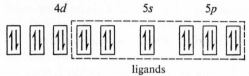

ligands

23.54 Cationic ammine complexes of rhodium(III) closely resemble the analogous compounds of cobalt and chromium. Compound types which have been characterized include, among others, $[Rh(NH_3)_6]X_3$, $[Rh\ en_3]X_3$, $[Rh(NH_3)_5(H_2O)]X_3$, $[Rh(NH_3)_5R]X_2$ (R = monovalent acid radical or OH^- group), and $[Rh\ py_4Cl_2]X$. Tris(ethylenediamine) complexes and other trichelates have been resolved into enantiomorphic forms.

23.55 In addition to the cationic complexes, nonelectrolyte and anionic ammine complexes are known. Examples of the latter types are $[Rh(NH_3)_3Br_3]$, $[Rh\ py_3Cl_3]$, $M^I[Rh\ py_2Cl_4]$, and $M^I_2[Rh(NH_3)Cl_5]$. The last class is apparently very labile to substitution, the halogens being easily removed by reaction with water.

23.56 Anionic complexes of tripositive rhodium with all the halogens have been obtained, those with fluorine, chlorine, and bromine being very well defined. The only type of fluoro complex known is $M^I_3[RhF_6]$. Four types of chloro and bromo compounds have been identified: $M^I_3[RhX_6]$, $M^I_2RhX_5$, $M^I_4RhX_7$, and $M^I_3Rh_2X_9$. The first two classes are the most common for chlorine, the last two being limited to a few salts of organic bases. For bromine, the binuclear complexes are much more numerous than the hexahalo derivatives, relatively few of the latter being known. No structural information is available for the pentahalo, heptahalo, or binuclear complexes and the formulas given should be taken only to indicate the ratios of the elements concerned.

23.57 Among other anionic complexes are the following: $M^I_3[Rh(CN)_6]$, $M^I_3[Rh(NO_2)_6]$, $M^I_3[Rh(SO_4)_3]$, $M^I_3[Rh(SO_3)_3]$, and $M^I_3[Rh(C_2O_4)_3]$. Solutions of the cyano complexes are particularly stable; they appear to be inert even when heated with concentrated sulfuric acid.

23.58 The predominant oxidation states of iridium are $+3$ and $+4$, with the former generally being by far the more stable. In the tripositive state both the apparently simple compounds and the complexes are similar to those of rhodium(III).

23.59 The best known "simple" tripositive iridium compounds are the oxide and halides. Anhydrous black iridium(III) oxide, Ir_2O_3, is formed by thermal decomposition of a mixture of potassium hexachloroiridate(IV), $K_2[IrCl_6]$, and sodium carbonate. A green hydrous oxide is formed on addition of dilute alkali to a solution of potassium hexachloroiridate(III), $K_3[IrCl_6]$, in an atmosphere of carbon dioxide. The green material is converted to a black substance on heating with concentrated alkali. The hydrated sesquioxide in alkaline medium is oxidized by air to the dioxide. When heated, the sesquioxide decomposes to metal and dioxide, the latter breaking down to metal and oxygen at temperatures above 1070°.

23.60 All iridium(III) halides except the fluoride have been prepared. The anhydrous chloride is produced by direct union of chlorine with the powdered metal at about 600°. The bromide and iodide are obtained as hydrates, *e.g.*, $IrBr_3 \cdot 4H_2O$ and $IrI_3 \cdot 3H_2O$, from solutions of the hydrated sesquioxide in the hydrohalic acids. The hydrates can be converted to the anhydrous compounds by dehydration *in vacuo* at elevated temperatures. A number of hydrates of the trichloride have been made, *e.g.*, $IrCl_3 \cdot 3H_2O$ and $IrCl_3 \cdot 1.5H_2O$. The hydrated chlorides dissolve in water to give dark green acidic solutions in which the chlorine apparently is bound to iridium in anionic complexes. The anhydrous trihalides are thermally unstable, decomposing at elevated temperatures to give first the lower halides (see 23.72) and finally the free metal.

23.61 In all of its numerous complex compounds iridium(III) exhibits a coordination number of six. Except for the halo complexes, in their relative inertness toward substitution and in the types of compounds formed iridium(III) complex compounds closely resemble the rhodium(III) complexes (sec. 23.57). The main classes of halide derivatives are $M^I_3[IrX_6]$ (X = Cl, Br, I) and $M^I_2[IrX_5(H_2O)]$ (X = Cl, Br); no heptahalo or binuclear complexes appear to have been identified. Hexahaloiridates(III) are obtained from the corresponding haloiridate(IV) compounds by reduction as in the example, the pentachloro

$$2Na_2[IrCl_6] + Na_2C_2O_4 = 2Na_3[IrCl_6] + 2CO_2$$

complexes being produced at the same time. Separation is effected by making use of solubility differences. The reduction potential for the $[IrCl_6]^{2-} - [IrCl_6]^{3-}$ couple in $1M$ hydrochloric acid has been determined to be 1.02 volts.

23.62 Iridium(IV) compounds include the oxide, halides, and a number of complex salts which are primarily anionic in nature.

23.63 The anhydrous oxide, IrO_2, is formed when the powdered metal is heated in air at temperatures not exceeding about 1070° (see above). The dioxide dissolves in hydrochloric acid with the formation of $H_2[IrCl_6]$. A dihydrate, $IrO_2 \cdot 2H_2O$, can be obtained by partially drying the product of reaction between molecular oxygen and an aqueous mixture of sodium hexachloroiridate(III) and potassium hydroxide. The blue-black hydrate is soluble in acids but insoluble in solutions of alkali. In a nitrogen atmosphere at 350° it is converted to the black anhydrous compound.

23.64 Two tetrahalides, the fluoride and chloride, have been characterized. The fluoride is produced when the hexafluoride (see 23.74) is reduced by the powdered metal at about 150°; the chloride, known definitely only in hydrated form, is obtained by the action of aqua regia on ammonium hexachloroiridate(IV). Neither halide is stable. The tetrafluoride, a yellow nonvolatile oil, is immediately converted to the hydrated dioxide by water and is decomposed by strong heating to give uncharacterized materials which are probably lower fluorides. The hydrated chloride loses both water and chlorine when gently heated, even in an atmosphere of chlorine.

23.65 Although a few other types, *e.g.*, ammines and oxalates, have been identified, the halogen compounds make up the main class of iridium(IV) complexes. These have the composition $M^I_2[IrX_6]$ and are known for all the halogens except iodine. Only two hexafluoroiridates(IV), $K_2[IrF_6]$ and $Pb[IrF_6]$, have been described. These are obtained together by heating the powdered metal with K_3HPbF_8 (see 13.117). The potassium compound can also be made by fusion of potassium hexanitroiridate(III), $K_3[Ir(NO_2)_6]$, with potassium hydrogen fluoride.[8] The chloro complexes are produced either by reaction of chlorine with a heated mixture of powdered iridium and alkali metal chloride or by the addition of the latter to a solution of hydrated dioxide in hydrochloric acid. The sodium salt is highly soluble in water at room temperature, but salts of larger alkali metal cations are relatively insoluble. The salts undergo slow hydrolysis in solution. Hexabromoiridates(IV) can be prepared in a manner similar to the second method cited for the chloro compounds.

Less Common Oxidation States **23.66** Compounds in which rhodium exhibits an oxidation state other than $+3$ are quite rare. The $+1$, $+2$, and $+4$ states have been characterized unequivocally, and there is inconclusive evidence that hexapositive rhodium can be obtained in solution by oxidation of the tripositive state, *e.g.*, by hypochlorite or electrolytically.

23.67 Interesting examples of rhodium(I) compounds are the complexes of the general formula $[Rh(CNR)_4]X$, where R is *p*-tolyl, *p*-chlorophenyl, or *p*-methoxyphenyl and X is perchlorate, chloride, or hexafluorophosphate.[9] These substances are made by reaction between the appropriate isonitrile and rhodium trichloride hydrate (see 23.51) in ethanol as solvent. The complexes are all diamagnetic and are believed to have a DSP^2 (square planar) configuration, inasmuch as rhodium(I) is isoelectronic with palladium(II) (see 23.78).

23.68 Although anhydrous rhodium(II) oxide and chloride have been reported, the evidence for their existence is very much open to question. There is no doubt, however, that the dipositive state can be stabilized by complex formation. Illustrative of complex types which have been identified are $[Rh\,py_6]X_2$ (X = halogen) and $[Rh(AsR_3)_4X_2]$ (AsR_3 = tertiary arsine). The pyridine complexes are produced by reduction of the corresponding compounds of tripositive rhodium by means of hypophosphorous acid in the presence of excess pyridine. Compounds with tertiary arsines, *e.g.*, $(CH_3)_2AsC_6H_5$, as ligands are obtained by the interaction of rhodium trihalides, the powdered metal, and the complexing agent in the presence of hypophosphorous acid in an inert atmosphere. The arsine derivatives are soluble in organic solvents, give no test for halide ion in the cold, and possess reducing properties.

[8] PEACOCK, *J. Chem. Soc.*, 3291 (1955).

[9] MALATESTA and VALLARINO, *J. Chem. Soc.*, 1867 (1956).

23.69 There appears to be no question of the existence of tetrapositive rhodium, although none of its compounds have been isolated in the pure condition. It is likely that fusion of the powdered metal with a mixture of alkali hydroxide and nitrate gives, at least in part, the dioxide, RhO_2. A dioxide hydrate, contaminated with sesquioxide, is undoubtedly formed when rhodium(III) in alkaline medium is treated with such potent oxidants as hypochlorite ion, or when solutions of hexachlororhodate(III) are anodically oxidized. The hydrated material cannot be dehydrated without loss of oxygen and complete conversion to sesquioxide.

23.70 A few compounds of iridium corresponding to the unfamiliar oxidation states of 0, +1, +2, and +6 have been identified.

23.71 Aside from the carbonyls (Table 13.4), there appears to be only one compound containing iridium(0). Reaction between bromopentammineiridium(III) bromide and potassium in liquid ammonia at $-33°$ results in the precipitation of a substance of the composition $Ir(NH_3)_5$.[10] Pentammineirid-

$$[Ir(NH_3)_5Br]Br_2 + \underbrace{3K^+ + 3e^-}_{metal} = Ir(NH_3)_5 + 3KBr$$

ium(0) is a pale yellow, diamagnetic solid which decomposes to free metal and ammonia at about 90°. The diamagnetism indicates that the compound should probably be formulated as a dimer.

23.72 In the monopositive state iridium is known only in the form of the halides IrCl, IrBr, and IrI. These compounds are products of the thermal decomposition of the trihalides, the dihalides being their immediate precursors. The monohalides are intensely colored (IrCl, coppery red; IrBr, brown; IrI, black), insoluble in acids, and resistant to the action of acids and alkalies. On strong heating they decompose to metal and halogen.

23.73 In addition to the dihalides (see above), compounds of iridium(II) include a sulfide, obtained by union of the elements, and a number of complexes, e.g., $K_4[Ir(CN)_6]$, $Na_6[Ir(SO_3)_4] \cdot 10H_2O$.

23.74 The only definitely characterized representative of +6 iridium is the hexafluoride, IrF_6. This compound is obtained by reaction between the elements in a fluorspar (CaF_2) or silica vessel at temperatures in the neighborhood of 200°. The hexafluoride is an extremely reactive volatile yellow solid (m.p., 44°; b.p., 53°). It is immediately decomposed by water with the evolution of oxygen and ozone and the formation of the dioxide hydrate and hydrofluoric acid. Reaction with chlorine gives iridium tetrafluoride and chlorine monofluoride whereas reaction with hydrogen gives the free metal.

Palladium and Platinum

Common Oxidation States **23.75** Palladium and platinum are much more similar in properties than are the members of each of the other platinum metal dyads. In both their simple and complex compounds, palladium and platinum

[10] WATT and MAYFIELD, *J. Am. Chem. Soc.*, **75**, 6178 (1953).

are primarily di- and tetrapositive, with the latter oxidation state being considerably more stable for platinum than for palladium.

23.76 Common simple palladium(II) compounds are the oxide, sulfide, halides, nitrate, and sulfate. The anhydrous oxide, PdO, can be prepared by reaction between the powdered metal and oxygen at red heat. It is a black substance which is insoluble in all acids and decomposes at high temperatures to the constituent elements. (The dissociation pressure of oxygen is 1 atm at 875°.) In the crystal each metal atom is joined to four oxygen atoms arranged in a plane. An acid-soluble hydrated monoxide of variable water content is formed by hydrolysis of the nitrate. Both the anhydrous compound and the hydrate are reduced by hydrogen, even at room temperature. The sulfide, PdS, is formed by heating the elements together or by precipitation from solutions of palladium(II) salts, e.g., $Pd(NO_3)_2$, with hydrogen sulfide. It is a dark (brown or blue) substance, insoluble in dilute hydrochloric acid and in ammonium sulfide solution. All the dihalides of palladium have been made, convenient methods of preparation being the following: PdF_2, by addition of hydrofluoric acid to solutions of the nitrate or by reduction of the trifluoride (see 23.93) with the free metal; $PdCl_2$, by direct union of the elements at red heat; $PdBr_2$, by combination of the elements in the presence of nitric acid; PdI_2, by metathesis in aqueous medium. Of the dihalides, only the chloride exhibits an appreciable water solubility, and from aqueous solutions there can be isolated the dark red 2-hydrate, $PdCl_2 \cdot 2H_2O$. The difluoride is apparently ionic in the solid state, having a structure in which each Pd^{2+} is surrounded octahedrally by six F^- and each of the latter by three metal ions at the corners of an equilateral triangle. On the other hand the anhydrous dichloride consists of infinite chains of square planar $PdCl_4$ groups. From solutions of the hydrated monoxide in nitric and sulfuric acids the compounds $Pd(NO_3)_2$ and $PdSO_4 \cdot 2H_2O$, respectively, can be isolated. These are deliquescent substances from whose aqueous solutions the hydrated oxide precipitates as a result of hydrolysis. The nitrate has been shown to be diamagnetic.[11] This is an interesting fact, for if the compound is ionic (as simple nitrates generally are) and the principle of maximum multiplicity is valid for Pd^{2+}, a moment corresponding to two unpaired electrons would be expected.

23.77 The simple compounds of dipositive platinum are very much like those of palladium, although the nitrate and sulfate appear not to have been made and there is some question regarding the existence of the difluoride. The oxide, PtO, has been obtained by reaction between the powdered metal and molecular oxygen at 420–440° and a pressure of 8 atm. The oxide has a crystal structure analogous to that of PdO. The hydroxide, $Pt(OH)_2$, has been made by the action of potassium hydroxide on a solution of potassium tetrachloroplatinate(II), $K_2[PtCl_4]$, in an inert atmosphere. The hydroxide is a black

[11] JANES, *J. Am. Chem. Soc.*, **57**, 471 (1935).

unstable substance which when moist is easily oxidized by air. When strongly heated it decomposes to metal and dioxide, and ultimately completely to metal. The known dihalides generally can be prepared by methods similar to those used for the corresponding palladium compounds and also from appropriate platinum(IV) compounds. For example, the dichloride is conveniently produced by thermal decomposition of the tetrachloride (see 23.85) or of chloroplatinic acid (see 23.89) (hexachloroplatinic(IV) acid), $H_2[PtCl_6]$; the dibromide can be obtained similarly. All the dihalides are practically insoluble in water. The dichloride dissolves in hydrochloric acid to give solutions containing the complex acid $H_2[PtCl_4]$, the reaction being accompanied by some decomposition to the free metal and $H_2[PtCl_6]$. Probably the outstanding difference between platinum(II) and palladium(II) in their simple compounds is the greater ease with which the former are converted to materials having the element in the tetrapositive state.

23.78 In their many complexes, dipositive palladium and platinum generally exhibit a coordination number of four, the metals being joined to the ligands by square planar DSP^2 bonds. The 4-coordinate complexes are invariably diamagnetic and have the configurations shown. The platinum(II) complexes

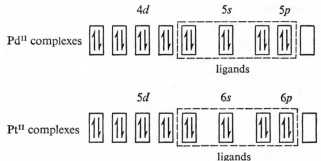

are fairly inert toward substitution, being in this regard somewhat more stable than the corresponding palladium compounds. Analogous palladium and platinum complexes are usually isomorphous.

23.79 The more important complexes of palladium(II) include a variety of compounds of the type $M^I_2[PdX_4]$ (X = Cl, Br, I, CN, NO_2) and the ammines. The ammines constitute two main types, as exemplified with ammonia as the ammine ligand: $[Pd(NH_3)_4]X_2$ and $[Pd(NH_3)_2X_2]$. The second type has been isolated in the form of *cis* and *trans* isomers.

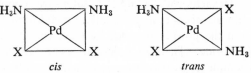

23.80 The halo anionic complexes can be obtained from the dihalides by union with appropriate metal halides. The tetrahalo derivatives can serve as sources of the other anionic complexes. The tetrammine complexes are generally formed by direct union of ammonia or amine with simple palladium(II) compounds and can be transformed to the nonelectrolytic diammine complexes by the action of acids.

23.81 As with palladium(II), the main types of complexes of dipositive platinum are those of composition $M^I_2[PtX_4]$ and the ammines. The best known of the anionic complexes are the tetrachloro derivatives; these are made by reaction of the simple chloride with a solution of alkali metal chloride or by reduction, e.g., by oxalate ion, of hexachloroplatinate(IV) salts, $M^I_2[PtCl_6]$, (see below). The ammine complexes consist of three principal types, as illustrated with ammonia as the ammine ligand: $[Pt(NH_3)_4]X_2$; $[Pt(NH_3)_3X]X$ (X may be the same or different); and $[Pt(NH_3)_2X_2]$. The last type, as would be expected, can be obtained as *cis* and *trans* isomers. With both platinum(II) and palladium(II) there are also many complex compounds containing organic sulfides (R_2S) and tertiary phosphines (R_3P) and arsines (R_3As) as ligands. For the most part, these are similar to the ammines in composition.

23.82 Relatively few compounds of tetrapositive palladium have been identified. Binary compounds include the oxide, sulfide, selenide, and telluride, whereas complexes, aside from a sulfide, appear to be confined almost exclusively to halo derivatives.

23.83 The dioxide, known only in hydrated form, is obtained as a dark red precipitate by reaction between alkali metal hydroxide and the hexachloropalladate(IV) ion. It is an unstable substance, losing oxygen slowly at room temperature. At 200° it is completely transformed to monoxide. The freshly precipitated dioxide is soluble both in dilute solutions of acids and in concentrated solutions of alkali. The disulfide can be produced in a number of ways, a common method being reaction between dichloride and sulfur at 400–500°. It is a black substance which dissociates above 600° to the monosulfide and is insoluble in strong acids. The diselenide and ditelluride are similar to the sulfide except that they are soluble in nitric acid.

23.84 A thiopalladate(IV) of the composition Na_2PdS_3 has been obtained by fusion of the monosulfide (see 23.76) with sulfur and sodium carbonate. It is a red-brown material which is immediately decomposed by water with the formation of the disulfide. Halo complexes are formed with chlorine and bromine and are primarily of the composition $M^I_2[PdX_6]$. A small number of diammines, e.g., $[Pd\ py_2Cl_2]Cl_2$, are also known. The hexahalopalladates(IV) are the most stable compounds of tetrapositive palladium, but even these are readily reduced. Hexachloropalladate(IV) salts are commonly produced by the action of chlorine or aqua regia on alkali metal tetrachloropalladate(II) compounds, or from the powdered metal by reaction with aqua regia in the presence of metal chloride. The bromo derivatives are similarly obtained from the palladium(II) complexes by oxidation with elementary bromine. The alkali metal hexahalo salts are all only slightly soluble in cold water and are destroyed with the evolution of free halogen when brought in contact with hot water. The solid compounds are thermally unstable; for example, $K_2[PdCl_6]$ evolves chlorine at temperatures above 175°. The standard potential for the half-reaction

$$[PdCl_6]^{2-} + 2e^- = [PdCl_4]^{2-} + 2Cl^-$$

has been found to be 1.29 volts.

23.85 Tetrapositive platinum forms binary compounds analogous to those described above for palladium, and in addition, a complete series of tetrahalides. The dioxide, obtained as a hydrate by reaction of platinum tetrachloride with aqueous sodium carbonate, is amphoteric in behavior and is soluble in both acids and alkalies, solution in the latter yielding hexahydroxoplatinate(IV) salts, $M^I_2[Pt(OH)_6]$. Like the corresponding palladium compound, it is thermally unstable and at high temperatures it decomposes to yield the free metal. The disulfide, diselenide, and ditelluride also closely resemble the analogous compounds of palladium, the latter two perhaps being more resistant to the action of acids than the corresponding palladium compounds. Of the tetrahalides the fluoride is made by direct union of the elements at red heat, the chloride by the thermal decomposition of chloroplatinic acid at 300° in an atmosphere of chlorine, the bromide by dissolution of the metal in a mixture of hydrobromic acid and bromine followed by removal of solvent and drying of the residue at 180°, and the iodide by treatment of a concentrated solution of $H_2[PtCl_6]$ with hot aqueous potassium iodide. The existence of the tetrahalides, and particularly the bromide and iodide, serves to emphasize the much greater stability of tetrapositive platinum as compared with the corresponding state for palladium. Platinum tetrafluoride is a yellow to red substance which is decomposed vigorously by water. The red-brown tetrachloride is readily soluble in water and can be recovered from the resulting solutions in hydrated forms. It is likely that in solution the chloride is present as the complex acid $H_2[PtCl_4(OH)_2]$. A substance of this composition (*i.e.*, $PtCl_4 \cdot 2H_2O$) can be obtained by heating the hydrates recovered from solution to 100°. The tetrabromide (brown-black) and tetraiodide (brown-black) exhibit low solubility in water. The chloride, bromide, and iodide undergo decomposition when heated to give free halogen and dihalide, the thermal stability decreasing in the expected order from chloride to iodide.

23.86 Platinum is the only member of the transition triads for which alkyl derivatives have been prepared. These substances, which may be regarded as compounds of the element in the +4 state, have formulas such as $(CH_3)_3PtI$, $(CH_3)_4Pt$, and $(CH_3)_3Pt - Pt(CH_3)_3$. The first compound, trimethylplatinum iodide, is obtained when platinum tetrachloride is treated with the Grignard reagent CH_3MgI. Reaction of the trimethyl derivative with sodium methyl, $NaCH_3$, gives the tetraalkyl compound, and with potassium metal the hexamethyl material. These substances are soluble in most organic media and stable to water and air. It has been shown that the compounds $(CH_3)_3PtCl$ and $(CH_3)_4Pt$ are tetrameric in the solid state.

23.87 In its complex compounds, platinum(IV) commonly exhibits a coordination number of six. The principal classes of complexes are the ammines, of which there are a large number, and the hexahaloplatinate(IV) salts.

23.88 Ammines of every type, *e.g.*, from $[Pt(NH_3)_6]Cl_4$ to $K[Pt(NH_3)Cl_5]$, have been characterized. The parent substance of the series cited, namely, hexammineplatinum(IV) chloride, is formed by reaction of liquid ammonia with ammonium hexachloroplatinate(IV), $(NH_4)_2[PtCl_6]$. The less highly ammoniated derivatives can be obtained in a variety of ways, frequently directly or indirectly from appropriate platinum(II) ammine complexes. For example, the diammine $[Pt(NH_3)_2Cl_4]$ is produced when dichlorodiammineplatinum(II), $[Pt(NH_3)_2Cl_2]$, is oxidized with chlorine, and the platinum(IV) diammine can be converted to $[Pt(NH_3)_5Cl]Cl_3$ by the action of concentrated aqueous ammonia. Of course, other amines, both monodentate, *e.g.*, CH_3NH_2, and polydentate, *e.g.*, en (ethylenediamine), can serve as ligands. The expected types of stereoisomerism for octahedral complexes (see 6.35 *ff.*) are found with the platinum(IV) ammines.

23.89 Of the hexahaloplatinate(IV) complexes (which have been obtained with all four halogens) the chloro derivatives are best known and are described briefly. Chloroplatinic acid (hexachloroplatinic(IV) acid), $H_2[PtCl_6]$, can be obtained as the 6-hydrate from the solution formed when platinum powder is treated with hydrochloric acid and chlorine. The acid is also formed as the main product of reaction of the metal with aqua regia. It is a brown-red deliquescent substance which dissolves readily in water, ethanol, or ether. The ammonium, potassium, rubidium, and cesium salts show small solubility in water and can be obtained from the acid by metathetical reactions. Under appropriate conditions, the bound chlorine in the complexes can be replaced by hydroxide ion to yield mixed derivatives, a common one being $M^I_2[PtCl_5(OH)]$. The hexachloroplatinate(IV) ion is not so powerful an oxidant as the corresponding palladium ion (see 23.84); the standard potential for the half-reaction shown is 0.68 volt.

$$[PtCl_6]^{2-} + 2e^- = [PtCl_4]^{2-} + 2Cl^-$$

Less Common Oxidation States **23.90** Oxidation states encountered less frequently than $+2$ and $+4$ for palladium and platinum are 0 and $+3$, and in addition there is reason to believe that platinum can exhibit the $+6$ state.

23.91 Palladium(0) isonitrile compounds of the composition $Pd(CNR)_2$ (R = phenyl, *p*-tolyl, *p*-anisyl) have been prepared by treatment of boiling alcoholic solutions of the palladium(II) complexes $Pd(CNR)_2I_2$ and isonitrile in a 1 : 2.1 molar ratio with an excess of concentrated alcoholic potassium hydroxide.[12] The diisonitrilepalladium(0) compounds are black diamagnetic substances whose insolubility in most solvents indicates a condensed structure. These compounds react with molecular iodine to give the original palladium(II) complexes and with triaryl phosphites to yield complex substances such as

[12] MALATESTA, *Rec. trav. chim.*, **75**, 644 (1956); *J. Chem. Soc.*, 3924 (1955).

$[Pd(CNR)((p\text{-}ClC_6H_4O)_3P)_3]$. The reaction sequence for the formation of the isonitrile palladium(0) complexes has been represented as follows.

$$Pd(CNR)_2I_2 + 2RNC + 2KOH = [Pd(CNR)_4](OH)_2 + 2KI$$
$$[Pd(CNR)_4](OH)_2 + RNC = Pd(CNR)_4 + RNCO + H_2O$$
$$Pd(CNR)_4 = Pd(CNR)_2 + 2RNC$$

Four-coordinate complexes of palladium(0) with triphenyl phosphite, $[Pd(P(OC_6H_5)_3)_4]$, and with a number of triarylphosphines, $[Pd(PAr_3)_4]$, have been obtained from the isonitrile compounds,[13] e.g.,

$$Pd(CNR)_2 + 4PAr_3 = [Pd(PAr_3)_4] + 2RNC.$$

These are white or yellow solids having high solubilities in organic solvents.

23.92 Analogous platinum(0) triarylphosphines have also been described, their preparation being accomplished by the following reaction.[13]

$$Na_2[PtCl_4] + 2KOH + 5PAr_3 = [Pt(PAr_3)_4] + 2NaCl + 2KCl + Ar_3PO + H_2O$$

Tetrammineplatinum(0), $Pt(NH_3)_4$, has been reported to have been made by the reduction of tetrammineplatinum(II) bromide by means of potassium in liquid ammonia.[14] (*Cf.* with $Ir(NH_3)_5$, sec. 23.71.) It is a yellowish-white solid which readily decomposes to elemental platinum and ammonia.

23.93 Compounds of tripositive palladium and platinum which appear to have been identified unequivocally include the fluoride of palladium and the trichloride, bromide, and iodide of platinum. Palladium(III) fluoride is formed by reaction between the constituent elements at 500° or by the action of fluorine on the dichloride at 200–250°. It is a reactive black hygroscopic substance, which on contact with water immediately decomposes with the liberation of oxygen. In the cold, it is reduced to the free metal by hydrogen. It is a paramagnetic compound, but its moment (2.05 Bohr magnetons),[15] like the moments of other apparently simple palladium metal compounds, is much lower than that expected in terms of the principle of maximum multiplicity. (On the basis of this principle Pd^{3+}, with a $4d^7$ configuration, would be expected to have three unpaired electrons with a spin-only moment of 3.87.) Platinum trichloride can be obtained by heating the tetrachloride (see 23.85) to 370°. It is a dark green substance which decomposes to the dichloride at 435°. It dissolves in hot water or warm concentrated hydrochloric acid, with disproportionation to the di- and tetrapositive states. The tribromide and triiodide are similar to the trichloride.

23.94 Only two compounds of platinum(VI), PtO_3 and PtF_6, appear to have been characterized definitely. The anodic oxidation of the hydrated dioxide (see 23.85) in potassium hydroxide solution at 0° gives a material which, on

[13] MALATESTA and ANGOLETTA, *Atti accad. nazl. Lincei*, Rend., Classe sci. fis. mat. e nat., **19**, 43 (1955); *Chem. Abstracts*, **57**, 929 (1957).
[14] WATT, WALLING, and MAYFIELD, *J. Am. Chem. Soc.*, **75**, 6175 (1953).
[15] NYHOLM and SHARPE, *J. Chem. Soc.*, 3579 (1952).

washing with acetic acid, yields a brown-red solid whose analysis corresponds closely to PtO_3. This is an extremely unstable substance; for example, when suspended in water it loses oxygen continuously. Reaction of a platinum filament with fluorine at 300 mm. pressure gives as the main product the nonvolatile tetrafluoride. In addition, a small amount of the volatile hexafluoride, m.p. 56.7°, is formed as a red-black material. This compound appears to be the least stable and most reactive of the known hexafluorides.[16]

[16] WEINSTOCK, CLAASSEN and MALM, *J. Am. Chem. Soc.*, **79**, 5832 (1957).

CHAPTER 24

THE COPPER FAMILY

Introduction

24.1 The copper family, following immediately after the transition triads, comprises the elements copper, silver, and gold, with atomic numbers 29, 47, and 79, respectively. Some properties of these elements are given in Table 24.1.

24.2 The atoms of all three members of this family possess ground state electronic configurations of the type $(n - 1)d^{10}ns^1$. In spite of the fact that the filling of the penultimate d level is completed with these elements, or in the case of silver, with the preceding element (Pd), some of the d electrons remain active with respect to compound formation. This is indicated by the fact that all three exhibit not only the monopositive oxidation state, which might be expected from the electronic configuration, but the higher oxidation states +2 (uncertain for gold) and +3, as well.

24.3 The monovalent state has been well characterized for all three elements, but it is only among the compounds of silver that it represents the most common state. The dipositive state is, of course, for copper the most familiar and important; silver is strongly oxidizing in its dipositive state; and no compounds of gold(II) appear to have been isolated. For copper and silver the +3 state is a very powerfully oxidizing one; for gold, however, it is less so, the most characteristic compounds of gold being those in which it exhibits +3 valence. The more important oxidation potential relationships are summarized.

GENERAL REFERENCES

KLEINBERG, *Unfamiliar Oxidation States and Their Stabilization*, University of Kansas Press, Lawrence, 1950, Ch. V.

LAIST, "Copper, Silver, and Gold," Vol. II of *Comprehensive Inorganic Chemistry*, edited by Sneed, Maynard and Brasted, D. Van Nostrand Company, Inc., New York, 1954.

LATIMER, *The Oxidation States of the Elements and Their Potentials in Aqueous Solutions*, 2nd Edition, Prentice-Hall, Inc., New York, 1952, Ch. 11.

REMY, *Treatise on Inorganic Chemistry* (translated and amended by J. S. Anderson), Elsevier Publishing Company, Amsterdam, 1956, Vol. II, Ch. 8.

SIDGWICK, *The Chemical Elements and Their Compounds*, Oxford University Press, London, 1950, pp. 103–92.

$$Cu \xrightarrow{-0.521} Cu^+ \xrightarrow{-0.153} Cu^{2+} \xrightarrow{(-1.8)} CuO^+$$
$$\underset{-0.337}{\big\lfloor\!\!\!-\!\!\!-\!\!\!\rightarrow}$$

$$Ag \xrightarrow{-0.799} Ag^+ \xrightarrow{-1.98} Ag^{2+} \xrightarrow{ca. -2.1} AgO^+$$

$$Au \xrightarrow{ca. -1.68} Au^+ \xrightarrow{-1.41} Au^{3+}$$
$$\underset{-1.50}{\big\lfloor\!\!\!-\!\!\!-\!\!\!\rightarrow}$$

24.4 It will be seen from these potentials that oxidation of metallic copper directly to Cu^{2+} and metallic gold to Au^{3+} is favored over oxidation to Cu^+ and Au^+, respectively. On the other hand oxidation of silver proceeds more easily to Ag^+ than to a higher state. The noble character of silver and, more especially, of gold is clearly evident in the large negative oxidation potentials for these elements.

TABLE 24.1

Some Properties of the Copper Family Elements

	Cu	Ag	Au
Natural isotopes	63 *, 65	107 *, 109	197
Density, g./cc.	8.94	10.50	19.32
Melting point, °C.	1083	960.5	1063
Boiling point, °C.	2325	1950	2600
Crystal ionic radius, Å			
M^+	0.93	1.21	1.37
M^{2+}	ca. 0.72		
Tetrahedral covalent radius, Å	1.35	1.53	1.50
Ionization potential, volts			
1st electron	7.724	7.574	9.22
2nd electron	20.287	21.48	20.5
3rd electron		36.10	
Electrode potential, $E°$, in volts, for			
$M = M^+ + e^-$	−0.521	−0.7991	ca. −1.68
$Cu = Cu^{2+} + 2e^-$	−0.337		
$Au = Au^{3+} + 3e^-$			−1.50

* More abundant isotope

24.5 Despite the number of oxidation states shown by this family only two simple (hydrated) ions, Cu^{2+} and Ag^+, are stable in aqueous solution. Although the Au^{3+} ion should be fairly stable toward reduction by water, simple gold(III) compounds undergo extensive hydrolysis. The strongly oxidizing copper(III), silver(II), and silver(III) ions, unless suitably stabilized in complexes or insoluble materials, are reduced by water. The monovalent ions, Cu^+ and Au^+, on the other hand, are unstable in aqueous solution with respect to the disproportionation reactions shown below, as the corresponding equilibrium constants clearly indicate.

$$2Cu^+ = Cu + Cu^{2+} \qquad K = 1.6 \times 10^6$$
$$3Au^+ = 2Au + Au^{3+} \qquad K = ca. \ 1 \times 10^{10}$$

Except for copper(II) and silver(I), therefore, the only compounds of these elements which are stable toward water are those which yield only very minute concentrations of the positive ion; that is, they are either insoluble compounds or stable complexes. Besides the restrictions imposed by their behavior in aqueous solution, the simple compounds of the strongly oxidizing species mentioned above suffer a severe limitation in number by the requirement that in order for the compound to be stable the anion must be difficult to oxidize.

The Elements

24.6 Although they are widely distributed, copper, silver, and gold occur in relatively low total quantities in the earth's crust, the estimated percentages being, respectively, 7×10^{-3}, 1×10^{-5}, and 5×10^{-7}. All three are found, at least to some extent, in the free state, as well as in combination. The most important natural source of copper is *chalcopyrite*, $CuFeS_2$. *Bornite*, Cu_3FeS_3, and other double sulfides, as well as *chalcocite*, Cu_2S, are also important. A number of oxidized ores, including *cuprite*, Cu_2O, *malachite*, $CuCO_3 \cdot Cu(OH)_2$, and *azurite*, $2CuCO_3 \cdot Cu(OH)_2$, may also serve as sources. Some copper is obtained from native ore. Silver is often found uncombined, but occurs more commonly in combination with sulfur, as in *argentite*, Ag_2S, and to some extent with halogens, as in *horn silver*, $AgCl$. Other elements, such as arsenic, antimony, lead, and copper, are frequently associated with it. Gold usually occurs in the free state, but is found also in some compounds, especially with tellurium, as in *calaverite*, $AuTe_2$.

24.7 The metallurgy of copper from a sulfide ore such as chalcopyrite is complex, and only a very brief outline of the major steps commonly employed will be given here. In a typical case the ore is subjected first to (1) concentration by flotation or gravity methods. Next follows (2) an oxidizing roast, in the course of which part of the sulfides present undergo oxidation, the sulfur being lost as the dioxide. Arsenic and antimony sulfides are commonly converted to oxides and volatilized in this step also. The next step, (3) smelting in a reverberatory matte furnace, eliminates a considerable amount of the iron in a silicate slag, and yields a "matte" consisting largely of Cu_2S and FeS. The molten matte, together with a flux, is put into a (4) converter, and a blast of air blown through, whereupon reactions typified by the following equations take place.

$$2FeS + 3O_2 = 2FeO + 2SO_2$$
$$FeO + SiO_2 = FeSiO_3 \ (\text{into slag; poured off})$$
$$2Cu_2S + 3O_2 = 2Cu_2O + 2SO_2$$
$$Cu_2S + 2Cu_2O = 6Cu + SO_2$$

The product, known as "blister copper," commonly contains as impurities small concentrations of such metals as Fe, Zn, Pb, Ag, and Au, and is subjected to

(5) refining. This may be accomplished in part by agitating the molten metal while air is blown on the surface to oxidize the more reactive impurity elements, forming a dross. Some Cu_2O is formed, too, and is reduced by stirring the metal with green wood poles. Electrolytic refining is also extensively employed, the blister copper serving as anode. Here copper and the more reactive metals are oxidized, while less reactive metals such as gold are not, but collect below the anode. At the cathode copper(II) ion is reduced in preference to the ions of more active metals, and thus a product of a high degree of purity can be obtained.

24.8 A large proportion of the silver produced is obtained as a by-product in the metallurgy of other elements, especially lead and copper. Where a primary silver ore is used extraction of the metal is usually accomplished by the cyanide process similar to that used for gold (see below).

24.9 Gold is most commonly extracted from its ores by the cyanide process, in which the crushed ore is leached with sodium cyanide solution, air being blown through the mixture. Gold(I) forms a very stable complex with cyanide ion, and metallic gold in the presence of excess cyanide is oxidized by the oxygen in the air with the formation of the complex, as represented by the following equation.

$$4Au + 8CN^- + O_2 + 2H_2O = 4Au(CN)_2^- + 4OH^-$$

The metal can be recovered from solution by the addition of metallic zinc. When the gold content of an ore justifies it, the cyanide extraction may be preceded by an amalgamation process in which the crushed ore and water are passed over amalgamated copper plates. Gold dissolves in the mercury, and the resulting amalgam, after removal from the plates, is subjected to distillation to effect separation of the metals.

24.10 Copper has a characteristic red color, is rather soft, but tough and ductile, and possesses high thermal and electrical conductivity, being exceeded only by silver in this last property. It undergoes only superficial oxidation in moist atmosphere, commonly forming a basic carbonate. When moderately heated it combines with oxygen to give copper(II) oxide; at high temperatures copper(I) oxide results. The metal combines with the halogens and with sulfur but not directly with nitrogen or carbon. As its oxidation potential indicates (Table 24.1), it is not normally oxidized by hydrogen ion, and dilute hydrochloric, sulfuric, or acetic acid do not attack it in the absence of air or other oxidizing agents or complexing agents. Nitric acid dissolves it, forming oxides of nitrogen; hot concentrated sulfuric acid also attacks it, with the production of sulfur dioxide. In both cases copper is oxidized to the +2 state.

24.11 Silver is a lustrous white metal, rather soft, and very ductile and malleable. Its thermal and electrical conductivities are higher than those of any other element. It is chemically less reactive than copper. Atmospheric oxygen does not attack it appreciably, but it reacts with ozone, especially when gently warmed. It reacts readily with sulfur and with solutions of sulfides or moist hydrogen sulfide to form black Ag_2S. The halogens attack the metal rather slowly. Silver is not attacked by nonoxidizing acids such as dilute sulfuric and hydrochloric acids, but oxidizing acids such as nitric or concentrated sulfuric acid readily dissolve it. It is resistant to alkalies and is only slightly attacked by molten alkali metal hydroxides.

24.12 Gold is a yellow, relatively soft metal, possessing the highest ductility and malleability of all the elements. It is the least reactive member of the copper family, and in many respects one of the least reactive of all the metals. It is not visibly attacked by oxygen nor by sulfur, although it combines readily with molten tellurium to give $AuTe_2$. Of the halogens, chlorine and bromine are the most reactive toward gold. Moist chlorine and liquid bromine react even at room temperature to give the corresponding gold(III) halides. Iodine reacts at moderately elevated temperatures to give AuI. Fluorine appears not to attack the metal except when it is rather strongly heated. Gold does not react significantly with alkalies nor with any of the common acids used singly, including nitric or sulfuric acids, dilute or concentrated. Mixtures of concentrated nitric and hydrochloric acids (aqua regia) readily dissolve it, however. In line with the general observation that the oxidation of a metal becomes less difficult in the presence of a suitable complexing agent, the oxidation of gold by aqua regia is favored by the possibility of forming the complex tetrachloraurate(III) ion, $AuCl_4^-$. A striking example of a similar effect is provided by the air oxidation of gold in the presence of cyanide ion, mentioned above. Although oxidation of the metal to the simple Au^+ and Au^{3+} ions is characterized by large negative potentials (Table 24.1), in the presence of cyanide ions the estimated standard oxidation potential assumes the rather large positive value shown below.

$$Au + 2CN^- = Au(CN)_2^- + e^- \qquad E° = 0.60 \text{ v.}$$

The Tripositive State

Copper(III) **24.13** The existence of simple compounds of copper(III) has not been definitely established, but a number of compounds containing copper(III) in anionic complexes have been obtained. The complexes represented in these compounds include the cuprate(III) ion, CuO_2^-, the hexafluorocuprate(III) ion, CuF_6^{3-}, the diperiodato complex, $[Cu(IO_6)_2]^{7-}$, and the ditellurato complex, $[Cu(TeO_6)_2]^{9-}$ or $[Cu(HTeO_6)_2]^{7-}$. Potassium cuprate(III), $KCuO_2$, is obtained [1] as a steel-blue product by heating a mixture of CuO and KO_2 (prepared *in situ* from partially oxidized potassium) in a dry oxygen atmosphere at 400 to 450°. The product has a characteristic X-ray pattern, differing from both KO_2 and CuO, and the copper is diamagnetic. The compound decomposes above 500° and is vigorously decomposed by water, yielding a dark brown precipitate which dissolves slowly in acids with the evolution of oxygen and the formation of copper(II) ion. No test for peroxide is shown. The analogous barium compound has been produced [2] by treatment of copper(II) chloride in cold, strongly

[1] WAHL and KLEMM, *Z. anorg. u. allgem. Chem.,* **270,** 69 (1952).
[2] SCHOLDER and VOELSKOW, *Z. anorg. u. allgem. Chem.,* **266,** 256 (1951).

alkaline medium with a large excess of potassium hypobromite, followed by rapid addition of the solution to aqueous barium chloride and chilling. The red hydrated compound, $Ba(CuO_2)_2 \cdot H_2O$, which precipitates is found to be sparingly soluble in water but to dissolve in acids with the evolution of oxygen, yielding copper(II) ion. Strontium cuprate(III) is more difficult to prepare pure, and the sodium compound appears to be quite unstable. The diamagnetic character of copper in these compounds points to planar four-coordination of the oxygen atoms about the metal, inner DSP^2 orbitals being used by the latter. This, in turn, suggests the probable existence of anionic chains in which each coordination square may, perhaps, share two opposite edges with its neighbors.

24.14 Potassium hexafluorocuprate(III), $K_3[CuF_6]$, is prepared [3] by treating a mixture of potassium and copper(II) chlorides in a 3 : 1 molar ratio with fluorine at 250°. The pale green product is decomposed by water, yielding an unidentified gas and copper(II) fluoride. In this compound copper has a magnetic moment of 2.8 Bohr magnetons, indicating $[CuF_6]^{3-}$ to be an outer orbital complex.

24.15 Compounds containing the diperiodatocuprate(III) complex have been prepared by anodic oxidation of a strongly alkaline solution of a copper(II) salt in the presence of potassium periodate. A diamagnetic, emerald green powder, analyzing for $K_7[Cu(IO_6)_2] \cdot 7H_2O$, was obtained in this manner. From it, $Na_7[Cu(IO_6)_2] \cdot 12H_2O$ was made by metathesis. A similar compound, $Na_7[Cu(IO_6)_2] \cdot 16H_2O$, results from the addition of $Na_2H_3IO_6$ to a solution of copper(II) chloride in strongly alkaline sodium hypochlorite.[4] At a somewhat elevated temperature the 12-hydrate is obtained. In dilute alkaline solution the diperiodatocopper(III) complex is a strong oxidizing agent, converting arsenite to arsenate, chromium(III) to chromate, cyanide to carbonate and nitrate, various sulfides to sulfates, and oxidizing a number of organic materials as well.

24.16 Oxidation of copper(II) chloride by means of strongly alkaline hypochlorite, followed by addition of sodium tellurate, $Na_2H_4TeO_6$ (instead of periodate) yields the brown crystalline product, $Na_9[Cu(TeO_6)_2] \cdot 20H_2O$.[4] Peroxydisulfate has also been used as the oxidizing agent instead of hypochlorite. For example, the addition of potassium peroxydisulfate, $K_2S_2O_8$, to a boiling solution containing tellurium dioxide, copper(II) sulfate, and potassium hydroxide, followed by introduction of excess sodium sulfate yields crystalline products corresponding to the formulas $Na_5H_4[Cu(TeO_6)_2] \cdot 18H_2O$ and $Na_7H_2[Cu(TeO_6)_2] \cdot 12H_2O$. Both the tellurato and the periodato complexes liberate oxygen and form copper(II) ion when treated with acid.

Silver(III) **24.17** The oxidation of silver(I) nitrate in strongly basic medium by means of potassium peroxydisulfate in the presence of periodate or tellurate yields compounds containing anionic periodato or tellurato complexes of silver(III) analogous to those described above for copper(III). Compounds prepared in this manner which have been isolated and analyzed include the

[3] KLEMM and HUSS, *Z. anorg. Chem.*, **258**, 221 (1949).
[4] LISTER, *Can. J. Chem.*, **31**, 638 (1953).

periodato compounds $K_6H[Ag(IO_6)_2] \cdot 10H_2O$, $K_7[Ag(IO_6)_2] \cdot KOH \cdot 8H_2O$, $K_6H[Ag(IO_6)_2] \cdot KOH \cdot 8H_2O$, and $Na_6K[Ag(IO_6)_2] \cdot NaOH \cdot H_2O$, and the tellurato compounds $Na_7H_2[Ag(TeO_6)_2] \cdot 14H_2O$ and $Na_6H_3[Ag(TeO_6)_2] \cdot 18H_2O$. They are yellow or orange in color. Magnetic measurements indicate silver to be diamagnetic in these substances.

24.18 The yellow fluorocomplex compounds, $KAgF_4$ and $CsAgF_4$, have also been described.[5] They are produced by heating a mixture of silver(I) salt and alkali metal salt in the appropriate proportions in a current of fluorine. The products are very reactive toward moisture. Silver is again found to have zero magnetic moment in these compounds, a result which indicates these complexes to be of the inner orbital DSP^2 type.

24.19 Silver(III) forms a very stable cationic complex with ethylenedibiguanide (edbg), in which the latter presumably acts as a quadridentate chelating agent, yielding a complex ion for which the structure shown has been postulated. When a mixture of silver(I) sulfate and ethylenedibiguanide sulfate in aqueous solution is treated with potassium peroxydisulfate, a red, sparingly soluble solid of composition corresponding to $[Ag\ edbg]_2(SO_4)_3 \cdot 7H_2O$ is slowly formed. Treatment of this compound with dilute alkali yields violet-red $[Ag\ edbg](OH)_3 \cdot 3H_2O$. From this, the orange-red nitrate and the dark red

perchlorate can be prepared. The molar conductivity of the nitrate is found to correspond to that of a terunivalent salt, in agreement with the formulation $[Ag\ edbg](NO_3)_3$. Moreover, these compounds react with acidified potassium iodide solution to liberate two equivalents of iodine per gram atom of silver, thus providing further evidence for the presence of tripositive silver in them. Magnetic measurements show them to be diamagnetic.

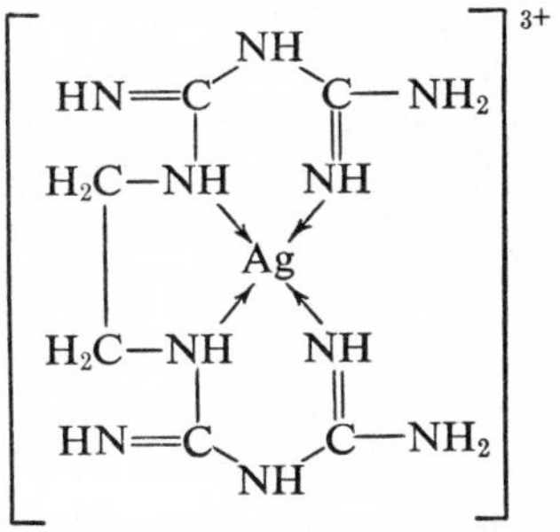

24.20 No binary compounds of silver(III) have been definitely characterized, although a material which may be an oxide or a basic silver(III) salt has been produced as a black precipitate from the reaction of a silver(I) salt with peroxydisulfate in approximately neutral solution. The wet, freshly separated solid shows two oxidizing equivalents per silver atom toward acidified oxalate or iron(II) sulfate solution, but when allowed to stand it rather rapidly loses part of its oxidizing ability, yielding a material which appears to contain both silver(III) and silver(II). The material gives no test for peroxide.

Gold(III) **24.21** The inorganic compounds of tripositive gold include binary compounds with oxygen, sulfur, and the halogens, a number of compounds containing gold as part of an anionic complex, and a few salts containing cationic complexes. Gold also forms a number of organo-metallic compounds; these, however, lie outside the scope of this work, and will not be discussed further.

[5] KLEMM, *Angew. Chem.*, **66**, 468 (1954).

24.22 Neither gold(III) oxide, Au_2O_3, nor sulfide, Au_2S_3, can be made by direct union of the elements, but must be prepared from other gold(III) compounds. The oxide can be obtained by careful heating (about 140–150°) of the hydrous oxide, which in turn is produced as a yellowish-brown precipitate by treatment of gold(III) chloride with alkali or alkaline earth metal hydroxide or carbonate. Preparation of the oxide in high purity is difficult, however, inasmuch as decomposition into the elements sets in at temperatures not very much higher than those required for dehydration of the hydrous oxide. The sulfide can be obtained by the action of hydrogen sulfide on a cold, dilute solution of chlorauric acid, $H[AuCl_4]$, or on a solution of gold(III) chloride in ether or on dry $Li[AuCl_4]$. The product, described as a black, graphitelike powder, decomposes extensively into the elements at about 200°.

24.23 Hydrous gold(III) oxide, also termed "gold(III) hydroxide" or "auric acid," is amphoteric. It is soluble in alkalies to give solutions from which aurate(III) salts, such as $NaAuO_2 \cdot H_2O$ and $KAuO_2 \cdot 3H_2O$, may be obtained; it dissolves in acids, also, if they are sufficiently concentrated, apparently forming such compounds as $H[AuCl_4]$, $H[Au(NO_3)_4]$, and $H[Au(SO_4)_2]$ in solution. The first two can actually be obtained in crystalline form as the hydrates $H[AuCl_4] \cdot 3H_2O$, $H[AuCl_4] \cdot 4H_2O$, and $H[Au(NO_3)_4] \cdot 3H_2O$, by careful evaporation of the corresponding acid solutions. Addition of an appropriate salt to the strongly acid solution, followed by evaporation, makes it possible to obtain such solid compounds as $K[AuCl_4]$, $K[Au(NO_3)_4]$, and $K[Au(SO_4)_2]$. Although complex nitrates and sulfates can thus be obtained, simple gold(III) nitrate and sulfate are not known. Dilution of the acidic nitrate or sulfate solutions with water results in hydrolysis and the precipitation of hydrous gold oxide.

24.24 Both gold(III) chloride and bromide can be produced by direct union of the elements. The chloride results when chlorine reacts with gold foil at about 200°, for example; the bromide is formed in the reaction of liquid bromine with gold. The chloride is a very hygroscopic, red, crystalline material; the bromide is dark brown in color, and is not hygroscopic. Both have been shown to consist of dimeric molecules, the chloride by vapor density measurements between 150° and 260°, the bromide by boiling point elevations produced in liquid bromine. Structural studies of some closely related organogold compounds suggest that the most probable structure of these compounds is one involving planar four-coordination of the halogen atoms around both gold atoms, corresponding to the formula given. When heated both the chloride and the bromide undergo decomposition into the corresponding gold(I) halide and free halogen.

$$Au_2X_6(s) = 2AuX(s) + 2X_2(g)$$

The equilibrium pressure of chlorine in the reaction is one atmosphere at about 250°, while that of bromine is estimated to reach one atmosphere at 178°.

24.25 Gold(III) iodide is less stable with respect to decomposition than are the bromide and iodide. It cannot be made by direct union of the elements, but is produced as a green precipitate when gold(III) chloride is added in suitable quantity to a solution of potassium iodide. On standing in air, even at room temperature, the iodide decomposes into gold(I) iodide and iodine.

24.26 Although the fluoride is thermally more stable than the other halides, decomposing extensively into the elements only at temperatures near 500°, it is best prepared, not by direct union of the elements, but by warming finely divided gold with bromine trifluoride, producing first $AuBrF_6$, which can then be decomposed at about 180° to give the orange-colored gold(III) fluoride, AuF_3. Unlike the other trihalides, the trifluoride does not react with the acid to give tetrafluorauric(III) acid. Instead, even in 40% HF solution, it hydrolyzes immediately, yielding a precipitate of the hydrous oxide. The salt $Na[AuF_4]$ can be made by the reaction between bromine trifluoride and $Na[AuCl_4]$, but it, too, is hydrolytically decomposed in water.

24.27 The tendency of gold(III) to form four-coordinated anionic complexes is well exemplified in the tetrahalo-acids and salts described above. X-ray examination of $K[AuBr_4] \cdot 2H_2O$ has shown the existence of planar $AuBr_4^-$ in the crystal; planar $AuCl_4^-$ has similarly been found in crystals of $Cs_2Au^IAu^{III}Cl_6$. Presumably this structure, involving the use of DSP^2 hybrid orbitals, is characteristic of the four-coordinated complexes of gold(III). Additional representative compounds containing other anionic complexes include $K[AuI_4]$, $H[Au(CN)_4] \cdot 3H_2O$, $K[Au(CN)_2Cl_2] \cdot H_2O$, $K[Au(CN)_2Br_2] \cdot 3H_2O$, $Na[Au(SCN)_4]$, $Na_5H_2[Au(IO_6)_2] \cdot 17H_2O$, and $Na_6H_3[Au(TeO_6)_2] \cdot 14H_2O$. Some of the complexes possess relatively high stability toward dissociation, as is illustrated by the values of the stability constants.

$$Au^{3+} + 4Cl^- = AuCl_4^- \qquad K = 2 \times 10^{21}$$
$$Au^{3+} + 4SCN^- = Au(SCN)_4^- \qquad K = ca.\ 10^{42}$$

On the other hand, the readiness with which AuF_4^-, $Au(NO_3)_4^-$, and $Au(SO_4)_2^-$, for example, undergo hydrolytic decomposition in water indicates that these complexes must be less stable in this respect.

24.28 Tripositive gold forms comparatively few types of cationic complexes. Among them are complexes with ammonia, with ethylenediamine, and with o-bis(dimethylarsino)benzene, illustrated by the representative compounds $[Au(NH_3)_4](NO_3)_3$, $[Au(NH_3)_4](ClO_4)_3$, $[Au\ en_2]Br_3$, and $[Au\ diarsine_2]I_3$. Here again gold appears to show the characteristic coordination number four. The last compound may actually represent an example of six-coordination, however, since the molar conductance of the salt in nitrobenzene corresponds to that of a uniunivalent salt, suggesting[6] the formulation $[Au\ diarsine_2I_2]I$. On similar grounds five-coordination is postulated for the compound $[Au\ diarsine_2I](ClO_4)_2$.

The Dipositive State

Copper(II) **24.29** The dipositive state is by far the most important oxidation state of copper. As has been pointed out (see 24.4) it is normally the state to

---

[6] HARRIS, NYHOLM and STEPHENSON, *Rec. trav. chim.*, **75**, 687 (1956).

which metallic copper goes upon oxidation. Moreover, the copper(II) ion is stable in water, and many compounds can be made by metathetical reactions as well as by direct oxidation of the metal. Not only is it possible to produce a variety of simple compounds, but since copper(II) ion is a good complex former, numerous coordination compounds can be obtained as well.

24.30 Copper(II) oxide, CuO, is obtained as a black, insoluble material, either by heating copper to a moderately elevated temperature in air or by thermal decomposition of the carbonate, hydroxide, or nitrate. It is weakly basic, dissolving in acids to give solutions of the corresponding salts. The oxide is readily reduced when heated with such agents as hydrogen or carbon monoxide.

24.31 The hydroxide is precipitated when solutions of copper(II) salts are treated with alkalies. It may be obtained either as a gelatinous material of variable water content or as a crystalline substance of composition corresponding to $Cu(OH)_2$.

24.32 The hydroxide, like the oxide, is predominantly basic, reacting with acids to give solutions of the corresponding copper(II) salts. It shows some amphoteric character, however, as is indicated by the significant increase in its solubility in the presence of strong bases. Moreover, from solutions of the hydroxide in concentrated alkalies solid hydroxocuprates such as $Na_2[Cu(OH)_4]$ and $Sr[Cu(OH)_4]$ may be obtained.

24.33 Only three of the copper(II) halides may be obtained as stable solid compounds, namely, the fluoride, chloride, and bromide. These may be produced in anhydrous form by reaction of copper metal with the appropriate halogen at elevated temperatures. The anhydrous fluoride is white, the chloride yellowish brown, and the bromide black. The compounds may be produced in solution by reaction of the hydrohalic acids with copper(II) oxide, hydroxide, or basic carbonate. The bromide and chloride are readily soluble in water, the fluoride sparingly so. Crystallization normally yields $CuF_2 \cdot 2H_2O$ and $CuCl_2 \cdot 2H_2O$; the bromide may be obtained as a hydrate or in anhydrous form, depending upon the temperature. Moderate heating of $CuF_2 \cdot 2H_2O$ results in the evolution of some HF with formation of a basic fluoride, $Cu(OH)F \cdot CuF_2$. When $CuCl_2 \cdot 2H_2O$ is moderately heated in a stream of HCl gas, anhydrous $CuCl_2$ is formed. Both the chloride and the bromide undergo thermal decomposition at high temperatures to give the copper(I) halide and free halogen. Copper(II) iodide has not been isolated, presumably because it is unstable with respect to this reaction under ordinarily attainable conditions. Crystals of anhydrous copper(II) chloride and bromide have both been shown to contain chains of the type shown, in which each copper atom shows planar four-coordination. In copper(II) chloride dihydrate, $CuCl_2 \cdot 2H_2O$, planar four-coordination is again shown in discrete units having the structure indicated.

24.34 Copper(II) sulfide, CuS, is formed when copper is heated in contact with sulfur. It is a black solid of very low solubility in water and is precipitated when solutions of copper(II) salts are treated with hydrogen sulfide, even in the presence of dilute acids. When strongly heated in the absence of air the compound undergoes decomposition to give copper(I) sulfide, Cu_2S.

24.35 A number of copper(II) salts of oxygen acids are known, among the most important of which are the nitrate and the sulfate. The former can be made by the action of nitric acid on the metal or on the oxide, hydroxide, or basic carbonate. It is normally crystallized from solution as the blue hexahydrate, $Cu(NO_3)_2 \cdot 6H_2O$, which loses water above about 26° to give the trihydrate, $Cu(NO_3)_2 \cdot 3H_2O$. Removal of the remaining water to give the anhydrous nitrate can be accomplished by dissolving the trihydrate in hot fuming nitric acid, then cooling the solution. Heating the trihydrate alone yields a basic compound instead of the anhydrous salt.

24.36 Copper(II) sulfate can be produced by the reaction of the metal with hot concentrated sulfuric acid or with air and warm dilute sulfuric acid. It is commonly crystallized from solution as the blue pentahydrate, "blue vitriol," $CuSO_4 \cdot 5H_2O$. Structural studies of this compound show four of the water molecules in a plane surrounding the copper atom, with the fifth water molecule being held by hydrogen bonds to two water molecules and to oxygen atoms of two sulfate ions. A series of lower hydrates may be obtained by moderate heating at suitable temperatures.

$$CuSO_4 \cdot 5H_2O \xrightarrow{53.7°} CuSO_4 \cdot 4H_2O \xrightarrow{102°} CuSO_4 \cdot 3H_2O \xrightarrow{113°} CuSO_4 \cdot H_2O$$

The last molecule of water can be driven off by prolonged heating between 200–300°, yielding white anhydrous $CuSO_4$.

24.37 The normal carbonate seems never to have been isolated; however, several basic carbonates are known, among them the naturally occurring minerals *azurite*, $Cu(OH)_2 \cdot 2CuCO_3$, and *malachite*, $Cu(OH)_2 \cdot CuCO_3$. Numerous other basic salts have been described, some representative examples being $Cu(NO_3)_2 \cdot 3Cu(OH)_2$, $CuCl_2 \cdot 3Cu(OH)_2$, $CuCl_2 \cdot Cu(OH)_2$, $CuBr_2 \cdot 3Cu(OH)_2$, $CuSO_4 \cdot 4Cu(OH)_2 \cdot 2H_2O$, and $Cu(C_2H_3O_2)_2 \cdot Cu(OH)_2$.

24.38 Copper(II) ion in solution readily forms cationic complexes with molecules containing a basic nitrogen atom which can serve as a donor group. The most familiar example is the intense violet-blue tetramminecopper(II) ion, $Cu(NH_3)_4^{2+}$, formed by the action of aqueous ammonia on a copper(II) salt. The stability constant for this complex ion is 2.1×10^{14}; it is sufficiently large that aqueous ammonia will dissolve a number of water-insoluble compounds, including the carbonate and hydroxide, though not the sulfide. Amines, polyamines, pyridine, and similar compounds form analogous complexes in solution. A number of solid compounds containing ammonia have been described, some common examples being $CuSO_4 \cdot 5NH_3$, $CuSO_4 \cdot 4NH_3 \cdot H_2O$, $CuCl_2 \cdot 4NH_3 \cdot H_2O$, $CuCl_2 \cdot 6NH_3$, and $Cu(OH)_2 \cdot 4NH_3 \cdot 3H_2O$. Neutral or anionic complexes are formed in solution with a variety of agents, such as thiocyanate, glycinate, oxalate, tartrate, chloride, and bromide ions. The halo complexes are not very stable in solution, but crystalline compounds having empirical formulas such as $KCuCl_3$, $K_2CuCl_4 \cdot 2H_2O$, $CsCuBr_3$, and $CsCuCl_3$ have been prepared. An X-ray study of $CsCuCl_3$ reveals the presence of infinite anionic chains (see 6.46) of the type $(CuCl_3)_n^{n-}$, in which each copper atom shows planar four-coordination. On the other hand, in $K_2CuCl_4 \cdot 2H_2O$, the complex unit is $[CuCl_2(H_2O)_2]$, possessing the same structure as in the copper(II) chloride dihydrate (see 24.33).

Silver(II) **24.39** Two binary compounds and several complex substances which appear to contain dipositive silver have been described. One of the binary compounds is a black solid of a composition corresponding to AgO, which is produced by the action of potassium peroxydisulfate on silver nitrate in alkaline solution. The compound dissolves in dilute sulfuric acid with the evolution of oxygen but gives no test for peroxide. In concentrated nitric or sulfuric acid it shows strong oxidizing power. The solid may be heated to 100° without change but decomposes at higher temperatures into silver metal and oxygen.

24.40 A second binary compound, AgF_2, is produced by the action of fluorine on silver or silver salts at temperatures somewhat below 450°. Above this temperature the compound decomposes completely into silver(I) fluoride and fluorine. AgF_2 is a powerful oxidizing and fluorinating agent. It reacts with water to liberate oxygen and ozone, oxidizes manganese(II) to permanganate, chromium(III) to chromate, and converts carbon tetrachloride to carbon tetrafluoride. The compound is paramagnetic, but the moment is less than that calculated for one unpaired electron.

24.41 A number of silver(II) complexes are known, most of them cationic. For example, $[Ag\ py_4]S_2O_8$, is obtained by the action of peroxydisulfate on aqueous silver nitrate containing an excess of pyridine. The orange-yellow crystals are isomorphous with those of the corresponding copper(II) salt; in view of the planar structure characteristic of four-coordinated copper(II), a similar structure for four-coordinated silver(II) complexes is indicated. Further evidence for the planar structure comes from X-ray examination of the copper(II) and silver(II) picolinates. These compounds are isomorphous, and the copper salt has been shown to have a *trans*-planar structure, suggesting a similar configuration for the silver(II) salt as shown.

24.42 Other compounds containing complexes of silver(II) with α, α'-dipyridyl or o-phenanthroline are represented by $[Ag\ dipy_2]S_2O_8$; by $[Ag\ dipy_3]X_2$, where $X = NO_3^-$, ClO_3^-, ClO_4^-; and by $[Ag\ o\text{-phen}_2]X_2$, where $X = NO_3^-$, ClO_3^-, HSO_4^-, or $\frac{1}{2}S_2O_8^{2-}$. The dipositive character of silver is shown by its quantitative oxidizing action toward iodides and oxalates. Moreover, magnetic measurements on a number of these salts yield values of 1.74–2.16 Bohr units for the magnetic moment of silver in them, consistent with the presence of one unpaired electron expected for the silver(II) ion.

Gold(II) **24.43** The existence of compounds containing dipositive gold has never been definitely established, although some evidence for the transient existence of gold(II) in solution has been advanced from kinetic studies.

The Monopositive State

Copper(I) **24.44** Because equilibrium in the disproportionation reaction lies

$$2Cu^+ = Cu + Cu^{2+}$$

far to the right, the only copper(I) compounds which are stable in contact with water are those which supply only minute concentrations of copper(I) ion. Therefore the only compounds which can be prepared in aqueous media are those which are very slightly soluble or in which the copper(I) state has been stabilized by complex formation.

24.45 Among the insoluble compounds of copper(I) are the oxide, chloride, bromide, iodide, cyanide, thiocyanate, and sulfide. When dry the oxide is red in color; the chloride, bromide, iodide, cyanide, and thiocyanate are white; and the sulfide is black. Most of these substances can be produced by the reduction of copper(II) ion in the presence of the appropriate precipitating agent. For example, the oxide, Cu_2O, is formed when a mild reducing agent such as glucose or hydrazine reacts with copper(II) in the presence of a strong base. The chloride may be prepared by warming a solution of copper(II) chloride in dilute hydrochloric acid with finely divided copper.

$$Cu^{2+} + 2Cl^- + Cu = 2CuCl(s)$$

Other reducing agents such as sulfur dioxide or tin(II) ion may be used instead of copper metal. Copper(I) bromide can be made similarly. The thiocyanate is readily obtained by reducing copper(II) ion with sulfur dioxide in the presence of thiocyanate ion. To produce copper(I) iodide or cyanide no additional reducing agent is necessary, since these anions themselves will reduce copper(II) ion, with the formation of free iodine or cyanogen and the precipitate.

$$2Cu^{2+} + 4I^- = 2CuI(s) + I_2$$
$$2Cu^{2+} + 4CN^- = 2CuCN(s) + (CN)_2$$

The sulfide, having a very low solubility, can be made by the action of hydrogen sulfide on a suspension of another copper(I) salt. The sulfide, oxide, chloride, and bromide are also produced from the corresponding copper(II) compounds by thermal decomposition at high temperatures (see 24.33–34).

24.46 Copper(I) oxide is basic in character. It reacts with the hydrohalic acids HCl, HBr, and HI to give the corresponding insoluble copper(I) halides. With dilute oxygen acids, however, it dissolves and undergoes disproportionation simultaneously.

$$Cu_2O + 2H^+ = Cu^{2+} + Cu + H_2O$$

It may be mentioned that copper(I) fluoride cannot be produced by the action of HF on copper(I) oxide. As a matter of fact, CuF appears not to be stable at ordinary temperatures. It is reported that when copper(II) fluoride, CuF_2, is heated to about 1200° the molten product contains about 70% CuF. However, when this material is cooled, disproportionation occurs according to the reaction $2CuF = CuF_2 + Cu$, and no CuF remains in the solid product. Attempts to prepare CuF in other ways have been unsuccessful.[7]

24.47 Copper(I) sulfate has been made by the reaction of copper(I) oxide with methyl sulfate at 160°.

$$Cu_2O + (CH_3)_2SO_4 = Cu_2SO_4 + CH_3OCH_3$$

The grayish-white solid is stable in dry air but it immediately undergoes disproportionation in water. The simple nitrate, $CuNO_3$, is not known but a number of its complexes have been prepared. For example, the compound $CuNO_3 \cdot 2NH_3$ can be made in liquid ammonia. Other compounds which have been described are $[Cu(CH_3CN)_4]NO_3$ and $[Cu(H_2NCSNH_2)_2]NO_3$.

24.48 Monopositive copper forms complexes with a number of agents, among them cyanide, thiocyanate, thiosulfate, and halide ions; ammonia, tertiary phosphines, and arsines; thiourea and thioacetamide. The most common coordination number is four, but two and three are also represented. Structural studies on the solid compounds have shown tetrahedral coordination of the four groups about the copper atom in $K_2[Cu(CN)_4]$ and $[Cu(CH_3CSNH_2)_4]Cl$. In the crystalline compound having the empirical formula K_2CuCl_3 the chlorine atoms are tetrahedrally arranged about the copper atom, each tetrahedron sharing two apices with adjacent tetrahedra, thus forming anionic chains $(CuCl_3)_n^{2n-}$. X-ray analysis of solid $K[Cu(CN)_2]$ has shown[8] it to have spiral anionic chains which may be schematically represented as shown. The three

$$-CN \rightarrow Cu-CN \rightarrow Cu-$$
$$\uparrow \qquad\quad \uparrow$$
$$CN \qquad\quad CN$$

bonds from each copper atom are not quite coplanar, nor are the bond angles equal. Presumably they represent the use of modified SP^2 hybrid orbitals by the metal atom.

Silver(I) **24.49** Silver forms a large number of compounds, both simple and complex, in which its oxidation state is $+1$. Many of the simple compounds are insoluble in water. Exceptions include the perchlorate, nitrate, fluoride, and chlorate, which are very soluble, and the sulfate, nitrite, and acetate, which are sparingly soluble. The insoluble compounds are commonly produced by metathetical reactions between the nitrate and a salt containing the precipitating anion.

[7] HAENDLER, TOWLE, BENNETT, and PATTERSON, *J. Am. Chem. Soc.*, **76**, 2178 (1954); CRAB-TREE, LEES, and LITTLE, *J. Inorg. Nucl. Chem.*, **1**, 213 (1956).
[8] CROMER, *J. Phys. Chem.*, **61**, 1388 (1957).

24.50 Silver(I) oxide is precipitated as a brownish-black solid when a strong base is added to a solution of a silver salt.

$$2Ag^+ + 2OH^- = Ag_2O(s) + H_2O$$

The oxide is basic in character, as is shown by the readiness with which it dissolves in acids and by the fact that suspensions of Ag_2O in water are distinctly alkaline. Moist silver(I) oxide, in fact, will absorb CO_2. In the presence of concentrated alkalies the solubility of the oxide is increased somewhat, indicating that it possesses a small degree of acidic character, also.

24.51 Solid silver(I) oxide undergoes perceptible decomposition into the elements at about 160°, and the equilibrium value of the oxygen pressure reaches one atmosphere at about 185–190°. The compound can be easily reduced by carbon monoxide or hydrogen.

24.52 Of the silver(I) halides the fluoride is very soluble, as has been mentioned; the chloride, bromide, and iodide are insoluble, their solubility products at 25° being 1.81×10^{-10}, 3.3×10^{-13}, and 8.5×10^{-17}, respectively. The fluoride is readily made by the action of hydrofluoric acid on silver oxide; evaporation of the solution commonly yields the dihydrate, $AgF \cdot 2H_2O$, one of the few hydrates formed by silver(I) salts. Above about 42° the dihydrate decomposes to give AgF. The other three halides are readily prepared by metathesis. They gradually undergo reduction in the light, a property which is extensively used in photography.

24.53 A so-called "sub-fluoride" of silver, of composition corresponding to the formula Ag_2F, has been described. It is obtained as a yellow- or bronze-colored crystalline solid from concentrated solutions of AgF which have dissolved metallic silver. The crystals contain close-packed layers of atoms occurring in the order Ag, Ag, F; the substance is considered to be intermediate between a salt and a metal.

24.54 Silver(I) sulfide, Ag_2S, having the lowest solubility of any of the silver(I) compounds, is readily precipitated from solutions or suspensions of other silver salts by means of hydrogen sulfide. The sulfide is also formed as a black solid on the surface of metallic silver which has come in contact with elemental sulfur, or with solutions of alkali metal sulfides or hydrogen sulfide in the presence of oxygen.

24.55 Of the silver(I) salts of the oxygen acids the nitrate, $AgNO_3$, is the most important. It is usually produced by dissolving metallic silver in nitric acid and crystallizing the compound from the solution. It is obtained in the form of colorless crystals, melting at 212°; they are very soluble in water, giving neutral solutions. The sparingly soluble sulfate, Ag_2SO_4, is commonly made from the metal by reaction with concentrated sulfuric acid. The very soluble perchlorate can be obtained by the action of aqueous perchloric acid on silver(I) oxide or carbonate or by metathesis between silver sulfate and barium perchlorate. Silver(I) perchlorate forms a monohydrate, $AgClO_4 \cdot H_2O$, which undergoes transition to the anhydrous salt above 43°.

24.56 Solutions containing silver(I) ion yield precipitates with a large number of anions. With CN^-, SCN^-, $[Fe(CN)_6]^{3-}$, $[Fe(CN)_6]^{4-}$, and IO_3^-, as well as with Cl^-, Br^-, I^-, and S^{2-}, precipitates can be obtained even in the presence of dilute nitric acid. The ions CrO_4^{2-}, $C_2O_4^{2-}$, SO_3^{2-}, $S_2O_3^{2-}$, BrO_3^-, and PO_3^- also yield precipitates with Ag^+ but require a lower hydrogen ion concentration such as that provided by dilute acetic acid, for example. Such ions as CO_3^{2-}, PO_4^{3-}, AsO_4^{3-}, AsO_3^{3-}, and BO_2^- give precipitates from neutral solutions. Differences in the solubility behavior, together with the characteristic colors shown by some of these precipitates, have been utilized in qualitative tests for a number of the anions.

24.57 Silver(I) ion forms complexes with molecules which contain a basic nitrogen atom such as ammonia, acridine, quinoline, and pyridine. It forms complexes, too, with molecules in which a sulfur atom serves as the donor atom; examples are thiourea, thioacetamide, and ethylenethiourea. A number of anions also enter into complexes with silver ion, among them hydroxide, chloride, bromide, iodide, thiosulfate, and cyanide. The most characteristic coordination number is two, but examples of four-coordination and even of three-coordination are known.

24.58 Silver(I) complexes exhibit a wide variation in stabilities with respect to dissociation in solution, as is illustrated by the stability constants.

$[Ag(OH)_2]^-$	4.0×10^3	$[Ag(S_2O_3)_2]^{3-}$	1.7×10^{13}
$[AgCl_2]^-$	4.5×10^5	$[Ag(CN)_2]^-$	5.6×10^{18}
$[Ag(NH_3)_2]^+$	1.6×10^7		

These differences are, of course, reflected in the behavior of the complexing agents toward the insoluble silver(I) compounds. For example, solutions of alkali metal cyanides will dissolve any of the insoluble compounds including the sulfide. The use of sodium thiosulfate as a "fixing" agent in photography is based upon the fact that solutions containing thiosulfate ion will dissolve silver halides as well as many other silver compounds. On the other hand aqueous ammonia does not dissolve the sulfide nor the iodide to any appreciable extent, but does dissolve many of the less insoluble compounds, such as the chloride, the carbonate, and the oxide. It should be mentioned that on standing ammoniacal solutions of silver salts deposit a dark-colored solid, called "fulminating silver." This material contains silver nitride, Ag_3N, and perhaps the imide, Ag_2NH; it is violently explosive, being sensitive to mechanical contact even when wet.

24.59 X-ray studies have shown the presence of linear $[H_3N \rightarrow Ag \leftarrow NH_3]^+$ in solid $[Ag(NH_3)_2]SO_4$, and linear $[NC \rightarrow Ag—CN]^-$ in $K[Ag(CN)_2]$. In $[Ag(SCNH_2CH_3)_4]Cl$, the four thioacetamide molecules are tetrahedrally coordinated to the silver atom. In the crystalline compounds of empirical formulas Cs_2AgCl_3, K_2AgI_3, Rb_2AgI_3, Cs_2AgI_3, and $(NH_4)_2AgI_3$ the silver atom again shows four-coordination; tetrahedral AgX_4 groups here share two corners to give anionic chains of the type $[AgX_3]_n^{2n-}$. Evidence for the formation of three-coordinated complexes in solution with thiourea [9] and with tertiary phosphines [10] has been obtained.

Gold(I) **24.60** The best characterized simple compounds of monopositive gold are the chloride, bromide, iodide, sulfide, and cyanide. A number of complex compounds are known, also.

24.61 Both AuCl and AuBr can be produced by careful heating of the corresponding gold(III) compounds. Gold(III) iodide gradually decomposes on standing at room temperature to form AuI. Gold(I) iodide is produced, also, when gold(III) oxide is dissolved in hydriodic acid. All three of the gold(I) halides decompose into the elements when heated to moderately elevated temperatures, the iodide being the least stable in this respect. The compounds are yellow to greenish-yellow in color, and all have low solubilities in water. In contact with water the chloride and bromide undergo decomposition. The

$$3AuX = 2Au + AuX_3$$

iodide reacts much more slowly under these conditions, presumably because of a lower solubility. Gold(I) fluoride is not known as a stable compound.

24.62 The existence of gold(I) oxide or hydroxide appears to be questionable. If either is formed in the reaction of an alkali with a gold(I) compound it must be unstable, since the final product appears to be a mixture of metallic gold and gold(III) oxide.

24.63 The sulfide, Au_2S, is obtained as a brownish-black solid by saturating a solution of $K[Au(CN)_2]$ with hydrogen sulfide, then adding hydrochloric acid. The solubility of the sulfide is very small, as indicated by the fact that it is not dissolved by concentrated hydrochloric acid.

24.64 Gold(I) cyanide can be made by decomposing $K[Au(CN)_2]$ with hydrochloric acid. Like the corresponding silver compound, it is insoluble in water and dilute acids. The crystal contains chains of the type indicated.

$$\rightarrow Au—CN \rightarrow Au—CN \rightarrow Au—CN \rightarrow$$

24.65 One of the most important complexes of monopositive gold is the cyano complex, $Au(CN)_2^-$. In consequence of its very large stability constant, the

$$Au^+ + 2CN^- = Au(CN)_2^- \qquad K = 4 \times 10^{28}$$

cyanoaurate(I) ion is stable in solution. Moreover, insoluble gold(I) compounds, including AuCN and Au_2S, are dissolved by excess alkali metal cyanide solutions. Crystalline compounds containing the complex, such as $K[Au(CN)_2]$, $Ba[Au(CN)_2]_2$, and $H[Au(CN)_2]$, can be prepared. Gold(I) also forms a complex with thiosulfate ion; aqueous thiosulfates will dissolve gold(I) iodide, for example. Solid compounds such as $Na_3[Au(S_2O_3)_2] \cdot \frac{1}{2}H_2O$ and $Ba_3[Au(S_2O_3)_2]_2$ can be obtained. The gold(I) halides show an increase in solubility in the

[9] FYFE, *J. Chem. Soc.*, 1955, p. 1032.
[10] AHRLAND and CHATT, *Chem. and Ind.*, 1955, p. 96.

presence of excess alkali metal halides, presumably because of the formation of complexes of the type AuX_2^-. These complexes are rather unstable, however, and disproportionation reactions occur more or less slowly, producing metallic gold and gold(III) compounds.

24.66 As the foregoing examples indicate, the characteristic coordination number of gold(I) is two. By analogy with the two-coordinated complexes of silver(I), a linear structure, involving the use of hybrid *SP* orbitals, is expected. This arrangement has been observed in the black crystalline compound of empirical formula $CsAuCl_3$. The structure of this substance is very similar to that of $Cs_2AgAuCl_6$, and undoubtedly the compound should be formulated $Cs_2Au^IAu^{III}Cl_6$. Half of the gold atoms are found to be two-coordinated, with the linear arrangement Cl—Au—Cl. The other half show the planar four-coordination characteristic of gold(III).

24.67 A series of compounds which presumably contain a four-coordinated cationic gold(I) complex with the bidentate molecule, *o*-bis(dimethylarsino)-benzene, have been described.[11] They are of the type [Au diarsine$_2$]X, in which X is a univalent ion such as ClO_4^-, Br^-, or I^-. Conductivity measurements in nitrobenzene indicate the compounds to be uniunivalent. The X-ray powder pattern of [Au diarsine$_2$]I is very similar to that of [Cu diarsine$_2$]I, suggesting tetrahedral four-coordination as a likely structure in this gold(I) complex.

[11] HARRIS, NYHOLM, and STEPHENSON, *Rec. trav. chim.*, **75**, 685 (1956).

CHAPTER 25

THE ZINC FAMILY

Introduction

25.1 The elements which comprise this family, zinc, cadmium, and mercury, with atomic numbers 30, 48, and 80, respectively, occur at the end of the three short transition series, and all possess in their outer electron levels the $(n - 1)d^{10}ns^2$ configuration. Unlike copper, silver, and gold, which immediately precede them and which, despite the possession of completed d levels, can use one or more d electrons in chemical reactions, the members of the zinc family utilize only the outer s electrons in reaction. This is indicated by the fact that all three metals form dipositive ions, and no oxidation states higher than $+2$ are known. Mercury forms, in addition, the unusual double ion, Hg_2^{2+}, in which its oxidation state is $+1$. Although some indications of the formation of monopositive cadmium have been reported, evidence for the existence of stable cadmium(I) compounds appears to be inconclusive.

25.2 The members of the zinc family occupy a somewhat unusual position with regard to classification in the periodic system. In a number of respects they resemble the representative metals more closely than they do the elements in the short transition series. Unlike the latter, for example, they possess relatively low melting and boiling points. Like the representative metals, their ions are colorless and diamagnetic. Moreover, like the metals in representative groups III–V, the lowest oxidation state ($+1$ in this case) becomes increasingly stable with increasing atomic number in the family.

GENERAL REFERENCES

LATIMER, *The Oxidation States of the Elements and Their Potentials in Aqueous Solutions*, 2nd Edition, Prentice-Hall, Inc., New York, 1952, Ch. 10.

PARTINGTON, *A Textbook of Inorganic Chemistry*, 6th Edition, Macmillan and Company, Ltd., London, 1950, Ch. XXXIX.

REMY, *Treatise on Inorganic Chemistry* (translated and amended by Anderson), Elsevier Publishing Company, Amsterdam, 1956, Vol. II, Ch. 9.

SIDGWICK, *The Chemical Elements and Their Compounds*, Oxford University Press, London, 1950, pp. 262–333.

25.3 On the other hand, like many of the transition metal ions, dipositive zinc, cadmium, and mercury readily form complexes with cyanide ion and with molecules containing nitrogen as the donor atom, such as ammonia and ethylenediamine, as well as with numerous other ligands. These elements might, therefore, be classed with the representative elements or with the short transition series elements, with some justification in either case. This dual character is suggested by the designation "terminal elements" which is sometimes applied to them.

25.4 Within the family there is a much closer similarity in properties between the first two elements than between the second and third, quite unlike the situation in the preceding transition groups. Indeed, in the trends of many properties there is a striking discontinuity between cadmium and mercury. From zinc to cadmium, for example, the first and second ionization potentials decrease somewhat in accord with the usual trend accompanying an increase in radius of the ion which is formed. With mercury, however, there is a sharp increase in these values despite the fact that the ionic radius of Hg^{2+} is larger than that of Cd^{2+} or Zn^{2+}. The first ionization potential of mercury, in fact, is larger than that of any other distinctly metallic element, being exceeded only in hydrogen, the inert gases, and some of the nonmetallic elements in representative groups IV–VII. The difficulty of removing the two outer s electrons from mercury appears to be a manifestation of the pronounced tendency of such electrons to behave as an "inert pair" in the post-lanthanide representative elements, a tendency which plays a prominent role in the chemistry of the elements thallium, lead, and bismuth which follow mercury.

25.5 The comparative inertness of the two s electrons in mercury is reflected in the noble character of the element. It is not attacked by oxygen at ordinary temperature, and reacts only very slowly near its boiling point to give mercury(II) oxide, which is readily decomposed at somewhat higher temperatures. Oxidation of the metal to the dipositive ion in aqueous solution is relatively difficult, also, as is indicated by the corresponding electrode potential (see Table 25.1).

25.6 In contrast to this behavior, zinc and cadmium undergo superficial oxidation in air at ordinary temperatures, and when strongly heated burn to give the corresponding oxides, which are stable up to rather elevated temperatures. The standard heats of formation ($-\Delta H°$) of zinc and cadmium oxides (83.17 and 60.86 kcal./mole, respectively, at 25°) are correspondingly much larger than for mercury(II) oxide (21.86 kcal./mole for the red modification). Both zinc and cadmium, moreover, are electropositive elements, reacting with nonoxidizing acids to liberate hydrogen. The fact that zinc, in spite of its higher first and second ionization potentials, can be more easily oxidized to the aqueous ion than can cadmium (see electrode potentials, Table 25.1) is to be ascribed to the distinctly greater heat of hydration of the smaller zinc ion.

25.7 Although the dipositive ions of zinc, cadmium, and mercury possess the same charge, roughly the same radii, and therefore the same ionic potential (see 6.124) as magnesium (0.66 Å), calcium (0.99 Å), and strontium (1.15 Å)

TABLE 25.1

Some Properties of the Metals of the Zinc Family

	Zn	Cd	Hg
Natural isotopes	64 *, 66, 67, 68, 70	106, 108, 110, 111, 112, 113, 114 *, 115, 116, 118	196, 198, 199, 200, 201, 202 *, 204
Density, g./cc.	7.13	8.64	13.596 (of liquid at 0°)
Melting point, °C.	419.5	320.9	−38.87
Boiling point, °C.	907	767	356.9
Tetrahedral covalent radius, Å	1.31	1.48	1.48
Crystal ionic radius, M^{2+}, Å	0.72	0.96	1.10
Heat of hydration ($-\Delta H$) of gaseous M^{2+} ion, kcal./mole	491.5	436.5	440.9
Ionization potential, volts			
1st electron	9.391	8.991	10.434
2nd electron	17.96	16.904	18.751
Electrode potential, $E°$, volts			
$M = M^{2+} + 2e^-$	+0.763	+0.403	−0.854

* Most abundant isotope

ions, respectively, the former show a distinctly greater tendency to form complexes, especially with the more polarizable ligands such as ammonia and amines and some of the halide ions. There is, however, a marked difference between zinc and cadmium on the one hand, and mercury on the other with respect to the stability of such complexes. Most of the complexes of zinc show somewhat higher stability constants than the corresponding complexes of cadmium, as might be expected both from the smaller size of the zinc ion and from the larger first and second ionization potentials of the atom (see 6.126). The difference is usually not very great, and in a few instances, notably with the halide and cyanide ions, the order of stability is reversed. The stability constants of the analogous mercury(II) complexes, however, are always larger than those of zinc and cadmium, often by many orders of magnitude. This behavior is illustrated by the values of the stability constant, K, shown.

	Zn	Cd	Hg
K for $[M(NH_3)_4]^{2+}$	2.9×10^9	1.3×10^7	2×10^{19}
K for $[M(H_2N—CH_2—CH_2—NH_2)_2]^{2+}$	2.3×10^{10}	1.0×10^{10}	2.6×10^{23}
K for $[M(CN)_4]^{2-}$	7.7×10^{16}	7.1×10^{18}	2.5×10^{41}

25.8 Although, as indicated above, mercury can exhibit four-coordination in its complexes, it has a pronounced tendency to show two-coordination. Thus the first two ligand groups acquired by mercury(II) are generally held much more firmly than the last two. This is illustrated by comparing the very large equilibrium constant for reaction (a) with the much smaller one for reaction (b).

(a) $\qquad$ $Hg^{2+} + 2NH_3 = [Hg(NH_3)_2]^{2+}$ $\qquad$ $K = 3.2 \times 10^{17}$
(b) $[Hg(NH_3)_2]^{2+} + 2NH_3 = [Hg(NH_3)_4]^{2+}$ $\qquad$ $K = 60$

Similar behavior is observed also in the chloro complexes; thus, solutions of mercury(II) chloride contain predominantly the species $HgCl_2$, with very little $HgCl_3^-$ and $HgCl_4^{2-}$. On the other hand, zinc shows no such preference for two-coordination, the four ligands all being held with approximately equal firmness. Toward some ligands, chloride ion and ammonia for example, cadmium appears to show some tendency to favor two-coordination, though its preference for this coordination number is much less pronounced than that exhibited by mercury.

25.9 The hydroxides of zinc and cadmium are only slightly soluble in water but dissolve in acids. Zinc hydroxide, in addition, is readily dissolved by strong alkalies, forming zincate ions such as $HZnO_2^-$ and ZnO_2^{2-}, or the essentially equivalent hydroxo complexes $Zn(OH)_3^-$ and $Zn(OH)_4^{2-}$. Cadmium hydroxide does not display this pronounced amphoteric behavior. Mercury hydroxides do not exist as stable solids, but mercury(II) oxide dissolves in water to a slight extent, presumably forming the hydroxide in solution. Although the latter appears to be an extremely weak base, it shows almost no amphoteric character and is not appreciably dissolved by alkali. This may, in part at least, be a consequence of the reluctance of mercury(II) to form three- or four-coordinated hydroxo complexes.

25.10 All three of the metals form dialkyl and diaryl compounds of the type R—M—R, those of cadmium being, in general, the least stable with respect to decomposition. The compounds of both zinc and cadmium are easily oxidized and react readily with oxygen and water. On the other hand the corresponding compounds of mercury are inert toward these agents. It has been suggested that the latter fact may also, perhaps, be attributed to the comparative unwillingness of mercury to expand its covalence beyond two in the formation of an activated intermediate.

Zinc and Cadmium

The Elements

25.11 The principal natural sources of zinc are the ores *sphalerite* or *zinc blende*, ZnS, and *smithsonite*, $ZnCO_3$. Other ores include *willemite*, Zn_2SiO_4, *zincite*, ZnO, *calamine*, $Zn_2(OH)_2SiO_3$, and *franklinite*, $(Zn, Mn)O \cdot Fe_2O_3$. Cadmium is commonly associated in low proportion with zinc, frequently as a substitutional impurity in sphalerite, occasionally as *greenockite*, CdS. Production of the metals commonly involves concentration of the ore as the first step, followed by roasting in air. Reduction may then be carried out either by pyrometallurgical or by electrochemical methods. In the pyrometallurgical process the roasted ore is sintered and subsequently smelted with carbon, whereupon the oxidized ore is reduced, chiefly by carbon monoxide, and the metals vaporized out and condensed. Partial separation of the cadmium may be effected by addition of a chloride to the roasted ore to bring about volatilization of cadmium chloride during the sintering step. Separation may also be achieved by fractional distillation of the metals obtained from the smelter, taking advantage of the lower boiling point of cadmium. In the electrochemical method the roasted ore is leached with sulfuric acid, interfering metals, including cadmium, are removed by reduction or precipitation, and zinc is deposited electrolytically from the sulfate solution. The cadmium obtained from the solution by chemical reduction is refined by dissolution in acid and subsequent electrodeposition.

25.12 Both zinc and cadmium are silvery white metals, which in the atmosphere acquire a thin adherent oxidized coating, probably a basic carbonate. When pure they possess rather low hardness, cadmium being softer than zinc. They are fairly malleable and ductile, but the presence of small amounts of impurities, especially in zinc, produces marked alterations in these properties. Both are oxidized by hydrogen ion, but because of the high overvoltage of hydrogen on the pure metals, the rate of reaction is very slow if the metals are of extremely high purity. Nitric acid readily attacks both, with the attendant production of nitrogen-containing reduction products which, in the case of zinc, may include hydroxylamine, hydrazine, and ammonium ion. Strong alkalies dissolve zinc, yielding molecular hydrogen and soluble zincates; cadmium is not dissolved by alkalies.

25.13 A number of the more important reactions of the metals are summarized in Table 25.2.

TABLE 25.2

Reactions of Zinc and Cadmium

Reaction	Remarks
$2M + O_2 = 2MO$	
$M + X_2 = MX_2$	X = halogen
$M + S = MS$	Also with Se and Te
$6M + P_4 = 2M_3P_2$	Similar reactions with As
$2M + P_4 = 2MP_2$	
$M + 2H^+ = M^{2+} + H_2$	Slow with pure metals
$M + OH^- + H_2O = HMO_2^- + H_2$	Zinc only

Compounds

Oxides and Related Compounds **25.14** The oxides of zinc and cadmium may be produced by strongly heating the metals in air or oxygen, by air oxidation of the sulfides at high temperature, or by thermal decomposition of various compounds, including the hydroxides, carbonates, and nitrates. Pure zinc oxide is white under ordinary conditions but undergoes a reversible color change to yellow at elevated temperatures. Its catalytic activity and general chemical reactivity appear to depend upon the extent of lattice imperfections in the solid, which in turn diminish as the temperature to which the oxide is subjected is raised. Cadmium oxide varies in color from greenish-yellow through brown to nearly black, depending upon its thermal treatment. Both zinc oxide and cadmium oxide are practically insoluble in water.

25.15 Addition of aqueous alkali or ammonia to a solution of a zinc salt yields a precipitate of zinc hydroxide which is ordinarily contaminated with adsorbed ions. By dissolution of the thoroughly washed precipitate in aqueous ammonia, followed by slow removal of ammonia from the solution, however, a white crystalline product can be obtained having a composition corresponding to $Zn(OH)_2$. Its solubility in water is approximately $1 \times 10^{-5}M$, at which concentration it nevertheless appears to be incompletely dissociated. It is readily dissolved by excess ammonia, through formation of the tetrammine-zinc(II) complex, and by excess alkali, with which it reacts to form soluble zincates as described above. Solid hydroxo-zincates of the compositions represented by $NaZn(OH)_3$ and $Na_2Zn(OH)_4$ can be obtained from solutions of the hydroxide in concentrated alkali.

25.16 Cadmium hydroxide, soluble in water to the extent of about $1 \times 10^{-5}M$, can be produced in a manner similar to that described for zinc hydroxide. It, too, is soluble in excess ammonia, with which cadmium ion forms a tetrammine complex. Unlike zinc hydroxide, however, its solubility is not greatly increased by the presence of excess hydroxide ion, although solid compounds of the compositions corresponding to $Cd(OH)_2 \cdot 2NaOH$, $Cd(OH)_2 \cdot 2Sr(OH)_2$, and $Cd(OH)_2 \cdot 2Ba(OH)_2$ have been prepared from cadmium hydroxide and very concentrated solutions of sodium hydroxide alone or mixed with the appropriate alkaline earth hydroxide. The distinct decrease in acidic character between zinc hydroxide and cadmium hydroxide is, of course, consistent with the usual trend toward decreasing acidity with increasing ionic size in a family.

25.17 The oxides and hydroxides are dissolved by acids, and numerous salts can be obtained in this manner. Many of the salts of both zinc and cadmium, including the chlorides, bromides, iodides, nitrates, sulfates, acetates, chlorates, and perchlorates, are soluble in water. As commonly crystallized from aqueous solution many of the solid compounds are hydrates, familiar examples being $Zn(NO_3)_2 \cdot 6H_2O$, $Cd(NO_3)_2 \cdot 4H_2O$, $ZnSO_4 \cdot 7H_2O$, and $CdSO_4 \cdot \frac{8}{3}H_2O$.

25.18 Common insoluble, or sparingly soluble, compounds of these metals, best obtained by metathetical reactions, include the fluorides, cyanides, carbonates, oxalates, ferrocyanides, phosphates, and sulfides, of which the last-named are the least soluble. Yellow cadmium sulfide can be precipitated from solutions of cadmium salts by means of hydrogen sulfide, even in the presence of dilute hydrochloric acid. Zinc sulfide, which is more soluble than the cadmium compound, can be obtained from weakly acid to alkaline solutions. Both compounds can be prepared from the elements, the reaction of zinc with sulfur being explosively violent if the materials are finely divided. Zinc sulfide is white, and the presence in it of small amounts of certain impurities, notably copper compounds, renders it fluorescent, although the pure compound does not possess this property.

25.19 Several well characterized basic salts of zinc and cadmium have been prepared as crystalline solids, examples of these being $Zn(NO_3)_2 \cdot 4Zn(OH)_2$, $ZnCl_2 \cdot Zn(OH)_2$, $ZnCl_2 \cdot 4Zn(OH)_2 \cdot H_2O$, and $CdCl_2 \cdot Cd(OH)_2$.

25.20 Neither zinc nor cadmium yields a peroxide as a result of direct union of the elements. However, materials containing peroxides in combination or admixture with hydroxide or oxide and water can be produced by treating alkaline solutions of the appropriate salts with hydrogen peroxide. Anhydrous products containing 70% or more of the peroxide have been obtained by the reaction of sodium superoxide with zinc or cadmium nitrate in liquid ammonia.[1]

Hydrides **25.21** The hydrides, ZnH_2 and CdH_2, can be prepared by reaction between lithium aluminum hydride and the respective dimethyl-metal compound in ether solution.

$$(CH_3)_2Zn + 2LiAlH_4 = ZnH_2 + 2LiAlH_3CH_3$$

Both hydrides are solids, insoluble in ether, zinc hydride being much the more stable of the two. It undergoes only slow decomposition at room temperature, whereas cadmium hydride decomposes very rapidly above about 0°.

Halides and Halo Complexes **25.22** The halides may be prepared by action of the hydrohalic acids on the hydroxides, oxides, or carbonates or on the metals themselves. Direct union of the elements can be employed also. With the exception of the fluorides, which are sparingly soluble, they are readily soluble in water, those of zinc being exceedingly so. Solutions of the zinc halides are somewhat acidic as a result of hydrolysis. All of the halides except cadmium fluoride form one or more hydrates, and all can be obtained in unhydrated form as well. For example, the stable solid phase in equilibrium with saturated solutions of zinc chloride above about 30° is $ZnCl_2$. Nevertheless, preparation of the anhydrous compound from the solid thus obtained cannot be satisfactorily accomplished simply by heating, since the adherent water is firmly held; strong heating is attended with some loss of HCl and formation of a basic product. Prolonged heating in a current of dry hydrogen chloride, however, yields the desired product.

25.23 Zinc and cadmium halides display a considerable amount of covalent character. One indication of this is the fact that molten zinc chloride (m.p. 315°), for example, is a relatively poor electrical conductor, its specific conductance at 319° being only 2×10^{-4} ohm^{-1} cm^{-1}. Moreover, zinc ion appears to form very stable complexes with chloride, and especially iodide in acetonitrile,[2] which

[1] SCHECHTER and KLEINBERG, *J. Am. Chem. Soc.*, **76**, 3297 (1954).
[2] KOLTHOFF and COETZEE, *J. Am. Chem. Soc.*, **79**, 870 (1957).

is normally a rather good ionizing solvent. Cadmium chloride (m.p. 568°) in the molten state shows good conductivity, but complex formation occurs in acetonitrile, and even in aqueous solution the soluble cadmium halides form autocomplexes yielding species of the types CdX^+, CdX_2, CdX_3^-, and to a smaller extent, CdX_4^{2-}. In the presence of excess halide ion, extensive formation of the tetrahalo complex occurs. The stability of these complexes increases from chloride to iodide, corresponding to the order of increasing polarizability of the halide ions. Although the covalent character of the anhydrous zinc halides is doubtless greater than that of the corresponding cadmium compounds, in aqueous solution the zinc halides show a lesser tendency to form halo complexes, which can probably be attributed to a stronger preference for water molecules on the part of the zinc ion. The large heat of hydration of gaseous Zn^{2+}, the high solubility of many zinc salts, and the extensive formation of hydrated salts all indicate a strong tendency to form aquo complexes.

Other Complexes   **25.24** Zinc and cadmium form complexes in solution with a variety of ligands, most numerous of which are those in which nitrogen is the donor atom. The complexes with ammonia and ethylenediamine have already been mentioned (see 25.7). Other ligands of similar character which are known to form complexes with these metals include 1,2-diaminopropane, 1,2,3-triaminopropane, diethylenetriamine, triethylenetetramine, β,β',β''-triaminotriethylamine, and *o*-phenanthroline. Numerous complexes are also formed with chelating ligands in which both nitrogen and oxygen act as donors, as, for example, 8-hydroxyquinoline, ethylenediaminetetraacetic acid, and the amino acids glycine, proline, tryptophane, and valine. Complexes with oxygen as donor atom exclusively include those with β-diketones such as acetylacetone, with salicylaldehyde, and with various hydroxyacids and dicarboxylic acids. Broadly speaking, the complexes in this last group are generally of lower stability than those in which nitrogen is the donor atom.

25.25 The most common coordination number of both zinc(II) and cadmium(II) in their complexes is four, although six is shown also in a few cases. In solution, for example, there is evidence that these ions may combine with as many as three molecules of ethylenediamine or *o*-phenanthroline. Since the inner *d* orbitals are completely filled in the metal ions, the four-coordinated complexes would be expected to use SP^3 hybrid orbitals and thus have a tetrahedral structure. This arrangement has been demonstrated by X-ray studies in a number of compounds, for example, in $K_2Zn(CN)_4$, $K_2Cd(CN)_4$, and some of the complex halides.

Mercury

The Element

25.26 The only important ore of mercury is the red sulfide *cinnabar*, HgS, with which may be associated small amounts of the black sulfide *metacinna-*

barite and metallic mercury. The metal is readily obtained by direct heating of the ore, whereupon the reaction shown occurs. At the temperatures employed,

$$HgS + O_2 = Hg + SO_2$$

mercury oxide is unstable, and the free element is thus distilled out and collected.

25.27 Mercury is unique in possessing the lowest melting point ($-38.87°$) and the highest volatility of all the metallic elements. Its specific electrical conductance at $0°$ is 1.58% that of silver. It shows a slight solubility in water, amounting in the absence of air to 0.02–0.03 mg. per liter at $30°$. Many metals dissolve in mercury to a significant extent, or combine with it to give inter-metallic compounds. Examples of metals forming amalgams in one or both of these ways include sodium, potassium, magnesium, silver, gold, copper, lead, tin, zinc, and cadmium. Chromium, manganese, nickel, and platinum are but slightly soluble, and iron, cobalt, and tungsten appear to be unaffected.

25.28 The comparatively low reactivity of the metal toward oxygen has been mentioned (see 25.5). It can be oxidized, however, by the halogens, by sulfur, and by oxidizing acids such as nitric and sulfuric acid. In most instances either the corresponding mercury(I) or mercury(II) compound may be obtained pre-dominantly, depending upon the proportions of reactants chosen and the conditions. This is a consequence of the fact that the potential for the oxidation of mercury to mercury(II) ion is somewhat more negative than that for the oxidation of the metal to mercury(I) ion, but not greatly so, as is shown by the potential relationships.

$$Hg \xrightarrow{-0.789} Hg_2^{2+} \xrightarrow{-0.920} Hg^{2+}$$
(with overarching -0.854)

These potentials yield for the system mercury, mercury(II) ion, and mercury(I) ion the value of the equilibrium constant shown.

$$Hg + Hg^{2+} \rightleftharpoons Hg_2^{2+} \qquad K = 166$$

In the presence of excess metal, therefore, the production of mercury(I) is favored, but in the absence of metal a strong oxidizing agent can convert Hg_2^{2+} to Hg^{2+}, as is indicated by the corresponding potential. Moreover, the above equilibrium may be readily displaced to the left through the formation of a weakly dissociated mercury(II) compound, or one that is much less soluble than the corresponding mercury(I) compound.

Mercury(II) Compounds

The Oxide and Related Compounds **25.29** Mercury(II) oxide, HgO, can be obtained as a red crystalline product by prolonged heating of mercury in air at temperatures just below its boiling point or by gentle heating of the nitrate. The oxide is precipitated, too, when excess alkali is added to a solution of a soluble mercury(II) salt, appearing under these conditions as a yellow product which has been shown by X-ray examination to differ from the red form only in being more finely divided. The oxide decomposes into its elements at temperatures somewhat above 500°.

25.30 The solubility of red mercury(II) oxide is 2.25×10^{-4} moles/1000 g. of water (the yellow form is slightly more soluble), and the resulting solution is weakly basic, indicating the formation of mercury(II) hydroxide in solution. The latter appears to be only weakly dissociated, however, the following value for the dissociation constant having been reported.

$$\frac{[Hg^{2+}][OH^-]^2}{[Hg(OH)_2]} = 1.8 \times 10^{-22}$$

Acids react with the oxide or its aqueous suspension to produce the corresponding mercury(II) salts. In aqueous alkalies the oxide is slightly more soluble; a value of 3.15×10^{-5} has been determined for the equilibrium constant corresponding to the reaction $HgO(s) + OH^- = HHgO_2^-$. No mercurates analogous to the compounds formed by zinc and cadmium hydroxides with alkalies have been isolated, however.

Halides **25.31** With the exception of the fluoride, the mercury(II) halides exhibit essentially covalent bonding. Solid mercury(II) chloride, for example, is a molecular crystal consisting of linear Cl—Hg—Cl molecules packed together. The compound sublimes without decomposition at 300°, and is soluble in alcohol, ether, and a number of other organic solvents. It is moderately soluble in water but undergoes only slight ionic dissociation in solution. The following values of the constants for the first and second dissociations have been cited.[3]

$$HgCl_2 = HgCl^+ + Cl^- \qquad K_1 = 3.30 \times 10^{-7}$$
$$HgCl^+ = Hg^{2+} + Cl^- \qquad K_2 = 1.84 \times 10^{-7}$$

Because the concentration of mercury(II) ion in such solutions is very low, hydrolysis occurs to a relatively small extent, sufficient, however, to make the solutions slightly acid.

25.32 Solid mercury(II) bromide is colorless, melts at 236°, and boils at 322°; its structure differs from that of the chloride, being intermediate between a molecular and a layer type of crystal. The solid iodide, HgI_2, consists of infinite square network layers in which each mercury atom is surrounded tetrahedrally by four iodine atoms. It exists in a red modification stable up to 127°, above which it undergoes transition to a yellow form. The compound sublimes at 140° and decomposes at temperatures above about 310°. The bromide is sparingly soluble in water (0.61g./100g. solution), the iodide practically insoluble (0.0059g./100g.); both are soluble in various organic solvents. The aqueous solubilities of the chloride, bromide, and iodide are all markedly increased in the presence of alkali or alkaline earth halides because of the formation of halo complexes (see 25.41 *ff.*).

---

[3] LINDGREN, JONSSON, and SILLÉN, *Acta Chem. Scand.*, **1**, 479 (1947).

25.33 Mercury(II) fluoride, as might be expected from the very low polarizability of the fluoride ion, behaves as an essentially ionic compound. The solid possesses an ionic lattice of the same type as that of calcium fluoride and melts at 645°. In water it undergoes extensive hydrolytic decomposition, which indicates that it probably ionizes normally upon being dissolved, thereby making available a considerable concentration of Hg^{2+} and F^-, both of which enter into hydrolytic reactions. Unlike the other halides it does not form halo complexes.

25.34 Mercury(II) chloride, frequently called "corrosive sublimate," is produced commercially by the action of excess chlorine on the heated metal. It can be made also by heating together solid mercury(II) sulfate and sodium chloride, from which the product sublimes. The other halides can be obtained similarly by direct combination of the elements, or they may be produced by action of the appropriate hydrohalic acid on mercury(II) oxide. In addition, the bromide and iodide, because of their limited solubility, are readily prepared by treating a solution of mercury(II) chloride or nitrate with the appropriate alkali metal halide. With the iodide, this method first precipitates the metastable yellow form of HgI_2, which changes rapidly into the stable red modification.

Other Simple Compounds **25.35** Mercury(II) nitrate is commonly obtained by the action of excess hot nitric acid on the metal. Evaporation of the solution yields the deliquescent monohydrate, $Hg(NO_3)_2 \cdot H_2O$, which, though soluble, is strongly hydrolyzed in the absence of free nitric acid.

25.36 The sulfate, $HgSO_4$, is similarly made by oxidation of the metal with hot concentrated sulfuric acid in excess; it may also be produced by action of the acid upon mercury(II) oxide. Like the nitrate it is hydrolyzed in aqueous solution and may yield basic products such as $HgSO_4 \cdot 2HgO$.

25.37 The perchlorate, like the nitrate, sulfate, and fluoride, is a soluble, strongly ionized salt which, because of the relatively high concentration of the metal ion in solution and the extreme weakness of the hydroxide, is extensively hydrolyzed. Since the first three are salts of strong acids, however, the hydrolytic reaction does not proceed as far in these cases as it does with the fluoride. It may be mentioned that the normal carbonate seems never to have been isolated.

25.38 On the other hand the cyanide, although the salt of a weak acid, is so very weakly dissociated in solution that little hydrolysis occurs. Ionic dissociation is so slight, in fact, that the solutions yield no precipitate with potassium hydroxide or iodide. Upon being heated to about 320° the compound decomposes to give cyanogen, according to the following equation.

$$Hg(CN)_2 = Hg + (CN)_2$$

25.39 Among the insoluble or sparingly soluble compounds of mercury(II), in addition to those described above, may be mentioned the thiocyanate, the phosphate, the oxalate, and the sulfide. The last of these has an exceedingly low solubility, its solubility product being of the order of 10^{-54}. All other mercury(II) compounds, including the complexes, can therefore be transposed by treatment with hydrogen sulfide, black HgS being precipitated. Frequently, double compounds of lighter color, such as $Hg(NO_3)_2 \cdot 2HgS$, are precipitated as intermediates and subsequently converted to the sulfide. The sulfide is scarcely attacked by concentrated acids but dissolves readily in hot aqua regia, undissociated mercury(II) chloride and complex chloromercurates being formed in solution. It is also dissolved by concentrated alkali sulfides, forming the complex thio-ion, $[HgS_2]^{2-}$.

25.40 Although the black form of HgS results from precipitation reactions or direct union of the elements, the red modification can be produced by subliming the black form or by digesting it with alkali polysulfide solution.

Complex Compounds   **25.41** As has been pointed out (see 25.8), mercury(II) has a pronounced tendency toward two-coordination, as is exemplified by the slight dissociation of $HgCl_2$, $Hg(CN)_2$, and $[Hg(NH_3)_2]^{2+}$. In these materials the mercury forms linear bonds involving the use of *SP* hybrid orbitals. With excess halide or cyanide ion or ammonia, four-coordinated complexes are formed. The slightly soluble bromide, iodide, and thiocyanate, for example, all dissolve in the presence of an excess of the anion, forming $[HgBr_4]^{2-}$, $[HgI_4]^{2-}$, and $[Hg(SCN)_4]^{2-}$; the chloride forms $[HgCl_4]^{2-}$ in solution. The stability of the tetrahalo complexes increases from chloride to iodide, the following values of stability constants having been reported: $[HgCl_4]^{2-}$, 9×10^{15}; $[HgBr_4]^{2-}$, 4.3×10^{21}; $[HgI_4]^{2-}$, 1.9×10^{30}.

25.42 Numerous solid complex compounds may be prepared, also, some examples being $K_2[Hg(CN)_4]$, $K_2[Hg(SCN)_4]$, $Zn[Hg(SCN)_4]$, $K_2[HgI_4] \cdot 2H_2O$, $K[HgCl_3]$, $K_2[HgCl_4]$, $[Hg(NH_3)_2]Cl_2$, and $[Hg(NH_3)_4](NO_3)_2$. X-ray analysis of the first compound shows a tetrahedral arrangement of the cyanides about the mercury atom, as would be expected for SP^3 bonds.

25.43 The ammonia complexes and related compounds of mercury(II) deserve special mention, since reactions with ammonia may yield ammine complexes or various ammonolytic products, depending upon the nature of the mercury salt and the conditions.

25.44 When aqueous mercury(II) chloride is treated with ammonia solution there is precipitated an ammonobasic mercury(II) chloride, formed according to the reaction shown. This reaction is reversible, and can be prevented by the

$$HgCl_2 + 2NH_3 = HgNH_2Cl + NH_4^+ + Cl^-$$

presence of a sufficiently high concentration of ammonium chloride. Under these conditions ammonia gives the diammine, $[Hg(NH_3)_2]Cl_2$, which can be crystallized from the solution. The compound can also be made by action of liquid ammonia on $HgCl_2$. When the diammine is dissolved in water it reacts to precipitate $HgNH_2Cl$ as above. Mercury(II) bromide reacts similarly to the chloride.

25.45 The more highly ionized salts, such as the nitrate, sulfate, or perchlorate, when treated with ammonia in aqueous solutions containing high concentrations of ammonium salts, yield the corresponding tetrammines, $[Hg(NH_3)_4](NO_3)_2$, etc. Some of these compounds in the solid state readily lose ammonia to give the diammines. If solutions of the salts named above are treated with ammonia in the absence of much ammonium salt, ammonolytic reactions occur which are different, however, from those observed with the halides. In the case under discussion, insoluble products of composition corresponding to $[Hg_2N]NO_3$, $[Hg_2N]ClO_4$, and the like are formed in reactions typified by the equation shown.

$$2Hg^{2+} + X^- + 4NH_3 = [Hg_2N]X + 3NH_4^+$$

Studies[4] of the structures of these compounds indicate the existence of an infinite three-dimensional network of Hg and N atoms, each of the former being linked linearly to two N atoms, with each N bonded tetrahedrally to four Hg atoms. The anions, and in some cases water molecules, are located within the channels present in the network and may be rather easily exchanged. Prolonged treatment of mercury(II) oxide with aqueous ammonia yields the related basic compound $[Hg_2N]OH \cdot 2H_2O$ (Millon's base).

Mercury(I) Compounds

Nature of the Mercury(I) Ion **25.46** The mercury(I) ion is unique among the metal cations in that it consists of two atoms linked together by a metal-metal bond, the resulting unit being dipositive. Evidence for the structure indicated

$$[Hg : Hg]^{2+}$$

comes from a number of sources: (1) The mathematical mass action expressions formulated for equilibria in reactions such as those shown remain constant as

$$2Hg + 2Ag^+ = Hg_2^{2+} + 2Ag$$
$$Hg + Hg^{2+} = Hg_2^{2+}$$

the concentrations of the ionic species are varied, whereas when written in accordance with the assumption that simple Hg^+ is formed, they do not. (2) The electrical conductivity of aqueous solutions of soluble mercury(I) salts shows a magnitude and concentration dependence like those of biunivalent salts, and unlike those of uniunivalent salts. (3) Structural studies of the solid mercury(I) halides, for example, show the arrangement X—Hg—Hg—X, the mercury atoms always occurring in pairs.

Compounds **25.47** From the equilibrium relationships involving mercury metal, mercury(II) ion, and mercury(I) ion (see 25.28), it would be expected that many compounds of the latter could be prepared by treating the corresponding mercury(II) compound with mercury. This is, indeed, the fact, provided the mercury(II) compound is neither extremely weakly dissociated nor much less soluble than the desired mercury(I) product. Since most mercury(I) compounds are insoluble, and are usually less soluble than the analogous

---

[4] LIPSCOMB, *Anal. Chem.*, **25**, 737 (1953).

mercury(II) compound, reduction of the latter by the metal can usually be accomplished. Even such soluble compounds as $Hg_2(NO_3)_2$ and $Hg_2(ClO_4)_2$ can be obtained by keeping solutions of $Hg(NO_3)_2$ and $Hg(ClO_4)_2$, respectively, in contact with mercury. Here, of course, the mercury(II) salts are strongly ionized, providing relatively high concentrations of Hg^{2+} for reaction.

25.48 A variation of this method is to use an excess of mercury with a suitable oxidizing agent. For example, mercury(I) chloride, long known as calomel, may be made by the action of a controlled amount of chlorine on an excess of the metal. Some mercury(II) chloride is also produced, but it may be washed out because the mercury(I) compound is insoluble. Mercury(I) nitrate and sulfate may be made by the action of nitric or sulfuric acids on excess mercury.

25.49 Most mercury(I) compounds, being insoluble, can also be prepared by metathesis, using solutions of the nitrate and a salt or acid containing the appropriate anion. The halides, for example, may be obtained in this way, as may also the sulfate, chromate, and phosphate.

25.50 The very soluble perchlorate, which crystallizes as $Hg_2(ClO_4)_2 \cdot 4H_2O$, and the nitrate, $Hg_2(NO_3)_2 \cdot 2H_2O$, are both hydrolyzed to some extent in water, but much less extensively than the corresponding mercury(II) compounds, although the nitrate in the absence of any free nitric acid may yield some insoluble basic material. That mercury(I) ion undergoes typically less extensive hydrolysis than mercury(II) is further indicated by the fact that the normal carbonate, Hg_2CO_3, can be precipitated by reaction of a soluble carbonate or bicarbonate with mercury(I) nitrate.

25.51 Quite unlike dipositive mercury, mercury(I) appears not to form complexes, none having been definitely characterized. This may arise in part from a weaker intrinsic tendency of mercury(I) to form stable complexes, associated, perhaps, with its undoubtedly much larger ionic size than mercury(II). Moreover, those ligands with which it might be expected to best form complexes probably give much more stable mercury(II) complexes, and therefore lead to disproportionation. This kind of behavior with cyanide ion and with ammonia is discussed in the following section.

Disproportionation Reactions **25.52** There are several examples of reactions between mercury(I) and other reagents which result in the formation of metallic mercury and a mercury(II) compound. For example, when a solution of a mercury(I) salt is treated with alkali hydroxide, a dark-colored precipitate is formed which X-ray examination shows to consist of mercury(II) oxide and mercury. The reaction may be represented by the following equation.

$$Hg_2^{2+} + 2OH^- = Hg + HgO + H_2O$$

The behavior of mercury(I) compounds toward hydrogen sulfide is similar, the products being metal and the very insoluble mercury(II) sulfide.

$$Hg_2^{2+} + H_2S = Hg + HgS + 2H^+$$

The action of cyanide ion on mercury(I) also leads to disproportionation, not through production of an insoluble mercury(II) compound, but as a result of the formation of the extremely weakly dissociated cyanide, $Hg(CN)_2$.

25.53 The oxide, hydroxide, sulfide, and cyanide of mercury(I), therefore, either do not exist, or, if formed at all, have only a transient existence, being unstable with respect to disproportionation into metal and the mercury(II) compound. It may be mentioned that mercury(I) compounds, the iodide for example, tend to be photosensitive with respect to this reaction.

25.54 The reaction of ammonia with mercury(I) compounds also results in disproportionation, metallic mercury and ammonolytic mercury(II) products or ammines being produced, depending upon conditions. Mercury(I) chloride, for example, in contact with gaseous ammonia for a prolonged period reacts as follows.

$$Hg_2Cl_2 + 2NH_3(g) = Hg + Hg(NH_3)_2Cl_2$$

However, dilute aqueous ammonia on the chloride gives either the ammonobasic mercury(II) chloride, $HgNH_2Cl$, or the chloride salt of Millon's base, $[Hg_2N]Cl$ (see 25.45), or both, the latter being favored by greater dilution of the ammonia. The reactions may be represented by the following equations.

$$Hg_2Cl_2 + 2NH_3 = Hg + HgNH_2Cl + NH_4^+ + Cl^-$$
$$2Hg_2Cl_2 + 4NH_3 = 2Hg + [Hg_2N]Cl + 3NH_4^+ + 3Cl^-$$

When soluble salts, such as $Hg_2(NO_3)_2$ or $Hg_2(ClO_4)_2$, are treated with ammonia in aqueous solution, the reaction appears to correspond to the following equation.

$$2Hg_2^{2+} + X^- + 4NH_3 = 2Hg + [Hg_2N]X + 3NH_4^+$$

SECTION C. *The Long Transition Series*

Chapter 26. The Rare-Earth, or Lanthanide, Elements   623

27. The Actinide Elements   641

THE RARE–EARTH, OR LANTHANIDE, ELEMENTS *

Introduction

26.1 On the basis of electronic configuration the rare-earth, or lanthanide, series is comprised of elements 58 to 71, in which the $4f$ orbitals are being filled (Table 26.1). Two other elements, lanthanum ($5d^16s^2$) and yttrium ($4d^15s^2$), although they contain no $4f$ electrons, are commonly included in the lanthanide series; these elements occur in nature associated with the lanthanides and are closely related to them in properties.

26.2 As would be expected for a series in which inner orbitals are being occupied, the lanthanides have properties characteristic of transition elements. Thus they are all metals; most of the ions are paramagnetic and many are colored; some of the elements exhibit variability in oxidation states. However, it should be emphasized that these elements differ in a number of important respects from transition elements in which inner d orbitals are being filled, largely because the f orbitals lie deeper in the atom and consequently are less readily available for chemical reaction and are better screened from the effects of surrounding electronic systems.

---

* The designation of these elements as *lanthanides* rather than as *rare-earths* appears to be gaining wide acceptance. The English refer to the same elements as *lanthanons*.

GENERAL REFERENCES

HOPKINS, *Chapters in the Chemistry of the Less Familiar Elements*, Stipes Publishing Co., Champaign, 1939, Ch. 6.

LATIMER, *The Oxidation States of the Elements and Their Potentials in Aqueous Solutions*, 2nd Edition, Prentice-Hall, Inc., New York, 1952, Ch. 20.

REMY, *Treatise on Inorganic Chemistry* (translated and amended by Anderson), Elsevier Publishing Company, Amsterdam, 1956, Vol. II, Ch. 10.

SIDGWICK, *The Chemical Elements and Their Compounds*, Oxford University Press, London, 1950, pp. 439–57.

VICKERY, *Chemistry of the Lanthanons*, Academic Press, Inc., New York, 1953.

YOST, RUSSELL and GARNER, *The Rare Earth Elements and Their Compounds*, John Wiley and Sons, Inc., New York, 1947.

TABLE 26.1

Electronic Configurations of the Lanthanide Elements *

(Xenon core not shown)

Element	Configuration	Element	Configuration
Cerium, $_{58}$Ce	$(4f^26s^2)$	Terbium, $_{65}$Tb	$(4f^96s^2)$
Praseodymium, $_{59}$Pr	$(4f^36s^2)$	Dysprosium, $_{66}$Dy	$(4f^{10}6s^2)$
Neodymium, $_{60}$Nd	$4f^46s^2$	Holmium, $_{67}$Ho	$(4f^{11}6s^2)$
Promethium, $_{61}$Pm	$(4f^56s^2)$	Erbium, $_{68}$Er	$(4f^{12}6s^2)$
Samarium, $_{62}$Sm	$4f^66s^2$	Thulium, $_{69}$Tm	$4f^{13}6s^2$
Europium, $_{63}$Eu	$4f^76s^2$	Ytterbium, $_{70}$Yb	$4f^{14}6s^2$
Gadolinium, $_{64}$Gd	$4f^75d^16s^2$	Lutetium, $_{71}$Lu	$4f^{14}5d^16s^2$

* MEGGERS, *Science*, **105**, 514 (1947). The symbols in parentheses represent extrapolations or predictions based on the analysis of spectra of neighboring elements.

Size Relationships **26.3** The entry of electrons into the inner $4f$ orbitals without significant change in the overlying $5s$, $5p$, $5d$, and $6s$ orbitals results in a regular increase in *effective* nuclear charge across the lanthanide series. The increase in effective nuclear charge is paralleled within the series by a monotonic decrease in size for ions of comparable charge, and with a few significant exceptions (see Table 26.2), for the neutral atoms themselves. Important chemical conse-

TABLE 26.2

Atomic (Single-Bond) and Ionic Radii of the Lanthanide Elements

Element	Atomic Number	Atomic Radius, Å *	Calculated Radius of Tripositive Ion, Å
(La	57	1.690	1.16)
Ce	58	1.646	1.14
Pr	59	1.648	1.12
Nd	60	1.642	1.10
Pm	61		1.08
Sm	62	1.66	1.07
Eu	63	1.850	1.05
Gd	64	1.614	1.03
Tb	65	1.592	1.02
Dy	66	1.589	1.00
Ho	67	1.580	0.99
Er	68	1.567	0.98
(Y	39	1.616	0.96)
Tm	69	1.562	0.96
Yb	70	1.699	0.95
Lu	71	1.557	0.93

* Taken from PAULING, *J. Am. Chem. Soc.*, **69**, 542 (1947). The inversions in order at Sm, Eu, and Yb are to be especially noted. It is interesting that these elements, in contrast to the other lanthanides can exist in the dipositive state. (See *Oxidation States*.)

quences of the *lanthanide contraction* have already been described (see 17.8 *ff.*), and others will be pointed out in this chapter.

Oxidation States **26.4** The lanthanide elements do not show nearly as wide a variety of oxidation states as do transition elements in which *d* orbitals are being occupied. The characteristic and most stable oxidation state of the lanthanides is +3; in this state the lanthanides have remarkably similar properties. The reason for the stability of the +3 state certainly is not apparent from the electronic configurations shown in Table 26.1. That most of the 4*f* electrons are tightly bound is shown by the fact that the maximum oxidation state exhibited by any of the lanthanides is +4, and this is found only for cerium, praseo-dymium, and terbium. In addition to the tri- and tetrapositive states, the +2 state is also known and this is definitely formed by samarium, europium, and ytterbium. In all three oxidation states the lanthanide elements show ionic behavior.

26.5 The tendency for lanthanide elements to give oxidation states other than the characteristic one of +3 can be correlated with their electronic configura-tions. On the basis of spectroscopic evidence, three configurations among the lanthanide ions have marked stability. The first and most stable configuration is that of La^{3+} which has the xenon structure and no 4*f* electrons; the second is that of Gd^{3+} with a half filled 4*f* level; the third stable configuration is that of Lu^{3+} with a completely filled 4*f* level. In Table 26.3 are summarized the known

TABLE 26.3

Oxidation States and Configurations of 4*f* Levels of the Lanthanide Elements

Element	Oxidation States and 4*f* Configurations		Element	Oxidation States and 4*f* Configurations	
Ce		III $(4f^1)$ IV $(4f^0)$	Tb		III $(4f^8)$ IV $(4f^7)$
Pr		III $(4f^2)$ IV $(4f^1)$	Dy		III $(4f^9)$
Nd		III $(4f^3)$	Ho		III $(4f^{10})$
Pm		III $(4f^4)$	Er		III $(4f^{11})$
Sm	II $(4f^6)$	III $(4f^5)$	Tm		III $(4f^{12})$
Eu	II $(4f^7)$	III $(4f^6)$	Yb	II $(4f^{14})$	III $(4f^{13})$
Gd		III $(4f^7)$	Lu		III $(4f^{14})$

oxidation states of the lanthanide elements, along with the corresponding con-figurations of the 4*f* levels. It is apparent that there is a direct parallelism be-tween the tendency of a lanthanide element to form either the di- or tetrapositive oxidation state and the actual or near attainment of the stable electronic con-figurations noted above, *i.e.*, of a 4*f* level which is void of electrons, half filled, or completely filled.

Colors of the Tripositive Ions **26.6** Most of the tripositive lanthanide ions are colored, only Ce^{3+}, Gd^{3+}, Yb^{3+}, and Lu^{3+} being colorless. There exists a striking periodicity in the colors of the ions, which appears to indicate that they arise from light absorption phenomena involving the 4*f* electrons. As is seen in Table 26.4, the colors of the first seven tripositive ions (including lanthanum) are the same or very similar to those of the last seven in reverse order. Thus

TABLE 26.4

Colors of the Tripositive Lanthanide Ions

	Atomic Number	Color		Atomic Number	Color
La³⁺	57	Colorless	Pm³⁺	61	
Lu³⁺	71	Colorless	Ho³⁺	67	Brownish yellow
Ce³⁺	58	Colorless	Sm³⁺	62	Pale yellow
Yb³⁺	70	Colorless	Dy³⁺	66	Yellowish
Pr³⁺	59	Yellow-green	Eu³⁺	63	Colorless
Tm³⁺	69	Pale green	Tb³⁺	65	Colorless
Nd³⁺	60	Red-violet	Gd³⁺	64	Colorless
Er³⁺	68	Rose			

an ion with n electrons more than lanthanum exhibits very much the same light absorption characteristics as one having $14 - n$ electrons more.

26.7 The spectra of tripositive lanthanide ions are characterized by the great sharpness of their absorption bands in the ultraviolet, visible, and near infrared regions, except for La³⁺ and Lu³⁺, which do not absorb in these regions. Absorption bands of materials containing representative elements or transition elements in which d orbitals are being occupied are ordinarily broad and diffuse and the bands found for the lanthanide ions have been attributed to electronic transitions involving $4f$ electrons, the sharpness of bands being evidence that the $4f$ electrons are but little affected by the electrical fields produced by environmental factors, e.g., solvent, negative ions.

Paramagnetic Properties of the Tripositive Ions **26.8** All the tripositive lanthanide ions, with the exception of La³⁺ which has no $4f$ electrons and Lu³⁺ in which this level is completely filled, are strongly paramagnetic due to the presence of unpaired $4f$ electrons. However, as a result of the high degree of screening of these electrons from the effects of surrounding electrical fields by overlying $5s$ and $5p$ levels, contributions of the orbital moments of the unpaired electrons are significant and the "spin-only" formula useful for compounds of the $3d$ transition series elements (see 4.134) cannot be employed to account for the observed magnetic moments of the lanthanide ions. Detailed exploration of this subject is beyond the scope of this text, but see 4.135–141.

Occurrence and Extraction

26.9 Minerals containing primarily lanthanide elements are found in relatively few localities and each mineral has present a number of the members of the series. Historically, the minerals have been grouped in two classes: (1) the *cerium group* "earths," containing mainly the lighter elements (lanthanum through europium); and (2) the *yttrium group* "earths," consisting largely of compounds of yttrium and the heavier series members, i.e., gadolinium through lutetium. One member of the series, promethium, has never been detected in nature, but is one of the products of nuclear fission, e.g., of uranium-235. The abundance of the individual lanthanide elements in the earth's crust is given in Table 26.5.

TABLE 26.5

Abundance of the Lanthanide Elements in the Earth's Crust *

(in p.p.m.)

(Y	31.0)	Sm	6.5	Ho	1.2
(La	19.0)	Eu	1.0	Er	2.4
Ce	44.0	Gd	6.3	Tm	0.3
Pr	5.6	Tb	1.0	Yb	2.6
Nd	24.0	Dy	4.3	Lu	0.7

* Taken from VICKERY, *Chemistry of the Lanthanons,* Academic Press, Inc., New York, 1953, p. 16.

26.10 The most common minerals are siliceous in nature; in addition, phosphates are numerous and significant as sources of the individual elements. At present the most important mineral is *monazite,* which, although predominantly a cerium group material, usually contains appreciable quantities of the heavier lanthanides. Monazite is largely a mixture of lanthanide phosphates having the following ranges of composition: cerium group elements, 49–74 per cent; yttrium group elements, 0–7.6 per cent; ThO_2 (thorium is probably present as silicate), 1–20 per cent.

26.11 In view of the siliceous character of most of the minerals and the presence of a variety of other metal impurities, the extraction of the lanthanides is ordinarily a rather complicated task, the specific method employed being dependent on the chemical make-up of the mineral. In general, however, a lanthanide mineral is treated in approximately the following fashion. The ground mineral is either digested with hot concentrated hydrochloric or sulfuric acid or fused with potassium acid sulfate or acid fluoride. Fusion with the latter agent is generally limited to minerals containing appreciable amounts of niobium or tantalum; these elements form soluble fluoro complexes and are thus effectively separated from the insoluble lanthanide fluorides. The latter are brought into solution by decomposition of the fused material with sulfuric acid. The digestion or fusion treatment results in the conversion of silicate to silica, which deposits from solution.

26.12 Passage of hydrogen sulfide into the solution of the lanthanide element sulfates precipitates acid insoluble sulfides, *e.g.,* of molybdenum, bismuth, copper, lead, etc. At this point, the lanthanides are precipitated as oxalates by means of the hot acid. Any thorium or zirconium present in the oxalate precipitate can be dissolved by boiling with ammonium oxalate solution.* The

* In extraction of the lanthanide elements from monazite, thorium is commonly precipitated by means of pyrophosphate ion prior to the conversion of the lanthanides to the insoluble oxalates.

lanthanide element oxalates can, if so desired, be converted to sulfates by careful ignition of a paste with concentrated sulfuric acid.

Separation

26.13 Because of the great similarity of the lanthanide elements in the common tripositive oxidation state, their separation from each other has long posed a problem to the chemist. The recent widespread rebirth of interest in these elements, arising from the knowledge that they are important products in nuclear fission, has intensified research on the separation problem, with the result that a rapid method is now available for separating the individual members in a high state of purity from complex mixtures of lanthanide elements. This method utilizes the ion-exchange technique and will be described in some detail.

26.14 The older slow and tedious procedures for the separation of the individual lanthanides in their tripositive state used fractional crystallization, precipitation, or decomposition. The first depended on slight differences in the solubilities of various salts, *e.g.*, double magnesium nitrates, double ammonium nitrates, etc. Fractional crystallization procedures are still of value for the removal of specific materials, but are outmoded for the separation of the members of the entire series. Fractional precipitation and decomposition methods were based on the slight basicity differences (see 26.23) between adjacent tripositive ions; the former technique utilized precipitation of such substances as hydroxides, oxalates, chromates, etc., and the latter, mainly thermal decomposition of nitrates and sulfates. The least basic lanthanide elements precipitate first and the least basic salt is decomposed first on heating.

26.15 It has proved possible to separate rapidly a few members of the lanthanide series by converting them from the characteristic tripositive oxidation state to other states (see 26.4) which have properties differing considerably from those exhibited in the characteristic oxidation state. Cerium has long been removed in a pure condition from lanthanide mixtures by oxidation in aqueous solution to the tetrapositive state by means of a strong oxidant, *e.g.*, bromate in neutral medium, chlorine in alkaline medium; cerium(IV), being much less basic than cerium(III), is precipitated from hot solution as a basic salt or as the dioxide. Concentration of praseodymium and terbium can also be obtained by an oxidation procedure. Although these elements cannot be converted to the +4 condition in aqueous solution, this state can be attained (in the form of oxides) by fusion with such oxidants as nitrates or chlorates. The unconverted tripositive lanthanides can be separated from the less basic tetrapositive praseodymium and terbium by extraction with water or a weakly acidic aqueous solution. Europium(III) can be practically quantitatively separated from solution of lanthanide mixtures by reduction to the dipositive condition, either electrolytically or by means of zinc amalgam, followed by precipitation as $EuSO_4$. If only small quantities of europium are present in the mixture, europium(II) sulfate is thrown down as mixed crystals with strontium sulfate. Zinc amalgam, but not electrolytic, reduction serves for the conversion of ytterbium(III) to the $+2$ state; precipitation with sulfate does not, however, remove the element quantitatively. Samarium(III) cannot be reduced by either of the methods suitable for europium(III). However, reduction by magnesium in ethanol medium containing hydrogen chloride results in the precipitation of samarium(II) chloride. All three lanthanides capable of assuming the dipositive condition can be converted to the metal amalgams by reduction in aqueous acetate solution with sodium amalgam; other lanthanide elements are unaffected. It should be pointed out that the specific methods outlined above for separation of lanthanide elements by oxidation or reduction reactions are still useful in spite of the advent of ion-exchange techniques.

26.16 The most effective tool at present available for the separation and purification of the lanthanide elements is that of ion-exchange, utilizing synthetic cation-exchange resins. The resins ordinarily employed are polymeric organic compounds containing sulfonic or carboxylic acid groups, the hydrogens of which are replaceable by other cations. When an aqueous solution of tripositive lanthanide ions is passed slowly through a long column of the resin, the lanthanides are fixed in a narrow band at the top of the column, the following equilibrium being established.

$$(1) \quad M^{3+} + 3HR \rightleftharpoons MR_3 + 3H^+ \quad (HR = \text{resin})$$

Some slight degree of separation of the lanthanide ions is effected in the initial exchange process, the ions of smaller hydrated ionic radius having a greater affinity for the resin than those of larger radius. For the lanthanide ions the order of hydrated radius size is the inverse of that of simple ionic size (Table 26.2 *); thus lanthanum ion is most readily bound to the resin and lutetium ion least tightly held.

26.17 The lanthanide ions fixed on the resin are next eluted by means of a complexing agent. Inasmuch as the stability (*i.e.*, with respect to dissociation) of lanthanide complexes increases progressively from lanthanum to lutetium (see 26.28), elution has the effect of supplementing to a considerable degree the original separation attained on the resin. This is illustrated below.

26.18 The most common eluant is a dilute solution of a mixture of ammonium citrate-citric acid † having a fixed pH somewhere in the range 4 to 7. A variety of complexes can be formed between lanthanide ions and citrate, because the nature of the citrate ion in solution is highly pH dependent. Passage of the

---

* As the size of the bare lanthanide ions decreases with increasing atomic number, the electric field in the neighborhood of the ion increases in strength; the attracting and orienting forces on solvent water molecules consequently increase and the extent of hydration and size of hydrated ion increase.

$$\text{CH}_2\text{COOH}$$
$$|$$
† Citric acid is a tricarboxylic acid of the constitution $\text{HO} - \text{C} - \text{COOH}$
$$|$$
$$\text{CH}_2\text{COOH}$$

citrate solution through the resin column containing the adsorbed lanthanides results first in the following reaction.

$$(2)\ 3NH_4^+ + MR_3 \rightleftharpoons M^{3+} + 3NH_4R$$

The lanthanide ion set free then complexes with citrate ion.

$$(3)\ M^{3+} + xA^{m-} \rightleftharpoons MA_x^{3-xm} \quad (A^{m-} = \text{one of the possible citrate ions})$$

The fraction of the total of M^{3+} found in the citrate complex is determined by the relative equilibrium constants of reactions (2) and (3). Below the band of adsorbed lanthanide ions ammonium citrate exchanges with the resin.

$$(4)\ NH_4^+ + HR \rightleftharpoons NH_4R + H^+$$

The hydrogen ion set free enters into competition with lanthanide ions for citrate anions.

$$(5)\ H^+ + A^{m-} \rightleftharpoons HA^{1-m}$$

This reaction drives equilibrium (3) to the left, increasing the concentration of lanthanide ions; the latter are then readsorbed on the resin in accordance with equation (1). Continued passage of ammonium citrate through the resin column causes the many-fold recurrence of the whole sequence of reactions noted above, and in this fashion lanthanide ions are moved down the column and eventually from the resin bed entirely. The order of elution parallels the increasing order of stability of citrate complexes, *i.e.*, lutetium is eluted first and lanthanum last. By careful control of experimental conditions extremely efficient separations are obtained.

The Metals

26.19 The availability of the lanthanides as a result of ion-exchange methods of separation has made possible the preparation of most of the metals in a high state of purity. The lighter lanthanides La, Ce, Pr, Nd, and Gd have been obtained in yields greater than 99 per cent by reduction of the anhydrous trichlorides with calcium in an inert (*e.g.*, argon) atmosphere.[1] The reduction, which is carried out in a tantalum crucible, proceeds exothermically at 550–600°, the final temperature of reaction being in the range 1000–1350° and high enough to melt the lanthanide metal. Under similar conditions of reaction, samarium, europium, and ytterbium, in the form of their trichlorides, are converted to the dipositive state. Samarium, 99.5 per cent pure, has been made by reduction of the anhydrous tribromide by means of barium at 1650–1700° in an argon atmosphere.[2] Heavier lanthanide metals cannot be prepared in good yield from the trichlorides, since the latter are too volatile at the temperatures at which the metals are molten. However, the metals (Tb, Dy, Y, Ho, Er, Tm) can be ob-

---

[1] SPEDDING and DAANE, *J. Am. Chem. Soc.*, **74**, 2783 (1952).
[2] ONSTOTT, *J. Am. Chem. Soc.*, **75**, 5128 (1953).

tained in a high state of purity by high temperature reduction of the trifluorides under conditions similar to those utilized for the lighter metals.[3] Ytterbium, which by this method is converted not to the metal but to the dipositive condition, can be prepared by the reduction *in vacuo* of the sesquioxide with lanthanum at elevated temperatures.[4] Samarium can be obtained in an analogous manner.

26.20 It has been only recently that accurate data on the physical properties of the lanthanide elements have been obtained. Melting point and boiling point values are listed in Table 26.6.

TABLE 26.6

Melting Points and Boiling Points of the Lanthanide Metals *

Element	Melting Point, °C.	Boiling Point, °C.	Element	Melting Point, °C.	Boiling Point, °C.
(La	920	3199)	Dy	1407	2600
Ce	804	3468	Ho	1461	2600
Pr	935	3127	Er	1497	2900
Nd	1024	3027	Tm	1450	1727
Pm	1035 †	2727 †	Yb	824	1427
Sm	1072	1900	Lu	1652	3327
Eu	826	1439	(Sc	1539	2727)
Gd	1312	3000	(Y	1509	2927)
Tb	1356	2800	(Ac	1050	3027) †

* Source: Dr. A. H. Daane, Institute for Atomic Research, Iowa State College.
† Estimated.

26.21 The lanthanide elements are extremely reactive. The lighter elements are readily tarnished in moist air, and with the exception of cerium which yields the dioxide, they burn at 200–400° to give sesquioxides. The oxidation is strongly exothermic, the heats of formation of the oxides in some instances being even greater than that of aluminum oxide.

Al_2O_3	CeO_2	Pr_2O_3	Nd_2O_3	Sm_2O_3	
−402.9	−233	−444.5	−442.0	−430	kcal. per mole

The lighter lanthanide metals combine directly with hydrogen, slowly at room temperature and rapidly at 300°, to give interstitial hydrides (see 9.15) of the approximate formula MH_3 (*e.g.*, $LaH_{2.8}$, $CeH_{2.8}$, $PrH_{2.7}$). The hydrides are brittle, amorphous substances, stable in dry air, but igniting on contact with water. The hydrogen can be completely removed by heating in a vacuum at temperatures above 1000°. At elevated temperatures the lanthanide elements unite directly with carbon, silicon, nitrogen, phosphorus, arsenic, sulfur, and the halogens. With the nonmetals of groups V, VI, and VII the compounds

[3] DAANE and SPEDDING, *J. Electrochem. Soc.*, **100**, 442 (1953).
[4] DAANE, DENNISON, and SPEDDING, *J. Am. Chem. Soc.*, **75**, 2272 (1953).

obtained are those expected from valence considerations. Union with carbon gives saltlike carbides of the composition MC_2.

26.22 The metals are all reactive toward water, liberating hydrogen slowly from cold and rapidly from warm water. They are about as electropositive (Table 26.7) as magnesium. It is to be noted that the standard electrode potentials decrease rather regularly from lanthanum to lutetium.

TABLE 26.7

Calculated Electrode Potentials of the Lanthanides *

(Reaction: $M = M(H_2O)_x^{3+} + 3e^-$)

Element	E°, Volts	Element	E°, Volts	Element	E°, Volts
(La	2.52)	Eu	2.41	Er	2.30
Ce	2.48	Gd	2.40	Tm	2.28
Pr	2.47	Tb	2.39	Yb	2.27
Nd	2.44	(Y	2.37)	Lu	2.25
Pm	2.42	Dy	2.35		
Sm	2.41	Ho	2.32		

* Data from LATIMER, *The Oxidation States of the Elements and Their Potentials in Aqueous Solutions*, 2nd. Edition, Prentice-Hall, Inc., New York, 1952, pp. 284 and 291.

The Tripositive Oxidation State

Simple Compounds **26.23** This oxidation state is a fairly basic one, and salts with anions derived from strong acids, *e.g.*, perchlorates, nitrates, sulfates, etc., are only slightly hydrolyzed. Moreover, the hydroxides readily absorb carbon dioxide from the air to give granular carbonates. As would be expected from the regular decrease in tripositive ionic radius along the series, basicity decreases with increasing atomic number.

26.24 Salts of the lanthanide elements ordinarily crystallize in hydrated form from aqueous solution. Among the more common salts the chlorides, bromides, iodides, sulfates, nitrates, acetates, perchlorates, and bromates are readily soluble in water, whereas the fluorides, oxalates, phosphates, and carbonates are relatively insoluble. The tripositive lanthanides have considerable tendency to form double salts and a number of them have been of value in separation procedures utilizing fractional crystallization (see 26.14). Among the more common double salts are the double nitrates with ammonium or dipositive cations, *e.g.*, $M^{III}(NO_3)_3 \cdot 2NH_4NO_3 \cdot 4H_2O$, $2M^{III}(NO_3)_3 \cdot 3Mg(NO_3)_2 \cdot 24H_2O$, and the double alkali metal sulfates, *e.g.*, $M^{III}_2(SO_4)_3 \cdot 3Na_2SO_4 \cdot xH_2O$, and carbonates, *e.g.*, $M^{III}_2(CO_3)_3 \cdot Na_2CO_3 \cdot 12H_2O$.

26.25 In solution, the tripositive state, for most of the lanthanides, is stable toward both oxidation and reduction. Only one element, namely cerium, can be converted to the tetrapositive state; only samarium, europium, and ytterbium can be reduced to the dipositive condition. The use of oxidation and reduction reactions in separation procedures has been discussed (see 26.15).

26.26 Lanthanide sesquioxides, except for those of cerium, praseodymium, and terbium, are readily obtained by thermal decomposition of hydroxides or the salts of many oxyacids, *e.g.*, carbonates, nitrates, oxalates, etc., as well as by direct union of the elements (see above). These methods are unsuitable for the preparation of the sesquioxides of the elements noted above because of their ready conversion at elevated temperatures to oxides containing the elements in the tetrapositive state. The sesquioxides of praseodymium and terbium can be prepared by reduction of higher oxides by means of hydrogen at 900°; cerium sesquioxide is more difficultly obtained, reduction of CeO_2 requiring a temperature of about 2000° and a hydrogen pressure of 150 atm. The sesquioxides are rather strong basic anhydrides, weaker than the alkaline earth metal oxides but stronger than magnesium oxide.

26.27 Treatment of a warm solution of a tripositive lanthanide salt with an excess of ammonia-water or alkali metal hydroxide results in the precipitation of the hydroxide, usually in a gelatinous form. A number of the lanthanide hydroxides, *e.g.*, those of neodymium and praseodymium, have been shown to be compounds truly having the constitution $M(OH)_3$; others, *e.g.*, the precipitated hydroxides of samarium and yttrium, are in reality hydrous oxides. The estimated solubility products of the lanthanide hydroxides, for example, $(M^{3+})(OH^-)^3$, decrease fairly regularly from a value of 1×10^{-19} for the lanthanum compound to 2.5×10^{-24} for lutetium hydroxide.

Complexes [5] **26.28** In comparison with ions derived from elements of the short transition series the tripositive lanthanide ions have relatively small tendency to form complex species. This can be attributed to two factors: (1) the unavailability of the deep-lying f orbitals for the formation of hybrid orbitals giving strong covalent bonds; and (2) the comparatively large radii of the ions (*e.g.*, Cr^{3+}, 0.62 Å; Fe^{3+}, 0.64 Å; Eu^{3+}, 1.05 Å), a property not conducive to the development of strong electrostatic interactions. Despite the factors unfavorable for the formation of complexes, such species are known. If it is assumed that there is some degree of covalent binding in the complexes, then the bonding must be of the "outer orbital" type, *i.e.*, it must involve orbitals of higher energy than $4f$, *e.g.*, $5d$, $6s$, $6p$. As might be supposed, the dissociative stability of the complexes increases with increasing atomic number (decreasing ionic size) of the lanthanide.

26.29 There is considerable evidence that in aqueous solution association occurs between tripositive lanthanide ions and various anions. Thus complexes with halide, sulfite, sulfate, thiosulfate, nitrate, pyrophosphate, and oxalate ions have been observed. The compositions and stabilities of a number of the complex species are given in Table 26.8. It is difficult or impossible to isolate these in the solid state as distinguishable complex species.

26.30 In addition to the complexes noted above, there exist those which contain a variety of organic ligands and often are sufficiently stable to permit isola-

[5] MOELLER, *Record Chem. Progress*, **14**, 69 (1953).

TABLE 26.8

Complexes of Some Lanthanides with Anions

Species	Dissociation Equilibrium	Instability Constant
CeF^{2+}	$CeF^{2+} \rightleftharpoons Ce^{3+} + F^-$	1.0×10^{-4}
$CeCl^{2+}$	$CeCl^{2+} \rightleftharpoons Ce^{3+} + Cl^-$	ca. 0.59–0.83
$CeBr^{2+}$	$CeBr^{2+} \rightleftharpoons Ce^{3+} + Br^-$	0.414
CeI^{2+}	$CeI^{2+} \rightleftharpoons Ce^{3+} + I^-$	extremely large
$CeSO_3^+$	$CeSO_3^+ \rightleftharpoons Ce^{3+} + SO_3^-$	9×10^{-9}
$CeSO_4^+$	$CeSO_4^+ \rightleftharpoons Ce^{3+} + SO_4^{2-}$	1.66×10^{-2}
$CeNO_3^{2+}$	$CeNO_3^{2+} \rightleftharpoons Ce^{3+} + NO_3^-$	ca. 0.4
$CeP_2O_7^-$	$CeP_2O_7^- \rightleftharpoons Ce^{3+} + P_2O_7^{4-}$	7×10^{-18}
$CeC_2O_4^+$	$CeC_2O_4^+ \rightleftharpoons Ce^{3+} + C_2O_4^{2-}$	3×10^{-7}
$NdC_2O_4^+$	$NdC_2O_4^+ \rightleftharpoons Nd^{3+} + C_2O_4^{2-}$	6.25×10^{-8}
$YbC_2O_4^+$	$YbC_2O_4^+ \rightleftharpoons Yb^{3+} + C_2O_4^{2-}$	5×10^{-8}

tion in the solid state. These compounds can be classified as nonchelated or chelated complexes. Specific
examples of the former type are rare. Perhaps the
best known are derivatives of antipyrene (ap), in which
the methyl-substituted nitrogen atom is believed to
function as the donor. Compounds of the type
[M ap$_6$]X$_3$ have been isolated, where M = La, Ce, Pr,
Nd, and Er, and X = Cl, I, NO$_3$, and ClO$_4$. It is worth noting that the tripositive lanthanide ions show little tendency to form complexes with the usual
donor molecules such as ammonia and simple amines.

26.31 Chelated complexes are much more common. These are either inner
complexes, *i.e.*, neutral molecules in which the ligand satisfies both the oxidation
number and coordination number of the lanthanide ion, or cationic or anionic
in character. Examples of inner complexes are those formed with 8-quinolinol
(8-hydroxyquinoline) and β-diketones.

26.32 With 5,7-dihalo-8-quinolinols and tripositive lanthanide ions compounds of the constitution shown are formed. These substances
are soluble in organic solvents and extractable
from aqueous into organic media. Whereas these
compounds are stable in water, analogous complexes formed with unsubstituted 8-quinolinol ap-
pear to undergo significant hydrolytic decomposition to yield basic products.

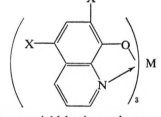

26.33 A variety of the chelates with β-diketones have been obtained by the
addition of the organic material to lanthanide metal salt in acidic solution,
followed by appropriate adjustment of the pH. Accurate pH control is necessary if the formation of basic products is to be avoided. The best known of
these complexes are the acetylacetonates (R = R' = CH$_3$), the dibenzoylmeth-

$$3 \; \begin{array}{c} R \\ | \\ C=O \\ | \\ CH_2 \\ | \\ C=O \\ | \\ R' \end{array} \;\; + \; M^{3+} \;\; = \;\; \left[\left(\begin{array}{c} R \\ | \\ C=O \\ | \\ CH \\ \| \\ C-O \\ | \\ R' \end{array} \right)_3 M \right] \;\; + \;\; 3H^+$$

ane chelates $(R = R' = C_6H_5)$, and the thenoyltrifluoroacetone chelates $(R = CF_3; \; R' = C_4H_3S)$. The compounds are water-insoluble, but dissolve readily in organic solvents, in which media they are monomolecular. The absorption spectra of the complexes in organic solvents are very similar to the spectra of the corresponding simple tripositive lanthanide ions in water solution (see 26.7). The absence of new absorption bands is proof that the $4f$ orbitals are not involved in the bonding between lanthanide ion and ligand.

26.34 The only cationic chelates which have been described are those having pyramidone (pd) as ligand. These compounds have the formula $[M \, pd_3]X_3$ and

pyramidone

have been prepared for La, Ce, Pr, Nd and Er, with $X = Cl$, Br, NO_3, and ClO_4. The lanthanide ion presumably exhibits a coordination number of six.

26.35 Among the anionic chelates the citrates have already been mentioned in connection with the ion-exchange separation of the lanthanides (see 26.18). None of the compounds have been isolated in solid form, but there is little question that a variety of complexes can be formed, since the nature of the citrate ion in solution is pH dependent. A similar situation exists for tartrate complexes.

26.36 Stable anionic complexes are formed between lanthanide ions and amino acids having more than one —CH_2COOH group on a nitrogen atom. Among the acids which have been utilized as complexing agents are the following.

$$RN(CH_2COOH)_2 \qquad N(CH_2COOH)_3$$
iminodiacetic acids   nitriloacetic acid

$$(HOOCCH_2)_2N—CH_2—CH_2—N(CH_2COOH)_2$$
ethylenediaminetetraacetic acid

With iminodiacetic acids complexes containing both one and two moles of ligand per gram ion of lanthanide are known. As expected, the complexes become increasingly more stable with decreasing size in lanthanide ion. The stability variations are sufficiently marked to make the iminodiacetic acids useful eluants in ion-exchange separations. The nitriloacetic acid chelates are of the type $[M(N(CH_2COO)_3)_2]^{3-}$, the dissociative stabilities again varying in the expected order.

26.37 The most stable anionic chelates appear to be obtained with ethylenediaminetetraacetic acid as ligand, solid compounds actually having been isolated. Reaction, at elevated temperatures, between aqueous suspensions of the acid and lanthanide sesquioxides yields crystalline compounds of the composition $H[MY] \cdot xH_2O$ (H_4Y = ethylenediaminetetraacetic acid). These substances are fairly strong acids. A number of salt types derived from the acid $H[MY]$ have also been prepared; among them are the sodium compounds, salts with lanthanide metal cations, i.e., $M[MY]_3 \cdot xH_2O$, which are glasslike, noncrystalline materials; and alkaloid derivatives. Infrared spectra of the compounds [6] have been interpreted as showing that in the anionic complex the ethylenediaminetetraacetate ligand occupies five coordination positions and possesses an uncomplexed carboxyl group. The sixth coordination position presumably is filled by a water molecule, the complex ion thus actually having the formula $[MY(H_2O)]^-$. The stability constants of these anionic chelates in aqueous solution have been determined from a study of the equilibrium below by means

$$M^{3+} + HY^{3-} \rightleftharpoons H[MY]$$

of a pH titration technique. The data are summarized in the form of association constants in Table 26.9 and show the expected order of stabilities.

TABLE 26.9

Stability Constants for
Lanthanide-Ethylenediaminetetraacetate Complexes

($K = [H(MY)]/[M^{3+}][HY^{3-}]$)

Lanthanide Element	Log K	Lanthanide Element	Log K
(La	15.30)	Gd	17.2
Ce	16.05	Dy	17.75
Pr	16.55	(Y	18.0)
Nd	16.75	Er	18.15
Sm	17.2	Yb	18.70

The Tetrapositive Oxidation State

26.38 Two phases of the chemistry of this oxidation state have already been discussed: (1) the relationship between its existence and the electronic configurations of the lanthanides (see 26.4); and (2) its significance in the separation of cerium, praseodymium, and terbium from lanthanide materials (see 26.15). In this section a number of additional specific aspects of the chemistry of the tetrapositive state are described.

[6] MOELLER, MOSS, and MARSHALL, *J. Am. Chem. Soc.*, **77**, 3182 (1955).

26.39 Of the three lanthanide elements which exhibit this oxidation state it is only with cerium that the +4 state is known both in solid compounds and in aqueous solution; for praseodymium and terbium only solid compounds have been characterized. Perhaps the best known cerium(IV) compound is the dioxide, CeO_2. This is easily obtained (as a white powder when pure) by the ignition in air of cerium(III) hydroxide or a salt of an oxyacid, *e.g.*, oxalate, carbonate, nitrate. The dioxide is considerably less basic than the corresponding cerium(III) compound, a fact consistent with the decrease in ionic size in passing from the +3 to the +4 state. The dioxide is extremely resistant to attack by hydrochloric or nitric acid or by alkali metal hydroxides. It can be dissolved by these acids when a reducing agent, *e.g.*, H_2O_2 or Sn^{2+}, is also present, cerium(IV) being converted to the tripositive condition.

26.40 Solutions of cerium(IV) can be obtained from the element in the tripositive state by treatment with a strong oxidizing agent such as peroxydisulfate or bismuthate in nitric acid medium. Reaction of cerium(IV) in solution with ammonia or an alkali metal hydroxide gives a yellow gelatinous hydrous oxide, $CeO_2 \cdot xH_2O$. This weakly basic substance is much more readily dissolved by acids than is the anhydrous oxide, and usually serves as the source of cerium(IV) solutions. It should be noted, however, that in reaction of the hydrous dioxide with hydrohalic acids, cerium(IV) solutions are obtained only with hydrofluoric acid; with concentrated solutions of the other hydrohalic acids free halogen is formed, cerium being reduced to the tripositive state.

26.41 Tetrapositive cerium has a considerable tendency to form double salts, in some of which the lanthanide element appears to be present as an anionic complex. The best-known "double salt" is $2NH_4NO_3 \cdot Ce(NO_3)_4$, which crystallizes from solution when cerium(IV) is treated with ammonium nitrate dissolved in concentrated nitric acid. There is some evidence that at least in the solid state this "double salt" is best formulated as a complex hexanitratocerate(IV), *i.e.*, $(NH_4)_2[Ce(NO_3)_6]$.

26.42 The outstanding characteristic of cerium(IV) solutions is their strong oxidizing power. The reduction potentials for this oxidation state have been measured in a number of acidic media and have been shown to vary with the acid present.

$$Ce^{4+} + e^- \rightleftharpoons Ce^{3+} \qquad E° = 1.44 \text{ v. (in 1 } M \text{ H}_2\text{SO}_4\text{)}; \; 1.61 \text{ v. (in }$$
$$0.5 - 2 \; M \text{ HNO}_3\text{)}; \; 1.70 \text{ v. (in 1 } M \text{ HClO}_4\text{)};$$
$$1.28 \text{ v. (in 2 } M \text{ HCl)}$$

If it is assumed that in perchloric acid solution the observed potential is for reaction involving the hydrated ions,* then the variation in potential in the other acidic media can be attributed to complex formation.

26.43 Tetrapositive praseodymium exists only in the form of the oxide. Ignition of the sesquioxide, carbonate, or nitrate, etc. (see 26.26) in air gives as the final product a black oxide of the formula Pr_6O_{11}. The pure dioxide (black) can

---

* The ClO_4^- ion has little coordinating tendency, and this assumption is reasonably valid.

be obtained by union of the sesquioxide and oxygen at elevated temperatures and pressures (*e.g.*, 375° and 15 atm. O_2 pressure) or by the fusion of Pr_6O_{11} with sodium chlorate.

26.44 Praseodymium(IV) is unstable in solution. Treatment of either Pr_6O_{11} or PrO_2 with nonreducing acids (*e.g.*, HNO_3, H_2SO_4) results in the reduction of praseodymium to the tripositive condition, with liberation of oxygen. The free halogens are evolved from hydrohalic acids. The standard potential for the reaction $Pr^{4+} + e^- = Pr^{3+}$ has been estimated to be 2.86 volts.

26.45 Terbium(IV) is known only in the solid state, in the forms of the oxide and fluoride. A brown oxide, Tb_4O_7, is produced in a manner analogous to that used to obtain Pr_6O_{11}. Tb_4O_7 is unstable at high temperatures, decomposing completely into the sesquioxide when heated at 800° in a nitrogen atmosphere. Pure TbO_2 is obtained by the action of atomic oxygen on Tb_4O_7 at 350°.[7] A brown oxide of the composition Tb_6O_{11} is formed by reaction between the sesquioxide and molecular oxygen at high temperatures and pressures. Reaction between anhydrous terbium trifluoride and elementary fluorine at atmospheric pressure gives the tetrafluoride.[8] The analogous cerium compound can be made in a similar fashion, but attempts to prepare the praseodymium derivative have proved unsuccessful. Terbium(IV) fluoride is inert to cold water.

The Dipositive Oxidation State

26.46 It has already been pointed out that the +2 state for the lanthanides is definitely found only for samarium, europium, and ytterbium (see 26.4), and methods for the attainment of this state in solution have been described (see 26.15). The preparation and properties of anhydrous lanthanide dihalides, the best-known compounds corresponding to this oxidation state, are now discussed; in addition, other significant chemical characteristics of the state are noted.

26.47 The dihalides are commonly produced from the anhydrous trihalides either by thermal decomposition in a high vacuum or by high temperature reduction with hydrogen, aluminum, or ammonia. (Most of the anhydrous lanthanide trihalides can be obtained conveniently by heating a mixture of ammonium halide and sesquioxide or hydrous oxide.) The modes of preparation and some properties of the known dihalides are summarized in Table 26.10.

26.48 In reactions the dihalides of europium and ytterbium are much more stable than the corresponding compounds of samarium. Samarium dihalides disproportionate extensively at temperatures somewhat above their melting points.

$$3SmX_2 = Sm + 2SmX_3$$

A similar reaction occurs for the ytterbium(II) halides, but decomposition appears to be much less extensive; europium dichloride apparently is stable at red heat. Aqueous solutions of the dihalides of samarium are extremely un-

[7] GRUEN, KOEHLER, and KATZ, *J. Am. Chem. Soc.*, **73**, 1475 (1951).
[8] CUNNINGHAM, FEAY, and ROLLIER, *J. Am. Chem. Soc.*, **76**, 3361 (1954).

TABLE 26.10

The Lanthanide Dihalides

Compound	Preparation	Properties
$SmCl_2$	$SmCl_3 + H_2$, Al, or NH_3; 600–650°	Red-brown; m.p. 740°; disproportionates at 1000°
$SmBr_2$	$SmBr_3 + H_2$; 600–650°	Dark brown; m.p. ca. 700°; disproportionates at high temperatures
SmI_2	Thermal decomposition of SmI_3 at 800–900°; $SmI_3 + H_2$ at 750°	Dark green; disproportionates at 680°
$EuCl_2$	$EuCl_3 + H_2$; 400–450°	White; apparently stable at red heat
$EuBr_2$	$EuBr_3 + HBr$; 350°	Chocolate-brown
EuI_2	$EuI_3 \cdot 6H_2O + H_2 + HI$; 600°	Dark brown-green
EuF_2	$EuF_3 + H_2$; above 900°	Yellow
$YbCl_2$	$YbCl_3 + H_2$ at 600–620°; thermal decomposition of $YbCl_3$, which begins at 870°	Colorless; disproportionates at high temperatures (before melting point is reached)
$YbBr_2$	Thermal decomposition of $YbBr_3$; begins at 700°	Black; disproportionates at high temperatures
YbI_2	Thermal decomposition of YbI_3; begins at 250°	Yellow-green; disproportionates at high temperatures

stable even in the absence of oxygen, hydrogen being evolved fairly rapidly; corresponding compounds of europium(II) and ytterbium(II) are much less readily oxidized by water, liberation of hydrogen occurring slowly at room temperature. Solutions of the dihalides of all three elements are oxidized rapidly in air as in the example given below.

$$12EuCl_2 + 3O_2 = 8EuCl_3 + 2Eu_2O_3$$

26.49 Potentials for the various lanthanide M(II)—M(III) couples have been determined and are summarized in Table 26.11. These data are indicative of the powerful reducing properties of the dipositive state, and in their trend are

TABLE 26.11

Oxidation Potentials of Lanthanide M(II)–M(III) Couples

Reaction	E Volts
$Sm^{2+} = Sm^{3+} + e^-$	1.55 * (10^{-3} M Sm^{3+} ion at dropping mercury electrode; in 10^{-3} N H_2SO_4; 10^{-1} M tetramethylammonium iodide supporting electrolyte)
$Eu^{2+} = Eu^{3+} + e^-$	0.43 (in very dilute HCOOH)
$Yb^{2+} = Yb^{3+} + e^-$	1.15 (at dropping mercury electrode)

* TIMNICK and GLOCKLER, *J. Am. Chem. Soc.*, **70**, 1347 (1948).

consistent with the observed chemical behavior of the three lanthanide elements in solution.

26.50 In their solubility behavior, compounds of the dipositive ions are very similar to corresponding strontium materials. Thus, they form insoluble sulfates (see 26.15), phosphates, and chromates.

CHAPTER 27

THE ACTINIDE ELEMENTS

Introduction: The Case for an Actinide Series

27.1 The synthesis in recent years of elements having atomic numbers greater than 92 has raised the question of their appropriate place in the periodic system. The available physical and chemical evidence leaves little doubt that in these transuranic elements $5f$ orbitals are being filled; therefore, on this basis the elements must be regarded as being members of a series analogous to the lanthanides in which $4f$ orbitals are being occupied. Extrapolation from previously observed trends in periodic arrangement suggests that the $5f$ series starts with thorium and that we are dealing with an *actinide* series (in the same sense that the $4f$ elements are members of a *lanthanide* series) rather than with a continuation of the $5d$ series begun at actinium.

La; Ce Pr Nd Pm Sm Eu Gd Tb Dy Ho Er Tm Yb Lu

Ac; Th Pa U Np Pu Am Cm Bk Cf Es Fm Md No

27.2 At first glance there are serious objections to this idea. In the first place, there is considerable question as to whether the elements before uranium (*i.e.*, Th and Pa) contain $5f$ electrons either in the gaseous atoms or in com-

GENERAL REFERENCES

The Actinide Elements, edited by Seaborg and Katz, McGraw-Hill Book Company, Inc., New York, 1954.

CORYELL, *Record Chem. Progress*, **12**, 55 (1951).

HAISSINSKY, *J. Chem. Soc.*, 1949 (Supp. Issue No. 2), S241.

LATIMER, *The Oxidation States of the Elements and Their Potentials in Aqueous Solutions*, 2nd Edition, Prentice-Hall, Inc., New York, 1952, Ch. 21.

LISTER, *Quart. Revs.*, IV, 20 (1950).

REMY, *Treatise on Inorganic Chemistry* (translated and amended by J. S. Anderson), Elsevier Publishing Company, Amsterdam, 1956, Vol. II, Ch. 14.

SEABORG, Ch. 3 in Vol. 1 of *Comprehensive Inorganic Chemistry*, edited by Sneed, Maynard, and Brasted, D. Van Nostrand Company, Inc., New York, 1953.

SEABORG, *Nucleonics*, **5**, 16 (1949).

pounds. Secondly, in terms of chemical properties thorium, protactinium, and uranium bear a much closer resemblance to the members of the titanium, vanadium, and chromium families, respectively, than they do to the transuranium elements. In spite of these factors, a strong case can be made for the actinide series. The evidence pointing to the existence of such a series is derived from five sources: (1) chemical properties; (2) absorption spectra of solid compounds and their aqueous solutions; (3) crystallographic data; (4) magnetic properties; and (5) spectroscopic information on gaseous species.

Chemical Properties **27.3** A summary of the known oxidation states of elements 89–98 is given in Table 27.1. The most pertinent fact to be derived

TABLE 27.1

Oxidation States of Elements 89–98 *

Atomic Number	Element	Oxidation States	Atomic Number	Element	Oxidation States
89	Ac (actinium)	**3**	94	Pu (plutonium)	3, **4**, 5, 6
90	Th (thorium)	(2), (3), **4**	95	Am (americium)	**3**, 4, 5, 6
91	Pa (protactinium)	(3), (4), **5**	96	Cm (curium)	**3**, (4)
92	U (uranium)	3, 4, 5, **6**	97	Bk (berkelium)	**3**, 4
93	Np (neptunium)	3, 4, **5**, 6	98	Cf (californium)	**3**

  * Extremely unstable states are shown in parentheses. The table includes oxidation states found in solid compounds formed only under drastic conditions, *e.g.*, Th(III) in ThI$_3$, Cm(IV) in CmO$_2$. Oxidation states in compounds possessing metallic character are omitted, *e.g.*, Np(II) in NpO, Am(II) in AmO. The most stable oxidation state for each element is given in boldface type.

from this tabulation is the striking stabilization of the lower oxidation states with increasing atomic number. This is brought out in a quantitative manner by the data in Table 27.2, in which are listed the standard oxidation potentials

TABLE 27.2

Some Oxidation Potentials of Elements 92 to 97

| Element | $E°$, VOLTS | | Element | $E°$, VOLTS | |
	(III)–(IV)	(IV)–(VI)		(III)–(IV)	(IV)–(VI)
$_{92}$U	+0.61 *	−0.33 *	$_{95}$Am	−2.32 ‡	−1.34 ‡
$_{93}$Np	−0.147 *	−0.944 *	$_{96}$Cm	< −2	
$_{94}$Pu	−0.97 †	−1.04 †	$_{97}$Bk	ca. −1.6	

  * In 1M HCl.
  † In 1M HClO$_4$.
  ‡ In acid solution (calculated values).

for the III—IV and IV—VI couples for the elements from uranium to berkelium (atomic numbers 92 to 97).

27.4 The most significant observations regarding oxidation state relationships among these elements are: (1) it is apparently impossible to convert tripositive curium in aqueous solution to either a higher or lower oxidation state, and (2) berkelium(III) can be oxidized to the tetrapositive state. These facts are entirely consistent with the actinide concept. Curium, on the assumption that the 5f series begins at thorium, should have seven 5f electrons and therefore should be analogous in behavior to gadolinium, which exhibits only the tripositive oxidation state. On the other hand, it would be expected that berkelium, the homolog of terbium, should be capable of forming the tetrapositive state, with the $5f^7$ configuration.

27.5 It should be pointed out that in terms of the actinide hypothesis, americium, the analog of europium, might be expected to possess a dipositive state in aqueous solution. That this state has not yet been definitely found in solution * can be attributed to the greater ease of removal of 5f electrons as compared to 4f electrons; thus a considerably stronger reducing agent might be required to convert tripositive americium to the +2 condition than is necessary for europium. The greater availability (*i.e.*, the lower binding energy) of 5f electrons can also account for the greater abundance of oxidation states higher than +3 for the actinide elements as compared to the lanthanides. The increasing stability of the +3 state for the actinides with increasing atomic number can then be explained in terms of increasing binding energy of the 5f electrons across the series to curium, where the 5f level is half filled.

27.6 Additional support for an actinide series comes from the properties of the free elements from thorium to curium. These substances are all highly active metals, differing relatively little in electropositive character (Table 27.6). In this regard they are similar to the lanthanide metals and different from the corresponding 5d elements hafnium to platinum, in which there is a marked transition from the strongly electropositive hafnium to the noble metals, osmium, iridium, and platinum.

27.7 Perhaps the most conclusive chemical evidence for the actinide concept is afforded by ion-exchange experiments on the separation of the tripositive transplutonic elements (Am, Cm, Bk, Cf). In Figure 27.1 the relative elution positions of these elements (from a cation exchange column with buffered ammonium citrate as eluant) are compared with the elution positions of the lanthanides presumed to be their homologs. It is evident that there is a remarkable analogy in elution spacings between the americium-curium-berkelium-californium group and the lanthanides proposed as homologs. The observed spacings are a reflection of relative changes in ionic radii which determine the relative stabilities of the citrate complexes. It is apparent that the same order of change in ionic radius is found in the transplutonic elements as occurs when the 4f level is being filled. It should be noted that the elution

---

* There is evidence, of an inconclusive nature, that +2 americium can exist in aqueous solution. Thus, tracer amounts of americium(III) when treated with sodium amalgam are precipitated with barium chloride on europium(II) sulfate as carrier.

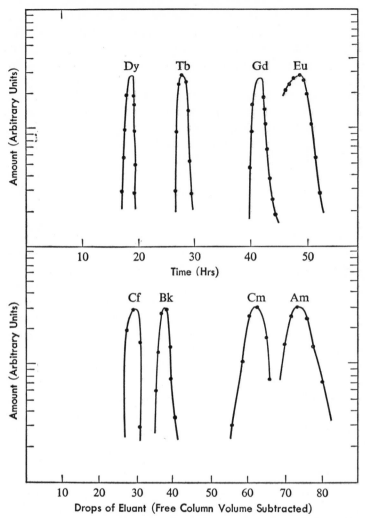

Fig. 27.1 Relative elution of homologous actinides and lanthanides. (Taken with modification from SEABORG, *Comprehensive Inorganic Chemistry*, Vol. I, edited by Sneed, Maynard, and Brasted, D. Van Nostrand Company, Inc., New York, 1953, p. 167.)

behavior of the transplutonic elements was actually predicted prior to their discovery, on the basis of their presumed analogy to the appropriate lanthanide elements.

Absorption Spectra Information **27.8** A characteristic property of tripositive lanthanide ions, dependent on electronic transitions involving 4f electrons, is the sharpness of the absorption bands in their spectra (see 26.7). A similar situation is observed for compounds of uranium, neptunium, plutonium, americium, and curium, both in the solid state and in aqueous solution, and is attributed to transitions involving 5f electrons. A number of observations have been made which are particularly pertinent with regard to support of the actinide concept. Thus the spectra of the lanthanides undergo simplification as the middle of the series (Gd, $4f^7$) is approached; an analogous simplification in spectra occurs with the heavy elements noted above as curium (proposed configuration $5f^7$) is approached. Moreover, in aqueous solution, U(IV), Np(V), and Pu(VI), each presumably having a $5f^2$ configuration, all display analogous absorption peaks in the near infrared region. Finally, the extreme sharpness of the absorption spectra of solid americium(III) chloride and bromide (Am(III), proposed configuration $5f^6$) is comparable only to the spectrum of europium(III) ($4f^6$) among the lanthanide ions.

Crystallographic Data **27.9** Crystal structure studies of compounds of the elements from thorium to americium appear to be best interpreted in terms of filling the $5f$ level in this region of the periodic system. Analogous compounds of these elements (*e.g.*, ThO_2–AmO_2) are almost always isostructural. In each series of isostructural compounds there is a monotonic decrease in lattice dimensions (decrease in ionic radius of the metallic constituent) with increasing atomic number, a contraction analogous to that observed for the lanthanide elements in which the $4f$ level is being filled. (It should be pointed out that generally there is also a decrease in size with increase in atomic number for a given valence state as electrons enter a d level. However, in this case a monotonic decrease is not found because d electrons exert a much greater influence on the nature of the binding in the crystal than do f electrons. Moreover, in systems where a d level is being occupied, the same structure type does not persist in compounds of analogous formulas.) The close analogy of the lanthanide contraction to that observed for the heavy elements is considered strong evidence that $5f$ orbitals are being filled in the latter.

27.10 Ionic radii for some of the actinide elements in various oxidation states, as calculated from crystal structure data, are given in Table 27.3. These data well illustrate the actinide contraction.

TABLE 27.3

Ionic Radii of Actinide Elements

Element	*Ionic Radius, Å, in Indicated Oxidation State* *			
	+3	+4	+5	+6
(Ac	1.11)			
Th	(1.08) †	0.99		
Pa	(1.05) †	0.96	0.90	
U	1.03	0.93	0.87	0.83
Np	1.01	0.92	0.88	0.82
Pu	1.00	0.90	0.87	0.81
Am	0.99	0.89	0.86	0.80

* Data taken from ZACHARIASEN, *The Actinide Elements*, edited by Seaborg and Katz, McGraw-Hill Book Co., Inc., New York, 1954, Ch. 18.

† Interpolated values.

Magnetic Properties **27.11** Although the magnetic susceptibility data available for compounds of the heaviest elements cannot at present be interpreted unequivocally, they strongly indicate that in these elements the *5f* level is being filled in the manner expected on the basis of the actinide concept. In Figure 27.2

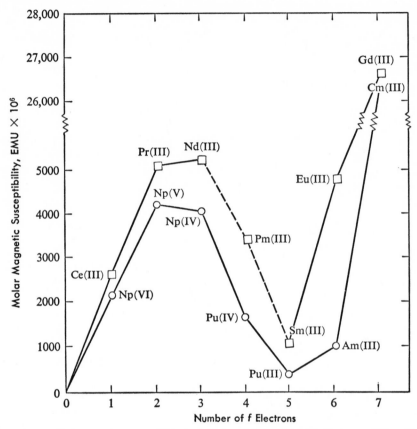

Fig. 27.2. Molar magnetic susceptibilities of some actinide and lanthanide ions. (Taken from *The Actinide Elements*, edited by Seaborg and Katz, McGraw-Hill Book Company, Inc., New York, 1954, p. 748.)

the molar magnetic susceptibilities of a number of tripositive lanthanide ions are plotted against the number of 4*f* electrons in these ions, and the susceptibility values are compared with those for a number of heaviest element species, the latter being arranged in increasing order of number of *5f* electrons on the assumption that the first *5f* electron enters at thorium. The striking similarity in the two plots is apparent.

Spectroscopic Information **27.12** Spectroscopic data lend additional weight to the actinide concept. Thus the spectrum of uranium has been interpreted to show the presence of three *5f* electrons in the lowest energy state of the neutral atom, which is consistent with the position this element occupies in an actinide series. Observations on the spectra of gaseous Th^+, Th^{2+}, and Th^{3+} species indicate that in the neutral atom the binding energies of $5f$ and $6d$ electrons lie very close together; actually gaseous Th^{3+} appears to have a $5f^1$ (beyond radon) ground configuration. There is such a strong analogy between the emission spectra of americium and europium that it appears likely that these elements have similar electronic configurations in the gaseous atoms. On the basis of the known europium structure, americium is assigned the configuration $5f^77s^2$ (beyond radon).

Summary **27.13** Considered in its totality the evidence for the existence of an actinide series is quite impressive, even though the first $5f$ electron may not appear at thorium. The outstanding chemical fact in support of the actinide concept is the remarkable stabilization of the tripositive state at curium, the element which would be the homolog of gadolinium in the lanthanide series and at which the $5f$ level would be half filled.

27.14 In Table 27.4 there are presented suggested electronic configurations for

TABLE 27.4

Suggested Electronic Configurations of the Actinide Elements

(Radon core not shown)

Element	Configuration	Element	Configuration
($_{89}$Ac	$6d\,7s^2$)	$_{94}$Pu	$5f^67s^2$ (or $5f^56d7s^2$)
$_{90}$Th	$6d^27s^2$ (or $5f6d7s^2$)	$_{95}$Am	$5f^77s^2$
$_{91}$Pa	$5f^26d7s^2$ (or $5f6d^27s^2$)	$_{96}$Cm	$5f^76d7s^2$
$_{92}$U	$5f^36d7s^2$	$_{97}$Bk	$5f^97s^2$
$_{93}$Np	$5f^57s^2$ (or $5f^46d7s^2$)	$_{98}$Cf	$5f^{10}7s^2$

the ground states of the neutral gaseous atoms for the elements actinium to californium. It must be emphasized that for the elements at the early part of the series it is difficult to assign electrons unambiguously to the $5f$ or $6d$ levels since the energy difference between the levels is extremely small in this region. Moreover, because of this small energy difference, in condensed systems, *i.e.*, in solid compounds and in ions in solutions, the electronic distributions may vary from those expected from the configurations of the gaseous atoms. Two points are clear, however. By the time uranium is reached, the $5f$ level definitely possesses lower energy than the $6d$, and as the series is further traversed the $5f$ electrons are bound progressively tighter in the compounds of the elements. At curium, the mid-point in the series, the $5f$ electrons are particularly firmly bound.

The Occurrence and Preparation of the Actinides

27.15 Of the actinide elements, all of which are radioactive, only those through uranium occur in nature to a significant extent. The transuranic elements are obtained synthetically by nuclear reactions. Two of these elements, neptunium and plutonium, are found in extremely minute amounts in uranium-containing ores.

27.16 Actinium exists in nature in small amounts in all uranium ores, primarily as the isotope of mass number 227, which results from the radioactive decay of uranium-235. The scarcity of actinium is illustrated by the fact

$$^{235}_{92}U \longrightarrow {}^{231}_{90}Th + {}^{4}_{2}He$$
$$\phantom{^{235}_{92}U \longrightarrow} \longrightarrow {}^{231}_{91}Pa + \beta^{-}$$
$$\phantom{^{235}_{92}U \longrightarrow \longrightarrow {}^{231}_{91}Pa} \longrightarrow {}^{227}_{89}Ac + {}^{4}_{2}He$$

that one ton of pure pitchblende (see 27.19) contains only 0.15 mg. of the element. In addition to isotope 227, one of mass number 228 also occurs to a slight extent on the surface of the earth, being a member of the thorium decay series ($^{232}_{90}Th \xrightarrow{-{}^{4}_{2}He} {}^{228}_{88}Ra \xrightarrow{-\beta^{-}} {}^{228}_{89}Ac \longrightarrow$ etc.). The isolation of actinium from uranium ores is a difficult task, not only because the element is present in such minute quantity, but also because it is found associated with much greater concentration of the lanthanides, which it largely resembles in chemical properties. The element is currently obtained synthetically in weighable quantities by transmutation of radium through intense neutron bombardment, its separation from radium and from elements resulting from the decay of actinium, e.g., thorium, polonium, lead, and bismuth, offering no great problem.

$$^{226}_{88}Ra + {}^{1}_{0}n \longrightarrow {}^{227}_{88}Ra + \gamma$$
$$\phantom{^{226}_{88}Ra + {}^{1}_{0}n \longrightarrow} \longrightarrow {}^{227}_{89}Ac + \beta^{-}$$

Actinium-227 has a half-life of 21.7 yr., decaying mainly by beta emission.

27.17 The main naturally occurring isotope of thorium is that of mass number 232. This is found widely distributed in nature, principally in the mineral *monazite* (see 26.10). It has been estimated that the average abundance of thorium in the earth's crust is only about 10 to 20 parts per million. Natural thorium decays by alpha emission, with a half-life of 1.39×10^{10} yr.

27.18 Protactinium in the form of the isotope ^{231}Pa is a constituent of all uranium ores, being a member of the uranium-235 decay chain. It is found to the extent of about 0.25 part per million parts of uranium, and the separation of the element in the pure form is tedious and difficult. The element has been produced artificially in gram amounts by the bombardment of thorium-230 (ionium) with neutrons, and this reaction serves as the main source of protactinium.

$$^{230}_{90}Th + {}^{1}_{0}n \longrightarrow {}^{231}_{90}Th + \gamma$$
$$\phantom{^{230}_{90}Th + {}^{1}_{0}n \longrightarrow} \longrightarrow {}^{231}_{91}Pa + \beta^{-}$$

Thorium-230 is one of the members of the uranium-238 decay series.

$$^{238}_{92}U \xrightarrow{-{}^{4}_{2}He} {}^{234}_{90}Th \xrightarrow{-\beta^{-}} {}^{234}_{91}Pa \xrightarrow{-\beta^{-}} {}^{234}_{92}U \xrightarrow{-{}^{4}_{2}He} {}^{230}_{90}Th$$

Protactinium-231 is an alpha-emitter, having a half-life of 3.43×10^{4} yr.

27.19 Uranium is widely distributed over the earth's surface, the average content in the earth's crust having been estimated to be 4×10^{-6} g. per g. of rock. Thus it is a more common element than cadmium, bismuth, mercury, or silver. The two principal uranium-containing minerals are *pitchblende* and *carnotite*. The former has essentially the composition U_3O_8, and the latter is a complex potassium uranyl vanadate, $K(UO_2)VO_4 \cdot \frac{3}{2}H_2O$. Three isotopes of uranium are found in nature — 234, 235, and 238, the relative abundance being 0.0051, 0.71, and 99.28%. These isotopes are all alpha-emitters and have half-lives of 2.48×10^5, 7.13×10^8, and 4.49×10^9 yr., respectively.

27.20 A large number of isotopes of the transuranic elements have been made by nuclear transmutations. The modes of preparation of some of the more common (*i.e.*, more accessible) isotopes for the elements neptunium through californium, along with some of their nuclear properties, are summarized in Table 27.5.

TABLE 27.5

The More Common Isotopes of Transuranic Elements

Element	Isotopic Species	Mode of Preparation *	Half-life and Type of Decay
Np	237	$^{238}U(n,2n)^{237}U \xrightarrow{-\beta^-} {}^{237}Np$	2.20×10^6 yr.; α
	239	$^{238}U(n,\gamma)^{239}U \xrightarrow{-\beta^-} {}^{239}Np$	2.33 da.; β^-
Pu	239	$^{239}Np \xrightarrow{-\beta^-} {}^{239}Pu$	24,360 yr.; α
	240	$^{238}U(\alpha,2n)^{240}Pu$	6,600 yr.; α
Am	241	$^{239}Pu(n,\gamma)^{240}Pu(n,\gamma)^{241}Pu \xrightarrow{-\beta^-} {}^{241}Am$	470 yr.; α
Cm	242	$^{241}Am(n,\gamma)^{242}Am \xrightarrow{-\beta^-} {}^{242}Cm$	162.5 da.; α
Bk	243	$^{241}Am(\alpha,2n)^{243}Bk$	4.6 hr.; mainly by β^- capture to yield ^{243}Cm.
	245	$^{241}Am(\alpha,p)^{244}Cm(d,n)^{245}Bk$	4.95 da.; mainly by β^- capture to yield ^{245}Cm.
Cf	244	$^{242}Cm(\alpha,2n)^{244}Cf$	45 min.; α
	246	$^{244}Cm(\alpha,2n)^{246}Cf$ or $^{238}U(^{12}C,4n)^{246}Cf$	35.7 hr.; α

* The reactions are interpreted as described for the following specific case:

$$^{238}U(n,2n)^{237}U \xrightarrow{-\beta^-} {}^{237}Np.$$

The bombardment of an atom of ^{238}U by a neutron of the appropriate energy is accompanied by the loss of two neutrons and the formation of an atom of ^{237}U. This in turn loses a beta particle to give ^{237}Np.

The Metals

27.21 Since this chapter is concerned primarily with the chemical relationships existing among the actinide elements, no attempt will be made to discuss the methods by which the elements are extracted in pure form from their various sources.* It is of interest, however, to note the procedures by which actinide metals have been prepared and to describe briefly their properties.

27.22 Thorium metal has been prepared in several ways: by reduction of simple and double halides with alkali and alkaline earth metals, particularly with sodium, at elevated temperatures; by decomposition of the tetraiodide on a hot tungsten filament; by electrolysis of molten mixtures of the tetrachloride or fluoride with sodium or potassium chloride; and by the high temperature reduction of the dioxide with magnesium or mixtures of sodium and calcium. All but the electrolytic procedure yield the powdered metal.

27.23 Protactinium has been made mainly by two methods: the decomposition of the vapor of the pentachloride, bromide, or iodide on a tungsten filament at high temperatures and a pressure of 10^{-5} to 10^{-6} mm. and the reduction of the tetrafluoride by barium metal at about 1500°.

27.24 Procedures analogous to those employed for thorium are applicable for the production of elementary uranium. Particularly good results appear to be obtained in an electrolytic process in which the bath consists of a fused eutectic mixture of sodium and calcium chlorides to which uranium tetrafluoride has been added.

27.25 Transuranic metals have been prepared by methods similar to those utilized for the lanthanides (see 26.19). Thus neptunium, plutonium, americium, and curium have been made by the reduction of the trifluorides with barium vapor at temperatures in the neighborhood of 1200° in beryllium oxide crucibles.

27.26 The actinide metals which have been prepared are all rather reactive substances. In the massive form they are silvery white and most of them are more or less readily attacked by moist air. At elevated temperatures they all react with the common nonmetals. The strongly electropositive character of the actinides is reflected in their estimated standard electrode potentials, which are summarized in Table 27.6. (No data are yet available for berkelium and californium.)

The Oxidation State Chemistry of Elements 89–98

27.27 The general oxidation state relationships existing among elements 89–98 have already been discussed with respect to the evidence in support of the actinide concept (see 27.3 *ff*.). In this section the chemistry of these elements is described in more detail, particular emphasis being placed on the relationships existing in solution and in selected solid compounds.

Actinium **27.28** This element, the prototype of the actinide series, on the basis of electronic configuration ($6d7s^2$, beyond radon) is actually a member of the scandium transition family. Both in solution and in its solid compounds it is solely tripositive. Actinium forms colorless compounds which are very

---

* Mention has been made of the ion-exchange technique for the separation of the transplutonic elements in their tripositive state (see 27.7). Ion-exchange and solvent extraction methods appear to offer great promise for rapid separation and purification of all the actinide elements.

TABLE 27.6

Electrode Potentials of the Actinide Elements

Element	Reaction	$E°$, Volts	Element	Reaction	$E°$, Volts
(Ac	$Ac = Ac(H_2O)_x^{3+} + 3e^-$	ca. 2.6)	U	$U = U(H_2O)_x^{3+} + 3e^-$	1.80
Th	$Th = Th(H_2O)_x^{4+} + 4e^-$	1.90	Np	$Np = Np(H_2O)_x^{3+} + 3e^-$	1.86
Pa	$Pa + 2H_2O = PaO_2^+$ $+ 4H^+ + 5e^-$	ca. 1.0	Pu	$Pu = Pu(H_2O)_x^{3+} + 3e^-$	2.03
			Am	$Am = Am(H_2O)_x^{3+} + 3e^-$	2.32

similar in properties to the corresponding lanthanum substances (see 26.23 ff.).

Thorium **27.29** Oxidation states of $+2$, $+3$, and $+4$ are known for this element, with the latter state being the only one capable of existence in aqueous solution. Tetrapositive thorium is closely similar to $+4$ zirconium and cerium in its properties.

27.30 Although thorium dioxide (ThO_2) and hydroxide appear to be entirely basic in their reactions, the tetrapositive ion undergoes a slight hydrolysis in aqueous solution and it has been assumed that the hydrolytic product is an ion of the form ThO^{2+} or $Th(OH)^{3+}$. Hydrolysis does not result in deposition of hydroxide even at acidities somewhat below 10^{-2} N. The solution chemistry of thorium is rather complex because of hydrolysis and the formation of polynuclear complexes at high thorium concentrations and low acidities. In solution tetrapositive thorium shows a strong tendency to form complexes with a wide variety of anions, *e.g.*, fluoride, chloride, iodate, nitrate, oxalate, etc. The ability of thorium to form complexes is indicated by the large number of "double salts" which have been isolated. Thus, for example, alkali metal "double salts" are formed with all the common anions, *e.g.*, $K_2Th(NO_3)_6$, $Na_4Th(P_2O_7)_2$, $KThF_5$, K_2ThCl_6.

27.31 Among the more common insoluble compounds are the dioxide, hydroxide, fluoride, iodate, pyrophosphate, and oxalate, the latter three being of some importance in the analytical chemistry of thorium. Thorium dioxide, obtained by thermal decomposition of the hydroxide or salt of an oxyacid, becomes one of the most refractory substances known when it has been ignited at high temperatures. The hydroxide forms as a gelatinous white precipitate upon addition of alkali hydroxide or ammonia water to a solution of a thorium salt. There is some question regarding the actual composition of the hydroxide. There appears to be good evidence that the compound $Th(OH)_4$ results if the gelatinous material is heated in the range 260 to 450°; above 470° it is converted to the dioxide.

27.32 Only two compounds containing thorium in oxidation states lower than $+4$ appear to have been definitely prepared. These are ThI_3 and ThI_2, and they are obtained by the reduction of thorium tetraiodide by means of elementary thorium at elevated temperatures. In contrast to the colorless nature of the tetraiodide, the lower iodides are black. They are unstable in water, reacting to give tetrapositive thorium and hydrogen.

Protactinium   **27.33** At present, relatively little is known about the chemistry of protactinium compounds. The main oxidation state is +5, and there is evidence for the existence of the tetrapositive and tripositive states.

27.34 Pentapositive protactinium shows a great tendency to form complexes with a variety of anions in aqueous solution. Complexing with fluoride ion is particularly strong, and as a result protactinium compounds are generally soluble in hydrofluoric acid. In the absence of complexing agents +5 protactinium is readily hydrolyzed with the formation of colloids. In this respect there is a marked resemblance to the behavior of niobium and tantalum. In solutions of low acid concentrations it appears that species of the types $Pa(OH)_{4.5}^{0.5+}$, $PaO(OH)_{2.5}^{0.5+}$, etc., are present, and in media of intermediate acid concentrations PaO^{3+} or $Pa(OH)_2^{3+}$ seems to be the predominant ion. It is possible that hydrated Pa^{5+} can exist in highly acidic aqueous solutions.

27.35 Pentapositive protactinium can be reduced in aqueous solution polarographically or by means of zinc amalgam. Reduction by the latter method appears to convert protactinium to the tetrapositive state. In this oxidation state the element is precipitated by fluoride, hydroxide, iodate, phosphate, and hypophosphate; is complexed by citrate, tartrate, and possibly carbonate; and is readily oxidized by air. In solutions containing oxalate ion, +5 protactinium is reduced polarographically in two irreversible one-electron steps, the second reduction stage $(Pa(IV) + e^- \rightarrow Pa(III))$ being hydrogen ion dependent. The potential for the reaction $Pa(V) + e^- \rightarrow Pa(IV)$ in oxalate medium was found to be about -1.5 volts.

27.36 Among the solid compounds of protactinium, oxides and halides have been most extensively studied. Thermal decomposition of the hydrated oxide, obtained by reaction of alkali with solutions of pentapositive protactinium, gives a dense white powder to which the formula Pa_2O_5 has been assigned. This substance in reality possesses the approximate composition Pa_4O_9. This can be reduced by hydrogen at about 1600° to give substances with lower oxygen content, with PaO_2 being a lower limit. Treatment of the dioxide with oxygen at 1100° gives Pa_2O_5. Both PaO_2 and Pa_2O_5 are completely basic in character.

27.37 Both penta- and tetrahalides of protactinium appear to have been made. The tetrafluoride is obtained as a high-melting, rust-colored substance by the action of a mixture of hydrogen fluoride and hydrogen on the dioxide at 500–600°. This compound is isostructural with ThF_4, UF_4, NpF_4, and PuF_4. Reaction between Pa_4O_9 and bromine trifluoride gives a volatile material which is assumed to be either PaF_5 or $PaOF_3$. A white volatile substance presumed to be $PaCl_5$ is formed by reaction of P_4O_9 with phosgene at 550° in a vacuum. This halide can be converted to $PaCl_4$ by treatment with hydrogen at 600°. Little definitive information is available on bromides and iodides of protactinium.

Uranium   **27.38** This element exhibits four well-defined oxidation states: +3, +4, +5, and +6. Of these, the tetra- and hexapositive states are most important. In aqueous solution the oxidation states exist as the ions U^{3+}, U^{4+}, UO_2^+, and UO_2^{2+} and show the following potential relationships in one molar hydrochloric acid.

$$U^{3+} \xrightarrow{\ 0.61\ } U^{4+} \xrightarrow{\ -0.62\ } UO_2^+ \xrightarrow{\ -0.05\ } UO_2^{2+}$$
$$\underset{-0.334}{\underline{\hspace{6cm}}}\uparrow$$

27.39 Solutions of tripositive uranium are formed by electrolytic reduction of the +4 or +6 species or by dissolving a uranium(III) halide (see below). Solutions containing the intense red +3 ion are unstable and are oxidized rather rapidly by water, with the formation of the tetrapositive state. Uranium(III) is also hydrolyzed by water, but the exact extent of hydrolysis is difficult to determine because of the oxidation reaction.

27.40 Solutions of +4 uranium have a characteristic green color and are considerably more stable toward oxidation than those of the tripositive ion. However, they are oxidized by molecular oxygen, the uranium being converted to the uranyl ion, UO_2^{2+}. Tetrapositive uranium is much more susceptible to hydrolysis than the +3 form, the reaction with water probably taking the course shown.

$$U^{4+} + 2H_2O \rightleftharpoons U(OH)^{3+} + H_3O^+$$

There is some evidence that in solution uranium(IV) forms complexes with a variety of anions, *e.g.*, chloride, sulfate, acetate, but little quantitative information is available regarding the nature of these complexes.

27.41 Pentapositive uranium in the form of UO_2^+ is obtained by reduction of uranyl ion (UO_2^{2+}) with hydrogen, zinc amalgam, or uranium(IV), or electrolytically at pH 2.5 to 3. UO_2^+ is extremely unstable, tending to disproportionate rapidly into uranium(IV) and (VI), except in the pH range 2 to 4, where the disproportionation reaction is slow.

27.42 Hexapositive uranium, UO_2^{2+} (probably hydrated), is the most common species of the element in aqueous solution. The ion has been shown to possess a linear structure. Solutions containing uranyl ion are yellow in color and distinctly acidic as a result of hydrolytic reaction. Hydrolysis leads to the production of polynuclear complex species, *e.g.*, $U_2O_5^{2+}$, $U_3O_8^{2+}$, $U_3O_8(OH)^+$, $U_3O_8(OH)_3^-$. In solution, the uranyl ion forms complexes with such anions as nitrate, acetate, cyanide, oxalate, phosphate, carbonate, etc. These complexes are predominantly anionic in character, but neutral and cationic species also appear to exist.

27.43 Many solid uranyl derivatives have been prepared. Among the more important simple salts are the nitrate hydrates (6, 3, and $2H_2O$), the carbonate, the oxalate trihydrate, the sulfate hydrates (3 and $1H_2O$), the acetate dihydrate, and the halides. The simple uranyl compounds are characterized by high solubility in certain organic solvents, *e.g.*, ethers, ketones, and esters, capable of complexing the uranium. In addition to the simple salts a large number of double salts (complexes) have been isolated. These include nitrates, *e.g.*, $MUO_2(NO_3)_3 \cdot xH_2O$ (M = NH_4, K, Rb, Cs, Tl); carbonates, *e.g.*, $M_4UO_2(CO_3)_3$

$(M = Na, K, NH_4)$; acetates, *e.g.*, $M^IUO_2(C_2H_3O_2)_3$, $M^{II}UO_2(C_2H_3O_2)_4$; oxalates, *e.g.*, $M^I_2UO_2(C_2O_4)_2$; and others. Generally the double salts exhibit low water solubility.

27.44 Aside from the uranyl compounds, the oxides, uranates, and halides are the best known solid uranium-containing substances.

27.45 Five oxides of uranium — UO_3, U_3O_8, U_2O_5, UO_2, and UO — have been characterized definitely. The monoxide shows metallic character and is not considered to be a normal oxide, in the sense that its crystal structure cannot be interpreted in terms of ordinary valence rules. Little is known of U_2O_5 which has been identified only recently. Studies on the uranium-oxygen system have shown it to be very complex because of the ease of solid solution formation, and uranium-oxygen materials of practically any composition between UO and UO_3 can be obtained.

27.46 Uranium trioxide is commonly prepared by the decomposition of uranyl nitrate at temperatures in the neighborhood of 300°. It exists in a number of crystalline modifications, the most common being an orange hexagonal form. When heated above about 500° it evolves oxygen and is converted to U_3O_8. The trioxide is amphoteric in behavior, reacting with acids to give uranyl salts and with metal hydroxides to form uranates (see below).

27.47 U_3O_8 is a greenish-black substance which is quite stable toward thermal decomposition. It is formed when any uranium oxide or substance yielding an oxide is strongly heated in air. At very high temperatures it evolves oxygen and goes over to the brown dioxide.

27.48 The dioxide is commonly made by the reduction of UO_3 or U_3O_8 with hydrogen at about 500°. It is difficultly soluble in most acids, but like all uranium oxides, it is transformed to uranyl nitrate by nitric acid. At high temperatures, the dioxide combines with chlorine to yield uranyl chloride, and is converted to the tetrachloride by reaction with powerful chlorinating agents and to the tetrafluoride by treatment with hydrogen fluoride.

27.49 The most common uranates derived from uranium(VI) are of the types $M^I_2UO_4$ and $M^I_2U_2O_7$. In addition, polyuranates containing up to seven uranium atoms per molecule have been described. All uranates, including those of the alkali metals, are insoluble in water but easily soluble in acids. Uranates are generally more stable thermally than the trioxide to which they are related, the stability being greatest for the alkali metal monouranates and decreasing with decreasing electropositive character of the metal and with increasing atomic ratio of uranium to metal. A number of methods have been utilized for the preparation of uranates: (1) fusion of UO_3 or U_3O_8 with metal chloride; (2) addition of soluble metal hydroxides to solutions of uranyl salts; and (3) ignition of metal-uranyl double salts, *e.g.*, $Mg(UO_2)_2(C_2H_3O_2)_6 \cdot 6H_2O$.

27.50 The uranium halides have been studied extensively. A list of the known compounds is given in Table 27.7, along with their melting points. The absence of pentahalides and hexahalides with bromine and iodine is noteworthy.

TABLE 27.7

The Halides of Uranium and Their Melting Points

Fluorides	Chlorides	Bromides	Iodides
UF$_6$ (subl. below m.p.)	UCl$_6$ (179°)		
UF$_5$ (dec. below 400°)	UCl$_5$ (327°, estd.)		
U$_2$F$_9$ (disproportionates on heating)			
U$_4$F$_{17}$ (disproportionates on heating)			
UF$_4$ (960°)	UCl$_4$ (590°)	UBr$_4$ (519°)	UI$_4$ (506°)
UF$_3$ (1430°, estd.)	UCl$_3$ (842°)	UBr$_3$ (752°)	UI$_3$ (680°, estd.)

27.51 Uranium tetrafluoride, obtained by the action of hydrogen fluoride on uranium dioxide at 500°, serves as the source of the other fluorides. Thus, the hexafluoride is commonly made by direct fluorination of the tetrafluoride at 350° and the trifluoride by reduction with hydrogen at 1000°. UF$_5$, U$_2$F$_9$, and U$_4$F$_{17}$ result from reaction between the solid tetrafluoride and the gaseous hexafluoride at rather low pressures and elevated temperatures.

27.52 Uranium hexafluoride, a colorless solid, is the most volatile uranium compound known, exhibiting a vapor pressure of 1 atm. at 56.5°. The volatility has been utilized in the separation of uranium-235 from uranium-238 by gaseous diffusion methods. In the vapor state the hexafluoride is mono-molecular and octahedral in structure. It is an extremely hygroscopic substance, reacting violently with water to give first uranyl fluoride, UO$_2$F$_2$, and finally the trioxide. It is a powerful fluorinating agent and vigorously attacks organic substances. Uranium pentafluoride and the intermediate fluorides U$_2$F$_9$ and U$_4$F$_{17}$ are unstable toward heat, disproportionating to the tetra- and hexa-fluorides. They are also readily decomposed by water, the tetrafluoride and uranyl fluoride being formed. Uranium tetrafluoride is stable with respect to decomposition to about 1100°. At elevated temperatures it reacts with an excess of atmospheric oxygen to form U$_3$O$_8$. It dissolves in water to the extent of about 0.10g. per liter at room temperature, and the resulting solutions appear to be hydrolyzed little, even at 100°. Oxidizing acids convert the tetrafluoride to the uranyl ion. Combination with metal fluorides yields such double salts as MUF$_5$, M$_2$UF$_6$, and M$_3$UF$_7$. Uranium trifluoride disproportionates to the metal and the tetrafluoride at temperatures above 1050°. Reaction with air at 900° gives U$_3$O$_8$. The trifluoride is insoluble in water, but is transformed to uranyl salts by hot oxidizing acids.

27.53 Uranium hexachloride can be prepared in a variety of ways: (1) dispro-portionation of the pentachloride in a high vacuum at 120–150°; (2) reaction of the penta- or tetrachloride with chlorine at 350°; and (3) reaction of the trioxide or a lower chloride with a liquid mixture of chlorine and carbon tetrachloride. The pure hexachloride can be obtained by sublimation at 75–100° and 10^{-4} mm. of mercury pressure. The pentachloride can be made by the direct union of the tetrachloride and elementary chlorine at 520–550° or by reaction of UO_3 or U_3O_8 with liquid carbon tetrachloride in a sealed tube at 250°.

$$2UO_3 + 6CCl_4 \overset{250°}{=} 2UCl_5 + 6COCl_2 + Cl_2$$

The tetrachloride, which is commonly obtained by treatment of the dioxide with such chlorinating agents as sulfur monochloride, carbon tetrachloride, thionyl chloride, etc., can also be prepared by direct union of the elements. The trichloride is commonly made by reduction of the tetrachloride with hydrogen at 525–550° and 7 atm. pressure or by reaction of the hydride (UH_3) with hydrogen chloride at 250–300°.

27.54 Like the corresponding fluoride, uranium hexachloride is very hygroscopic; it reacts violently with water to yield uranyl chloride. It undergoes halogen exchange with liquid hydrogen fluoride to form the hexafluoride. In the neighborhood of 150° the hexachloride is decomposed in a complex fashion. The pentachloride is less stable thermally than the hexachloride, irreversible decomposition to chlorine and the tetrachloride beginning below 100°. At 100–175° in a high vacuum the pentachloride disproportionates.

$$2UCl_5 = UCl_4 + UCl_6$$

It completely exchanges halogen with liquid hydrogen fluoride. Both UCl_6 and UCl_5 are soluble without reaction in carbon tetrachloride. Uranium tetrachloride is extremely soluble in water, solution at room temperature being accompanied by considerable hydrolysis (to give $UOCl_2$) and also by oxidation by the water. At 250° the tetrachloride is converted by air to U_3O_8. It forms complex compounds with a variety of Lewis bases, *e.g.*, Na_2UCl_6, $UCl_4 \cdot 12NH_3$. The trichloride is readily oxidized; thus air converts it to uranyl chloride and the tetrachloride, and bromine and iodine react to yield mixed tetrahalides. Both uranium trichloride and tetrachloride are soluble in strongly polar solvents, *e.g.*, acetic acid, and insoluble in nonpolar media, *e.g.*, carbon tetrachloride.

27.55 With bromine and iodine uranium forms only tetra- and trihalides. These compounds can be prepared by direct union of the elements at elevated temperatures, as well as by other specific methods.

$$UH_3 + 3HBr \overset{300°}{=} UBr_3 + 3H_2$$

$$UO_2 + 2C + 2Br_2 \overset{\Delta}{=} UBr_4 + 2CO$$

$$2UI_4 + H_2 \overset{\Delta}{=} 2UI_3 + 2HI$$

27.56 Uranium tetrabromide is similar to the tetrachloride in most of its properties. The tetraiodide, unlike the other uranium tetrahalides, is thermally unstable and is decomposed at relatively low temperatures to the triiodide. Both the tribromide and triiodide are easily oxidized, *e.g.*, by water, to yield uranium(IV).

The Transuranic Elements 93–98 **27.57** These elements are discussed as a unit in order to emphasize the striking trend with respect to stabilization of the tripositive oxidation state with increasing atomic number, a trend of paramount importance as evidence in support of the actinide concept (27.3 *ff.*).

27.58 Neptunium and plutonium (elements 93 and 94) are similar in their chemistry to uranium, exhibiting the same oxidation states. There is, however, a significant difference in the relative stabilities of these states for the three elements, a general increase occurring in stability of the lower states from uranium to plutonium (Table 27.1). Thus, the most prominent oxidation state in aqueous solution for the elements is $+6$, $+5$, and $+4$, respectively. The stability differences are utilized in the separation of these elements from each other.

27.59 The ionic species of neptunium and plutonium which exist in aqueous solution are analogous to those of uranium. The potential relationships among the aqueous neptunium and plutonium species are shown (*cf.* 27.38). As is

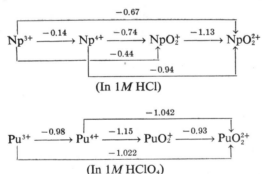

(In 1*M* HCl)

(In 1*M* HClO₄)

indicated by the potential diagram, the NpO_2^+ species is fairly stable toward disproportionation, a striking contrast to the behavior of the analogous uranium and plutonium ions. The potentials of the various plutonium couples lie so close to each other that all the intermediate oxidation states of this element tend to undergo disproportionation. The potentials listed in the diagrams can be modified significantly by changes in hydrogen ion concentration or by the presence of anions, *e.g.*, fluoride, oxalate, sulfate, capable of forming complexes with the various cationic species.

27.60 Tripositive neptunium can be obtained in dilute hydrochloric acid solution by reduction of higher states, either electrolytically at a mercury cathode or by catalytic hydrogenation. Neptunium(III) is rapidly air oxidized to the tetrapositive state. The latter state can also be made by reduction of neptunium(V) or (VI) in a number of ways, *e.g.*, with oxalic acid in dilute sulfuric acid at 75°, or with tin(II) in dilute hydrochloric acid in the presence of iron(II) as catalyst. Solutions of neptunium(V) can be prepared by oxidation of the tetrapositive state, *e.g.*, by stoichiometric quantities of cerium(IV), or by reduction of neptunium(VI), NpO_2^{2+}, with tin(II) or hydroxylamine hydrochloride. The hexapositive state is obtained by oxidation of any of the lower states with moderately strong oxidizing agents, *e.g.*, dipositive silver, bromate, or cerium(IV). In aqueous solution neptunium species are characteristically colored: Np^{3+}, pale purple; Np^{4+}, pale yellow-green; NpO_2^+, green-blue; and NpO_2^{2+}, color dependent on nature of acid present. In precipitation reactions tripositive neptunium is closely similar to the +3 lanthanides; tetrapositive neptunium resembles cerium(IV) and other +4 actinides; and the NpO_2^{2+} ion is very much like the corresponding uranium species. Little is known about neptunium complexes in solution.

27.61 Although plutonium-239 is a difficult element to work with because of its high specific alpha radioactivity (one milligram emits 1.4×10^8 alpha particles per minute) and because of the pronounced tendency for intermediate oxidation states to disproportionate, there is considerable information regarding the behavior of ionic species of this element in aqueous solution. Pure solutions of Pu^{3+} (blue-lavender) and PuO_2^{2+} (pink-orange) are readily obtained, the former by treatment of solutions of higher oxidation states with such reducing agents as sulfur dioxide or hydroxylamine and the latter by oxidation of lower states with bromate or ozone. Plutonium(IV), as Pu^{4+} (yellow-brown), can be prepared in a fairly pure condition by treatment of the hydroxide with perchloric acid solution. The disproportionation reaction is rather slow at room temper-

$$3Pu^{4+} + 2H_2O = 2Pu^{3+} + PuO_2^{2+} + 4H^+$$

ature. Plutonium(V), PuO_2^+, is formed as an initial product in the reduction of PuO_2^{2+} by reagents such as iron(II), sulfur dioxide or hydroxylamine (see above). The PuO_2^+ ion is intermediate between UO_2^+ (see 27.41) and NpO_2^+ in stability toward disproportionation. Although it is fairly stable at hydrogen ion concentrations in the range 10^{-9}–$0.5M$, in more strongly acidic solutions it undergoes the following reaction.

$$2PuO_2^+ + 4H^+ = PuO_2^{2+} + Pu^{4+} + 2H_2O$$

27.62 All the aqueous plutonium species tend to hydrolyze, the order of decreasing hydrolytic stability being PuO_2^+, Pu^{3+}, PuO_2^{2+}, Pu^{4+}. Thus, Pu^{4+} begins to undergo hydrolysis even in solutions tenth molar in hydrogen ion, PuO_2^{2+} at about pH 5, Pu^{3+} at approximately pH 7, and PuO_2^+ in the neighborhood of pH 9. The process of hydrolysis is considered to involve proton transfer from one of the water molecules of the hydrated ion to an adjacent water molecule (see example).

$$Pu(H_2O)_x^{4+} + H_2O = Pu(OH)(H_2O)_{x-1}^{3+} + H_3O^+$$

The hydrolysis of Pu^{4+} is accompanied by formation of a colloidal polymer of variable composition.

27.63 In precipitation reactions Pu^{3+}, Pu^{4+}, and PuO_2^{2+} are similar to the corresponding neptunium species (see above). Among the more common compounds of Pu^{3+} and Pu^{4+} obtainable by precipitation reactions are the fluorides, oxalates, hexacyanoferrates(III), and hydroxides. A potassium salt containing +5 plutonium can be precipitated from concentrated carbonate solution, but the compound has not been characterized. Indeed, no solid compounds of plutonium(V) are definitely known. A plutonium(VI) compound of interest, obtained by precipitation from aqueous solution, is $NaPuO_2(C_2H_3O_2)_3$. This substance is isomorphous with the analogous uranium and neptunium compounds.

27.64 In contrast to the lack of data regarding neptunium complexes, a considerable amount of qualitative information is available about plutonium complexes in aqueous solution. Tripositive plutonium ion, like the corresponding lanthanide ions, has a relatively small tendency to form complexes. Evidence of a qualitative nature has been obtained for the existence of complexes with chloride ion in solutions containing relatively high concentrations of hydrochloric acid, with nitrate ion in solutions of nitric acid, and with carbonate ion in potassium carbonate solution. Tetrapositive plutonium, as a result of its higher charge and smaller radius, forms complexes more readily than does Pu^{3+}. Evidence has been obtained for such species with chloride, fluoride, nitrate, acetate, sulfate, sulfite, citrate, oxalate, carbonate, and phosphate ions. The great bulk of the data comes from the spectral changes occurring when Pu^{4+} comes in contact with these ions in solution; in only a few instances have the compositions of the complexes in solution been determined unequivocally. There appears to be little question that with some of the anions, at least, a variety of complexes may be formed depending upon the relative concentration of anion and cation. No evidence has been obtained for complexes of plutonium(V). There appears to be little doubt that plutonium(VI) (PuO_2^{2+}) forms complexes with nitrate, chloride, sulfate, and carbonate ions, but the exact nature of the species is unknown.

27.65 Examination of the solid compounds of neptunium and plutonium brings out clearly the trend toward stabilization of the lower oxidation states with increasing atomic number across the actinide series. Of particular interest are the oxides and halides.

27.66 No oxide of the composition MO_3, corresponding to UO_3, has been prepared for either neptunium or plutonium. For both elements a monoxide is known, but in each case the compound, like UO, is definitely metallic in character and probably is best regarded as an interstitial compound. The dioxides are the most important oxides of both neptunium and plutonium. The dioxides are obtained by the ignition in air (for NpO_2 at temperatures in the neighborhood of 1000°; for PuO_2 at 700–800°) of decomposable oxy compounds, *e.g.*, nitrates, oxalates, etc., containing the transuranium element in any oxidation state. No higher oxide than the dioxide has been prepared for plutonium. An oxide of variable composition, $PuO_{1.5-1.75}$, has been obtained by decomposition of PuO_2 on a tantalum or iridium filament at 1650–1800° in a high vacuum. For neptunium, the oxide Np_3O_8, isomorphous with U_3O_8, is formed when Np(V) or Np(VI) compounds are ignited in air at 275–450°. Substances intermediate in composition between NpO_2 and Np_3O_8 have also been characterized.

27.67 A summary of the anhydrous halides of neptunium and plutonium, together with their methods of preparation and their heats of formation, is given in Table 27.8. An outstanding characteristic of all the plutonium halides, except the trifluoride, is their extremely hygroscopic nature. A number of fluoro and chloro complexes of plutonium have been reported: $NaPuF_4$, M^IPuF_5, $M^I_2Pu_2F_9$, $M^I_2PuCl_6$. The complexes of plutonium(IV) are obtained by precipitation reactions from media containing the appropriate hydrohalic acid. The existence of the chloro compounds is particularly noteworthy, inasmuch as solid plutonium tetrachloride has not been isolated, although there is evidence that the gaseous species may be formed when the trichloride vapor and chlorine are brought together.

$$2PuCl_3(g) + Cl_2(g) \rightleftharpoons 2PuCl_4(g)$$

27.68 In acidic aqueous solution americium definitely exhibits +3, +5, and +6 oxidation states, but there is no unequivocal evidence for the existence of dipositive and tetrapositive states. Ionic species in these oxidation states have formulas corresponding to those of uranium, neptunium, and plutonium in corresponding states — Am^{3+}, AmO_2^+, and AmO_2^{2+}. The characteristically pink tripositive state is by far the most stable form of americium in aqueous solution. Among the oxidation potentials for the various ions in acidic solution shown, the Am(III)—Am(V) and Am(IV)—Am(V) couples were calculated from the other values.

$$
\begin{array}{c}
\overset{-1.7}{\overbrace{\hspace{5cm}}} \\
Am^{3+} \xrightarrow{(-2.32)} (Am^{4+}) \xrightarrow{(-1.08)} AmO_2^+ \xrightarrow{-1.64} AmO_2^{2+} \\
\underset{(-1.68)}{\underbrace{\hspace{5cm}}}
\end{array}
$$

27.69 In acid solution, strong oxidizing agents, e.g., $S_2O_8^{2-}$, convert americium(III) to AmO_2^{2+}. A compound, presumably $NaAmO_2(C_2H_3O_2)_3$, isostructural with $NaUO_2(C_2H_3O_2)_3$ and $NaPuO_2(C_2H_3O_2)_3$, can be precipitated by addition of sodium acetate. In solution, americium(VI) undergoes autoreduction, undoubtedly because of reaction with decomposition products of water resulting from the radioactivity of americium. Pentapositive americium cannot be isolated from acid solution, but can be obtained in the form of an insoluble compound of unknown composition by oxidation of americium(III) by sodium hypochlorite in carbonate solution. The attainment of the +5 state in alkaline solution is consistent with estimated potential values in this medium.

$$Am \xrightarrow{2.71} Am(OH)_3 \xrightarrow{0.4} Am(OH)_4 \xrightarrow{-0.7} AmO_2OH \xrightarrow{-1.1} AmO_2(OH)_2$$

In acid medium, americium(V) disproportionates to the tri- and hexapositive states.

27.70 Except in the oxides, the most stable oxidation state for americium

TABLE 27.8

The Halides of Neptunium and Plutonium

Fluorides	Method of Preparation	Color	Melting Point, °C.	Heat of Formation (ΔH), kcal./mole
NpF_6	$2NpF_3 + 3F_2 \overset{\Delta}{\underset{\text{Ni filament}}{=}} 2NpF_6$	White	53	-463 ± 3 for $NpF_6(g)$
NpF_4	$NpF_3 + \frac{1}{4}O_2 + HF \overset{500°}{=} NpF_4 + \frac{1}{2}H_2O$	Light green		-428 ± 3
NpF_3	$NpO_2 + \frac{1}{2}H_2 + 3HF \overset{500°}{=} NpF_3 + 2H_2O$	Purple		-360 ± 3
PuF_6	$PuF_4 + F_2 \overset{600-700°}{=} PuF_6$	White to pale brown	50.7	ca. 7
PuF_4	$PuO_2 + 4HF \overset{500°}{\underset{\text{in } O_2}{=}} PuF_4 + 2H_2O$ or $2PuF_3 + F_2 \overset{300°}{=} 2PuF_4$	Pale brown		-424 ± 4
PuF_3	$2PuO_2 + 6HF + H_2 \overset{550-600°}{=} 2PuF_3 + 4H_2O$ or $Pu^{3+} + 3HF \overset{H_2O}{=} PuF_3 + 3H^+$	Purple	1425	-375 ± 1
Chlorides				
$NpCl_4$	$NpO_2 + CCl_4 \overset{530°}{=} NpCl_4 + CO_2$	Reddish-brown		-237 ± 1
$NpCl_3$	$2NpCl_4 + H_2 \overset{450°}{=} 2NpCl_3 + 2HCl$	White	ca. 800	-216 ± 2
$PuCl_3$	$PuO_2 + CCl_4 \overset{700-800°}{=} PuCl_3 + CO_2 + \frac{1}{2}Cl_2$	Green	760	-230.1
Bromides				
$NpBr_4$	$3NpO_2 + 4AlBr_3 \overset{350°}{=} 3NpBr_4 + 2Al_2O_3$	Reddish-brown	740	-197.5 ± 1
$NpBr_3$	$3NpO_2 + Al + 3AlBr_3 \overset{350-400°}{=} 3NpBr_3 + 2Al_2O_3$	Green		-195 ± 1
$PuBr_3$	$PuO_2 + 4HBr = PuBr_3 + 2H_2O + \frac{1}{2}Br_2$	Green	680	-198.8
Iodides				
NpI_3	$3NpO_2 + 4AlI_3 \overset{350-400°}{=} 3NpI_3 + \frac{3}{2}I_2 + 2Al_2O_3$	Brown?		-141 ± 1
PuI_3	$Pu + 3HI \overset{450°}{\underset{100 \text{ mm.}}{=}} PuI_3 + \frac{3}{2}H_2$	Bright green	770	ca. -190

in solid compounds is +3. Americium(III), as expected, has solubility characteristics of the tripositive lanthanides and gives insoluble compounds with hydroxide, fluoride, oxalate, carbonate, and phosphate ions. The anhydrous trihalides are prepared by methods similar to those utilized for analogous neptunium and plutonium compounds. The tetrafluoride is the only halide containing americium in a higher oxidation state than +3. This compound is prepared by the direct fluorination of the trifluoride at temperatures not exceeding about 730°. It is interesting that it has not yet been found possible to obtain it from the dioxide (see below) by reaction with oxygen-hydrogen fluoride mixtures at elevated temperatures, a method suitable for the preparation of neptunium and plutonium tetrafluorides.

27.71 Two oxides of americium, Am_2O_3 and AmO_2, are known. The latter, which is the more stable, is formed as a black substance when the hydrous oxide or oxalate of americium(III) is heated in air at temperatures below 1000°. The dioxide has a fluorite structure,* being isomorphous with UO_2, NpO_2, and PuO_2. This type of structure is particularly stable in actinide element-oxygen systems. Reduction of AmO_2 with hydrogen at 750° yields the orange-red sesquioxide.

27.72 Curium, the actinide analog of the lanthanide element gadolinium, appears to be exclusively tripositive in aqueous solution. Attempts to oxidize or reduce +3 curium in either acidic or alkaline medium have been unsuccessful. It should be emphasized that experiments with macroscopic amounts of curium in solution are complicated by its high specific alpha radioactivity (one microgram of ^{242}Cm corresponds to about 10^{11} disintegrations per minute). The intense alpha activity results in the rapid decomposition of water, giving rise to species (H_2O_2, OH, etc.) possessing strong reducing power. The stability of the +3 state for curium has been cited as a major piece of evidence in support of the actinide concept (see 27.13). As would be expected, curium(III) compounds exhibit solubility behavior similar to that of the tripositive lanthanides.

27.73 Although curium is characteristically tripositive in its solid compounds also, there is excellent evidence for the existence of curium(IV) oxide, CmO_2. The ignition of curium(III) oxide (containing ^{244}Cm, alpha-emitter; half-life 19.2 yr.) in one atmosphere of oxygen at about 650°, followed by slow cooling, gives a black material, X-ray analysis of which appears to show unequivocally that it is an oxide with an O/Cm ratio very nearly two.[1] The formation of the dioxide again emphasizes the importance of the fluorite-type structure in actinide-oxygen systems. The dioxide decomposes at 600° to give colorless curium(III) oxide.†

[1] ASPREY, ELLINGER, FRIED, and ZACHARIASEN, *J. Am. Chem. Soc.*, **77**, 1707 (1955).

* In fluorite (CaF_2), each Ca^{2+} ion is surrounded by eight F^- ions at the corners of a cube, and each F^- by four Ca^{2+} ions at the corners of a regular tetrahedron.

† Curium tetrafluoride has recently been obtained in the solid state by reaction of fluorine on the trifluoride at elevated temperatures. (ASPREY, ELLINGER, FRIED, and ZACHARIASEN, *J. Am. Chem. Soc.*, **79**, 5825 (1957).) The existence of this compound and also the dioxide suggests that the $5f^7$ configuration may not possess the special stability which seems to characterize the $4f^7$ configuration (in Gd^{3+}).

27.74 The chemical properties of berkelium and californium (atomic numbers 97 and 98) have been determined entirely with the use of tracer amounts of these elements. On the basis of their ion-exchange behavior (see 27.7) and the oxidation states which exist, there is little doubt that berkelium and californium are lanthanidelike elements. Thus berkelium, like its lanthanide homolog terbium, exhibits both +3 and +4 oxidation states, with the former state being predominant. Evidence for the tetrapositive state is afforded by the fact that treatment of a solution of berkelium(III) with acid solutions of such oxidizing agents as bromate or dichromate gives a species which is carried appreciably by zirconium(IV) phosphate. Oxidation can also be effected by cerium(IV) and the berkelium carried by the tetrapositive lanthanide iodate. The oxidation potential of the Bk(III)—Bk(IV) couple has been estimated to be about −1.6 volts.

27.75 Californium appears to exist in solution solely in the tripositive state, in complete analogy with the behavior of dysprosium, its lanthanide homolog. Attempts to oxidize +3 californium with a variety of strong oxidizing agents have been unsuccessful.

Elements 99 to 102

27.76 Elements 99 and 100 were first obtained from uranium which had been subjected to extremely intensive neutron bombardment during the course of a thermonuclear explosion.[2] After chemical removal of the lanthanide elements formed in the fission of the uranium, the tripositive actinides were separated by an ion-exchange method in which californium-246 (half-life 36 hr.; alpha-emitter) was employed as a tracer. On the basis of predicted elution behavior of the actinide elements (see 27.7), the presence of elements 99 and 100 was demonstrated. The detected isotope of element 99 was shown to have a mass number of 253 and to decay by alpha emission, with a half-life of about 20 days. This element is formed as a result of the beta decay of californium-253, which in turn arises from the beta decay of uranium-253 and its daughters. The alpha-active element 100 (half-life about 16 hr.) was assigned a mass number of 255; this element is produced by the beta decay of $^{255}99$, which originates through beta emission by uranium-255 and daughters.

27.77 Elements 99 and 100 have also been formed by repeated neutron capture in nuclear reactors, reaction sequences such as the one depicted below occurring:[3]

$$^{239}_{94}\text{Pu} \xrightarrow{+2^{1}_{0}n} {}^{241}_{94}\text{Pu} \xrightarrow{-\beta^-} {}^{241}_{95}\text{Am} \xrightarrow{+1^{1}_{0}n} {}^{242}_{95}\text{Am} \xrightarrow{-\beta^-} {}^{242}_{96}\text{Cm}$$

$$^{242}_{96}\text{Cm} \xrightarrow{+7^{1}_{0}n} {}^{249}_{96}\text{Cm} \xrightarrow{-\beta^-} {}^{249}_{97}\text{Bk} \xrightarrow{+1^{1}_{0}n} {}^{250}_{97}\text{Bk} \xrightarrow{-\beta^-} {}^{250}_{98}\text{Cf}$$

$$^{250}_{98}\text{Cf} \xrightarrow{+3^{1}_{0}n} {}^{253}_{98}\text{Cf} \xrightarrow{-\beta^-} {}^{253}99 \xrightarrow{+1^{1}_{0}n} {}^{254}99 \xrightarrow{-\beta^-} {}^{254}100$$

[2] GHIORSO ET AL., *Phys. Rev.*, **99**, 1048 (1955).
[3] *Chem. and Eng. News*, **33**, 1956 (1955).

An inherent difficulty in producing transcalifornium elements by this method is the high probability that some of the intermediate heavy nuclei formed are so unstable that they undergo spontaneous fission and thus interrupt the neutron capture-beta decay processes. Extremely small quantities of 99 and 100 have also been made by bombardment of uranium with heavier particles than neutrons. Thus a few atoms of 99 have been obtained by use of accelerated nitrogen nuclei as the bombarding particles, and element 100 has been formed by means of bombardment with high energy oxygen ions.

27.78 Element 101, to the extent of 17 atoms, has been reported to have been made by reaction of element 99 with 41 mev alpha particles. The isotope formed, mass number 256, decays by spontaneous fission.

27.79 Element 102 has been reported to have been synthesized by bombardment of curium-244 with carbon-13 ions.[4,*]

$$_{96}^{244}Cm + _{6}^{13}C = {}^{251}102 \text{ (or } {}^{253}102) + 6_{0}^{1}n \text{ (or } 4_{0}^{1}n)$$

27.80 The names einsteinium (Es), fermium (Fm), mendelevium (Md), and nobelium (No) have been suggested for elements 99, 100, 101, and 102, respectively.

[4] *Chem. and Eng. News*, **35**, 15 (1957).

[*] Attempts to confirm this synthesis have been unsuccessful. However, bombardment of a mixture of curium isotopes (95% ^{244}Cm and 4.5% ^{246}Cm) on a very thin nickel foil with monoenergetic ^{12}C ions at energies from 60–100 mev gave evidence for the formation of an isotope of element 102, having a half-life of 3 sec., the reaction being $_{96}^{246}Cm + _{6}^{12}C = {}_{102}^{254}X + 4_{0}^{1}n$ (GHIORSO, SIKKELAND, WALTON, and SEABORG, *Phys. Rev. Lett.*, **1**, 17, 18 (1958)).

INDEX

Acetic acid, *see also* Nonaqueous solvents
  dimerization, 197–198
Acetylene, bonding, 180–181
Acid-base concepts,
  Brönsted-Lowry, 269–272, 286
  early history, 268, 269
  hydrogen concept, 269
  Lewis Electronic, 269, 282–285, 286
  Solvent System, 269, 272–282
Acid-base reactions,
  in acetic acid, 275, 276
  general, 282–284
  at high temperatures, 285–287
  in liquid ammonia, 273, 274
  in selenium(IV) oxychloride, 280–282
  in sulfur dioxide, 277–279
  in water, 270, 271
Acidity,
  relation to reducing strength, 123–124
  relation to stability of oxidation states, 125
Actinide elements, *see also individual elements*
  absorption spectra, 644, 645
  actinide contraction, 645
  common isotopes of transuranic elements, 649
  electronic configurations, 67–68, 646, 647
  elution behavior, 643, 644
  evidence for actinide series, 641–647
  ionic radii, 645
  magnetic properties, 137–138, 646
  occurrence and preparation, 647–649
  oxidation potentials, 642, 651
  oxidation state relationships, 642, 643
  preparation of metals, 650
Actinium, *see also* Actinide elements
  properties, 650, 651
Action integrals, 18
Activity, 110
Activity coefficient, 110, 127–128
Alkali metals,
  complexes, 310–313
  electronic configurations, 301
  general properties, 64, 301–303
  general reactions, 303
  halides, lattice energies, 155–156
    melting and boiling points, 158
    thermochemical data, 157
  hydrides, 152–153, 176, 322
  ionization energies and ionic bonding, 152
  liquid ammonia solutions, 305, 306–310
  lithium, "anomalous" behavior, 303, 304
  ozonides, 304
  physical properties, 64, 302
  reactions with oxygen, 304–306

Alkali metals (*cont.*)
  sodium peroxide, 304
  stability of carbonates, 304
  superoxides, 304–306
Alkaline earth metals, *see also* Representative
    group II elements
  carbides, 322
  complexes, 323, 324
  electronic configurations, 314
  general chemical characteristics, 322, 323
  halides, melting and boiling points, 158
  hydrides, 322
  hydroxides, 323
  oxides, 322, 323
  reactions with oxygen, 322, 323
Alpha particles, 11
Aluminum, *see also* Representative group III
    elements *and* Representative group
    III metals
  aluminum(I), 342, 343
  complexes of tripositive state, 340, 341
  lithium aluminum hydride, 334, 341, 342
  sesquioxide and related compounds, 338
  trihalides, 339, 340
  trimethyl dimer, 204–205
Americium, *see also* Actinide elements
  hexapositive state, 660
  oxidation state relationships, 660
  oxides, 662
  pentapositive state, 660
  tetrapositive state, 660, 662
  tripositive state, 660, 662
Ammonia, *see also* Liquid ammonia
  amine complexes, 213–217
  bond angle, 178, 183–184
  boron trifluoride addition compound, 183, 193
  preparation and properties, 386–388
Angular momentum, 18–19
  operators, 31–32
  quantization, 25, 50–51
Anti-bonding orbitals, 167–168, 170, 173–174
Antiferromagnetism, 133, 140
Antimony, *see also* Representative group V
    elements *and* Representative group V
    metals
  pentahalides and derivatives, 415, 416, 417
  pentoxides and oxyacids, 417, 418
  sesquioxides and related compounds, 420, 421
  trihalides and derivatives, 418, 419
  tripositive cation, 421
Antisymmetric state,
  hydrogen molecule, 173–175
  hydrogen molecule ion, 169–171

Aqua regia, 401, 402
Arsenic, *see also* Representative group V elements *and* Representative group V metals
  pentahalides and derivatives, 415, 416
  pentoxides and oxyacids, 417
  sesquioxides and related compounds, 420
  trihalides and derivatives, 418, 419
Arsine, bond angle, 185
Artificial transmutation, 14
Astatine, 484, 485
Atomic crystals, 206
Atomic number, 12, 16
Atomic orbitals, 46, 48, 166
  overlap, 171
Atomic radius, 81–91
  relation to ionization potential, 93
Atomic spectra, 49
Atomic structure,
  Bohr's model, 17–27
  Lenard's hypothesis, 11
  many-electron atoms, 26–27, 43–48
  modern concept, 15
  Rutherford's hypothesis, 11, 14
  Thomson's hypothesis, 11
Atomic theory,
  chemical development, 3–9
  Dalton's, 4
  physical development, 9–16
Atomic volume, 6–7, 69, 70
Atomic weights, 5
Avogadro's hypothesis, 5
Azides, *see* Hydrazoic acid and derivatives

Barium, *see* Alkaline earth metals *and* Representative group II elements
Benzene,
  atomic orbital theory, 190
  bond length, 89
  heats of fusion and vaporization, 159
  molecular orbital theory, 190–191
  resonance energy, 190
  resonance structures, 90, 189
  thermochemical data, 189
Berkelium, *see also* Actinide elements
  oxidation states, 663
Beryllium, 317–320; *see also* Representative group II elements
  bonding, 182
  complexes, 317–320
  electronic configuration, 314
  general chemical characteristics, 317
  halides, 158
  halides, conductivity, 316
  hydroxide, 317
  physical properties, 315
Beta particles, 11
Biradicals, paramagnetism, 138

Bismuth, *see also* Representative group V elements *and* Representative group V metals
  pentahalides and derivatives, 415, 416
  pentoxides and oxyacids, 417, 418
  sesquioxide and related compounds, 420, 421
  trihalides and derivatives, 418, 419
  tripositive cation, 421
Bohr magneton, 136
Bohr theory of atomic structure, 12, 17–27
Bohr-Wilson-Sommerfeld theory, 18, 28
Bond angles,
  first row elements, 182–185
  and hybrid orbitals, table, 186
  measurement, 177
  theory, 177–181
Bond energies, 102–105
  additivity, 103
  measurement, 103
  multiple carbon-carbon bonds, 181
  relation to electronegativity, 104, 196
  table, 104
Bond length, 82
  additivity, 82
  hydrogen molecule, 174
  hydrogen molecule ion, 166
  and ionic character, 88
  and resonance, 89–91
  and stability ratio, 106
Bond strength, 179–181
  hybrid orbitals, 185
  sigma and pi bonds, 180
Bonding orbitals, 167–168, 170, 173–175, 178
Borates, 329
Borazene, *see* Borazole
Borazole, 335
Boric acids, 329
Borine carbonyl, 335
Born-Haber cycle,
  electron affinity, 101
  lattice energies, 156–157
  oxidation potentials, 116, 118
  solubility, 160–161
Borohydrides, 298, 299, 336–337
Boron, *see also* Representative group III elements
  bonding, 182–183
  borazole, 335
  borine carbonyl, 335
  borohydrides, 298, 299, 336–337
  general chemical characteristics, 328
  general reactions, 328
  halides, 331
  halides, complexes, 331–333
  hydrides, 202–204, 298, 333–336
  oxide, 328, 329
  oxyacids, 329
  polyhydroxy complexes, 329, 330
  salts of oxyacids, 329

Brillouin zones, 144
Bromine, *see* Halogens
Brönsted-Lowry acid-base concept, 269–272, 286

Cadmium, *see also* Zinc family
  basic salts, 613
  complex compounds, 614
  general reactions, 611
  hydride, 613
  occurrence, 610
  oxide and related compounds, 611, 612
  preparation, 610, 611
  reducing strength, 130
  simple salts, 612, 613, 614
Calcium, *see* Alkaline earth metals *and* Representative group II elements
Californium, *see also* Actinide elements
  tripositive state, 663
Carbides,
  alkaline earth, 322
  boron, 352
  interstitial, 350–352
  reactive type with transition elements, 350, 352
  saltlike, 350, 351
  silicon, 352
Carbon, *see also* Representative group IV elements, Diamond, Graphite
  binary compounds with metals, 322, 350–352
  bond angles, 178–181
  bond length, 82
  carbonic acid and salts, 355, 356
  carbonyl halides of transition elements, 362
  carbonyl hydrides, 361, 362
  carbonyls, 241, 259, 358–362
  catenation, 347
  cyanogen, 356, 357
  diamond, 207, 348
  dioxide, 355
    dipole moment, 162
    heats of fusion and vaporization, 159
    resonance structures, 188
  four-covalent, 352, 353
  graphite, 89, 91, 348–350
  "graphitic" compounds, 349, 350
  hydrocyanic acid and salts, 357
  methane, 144, 178, 187
  monoxide, 354, 355, 358–362
  multiple bonded, 179–181, 348, 353–364
  promotion, 177
  suboxide, 353, 354
  tendency for self-linkage, 347
  tetrahalides, 353
    bond angle of tetrachloride, 178
    dipole moment of tetrachloride, 162
  valence, 10, 177
Carbonyl halides of transition metals, 362

Carbonyl hydrides, 361, 362
Carbonyls, 241, 259, 358–362
  derivatives of, 361, 362
Carborundum, 352
Cathode rays, 10
Cell process,
  electrical work, 109
  electrode reactions, 108
Cerium, *see* Lanthanide elements
Cerium(IV) oxidation, 128
Cesium, *see also* Alkali metals
  ionic bonding, 151
Chelation, *see* Coordination compounds
Chlorine, *see also* Halogens
  chloride-chlorate couple, 124
  ionic bonding, 150–151
Chlorine dioxide, three-electron bond, 191
Chromium, *see also* Chromium family
  carbonyl, 358, 359
  chromates(VI) and polychromates, 516, 517
  chromium(III) complexes, 525, 526
  chromium(II) compounds, 527, 528
  chromium(IV) compounds, 523, 524
  chromium(V) compounds, 521, 522
  chromium(III) oxide, 525
  chromium(VI) oxide and related compounds, 516, 517
  general reactions, 515, 516
  oxyhalide complexes of chromium(VI), 521
  oxyhalides of chromium(VI), 519, 520
  preparation, 514, 515
  trihalide hydrate isomers, 223, 525
  trihalides, 525
Chromium family,
  dipositive state, 527–529
  general properties, 513–516
  general reactions, 515, 516
  hexapositive state, 516–521
  occurrence, 515
  oxidation state relationships, 513, 514
  pentapositive state, 521–523
  physical properties, 515
  preparation, 514, 515
  tetrapositive state, 523, 524
  tripositive state, 525–527
  valence shell configurations, 513
Chromyl halides, 519, 520
Closed shells, 45, 47
Cobalt, *see also* Transition triads I
  carbonyl hydride, 361, 362
  carbonyls, 358, 359
  cobalt(–I) compounds, 361, 362, 563, 564
  cobalt(0) compounds, 358, 359, 563
  cobalt(I) compounds, 562, 563
  cobalt(IV) compounds, 550, 551
  cobalt(II) simple salts, 560
  cobalt(III) simple salts, 553, 554
  complex compounds of cobalt(II), 560, 561

Cobalt (*cont.*)
  complex compounds of cobalt(III), 131, 213, 214, 215, 222, 223, 224, 225, 226, 227, 228, 242, 243, 556, 557
  general reactions, 548, 549
  occurrence, 548
  oxide of cobalt(II) and related compounds, 559
  preparation, 548
  sesquioxide and related compounds, 553
Complex atoms, 43–57
  Bohr theory, 26–27
  ground state configurations, 45, 47
Complex compounds, *see* Coordination compounds
Conductance,
  electronic, 143–144
  ionic, 161
Constant-energy radii, 89
Coordination compounds,
  chelation, 219, 226
  coordination number, 216
  coordination number and structure, 229–252
  effective atomic number, 217, 218
  inner orbital, 246–249, 265–267
  isomerism, 222–229; *see also* Isomerism, coordination compounds
  lability, 212, 265–267
  ligand field theory, 249–251
  ligands, 214, 218, 219
  nomenclature, 220–222
  orbital theory and magnetic properties, 234, 235, 236, 241, 244–248
  orbital theory and structure, 229, 230, 231, 234, 235, 236, 244–248
  outer orbital, 246–249, 265–267
  penetration complexes, 213
  polynuclear, 220, 252–255
  stability, 212, 255–265
  Werner coordination theory, 214–217
Coordination number,
  complex compounds, 216
  crystal, 80
Copper, *see also* Copper family
  complex compounds of copper(I), 602
  complex compounds of copper(II), 235, 236, 599, 600
  copper(III) compounds, 593, 594
  copper(I)-copper(II) couple, 131
  copper(I) simple compounds, 145, 601–602
  dihalides, 598
  disproportionation of copper(I), 601
  general properties, 590, 592
  oxidation by bromate ion, 126
  oxide of copper(II) and derivatives, 598
  oxyacid salts of copper(II), 599
  preparation, 591, 592
  sulfides, 599
Copper family,
  occurrence, 591
  oxidation state relationships, 589, 590, 591
  physical properties, 590
  valence shell configurations, 589
Coulomb integral, 170
  hydrogen molecule, 173
Covalent bonds, 148–149, 192–197
  coordinate, 192–193
  in crystals, 159
  Fajan's rules, 164
  general properties, 206–207
  in metals, 205
  normal, 192
  physical interpretation, 170, 172, 175
  polar, 192–197
  quantum mechanical basis, 165–187
  relation to polarizability, 196
Covalent radii, 81–89
  multiple bond, 83, 86
  octahedral, 83, 85, 186
  single bond, 81–83, 87, 186
  square, 83, 186
  tetrahedral, 83, 85, 186
  variation with structure, 86, 88
Crystal energy, 101
Curie law, 135, 139–140
Curie-Weiss law, 135
Curium, *see also* Actinide elements
  tetrapositive state, 662
  tripositive state, 662
Cyanides,
  complex, 258, 259, 362–364
  simple, 357
Cyanogen, 189, 356, 357

Dalton's atomic theory, 4
Daniell cell, 106–108
de Broglie's hypothesis, 29
Degeneracy,
  complex atoms, 51
  energy states, 21
  hydrogen molecule ion, 167
  hydrogenlike atoms, 36, 42
Deuterium, *see* Hydrogen
Deuteron, 15
Dewar structures, 90, 189
Diagonal relationship, 65
Diamagnetism, 132, 134–135
Diamond, 207, 348
Diatomic molecules, electronic configurations, 168
Diborane, 333–335
Differentiating electron, 62–63
Dimerization, formic and acetic acids, 197–198
Diphosphine, 404, 405
Dipole-dipole forces, 162–163
Dipole moments, 162, 163, 194, 239, 240, 241

Disproportionation, 120
Döbereiner's triads, 6
Double bond, 179–181
Double salts, 211, 212
Dulong and Petit's Rule, 5, 69
Dysprosium, *see* Lanthanide elements

Effective atomic number, 217, 218, 360
Effective nuclear charge, 73
Eigenfunctions, 29
  hydrogenlike atoms, 34–35
  of spin operator, 41
Eigenvalues, 29
  hydrogenlike atoms, 36
Einsteinium, 663, 664; *see also* Actinide
  elements
Electrical properties of metals, 142–146
Electrode potentials, 106–132
  applications, 119–132
  calculation of, 121
  and chemical equilibrium, 126–128
  dependence on activity, 122
  origin, 109
  relation to ionization potentials, 109–110
  stabilization of oxidation states, 120, 128–
    132
Electrode reactions,
  and cell process, 108
  dependence on acidity, 124
Electromotive force, 106
  and chemical change, 107, 119, 124–125
  relation to electrical work, 109
  sign conventions, 107–108
  single electrode potentials, 108
Electron,
  bonding, 167–168
  discovery, 10
Electron affinity, 99–102
  dependence on structure, 100, 102
  and ionization potential, 99–100
  measurement, 101
  relation to ionic bonding, 151–152
  and standard oxidation potentials, 118
  table, 101
Electron deficient bonds, 202–205
Electron density, sigma and pi bonds, 180–181
Electron diffraction, 84
Electron orbits,
  Bohr, 18
  relation to diamagnetism, 134
Electron pair bond, 176–177
  and resonance, 191
Electron pairing, 62, 135, 150, 165, 176
Electron sharing, 148–150
Electron shells, 63
Electron spin, 40–42
  and ferromagnetism, 139
  hydrogen molecule, 174
  and magnetic moment, 133

Electron spin (*cont.*)
  and maximum covalency, 176
  operators, 42
  pairing, 165
Electron spin resonance, 141
Electron transfer, 148–149
Electronegativity, 88, 102–106
  relation to bond character, 106
  relation to bond energy, 105
  relation to bond polarity, 194–195
  relation to dipole moments, 162
  relation to ionic bond formation, 153
  relation to ionization potential and electron
    affinity, 102
  table, 105
  variation with structure, 102, 106
Electronic configurations, 45, 47–48, 57
  closed, 52
  diatomic molecules, 168
  elements, table, 56
  many-electron molecules, 175
Electrostatic interactions in crystals, 154
Energy level diagram, 22
  complex atom, 52
  helium, 53
  nitrogen, 55
  relation to ionization potentials, 95
  sodium, 54
Enthalpy changes, 117
Entropy changes, 117
Equilibrium constant, 126
  calculation from standard potentials, 126–
    128
Erbium, *see* Lanthanide elements
Ethyl alcohol, proton resonance, 141
Ethylene, structure, 179–180
Europium, *see* Lanthanide elements
Exchange energy, 170–172, 187
Exchange integral, 170–172
  aromatic systems, 190
  hydrogen molecule, 173
  relation to bonding strength, 171, 174–176
Excited states, 21
Exclusion Principle, 42–44, 102
  in hydrogen molecule, 174
  and molecular orbitals, 167
  relation to electron pairing, 150
  relation to ferromagnetism, 139

Fajan's rules, 13, 164
Fermium, 663, 664; *see also* Actinide ele-
  ments
Ferrimagnetism, 133, 140
Ferromagnetic resonance, 141
Ferromagnetism, 132–133, 138–140
  alignment of magnetic moments, 139
  effect of temperature, 139
  relation to structure, 140
Fluoride ion, anomalous size, 157

Fluorine, *see also* Halogens
  ionic bonding, 151
  ionic character in compounds, 195
Formal potentials, 128
Formic acid,
  dimerization, 197–198
  hydrogen bonding, 199
Free energy change, 109, 117, 119
  and equilibrium, 126
  and spontaneous chemical change, 119–120
  standard value, 122

Gadolinium, *see* Lanthanide elements
Gallium, *see also* Representative group III
    elements *and* Representative group
    III metals
  complexes of tripositive state, 340, 341
  lower oxidation states, 343, 344
  sesquioxide and related compounds, 338
  trihalides, 339
Galvanic cell, 106
Gay-Lussac's law, 5
Germanium, *see also* Representative group
    IV elements *and* Representative group
    IV metals
  complexes of germanium(IV), 373, 374
  dihalides and derivatives, 376, 377
  dioxide and related compounds, 374, 375
  hydrides, 371, 372
  monoxide and derivatives, 375, 376
  tetrahalides, 372, 373
Gold, *see also* Copper family
  complex compounds of gold(I), 229, 605,
    606
  complex compounds of gold(III), 596, 597
  general properties, 590, 593
  gold(I) simple compounds, 605
  oxide of gold(III) and derivatives, 596
  preparation from ores, 592
  trihalides, 596, 597
Graphite, 348–350
  bond distances, 89
  structure, 91
Ground state, 21
  oxygen molecule, 182

Hafnium, *see* Titanium family
Half bonds, 204
Halic acids and halates, 477, 478, 480, 481
Halogens,
  binary compounds with oxygen, 472–477
  bromine monochloride, 461, 462, 463
  bromine monofluoride, 461, 462, 463
  bromine oxides, 473, 475, 476
  bromine pentafluoride, 461, 465, 466
  bromine trifluoride, 461, 463, 464, 465
  cationic behavior, 458, 461, 482–484
  chlorine monofluoride, 461, 462, 463
  chlorine oxides, 191, 473, 474, 475

Halogens (*cont.*)
  chlorine trifluoride, 461, 463, 464
  complexes of monopositive bromine, 483,
    484
  complexes of monopositive iodine, 482, 483
  electron affinity and ionic bonding, 152
  electronic configurations, 456
  enneaiodide anion, 467, 468
  general properties, 456–461
  general reactions, 460
  halic acids and halates, 477, 478, 480, 481
  halous acids and halites, 477, 478, 479, 480
  heptaiodide anion, 467, 468
  hydrogen halides, physical properties, 471
    preparation, 470, 471
    thermal stability, 471
  hydrohalic acids, 471, 472
  hypohalous acids and hypohalites, 477,
    478, 479
  interhalogens, 461–466
    physical constants, 461
    of type XX', 461, 462, 463
    of type XX'_3, 461, 463–465
    of type XX'_5, 461, 465, 466
  iodine heptafluoride, 461, 465, 466
  iodine monobromide, 461, 462, 463
  iodine monochloride, 461, 462, 463, 505
  iodine-oxygen compounds, 472, 473, 476,
    477
  iodine pentafluoride, 461, 465, 466
  iodine trichloride, 461, 463, 464
  oxyacids and salts, 477–482
  oxyacids and salts, potential diagrams, 478
  oxygen fluorides, 473, 474
  pentaiodide anion, 467, 468
  perhalic acids and perhalates, 477, 478, 481,
    482
  physical properties, 457
  polyhalide anions of type X_n^-, 466, 467, 468
    of type XX'^-_n, 466, 467, 468–470
    of type $XX'X''^-_n$, 466, 467, 470
  polyhalide complexes, 466–470
  trihalide anions, 466, 467, 468
  tripositive iodine, cationic behavior, 484
Halous acids and halites, 477, 478, 479, 480
Hamiltonian operator, 29–30
  hydrogen molecule, 173
  space and spin terms, 41
Heat of dissociation, halogens, 157
Heat of formation, alkali metal halides, 157
Heat of solution, 160–161
Heat of sublimation,
  alkali metals, 157
  dependence on interionic forces, 158
Heavy water, 299, 300
Heisenberg Uncertainty Principle, 28, 30–
  31
Heitler and London atomic orbital theory,
  165

Helium molecule ion, 191
Heteropolyacids and salts, 253–255
Holmium, *see* Lanthanide elements
Huggins constant-energy relationship, 88–89, 105–106
Hund and Mulliken molecular orbital theory, 165
Hund's rule of maximum multiplicity, 61–62, 249
Hybrid orbitals, 178–187
    linear SP, 181–182
    octahedral D^2SP^3, 185
    table, 186
    tetragonal plane DSP^2, 185
    tetrahedral SP^3, 178–179, 183–184
    trigonal plane SP^2, 179–180, 183
    and unshared pairs, 187
Hybridization, 178–181
    long period elements, 185
    methyl radical, 183
    nitrogen and oxygen, 183
Hydration energy, 116–119
Hydrazine, 388, 389
Hydrazoic acid and derivatives, 390–392
Hydrides,
    alkali metal, 322
    alkaline earth metal, 322
    bonding, 152–153
    boron, 333–337
    classes, 297–299
Hydrogen,
    deuterium, 295, 299, 300
    exchange reactions, 300
    hydrides, 296–299
    isotopes, 295
    ortho, 296, 299
    para, 296, 299
    properties, 295, 296
    tritium, 295
Hydrogen atom,
    Bohr orbits, 19, 23–24
    Bohr quantum conditions, 19–20
    electron affinity and ionic bonding, 152
    energy levels, 20–21
    ionization energy and ionic bonding, 152
    spectrum, 22–23
    wave-mechanical model, 32–40
Hydrogen bonding, 197–202
    conditions for, 198
    in crystals, 201
    effect on properties, 200
    intramolecular, 201
    relation to solubility, 200–201
    in water, 200, 202
Hydrogen cyanide, 357
Hydrogen halides, 470–472
Hydrogen molecule,
    atomic orbital theory, 172–174
    bond length, 88

Hydrogen molecule (*cont.*)
    energy and bond length, 173–174
    ionic contribution to bond, 153
    molecular orbital theory, 174–175
    structure, 165
Hydrogen molecule ion, 166–172
    approximate theory, 169–172
    energy, 166–167, 170–172
    molecular orbitals, 165–168
    resonance, 171
Hydrogen peroxide, *see* Oxygen
Hydrogen selenide, 436, 437
    bond angle, 185
Hydrogen sulfide, 436, 437
    bond angle, 185
Hydroxylamine, 389, 390
Hydroxyl bonds, 202
Hypohalous acids and hypohalites, 477, 478, 479

Ice, hydrogen bonding, 200, 202
Indium, *see also* Representative group III elements *and* Representative group III metals
    complexes of tripositive state, 340, 341
    lower oxidation states, 343, 344
    sesquioxide and related compounds, 338, 339
    trihalides, 339, 340
Inert pair, 65, 135
Inert gases,
    electronic configurations and stability, 148–149
    hydrates, dipole-polarizability interactions, 163
    liquefaction and crystallization, 163
    polarizability, 163
Interhalogens, *see* Halogens
Interionic forces,
    in ionic compounds, 158
    in solution, 110
    and thermodynamic properties, 158–159
Intermetallic compounds, bonding, 205–206
Intermolecular forces, 70, 72
Iodine, *see* Halogens
Ion-dipole forces, 162–163
Ionic bonds, 148–161
    dependence on structure, 153
    and electrical conductivity, 161
    and electronegativity, 153
    general properties, 153
    and solubility, 159
Ionic character, 88
    hydrogen compounds, 176, 194–195
    hydrogen molecule, 172
    hydrogen-oxygen bond, 195
    relation to electronegativity, 195
Ionic potential, 257, 258

Ionic radii, 72–81
  and coordination number, 80
  crystal, 73, 75, 76
  relation to lattice energy, 155
  relation to solubility, 161
  tables, 74–76
  univalent, 73–74
  variation with structure, 75–81
Ionization potential, 60, 91–99, 143
  dependence on structure, 93–95, 98–99
  and lanthanide contraction, 99
  and standard oxidation potential, 116–117
  table, 96–97
Iridium, *see also* Transition triads II
  carbonyls, 358, 360
  hexafluoride, 581
  iridium(I) compounds, 581
  iridium(II) compounds, 581
  iridium(III) compounds, 578, 579
  iridium(IV) compounds, 579, 580
  pentammineiridium(0), 581
Iron, *see also* Transition triads I
  carbonyl hydride, 361, 362
  carbonyls, 241, 358, 360
  complex compounds of iron(II), 560
  complex compounds of iron(III), 555, 556
  ferrates(VI), 549
  general reactions, 548, 549
  iron($-$II) compounds, 361, 362, 564
  iron(IV) compounds, 550, 551
  iron(II) simple salts, 559, 560
  occurrence, 548
  oxide of iron(II) and related compounds,
      127, 558, 559
  pentapositive state, 549
  preparation, 548
  sesquioxide and related compounds, 552,
      553
  trihalides, 554
Isoelectronic sequence, 73
Isomerism, coordination compounds,
  coordination, 224
  hydrate, 223, 224
  ionization, 223
  ligand, 224
  linkage, 224, 225
  polymerism, 222, 223
  stereoisomerism, 225–229, 230, 231, 232,
      233, 236–240, 241–244
Isopolyacids and salts, 253–255
Isotopes, 14

Kekulé structures, 90, 189
Kossel theory of valence, 148–149

Lanthanide contraction, 79, 81, 99, 489, 490,
    624
Lanthanide elements,
  atomic radii, 624

Lanthanide elements (*cont.*)
  chemical properties, 631, 632
  colors of tripositive ions, 625, 626
  configuration and properties, 67–68, 624
  dipositive state, 638–640
  extraction, 627, 628
  general properties, 623–626
  magnetic moments, 137–138, 626
  occurrence, 626, 627
  oxidation potentials, 632, 637, 639
  oxidation states, 625
  physical properties, 631
  preparation of metals, 630, 631
  radii of tripositive ions, 624
  separation, 628–630
  tetrapositive state, 636–638
  tripositive state, complex compounds, 633–
      636
  tripositive state, simple compounds, 632,
      633
Lanthanum, *see* Lanthanide elements
Lattice energy, 101, 154–158
  dependence on structure, 155–157
  relation to fusion, sublimation, vaporiza-
      tion, 158
Laws of Chemical Combination, 4
Lead, *see also* Representative group IV
      elements *and* Representative group
      IV metals
  complexes of lead(IV), 373, 374
  dihalides and derivatives, 376, 377
  dioxide and related compounds, 374, 375
  hydride, 371, 372
  monoxide and derivatives, 375, 376
  tetrahalides, 372, 373
Lewis Electronic acid-base concept, 269, 282–
      285, 286
Lewis theory of valence, 148–149, 165
Ligand field theory, 249–251
Liquid ammonia, *see also* Nonaqueous
      solvents
  reductions in, 305, 308–310
  solutions of alkali metals, 306–310
  solutions of alkaline earth metals, 322
Lithium, *see also* Alkali metals
  "anomalous" behavior, 117, 157–158, 303,
      304
  heat of sublimation, 157
  hydration energy, 117, 158
  ionization energy, 157
Lithium aluminum hydride, 334, 341, 342
Lutetium, *see* Lanthanide elements

Madelung constant, 154
Magnesium, *see also* Representative group
      II elements
  complexes, 321
  electronic configuration, 314
  general chemical characteristics, 321

Magnesium (*cont.*)
  hydroxide, 321
  physical properties, 315
  salts, hydrolysis, 321
Magnetic moment, 133
  and electron spin, 133, 137
  lanthanides and actinides, 137–138
  and orbital electronic motion, 133
  orientation in magnetic field, 135
  quantum mechanical theory, 136
  relation to chemical binding and structure, 138
  transition elements, 136
Magnetic resonance, 140–142
Magnetic susceptibility, 134–135
  ferromagnetic, 139
Manganese, *see also* Manganese family
  carbonyl, 358
  complexes of manganese(III), 131, 541
  compounds of manganese(II), 542, 543
  dioxide, 538, 539
  general reactions, 533
  halo complexes of manganese(IV), 539, 540
  heptoxide and related compounds, 534, 535
  manganates(IV), 539
  manganates(V), 537
  manganates(VI), 536
  manganese(0), 544
  manganese(I), 543, 544
  manganese dioxide-manganese(II) couple, 123
  manganese(III) simple salts, 541
  occurrence, 533
  oxyhalides of manganese(VII), 535, 536
  preparation, 533
  sesquioxide and related compounds, 541
Manganese family,
  dipositive state, 542, 543
  general properties, 530–532
  heptapositive state, 534–536
  hexapositive state, 536, 537
  oxidation state relationships, 531, 532
  pentapositive state, 537, 538
  physical properties, 530
  tetrapositive state, 538–540
  tripositive state, 540–542
  valence shell configurations, 530
Many-electron atoms, *see* Complex atoms
Matrix elements, 31
Maximum covalency, 176–177, 184–185
Maximum multiplicity, principle of, 61–62, 249
Mendeléeff's periodic table, 5–9
Mendelevium, 664; *see also* Actinide elements
Mercury, *see also* Zinc family
  bonding, 182
  complex compounds of mercury(II), 618, 619

Mercury (*cont.*)
  compounds of mercury(I), 619, 620
  disproportionation of mercury(I), 620, 621
  mercury(II) simple compounds, 616, 617, 618
  occurrence, 614, 615
  oxidation state relationships, 615
  oxide of mercury(II) and related compounds, 615, 616
  preparation, 615
  reducing strength, 130
  structure of mercury(I) ion, 619
Metallic bond, 205–206
Metals,
  covalent bonding, 205
  electrical and thermal conductivity, 143
  electron gas model, 143
  electronic heat capacity, 144
  physical properties and structure, 143
  quantum mechanical theory, 144
Methane,
  bond angle, 178
  resonance, 187
Methyl radical, structure and bonding, 183
Methylene radical, structure and bonding, 182
Millon's base, 619
Molar refraction, 163–164
Molecular crystals, 206
Molecular orbitals, 165–168
  bonding and anti-bonding, 167
Molybdenum, *see also* Chromium family
  carbonyl, 358, 359, 360, 361
  fluoro complexes of molybdenum(VI), 519
  general reactions, 515, 516
  hexafluoride, 518, 519
  molybdates(VI) and polymolybdates, 253, 254, 255, 517, 518
  molybdenum(II) compounds, 527, 528, 529
  molybdenum(III) compounds, 525, 526, 527
  molybdenum(IV) compounds, 524
  molybdenum(V) compounds, 522, 523
  molybdenum(VI) oxide and related compounds, 516, 517, 518
  octacyanomolybdate(IV), 252, 524
  oxyfluoro complexes of molybdenum(VI), 521
  oxyhalides of molybdenum(VI), 519, 520
  preparation, 515
Mulliken's electronegativity postulate, 102, 105
Multiple bonds, 179–182
  carbon, 179–181, 182
  nitrogen, 181–182
  oxygen, 181–182

Neodymium, *see* Lanthanide elements
Neptunium, *see also* Actinide elements
  halides, 661
  hexapositive state, 658, 661

Neptunium (*cont.*)
  oxidation state relationships, 657
  oxides, 659, 660
  pentapositive state, 658
  tetrapositive state, 658, 661
  tripositive state, 657, 658, 661
Nernst equation, 121–122
Neutron, discovery, 14
Neutron diffraction, 84
Newland's Law of Octaves, 6
Nickel, *see also* Transition triads I
  carbonyl, 241, 359, 360, 361
  complex compounds of nickel(II), 130, 234, 235, 561, 562
  complex compounds of nickel(III), 557, 558
  compounds of nickel(0), 241, 309, 359, 360, 361, 563, 564
  compounds of nickel(IV), 550, 551, 552
  cyano complex of nickel(I), 309, 563
  general reactions, 548, 549
  nickel(II) simple salts, 130, 560
  occurrence, 548
  oxide of nickel(II) and related compounds, 559
  preparation, 548
  sesquioxide, 554
Niobium, *see also* Vanadium family
  general reactions, 501, 502
  niobates(V) and polyniobates, 503
  niobium(III) compounds, 511
  niobium(IV) compounds, 509
  niobium(II) oxide, 512
  oxyhalide compounds of niobium(V), 505–507
  pentahalides and halo complexes, 251, 252, 504, 505
  pentoxide and related compounds, 502, 503
  preparation, 501
Nitrides,
  covalent, 385
  interstitial, 385
  ionic, 384, 385
Nitrogen, *see also* Representative group V elements
  ammonia, 386–388
  bond angle, 178, 183–184
  dinitrogen pentoxide, 395, 400
  dinitrogen tetroxide, 395, 399, 400
  halides, 392, 393
  hydrazine, 388, 389
  hydrazoic acid and derivatives, 390–392
  hydronitrogens, 386–392
  hydroxylamine, 389, 390
  hyponitrous acid, 396
  nitric acid and nitrates, 400–402
  nitric oxide, 191, 395–397
  nitrides, 384, 385
  nitrogen dioxide, 395, 399, 400

Nitrogen (*cont.*)
  nitrogen(I) oxide, 395, 396
  nitrogen(II) oxide, 395–397
  nitrogen(III) oxide, 395, 397, 398
  nitrogen(V) oxide, 395, 400
  nitrogen(IV) oxides, 395, 399, 400
  nitrogen sesquioxide, 395, 397, 398
  nitrous acid and nitrites, 398, 399
  nitrous oxide, 395, 396
  oxides and related compounds, 395–402
  oxyhalides, 393–395
  properties, 384
  triple bond and stability, 182
Nitronium ion, 402
Nitrosyl halides, 393, 394, 401
Nitryl halides, 393–395
Nobelium, 664; *see also* Actinide elements
No-electron bonds, 203
Nonaqueous solvents,
  acetic acid, 275–277
  bromine trifluoride, 464, 465
  iodine monochloride, 505
  liquid ammonia, 272–274, 305, 306–310, 322
  selenium(IV) oxychloride, 279–282
  sulfur dioxide, 274, 275, 277–279
Nuclear fission, 15–16
Nuclear magnetic resonance, 141
  structural information, 141–142
Nuclear reactions, 15–16
Nucleus, constitution, 14

Odd molecules,
  and electron pairing, 177
  paramagnetism, 138
One-electron bond, 150, 166–172, 191, 203
  boron hydrides, 191, 203
  physical interpretation, 170, 172
  requirements, 191
Osmium, *see also* Transition triads II
  carbonyls, 358, 360
  complex compounds of osmium(VIII), 573, 574
  osmium(II) compounds, 575, 576
  osmium(III) compounds, 576
  osmium(IV) compounds, 571, 572
  osmium(VI) compounds, 572, 573
  tetroxide, 573
Overlap integral, 171–172
  hydrogen molecule, 173, 175
Oxidation potentials, 108–132
  dependence on structure, 116–117
  relation to reducing and oxidizing power, 110, 118–119
  tables, 111–115
Oxidation states, stabilization, 129, 130–132
Oxidizing power,
  relation to acidity, 123–124
  relation to complex formation, 130

Oxygen, *see also* Representative group VI elements
  bond angle, 177, 183
  hydrogen peroxide, 429–431
  hydroperoxides, 431
  metallic oxides, general properties, 432–434
  molar refraction, 164
  nonmetallic oxides, general properties, 432
  ozone, 187, 427
  paramagnetism, 138, 182
  peroxy acids and salts, 431, 432, 450, 451
  properties, 426, 427
  unpaired electrons, 177
  water, 427–429
Ozone, 187, 427

Palladium, *see also* Transition triads II
  complex compounds of palladium(II), 583, 584
  complex compounds of palladium(IV), 584, 585
  compounds of palladium(0), 586, 587
  palladium(II) simple compounds, 582
  palladium(IV) simple compounds, 584
  trifluoride, 587
Parabola method, 14
Paramagnetic resonance, 141–142
Paramagnetism, 132–133, 135–138
  in crystalline or liquid state, 136
  and unpaired electrons, 138
Pauli Principle, *see* Exclusion Principle
Pauling's bond character relation, 195
Pauling's bond energy postulate, 104–105
Penetrating electrons, 47, 60–61, 78, 94
Penicillin, 83
Perhalic acids and perhalates, 477, 478, 481, 482
Periodic classification, 58–68
  Bohr's, 63
  long transition series elements, 63, 66–68
  representative elements, 63, 64
  short transition series elements, 63, 66
Periodic Law, 6, 13
Periodic table, 6–9, 59, 66
  short period form, 66
Peroxides, 304, 305, 431
Peroxy acids and salts, *see* Oxygen
Peroxysulfuric acids and salts, 450, 451
Phenols, resonance and hydrogen bonding, 198
Phosphine, 185, 403, 404, 405
Phosphonium salts, 404, 405
Phosphorus, *see also* Representative group V elements
  allotropic forms, 402–404
  diphosphoric acid, 410, 413
  halides and related compounds, 405–408
  hexafluorophosphates, 407
  hydrides, 403, 404, 405

Phosphorus (*cont.*)
  hypophosphoric acid, 410, 411, 412
  hypophosphorous acid, 410, 411
  metaphosphates, 413, 414
  metaphosphoric acid, 410, 414
  occurrence, 402
  orthophosphates, 413
  orthophosphoric acid, 410, 412
  oxides, 409, 410
  oxyacids and salts, 410–414
  oxyhalides, 408
  pentahalides, 406, 407
  pentahalides, bonding, 185
  pentoxide, 409, 410
  phosphites, 411
  phosphoric acids and salts, 410, 412–414
  phosphorous acid, 410, 411
  phosphorus(III) oxide, 409
  phosphorus(V) oxide, 409, 410
  preparation, 402
  pyrophosphates, 413
  pyrophosphoric acid, 410, 413
  reactions of the element, 403
  sesquioxide, 409
  structure, 403
  tetrahalides, 407, 408
  thiohalides, 408
  trihalides, 405, 406
  triphosphates, 413, 414
Photoelectric effect, 11, 143
Pi bonds, 180–181
Platinum, *see also* Transition triads II
  alkyl derivatives, 204, 585
  complex compounds of platinum(II), 216, 225, 232, 233, 234, 236, 237, 238, 239, 584
  complex compounds of platinum(IV), 216, 217, 585, 586
  compounds of platinum(0), 587
  compounds of platinum(VI), 587, 588
  platinum(II) simple compounds, 582, 583
  platinum(IV) simple compounds, 585
  tetramethyl tetramer, 204
  trihalides, 587
Platinum metals, *see* Transition triads II *and also individual elements*
Plutonium, *see also* Actinide elements
  halides, 660, 661
  hexapositive state, 658, 659, 661
  oxidation state relationships, 657
  oxides, 659, 660
  pentapositive state, 658, 659
  tetrapositive state, 658, 659, 660, 661
  tripositive state, 658, 659, 661
Polarizability, 72, 134
  and coordination, 164
  and electronegativity, 197
  of halide ions, 163
  and induced dipoles, 163

Polarizability (*cont.*)
  of inert gases, 163
  and lattice energy, 155
  relation to structure, 163
  and solubility, 161
Polarization and covalent bonding, 196
Polarization interactions,
  in crystals, 154
  and Fajan's rules, 164
  with ions and dipoles, 163
Polonium, 455; *see also* Representative group
  VI elements
Positive rays, 10
Potassium, *see also* Alkali metals
  ionic bonding, 150–151
Potentiometric titration, 128
Praseodymium, *see* Lanthanide elements
Probability distribution functions, 30, 47
  alkali metal ions, 48–49
  in crystals, 154
  hydrogenlike atoms, 37–40
Promethium, *see* Lanthanide elements
Promotion, 61, 177, 182–184
  in beryllium, 182
  in carbon, 177
  in nitrogen and oxygen, 183–184
  requirements for, 177
Protactinium, 652; *see also* Actinide elements
Proteins, hydrogen bonds in, 201
Protonated double bond, 203, 334
  conditions for, 204
Protons, 14
Prout's hypothesis, 5

Quantum numbers, 20, 30, 42, 50
  azimuthal, 20–21, 33
  hydrogen molecule ion, 166
  magnetic, 20–21, 33, 166
  principal, 20–21, 34
  radial, 20
  resultant, 50–51
  spin, 42
  total, 20–21
Quantum restrictions, 18
Quenching of orbital magnetic contribution,
  136

Radioactive disintegration, 13, 15
Radioactive elements, discovery, 11
Radium,
  electronic configuration, 314
  physical properties, 315
Radius ratio, 79
Rare-earth elements, *see* Lanthanide elements
Reaction quotient, 126
Reducing strength,
  and acidity, 123–124
  and complex formation, 130
Reinecke's salt, 526

Representative elements, perspective, 291–294
Representative group I elements, *see* Alkali
  metals
Representative group II elements, *see also*
  Alkaline earth metals, Beryllium,
  Magnesium, Radium
  electronic configurations, 314
  general properties, 314–317
  general reactions, 316, 317
  physical properties, 315
  stability of carbonates, 316
Representative group III elements, *see also*
  Representative group III metals *and*
  individual elements
  electronic configurations, 325
  general properties, 325–328
  physical properties, 326
Representative group III metals, *see also*
  Representative group III elements *and*
  Aluminum, Gallium, Indium, Thallium
  complexes, 340–342
  general characteristics, 337
  general reactions, 337
  lower oxidation states, 342–344
  oxides and hydroxides, 338, 339
  trihalides, 339, 340
  tripositive oxidation state, 338–342
Representative group IV elements, *see also*
  Representative group IV metals *and*
  individual elements
  electronic configurations, 345
  general properties, 345–348
  physical properties, 345, 346
Representative group IV metals, *see also*
  Representative group IV elements *and*
  Germanium, Lead, Tin
  derivatives of tetrahalides, 373, 374
  dihalides and derivatives, 376, 377
  dioxides and derivatives, 374, 375
  dipositive state, 375–377
  general properties, 370, 371
  general reactions, 370
  hydrides, 371, 372
  monoxides, 375, 376
  oxidation potential relationships, 371
  tetrahalides, 372, 373
  tetrapositive state, 371–375
Representative group V elements, *see also*
  Representative group V metals *and*
  individual elements
  electronic configurations, 378
  general properties, 378–383
  oxidation state relationships, 379–383
  physical properties, 379
Representative group V metals, *see also*
  Representative group V elements *and*
  Antimony, Arsenic, Bismuth
  general properties, 414, 415
  pentahalides and derivatives, 415–417

Representative group V metals (*cont.*)
  pentapositive state, 415–418
  pentoxides and oxyacids, 417, 418
  sesquioxides and related compounds, 420, 421
  trihalides and derivatives, 418, 419
  tripositive cations, 421
  tripositive state, 418–421
Representative group VI elements, *see also individual elements*
  electronic configurations, 422
  general properties, 422–426
  physical properties, 423
Representative group VII elements, *see Halogens*
Residual valence, 202
Resonance, 89–91, 187–191
  in aromatic systems, 190
  and bond lengths, 91
  formic acid dimer, 199
  graphite, 207
  helium molecule ion, 191
  hydrogen molecule, 175
  hydrogen molecule ion, 171
  metals, 205
  ozone, 187
  phosphorus pentafluoride and sulfur hexafluoride, 185
  requirements for, 188
Resonance energy, 91, 189–191
Resonance hybrid, symmetry in, 199
Resonance stabilization, 90, 199
Rhenide ion, 544
Rhenium, *see also* Manganese family
  carbonyl, 358
  complexes of rhenium(V), 538
  dioxide and related compounds, 539
  dipositive state, 543
  general reactions, 533, 534
  halo complexes of rhenium(IV), 540
  heptasulfide, 535
  heptoxide and related compounds, 534, 535
  hexafluoride, 537
  occurrence, 533
  oxide of rhenium(VI), 536
  oxyhalides of rhenium(VI), 537
  oxyhalides of rhenium(VII), 536, 537
  pentachloride, 538
  preparation, 533
  rhenate(V), 537, 538
  rhenium(−I), 544
  rhenium(I), 544
  tetrafluoride, 540
  trihalides and related halo complexes, 541, 542
Rhodium, *see also* Transition triads II
  carbonyls, 358, 360
  rhodium(I) compounds, 580
  rhodium(II) compounds, 580

Rhodium (*cont.*)
  rhodium(III) compounds, 577, 578
  tetrapositive state, 581
Rotational spectra, 84
Rubidium, *see* Alkali metals
Rule of Eight, 149
Rule of Two, 150
Ruthenium, *see also* Transition triads II
  carbonyls, 358, 360
  ruthenium(II) compounds, 568, 569
  ruthenium(III) compounds, 569, 570
  ruthenium(IV) compounds, 574
  ruthenium(V) compounds, 574
  ruthenium(VI) compounds, 575
  ruthenium(VII) compounds, 575
  tetroxide, 575
Rydberg constant, 21

Salicylaldehyde, hydrogen bonding, 201
Salicylic acid, hydrogen bonding, 201
Samarium, *see* Lanthanide elements
Schrödinger's amplitude equation, 30
Screening effect, 45–46, 47, 60–61, 73, 78
Selection rule, 53–54
Selenium, *see also* Representative group VI elements
  allotropic forms, 435, 436
  complex halides, 442
  dioxide, 442, 443
  general chemical properties, 436
  halides, 438–442
  hydrides and derivatives, 436–438
  oxyhalides, 444–446
  selenic acid and salts, 448, 449, 450
  selenious acid and salts, 446–448
  trioxide, 442, 444
Selenium(IV) oxychloride, *see* Nonaqueous solvents *and* Selenyl halides
Selenium(IV) oxyhalides, *see* Selenyl halides
Selenyl halides, 444–446
Self-consistent fields, 48
Semiconductors, 144–145
Sigma bonds, 180–181
Silanes, 365, 366
Silicates, 365
Silicon, *see also* Representative group IV elements
  bond energies with other elements, 347, 348
  dioxide and derivatives, 364, 365
  halides, 366–369
  hydrides, 365, 366
  monoxide, 364
  oxyhalides, 369, 370
  preparation, 364
  reactions, 364
Silver, *see also* Copper family
  complex compounds of silver(I), 229, 604, 605
  compounds of silver(II), 600, 601

Silver (*cont.*)
  compounds of silver(III), 594, 595
  general properties, 127, 590, 592, 593
  silver(I) simple compounds, 602, 603, 604
  silver-silver chloride electrode, 123
  "sub-fluoride," 603
Sodium, *see also* Alkali metals
  sodium sulfate decahydrate, solubility and
      temperature, 160
Solubility, ionic compounds, 161
Solvation, 159–161
Solvation and hydrogen bonding, 201
Solvent system acid-base concept, 269, 272–
      282
Space functions, 41, 174
Spallation, 15
Specific heat, 5, 144
Spherical harmonics, 33
Spin functions, 41, 174
Stability of oxidation states, relation to elec-
      trode potentials, 130
Stability ratio, 106
Standard states, 110
Stationary states, 18, 30
  complex atoms, 27
  hydrogenlike atoms, 36
Strontium, *see* Alkaline earth metals
Sulfur, *see also* Representative group VI
      elements
  allotropic forms, 434, 435
  dioxide, 274, 275, 277–279, 442, 443
  dithionic acid and salts, 453
  dithionous acid and salts, 451, 452
  general chemical properties, 436
  halides, 438–442
  hexafluoride, bonding, 185
  hydrides and derivatives, 436–438
  molecular species, 434, 435
  oxyhalides, 444–446
  peroxysulfuric acids and salts, 450, 451
  polythionic acids and salts, 453, 454
  pyrosulfates, 449, 450
  sulfuric acid and salts, 448, 449
  sulfurous acid and salts, 446–448
  sulfuryl halides, 445, 446
  thiosulfates, 452, 453
  trioxide, 442, 443, 444
Superconductors, 145–146
Superoxides, 304–306
Symmetric state,
  hydrogen molecule, 173–175
  hydrogen molecule ion, 169–171

Tantalum, *see also* Vanadium family
  dichloride, 512
  fluorotantalates, 252, 504, 505
  general reactions, 501, 502
  oxyhalo complexes of tantalum(V), 506,
      507

Tantalum (*cont.*)
  pentahalides, 503, 504
  pentoxide and related compounds, 502, 503
  preparation, 501
  tantalates(V) and polytantalates, 503
  tantalum(III) compounds, 511
  tantalum(IV) compounds, 509
Technetium, *see also* Manganese family
  dioxide, 539
  heptasulfide, 535
  heptoxide and related compounds, 534, 535
  hexachlorotechnetate(IV), 540
  preparation, 533
Tellurium, *see also* Representative group VI
      elements
  complex halides, 442
  dioxide, 442, 443
  general chemical properties, 436
  halides, 438–442
  hydrides and derivatives, 436–438
  physical characteristics, 436
  telluric acids and salts, 449, 450
  tellurous acid and salts, 446–448
  trioxide, 442, 444
Terbium, *see* Lanthanide elements
Term symbol, 51
Terminal elements, 64, 487, 608
Tetrahedral bonding, 178–179
Thallium, *see also* Representative group III
      elements *and* Representative group
      III metals
  complexes of tripositive state, 340, 341
  sesquioxide, 339
  stability of oxidation states, 125
  thallium(I), 342
  trihalides, 339
Thermionic emission, 11, 143
Thionyl halides, 444–446
Thorium, 651; *see also* Actinide elements
Three-atom orbitals, 204
Three-electron bond, 150, 191
  oxygen, nitric oxide, chlorine dioxide, 191
  requirements, 191
Thulium, *see* Lanthanide elements
Tin, *see also* Representative group IV ele-
      ments *and* Representative group IV
      metals
  complexes of tin(IV), 373, 374
  dihalides and derivatives, 376, 377
  dioxide and related compounds, 374, 375
  hydride, 371, 372
  monoxide and derivatives, 375, 376
  tetrahalides, 372, 373
Titanium, *see also* Titanium family
  dioxide and related compounds, 493, 494
  general reactions, 493
  hexafluorotitanates, 496
  oxyacid salts, 496
  preparation, 493

Titanium (*cont.*)
  tetrahalides and derivatives, 494–496
  titanates, 494
  titanium(II) compounds, 498
  titanium(III) compounds, 497, 498
Titanium family,
  general properties, 491, 492, 493
  general reactions, 493
  lower oxidation states, 497, 498
  occurrence, 492
  physical properties, 492
  tetrapositive state, 493–497
  valence shell configurations, 491
Transition elements, long series, *see* Lanthanide elements *and* Actinide elements
Transition elements, short series, *see also*,
  e.g., Titanium family, Vanadium
  family, *etc., and individual elements*
  oxidation states, general relationships, 487,
    488
  oxidation states, maximum, 488
  perspective, 487–490
  valence electrons, 487
Transition probabilities, 34
Transition triads, 66–67
Transition triads I, *see also* Iron, Cobalt,
  Nickel
  dipositive state, 558–562
  hexapositive state, 549
  oxidation state relationships, 546, 547
  pentapositive state, 549
  physical properties, 546
  tetrapositive state, 550–552
  tripositive state, 552–558
  valence shell configurations, 545
Transition triads II, *see also* Ruthenium,
  Osmium, Rhodium, Iridium, Palladium, Platinum
  general reactions, 567, 568
  occurrence, 566, 567
  oxidation states, summary, 565, 566
  physical properties, 566
  valence shell configurations, 565
Transitions between stationary states, 18, 22,
  27
Triiodide ion, 467, 468
  ion-polarizability interaction, 163
Trimethylammonium hydroxide, 197
Triple bond,
  carbon, 180–181
  nitrogen, 182
Tritium, *see* Hydrogen
Triton, 15
Tungsten, *see also* Chromium family
  carbonyl, 358–361
  fluoro complexes of tungsten(VI), 519
  general reactions, 515, 516
  hexahalides, 518, 519
  oxyfluoro complexes of tungsten(VI), 521

Tungsten (*cont.*)
  oxyhalides of tungsten(VI), 519, 520, 521
  preparation, 515
  tungstates(VI) and polytungstates, 253,
    254, 255, 517, 518
  tungsten(II) compounds, 525, 526, 527
  tungsten(III) compounds, 525, 526, 527
  tungsten(IV) compounds, 524
  tungsten(V) compounds, 522, 523
  tungsten(VI) oxide and related compounds,
    516, 517, 518

Uncertainty principle, 28, 30–31
United atom, 166
Unshared pair, 181
  and bond angles, 186–187
Uranium, *see also* Actinide elements
  halides, 654–657
  hexapositive state, 653, 654, 655, 656
  oxidation state relationships, 652, 653
  oxides, 654
  pentapositive state, 653, 654, 655, 656
  tetrapositive state, 653, 654, 655, 656
  tripositive state, 653, 655, 656
  uranates, 654
  uranyl compounds, 653, 654

Valence, 147
  relation to solubility of ionic compounds,
    161
Valence bands, 144
Valence electrons, 47, 92, 144
  in solid metals, 206
Valence forces, 148, 163
  dipole-dipole, 163
  ion-dipole, 163
  polarization interactions, 163
  relation to atomic structure, 148
Valence shell, expansion of, 185
Van der Waals forces, 198, 206–207
Van der Waals repulsion energy, 154
Vanadium, *see also* Vanadium family
  general reactions, 501, 502
  oxy compounds of vanadium(IV), 507, 508
  oxyhalides of vanadium(III), 510
  oxyhalides of vanadium(V), 505–507
  pentahalides and halo complexes, 503–505
  pentoxide and related compounds, 502, 503
  preparation, 501
  tetrahalides, 507
  trihalides, 509, 510
  vanadates(IV), 507
  vanadates(V) and polyvanadates, 502, 503
  vanadium(III) complexes, 510, 511
  vanadium(III) oxide, 509
  vanadium(IV) oxide, 507
  vanadium(II) simple compounds, 511, 512
  vanadium(III) sulfate, 510
  vanadyl compounds, 507, 508

Vanadium family,
  dipositive state, 511, 512
  general properties, 499–502
  general reactions, 501, 502
  occurrence, 500, 501
  oxidation state relationships, 499, 500
  pentapositive state, 502–507
  physical properties, 500
  preparation, 501
  tetrapositive state, 507–509
  tripositive state, 509–511
  valence shell configurations, 499
Vector model of atom, 50

Water, *see also* Oxygen
  bond angle, 177, 183–184
  dielectric constant, 160
  dipole moment, 163, 195
  heats of fusion and vaporization, 159
Wave function, 29
  in crystals, 154
  determinantal form, 44
  and ferromagnetism, 139
  hydrogen atom, 46–48
  hydrogen molecule, 172–175
  hydrogen molecule ion, 169
  lithium hydride, 176
  many-electron atom, 43
  metals, 144
Wave mechanics, elementary principles, 29–32

X-ray diffraction, 83–84
X-rays, discovery, 11

Ytterbium, *see* Lanthanide elements
Yttrium, *see* Lanthanide elements

Zeeman effect, 26
Zero point energy, crystal lattice, 154–155
Zinc, *see also* Zinc family
  basic salts, 613
  complex compounds, 130, 613, 614
  general reactions, 611
  hydride, 613
  occurrence, 610
  oxide and related compounds, 145, 611, 612
  preparation, 610, 611
  simple salts, 130, 612, 613
Zinc family,
  general properties, 607–610
  physical properties, 609
  valence shell configurations, 607
Zirconium, *see also* Titanium family
  dioxide and related compounds, 493, 494
  fluoro complexes of zirconium(IV), 251, 496
  general reactions, 493
  oxyacid salts, 497
  preparation, 493
  tetrahalides and derivatives, 494–496
  zirconium(III) compounds, 498
  zirconium(II) halides, 498